PEARSON

ALWAYS LEARNING

Lisa A. Urry • Michael L. Cain • Steven A. Wasserman
Peter V. Minorsky • Jane B. Reece

Campbell Biology in Focus

Second Custom Edition for BIO 110: General Biology
West Chester University

Taken from:
Campbell Biology in Focus, Second Edition
by Lisa A. Urry, Michael L. Cain, Steven A. Wasserman,
Peter V. Minorsky, and Jane B. Reece

Pearson Education, Inc., 330 Hudson Street, New York, New York 10013
A Pearson Education Company
www.pearsoned.com

Printed in the United States of America

000200010272052043

CM

PEARSON   ISBN 10: 1-323-46465-4
ISBN 13: 978-1-323-46465-6

Detailed Contents

1 **Introduction: Evolution and the Foundations of Biology 2**

OVERVIEW Inquiring About Life 2

CONCEPT 1.1 The study of life reveals common themes 3
  Theme: New Properties Emerge at Successive Levels of Biological Organization 3
  Theme: Life's Processes Involve the Expression and Transmission of Genetic Information 6
  Theme: Life Requires the Transfer and Transformation of Energy and Matter 8
  Theme: Organisms Interact with Other Organisms and the Physical Environment 8
  Evolution, the Core Theme of Biology 9

CONCEPT 1.2 The Core Theme: Evolution accounts for the unity and diversity of life 10
  Classifying the Diversity of Life 10
  Unity in the Diversity of Life 11
  Charles Darwin and the Theory of Natural Selection 11
  The Tree of Life 12

CONCEPT 1.3 In studying nature, scientists form and test hypotheses 13
  Exploration and Discovery 13
  Gathering and Analyzing Data 13
  Forming and Testing Hypotheses 14
  The Flexibility of the Scientific Process 15
  A Case Study in Scientific Inquiry: Investigating Coat Coloration in Mouse Populations 16
  Experimental Variables and Controls 16
  Theories in Science 17
  Science as a Social Process 18

UNIT 1 Chemistry and Cells 21

2 **The Chemical Context of Life 22**

OVERVIEW A Chemical Connection to Biology 22

CONCEPT 2.1 Matter consists of chemical elements in pure form and in combinations called compounds 22
  Elements and Compounds 22
  The Elements of Life 23
  Evolution of Tolerance to Toxic Elements 23

CONCEPT 2.2 An element's properties depend on the structure of its atoms 23
  Subatomic Particles 24
  Atomic Number and Atomic Mass 24
  Isotopes 24
  The Energy Levels of Electrons 25
  Electron Distribution and Chemical Properties 26

CONCEPT 2.3 The formation and function of molecules depend on chemical bonding between atoms 27
  Covalent Bonds 27
  Ionic Bonds 29
  Weak Chemical Bonds 30
  Molecular Shape and Function 30

CONCEPT 2.4 Chemical reactions make and break chemical bonds 31

CONCEPT 2.5 Hydrogen bonding gives water properties that help make life possible on Earth 32
  Cohesion of Water Molecules 33
  Moderation of Temperature by Water 34
  Floating of Ice on Liquid Water 35
  Water: The Solvent of Life 36
  Acids and Bases 37

3 **Carbon and the Molecular Diversity of Life 43**

OVERVIEW Carbon Compounds and Life 43

CONCEPT 3.1 Carbon atoms can form diverse molecules by bonding to four other atoms 44
  The Formation of Bonds with Carbon 44
  Molecular Diversity Arising from Variation in Carbon Skeletons 45
  The Chemical Groups Most Important to Life 46
  ATP: An Important Source of Energy for Cellular Processes 48

CONCEPT 3.2 Macromolecules are polymers, built from monomers 48
  The Synthesis and Breakdown of Polymers 48
  The Diversity of Polymers 49

CONCEPT 3.3 Carbohydrates serve as fuel and building material 49
  Sugars 49
  Polysaccharides 51

CONCEPT 3.4 Lipids are a diverse group of hydrophobic molecules 53
  Fats 53
  Phospholipids 54
  Steroids 55

CONCEPT 3.5 Proteins include a diversity of structures, resulting in a wide range of functions 55
  Amino Acid Monomers 56
  Polypeptides (Amino Acid Polymers) 58
  Protein Structure and Function 58

CONCEPT 3.6 Nucleic acids store, transmit, and help express hereditary information 64
  The Roles of Nucleic Acids 64
  The Components of Nucleic Acids 64
  Nucleotide Polymers 65
  The Structures of DNA and RNA Molecules 66

CONCEPT 3.7 Genomics and proteomics have transformed biological inquiry and applications 66
  DNA and Proteins as Tape Measures of Evolution 67

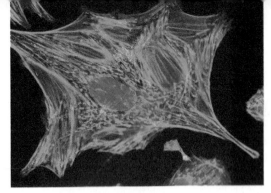

4 · A Tour of the Cell 72

OVERVIEW The Fundamental Units of Life 72

CONCEPT 4.1 Biologists use microscopes and the tools of biochemistry to study cells 73
- Microscopy 73
- Cell Fractionation 75

CONCEPT 4.2 Eukaryotic cells have internal membranes that compartmentalize their functions 75
- Comparing Prokaryotic and Eukaryotic Cells 75
- A Panoramic View of the Eukaryotic Cell 77

CONCEPT 4.3 The eukaryotic cell's genetic instructions are housed in the nucleus and carried out by the ribosomes 80
- The Nucleus: Information Central 80
- Ribosomes: Protein Factories 82

CONCEPT 4.4 The endomembrane system regulates protein traffic and performs metabolic functions in the cell 82
- The Endoplasmic Reticulum: Biosynthetic Factory 83
- The Golgi Apparatus: Shipping and Receiving Center 84
- Lysosomes: Digestive Compartments 85
- Vacuoles: Diverse Maintenance Compartments 86
- The Endomembrane System: A Review 87

CONCEPT 4.5 Mitochondria and chloroplasts change energy from one form to another 87
- The Evolutionary Origins of Mitochondria and Chloroplasts 88
- Mitochondria: Chemical Energy Conversion 88
- Chloroplasts: Capture of Light Energy 89
- Peroxisomes: Oxidation 90

CONCEPT 4.6 The cytoskeleton is a network of fibers that organizes structures and activities in the cell 90
- Roles of the Cytoskeleton: Support and Motility 90
- Components of the Cytoskeleton 91

CONCEPT 4.7 Extracellular components and connections between cells help coordinate cellular activities 94
- Cell Walls of Plants 94
- The Extracellular Matrix (ECM) of Animal Cells 95
- Cell Junctions 96
- The Cell: A Living Unit Greater Than the Sum of Its Parts 97

5 · Membrane Transport and Cell Signaling 100

OVERVIEW Life at the Edge 100

CONCEPT 5.1 Cellular membranes are fluid mosaics of lipids and proteins 100
- The Fluidity of Membranes 101
- Evolution of Differences in Membrane Lipid Composition 102
- Membrane Proteins and Their Functions 103
- The Role of Membrane Carbohydrates in Cell-Cell Recognition 104
- Synthesis and Sidedness of Membranes 104

CONCEPT 5.2 Membrane structure results in selective permeability 105
- The Permeability of the Lipid Bilayer 105
- Transport Proteins 105

CONCEPT 5.3 Passive transport is diffusion of a substance across a membrane with no energy investment 105
- Effects of Osmosis on Water Balance 106
- Facilitated Diffusion: Passive Transport Aided by Proteins 108

CONCEPT 5.4 Active transport uses energy to move solutes against their gradients 109
- The Need for Energy in Active Transport 109
- How Ion Pumps Maintain Membrane Potential 110
- Cotransport: Coupled Transport by a Membrane Protein 111

CONCEPT 5.5 Bulk transport across the plasma membrane occurs by exocytosis and endocytosis 112
- Exocytosis 112
- Endocytosis 112

CONCEPT 5.6 The plasma membrane plays a key role in most cell signaling 114
- Local and Long-Distance Signaling 114
- The Three Stages of Cell Signaling: A Preview 115
- Reception, the Binding of a Signaling Molecule to a Receptor Protein 115
- Transduction by Cascades of Molecular Interactions 117
- Response: Regulation of Transcription or Cytoplasmic Activities 119

6 · An Introduction to Metabolism 122

OVERVIEW The Energy of Life 122

CONCEPT 6.1 An organism's metabolism transforms matter and energy 122
- Metabolic Pathways 122
- Forms of Energy 123
- The Laws of Energy Transformation 124

CONCEPT 6.2 The free-energy change of a reaction tells us whether or not the reaction occurs spontaneously 125
- Free-Energy Change (ΔG), Stability, and Equilibrium 125
- Free Energy and Metabolism 126

CONCEPT 6.3 ATP powers cellular work by coupling exergonic reactions to endergonic reactions 128
- The Structure and Hydrolysis of ATP 128
- How the Hydrolysis of ATP Performs Work 129
- The Regeneration of ATP 130

CONCEPT 6.4 Enzymes speed up metabolic reactions by lowering energy barriers 131
- The Activation Energy Barrier 131
- How Enzymes Speed Up Reactions 132
- Substrate Specificity of Enzymes 132
- Catalysis in the Enzyme's Active Site 133
- Effects of Local Conditions on Enzyme Activity 135
- The Evolution of Enzymes 136

11   Mendel and the Gene Idea 214

OVERVIEW Drawing from the Deck of Genes 214

CONCEPT 11.1 Mendel used the scientific approach to identify two laws of inheritance 215
- Mendel's Experimental, Quantitative Approach 215
- The Law of Segregation 215
- The Law of Independent Assortment 219

CONCEPT 11.2 Probability laws govern Mendelian inheritance 221
- The Multiplication and Addition Rules Applied to Monohybrid Crosses 221
- Solving Complex Genetics Problems with the Rules of Probability 222

CONCEPT 11.3 Inheritance patterns are often more complex than predicted by simple Mendelian genetics 223
- Extending Mendelian Genetics for a Single Gene 223
- Extending Mendelian Genetics for Two or More Genes 225
- Nature and Nurture: The Environmental Impact on Phenotype 226
- A Mendelian View of Heredity and Variation 226

CONCEPT 11.4 Many human traits follow Mendelian patterns of inheritance 228
- Pedigree Analysis 228
- Recessively Inherited Disorders 229
- Dominantly Inherited Disorders 231
- Multifactorial Disorders 231
- Genetic Counseling Based on Mendelian Genetics 231

12   The Chromosomal Basis of Inheritance 236

OVERVIEW Locating Genes Along Chromosomes 236

CONCEPT 12.1 Morgan showed that Mendelian inheritance has its physical basis in the behavior of chromosomes: *scientific inquiry* 238
- Morgan's Choice of Experimental Organism 238
- Correlating Behavior of a Gene's Alleles with Behavior of a Chromosome Pair 238

CONCEPT 12.2 Sex-linked genes exhibit unique patterns of inheritance 239
- The Chromosomal Basis of Sex 239
- Inheritance of X-Linked Genes 240
- X Inactivation in Female Mammals 241

CONCEPT 12.3 Linked genes tend to be inherited together because they are located near each other on the same chromosome 242
- How Linkage Affects Inheritance 242
- Genetic Recombination and Linkage 243
- Mapping the Distance Between Genes Using Recombination Data: *Scientific Inquiry* 245

CONCEPT 12.4 Alterations of chromosome number or structure cause some genetic disorders 248
- Abnormal Chromosome Number 248
- Alterations of Chromosome Structure 249
- Human Disorders Due to Chromosomal Alterations 249

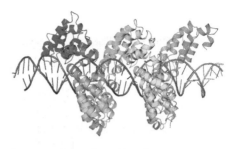

13   The Molecular Basis of Inheritance 253

OVERVIEW Life's Operating Instructions 253

CONCEPT 13.1 DNA is the genetic material 254
- The Search for the Genetic Material: *Scientific Inquiry* 254
- Building a Structural Model of DNA: *Scientific Inquiry* 256

CONCEPT 13.2 Many proteins work together in DNA replication and repair 259
- The Basic Principle: Base Pairing to a Template Strand 260
- DNA Replication: *A Closer Look* 260
- Proofreading and Repairing DNA 266
- Evolutionary Significance of Altered DNA Nucleotides 266
- Replicating the Ends of DNA Molecules 267

CONCEPT 13.3 A chromosome consists of a DNA molecule packed together with proteins 267

CONCEPT 13.4 Understanding DNA structure and replication makes genetic engineering possible 270
- DNA Cloning: Making Multiple Copies of a Gene or Other DNA Segment 270
- Using Restriction Enzymes to Make a Recombinant DNA Plasmid 271
- Amplifying DNA: The Polymerase Chain Reaction (PCR) and Its Use in Cloning 272
- DNA Sequencing 273
- Editing Genes and Genomes 274

14   Gene Expression: From Gene to Protein 278

OVERVIEW The Flow of Genetic Information 278

CONCEPT 14.1 Genes specify proteins via transcription and translation 279
- Evidence from the Study of Metabolic Defects 279
- Basic Principles of Transcription and Translation 280
- The Genetic Code 282

CONCEPT 14.2 Transcription is the DNA-directed synthesis of RNA: *a closer look* 284
- Molecular Components of Transcription 284
- Synthesis of an RNA Transcript 284

CONCEPT 14.3 Eukaryotic cells modify RNA after transcription 286
- Alteration of mRNA Ends 286
- Split Genes and RNA Splicing 287

CONCEPT 14.4 Translation is the RNA-directed synthesis of a polypeptide: *a closer look* 288
- Molecular Components of Translation 288
- Building a Polypeptide 291
- Completing and Targeting the Functional Protein 292
- Making Multiple Polypeptides in Bacteria and Eukaryotes 296

CONCEPT 14.5 Mutations of one or a few nucleotides can affect protein structure and function 298
- Types of Small-Scale Mutations 298
- New Mutations and Mutagens 300
- What Is a Gene? *Revisiting the Question* 300

CONCEPT **6.5** Regulation of enzyme activity helps control metabolism 136
    Allosteric Regulation of Enzymes 137
    Organization of Enzymes Within the Cell 138

7 Cellular Respiration and Fermentation 141

OVERVIEW Life Is Work 141

CONCEPT **7.1** Catabolic pathways yield energy by oxidizing organic fuels 142
    Catabolic Pathways and Production of ATP 142
    Redox Reactions: Oxidation and Reduction 142
    The Stages of Cellular Respiration: *A Preview* 145

CONCEPT **7.2** Glycolysis harvests chemical energy by oxidizing glucose to pyruvate 147

CONCEPT **7.3** After pyruvate is oxidized, the citric acid cycle completes the energy-yielding oxidation of organic molecules 148

CONCEPT **7.4** During oxidative phosphorylation, chemiosmosis couples electron transport to ATP synthesis 149
    The Pathway of Electron Transport 150
    Chemiosmosis: The Energy-Coupling Mechanism 151
    An Accounting of ATP Production by Cellular Respiration 153

CONCEPT **7.5** Fermentation and anaerobic respiration enable cells to produce ATP without the use of oxygen 154
    Types of Fermentation 156
    Comparing Fermentation with Anaerobic and Aerobic Respiration 156
    The Evolutionary Significance of Glycolysis 157

CONCEPT **7.6** Glycolysis and the citric acid cycle connect to many other metabolic pathways 157
    The Versatility of Catabolism 157
    Biosynthesis (Anabolic Pathways) 158

8 Photosynthesis 161

OVERVIEW The Process That Feeds the Biosphere 161

CONCEPT **8.1** Photosynthesis converts light energy to the chemical energy of food 162
    Chloroplasts: The Sites of Photosynthesis in Plants 162
    Tracking Atoms Through Photosynthesis: *Scientific Inquiry* 163
    The Two Stages of Photosynthesis: *A Preview* 164

CONCEPT **8.2** The light reactions convert solar energy to the chemical energy of ATP and NADPH 165
    The Nature of Sunlight 165
    Photosynthetic Pigments: The Light Receptors 166
    Excitation of Chlorophyll by Light 168
    A Photosystem: A Reaction-Center Complex Associated with Light-Harvesting Complexes 169

    Linear Electron Flow 170
    A Comparison of Chemiosmosis in Chloroplasts and Mitochondria 171

CONCEPT **8.3** The Calvin cycle uses the chemical energy of ATP and NADPH to reduce CO_2 to sugar 173
    Evolution of Alternative Mechanisms of Carbon Fixation in Hot, Arid Climates 175
    The Importance of Photosynthesis: *A Review* 176

9 The Cell Cycle 182

OVERVIEW The Key Roles of Cell Division 182

CONCEPT **9.1** Most cell division results in genetically identical daughter cells 183
    Cellular Organization of the Genetic Material 183
    Distribution of Chromosomes During Eukaryotic Cell Division 183

CONCEPT **9.2** The mitotic phase alternates with interphase in the cell cycle 185
    Phases of the Cell Cycle 185
    The Mitotic Spindle: *A Closer Look* 185
    Cytokinesis: *A Closer Look* 188
    Binary Fission in Bacteria 190
    The Evolution of Mitosis 191

CONCEPT **9.3** The eukaryotic cell cycle is regulated by a molecular control system 192
    Evidence for Cytoplasmic Signals 192
    Checkpoints of the Cell Cycle Control System 192
    Loss of Cell Cycle Controls in Cancer Cells 195

UNIT 2 Genetics 199

10 Meiosis and Sexual Life Cycles 200

OVERVIEW Variations on a Theme 200

CONCEPT **10.1** Offspring acquire genes from parents by inheriting chromosomes 201
    Inheritance of Genes 201
    Comparison of Asexual and Sexual Reproduction 201

CONCEPT **10.2** Fertilization and meiosis alternate in sexual life cycles 202
    Sets of Chromosomes in Human Cells 202
    Behavior of Chromosome Sets in the Human Life Cycle 203
    The Variety of Sexual Life Cycles 204

CONCEPT **10.3** Meiosis reduces the number of chromosome sets from diploid to haploid 205
    The Stages of Meiosis 205
    Crossing Over and Synapsis During Prophase I 208
    A Comparison of Mitosis and Meiosis 208

CONCEPT **10.4** Genetic variation produced in sexual life cycles contributes to evolution 210
    Origins of Genetic Variation Among Offspring 210
    The Evolutionary Significance of Genetic Variation Within Populations 212

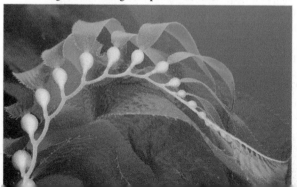

UNIT 3 Evolution 378

19 Descent with Modification 379

OVERVIEW Endless Forms Most Beautiful 379

CONCEPT 19.1 The Darwinian revolution challenged traditional views of a young Earth inhabited by unchanging species 380
Scala Naturae and Classification of Species 380
Ideas About Change over Time 380
Lamarck's Hypothesis of Evolution 381

CONCEPT 19.2 Descent with modification by natural selection explains the adaptations of organisms and the unity and diversity of life 382
Darwin's Research 382
Ideas from The Origin of Species 384

CONCEPT 19.3 Evolution is supported by an overwhelming amount of scientific evidence 387
Direct Observations of Evolutionary Change 387
Homology 389
The Fossil Record 390
Biogeography 391
What Is Theoretical About Darwin's View of Life? 392

20 Phylogeny 395

OVERVIEW Investigating the Evolutionary History of Life 395

CONCEPT 20.1 Phylogenies show evolutionary relationships 396
Binomial Nomenclature 396
Hierarchical Classification 396
Linking Classification and Phylogeny 397
What We Can and Cannot Learn from Phylogenetic Trees 398
Applying Phylogenies 398

CONCEPT 20.2 Phylogenies are inferred from morphological and molecular data 399
Morphological and Molecular Homologies 399
Sorting Homology from Analogy 399
Evaluating Molecular Homologies 400

CONCEPT 20.3 Shared characters are used to construct phylogenetic trees 401
Cladistics 401
Phylogenetic Trees with Proportional Branch Lengths 402
Maximum Parsimony 405
Phylogenetic Trees as Hypotheses 405

CONCEPT 20.4 Molecular clocks help track evolutionary time 406
Molecular Clocks 406
Applying a Molecular Clock: Dating the Origin of HIV 407

CONCEPT 20.5 New information continues to revise our understanding of evolutionary history 408
From Two Kingdoms to Three Domains 408
The Important Role of Horizontal Gene Transfer 409

21 The Evolution of Populations 413

OVERVIEW The Smallest Unit of Evolution 413

CONCEPT 21.1 Genetic variation makes evolution possible 414
Genetic Variation 414
Sources of Genetic Variation 415

CONCEPT 21.2 The Hardy-Weinberg equation can be used to test whether a population is evolving 417
Gene Pools and Allele Frequencies 417
The Hardy-Weinberg Equation 417

CONCEPT 21.3 Natural selection, genetic drift, and gene flow can alter allele frequencies in a population 421
Natural Selection 421
Genetic Drift 421
Gene Flow 423

CONCEPT 21.4 Natural selection is the only mechanism that consistently causes adaptive evolution 424
Natural Selection: A Closer Look 424
The Key Role of Natural Selection in Adaptive Evolution 426
Balancing Selection 426
Sexual Selection 427
Why Natural Selection Cannot Fashion Perfect Organisms 430

22 The Origin of Species 434

OVERVIEW That "Mystery of Mysteries" 434

CONCEPT 22.1 The biological species concept emphasizes reproductive isolation 434
The Biological Species Concept 435
Other Definitions of Species 438

CONCEPT 22.2 Speciation can take place with or without geographic separation 439
Allopatric ("Other Country") Speciation 439
Sympatric ("Same Country") Speciation 440
Allopatric and Sympatric Speciation: A Review 443

CONCEPT 22.3 Hybrid zones reveal factors that cause reproductive isolation 444
Patterns Within Hybrid Zones 445
Hybrid Zones over Time 445

CONCEPT 22.4 Speciation can occur rapidly or slowly and can result from changes in few or many genes 446
The Time Course of Speciation 447
Studying the Genetics of Speciation 448
From Speciation to Macroevolution 449

UNIT 7 Ecology 839

40 Population Ecology and the Distribution of Organisms 840

OVERVIEW Discovering Ecology 840

CONCEPT 40.1 Earth's climate influences the distribution of terrestrial biomes 843
  Global Climate Patterns 843
  Regional Effects on Climate 843
  Climate and Terrestrial Biomes 844
  General Features of Terrestrial Biomes 845

CONCEPT 40.2 Aquatic biomes are diverse and dynamic systems that cover most of Earth 849

CONCEPT 40.3 Interactions between organisms and the environment limit the distribution of species 852
  Dispersal and Distribution 852
  Biotic Factors 853
  Abiotic Factors 853

CONCEPT 40.4 Biotic and abiotic factors affect population density, dispersion, and demographics 854
  Density and Dispersion 854
  Demographics 856

CONCEPT 40.5 The exponential and logistic models describe the growth of populations 857
  Changes in Population Size 857
  Exponential Growth 858
  Carrying Capacity 858
  The Logistic Growth Model 859
  The Logistic Model and Real Populations 860

CONCEPT 40.6 Population dynamics are influenced strongly by life history traits and population density 861
  "Trade-offs" and Life Histories 861
  Population Change and Population Density 862
  Mechanisms of Density-Dependent Population Regulation 862
  Population Dynamics 862

41 Species Interactions 867

OVERVIEW Communities in Motion 867

CONCEPT 41.1 Interactions within a community may help, harm, or have no effect on the species involved 868
  Competition 868
  Exploitation 869
  Positive Interactions 872

CONCEPT 41.2 Diversity and trophic structure characterize biological communities 873
  Species Diversity 873
  Diversity and Community Stability 875
  Trophic Structure 875
  Species with a Large Impact 876
  Bottom-Up and Top-Down Controls 877

CONCEPT 41.3 Disturbance influences species diversity and composition 878
  Characterizing Disturbance 878
  Ecological Succession 879
  Human Disturbance 880

CONCEPT 41.4 Biogeographic factors affect community diversity 881
  Latitudinal Gradients 881
  Area Effects 882

CONCEPT 41.5 Pathogens alter community structure locally and globally 883
  Effects on Community Structure 883
  Community Ecology and Zoonotic Diseases 883

42 Ecosystems and Energy 886

OVERVIEW Transformed to Tundra 886

CONCEPT 42.1 Physical laws govern energy flow and chemical cycling in ecosystems 887
  Conservation of Energy 887
  Conservation of Mass 887
  Energy, Mass, and Trophic Levels 888

CONCEPT 42.2 Energy and other limiting factors control primary production in ecosystems 888
  Ecosystem Energy Budgets 889
  Primary Production in Aquatic Ecosystems 890
  Primary Production in Terrestrial Ecosystems 891

CONCEPT 42.3 Energy transfer between trophic levels is typically only 10% efficient 892
  Production Efficiency 892
  Trophic Efficiency and Ecological Pyramids 893

CONCEPT 42.4 Biological and geochemical processes cycle nutrients and water in ecosystems 895
  Decomposition and Nutrient Cycling Rates 895
  Biogeochemical Cycles 895
  Case Study: Nutrient Cycling in the Hubbard Brook Experimental Forest 898

CONCEPT 42.5 Restoration ecologists return degraded ecosystems to a more natural state 899

    Bioremediation 899
    Biological Augmentation 901
    Ecosystems: *A Review* 901

Appendix A   Answers A-1

Appendix B   Periodic Table of the Elements B-1

Appendix C   The Metric System C-1

Appendix D   A Comparison of the Light Microscope and the Electron Microscope D-1

Appendix E   Classification of Life E-1

Appendix F   Scientific Skills Review F-1

Credits   CR-1

Glossary   G-1

Index   I-1

1 Introduction: Evolution and the Foundations of Biology

KEY CONCEPTS

1.1 The study of life reveals common themes

1.2 The Core Theme: Evolution accounts for the unity and diversity of life

1.3 In studying nature, scientists form and test hypotheses

▲ **Figure 1.1 What can this beach mouse (*Peromyscus polionotus*) teach us about biology?**

Inquiring About Life

There are few hiding places for a mouse among the sparse clumps of beach grass that dot the brilliant white sand dunes along the Florida seashore. However, the beach mice that live there have light, dappled fur, allowing them to blend into their surroundings **(Figure 1.1)**. Mice of the same species (*Peromyscus polionotus*) also inhabit nearby inland areas. These mice are much darker in color, as are the soil and vegetation where they live **(Figure 1.2)**. For both beach mice and inland mice, the close color match of coat (fur) and environment is vital for survival, since hawks, herons, and other sharp-eyed predators periodically scan the landscape for prey. How has the color of each group of mice come to be so well matched, or *adapted*, to the local background?

An organism's adaptations to its environment, such as the mouse's protective camouflage, are the result of **evolution**, the process of change over time that has

▲ **Figure 1.2 An inland mouse of the species *Peromyscus polionotus*.** This mouse has a much darker back, side, and face than mice of the same species that inhabit sand dunes.

resulted in the astounding array of organisms found on Earth. Evolution is the fundamental principle of biology and the core theme of this book.

Posing questions about the living world and seeking answers through scientific inquiry are the central activities of **biology**, the scientific study of life. Biologists' questions can be ambitious. They may ask how a single tiny cell becomes a tree or a dog, how the human mind works, or how the different forms of life in a forest interact. When questions occur to you as you observe the living world, you are thinking like a biologist.

How do biologists make sense of life's diversity and complexity? This opening chapter sets up a framework for answering this question. We begin with a panoramic view of the biological "landscape," organized around a set of unifying themes. We'll then focus on biology's core theme, evolution. Finally, we'll examine the process of scientific inquiry—how scientists ask and attempt to answer questions about the natural world.

The study of life reveals common themes

Biology is a subject of enormous scope, and exciting new biological discoveries are being made every day. How can you organize and make sense of all the information you'll encounter as you study biology? Focusing on a few big ideas will help. Here are five unifying themes—ways of thinking about life that will still hold true decades from now:

- Organization
- Information
- Energy and Matter
- Interactions
- Evolution

In this chapter, we'll briefly define and explore each theme.

Theme: New Properties Emerge at Successive Levels of Biological Organization

ORGANIZATION The study of life on Earth extends from the microscopic scale of the molecules and cells that make up organisms to the global scale of the entire living planet. As biologists, we can divide this enormous range into different levels of biological organization.

In **Figure 1.3**, we zoom in from space to take a closer and closer look at life in a mountain meadow. This journey, depicted in the figure as a series of numbered steps, highlights the hierarchy of biological organization.

Zooming in at ever-finer resolution illustrates the principle that underlies *reductionism*, an approach that reduces complex systems to simpler components that are more manageable to study. Reductionism is a powerful strategy in biology. For example, by studying the molecular structure of DNA that had been extracted from cells, James Watson and Francis Crick inferred the chemical basis of biological inheritance. Despite its importance, reductionism provides an incomplete view of life, as we'll discuss next.

Emergent Properties

Let's reexamine Figure 1.3, beginning this time at the molecular level and then zooming out. Viewed this way, we see that novel properties emerge at each level that are absent from the preceding one. These **emergent properties** are due to the arrangement and interactions of parts as complexity increases. For example, although photosynthesis occurs in an intact chloroplast, it will not take place if chlorophyll and other chloroplast molecules are simply mixed in a test tube. The coordinated processes of photosynthesis require a specific organization of these molecules in the chloroplast. In general, isolated components of living systems—the objects

of study in a reductionist approach—lack a number of significant properties that emerge at higher levels of organization.

Emergent properties are not unique to life. A box of bicycle parts won't transport you anywhere, but if they are arranged in a certain way, you can pedal to your chosen destination. Compared with such nonliving examples, however, biological systems are far more complex, making the emergent properties of life especially challenging to study.

To fully explore emergent properties, biologists complement reductionism with **systems biology**, the exploration of the network of interactions that underlie the emergent properties of a system. A single leaf cell can be considered a system, as can a frog, an ant colony, or a desert ecosystem. By examining and modeling the dynamic behavior of an integrated network of components, systems biology enables us to pose new kinds of questions. For example, how do networks of genes in our cells produce oscillations in the activity of the molecules that generate our 24-hour cycle of wakefulness and sleep? At a larger scale, how does a gradual increase in atmospheric carbon dioxide alter ecosystems and the entire biosphere? Systems biology can be used to study life at all levels.

Structure and Function

At each level of biological organization, we find a correlation between structure and function. Consider a leaf in Figure 1.3: Its thin, flat shape maximizes the capture of sunlight by chloroplasts. Because such correlations of structure and function are common in all forms of life, analyzing a biological structure gives us clues about what it does and how it works. A good example from the animal kingdom is the hummingbird. The hummingbird's anatomy allows its wings to rotate at the shoulder, so hummingbirds have the ability, unique among birds, to fly backward or hover in place. While hovering, the birds can extend their long slender beaks into flowers and feed on nectar. Such an elegant match of form and function in the structures of life is explained by natural selection, as we'll explore shortly.

The Cell: An Organism's Basic Unit of Structure and Function

The cell is the smallest unit of organization that can perform all activities required for life. In fact, the actions of an organism are all based on the activities of its cells. For instance, the movement of your eyes as you read this sentence results from the activities of muscle and nerve cells. Even a process that occurs on a global scale, such as the recycling of carbon atoms, is the cumulative product of cellular functions,

◄ 1 The Biosphere

Even from space, we can see signs of Earth's life—in the green mosaic of the forests, for example. We can also see the entire **biosphere**, which consists of all life on Earth and all the places where life exists: most regions of land, most bodies of water, the atmosphere to an altitude of several kilometers, and even sediments far below the ocean floor.

◄ 2 Ecosystems

Our first scale change brings us to a North American mountain meadow, which is an example of an ecosystem, as are tropical forests, grasslands, deserts, and coral reefs. An **ecosystem** consists of all the living things in a particular area, along with all the nonliving components of the environment with which life interacts, such as soil, water, atmospheric gases, and light.

► 3 Communities

The array of organisms inhabiting a particular ecosystem is called a biological **community**. The community in our meadow ecosystem includes many kinds of plants, various animals, mushrooms and other fungi, and enormous numbers of diverse microorganisms, such as bacteria, that are too small to see without a microscope. Each of these forms of life belongs to a *species*—a group whose members can only reproduce with other members of the group.

► 4 Populations

A **population** consists of all the individuals of a species living within the bounds of a specified area. For example, our meadow includes a population of lupine (some of which are shown here) and a population of mule deer. A community is therefore the set of populations that inhabit a particular area.

▲ 5 Organisms

Individual living things are called **organisms**. Each plant in the meadow is an organism, and so is each animal, fungus, and bacterium.

including the photosynthetic activity of chloroplasts in leaf cells.

All cells share certain characteristics, such as being enclosed by a membrane that regulates the passage of materials between the cell and its surroundings. Nevertheless, we distinguish two main forms of cells: prokaryotic and eukaryotic. The cells of two groups of single-celled microorganisms—bacteria and archaea—are prokaryotic. All other forms of life, including plants and animals, are composed of eukaryotic cells.

A **eukaryotic cell** contains membrane-enclosed organelles (**Figure 1.4**). Some organelles, such as the DNA-containing nucleus, are found in the cells of all eukaryotes; other organelles are specific to particular cell types. For example, the chloroplast in Figure 1.3 is an organelle found only in eukaryotic cells that carry out photosynthesis. In contrast to eukaryotic cells, a **prokaryotic cell** lacks a nucleus or other membrane-enclosed organelles. Furthermore, prokaryotic cells are generally smaller than eukaryotic cells, as shown in Figure 1.4.

▼ 6 Organs

The structural hierarchy of life continues to unfold as we explore the architecture of a complex organism. A leaf is an example of an **organ**, a body part that is made up of multiple tissues and has specific functions in the body. Leaves, stems, and roots are the major organs of plants. Within an organ, each tissue has a distinct arrangement and contributes particular properties to organ function.

▼ 7 Tissues

Viewing the tissues of a leaf requires a microscope. Each **tissue** is a group of cells that work together, performing a specialized function. The leaf shown here has been cut on an angle. The honeycombed tissue in the interior of the leaf (left side of photo) is the main location of photosynthesis, the process that converts light energy to the chemical energy of sugar. The jigsaw puzzle–like "skin" on the surface of the leaf is a tissue called epidermis (right side of photo). The pores through the epidermis allow entry of the gas CO_2, a raw material for sugar production.

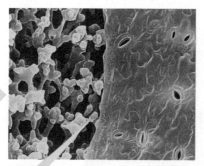

50 µm

▶ 8 Cells

The **cell** is life's fundamental unit of structure and function. Some organisms consist of a single cell, which performs all the functions of life. Other organisms are multicellular and feature a division of labor among specialized cells. Here we see a magnified view of a cell in a leaf tissue. This cell is about 40 micrometers (µm) across—about 500 of them would reach across a small coin. Within these tiny cells are even smaller green structures called chloroplasts, which are responsible for photosynthesis.

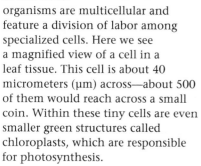

Cell   10 µm

▼ 9 Organelles

Chloroplasts are examples of **organelles**, the various functional components present in cells. The image below, taken by a powerful microscope, shows a single chloroplast.

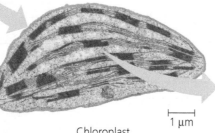

Chloroplast   1 µm

▼ 10 Molecules

Our last scale change drops us into a chloroplast for a view of life at the molecular level. A **molecule** is a chemical structure consisting of two or more units called atoms, represented as balls in this computer graphic of a chlorophyll molecule.

Chlorophyll is the pigment that makes a leaf green, and it absorbs sunlight during photosynthesis. Within each chloroplast, millions of chlorophyll molecules are organized into systems that convert light energy to the chemical energy of food.

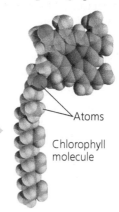

Atoms

Chlorophyll molecule

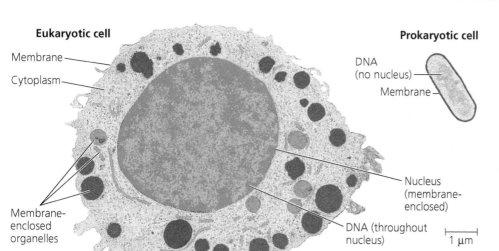

Eukaryotic cell

Membrane

Cytoplasm

Membrane-enclosed organelles

Prokaryotic cell

DNA (no nucleus)

Membrane

Nucleus (membrane-enclosed)

DNA (throughout nucleus)

1 µm

◀ **Figure 1.4 Contrasting eukaryotic and prokaryotic cells in size and complexity.** Cells vary in size, but eukaryotic cells are generally much larger than prokaryotic cells.

Theme: Life's Processes Involve the Expression and Transmission of Genetic Information

INFORMATION Within cells, structures called chromosomes contain genetic material in the form of **DNA (deoxyribonucleic acid)**. In cells that are preparing to divide, the chromosomes may be made visible using a dye that appears blue when bound to the DNA **(Figure 1.5)**.

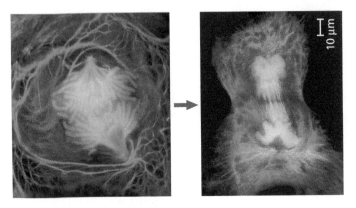

▲ **Figure 1.5 A lung cell from a newt divides into two smaller cells that will grow and divide again.**

DNA, the Genetic Material

Each chromosome contains one very long DNA molecule with hundreds or thousands of **genes**, each a section of the DNA of the chromosome. Transmitted from parents to offspring, genes are the units of inheritance. They encode the information necessary to build all of the molecules synthesized within a cell, which in turn establish that cell's identity and function. You began as a single cell stocked with DNA inherited from your parents. The replication of that DNA during each round of cell division transmitted copies of the DNA to what eventually became the trillions of cells of your body. As the cells grew and divided, the genetic information encoded by the DNA directed your development **(Figure 1.6)**.

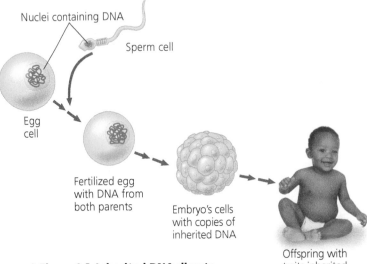

▲ **Figure 1.6 Inherited DNA directs development of an organism.**

The molecular structure of DNA accounts for its ability to store information. A DNA molecule is made up of two long chains, called strands, arranged in a double helix. Each chain is made up of four kinds of chemical building blocks called nucleotides, abbreviated A, T, C, and G **(Figure 1.7)**. Specific sequences of these four nucleotides encode the information in genes. The way DNA encodes information is analogous to how we arrange the letters of the alphabet into words and phrases with specific meanings. The word *rat*, for example, evokes a rodent; the words *tar* and *art*, which contain the same letters, mean very different things. We can think of the set of nucleotides as a four-letter alphabet.

For many genes, the sequence provides the blueprint for making a protein. For instance, a given bacterial gene may specify a particular protein (an enzyme) required to assemble the cell membrane, while a certain human gene may denote a different protein (an antibody) that helps fight off infection. Overall, proteins are major players in building and maintaining the cell and in carrying out its activities.

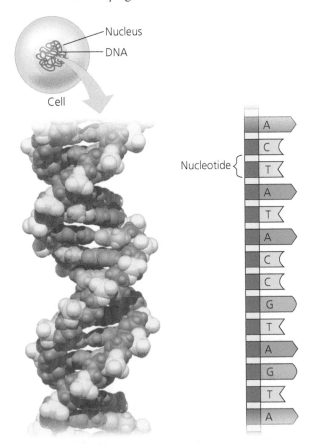

(a) DNA double helix. This model shows the atoms in a segment of DNA. Made up of two long chains (strands) of building blocks called nucleotides, a DNA molecule takes the three-dimensional form of a double helix.

(b) Single strand of DNA. These geometric shapes and letters are simple symbols for the nucleotides in a small section of one strand of a DNA molecule. Genetic information is encoded in specific sequences of the four types of nucleotides. Their names are abbreviated A, T, C, and G.

▲ **Figure 1.7 DNA: The genetic material.**

Genes control protein production indirectly, using a related molecule called mRNA as an intermediary (**Figure 1.8**). The sequence of nucleotides along a gene is transcribed into mRNA, which is then translated into a chain of protein building blocks called amino acids. Once completed, this chain forms a specific protein with a unique shape and function. The entire process by which the information in a gene directs the production of a cellular product is called **gene expression**.

In carrying out gene expression, all forms of life employ essentially the same genetic code: A particular sequence of nucleotides says the same thing in one organism as it does in another. Differences between organisms reflect differences between their nucleotide sequences rather than between their genetic codes. This universality of the genetic code is a strong piece of evidence that all life is related. Comparing the sequences in several species for a gene that codes for a particular protein can provide valuable information both about the protein and about the evolutionary relationship of the species to each other.

The mRNA molecule in Figure 1.8 is translated into a protein, but other cellular RNAs function differently. For example, we have known for decades that some types of RNA are actually components of the cellular machinery that manufactures proteins. Recently, scientists have discovered whole new classes of RNA that play other roles in the cell, such as regulating the function of protein-coding genes. Genes also specify all of these RNAs, and their production is also referred to as gene expression. By carrying the instructions for making proteins and RNAs and by replicating with each cell division, DNA ensures faithful inheritance of genetic information from generation to generation.

Genomics: Large-Scale Analysis of DNA Sequences

The entire "library" of genetic instructions that an organism inherits is called its **genome**. A typical human cell has two similar sets of chromosomes, and each set has approximately 3 billion nucleotide pairs of DNA. If the one-letter abbreviations for the nucleotides of one strand in a set were written in letters the size of those you are now reading, the genomic text would fill about 700 biology textbooks.

Since the early 1990s, the pace at which researchers can determine the sequence of a genome has accelerated at an astounding rate, enabled by a revolution in technology. The genome sequence—the entire sequence of nucleotides for a representative member of a species—is now known for humans and many other animals, as well as numerous plants, fungi, bacteria, and archaea. To make sense of the deluge of data from genome-sequencing projects and the growing catalog of known gene functions, scientists are applying a systems biology approach at the cellular and molecular levels. Rather than investigating a single gene at a time, researchers study whole sets of genes in one or more species—an approach called **genomics**. Likewise, the term **proteomics** refers to the study of sets of proteins and their properties. (The entire set of proteins expressed by a given cell or group of cells is called a **proteome**.)

▼ **Figure 1.8 Gene expression: Cells use information encoded in a gene to synthesize a functional protein.**

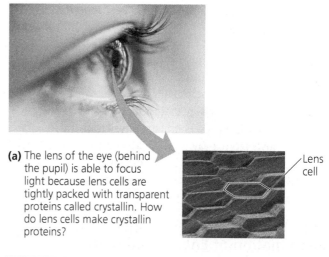

(a) The lens of the eye (behind the pupil) is able to focus light because lens cells are tightly packed with transparent proteins called crystallin. How do lens cells make crystallin proteins?

Lens cell

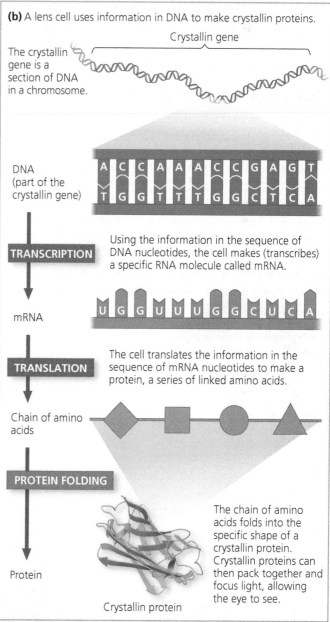

(b) A lens cell uses information in DNA to make crystallin proteins.

Crystallin gene

The crystallin gene is a section of DNA in a chromosome.

DNA (part of the crystallin gene)

A C C A A A C C G A G T
T G G T T T G G C T C A

TRANSCRIPTION

Using the information in the sequence of DNA nucleotides, the cell makes (transcribes) a specific RNA molecule called mRNA.

mRNA

U G G U U U G G C U C A

TRANSLATION

The cell translates the information in the sequence of mRNA nucleotides to make a protein, a series of linked amino acids.

Chain of amino acids

PROTEIN FOLDING

The chain of amino acids folds into the specific shape of a crystallin protein. Crystallin proteins can then pack together and focus light, allowing the eye to see.

Protein

Crystallin protein

Three important research developments have made the genomic and proteomic approaches possible. One is "high-throughput" technology, tools that can analyze many biological samples very rapidly. The second major development is **bioinformatics**, the use of computational tools to store, organize, and analyze the huge volume of data that results from high-throughput methods. The third key development is the formation of interdisciplinary research teams—groups of diverse specialists that may include computer scientists, mathematicians, engineers, chemists, physicists, and, of course, biologists from a variety of fields. Researchers in such teams aim to learn how the activities of all the proteins and RNAs encoded by the DNA are coordinated in cells and in whole organisms.

Theme: Life Requires the Transfer and Transformation of Energy and Matter

ENERGY AND MATTER Moving, growing, reproducing, and the various cellular activities of life are work, and work requires energy. The input of energy, primarily from the sun, and the transformation of energy from one form to another make life possible **(Figure 1.9)**. When a plant's leaves absorb sunlight, molecules within the leaves convert the energy of sunlight to the chemical energy of food, such as sugars, in the process of photosynthesis. The chemical energy in food molecules is then passed along by plants and other photosynthetic organisms (producers) to consumers. A consumer is an organism that obtains its energy by feeding on other organisms or their remains.

When an organism uses chemical energy to perform work, such as muscle contraction or cell division, some of that energy is lost to the surroundings as heat. As a result, energy flows *through* an ecosystem, usually entering as light and exiting as heat. In contrast, chemical elements remain *within* an ecosystem, where they are used and then recycled (see Figure 1.9).

Chemicals that a plant absorbs from the air or soil may be incorporated into the plant's body and then passed to an animal that eats the plant. Eventually, these chemicals will be returned to the environment by decomposers, such as bacteria and fungi, that break down waste products, organic debris, and the bodies of dead organisms. The chemicals are then available to be taken up by plants again, thereby completing the cycle.

Theme: Organisms Interact with Other Organisms and the Physical Environment

INTERACTIONS Every organism in an ecosystem interacts with other organisms. A flowering plant, for example, interacts with soil microorganisms associated with its roots, insects that pollinate its flowers, and animals that eat its leaves and petals. Interactions between organisms include those that are mutually beneficial (as when fish eat small parasites on a turtle, shown in **Figure 1.10**), and those in which one species benefits and the other is harmed (as when a lion kills and eats a zebra). In some interactions between species both are harmed (as when two plants compete for a soil resource that is in short supply).

Each organism in an ecosystem also interacts continuously with physical factors in its environment. The leaves of a flowering plant, for example, absorb light from the sun, take in carbon dioxide from the air, and release oxygen to the air. The environment is also affected by the organisms living there. For example, a plant takes up water and minerals from the soil through its roots, and its roots break up rocks, thereby contributing to the formation of soil. On a global scale, plants and other photosynthetic organisms have generated all the oxygen in the atmosphere.

Like other organisms, we humans interact with our environment. Unfortunately, our interactions sometimes have dire consequences. For example, over the past 150 years, humans have greatly increased the burning of fossil fuels (coal, oil, and gas). This practice releases large amounts of carbon dioxide

▶ **Figure 1.9 Energy flow and chemical cycling.** There is a one-way flow of energy in an ecosystem: During photosynthesis, plants convert energy from sunlight to chemical energy (stored in food molecules such as sugars), which is used by plants and other organisms to do work and is eventually lost from the ecosystem as heat. In contrast, chemicals cycle between organisms and the physical environment.

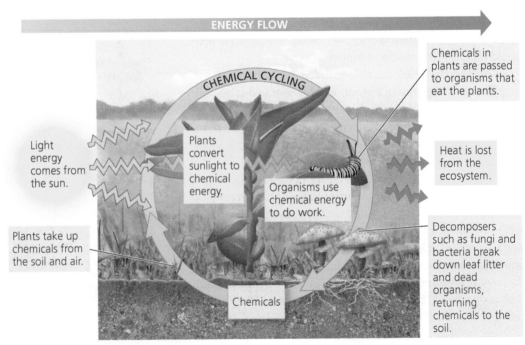

ENERGY FLOW

CHEMICAL CYCLING

Light energy comes from the sun.

Plants convert sunlight to chemical energy.

Organisms use chemical energy to do work.

Chemicals in plants are passed to organisms that eat the plants.

Heat is lost from the ecosystem.

Plants take up chemicals from the soil and air.

Chemicals

Decomposers such as fungi and bacteria break down leaf litter and dead organisms, returning chemicals to the soil.

▶ **Figure 1.10 A mutually beneficial interaction between species.** These fish feed on small organisms living on the sea turtle's skin and shell. The sea turtle benefits from the removal of parasites, and the fish gain a meal and protection from enemies. For more examples of mutually beneficial relationships (mutualisms), see Make Connections Figure 29.10.

(CO_2) and other gases into the atmosphere. About half of this CO_2 stays in the atmosphere, causing heat to be trapped close to Earth's surface (see Figure 43.26). Scientists calculate that the CO_2 that human activities have added to the atmosphere has increased the average temperature of the planet by about 1°C since 1900. At the current rates that CO_2 and other gases are being added to the atmosphere, global models predict an additional rise of at least 3°C before the end of this century.

This ongoing global warming is a major aspect of **climate change**, a directional change to the global climate that lasts for three decades or more (as opposed to short-term changes in the weather). But global warming is not the only way the climate is changing: wind and precipitation patterns are also shifting, and extreme weather events such as storms and droughts are occurring more often. Climate change has already affected organisms and their habitats all over the planet. For example, polar bears have lost much of the ice platform from which they hunt, leading to food shortages and increased mortality rates. As habitats deteriorate, hundreds of plant and animal species are shifting their ranges to more suitable locations—but for some, there is insufficient suitable habitat, or they may not be able to migrate quickly enough. As a result, the populations of many species are shrinking in size or even disappearing **(Figure 1.11)**.

This trend can ultimately result in extinction, the permanent loss of a species. As we'll discuss in greater detail in Concept 43.4, the consequences of these changes for humans and other organisms may be profound.

Evolution, the Core Theme of Biology

Having considered four of the unifying themes that run through this text (organization, information, energy and matter, and interactions), let's now turn to biology's core theme—evolution. Evolution makes sense of everything we know about living organisms. As the fossil record clearly shows, life has been evolving on Earth for billions of years, resulting in a vast diversity of past and present organisms. But along with the diversity there is also unity. For example, while sea horses, jackrabbits, hummingbirds, crocodiles, and giraffes all look very different, their skeletons are organized in the same basic way.

The scientific explanation for the unity and diversity of organisms—as well as for the adaptation of organisms to their particular environments—is **evolution**: the concept that the organisms living on Earth today are the modified descendants of common ancestors. As a result of descent with modification, two species share certain traits (unity) simply because they have descended from a common ancestor. Furthermore, we can account for differences between two species (diversity) with the idea that certain heritable changes occurred after the two species diverged from their common ancestor. An abundance of evidence of different types supports the occurrence of evolution and the theory that describes how it takes place, which we'll discuss in detail in Chapters 19–23. Meanwhile, in the next section, we'll continue our introduction to the fundamental concept of evolution.

▶ **Figure 1.11 Threatened by global warming.** A warmer environment causes lizards in the genus *Sceloporus* to spend more time in refuges from the heat, reducing the time available for foraging. The lizards' food intake drops, decreasing their reproductive success. Indeed, surveys of 200 populations of *Sceloporus* species in Mexico show that 12% of these populations have disappeared since 1975. For more examples of how climate change is affecting life on Earth, see Make Connections Figure 43.28.

CONCEPT CHECK 1.1

1. Starting with the molecular level in Figure 1.3, write a sentence that includes components from the previous (lower) level of biological organization, for example, "A molecule consists of *atoms* bonded together." Continue with organelles, moving up the biological hierarchy.
2. Identify the theme or themes exemplified by (a) the sharp quills of a porcupine, (b) the development of a multicellular organism from a single fertilized egg, and (c) a hummingbird using sugar to power its flight.
3. **WHAT IF?** For each theme discussed in this section, give an example not mentioned in the text.

For suggested answers, see Appendix A.

CONCEPT 1.2

The Core Theme: Evolution accounts for the unity and diversity of life

EVOLUTION Diversity is a hallmark of life. Biologists have identified and named about 1.8 million species of organisms, and estimates of the number of living species range from about 10 million to over 100 million. These remarkably diverse forms of life arose by evolutionary processes. Before exploring evolution further, however, let's first consider how biologists organize the enormous variety of life forms on this planet into manageable and informative groupings.

Classifying the Diversity of Life

Humans have a tendency to group diverse items according to their similarities and relationships to each other. Following this inclination, biologists have long used careful comparisons of form and function to classify life-forms into a hierarchy of increasingly inclusive groups. Consider, for example, the species known as the leopard (*Panthera pardus*). Leopards belong to the same genus (*Panthera*) as tigers and lions. Bringing together several similar genera forms a family, which in turn is a component of an order and then a class. For the leopard, this means being grouped with cougars, cheetahs, and others in the family Felidae, with wolves in the order Carnivora, and with dolphins (and us) in the class Mammalia (see Figure 20.3). These animals can be classified into still broader groupings: the phylum Chordata and the kingdom Animalia.

In the last few decades, new methods of assessing species relationships, especially comparisons of DNA sequences, have led to a reevaluation of the larger groupings. Although this reevaluation is ongoing, there is consensus among biologists that the kingdoms of life, whatever their number, can be further grouped into three higher levels of classification called domains: Bacteria, Archaea, and Eukarya **(Figure 1.12)**.

▼ **Figure 1.12 The three domains of life.**

(a) Domain Bacteria

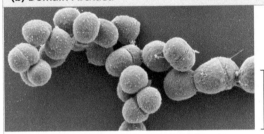

Bacteria are the most diverse and widespread prokaryotes and are now classified into multiple kingdoms. Each rod-shaped structure in this photo is a bacterial cell.

(b) Domain Archaea

Domain Archaea includes multiple kingdoms. Some of the prokaryotes known as **archaea** live in Earth's extreme environments, such as salty lakes and boiling hot springs. Each round structure in this photo is an archaeal cell.

(c) Domain Eukarya

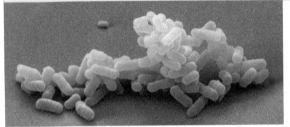

◀ **Kingdom Animalia** consists of multicellular eukaryotes that ingest other organisms.

▲ **Kingdom Plantae** (land plants) consists of terrestrial multicellular eukaryotes that carry out photosynthesis, the conversion of light energy to the chemical energy in food.

▶ **Kingdom Fungi** is defined in part by the nutritional mode of its members (such as this mushroom), which absorb nutrients from outside their bodies.

▶ **Protists** are mostly unicellular eukaryotes and some relatively simple multicellular relatives. Pictured here is an assortment of protists inhabiting pond water. Scientists are currently debating how to classify protists in a way that accurately reflects their evolutionary relationships.

The organisms making up two of the three domains—**Bacteria** and **Archaea**—are prokaryotic. All the eukaryotes (organisms with eukaryotic cells) are grouped in domain **Eukarya**. This domain includes three kingdoms of multicellular eukaryotes: Plantae, Fungi, and Animalia. These three kingdoms are distinguished partly by their modes of nutrition. Plants produce their own sugars and other food molecules by photosynthesis; fungi absorb dissolved nutrients from their surroundings; and animals obtain food by eating and digesting other organisms. Animalia is, of course, our own kingdom.

The most numerous and diverse eukaryotes are the mostly single-celled protists. Although protists once were placed in a single kingdom, they are now classified into several groups. One major reason for this change is the recent DNA evidence showing that some protists are less closely related to other protists than they are to plants, animals, or fungi.

Unity in the Diversity of Life

Although diversity is apparent in the many forms of life, there is also remarkable unity. Consider, for example, the similar skeletons of different animals and the universal genetic language of DNA (the genetic code), both mentioned earlier. In fact, similarities between organisms are evident at all levels of the biological hierarchy.

How can we account for life's dual nature of unity and diversity? The process of evolution, explained next, illuminates both the similarities and differences in the world of life. It also introduces another dimension of biology: the passage of time. The history of life, as documented by fossils and other evidence, is the saga of an ever-changing Earth billions of years old, inhabited by an evolving cast of living forms **(Figure 1.13)**.

▲ **Figure 1.13 Digging into the past.** Paleontologists carefully excavate the hind leg of a long-necked dinosaur (*Rapetosaurus krausei*) from rocks in Madagascar.

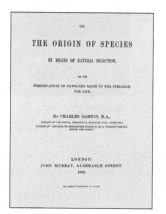

▶ **Figure 1.14 Charles Darwin as a young man.** His revolutionary book, which is commonly referred to as *The Origin of Species*, was first published in 1859.

Charles Darwin and the Theory of Natural Selection

An evolutionary view of life came into sharp focus in 1859, when Charles Darwin published one of the most important and influential books ever written, *On the Origin of Species by Means of Natural Selection* **(Figure 1.14)**. *The Origin of Species* articulated two main points. The first was that species arise from a succession of ancestors that were different from them. Darwin called this process "descent with modification." This insightful phrase captured the duality of life's unity and diversity—unity in the kinship among species that descended from common ancestors and diversity in the modifications that evolved as species branched from their common ancestors **(Figure 1.15)**. Darwin's second main point was his proposal that "natural selection" is a primary cause of descent with modification.

▼ **American flamingo**   ▼ **European robin**   ▼ **Gentoo penguin**

▲ **Figure 1.15 Unity and diversity among birds.** These three birds are variations on a common body plan. For example, each has feathers, a beak, and wings, although these features are highly specialized for the birds' diverse lifestyles.

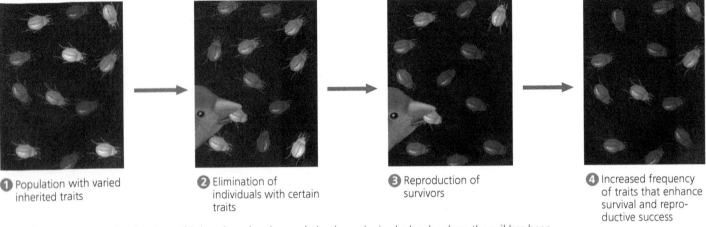

① Population with varied inherited traits

② Elimination of individuals with certain traits

③ Reproduction of survivors

④ Increased frequency of traits that enhance survival and reproductive success

▲ **Figure 1.16 Natural selection.** This imaginary beetle population has colonized a locale where the soil has been blackened by a recent brush fire. Initially, the population varies extensively in the inherited coloration of the individuals, from very light gray to charcoal. For hungry birds that prey on the beetles, it is easiest to spot the beetles that are lightest in color.

Darwin developed his theory of natural selection from observations that by themselves were neither new nor profound. However, although others had described the pieces of the puzzle, it was Darwin who saw how they fit together. His three essential observations were the following: First, individuals in a population vary in their traits, many of which seem to be heritable (passed on from parents to offspring). Second, a population can produce far more offspring than can survive to produce offspring of their own. Competition is thus inevitable. Third, species generally are suited to their environments—in other words, they are adapted to their circumstances. For instance, a common adaptation among birds that eat mostly hard seeds is an especially strong beak.

By making inferences from these three observations, Darwin arrived at his theory of evolution. He reasoned that individuals with inherited traits that are better suited to the local environment are more likely to survive and reproduce than are less well-suited individuals. Over many generations, a higher and higher proportion of individuals in a population will have the advantageous traits. Darwin called this mechanism of evolutionary adaptation **natural selection** because the natural environment consistently "selects" for the propagation of certain traits among naturally occurring variant traits in the population **(Figure 1.16)**.

The Tree of Life

For another example of unity and diversity, consider the human arm. The bones, joints, nerves, and blood vessels in your forelimb are very similar to those in the foreleg of a horse, the flipper of a whale, and the wing of a bat. Indeed, all mammalian forelimbs are anatomical variations of a common architecture. According to the Darwinian concept of descent with modification, the shared anatomy of mammalian limbs reflects inheritance of the limb structure from a common ancestor—the "prototype" mammal from which all other mammals descended. The diversity of mammalian forelimbs results from modification by natural selection operating over millions of years in different environmental contexts.

Darwin proposed that natural selection, by its cumulative effects over long periods of time, could cause an ancestral species to give rise to two or more descendant species. This could occur, for example, if one population of organisms fragmented into several subpopulations isolated in different environments. In these separate arenas of natural selection, one species could gradually radiate into multiple species as the geographically isolated populations adapted over many generations to different environmental conditions.

The "family tree" of six finch species shown in **Figure 1.17** illustrates a famous example of the process of radiation. Darwin collected specimens of finches during his 1835 visit to the remote Galápagos Islands, 900 kilometers (km) west of South America. The Galápagos finches are believed to have descended from an ancestral finch species that reached the archipelago from South America or the Caribbean. Over time, the Galápagos finches diversified from their ancestor as populations became adapted to different food sources on their particular islands. Years after Darwin collected the finches, researchers began to sort out their evolutionary relationships, first from anatomical and geographic data and more recently using DNA sequence comparisons.

Biologists' diagrams of such evolutionary relationships generally take treelike forms, though the trees are often turned sideways, as in Figure 1.17. Tree diagrams make sense: Just as an individual has a genealogy that can be diagrammed as a family tree, each species is one twig of a branching tree of life extending back in time through ancestral species more and more remote. Species that are very similar, such as the Galápagos finches, share a relatively recent common ancestor. Through an ancestor that lived much farther back in time, finches are related to sparrows, hawks, penguins, and all other birds. Furthermore, finches and other birds are related to us through a common ancestor even more ancient. Trace life back far enough, and we reach the early prokaryotes that inhabited Earth 3.5 billion years ago. We can recognize their vestiges in our own cells—in the universal genetic code, for example. Indeed, all of life is connected through its long evolutionary history.

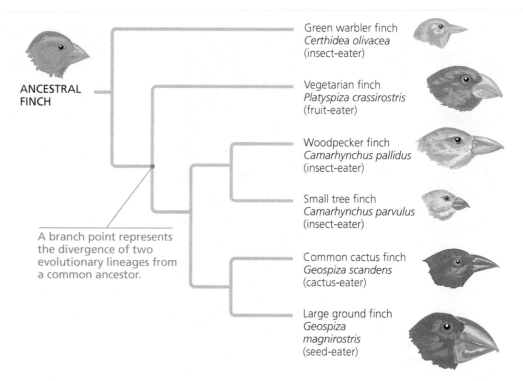

► **Figure 1.17 Descent with modification: finches on the Galápagos Islands.** This "tree" diagram illustrates a current model for the evolutionary relationships of finches on the Galápagos. Note the various beaks, which are adapted to particular food sources. For example, heavier, thicker beaks are better at cracking seeds, while more slender beaks are better at grasping insects.

ANCESTRAL FINCH

Green warbler finch
Certhidea olivacea
(insect-eater)

Vegetarian finch
Platyspiza crassirostris
(fruit-eater)

Woodpecker finch
Camarhynchus pallidus
(insect-eater)

Small tree finch
Camarhynchus parvulus
(insect-eater)

Common cactus finch
Geospiza scandens
(cactus-eater)

Large ground finch
Geospiza magnirostris
(seed-eater)

A branch point represents the divergence of two evolutionary lineages from a common ancestor.

CONCEPT CHECK 1.2

1. How is a mailing address analogous to biology's hierarchical classification system?
2. Explain why "editing" is an appropriate metaphor for how natural selection acts on a population's heritable variation.
3. **DRAW IT** Recent evidence indicates that fungi and animals are more closely related to each other than either of these kingdoms is to plants. Draw a simple branching pattern that symbolizes the proposed relationship between these three kingdoms of multicellular eukaryotes.

For suggested answers, see Appendix A.

CONCEPT 1.3

In studying nature, scientists form and test hypotheses

Science is a way of knowing—an approach to understanding the natural world. It developed out of our curiosity about ourselves, other life forms, our planet, and the universe.

At the heart of science is **inquiry**, a search for information and explanations of natural phenomena. There is no formula for successful scientific inquiry, no single scientific method that researchers must rigidly follow. As in all quests, science includes elements of challenge, adventure, and luck, along with careful planning, reasoning, creativity, patience, and the persistence to overcome setbacks. Such diverse elements of inquiry make science far less structured than most people realize. That said, it is possible to highlight certain characteristics that help to distinguish science from other ways of describing and explaining nature.

Scientists use a process of inquiry that includes making observations, forming logical explanations (*hypotheses*), and

testing them. The process is necessarily repetitive: In testing a hypothesis, our observations may inspire revision of the original hypothesis or formation of a new one, thus leading to further testing. In this way, scientists circle closer and closer to their best estimation of the laws governing nature.

Exploration and Discovery

Biology, like other sciences, begins with careful observation. In gathering information, biologists often use tools, such as microscopes, precision thermometers, or high-speed cameras, that extend their senses or facilitate careful measurement. Observations can reveal valuable information about the natural world. For example, a series of detailed observations have shaped our understanding of cell structure. Another set of observations is currently expanding our databases of genome sequences from diverse species and of genes whose expression is altered in diseases.

In exploring nature, biologists also rely heavily on the scientific literature, the published contributions of fellow scientists. By reading about and understanding past studies, scientists can build on the foundation of existing knowledge, focusing their investigations on observations that are original and on hypotheses that are consistent with previous findings. Identifying publications relevant to a new line of research is now easier than at any point in the past, thanks to indexed and searchable electronic databases.

Gathering and Analyzing Data

Recorded observations are called **data**. Put another way, data are items of information on which scientific inquiry is based. Some data are *qualitative*, such as descriptions of what is observed. For example, British primate researcher Jane Goodall spent decades recording her observations of chimpanzee behavior during field research in a Tanzanian jungle

▲ **Figure 1.18 Jane Goodall collecting qualitative data on chimpanzee behavior.** Goodall recorded her observations in field notebooks, often with sketches of the animals' behavior.

(Figure 1.18). She also documented her observations with photographs and movies.

In her studies, Goodall also gathered and recorded volumes of *quantitative* data, such as the frequency and duration of specific behaviors for different members of a group of chimpanzees in a variety of situations. Quantitative data are generally expressed as numerical measurements and often organized into tables or graphs. Scientists analyze their data using a type of mathematics called *statistics* to test whether their results are significant or merely due to random fluctuations. All results presented in this text have been shown to be statistically significant.

Collecting and analyzing observations can lead to important conclusions based on a type of logic called **inductive reasoning**. Through induction, we derive generalizations from a large number of specific observations. The generalization "All organisms are made of cells" was based on two centuries of microscopic observations made by biologists examining cells in diverse biological specimens. Careful observations and data analyses, along with the generalizations reached by induction, are fundamental to our understanding of nature.

Forming and Testing Hypotheses

Our innate curiosity often stimulates us to pose questions about the natural basis for the phenomena we observe in the world. What *caused* the different chimpanzee behaviors observed in the wild? What *explains* the variation in coat color among the mice of a single species, shown in Figures 1.1 and 1.2? In science, answering such questions usually involves forming and testing logical explanations—that is, hypotheses.

In science, a **hypothesis** is an explanation, based on observations and assumptions, that leads to a testable prediction.

Said another way, a hypothesis is an explanation on trial. The hypothesis is usually a rational accounting for a set of observations, based on the available data and guided by inductive reasoning. A scientific hypothesis must lead to predictions that can be tested by making additional observations or by performing experiments. An **experiment** is a scientific test, often carried out under controlled conditions.

We all make observations and develop questions and hypotheses in solving everyday problems. Let's say, for example, that your desk lamp is plugged in and turned on but the bulb isn't lit. That's an observation. The question is obvious: Why doesn't the lamp work? Two reasonable hypotheses based on your experience are that (1) the bulb is burnt out or (2) the lamp is broken. Each of these hypotheses leads to predictions you can test with experiments. For example, the burnt-out bulb hypothesis predicts that replacing the bulb will fix the problem. Figuring things out in this way by trial and error is a hypothesis-based approach.

Deductive Reasoning

A type of logic called deduction is also built into the use of hypotheses in science. While induction entails reasoning from a set of specific observations to reach a general conclusion, **deductive reasoning** involves logic that flows in the opposite direction, from the general to the specific. From general premises, we extrapolate to the specific results we should expect if the premises are true. In the scientific process, deductions usually take the form of predictions of results that will be found if a particular hypothesis (premise) is correct. We then test the hypothesis by carrying out experiments or observations to see whether or not the results are as predicted. This deductive testing takes the form of "*If . . . then*" logic. In the case of the desk lamp example: *If* the burnt-out bulb hypothesis is correct, *then* the lamp should work when you replace the bulb with a new one.

We can use the desk lamp example to illustrate two other key points about the use of hypotheses in science. First, one can always devise additional hypotheses to explain a set of observations. For instance, another of the many possible alternative hypotheses to explain our dead desk lamp is that the wall outlet is faulty. Although you could design an experiment to test this hypothesis, we can never test all possible explanations. Second, we can never *prove* that a hypothesis is true. The burnt-out bulb hypothesis is the most likely explanation, but testing supports that hypothesis *not* by proving that it is correct, but rather by not finding that it is false. For example, if replacing the bulb fixed the desk lamp, it might have been because the bulb we replaced was good but not screwed in properly.

Although a hypothesis can never be proved beyond the shadow of a doubt, testing it in various ways can significantly increase our confidence in its validity. Often, rounds of hypothesis formulation and testing lead to a scientific consensus—the shared conclusion of many scientists that a particular hypothesis explains the known data well and stands up to experimental testing.

Questions That Can and Cannot Be Addressed by Science

Scientific inquiry is a powerful way to learn about nature, but there are limitations to the kinds of questions it can answer. A scientific hypothesis must be *testable*; there must be some observation or experiment that could reveal if such an idea is more likely to be true or false. For example, the hypothesis that a burnt-out bulb is the sole reason the lamp doesn't work would not be supported if replacing the bulb with a new one didn't fix the lamp.

Not all hypotheses meet the criteria of science: You wouldn't be able to test the hypothesis that invisible ghosts are fooling with your desk lamp! Because science only deals with natural, testable explanations for natural phenomena, it can neither support nor contradict the invisible ghost hypothesis, nor whether spirits or elves cause storms, rainbows, or illnesses. Such supernatural explanations are simply outside the bounds of science, as are religious matters, which are issues of personal faith.

▶ **Figure 1.19 The process of science: A realistic model.** The process of science is not linear, but instead involves backtracking, repetition, and feedback between different steps of the process. This illustration is based on a model (How Science Works) from the website Understanding Science.

The Flexibility of the Scientific Process

The way that researchers answer questions about the natural and physical world is often idealized as the scientific method. However, very few scientific studies adhere rigidly to the sequence of steps that are typically used to describe this approach. For example, a scientist may start to design an experiment, but then backtrack after realizing that more preliminary observations are necessary. In other cases, observations remain too puzzling to prompt well-defined questions until further study provides a new context in which to view those observations. For example, scientists could not unravel the details of how genes encode proteins until *after* the discovery of the structure of DNA (an event that took place in 1953).

A more realistic model of the scientific process is shown in **Figure 1.19**. The focus of this model, shown in the central circle in the figure, is the forming and testing of hypotheses. This core set of activities is the reason that science does so well in explaining phenomena in the natural world. These activities, however, are shaped by exploration and discovery (upper circle)

EXPLORATION AND DISCOVERY
- Observing nature
- Asking questions
- Reading the scientific literature

FORMING AND TESTING HYPOTHESES

Testing Ideas
- Forming hypotheses
- Predicting results
- Doing experiments and/or making observations
- Gathering data
- Analyzing results

Interpreting Results
Data may...
- Support a hypothesis
- Contradict a hypothesis
- Inspire a revised or new hypothesis

SOCIETAL BENEFITS AND OUTCOMES
- Developing technology
- Informing policy
- Solving problems
- Building knowledge

COMMUNITY ANALYSIS AND FEEDBACK
- Feedback and peer review
- Replication of findings
- Publication
- Consensus building

and influenced by interactions with other scientists and with society more generally (lower circles). For example, the community of scientists influences which hypotheses are tested, how test results are interpreted, and what value is placed on the findings. Similarly, societal needs—such as the push to cure cancer or understand the process of climate change—may help shape what research projects are funded and how extensively the results are discussed.

Now that we have highlighted the key features of scientific inquiry—making observations and forming and testing hypotheses—you should be able to recognize these features in a case study of actual scientific research.

A Case Study in Scientific Inquiry: Investigating Coat Coloration in Mouse Populations

Our case study begins with a set of observations and inductive generalizations. Color patterns of animals vary widely in nature, sometimes even among members of the same species. What accounts for such variation? As you may recall, the two mice depicted at the beginning of this chapter are members of the same species (*Peromyscus polionotus*), but they have different coat (fur) color patterns and reside in different environments. The beach mouse lives along the Florida seashore, a habitat of brilliant white sand dunes with sparse clumps of beach grass. The inland mouse lives on darker, more fertile soil farther inland **(Figure 1.20)**. Even a brief glance at the photographs in Figure 1.20 reveals a striking match of mouse coloration to its habitat. The natural predators of these mice, including hawks, owls, foxes, and coyotes, all use their sense of sight to hunt for prey. It was logical, therefore, for Francis B. Sumner, a naturalist studying populations of these mice in the 1920s, to hypothesize that their coloration patterns had evolved as adaptations that camouflage the mice in their native environments, protecting them from predation.

As obvious as the camouflage hypothesis may seem, it still required testing. In 2010, biologist Hopi Hoekstra of Harvard University and a group of her students headed to Florida to test the prediction that mice with coloration that did not match their habitat would be preyed on more heavily than the native, well-matched mice. **Figure 1.21** summarizes this field experiment, introducing a format we will use throughout the book to walk through other examples of biological inquiry.

The researchers built hundreds of models of mice and spray-painted them to resemble either beach or inland mice, so that the models differed only in their color patterns. The researchers placed equal numbers of these model mice randomly in both habitats and left them overnight. The mouse models resembling the native mice in the habitat were the *control* group (for instance, light-colored mouse models in the beach habitat), while the models with the non-native coloration were the *experimental* group (for example, darker models in the beach habitat). The following morning, the team counted and recorded signs of predation events, which ranged from bites and gouge marks on some models to the outright disappearance of other models. Judging by the shape of the predators' bites and the tracks surrounding the experimental sites, the predators appeared to be split fairly evenly between mammals (such as foxes and coyotes) and birds (such as owls, herons, and hawks).

For each environment, the researchers then calculated the percentage of predator attacks that targeted camouflaged models. The results were clear-cut: Camouflaged models showed much lower predation rates than those lacking camouflage in both the dune habitat (where light mice were less vulnerable) and the inland habitat (where dark mice were less vulnerable). The data thus fit the key prediction of the camouflage hypothesis.

Experimental Variables and Controls

In carrying out an experiment, a researcher often manipulates a factor in a system and observes the effects of this change. The mouse camouflage experiment described in Figure 1.21 is an example of a **controlled experiment**, one that is designed to compare an experimental group (the non-camouflaged models, in this case) with a control group (the camouflaged

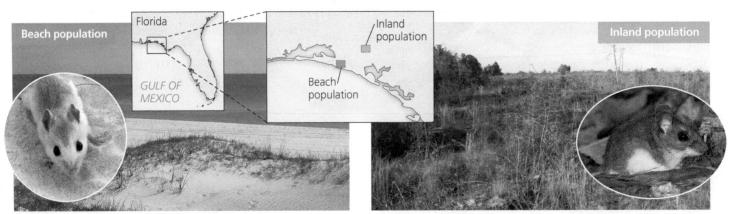

Beach mice living on sparsely vegetated sand dunes along the coast have light tan, dappled fur on their backs that allows them to blend into their surroundings, providing camouflage.

Members of the same species living about 30 km inland have dark fur on their backs, camouflaging them against the dark ground of their habitat.

▲ **Figure 1.20 Different coloration in beach and inland populations of *Peromyscus polionotus*.**

▼ Figure 1.21 Inquiry

Does camouflage affect predation rates on two populations of mice?

Experiment Hopi Hoekstra and colleagues tested the hypothesis that coat coloration provides camouflage that protects beach and inland populations of *Peromyscus polionotus* mice from predation in their habitats. The researchers spray-painted mouse models with light or dark color patterns that matched those of the beach and inland mice and placed models with each of the patterns in both habitats. The next morning, they counted damaged or missing models.

Results For each habitat, the researchers calculated the percentage of attacked models that were camouflaged or non-camouflaged. In both cases, the models whose pattern did not match their surroundings suffered much higher "predation" than did the camouflaged models.

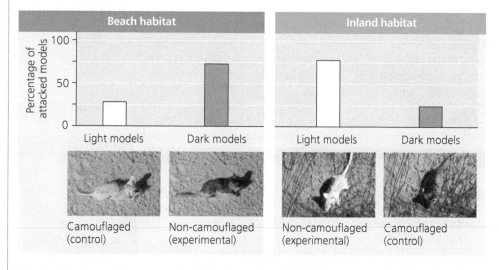

Conclusion The results are consistent with the researchers' prediction that mouse models with camouflage coloration would be preyed on less often than non-camouflaged mouse models. Thus, the experiment supports the camouflage hypothesis.

Data from S. N. Vignieri, J. G. Larson, and H. E. Hoekstra, The selective advantage of crypsis in mice, *Evolution* 64:2153–2158 (2010).

INTERPRET THE DATA *The bars indicate the percentage of the attacked models that were either light or dark. Assume 100 mouse models were attacked in each habitat. For the beach habitat, how many were light models? Dark models? Answer the same questions for the inland habitat.*

models). Both the factor that is manipulated and the factor that is subsequently measured are experimental **variables**— a feature or quantity that varies in an experiment. In our example, the color of the mouse model was the **independent variable**—the factor manipulated by the researchers. The **dependent variable** is the factor being measured that is predicted to be affected by the independent variable; in this case, the researchers measured the amount of predation in response to variation in color of the mouse model. Ideally, the experimental and control groups differ in only one independent variable—in the mouse experiment, color.

Without the control group of camouflaged models, the researchers would not have been able to rule out other factors as causes of the more frequent attacks on the non-camouflaged models—such as different numbers of predators or different temperatures in the various test areas. The clever experimental design left coloration as the only factor that could account for the low predation rate on models camouflaged with respect to the surrounding environment.

A common misconception is that the term *controlled experiment* means that scientists control all features of the experimental environment. But that's impossible in field research and can be very difficult even in a highly regulated laboratory setting. Researchers usually "control" unwanted variables not by *eliminating* them but by *canceling out* their effects using control groups.

Theories in Science

"It's just a theory!" Our everyday use of the term *theory* often implies an untested speculation. But the term *theory* has a different meaning in science. What is a scientific theory, and how is it different from a hypothesis or from mere speculation?

First, a scientific **theory** is much broader in scope than a hypothesis. *This* is a hypothesis: "Coat coloration well-matched to their habitat is an adaptation that protects mice from predators." But *this* is a theory: "Evolutionary adaptations arise by natural selection." This theory proposes that natural selection accounts for an enormous variety of adaptations, of which coat color in mice is but one example.

Second, a theory is general enough to spin off many new, testable hypotheses. For example, the theory of natural selection motivated two researchers at Princeton University, Peter and Rosemary Grant, to test the specific hypothesis that the beaks of Galápagos finches evolve in response to changes in the types of available food. (For their results, see the introduction to Chapter 21.)

And third, compared to any one hypothesis, a theory is generally supported by a much greater body of evidence. Those theories that become widely adopted in science (such as the theory of natural selection or the theory of gravity) explain a great diversity of observations and are supported by a vast accumulation of evidence.

In spite of the body of evidence supporting a widely accepted theory, scientists will sometimes modify or even reject theories when new research produces results that don't fit. For example, biologists once lumped bacteria and archaea together as a kingdom of prokaryotes. When new methods for comparing cells and molecules could be used to test such relationships, the evidence led scientists to reject the theory that bacteria and archaea are members of the same kingdom. If there is "truth" in science, it is conditional, based on the weight of available evidence.

Science as a Social Process

The great scientist Sir Isaac Newton once said: "To explain all nature is too difficult a task for any one man or even for any one age. 'Tis much better to do a little with certainty, and leave the rest for others that come after you." Anyone who becomes a scientist, driven by curiosity about nature, is sure to benefit from the rich storehouse of discoveries by others who have come before. In fact, while movies and cartoons sometimes portray scientists as loners working in isolated labs, science is an intensely social activity. Most scientists work in teams, which often include graduate and undergraduate students.

Science is continuously vetted through the expectation that observations and experiments must be repeatable and hypotheses must be testable. Scientists working in the same research field often check one another's claims by attempting to confirm observations or repeat experiments. In fact, Hopi Hoekstra's experiment benefited from the work of another researcher, D. W. Kaufman, four decades earlier. You can study the design of Kaufman's experiment and interpret the results in the **Scientific Skills Exercise**.

If scientific colleagues cannot repeat experimental findings, this failure may reflect an underlying weakness in the original claim, which will then have to be revised. In this sense, science polices itself. Adherence to high professional standards in reporting results is central to the scientific endeavor, since the validity of experimental data is key to designing further inquiry.

Biologists may approach questions from different angles. Some biologists focus on ecosystems, while others study natural phenomena at the level of organisms or cells. This text is divided into units that focus on biology observed at different levels and investigated through different approaches. Yet any given problem can be addressed from many perspectives, which in fact complement each other. For example, Hoekstra's work uncovered at least one genetic mutation that underlies the differences

---

Scientific Skills Exercise

Interpreting a Pair of Bar Graphs

How Much Does Camouflage Affect Predation on Mice by Owls with and without Moonlight? D. W. Kaufman hypothesized that the extent to which the coat color of a mouse contrasted with the color of its surroundings would affect the rate of nighttime predation by owls. He also hypothesized that contrast would be affected by the amount of moonlight. In this exercise, you will analyze data from his studies of owl-mouse predation that tested these hypotheses.

How the Experiment Was Done Pairs of mice (*Peromyscus polionotus*) with different coat colors, one light brown and one dark brown, were released simultaneously into an enclosure that contained a hungry owl. The researcher recorded the color of the mouse that was first caught by the owl. If the owl did not catch either mouse within 15 minutes, the test was recorded as a zero. The release trials were repeated multiple times in enclosures with either a dark-colored soil surface or a light-colored soil surface. The presence or absence of moonlight during each assay was recorded.

Data from the Experiment

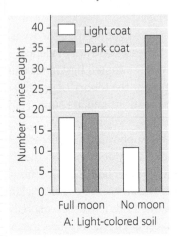
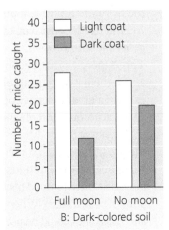

Data from D. W. Kaufman, Adaptive coloration in *Peromyscus polionotus*: Experimental selection by owls, *Journal of Mammalogy* 55:271–283 (1974).

INTERPRET THE DATA

1. First, make sure you understand how the graphs are set up. Graph A shows data from the light-colored soil enclosure and graph B from the dark-colored enclosure, but in all other respects the graphs are the same. (a) There is more than one independent variable in these graphs. What are the independent variables, the variables that were tested by the researcher? Which axis of the graphs has the independent variables? (b) What is the dependent variable, the response to the variables being tested? Which axis of the graphs has the dependent variable? (For additional information about graphs, see the Scientific Skills Review in Appendix F and in the Study Area in MasteringBiology.)

2. (a) How many dark brown mice were caught in the light-colored soil enclosure on a moonlit night? (b) How many dark brown mice were caught in the dark-colored soil enclosure on a moonlit night? (c) On a moonlit night, would a dark brown mouse be more likely to escape predation by owls on dark- or light-colored soil? Explain your answer.

3. (a) Is a dark brown mouse on dark-colored soil more likely to escape predation under a full moon or with no moon? (b) What about a light brown mouse on light-colored soil? Explain.

4. (a) Under which conditions would a dark brown mouse be most likely to escape predation at night? (b) A light brown mouse?

5. (a) What combination of independent variables led to the highest predation level in enclosures with light-colored soil? (b) What combination of independent variables led to the highest predation level in enclosures with dark-colored soil?

6. Thinking about your answers to question 5, provide a simple statement describing conditions that are especially deadly for either color of mouse.

7. Combining the data from both graphs, estimate the number of mice caught in moonlight versus no-moonlight conditions. Which condition is optimal for predation by the owl? Explain.

(MB) A version of this Scientific Skills Exercise can be assigned in MasteringBiology.

between beach and inland mouse coloration. Because the biologists in her lab have different specialties, her research group has been able not only to characterize evolutionary adaptations, but also to define the molecular basis for particular adaptations in the DNA sequence of the mouse genome.

The research community is part of society at large. The relationship of science to society becomes clearer when we add technology to the picture. The goal of **technology** is to *apply* scientific knowledge for some specific purpose. Because scientists put new technology to work in their research, science and technology are interdependent.

In centuries past, many major technological innovations originated along trade routes, where a rich mix of different cultures ignited new ideas. For example, the printing press was invented around 1440 by Johannes Gutenberg, living in what is now Germany. This invention relied on several innovations from China, including paper and ink, and from Iraq, where technology was developed for the mass production of paper. Like technology, science stands to gain much from embracing a diversity of backgrounds and viewpoints among its practitioners.

The scientific community reflects the customs and behaviors of society at large. It is therefore not surprising that until recently, women and certain racial and ethnic groups have faced huge obstacles in their pursuit to become professional scientists. Over the past 50 years, changing attitudes about career choices have increased the proportion of women in biology, and women now constitute roughly half of undergraduate majors and Ph.D. students in the field. The pace of change has been slow at higher levels in the profession, however, and women and many racial and ethnic groups are still significantly underrepresented in many branches of science. This lack of diversity hampers the progress of science. The more voices that are heard at the table, the more robust and productive the scientific conversation will be. The authors of this textbook welcome all students to the community of biologists, wishing you the joys and satisfactions of this exciting field of science.

CONCEPT CHECK 1.3

1. Contrast inductive reasoning with deductive reasoning.
2. What qualitative observation led to the quantitative study outlined in Figure 1.21?
3. Why is natural selection called a theory?
4. How does science differ from technology?

   For suggested answers, see Appendix A.

---

1 Chapter Review

Go to **MasteringBiology®** for Assignments, the eText, and the Study Area with Animations, Activities, Vocab Self-Quiz, and Practice Tests.

SUMMARY OF KEY CONCEPTS

VOCAB SELF-QUIZ

goo.gl/gbai8v

CONCEPT 1.1

The study of life reveals common themes (pp. 3–9)

Theme: Organization

- The hierarchy of life unfolds as follows: biosphere > ecosystem > community > population > organism > organ system > organ > tissue > cell > organelle > molecule > atom. With each step up, new properties emerge (**emergent properties**) as a result of interactions among components at the lower levels.
- Structure and function are correlated at all levels of biological organization. The cell is the lowest level of organization that can perform all activities required for life. Cells are either prokaryotic or eukaryotic. **Eukaryotic cells** have a DNA-containing nucleus and other membrane-enclosed organelles. **Prokaryotic cells** lack such organelles.

Theme: Information

- Genetic information is encoded in the nucleotide sequences of **DNA**. It is DNA that transmits heritable information from parents to offspring. DNA sequences (called **genes**) program a cell's protein production by being transcribed into mRNA and then translated into specific proteins, a process called **gene expression**. Gene expression also produces RNAs that are not translated into proteins but serve other important functions.

Theme: Energy and Matter

- Energy flows through an ecosystem. All organisms must perform work, which requires energy. Producers convert energy from sunlight to chemical energy, some of which is then passed on to consumers (the rest is lost from the ecosystem as heat). Chemicals cycle between organisms and the environment.

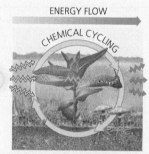

Theme: Interactions

- Organisms interact continuously with physical factors. Plants take up nutrients from the soil and chemicals from the air and use energy from the sun. Interactions among plants, animals, and other organisms affect the participants in varying ways.

Core Theme: Evolution

- Evolution accounts for the unity and diversity of life and also for the match of organisms to their environments.

? *Thinking about the muscles and nerves in your hand, how does the activity of text messaging reflect the five unifying themes of biology described in this chapter?*

The Core Theme: Evolution accounts for the unity and diversity of life (pp. 10–13)

- Biologists classify species according to a system of broader and broader groups. Domain **Bacteria** and domain **Archaea** consist of prokaryotes. Domain **Eukarya**, the eukaryotes, includes various groups of protists as well as plants, fungi, and animals. As diverse as life is, there is also evidence of remarkable unity, which is revealed in the similarities between different kinds of organisms.
- Darwin proposed **natural selection** as the mechanism for evolutionary adaptation of populations to their environments. Natural selection is the evolutionary process that occurs when a population is exposed to environmental factors that consistently cause individuals with certain heritable traits to have greater reproductive success than do individuals with other heritable traits.
- Each species is one twig of a branching tree of life extending back in time through more and more remote ancestral species. All of life is connected through its long evolutionary history.

? *How could natural selection have led to the evolution of adaptations such as camouflaging coat color in beach mice?*

In studying nature, scientists form and test hypotheses (pp. 13–19)

- In scientific **inquiry**, scientists make and record observations (collect **data**) and use **inductive reasoning** to draw a general conclusion, which can be developed into a testable **hypothesis**. **Deductive reasoning** makes predictions that can be used to test hypotheses. Scientific hypotheses must be testable.
- **Controlled experiments**, such as the investigation of coat color in mouse populations, are designed to demonstrate the effect of one **variable** by testing control groups and experimental groups differing in only that one variable.
- A scientific **theory** is broad in scope, generates new hypotheses, and is supported by a large body of evidence.
- Observations and experiments must be repeatable, and hypotheses must be testable. Biologists approach questions at different levels; their approaches complement each other. **Technology** is a method or device that applies scientific knowledge for some specific purpose that affects society as well as for scientific research. Diversity among scientists promotes progress in science.

? *What are the roles of gathering and interpreting data in scientific inquiry?*

TEST YOUR UNDERSTANDING

PRACTICE TEST

goo.gl/CRZjvS

Level 1: Knowledge/Comprehension

1. All the organisms on your campus make up
   - (A) an ecosystem.
   - (B) a community.
   - (C) a population.
   - (D) a taxonomic domain.

2. Which of the following best demonstrates the unity among all organisms?
   - (A) emergent properties
   - (B) descent with modification
   - (C) DNA structure and function
   - (D) natural selection

3. A controlled experiment is one that
   - (A) proceeds slowly enough that a scientist can make careful records of the results.
   - (B) tests experimental and control groups in parallel.
   - (C) is repeated many times to make sure the results are accurate.
   - (D) keeps all variables constant.

4. Which of the following statements best distinguishes hypotheses from theories in science?
   - (A) Theories are hypotheses that have been proved.
   - (B) Hypotheses are guesses; theories are correct answers.
   - (C) Hypotheses usually are relatively narrow in scope; theories have broad explanatory power.
   - (D) Theories are proved true; hypotheses are often contradicted by experimental results.

Level 2: Application/Analysis

5. Which of the following best describes the logic of scientific inquiry?
   - (A) If I generate a testable hypothesis, tests and observations will support it.
   - (B) If my prediction is correct, it will lead to a testable hypothesis.
   - (C) If my observations are accurate, they will support my hypothesis.
   - (D) If my hypothesis is correct, I can expect certain test results.

6. **DRAW IT** With rough sketches, draw a biological hierarchy similar to the one in Figure 1.3 but using a coral reef as the ecosystem, a fish as the organism, its stomach as the organ, and DNA as the molecule. Include all levels in the hierarchy.

Level 3: Synthesis/Evaluation

7. **SCIENTIFIC INQUIRY**
   Based on the results of the mouse coloration case study, propose a hypothesis researchers might use to further study the role of predators in the natural selection process.

8. **SCIENTIFIC INQUIRY**
   Scientists search the scientific literature by means of electronic databases such as PubMed, a free online database maintained by the National Center for Biotechnology Information. Use PubMed to find the abstract of a scientific article that Hopi Hoekstra published in 2014 or later.

9. **FOCUS ON EVOLUTION**
   In a short essay (100–150 words), describe Darwin's view of how natural selection resulted in both unity and diversity of life on Earth. Include in your discussion some of his evidence. (See tips for writing good essays and a suggested grading rubric in the Study Area of MasteringBiology under "Writing Tips and Rubric.")

10. **FOCUS ON INFORMATION**
    A typical prokaryotic cell has about 3,000 genes in its DNA, while a human cell has almost 21,000 genes. About 1,000 of these genes are present in both types of cells. (a) Based on your understanding of evolution, explain how such different organisms could have this same subset of 1,000 genes. (b) What sorts of functions might these shared genes have? Justify your choices.

11. **SYNTHESIZE YOUR KNOWLEDGE**

Can you pick out the mossy leaf-tailed gecko lying against the tree trunk in this photo? How is the appearance of the gecko a benefit in terms of survival? Given what you learned about evolution, natural selection, and genetic information in this chapter, describe how the gecko's coloration might have evolved.

For selected answers, see Appendix A.

Unit 1 Chemistry and Cells

2 The Chemical Context of Life

The structures and functions of living organisms are based on the **chemistry** of atoms and molecules.

3 Carbon and the Molecular Diversity of Life

The carbon atom is the foundation of all organic molecules, and its versatility gives rise to the **molecular diversity of life.**

4 A Tour of the Cell

The basic structural and functional unit of life is the **cell.**

5 Membrane Transport and Cell Signaling

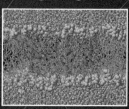

The **plasma membrane** regulates the passage of substances into and out of the cell and enables **signaling** between cells.

6 An Introduction to Metabolism

The cellular processes that transform matter and energy make up **cell metabolism.**

7 Cellular Respiration and Fermentation

Organisms obtain energy from food by breaking it down by means of **cellular respiration** or **fermentation.**

8 Photosynthesis

Photosynthesis is the basis of life on planet Earth: Photosynthetic organisms capture light energy and use it to make the food that all organisms depend on.

9 The Cell Cycle

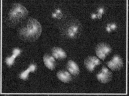

A eukaryotic cell grows and then divides in two, passing along identical genetic information to its daughter cells via **mitosis.** The **cell cycle** describes this progression.

Chemistry and Cells

2 The Chemical Context of Life
3 Carbon and the Molecular Diversity of Life
4 A Tour of the Cell
5 Membrane Transport and Cell Signaling
6 An Introduction to Metabolism
7 Cellular Respiration and Fermentation
8 Photosynthesis
9 The Cell Cycle

Ecology 1
Animals
Plants
History of Life
Evolution
Genetics

2 The Chemical Context of Life

KEY CONCEPTS

2.1 Matter consists of chemical elements in pure form and in combinations called compounds

2.2 An element's properties depend on the structure of its atoms

2.3 The formation and function of molecules depend on chemical bonding between atoms

2.4 Chemical reactions make and break chemical bonds

2.5 Hydrogen bonding gives water properties that help make life possible on Earth

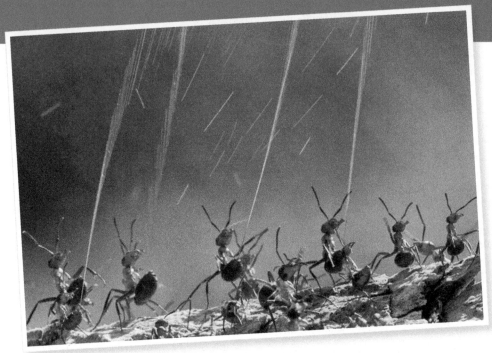

▲ Figure 2.1 **What weapon are these wood ants shooting into the air?**

A Chemical Connection to Biology

Like other animals, ants have mechanisms that defend them from attack. Wood ants live in colonies of hundreds or thousands, and the colony as a whole has a particularly effective way of dealing with enemies. When threatened from above, the ants shoot volleys of formic acid into the air from their abdomens, and the acid bombards the potential predator, such as a hungry bird **(Figure 2.1)**. Formic acid is produced by many species of ants and got its name from the Latin word for ant, *formica*. In quite a few ant species, the formic acid isn't shot out, but probably serves as a disinfectant that protects the ants against microbial parasites. Scientists have long known that chemicals play a major role in insect communication, the attraction of mates, and defense against predators.

Research on ants and other insects is a good example of how relevant chemistry is to the study of life. Unlike college courses, nature is not neatly packaged into individual sciences—biology, chemistry, physics, and so forth. Biologists specialize in the study of life, but organisms and their environments are natural systems to which the concepts of chemistry and physics apply. Biology is multidisciplinary.

This unit of chapters introduces some basic concepts of chemistry that apply to the study of life. Somewhere in the transition from molecules to cells, we will cross the blurry boundary between nonlife and life. This chapter focuses on the chemical components that make up all matter, with a final section on the substance that supports all of life—water.

CONCEPT 2.1

Matter consists of chemical elements in pure form and in combinations called compounds

Organisms are composed of **matter**, which is anything that takes up space and has mass. Matter exists in many forms. Rocks, metals, oils, gases, and living organisms are a few examples of what seems to be an endless assortment of matter.

Elements and Compounds

Matter is made up of elements. An **element** is a substance that cannot be broken down to other substances by chemical reactions. Today, chemists recognize 92 elements occurring in nature; gold, copper, carbon, and oxygen are examples. Each element has a symbol, usually the first letter or two of its name. Some symbols are derived from Latin or German; for instance, the symbol for sodium is Na, from the Latin word *natrium*.

A **compound** is a substance consisting of two or more different elements combined in a fixed ratio. Table salt, for example, is sodium chloride (NaCl), a compound composed of the elements sodium (Na) and chlorine (Cl) in a 1:1 ratio. Pure sodium is a metal, and pure chlorine is a poisonous gas. When chemically combined, however, sodium and chlorine form an edible compound. Water (H_2O), another compound, consists of the elements hydrogen (H) and oxygen (O) in a 2:1 ratio. These are simple examples of organized matter having *emergent properties*: A compound has chemical and physical characteristics different from those of its constituent elements **(Figure 2.2)**.

The Elements of Life

Of the 92 natural elements, about 20–25% are **essential elements** that an organism needs to live a healthy life and reproduce. The essential elements are similar among organisms, but there is some variation—for example, humans need 25 elements, but plants need only 17.

Relative amounts of all the elements in the human body are listed in **Table 2.1**. Just four elements—oxygen (O), carbon (C), hydrogen (H), and nitrogen (N)—make up approximately 96% of living matter. Calcium (Ca), phosphorus (P), potassium (K), sulfur (S), and a few other elements account for most of the remaining 4% or so of an organism's mass. **Trace elements** are required by an organism in only minute quantities. Some trace elements, such as iron (Fe), are needed by all forms of life; others are required only by certain species. For example, in vertebrates (animals with backbones), the element iodine (I) is an essential ingredient of a hormone produced by the thyroid gland. A daily intake of only 0.15 milligram (mg) of iodine is adequate for normal activity of the human thyroid. An iodine deficiency in the diet causes the thyroid gland to grow to abnormal size, a condition called goiter. Consuming seafood or iodized salt reduces the incidence of goiter.

Sodium   **Chlorine**   **Sodium chloride**

▲ **Figure 2.2 The emergent properties of a compound.** The metal sodium combines with the poisonous gas chlorine, forming the edible compound sodium chloride, or table salt.

Table 2.1 Elements in the Human Body

Element	Symbol	Percentage of Body Mass (including water)	
Oxygen	O	65.0%	
Carbon	C	18.5%	96.3%
Hydrogen	H	9.5%	
Nitrogen	N	3.3%	
Calcium	Ca	1.5%	
Phosphorus	P	1.0%	
Potassium	K	0.4%	
Sulfur	S	0.3%	3.7%
Sodium	Na	0.2%	
Chlorine	Cl	0.2%	
Magnesium	Mg	0.1%	

Trace elements (less than 0.01% of mass): Boron (B), chromium (Cr), cobalt (Co), copper (Cu), fluorine (F), iodine (I), iron (Fe), manganese (Mn), molybdenum (Mo), selenium (Se), silicon (Si), tin (Sn), vanadium (V), zinc (Zn)

INTERPRET THE DATA *Given the makeup of the human body, what compound do you think accounts for the high percentage of oxygen?*

Evolution of Tolerance to Toxic Elements

EVOLUTION Some naturally occurring elements are toxic to organisms. In humans, for instance, the element arsenic has been linked to numerous diseases and can be lethal. Some species, however, have become adapted to environments containing elements that are usually toxic. For example, sunflower plants can take up lead, zinc, and other heavy metals in concentrations that would kill most organisms. This capability enabled sunflowers to be used to detoxify contaminated soils after Hurricane Katrina. Presumably, variants of ancestral sunflower species were able to grow in soils with heavy metals, and subsequent natural selection resulted in their survival and reproduction.

CONCEPT CHECK 2.1

1. Is a trace element an essential element? Explain.
2. **WHAT IF?** In humans, iron is a trace element required for the proper functioning of hemoglobin, the molecule that carries oxygen in red blood cells. What might be the effects of an iron deficiency?

For suggested answers, see Appendix A.

CONCEPT 2.2

An element's properties depend on the structure of its atoms

Each element consists of a certain type of atom that is different from the atoms of any other element. An **atom** is the smallest unit of matter that still retains the properties of an element. Atoms are so small that it would take about a million of them to stretch across the period at the end of this sentence. We symbolize atoms with the same abbreviation used for the element that is made up of those atoms. For example, the symbol C stands for both the element carbon and a single carbon atom.

Subatomic Particles

Although the atom is the smallest unit having the properties of an element, these tiny bits of matter are composed of even smaller parts, called *subatomic particles*. Using high-energy collisions, physicists have produced more than a hundred types of particles from the atom, but only three kinds of particles are relevant here: **neutrons**, **protons**, and **electrons**. Protons and electrons are electrically charged. Each proton has one unit of positive charge, and each electron has one unit of negative charge. A neutron, as its name implies, is electrically neutral.

Protons and neutrons are packed together tightly in a dense core, or **atomic nucleus**, at the center of an atom; protons give the nucleus a positive charge. The rapidly moving electrons form a "cloud" of negative charge around the nucleus, and it is the attraction between opposite charges that keeps the electrons in the vicinity of the nucleus. **Figure 2.3** shows two commonly used models of the structure of the helium atom as an example.

The neutron and proton are almost identical in mass, each about 1.7×10^{-24} gram (g). Grams and other conventional units are not very useful for describing the mass of objects that are so minuscule. Thus, for atoms and subatomic particles (and for molecules, too), we use a unit of measurement called the **dalton** (the same as the *atomic mass unit*, or *amu*). Neutrons and protons have masses close to 1 dalton. Because the mass of an electron is only about 1/2,000 that of a neutron or proton, we can ignore electrons when computing the total mass of an atom.

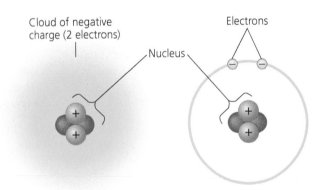

Cloud of negative charge (2 electrons)

Nucleus

Electrons

(a) This model shows the two electrons as a cloud of negative charge, a result of their motion around the nucleus.

(b) In this more simplified model, the electrons are shown as two small yellow spheres on a circle around the nucleus.

▲ **Figure 2.3 Simplified models of a helium (He) atom.** The helium nucleus consists of 2 neutrons (brown) and 2 protons (pink). Two electrons (yellow) exist outside the nucleus. These models are not to scale; they greatly overestimate the size of the nucleus in relation to the electron cloud.

Atomic Number and Atomic Mass

Atoms of the various elements differ in their number of subatomic particles. All atoms of a particular element have the same number of protons in their nuclei. This number of protons, which is unique to that element, is called the **atomic number** and is written as a subscript to the left of the symbol for the element. The abbreviation $_2$He, for example, tells us that an atom of the element helium has 2 protons in its nucleus. Unless otherwise indicated, an atom is neutral in electrical charge, which means that its protons must be balanced by an equal number of electrons. Therefore, the atomic number tells us the number of protons and also the number of electrons in an electrically neutral atom.

We can deduce the number of neutrons from a second quantity, the **mass number**, which is the total number of protons and neutrons in the nucleus of an atom. The mass number is written as a superscript to the left of an element's symbol. For example, we can use this shorthand to write an atom of helium as $_2^4$He. Because the atomic number indicates how many protons there are, we can determine the number of neutrons by subtracting the atomic number from the mass number: The helium atom $_2^4$He has 2 neutrons. For sodium (Na):

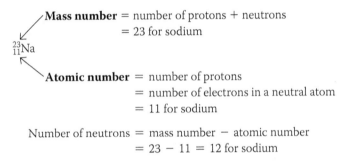

$_{11}^{23}$Na

Mass number = number of protons + neutrons
= 23 for sodium

Atomic number = number of protons
= number of electrons in a neutral atom
= 11 for sodium

Number of neutrons = mass number − atomic number
= 23 − 11 = 12 for sodium

The simplest atom is hydrogen $_1^1$H, which has no neutrons; it consists of a single proton with a single electron.

Because the contribution of electrons to mass is negligible, almost all of an atom's mass is concentrated in its nucleus. Neutrons and protons each have a mass very close to 1 dalton, so the mass number is close to, but slightly different from, the total mass of an atom, called its **atomic mass**. For example, the mass number of sodium ($_{11}^{23}$Na) is 23, but its atomic mass is 22.9898 daltons.

Isotopes

All atoms of a given element have the same number of protons, but some atoms have more neutrons than other atoms of the same element and thus have greater mass. These different atomic forms of the same element are called **isotopes** of the element. In nature, an element may occur as a mixture of its isotopes. As an example, the element carbon, which has the atomic number 6, has three naturally occurring isotopes. The most common isotope is carbon-12, $_6^{12}$C, which accounts for about 99% of the carbon in nature. The isotope $_6^{12}$C has 6 neutrons. Most of the remaining 1% of carbon consists of atoms of the isotope $_6^{13}$C, with 7 neutrons. A third, even rarer isotope, $^{14}_6\text{C}$, has 8 neutrons. Notice that all three isotopes of carbon have 6 protons; otherwise, they would not be carbon. Although the isotopes of an element have slightly different masses, they behave identically in chemical reactions. (For an element with more than one naturally occurring isotope, the atomic mass is an average of those isotopes, weighted by their abundance. Thus carbon has an atomic mass of 12.01 daltons.)

Both ^{12}C and ^{13}C are stable isotopes, meaning that their nuclei do not have a tendency to lose subatomic particles, a process called decay. The isotope ^{14}C, however, is unstable, or radioactive. A **radioactive isotope** is one in which the nucleus decays spontaneously, giving off particles and energy. When the radioactive decay leads to a change in the number of protons, it transforms the atom to an atom of a different element. For example, when an atom of ^{14}C decays, it becomes an atom of nitrogen.

Radioactive isotopes have many useful applications in biology. For example, researchers use measurements of radioactivity in fossils to date these relics of past life (see Concept 23.1). Radioactive isotopes are also useful as tracers to follow atoms through metabolism, the chemical processes of an organism. Cells can use radioactive atoms just as they would use nonradioactive isotopes of the same element. The radioactive isotopes are incorporated into biologically active molecules, which can then be tracked by monitoring the radioactivity.

Radioactive tracers are important diagnostic tools in medicine. For example, certain kidney disorders can be diagnosed by injecting small doses of substances containing radioactive isotopes into the blood and then measuring the amount of tracer excreted in the urine. Radioactive tracers are also used in combination with sophisticated imaging instruments, such as PET scanners, that can monitor the growth and metabolism of cancers in the body **(Figure 2.4)**.

Although radioactive isotopes are very useful in biological research and medicine, radiation from decaying isotopes also poses a hazard to life by damaging cellular molecules. The severity of this damage depends on the type and amount of radiation an organism absorbs. One of the most serious environmental threats is radioactive fallout from nuclear accidents. The doses of most isotopes used in medical diagnosis, however, are relatively safe.

▶ Figure 2.4 **A PET scan, a medical use for radioactive isotopes.** PET (positron-emission tomography) detects locations of intense chemical activity in the body. The bright yellow spot marks an area with an elevated level of radioactively labeled glucose, which in turn indicates high metabolic activity, a hallmark of cancerous tissue.

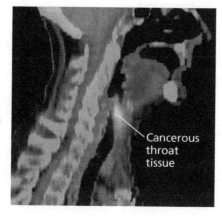

Cancerous throat tissue

The Energy Levels of Electrons

The simplified models of the atom in Figure 2.3 greatly exaggerate the size of the nucleus relative to that of the whole atom. If an atom of helium were the size of a typical football stadium, the nucleus would be the size of a pencil eraser in the center of the field. Moreover, the electrons would be like two tiny gnats buzzing around the stadium. Atoms are mostly empty space.

When two atoms approach each other during a chemical reaction, their nuclei do not come close enough to interact. Of the three kinds of subatomic particles we have discussed, only electrons are directly involved in the chemical reactions between atoms.

An atom's electrons vary in the amount of energy they possess. **Energy** is defined as the capacity to cause change—for instance, by doing work. **Potential energy** is the energy that matter possesses because of its location or structure. For example, water in a reservoir on a hill has potential energy because of its altitude. When the gates of the reservoir's dam are opened and the water runs downhill, the energy can be used to do work, such as moving the blades of turbines to generate electricity. Because energy has been expended, the water has less energy at the bottom of the hill than it did in the reservoir. Matter has a natural tendency to move toward the lowest possible state of potential energy; in our example, the water runs downhill. To restore the potential energy of a reservoir, work must be done to elevate the water against gravity.

The electrons of an atom have potential energy due to their distance from the nucleus **(Figure 2.5)**. The negatively charged

(a) A ball bouncing down a flight of stairs can come to rest only on each step, not between steps. Similarly, an electron can exist only at certain energy levels, not between levels.

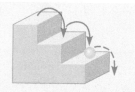

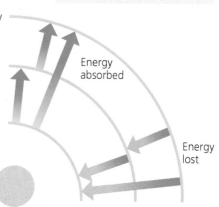

Third shell (highest energy level in this model)

Second shell (higher energy level)

First shell (lowest energy level)

Energy absorbed

Energy lost

Atomic nucleus

(b) An electron can move from one shell to another only if the energy it gains or loses is exactly equal to the difference in energy between the energy levels of the two shells. Arrows in this model indicate some of the stepwise changes in potential energy that are possible.

▲ Figure 2.5 **Energy levels of an atom's electrons.** Electrons exist only at fixed levels of potential energy called electron shells.

electrons are attracted to the positively charged nucleus. It takes work to move a given electron farther away from the nucleus, so the more distant an electron is from the nucleus, the greater its potential energy. Unlike the continuous flow of water downhill, changes in the potential energy of electrons can occur only in steps of fixed amounts. An electron having a certain amount of energy is something like a ball on a staircase (Figure 2.5a). The ball can have different amounts of potential energy, depending on which step it is on, but it cannot spend much time between the steps. Similarly, an electron's potential energy is determined by its energy level. An electron can exist only at certain energy levels, not between them.

An electron's energy level is correlated with its average distance from the nucleus. Electrons are found in different **electron shells**, each with a characteristic average distance and energy level. In diagrams, shells can be represented by concentric circles (Figure 2.5b). The first shell is closest to the nucleus, and electrons in this shell have the lowest potential energy. Electrons in the second shell have more energy, and electrons in the third shell even more energy. An electron can move from one shell to another, but only by absorbing or losing an amount of energy equal to the difference in potential energy between its position in the old shell and that in the new shell. When an electron absorbs energy, it moves to a shell

farther out from the nucleus. For example, light energy can excite an electron to a higher energy level. (Indeed, this is the first step taken when plants harness the energy of sunlight for photosynthesis, the process that produces food from carbon dioxide and water. You'll learn more about photosynthesis in Chapter 8.) When an electron loses energy, it "falls back" to a shell closer to the nucleus, and the lost energy is usually released to the environment as heat. For example, sunlight excites electrons in the surface of a car to higher energy levels. When the electrons fall back to their original levels, the car's surface heats up. This thermal energy can be transferred to the air or to your hand if you touch the car.

Electron Distribution and Chemical Properties

The chemical behavior of an atom is determined by the distribution of electrons in the atom's electron shells. Beginning with hydrogen, the simplest atom, we can imagine building the atoms of the other elements by adding 1 proton and 1 electron at a time (along with an appropriate number of neutrons). **Figure 2.6**, a modified version of what is called the *periodic table of the elements*, shows this distribution of electrons for the first 18 elements, from hydrogen ($_1$H) to argon ($_{18}$Ar). The elements are arranged in three rows, or *periods*, corresponding to the number of electron shells in their atoms. The

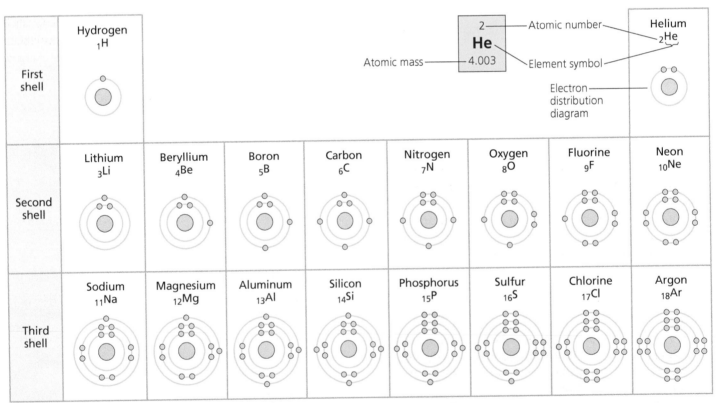

▲ **Figure 2.6 Electron distribution diagrams for the first 18 elements in the periodic table.** In a standard periodic table (see Appendix B), information for each element is presented as shown for helium in the inset. In the diagrams in this table, electrons are represented as yellow dots and electron shells as concentric circles. These diagrams are a convenient way to picture the distribution of an atom's electrons among its electron shells, but these simplified models do not accurately represent the shape of the atom or the location of its electrons. The elements are arranged in rows, each representing the filling of an electron shell. As electrons are added, they occupy the lowest available shell.

? *What is the atomic number of magnesium? How many protons and electrons does it have? How many electron shells? How many valence electrons?*

left-to-right sequence of elements in each row corresponds to the sequential addition of electrons and protons. (See Appendix B for the complete periodic table.)

Hydrogen's 1 electron and helium's 2 electrons are located in the first shell. Electrons, like all matter, tend to exist in the lowest available state of potential energy. In an atom, this state is in the first shell. However, the first shell can hold no more than 2 electrons; thus, hydrogen and helium are the only elements in the first row of the table. In an atom with more than 2 electrons, the additional electrons must occupy higher shells because the first shell is full. The next element, lithium, has 3 electrons. Two of these electrons fill the first shell, while the third electron occupies the second shell. The second shell holds a maximum of 8 electrons. Neon, at the end of the second row, has 8 electrons in the second shell, giving it a total of 10 electrons.

The chemical behavior of an atom depends mostly on the number of electrons in its *outermost* shell. We call those outer electrons **valence electrons** and the outermost electron shell the **valence shell**. In the case of lithium, there is only 1 valence electron, and the second shell is the valence shell. Atoms with the same number of electrons in their valence shells exhibit similar chemical behavior. For example, fluorine (F) and chlorine (Cl) both have 7 valence electrons, and both form compounds when combined with the element sodium (Na): Sodium fluoride (NaF) is commonly added to toothpaste to prevent tooth decay, and, as described earlier, NaCl is table salt (see Figure 2.2). An atom with a completed valence shell is unreactive; that is, it will not interact readily with other atoms. At the far right of the periodic table are helium, neon, and argon, the only three elements shown in Figure 2.6 that have full valence shells. These elements are said to be *inert*, meaning chemically unreactive. All the other atoms in Figure 2.6 are chemically reactive because they have incomplete valence shells.

Notice that as we "build" the atoms in Figure 2.6, the first 4 electrons added to the second and third shells are not shown in pairs; only after 4 electrons are present do the next electrons complete pairs. The reactivity of an atom arises from the presence of one or more unpaired electrons in its valence shell. As you will see in the next section, atoms interact in a way that completes their valence shells. When they do so, it is the *unpaired* electrons that are involved.

CONCEPT CHECK 2.2

1. A nitrogen atom has 7 protons, and the most common isotope of nitrogen has 7 neutrons. A radioactive isotope of nitrogen has 8 neutrons. Write the atomic number and mass number of this radioactive nitrogen as a chemical symbol with a subscript and superscript.

2. How many electrons does fluorine have? How many electron shells? How many electrons are needed to fill the valence shell?

3. **WHAT IF?** In Figure 2.6, if two or more elements are in the same row, what do they have in common? If two or more elements are in the same column, what do they have in common?

For suggested answers, see Appendix A.

The formation and function of molecules depend on chemical bonding between atoms

Now that we have looked at the structure of atoms, we can move up the hierarchy of organization and see how atoms combine to form molecules and ionic compounds. Atoms with incomplete valence shells can interact with certain other atoms in such a way that each partner completes its valence shell: The atoms either share or transfer valence electrons. These interactions usually result in atoms staying close together, held by attractions called **chemical bonds**. The strongest kinds of chemical bonds are covalent bonds and ionic bonds (when in dry ionic compounds; ionic bonds are weak when in aqueous solutions).

Covalent Bonds

A **covalent bond** is the sharing of a pair of valence electrons by two atoms. For example, let's consider what happens when two hydrogen atoms approach each other. Recall that hydrogen has 1 valence electron in the first shell, but the shell's capacity is 2 electrons. When the two hydrogen atoms come close enough for their electron shells to overlap, they can share their electrons **(Figure 2.7)**. Each hydrogen atom is now associated with 2 electrons in what amounts to a completed valence shell. Two or more atoms held together by covalent bonds constitute a **molecule**, in this case a hydrogen molecule.

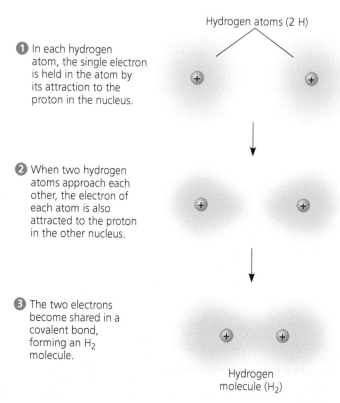

Hydrogen atoms (2 H)

❶ In each hydrogen atom, the single electron is held in the atom by its attraction to the proton in the nucleus.

❷ When two hydrogen atoms approach each other, the electron of each atom is also attracted to the proton in the other nucleus.

❸ The two electrons become shared in a covalent bond, forming an H_2 molecule.

Hydrogen molecule (H_2)

▲ **Figure 2.7 Formation of a covalent bond.**

Figure 2.8a shows several ways of representing a hydrogen molecule. Its *molecular formula*, H_2, simply indicates that the molecule consists of two atoms of hydrogen. Electron sharing can be depicted by an electron distribution diagram or by a *structural formula*, H—H, where the line represents a **single bond**, a pair of shared electrons. A space-filling model comes closest to representing the actual shape of the molecule.

Oxygen has 6 electrons in its second electron shell and therefore needs 2 more electrons to complete its valence shell. Two oxygen atoms form a molecule by sharing *two* pairs of valence electrons **(Figure 2.8b)**. The atoms are thus joined by a **double bond** ($O{=}O$).

Each atom that can share valence electrons has a bonding capacity corresponding to the number of covalent bonds the atom can form. When the bonds form, they give the atom a full complement of electrons in the valence shell. The bonding capacity of oxygen, for example, is 2. This bonding capacity is called the atom's **valence** and usually equals the number of electrons required to complete the atom's outermost (valence) shell. See if you can determine the valences of hydrogen, oxygen, nitrogen, and carbon by studying the electron distribution diagrams in Figure 2.6. You can see that the valence of hydrogen is 1; oxygen, 2; nitrogen, 3; and carbon, 4. (The situation is more complicated for phosphorus, in the third row of the periodic table, which can have a valence of 3 or 5 depending on the combination of single and double bonds it makes.)

The molecules H_2 and O_2 are pure elements rather than compounds because a compound is a combination of two or more *different* elements. Water, with the molecular formula H_2O, is a compound. Two atoms of hydrogen are needed to satisfy the valence of one oxygen atom. **Figure 2.8c** shows the structure of a water molecule. Water is so important to life that the last section of this chapter, Concept 2.5, is devoted to its structure and behavior.

Methane, the main component of natural gas, is a compound with the molecular formula CH_4. It takes four hydrogen atoms, each with a valence of 1, to complement one atom of carbon, with its valence of 4 **(Figure 2.8d)**. (We will look at many other compounds of carbon in Chapter 3.)

Atoms in a molecule attract shared bonding electrons to varying degrees, depending on the element. The attraction of a particular atom for the electrons of a covalent bond is called its **electronegativity**. The more electronegative an atom is, the more strongly it pulls shared electrons toward itself. In a covalent bond between two atoms of the same element, the electrons are shared equally because the two atoms have the same electronegativity—the tug-of-war is at a standoff. Such a bond is called a **nonpolar covalent bond**. For example, the single bond of H_2 is nonpolar, as is the double bond of O_2. However, when an atom is bonded to a more electronegative atom, the electrons of the bond are not shared equally. This type of bond is called a **polar covalent bond**. Such bonds vary in their polarity, depending on the relative electronegativity of the two atoms. For example, the bonds between the oxygen and hydrogen atoms of a water molecule are quite polar **(Figure 2.9)**. Oxygen is one of the most electronegative elements, attracting shared electrons much more strongly than hydrogen does. In a covalent bond between oxygen and hydrogen, the electrons spend more time near the oxygen nucleus than they do near the hydrogen nucleus. Because electrons have a negative charge and are pulled toward oxygen in a water molecule, the oxygen atom has a partial negative charge (indicated by the Greek letter δ with a

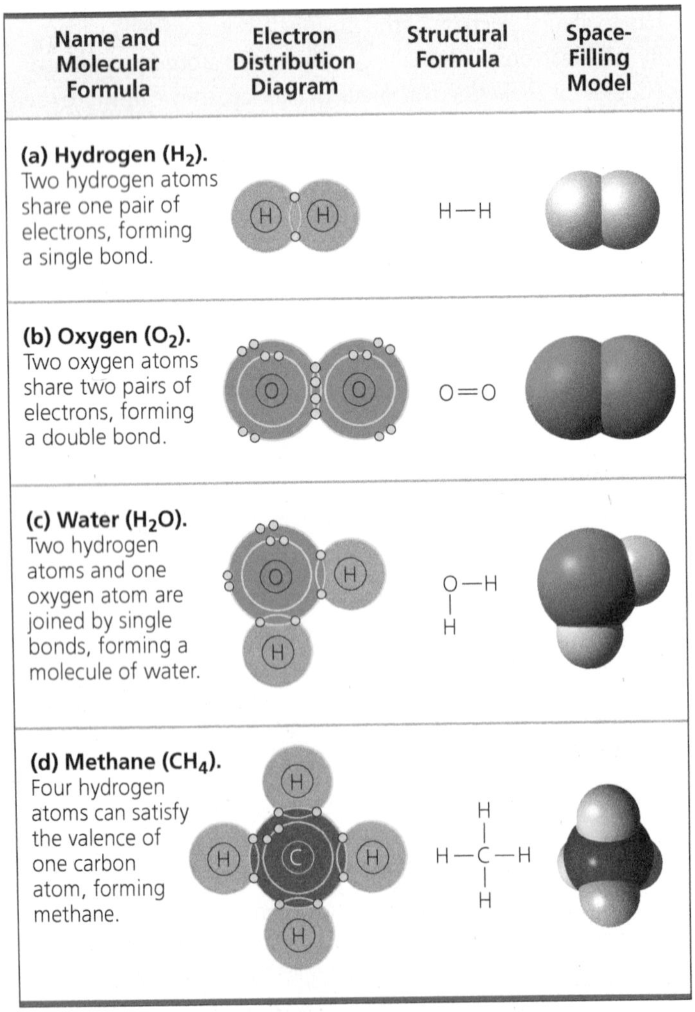

Name and Molecular Formula	Electron Distribution Diagram	Structural Formula	Space-Filling Model
(a) Hydrogen (H_2). Two hydrogen atoms share one pair of electrons, forming a single bond.		H—H	
(b) Oxygen (O_2). Two oxygen atoms share two pairs of electrons, forming a double bond.		O=O	
(c) Water (H_2O). Two hydrogen atoms and one oxygen atom are joined by single bonds, forming a molecule of water.		O—H $\vert$ H	
(d) Methane (CH_4). Four hydrogen atoms can satisfy the valence of one carbon atom, forming methane.		H $\vert$ H—C—H $\vert$ H	

▲ **Figure 2.8 Covalent bonding in four molecules.** The number of electrons required to complete an atom's valence shell generally determines how many covalent bonds that atom will form. This figure shows several ways of indicating covalent bonds.

Because oxygen (O) is more electronegative than hydrogen (H), shared electrons are pulled more toward oxygen.

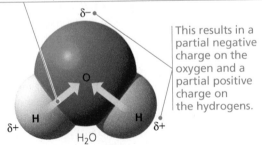

This results in a partial negative charge on the oxygen and a partial positive charge on the hydrogens.

▲ **Figure 2.9 Polar covalent bonds in a water molecule.**

minus sign, δ−, or "delta minus"), and each hydrogen atom has a partial positive charge (δ+, or "delta plus"). In contrast, the individual bonds of methane (CH_4) are much less polar because the electronegativities of carbon and hydrogen are similar.

Ionic Bonds

In some cases, two atoms are so unequal in their attraction for valence electrons that the more electronegative atom strips an electron completely away from its partner. The two resulting oppositely charged atoms (or molecules) are called **ions**. A positively charged ion is called a **cation**, while a negatively charged ion is called an **anion**. Because of their opposite charges, cations and anions attract each other; this attraction is called an **ionic bond**. Note that the transfer of an electron is not, by itself, the formation of a bond; rather, it allows a bond to form because it results in two ions of opposite charge. Any two such ions can form an ionic bond—the ions do not need to have acquired their charge by an electron transfer with each other.

This is what happens when an atom of sodium ($_{11}Na$) encounters an atom of chlorine ($_{17}Cl$) **(Figure 2.10)**. A sodium atom has a total of 11 electrons, with its single valence electron in the third electron shell. A chlorine atom has a total of 17 electrons, with 7 electrons in its valence shell. When these two atoms meet, the lone valence electron of sodium is transferred to the chlorine atom, and both atoms end up with their valence shells complete. (Because sodium no longer has an electron in the third shell, the second shell is now the valence shell.)

The electron transfer between the two atoms moves one unit of negative charge from sodium to chlorine. Sodium, now with 11 protons but only 10 electrons, has a net electrical charge of 1+; the sodium atom has become a cation. Conversely, the chlorine atom, having gained an extra electron, now has 17 protons and 18 electrons, giving it a net electrical charge of 1−; it has become a chloride ion—an anion.

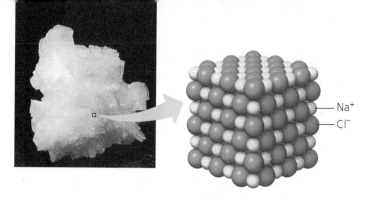

▲ **Figure 2.11 A sodium chloride (NaCl) crystal.** The sodium ions (Na^+) and chloride ions (Cl^-) are held together by ionic bonds. The formula NaCl tells us that the ratio of Na^+ to Cl^- is 1:1.

Compounds formed by ionic bonds are called **ionic compounds**, or **salts**. We know the ionic compound sodium chloride (NaCl) as table salt **(Figure 2.11)**. Salts are often found in nature as crystals of various sizes and shapes. Each salt crystal is an aggregate of vast numbers of cations and anions bonded by their electrical attraction and arranged in a three-dimensional lattice. Unlike a covalent compound, which consists of molecules having a definite size and number of atoms, an ionic compound does not consist of molecules. The formula for an ionic compound, such as NaCl, indicates only the ratio of elements in a crystal of the salt. "NaCl" by itself is not a molecule.

Not all salts have equal numbers of cations and anions. For example, the ionic compound magnesium chloride ($MgCl_2$) has two chloride ions for each magnesium ion. Magnesium ($_{12}Mg$) must lose 2 outer electrons if the atom is to have a complete valence shell, so it has a tendency to become a cation with a net charge of 2+ (Mg^{2+}). One magnesium cation can therefore form ionic bonds with two chloride anions (Cl^-).

The term *ion* also applies to entire molecules that are electrically charged. In the salt ammonium chloride (NH_4Cl), for instance, the anion is a single chloride ion (Cl^-), but the cation is ammonium (NH_4^+), a nitrogen atom covalently bonded to four hydrogen atoms. The whole ammonium ion has an electrical charge of 1+ because it has given up 1 electron and thus is 1 electron short.

Environment affects the strength of ionic bonds. In a dry salt crystal, the bonds are so strong that it takes a hammer and chisel to break enough of them to crack the crystal in two. If the same salt crystal is dissolved in water, however, the ionic bonds are much weaker because each ion is partially shielded by its interactions with water molecules. Most drugs are manufactured as salts because they are quite stable when dry but can dissociate (come apart) easily in water.

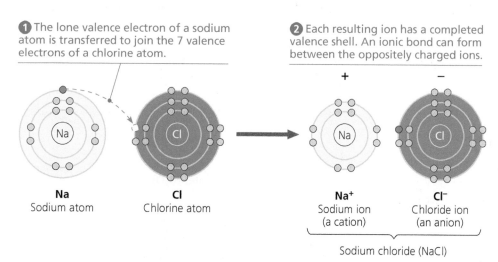

❶ The lone valence electron of a sodium atom is transferred to join the 7 valence electrons of a chlorine atom.

❷ Each resulting ion has a completed valence shell. An ionic bond can form between the oppositely charged ions.

Na	**Cl**
Sodium atom	Chlorine atom

+	−
Na⁺	**Cl⁻**
Sodium ion (a cation)	Chloride ion (an anion)

Sodium chloride (NaCl)

▲ **Figure 2.10 Electron transfer and ionic bonding.** The attraction between oppositely charged atoms, or ions, is an ionic bond. An ionic bond can form between any two oppositely charged ions, even if they have not been formed by transfer of an electron from one to the other.

Weak Chemical Bonds

In organisms, most of the strongest chemical bonds are co-valent bonds, which link atoms to form a cell's molecules. But weaker bonding within and between molecules is also indispensable in the cell, contributing greatly to the emergent properties of life. Many large biological molecules are held in their functional form by weak bonds. In addition, when two molecules in the cell make contact, they may adhere temporarily by weak bonds. The reversibility of weak bonding can be an advantage: Two molecules can come together, respond to one another in some way, and then separate.

Several types of weak chemical bonds are important in organisms. One is the ionic bond as it exists between ions disso-ciated in water, which we just discussed. Hydrogen bonds and van der Waals interactions are also crucial to life.

Hydrogen Bonds

Among the various kinds of weak chemical bonds, hydrogen bonds are so central to the chemistry of life that they deserve special attention. When a hydrogen atom is covalently bonded to an electronegative atom, the hydrogen atom has a partial positive charge that allows it to be attracted to a different electronegative atom nearby. This noncovalent attraction between a hydrogen and an electronegative atom is called a **hydrogen bond**. In living cells, the electronegative partners are usually oxygen or nitrogen atoms. Refer to **Figure 2.12** to examine the simple case of hydro-gen bonding between water (H_2O) and ammonia (NH_3).

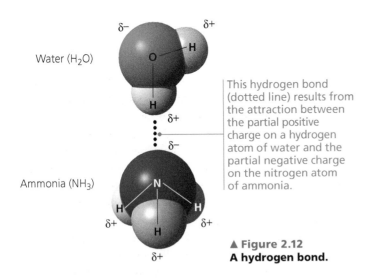

Water (H_2O)

Ammonia (NH_3)

This hydrogen bond (dotted line) results from the attraction between the partial positive charge on a hydrogen atom of water and the partial negative charge on the nitrogen atom of ammonia.

▲ **Figure 2.12**
A hydrogen bond.

Van der Waals Interactions

Even a molecule with nonpolar covalent bonds may have posi-tively and negatively charged regions. Electrons are not always symmetrically distributed in such a molecule; at any instant, they may accumulate by chance in one part of the molecule or another. The results are ever-changing regions of positive and negative charge that enable all atoms and molecules to stick to one another. These **van der Waals interactions** are indi-vidually weak and occur only when atoms and molecules are

very close together. When many such interactions occur simultaneously, however, they can be powerful: Van der Waals interactions allow the gecko lizard, shown here, to walk straight up a wall! A gecko toe has hundreds of thou-sands of tiny hairs with multiple projections on each, which help to maximize surface contact with the wall. The van der Waals interactions between the mol-ecules of the foot and those of the wall's surface are so numer-ous that despite their individual weakness, together they can support the gecko's body weight. This discovery has inspired development of an artificial adhesive called Geckskin: A patch the size of an index card can hold a 700-pound weight to a wall!

Van der Waals interactions, hydrogen bonds, ionic bonds in water, and other weak bonds may form not only between molecules but also between parts of a large molecule, such as a protein. The cumulative effect of weak bonds is to reinforce the three-dimensional shape of the molecule. (You will learn more about the very important biological roles of weak bonds in Concept 3.5.)

Molecular Shape and Function

A molecule has a characteristic size and shape, which are key to its function in the living cell. A molecule consisting of two atoms, such as H_2 or O_2, is always linear, but most molecules with more than two atoms have more complicated shapes. To take a very simple example, a water molecule (H_2O) is shaped roughly like a V, with its two covalent bonds spread apart at an angle of 104.5° **(Figure 2.13)**. A methane molecule (CH_4) has a geometric shape called a tetrahedron, a pyramid with a triangular base. The carbon nucleus is inside, at the center, with its four covalent bonds radiating to hydrogen nuclei at the

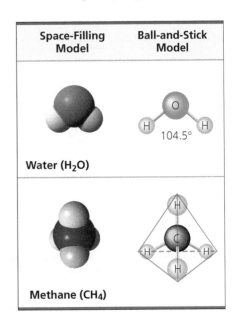

Space-Filling Model	Ball-and-Stick Model

Water (H_2O)

Methane (CH_4)

▶ **Figure 2.13**
Models showing the shapes of two small molecules.
Each of the molecules, water and methane, is represented in two different ways.

corners of the tetrahedron. Larger molecules containing multiple carbon atoms, including many of the molecules that make up living matter, have more complex overall shapes. However, the tetrahedral shape of a carbon atom bonded to four other atoms is often a repeating motif within such molecules.

Molecular shape is crucial in biology: It determines how biological molecules recognize and respond to one another with specificity. Biological molecules often bind temporarily to each other by forming weak bonds, but only if their shapes are complementary. Consider the effects of opiates (drugs derived from opium); morphine and heroin are two examples. Opiates relieve pain and alter mood by weakly binding to specific receptor molecules on the surfaces of brain cells. Why would brain cells carry receptors for opiates, compounds that are not made by the body? In 1975, the discovery of endorphins answered this question. Endorphins are signaling molecules made by the pituitary gland that bind to the receptors, relieving pain and producing euphoria during times of stress, such as intense exercise. Opiates have shapes similar to endorphins and mimic them by binding to endorphin receptors in the brain. That is why opiates and endorphins have similar effects **(Figure 2.14)**.

Key

■	Carbon	■	Nitrogen
▨	Hydrogen	▨	Sulfur
		■	Oxygen

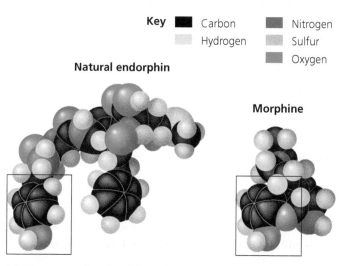

(a) Structures of endorphin and morphine. The boxed portion of the endorphin molecule (left) binds to receptor molecules on target cells in the brain. The boxed portion of the morphine molecule (right) is a close match.

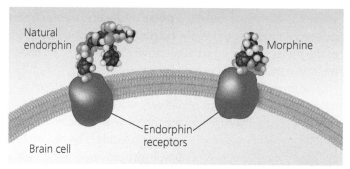

(b) Binding to endorphin receptors. Both endorphin and morphine can bind to endorphin receptors on the surface of a brain cell.

▲ **Figure 2.14 A molecular mimic.** Morphine affects pain perception and emotional state by mimicking the brain's natural endorphins.

The role of molecular shape in brain chemistry illustrates the match between structure and function in biological organization, one of biology's unifying themes.

CONCEPT CHECK 2.3
1. Why does the structure $H—C\!=\!C—H$ fail to make sense chemically?
2. What holds the atoms together in a crystal of magnesium chloride ($MgCl_2$)?
3. **WHAT IF?** If you were a pharmaceutical researcher, why would you want to learn the three-dimensional shapes of naturally occurring signaling molecules?

For suggested answers, see Appendix A.

CONCEPT 2.4

Chemical reactions make and break chemical bonds

The making and breaking of chemical bonds, leading to changes in the composition of matter, are called **chemical reactions**. An example is the reaction between hydrogen and oxygen molecules that forms water:

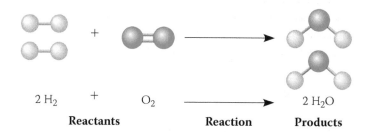

$2\,H_2$	$+$	O_2		$2\,H_2O$
Reactants			**Reaction**	**Products**

This reaction breaks the covalent bonds of H_2 and O_2 and forms the new bonds of H_2O. When we write the equation for a chemical reaction, we use an arrow to indicate the conversion of the starting materials, called the **reactants**, to the resulting materials, or **products**. The coefficients indicate the number of molecules involved; for example, the coefficient 2 in front of H_2 means that the reaction starts with two molecules of hydrogen. Notice that all atoms of the reactants must be accounted for in the products. Matter is conserved in a chemical reaction: Reactions cannot create or destroy atoms but can only rearrange (redistribute) the electrons among them.

Photosynthesis, which takes place within the cells of green plant tissues, is an important biological example of how chemical reactions rearrange matter. Humans and other animals ultimately depend on photosynthesis for food and oxygen, and this process is at the foundation of almost all ecosystems. The following chemical shorthand summarizes the process of photosynthesis:

$$6\,CO_2 + 6\,H_2O \rightarrow C_6H_{12}O_6 + 6\,O_2$$

The raw materials of photosynthesis are carbon dioxide (CO_2), which is taken from the air, and water (H_2O), which is

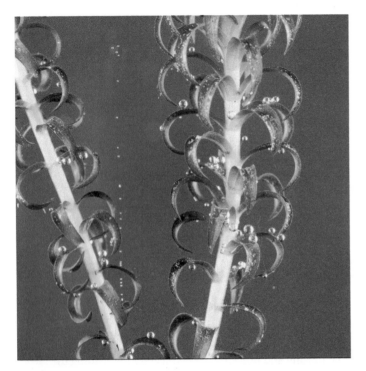

▲ **Figure 2.15 Photosynthesis: a solar-powered rearrangement of matter.** *Elodea*, a freshwater plant, produces sugar by rearranging the atoms of carbon dioxide and water in the chemical process known as photosynthesis, which is powered by sunlight. Much of the sugar is then converted to other food molecules. Oxygen gas (O_2) is a by-product of photosynthesis; notice the bubbles of O_2-containing gas escaping from the leaves submerged in water.

❓ *Explain how this photo relates to the reactants and products in the equation for photosynthesis given in the text. (You will learn more about photosynthesis in Chapter 8.)*

absorbed from the soil. Within the plant cells, sunlight powers the conversion of these ingredients to a sugar called glucose ($C_6H_{12}O_6$) and oxygen molecules (O_2), a by-product that the plant releases into the surroundings **(Figure 2.15)**. Although photosynthesis is actually a sequence of many chemical reactions, we still end up with the same number and types of atoms that we had when we started. Matter has simply been rearranged, with an input of energy provided by sunlight.

All chemical reactions are reversible, with the products of the forward reaction becoming the reactants for the reverse reaction. For example, hydrogen and nitrogen molecules can combine to form ammonia, but ammonia can also decompose to regenerate hydrogen and nitrogen:

$$3\,H_2 + N_2 \rightleftharpoons 2\,NH_3$$

The two opposite-headed arrows indicate that the reaction is reversible.

One of the factors affecting the rate of a reaction is the concentration of reactants. The greater the concentration of reactant molecules, the more frequently they collide with one another and have an opportunity to react and form products. The same holds true for products. As products accumulate, collisions resulting in the reverse reaction become more frequent. Eventually, the forward and reverse reactions occur at the same rate, and the relative concentrations of products and reactants stop changing. The point at which the reactions offset one another exactly is called **chemical equilibrium**. This is a dynamic equilibrium; reactions are still going on, but with no net effect on the concentrations of reactants and products. Equilibrium does *not* mean that the reactants and products are equal in concentration, but only that their concentrations have stabilized at a particular ratio. The reaction involving ammonia reaches equilibrium when ammonia decomposes as rapidly as it forms. In some chemical reactions, the equilibrium point may lie so far to the right that these reactions go essentially to completion; that is, virtually all the reactants are converted to products.

To conclude this chapter, we focus on water, the substance in which all the chemical processes of organisms occur.

CONCEPT CHECK 2.4

1. Which type of chemical reaction occurs faster at equilibrium, the formation of products from reactants or that of reactants from products?
2. **WHAT IF?** Write an equation that uses the products of photosynthesis as reactants and the reactants of photosynthesis as products. Add energy as another product. This new equation describes a process that occurs in your cells. Describe this equation in words. How does this equation relate to breathing?

For suggested answers, see Appendix A.

CONCEPT 2.5

Hydrogen bonding gives water properties that help make life possible on Earth

All organisms are made mostly of water and live in an environment dominated by water. Most cells are surrounded by water, and cells themselves are about 70–95% water. Water is so common that it is easy to overlook the fact that it is an exceptional substance with many extraordinary qualities. We can trace water's unique behavior to the structure and interactions of its molecules. As you saw in Figure 2.9, the connections between the atoms of a water molecule are polar covalent bonds. The unequal sharing of electrons and water's V-like shape make it a **polar molecule**, meaning that its overall charge is unevenly distributed: The oxygen region of the molecule has a partial negative charge ($\delta-$), and each hydrogen has a partial positive charge ($\delta+$).

The properties of water arise from attractions between oppositely charged atoms of different water molecules: The slightly positive hydrogen of one molecule is attracted to the slightly negative oxygen of a nearby molecule. The two molecules are thus held together by a hydrogen bond. When water is in its liquid form, its hydrogen bonds are very fragile, each only about 1/20 as strong as a covalent bond. The hydrogen bonds form, break, and re-form with great frequency. Each lasts only a few trillionths of a second, but the molecules are

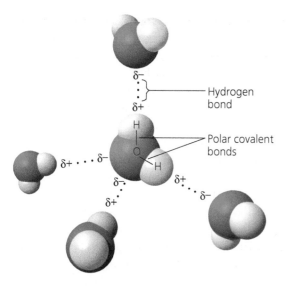

▲ **Figure 2.16 Hydrogen bonds between water molecules.** The charged regions in a water molecule are due to its polar covalent bonds. Oppositely charged regions of neighboring water molecules are attracted to each other, forming hydrogen bonds. Each molecule can hydrogen-bond to multiple partners, and these associations are constantly changing.

DRAW IT *Draw partial charges on all the atoms of the water molecule on the far left, and draw two more water molecules hydrogen-bonded to it.*

constantly forming new hydrogen bonds with a succession of partners. Therefore, at any instant, most of the water molecules are hydrogen-bonded to their neighbors **(Figure 2.16)**. The extraordinary properties of water emerge from this hydrogen bonding, which organizes water molecules into a higher level of structural order. We will examine four emergent properties of water that contribute to Earth's suitability as an environment for life: cohesive behavior, ability to moderate temperature, expansion upon freezing, and versatility as a solvent. After that, we'll discuss a critical aspect of water chemistry—acids and bases.

Cohesion of Water Molecules

Water molecules stay close to each other as a result of hydrogen bonding. At any given moment, many of the molecules in liquid water are linked by multiple hydrogen bonds. These linkages make water more structured than most other liquids. Collectively, the hydrogen bonds hold the substance together, a phenomenon called **cohesion**.

Cohesion due to hydrogen bonding contributes to the transport of water and dissolved nutrients against gravity in plants **(Figure 2.17)**. Water from the roots reaches the leaves through a network of water-conducting cells. As water evaporates from a leaf, hydrogen bonds cause water molecules leaving the veins to tug on molecules farther down, and the upward pull is transmitted through the water-conducting cells all the way to the roots. **Adhesion**, the clinging of one substance to another, also plays a role. Adhesion of water to cell walls by hydrogen bonds helps counter the downward pull of gravity.

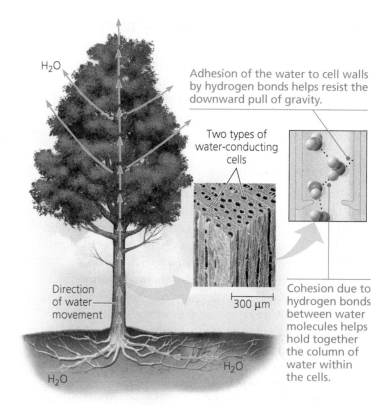

▲ **Figure 2.17 Water transport in plants.** Evaporation from leaves pulls water upward from the roots through water-conducting cells. Because of the properties of cohesion and adhesion, the tallest trees can transport water more than 100 m upward—approximately one-quarter the height of the Empire State Building in New York City.

ANIMATION Visit the Study Area in **MasteringBiology** for the BioFlix® 3-D Animation on Water Transport in Plants.

Related to cohesion is **surface tension**, a measure of how difficult it is to stretch or break the surface of a liquid. The hydrogen bonds in water give it an unusually high surface tension, making it behave as though it were coated with an invisible film. You can observe the surface tension of water by slightly overfilling a drinking glass; the water will stand above the rim. The spider in **Figure 2.18** takes advantage of the surface tension of water to walk across a pond without breaking the surface.

▶ **Figure 2.18 Walking on water.** The high surface tension of water, resulting from the collective strength of its hydrogen bonds, allows this raft spider to walk on the surface of a pond.

Moderation of Temperature by Water

Water moderates air temperature by absorbing heat from air that is warmer and releasing the stored heat to air that is cooler. Water is effective as a heat bank because it can absorb or release a relatively large amount of heat with only a slight change in its own temperature. To understand this capability of water, we must first look briefly at temperature and heat.

Temperature and Heat

Anything that moves has **kinetic energy**, the energy of motion. Atoms and molecules have kinetic energy because they are always moving, although not necessarily in any particular direction. The faster a molecule moves, the greater its kinetic energy. The kinetic energy associated with the random movement of atoms or molecules is called **thermal energy**. Thermal energy is related to temperature, but they are not the same thing. **Temperature** represents the *average* kinetic energy of the molecules in a body of matter, regardless of volume, whereas the thermal energy of a body of matter reflects the *total* kinetic energy and thus depends on the matter's volume. When water is heated in a coffeemaker, the average speed of the molecules increases, and the thermometer records this as a rise in temperature of the liquid. The total amount of thermal energy also increases in this case. Note, however, that although the pot of coffee has a much higher temperature than, say, the water in a swimming pool, the swimming pool contains more thermal energy because of its much greater volume.

Whenever two objects of different temperature are brought together, thermal energy passes from the warmer to the cooler object until the two are the same temperature. Molecules in the cooler object speed up at the expense of the thermal energy of the warmer object. An ice cube cools a drink not by adding coldness to the liquid, but by absorbing thermal energy from the liquid as the ice itself melts. Thermal energy in transfer from one body of matter to another is defined as **heat**.

One convenient unit of heat used in this book is the **calorie (cal)**. A calorie is the amount of heat it takes to raise the temperature of 1 g of water by 1°C. Conversely, a calorie is also the amount of heat that 1 g of water releases when it cools by 1°C. A **kilocalorie (kcal)**, 1,000 cal, is the quantity of heat required to raise the temperature of 1 kilogram (kg) of water by 1°C. (The "calories" on food packages are actually kilocalories.) Another energy unit used in this book is the **joule (J)**. One joule equals 0.239 cal; one calorie equals 4.184 J.

Water's High Specific Heat

The ability of water to stabilize temperature stems from its relatively high specific heat. The **specific heat** of a substance is defined as the amount of heat that must be absorbed or lost for 1 g of that substance to change its temperature by 1°C. We already know water's specific heat because we have defined a calorie as the amount of heat that causes 1 g of water to change its temperature by 1°C. Therefore, the specific heat of water is 1 calorie per gram per degree Celsius, abbreviated as $1 \, cal/(g \cdot °C)$. Compared with most other substances, water has an unusually high specific heat. As a result, water will change its temperature less than other liquids when it absorbs or loses a given amount of heat. The reason you can burn your fingers by touching the side of an iron pot on the stove when the water in the pot is still lukewarm is that the specific heat of water is ten times greater than that of iron. In other words, the same amount of heat will raise the temperature of 1 g of the iron much faster than it will raise the temperature of 1 g of the water. Specific heat can be thought of as a measure of how well a substance resists changing its temperature when it absorbs or releases heat. Water resists changing its temperature; when it does change its temperature, it absorbs or loses a relatively large quantity of heat for each degree of change.

We can trace water's high specific heat, like many of its other properties, to hydrogen bonding. Heat must be absorbed in order to break hydrogen bonds; by the same token, heat is released when hydrogen bonds form. A calorie of heat causes a relatively small change in the temperature of water because much of the heat is used to disrupt hydrogen bonds before the water molecules can begin moving faster. And when the temperature of water drops slightly, many additional hydrogen bonds form, releasing a considerable amount of energy in the form of heat.

What is the relevance of water's high specific heat to life on Earth? A large body of water can absorb and store a huge amount of heat from the sun in the daytime and during summer while warming up only a few degrees. At night and during winter, the gradually cooling water can warm the air. This capability of water serves to moderate air temperatures in coastal areas **(Figure 2.19)**. The high specific heat of water also tends to stabilize ocean temperatures, creating a favorable environment for marine life. Thus, because of its high specific heat, the water that covers most of Earth keeps temperature fluctuations on land and in water within limits that permit life. Also, because organisms are made primarily of water, they are better able to resist changes in their own temperature than if they were made of a liquid with a lower specific heat.

▲ Figure 2.19 **Temperatures for the Pacific Ocean and Southern California on an August day.**

INTERPRET THE DATA *Explain the pattern of temperatures shown in this diagram.*

Evaporative Cooling

Molecules of any liquid stay close together because they are attracted to one another. Molecules moving fast enough to overcome these attractions can depart the liquid and enter the air as a gas (vapor). This transformation from a liquid to a gas is called vaporization, or *evaporation*. Recall that the speed of molecular movement varies and that temperature is the *average* kinetic energy of molecules. Even at low temperatures, the speediest molecules can escape into the air. Some evaporation occurs at any temperature; a glass of water at room temperature, for example, will eventually evaporate completely. If a liquid is heated, the average kinetic energy of molecules increases and the liquid evaporates more rapidly.

Heat of vaporization is the quantity of heat a liquid must absorb for 1 g of it to be converted from the liquid to the gaseous state. For the same reason that water has a high specific heat, it also has a high heat of vaporization relative to most other liquids. To evaporate 1 g of water at 25°C, about 580 cal of heat is needed—nearly double the amount needed to vaporize a gram of alcohol, for example. Water's high heat of vaporization is another emergent property resulting from the strength of its hydrogen bonds, which must be broken before the molecules can exit from the liquid in the form of water vapor.

The high amount of energy required to vaporize water has a wide range of effects. On a global scale, for example, it helps moderate Earth's climate. A considerable amount of solar heat absorbed by tropical seas is consumed during the evaporation of surface water. Then, as moist tropical air circulates poleward, it releases heat as it condenses and forms rain. On an organismal level, water's high heat of vaporization accounts for the severity of steam burns. These burns are caused by the heat energy released when steam condenses into liquid on the skin.

As a liquid evaporates, the surface of the liquid that remains behind cools down (its temperature decreases). This **evaporative cooling** occurs because the "hottest" molecules, those with the greatest kinetic energy, are the ones most likely to leave as gas. It is as if the hundred fastest runners at a college transferred to another school; the average speed of the remaining students would decline.

Evaporative cooling of water contributes to the stability of temperature in lakes and ponds and also provides a mechanism that prevents terrestrial organisms from overheating. For example, evaporation of water from the leaves of a plant helps keep the tissues in the leaves from becoming too warm in the sunlight. Evaporation of sweat from human skin dissipates body heat and helps prevent overheating on a hot day or when excess heat is generated by strenuous activity. High humidity on a hot day increases discomfort because the high concentration of water vapor in the air inhibits the evaporation of sweat from the body.

Floating of Ice on Liquid Water

Water is one of the few substances that are less dense as a solid than as a liquid. In other words, ice floats on liquid water. While other materials contract and become denser when they solidify, water expands. The cause of this exotic behavior is, once again, hydrogen bonding. At temperatures above 4°C, water behaves like other liquids, expanding as it warms and contracting as it cools. As the temperature falls from 4°C to 0°C, water begins to freeze because more and more of its molecules are moving too slowly to break hydrogen bonds. At 0°C, the molecules become locked into a crystalline lattice, each water molecule hydrogen-bonded to four partners (**Figure 2.20**). The hydrogen bonds keep the molecules at "arm's length," far enough apart to make ice about 10% less dense than liquid water at 4°C. When ice absorbs enough heat for its temperature to rise above 0°C, hydrogen bonds between molecules are disrupted. As the crystal collapses, the ice melts, and molecules are free to slip closer together. Water reaches its greatest density at 4°C and then begins to expand as the molecules move faster.

The ability of ice to float due to its lower density is an important factor in the suitability of the environment for life. If ice sank, then eventually all ponds, lakes, and even oceans

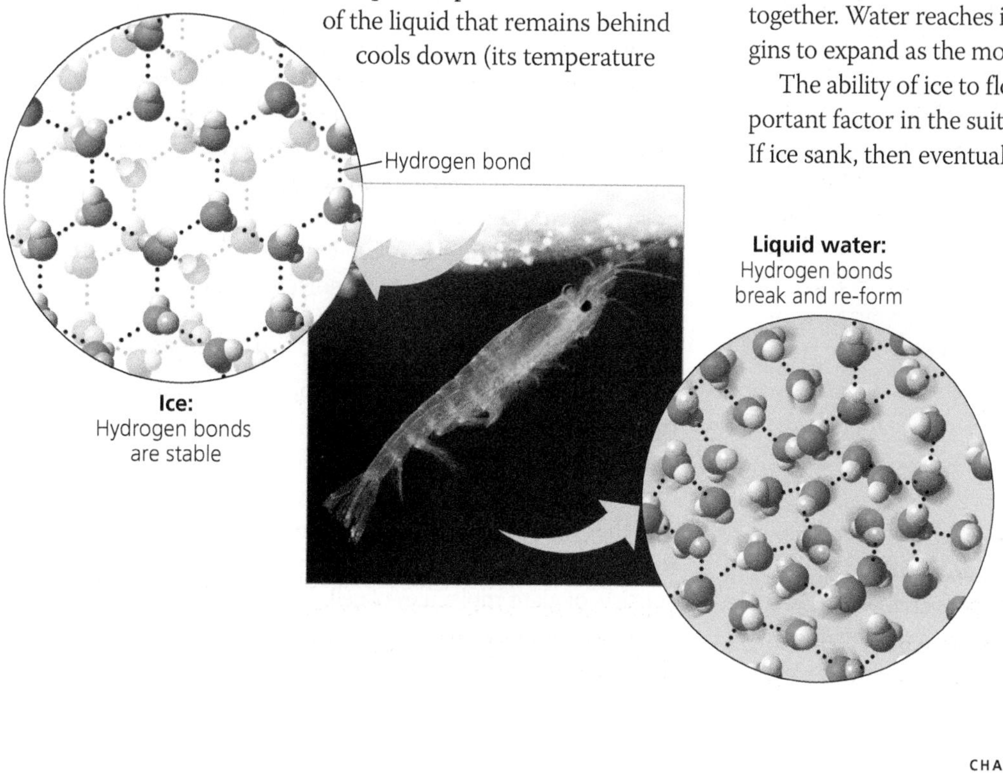

Hydrogen bond

Ice:
Hydrogen bonds
are stable

Liquid water:
Hydrogen bonds
break and re-form

◀ **Figure 2.20 Ice: crystalline structure and floating barrier.** In ice, each molecule is hydrogen-bonded to four neighbors in a three-dimensional crystal. Because the crystal is spacious, ice has fewer molecules than an equal volume of liquid water. In other words, ice is less dense than liquid water. Floating ice becomes a barrier that insulates the liquid water below from the colder air. The marine organism shown here is a type of shrimp called krill; it was photographed beneath floating ice in the Southern Ocean near Antarctica.

WHAT IF? *If water did not form hydrogen bonds, what would happen to the shrimp's habitat, shown here?*

would freeze solid, making life as we know it impossible on Earth. During summer, only the upper few inches of the ocean would thaw. Instead, when a deep body of water cools, the floating ice insulates the liquid water below, preventing it from freezing and allowing life to exist under the frozen surface, as shown in the photo in Figure 2.20.

Water: The Solvent of Life

A sugar cube placed in a glass of water will dissolve. Eventually, the glass will contain a uniform mixture of sugar and water; the concentration of dissolved sugar will be the same everywhere in the mixture. A liquid that is a completely homogeneous mixture of two or more substances is called a **solution**. The dissolving agent of a solution is the **solvent**, and the substance that is dissolved is the **solute**. In this case, water is the solvent and sugar is the solute. An **aqueous solution** is one in which the solute is dissolved in water; water is the solvent.

Water is a very versatile solvent, a quality we can trace to the polarity of the water molecule. Suppose, for example, that a spoonful of table salt, the ionic compound sodium chloride (NaCl), is placed in water **(Figure 2.21)**. At the surface of each grain, or crystal, of salt, the sodium and chloride ions are exposed to the solvent. These ions and regions of the water molecules are attracted to each other due to their opposite charges. The oxygen regions of the water molecules are negatively

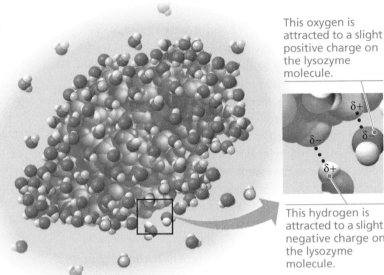

This oxygen is attracted to a slight positive charge on the lysozyme molecule.

This hydrogen is attracted to a slight negative charge on the lysozyme molecule.

▲ **Figure 2.22 A water-soluble protein.** Human lysozyme is a protein found in tears and saliva that has antibacterial action. This model shows the lysozyme molecule (purple) in an aqueous environment. Ionic and polar regions on the protein's surface attract the slightly charged regions of water molecules.

charged and are attracted to sodium cations. The hydrogen regions are positively charged and are attracted to chloride anions. As a result, water molecules surround the individual sodium and chloride ions, separating and shielding them from one another. The sphere of water molecules around each dissolved ion is called a **hydration shell**. Working inward from the surface of each salt crystal, water eventually dissolves all the ions. The result is a solution of two solutes, sodium cations and chloride anions, homogeneously mixed with water, the solvent. Other ionic compounds also dissolve in water. Seawater, for instance, contains a great variety of dissolved ions, as do living cells.

A compound does not need to be ionic to dissolve in water; many compounds made up of nonionic polar molecules, such as sugars, are also water-soluble. Such compounds dissolve when water molecules surround each of the solute molecules, forming hydrogen bonds with them. Even molecules as large as proteins can dissolve in water if they have ionic and polar regions on their surface **(Figure 2.22)**. Many different kinds of polar compounds are dissolved (along with ions) in the water of such biological fluids as blood, the sap of plants, and the liquid within all cells. Water is the solvent of life.

Hydrophilic and Hydrophobic Substances

Any substance that has an affinity for water is said to be **hydrophilic** (from the Greek *hydro*, water, and *philos*, loving). In some cases, substances can be hydrophilic without actually dissolving. For example, some molecules in cells are so large that they do not dissolve. Another example of a hydrophilic substance that does not dissolve is cotton, a plant product. Cotton consists of giant molecules of cellulose, a compound with numerous regions of partial positive and partial negative charges that can form hydrogen bonds with water. Water adheres to the

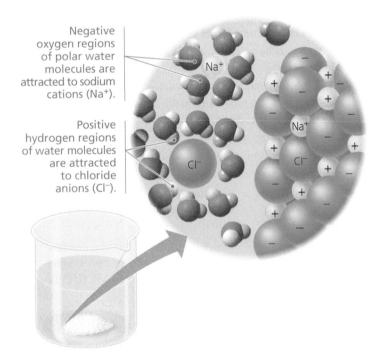

Negative oxygen regions of polar water molecules are attracted to sodium cations (Na⁺).

Positive hydrogen regions of water molecules are attracted to chloride anions (Cl⁻).

▲ **Figure 2.21 Table salt dissolving in water.** A sphere of water molecules, called a hydration shell, surrounds each solute ion.

WHAT IF? *What would happen if you heated this solution for a long time?*

cellulose fibers. Thus, a cotton towel does a great job of drying the body, yet it does not dissolve in the washing machine. Cellulose is also present in the walls of plant cells that conduct water; you read earlier how the adhesion of water to these hydrophilic walls helps water move up the plant against gravity.

There are, of course, substances that do not have an affinity for water. Substances that are nonionic and nonpolar (or otherwise cannot form hydrogen bonds) actually seem to repel water; these substances are said to be **hydrophobic** (from the Greek *phobos*, fearing). An example from the kitchen is vegetable oil, which, as you know, does not mix stably with water-based substances such as vinegar. The hydrophobic behavior of the oil molecules results from a prevalence of relatively nonpolar covalent bonds, in this case bonds between carbon and hydrogen, which share electrons almost equally. Hydrophobic molecules related to oils are major ingredients of cell membranes. (Imagine what would happen to a cell if its membrane dissolved!)

Solute Concentration in Aqueous Solutions

Most of the chemical reactions in organisms involve solutes dissolved in water. To understand such reactions, we must know how many atoms and molecules are involved and be able to calculate the concentration of solutes in an aqueous solution (the number of solute molecules in a volume of solution).

When carrying out experiments, we use mass to calculate the number of molecules. We first calculate the **molecular mass**, which is simply the sum of the masses of all the atoms in a molecule. As an example, let's calculate the molecular mass of table sugar (sucrose), $C_{12}H_{22}O_{11}$, by multiplying the number of atoms by the atomic mass of each element (see Appendix B). In round numbers, sucrose has a molecular mass of $(12 \times 12) + (22 \times 1) + (11 \times 16) = 342$ daltons. Because we can't measure out small numbers of molecules, we usually measure substances in units called moles. Just as a dozen always means 12 objects, a **mole (mol)** represents an exact number of objects: 6.02×10^{23}, which is called Avogadro's number. There are 6.02×10^{23} daltons in 1 g. Once we determine the molecular mass of a molecule such as sucrose, we can use the same number (342), but with the unit *gram*, to represent the mass of 6.02×10^{23} molecules of sucrose, or 1 mol of sucrose. To obtain 1 mol of sucrose in the lab, therefore, we weigh out 342 g.

The practical advantage of measuring a quantity of chemicals in moles is that a mole of one substance has exactly the same number of molecules as a mole of any other substance. Measuring in moles makes it convenient for scientists working in the laboratory to combine substances in fixed ratios of molecules.

How would we make a liter (L) of solution consisting of 1 mol of sucrose dissolved in water? We would measure out 342 g of sucrose and then add enough water to bring the total volume of the solution up to 1 L. At that point, we would have a 1-molar (1 *M*) solution of sucrose. **Molarity**—the number of moles of solute per liter of solution—is the unit of concentration most often used by biologists for aqueous solutions.

Acids and Bases

Occasionally, a hydrogen atom participating in a hydrogen bond between two water molecules shifts from one molecule to the other. When this happens, the hydrogen atom leaves its electron behind, and what is actually transferred is a **hydrogen ion** (H^+), a single proton with a charge of $1+$. The water molecule that lost a proton is now a **hydroxide ion** (OH^-), which has a charge of $1-$. The proton binds to the other water molecule, making that molecule a **hydronium ion** (H_3O^+):

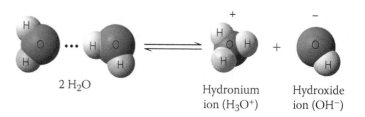

$2\ H_2O$ Hydronium ion (H_3O^+)   Hydroxide ion (OH^-)

By convention, H^+ (the hydrogen ion) is used to represent H_3O^+ (the hydronium ion), and we follow that practice here. Keep in mind, though, that H^+ does not exist on its own in an aqueous solution. It is always associated with a water molecule in the form of H_3O^+.

As indicated by the double arrows, this is a reversible reaction that reaches a state of dynamic equilibrium when water molecules dissociate at the same rate that they are being reformed from H^+ and OH^-. At this equilibrium point, the concentration of water molecules greatly exceeds the concentrations of H^+ and OH^-. In pure water, only one water molecule in every 554 million is dissociated; the concentration of each ion in pure water is $10^{-7}\ M$ (at 25°C). This means there is only one ten-millionth of a mole of hydrogen ions per liter of pure water and an equal number of hydroxide ions.

Although the dissociation of water is reversible and statistically rare, it is exceedingly important in the chemistry of life. H^+ and OH^- are very reactive. Changes in their concentrations can drastically affect a cell's proteins and other complex molecules. As we have seen, the concentrations of H^+ and OH^- are equal in pure water, but adding certain kinds of solutes, called acids and bases, disrupts this balance.

What would cause an aqueous solution to have an imbalance in H^+ and OH^- concentrations? When acids dissolve in water, they donate additional H^+ to the solution. An **acid** is a substance that increases the hydrogen ion concentration of a solution. For example, when hydrochloric acid (HCl) is added to water, hydrogen ions dissociate from chloride ions:

$$HCl \rightarrow H^+ + Cl^-$$

This source of H^+ (dissociation of water is the other source) results in an acidic solution—one having more H^+ than OH^-.

A substance that *reduces* the hydrogen ion concentration of a solution is called a **base**. Some bases reduce the H^+ concentration directly by accepting hydrogen ions. Ammonia (NH_3), for instance, acts as a base when the unshared electron pair in nitrogen's valence shell attracts a hydrogen ion from the solution, resulting in an ammonium ion (NH_4^+):

$$NH_3 + H^+ \rightleftharpoons NH_4^+$$

Other bases reduce the H^+ concentration indirectly by dissociating to form hydroxide ions, which combine with hydrogen ions and form water. One such base is sodium hydroxide (NaOH), which in water dissociates into its ions:

$$NaOH \rightarrow Na^+ + OH^-$$

In either case, the base reduces the H^+ concentration. Solutions with a higher concentration of OH^- than H^+ are known as basic solutions. A solution in which the H^+ and OH^- concentrations are equal is said to be neutral.

Notice that single arrows were used in the reactions for HCl and NaOH. These compounds dissociate completely when mixed with water, so hydrochloric acid is called a strong acid and sodium hydroxide a strong base. In contrast, ammonia is a relatively weak base. The double arrows in the reaction for ammonia indicate that the binding and release of hydrogen ions are reversible reactions, although at equilibrium there will be a fixed ratio of NH_4^+ to NH_3.

Weak acids are acids that reversibly release and accept back hydrogen ions. An example is carbonic acid:

$$\underset{\substack{\text{Carbonic} \\ \text{acid}}}{H_2CO_3} \rightleftharpoons \underset{\substack{\text{Bicarbonate} \\ \text{ion}}}{HCO_3^-} + \underset{\substack{\text{Hydrogen} \\ \text{ion}}}{H^+}$$

Here the equilibrium so favors the reaction in the left direction that when carbonic acid is added to pure water, only 1% of the molecules are dissociated at any particular time. Still, that is enough to shift the balance of H^+ and OH^- from neutrality.

The pH Scale

In any aqueous solution at 25°C, the *product* of the H^+ and OH^- concentrations is constant at 10^{-14}. This can be written

$$[H^+][OH^-] = 10^{-14}$$

In such an equation, brackets indicate molar concentration. In a neutral solution at room temperature (25°C), $[H^+] = 10^{-7}$ and $[OH^-] = 10^{-7}$. In this case, $10^{-7} \times 10^{-7} = 10^{-14}$. If enough acid is added to a solution to increase $[H^+]$ to $10^{-5}\,M$, then $[OH^-]$ will decline by an equivalent factor to $10^{-9}\,M$ (note that $10^{-5} \times 10^{-9} = 10^{-14}$). This constant relationship expresses the behavior of acids and bases in an aqueous solution. An acid not only adds hydrogen ions to a solution, but also removes hydroxide ions because of the tendency for H^+ to combine with OH^-, forming water. A base has the opposite effect, increasing OH^- concentration but also reducing H^+ concentration by the formation of water. If enough of a base is added to raise the OH^- concentration to 10^{-4} M, it will cause the H^+ concentration to drop to $10^{-10}\,M$. Whenever we know the concentration of either H^+ or OH^- in an aqueous solution, we can deduce the concentration of the other ion.

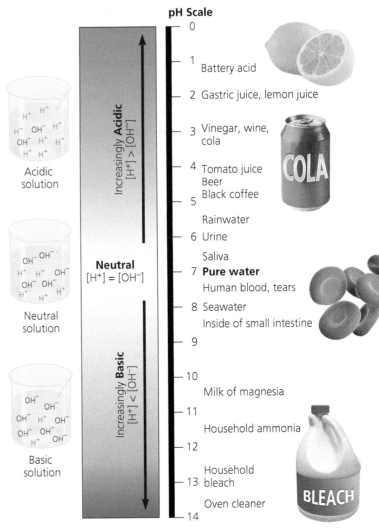

▲ **Figure 2.23 The pH scale and pH values of some aqueous solutions.**

Because the H^+ and OH^- concentrations of solutions can vary by a factor of 100 trillion or more, scientists have developed a way to express this variation more conveniently than in moles per liter. The pH scale **(Figure 2.23)** compresses the range of H^+ and OH^- concentrations by employing logarithms. The **pH** of a solution is defined as the negative logarithm (base 10) of the hydrogen ion concentration:

$$pH = -\log[H^+]$$

For a neutral aqueous solution, $[H^+]$ is $10^{-7}\,M$, giving us

$$-\log 10^{-7} = -(-7) = 7$$

Notice that pH *declines* as H^+ concentration *increases*. Notice, too, that although the pH scale is based on H^+ concentration, it also implies OH^- concentration. A solution of pH 10 has a hydrogen ion concentration of $10^{-10}\,M$ and a hydroxide ion concentration of $10^{-4}\,M$.

The pH of a neutral aqueous solution at 25°C is 7, the midpoint of the pH scale. A pH value less than 7 denotes an acidic solution; the lower the number, the more acidic the solution. The pH for basic solutions is above 7. Most biological fluids, such as blood and saliva, are within the range of pH 6–8. There are a few exceptions, however, including the strongly acidic digestive juice of the human stomach, which has a pH of about 2.

Remember that each pH unit represents a tenfold difference in H^+ and OH^- concentrations. It is this mathematical feature that makes the pH scale so compact. A solution of pH 3 is not twice as acidic as a solution of pH 6, but a thousand times ($10 \times 10 \times 10$) more acidic. When the pH of a solution changes slightly, the actual concentrations of H^+ and OH^- in the solution change substantially.

Buffers

The internal pH of most living cells is close to 7. Even a slight change in pH can be harmful because the chemical processes of the cell are very sensitive to the concentrations of hydrogen and hydroxide ions. The pH of human blood is very close to 7.4, which is slightly basic. A person cannot survive for more than a few minutes if the blood pH drops to 7 or rises to 7.8, and a chemical system exists in the blood that maintains a stable pH. If 0.01 mol of a strong acid is added to a liter of pure water, the pH drops from 7.0 to 2.0. If the same amount of acid is added to a liter of blood, however, the pH decrease is only from 7.4 to 7.3. Why does the addition of acid have so much less of an effect on the pH of blood than it does on the pH of water?

The presence of substances called buffers allows biological fluids to maintain a relatively constant pH despite the addition of acids or bases. A **buffer** is a substance that minimizes changes in the concentrations of H^+ and OH^- in a solution. It does so by accepting hydrogen ions from the solution when they are in excess and donating hydrogen ions to the solution when they have been depleted. Most buffer solutions contain a weak acid and its corresponding base, which combine reversibly with hydrogen ions.

Several buffers contribute to pH stability in human blood and many other biological solutions. One of these is carbonic acid (H_2CO_3), which is formed when CO_2 reacts with water in blood plasma. As mentioned earlier, carbonic acid dissociates to yield a bicarbonate ion (HCO_3^-) and a hydrogen ion (H^+):

	Response to a rise in pH			
H_2CO_3	$\rightleftharpoons$	HCO_3^-	$+$	H^+
H^+ donor (acid)	Response to a drop in pH	H^+ acceptor (base)		Hydrogen ion

The chemical equilibrium between carbonic acid and bicarbonate acts as a pH regulator, the reaction shifting left or right as other processes in the solution add or remove hydrogen ions. If the H^+ concentration in blood begins to fall (that is, if pH rises), the reaction proceeds to the right and more carbonic acid dissociates, replenishing hydrogen ions. But when the H^+ concentration in blood begins to rise (when pH drops), the reaction proceeds to the left, with HCO_3^- (the base) removing the hydrogen ions from the solution and forming H_2CO_3. Thus, the carbonic acid–bicarbonate buffering system consists of an acid and a base in equilibrium with each other. Most other buffers are also acid-base pairs.

Acidification: A Threat to Our Oceans

Among the many threats to water quality posed by human activities is the burning of fossil fuels, which releases CO_2 into the atmosphere. The resulting increase in atmospheric CO_2 levels has caused global warming (see Concept 43.4). In addition, about 25% of human-generated CO_2 is absorbed by the oceans. In spite of the huge volume of water in the oceans, scientists worry that the absorption of so much CO_2 will harm marine ecosystems.

Recent data have shown that such fears are well founded. When CO_2 dissolves in seawater, it reacts with water to form carbonic acid, which lowers ocean pH. This process, known as **ocean acidification**, alters the delicate balance of conditions for life in the oceans (**Figure 2.24**). Based on measurements of CO_2 levels in air bubbles trapped in ice over thousands of years, scientists calculate that the pH of the oceans is 0.1 pH unit lower now than at any time in the past 420,000 years. Recent studies predict that it will drop another 0.3–0.5 pH unit by the end of this century.

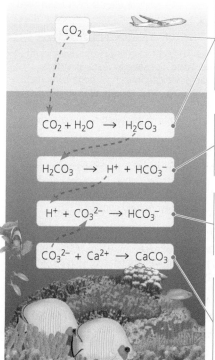

Some carbon dioxide (CO_2) in the atmosphere dissolves in the ocean, where it reacts with water to form carbonic acid (H_2CO_3).

$CO_2 + H_2O \rightarrow H_2CO_3$

Carbonic acid dissociates into hydrogen ions (H^+) and bicarbonate ions (HCO_3^-).

$H_2CO_3 \rightarrow H^+ + HCO_3^-$

The added H^+ combines with carbonate ions (CO_3^{2-}), forming more HCO_3^-.

$H^+ + CO_3^{2-} \rightarrow HCO_3^-$

Less CO_3^{2-} is available for calcification — the formation of calcium carbonate ($CaCO_3$) — by marine organisms such as corals.

$CO_3^{2-} + Ca^{2+} \rightarrow CaCO_3$

▲ **Figure 2.24 Atmospheric CO_2 from human activities and its fate in the ocean.**

WHAT IF? *Would lowering the ocean's carbonate concentration have any effect, even indirectly, on organisms that don't form $CaCO_3$? Explain.*

As seawater acidifies, the extra hydrogen ions combine with carbonate ions (CO_3^{2-}) to form bicarbonate ions (HCO_3^-), thereby reducing the carbonate ion concentration (see Figure 2.24). Scientists predict that ocean acidification will cause the carbonate ion concentration to decrease by 40% by the year 2100. This is of great concern because carbonate ions are required for calcification, the production of calcium carbonate ($CaCO_3$), by many marine organisms, including reef-building corals and animals that build shells. The **Scientific Skills Exercise** allows you to work with data from an experiment examining the effect of carbonate ion concentration on coral reefs. Coral reefs are sensitive ecosystems that act as havens for a great diversity of marine life. The disappearance of coral reef ecosystems would be a tragic loss of biological diversity.

CONCEPT CHECK 2.5

1. Describe how properties of water contribute to the upward movement of water in a tree.
2. How can the freezing of water crack boulders?
3. Compared with a basic solution at pH 9, the same volume of an acidic solution at pH 4 has _____ times as many hydrogen ions (H^+).
4. **WHAT IF?** What would be the effect on the properties of the water molecule if oxygen and hydrogen had equal electronegativity?
5. **INTERPRET THE DATA** The concentration of the appetite-regulating hormone ghrelin is about 1.3×10^{-10} *M* in the blood of a fasting person. How many molecules of ghrelin are in 1 L of blood?

For suggested answers, see Appendix A.

Scientific Skills Exercise

Interpreting a Scatter Plot with a Regression Line

How Does the Carbonate Ion Concentration of Seawater Affect the Calcification Rate of a Coral Reef? Scientists predict that acidification of the ocean due to higher levels of atmospheric CO_2 will lower the concentration of dissolved carbonate ions, which living corals use to build calcium carbonate reef structures. In this exercise, you will analyze data from a controlled experiment that examined the effect of carbonate ion concentration ($[CO_3^{2-}]$) on calcium carbonate deposition, a process called calcification.

How the Experiment Was Done For several years, scientists conducted research on ocean acidification using a large coral reef aquarium at Biosphere 2 in Arizona. They measured the rate of calcification by the reef organisms and examined how the calcification rate changed with differing amounts of dissolved carbonate ions in the seawater.

Data from the Experiment The black data points in the graph form a scatter plot. The red line, known as a linear regression line, is the best-fitting straight line for these points. These data are from one set of experiments, in which the pH, temperature, and calcium ion concentration of the seawater were held constant.

Data from C. Langdon et al., Effect of calcium carbonate saturation state on the calcification rate of an experimental coral reef, *Global Biogeochemical Cycles* 14:639–654 (2000).

INTERPRET THE DATA

1. When presented with a graph of experimental data, the first step in your analysis is to determine what each axis represents. (a) In words, explain what is being shown on the *x*-axis. Be sure to include the units. (b) What is being shown on the *y*-axis (including units)? (c) Which variable is the independent variable—the variable that was *manipulated* by the researchers? (d) Which variable is the dependent variable—the variable that responded to or depended on the treatment, which was *measured* by the researchers? (For additional information about graphs, see the Scientific Skills Review in Appendix F and in the Study Area in MasteringBiology.)

2. Based on the data shown in the graph, describe in words the relationship between carbonate ion concentration and calcification rate.

3. (a) If the seawater carbonate ion concentration is 270 μmol/kg, what is the approximate rate of calcification, and approximately how many days would it take 1 square meter of reef to accumulate 30 mmol of calcium carbonate ($CaCO_3$)? (b) If the seawater carbonate ion concentration is 250 μmol/kg, what is the approximate rate of calcification, and approximately how many days would it take 1 square meter of reef to accumulate 30 mmol of calcium carbonate? (c) If carbonate ion concentration decreases, how does the calcification rate change, and how does that affect the time it takes coral to grow?

4. (a) Referring to the reactions in Figure 2.24, determine which step of the process is measured in this experiment. (b) Are the results of this experiment consistent with the hypothesis that increased atmospheric $[CO_2]$ will slow the growth of coral reefs? Why or why not?

(MB) A version of this Scientific Skills Exercise can be assigned in MasteringBiology.

2 Chapter Review

Go to **MasteringBiology®** for Assignments, the eText, and the Study Area with Animations, Activities, Vocab Self-Quiz, and Practice Tests.

SUMMARY OF KEY CONCEPTS

VOCAB SELF-QUIZ

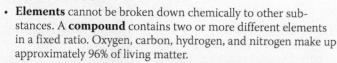

goo.gl/gbai8v

CONCEPT 2.1

Matter consists of chemical elements in pure form and in combinations called compounds (pp. 22–23)

- **Elements** cannot be broken down chemically to other substances. A **compound** contains two or more different elements in a fixed ratio. Oxygen, carbon, hydrogen, and nitrogen make up approximately 96% of living matter.

? *In what way does the need for iodine or iron in your diet differ from your need for calcium or phosphorus?*

CONCEPT 2.2

An element's properties depend on the structure of its atoms (pp. 23–27)

- An **atom**, the smallest unit of an element, has the following components:

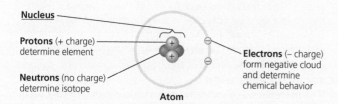

Nucleus

Protons (+ charge) determine element

Neutrons (no charge) determine isotope

Electrons (– charge) form negative cloud and determine chemical behavior

Atom

- An electrically neutral atom has equal numbers of electrons and protons; the number of protons determines the **atomic number**. **Isotopes** of an element differ from each other in neutron number and therefore mass. Unstable isotopes give off particles and energy as radioactivity.
- In an atom, electrons occupy specific **electron shells**; the electrons in a shell have a characteristic energy level. Electron distribution in shells determines the chemical behavior of an atom. An atom that has an incomplete outer shell, the **valence shell**, is reactive.

DRAW IT *Draw the electron distribution diagrams for neon ($_{10}$Ne) and argon ($_{18}$Ar). Why are they chemically unreactive?*

CONCEPT 2.3

The formation and function of molecules depend on chemical bonding between atoms (pp. 27–31)

- **Chemical bonds** form when atoms interact and complete their valence shells. **Covalent bonds** form when pairs of electrons are shared. H_2 has a **single bond**: H — H. A **double bond** is the sharing of two pairs of electrons, as in O＝O.
- **Molecules** consist of two or more covalently bonded atoms. The attraction of an atom for the electrons of a covalent bond is its **electronegativity**. Electrons of a **polar covalent bond** are pulled closer to the more electronegative atom, such as the oxygen in H_2O.
- An **ion** forms when an atom or molecule gains or loses an electron and becomes charged. An **ionic bond** is the attraction between two oppositely charged ions, such as Na^+ and Cl^-.
- Weak bonds reinforce the shapes of large molecules and help molecules adhere to each other. A **hydrogen bond** is an attraction between a hydrogen atom carrying a partial positive charge ($\delta+$) and an electronegative atom ($\delta-$). **Van der Waals interactions** occur between transiently positive and negative regions of molecules.
- Molecular shape is usually the basis for the recognition of one biological molecule by another.

? *In terms of electron sharing between atoms, compare nonpolar covalent bonds, polar covalent bonds, and the formation of ions.*

CONCEPT 2.4

Chemical reactions make and break chemical bonds (pp. 31–32)

- **Chemical reactions** change **reactants** into **products** while conserving matter. All chemical reactions are theoretically reversible. **Chemical equilibrium** is reached when the forward and reverse reaction rates are equal.

? *What would happen to the concentration of products if more reactants were added to a reaction that was in chemical equilibrium? How would this addition affect the equilibrium?*

CONCEPT 2.5

Hydrogen bonding gives water properties that help make life possible on Earth (pp. 32–40)

- A **hydrogen bond** forms when the slightly negatively charged oxygen of one water molecule is attracted to the slightly positively charged hydrogen of a nearby water molecule. Hydrogen bonding between water molecules is the basis for water's properties.

- Hydrogen bonding keeps water molecules close to each other, giving water **cohesion**. Hydrogen bonding is also responsible for water's **surface tension**.
- Water has a high **specific heat**: Heat is absorbed when hydrogen bonds break and is released when hydrogen bonds form. This helps keep temperatures relatively steady, within limits that permit life. **Evaporative cooling** is based on water's high **heat of vaporization**. The evaporative loss of the most energetic water molecules cools a surface.
- Ice floats because it is less dense than liquid water. This property allows life to exist under the frozen surfaces of lakes and seas.

Ice: stable hydrogen bonds   **Liquid water:** transient hydrogen bonds

- Water is an unusually versatile **solvent** because its polar molecules are attracted to ions and polar substances that can form hydrogen bonds. **Hydrophilic** substances have an affinity for water; **hydrophobic** substances do not. **Molarity**, the number of moles of **solute** per liter of **solution**, is used as a measure of solute concentration in solutions. A **mole** is a certain number of molecules of a substance. The mass of a mole of a substance in grams is the same as the **molecular mass** in daltons.

- A water molecule can transfer an H^+ to another water molecule to form H_3O^+ (represented simply by H^+) and OH^-.
- The concentration of H^+ is expressed as **pH**; $pH = -\log[H^+]$. A **buffer** consists of an acid-base pair that combines reversibly with hydrogen ions, allowing it to resist pH changes.
- The burning of fossil fuels increases the amount of CO_2 in the atmosphere. Some CO_2 dissolves in the oceans, causing **ocean acidification**, which has potentially grave consequences for coral reefs.

Acidic $[H^+] > [OH^-]$ — 0

Acids donate H^+ in aqueous solutions.

Neutral $[H^+] = [OH^-]$ — 7

Bases donate OH^- or accept H^+ in aqueous solutions.

Basic $[H^+] < [OH^-]$ — 14

? *Describe how the properties of water result from the molecule's polar covalent bonds and how these properties contribute to Earth's suitability for life.*

TEST YOUR UNDERSTANDING

PRACTICE TEST

goo.gl/CRZjvS

Level 1: Knowledge/Comprehension

1. The reactivity of an atom arises from
   (A) the average distance of the outermost electron shell from the nucleus.
   (B) the existence of unpaired electrons in the valence shell.
   (C) the sum of the potential energies of all the electron shells.
   (D) the potential energy of the valence shell.

2. Which of the following statements correctly describes any chemical reaction that has reached equilibrium?
   (A) The concentrations of products and reactants are equal.
   (B) The reaction is now irreversible.
   (C) Both forward and reverse reactions have halted.
   (D) The rates of the forward and reverse reactions are equal.

3. Many mammals control their body temperature by sweating. Which property of water is most directly responsible for the ability of sweat to lower body temperature?
   (A) water's change in density when it condenses
   (B) water's ability to dissolve molecules in the air
   (C) the release of heat by the formation of hydrogen bonds
   (D) the absorption of heat by the breaking of hydrogen bonds

4. We can be sure that a mole of table sugar and a mole of vitamin C are equal in their
   (A) mass.   (C) number of atoms.
   (B) volume.   (D) number of molecules.

5. Measurements show that the pH of a particular lake is 4.0. What is the hydrogen ion concentration of the lake?
   (A) $4.0\,M$ (B) $10^{-4}\,M$ (C) $10^4\,M$ (D) $10^{-10}\,M$

Level 2: Application/Analysis

6. The atomic number of sulfur is 16. Sulfur combines with hydrogen by covalent bonding to form a compound, hydrogen sulfide. Based on the number of valence electrons in a sulfur atom, predict the molecular formula of the compound.
   (A) HS   (B) HS_2 (C) H_2S (D) H_3S_2

7. What coefficients must be placed in the following blanks so that all atoms are accounted for in the products?
   $$C_6H_{12}O_6 \rightarrow \underline{\quad} C_2H_6O + \underline{\quad} CO_2$$
   (A) 1; 2   (B) 3; 1   (C) 1; 3   (D) 2; 2

8. A slice of pizza has 500 kcal. If we could burn the pizza and use all the heat to warm a 50-L container of cold water, what would be the approximate increase in the temperature of the water? (*Note*: A liter of cold water weighs about 1 kg.)
   (A) 50°C   (B) 5°C   (C) 1°C   (D) 10°C

9. **DRAW IT** Draw the hydration shells that form around a potassium ion and a chloride ion when potassium chloride (KCl) dissolves in water. Label the positive, negative, and partial charges on the atoms.

10. **MAKE CONNECTIONS** What do climate change (see Concept 1.1) and ocean acidification have in common?

Level 3: Synthesis/Evaluation

11. **SCIENTIFIC INQUIRY**
    Female luna moths (*Actias luna*) attract males by emitting chemical signals that spread through the air. A male hundreds of meters away can detect these molecules and fly toward their source. The sensory organs responsible for this behavior are the comblike antennae visible in the photograph shown here. Each filament of an antenna is equipped with thousands of receptor cells that detect the sex attractant. (a) Based on what you learned in this chapter, propose a hypothesis to account for the ability of the male moth to detect a specific molecule in the presence of many other molecules in the air. (b) Describe predictions your hypothesis enables you to make. (c) Design an experiment to test one of these predictions.

12. **FOCUS ON EVOLUTION**
    The percentages of naturally occurring elements making up the human body are similar to the percentages of these elements found in other organisms. How could you account for this similarity among organisms? Explain your thinking.

13. **FOCUS ON ORGANIZATION**
    Several emergent properties of water contribute to the suitability of the environment for life. In a short essay (100–150 words), describe how the ability of water to function as a versatile solvent arises from the structure of water molecules.

14. **SYNTHESIZE YOUR KNOWLEDGE**

How do cats drink? Scientists using high-speed video have shown that cats use an interesting technique to drink aqueous substances like water and milk. Four times a second, the cat touches the tip of its tongue to the water and draws a column of water up into its mouth (as you can see in the photo), which then shuts before gravity can pull the water back down. Describe how the properties of water allow cats to drink in this fashion, including how water's molecular structure contributes to the process.

For selected answers, see Appendix A.

3 Carbon and the Molecular Diversity of Life

KEY CONCEPTS

3.1 Carbon atoms can form diverse molecules by bonding to four other atoms

3.2 Macromolecules are polymers, built from monomers

3.3 Carbohydrates serve as fuel and building material

3.4 Lipids are a diverse group of hydrophobic molecules

3.5 Proteins include a diversity of structures, resulting in a wide range of functions

3.6 Nucleic acids store, transmit, and help express hereditary information

3.7 Genomics and proteomics have transformed biological inquiry and applications

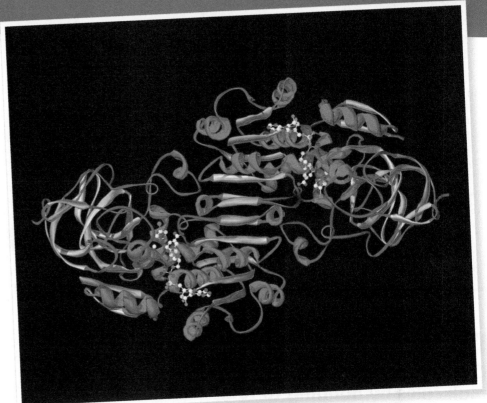

▲ **Figure 3.1 Why is the structure of a protein important for its function?**

Carbon Compounds and Life

Water is the universal medium for life on Earth, but water aside, living organisms are made up of chemicals based mostly on the element carbon. Of all chemical elements, carbon is unparalleled in its ability to form molecules that are large, complex, and varied. Hydrogen (H), oxygen (O), nitrogen (N), sulfur (S), and phosphorus (P) are other common ingredients of these compounds, but it is the element carbon (C) that accounts for the enormous variety of biological molecules. For historical reasons, a compound containing carbon is said to be an **organic compound**; furthermore, almost all organic compounds associated with life contain hydrogen atoms in addition to carbon atoms. Different species of organisms and even different individuals within a species are distinguished by variations in their large organic compounds.

Given the rich complexity of life on Earth, it may surprise you to learn that the critically important large molecules of all living things—from bacteria to elephants—fall into just four

main classes: carbohydrates, lipids, proteins, and nucleic acids. On the molecular scale, members of three of these classes—carbohydrates, proteins, and nucleic acids—are huge and are therefore called **macromolecules**. For example, a protein may consist of thousands of atoms that form a molecular colossus with a mass well over 100,000 daltons. Considering the size and complexity of macromolecules, it is noteworthy that biochemists have determined the detailed structure of so many of them. The image in **Figure 3.1** is a molecular model of a protein called alcohol dehydrogenase, which breaks down alcohol in the body. The structures of macromolecules can provide important information about their functions.

In this chapter, we'll first investigate the properties of small organic molecules and then go on to discuss the larger biological molecules. After considering how macromolecules are built, we'll examine the structure and function of all four classes of large biological molecules. Like small molecules, large biological molecules exhibit unique emergent properties arising from the orderly arrangement of their atoms.

▼ Figure 3.2 The shapes of three simple organic molecules.

Molecule and Molecular Shape	Molecular Formula	Structural Formula	Ball-and-Stick Model (molecular shape in pink)	Space-Filling Model
(a) Methane. When a carbon atom has four single bonds to other atoms, the molecule is tetrahedral.	CH_4	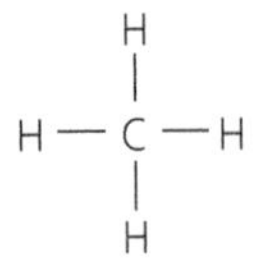	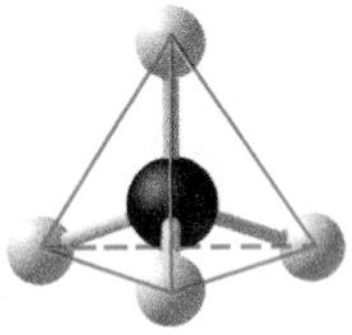	
(b) Ethane. A molecule may have more than one tetrahedral group of single-bonded atoms. (Ethane consists of two such groups.)	C_2H_6	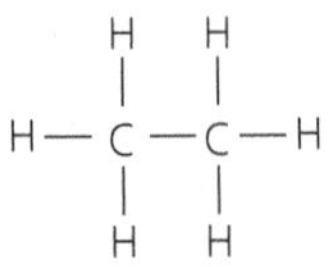	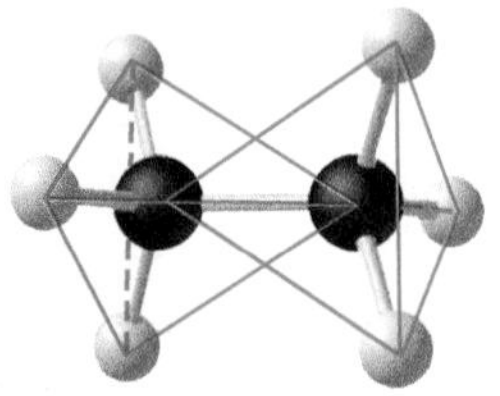	
(c) Ethene (ethylene). When two carbon atoms are joined by a double bond, all atoms attached to those carbons are in the same plane, and the molecule is flat.	C_2H_4	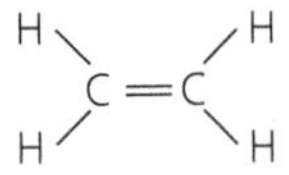	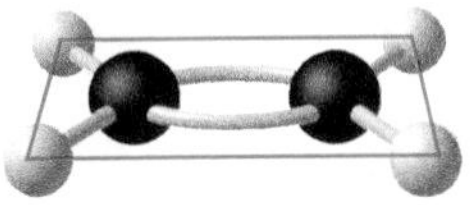	

CONCEPT 3.1

Carbon atoms can form diverse molecules by bonding to four other atoms

The key to an atom's chemical characteristics is its electron configuration. This configuration determines the kinds and number of bonds an atom will form with other atoms, and it is the source of carbon's versatility.

The Formation of Bonds with Carbon

Carbon has 6 electrons, with 2 in the first electron shell and 4 in the second shell; thus, it has 4 valence electrons in a shell that can hold up to 8 electrons. A carbon atom usually completes its valence shell by sharing its 4 electrons with other atoms so that 8 electrons are present. Each pair of shared electrons constitutes a covalent bond (see Figure 2.8d). In organic molecules, carbon usually forms single or double covalent bonds. Each carbon atom acts as an intersection point from which a molecule can branch off in as many as four directions. This enables carbon to form large, complex molecules.

When a carbon atom forms four single covalent bonds, the bonds angle toward the corners of an imaginary tetrahedron. The bond angles in methane (CH_4) are 109.5° **(Figure 3.2a)**, and they are roughly the same in any group of atoms where carbon has four single bonds. For example, ethane (C_2H_6) is shaped like two overlapping tetrahedrons **(Figure 3.2b)**.

In molecules with more carbons, every grouping of a carbon bonded to four other atoms has a tetrahedral shape. But when two carbon atoms are joined by a double bond, as in ethene (C_2H_4), the atoms joined to those carbons are in the same plane as the carbons **(Figure 3.2c)**. We find it convenient to write molecules as structural formulas, as if the molecules being represented are two-dimensional, but keep in mind that molecules are three-dimensional and that the shape of a molecule is central to its function.

The electron configuration of carbon gives it covalent compatibility with many different elements. **Figure 3.3** shows electron distribution diagrams for carbon and its most frequent partners—hydrogen, oxygen, and nitrogen. These are the four main atoms in organic molecules. The number of unpaired electrons in the valence shell of an atom is generally equal to the atom's **valence**, the number of covalent bonds it can form. Let's consider how valence and the rules of covalent bonding

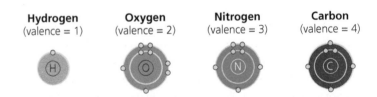

▲ **Figure 3.3 Valences of the major elements of organic molecules.** Valence is the number of covalent bonds an atom can form. It is generally equal to the number of electrons required to complete the valence (outermost) shell (see Figure 2.6). Note that carbon can form four bonds.

apply to carbon atoms with partners other than hydrogen. We'll first look at the simple example of carbon dioxide.

In the carbon dioxide molecule (CO_2), a single carbon atom is joined to two atoms of oxygen by double covalent bonds. The structural formula for CO_2 is shown here:

$$O=C=O$$

Each line in a structural formula represents a pair of shared electrons. Thus, the two double bonds in CO_2 have the same number of shared electrons as four single bonds. The arrangement completes the valence shells of all atoms in the molecule:

Because CO_2 is a very simple molecule and lacks hydrogen, it is often considered inorganic, even though it contains carbon. Whether we call CO_2 organic or inorganic, however, it is clearly important to the living world as the source of carbon for all organic molecules in organisms.

Carbon dioxide is a molecule with only one carbon atom. But a carbon atom can also use one or more valence electrons to form covalent bonds to other carbon atoms, linking the atoms into chains, as shown here for C_3H_8:

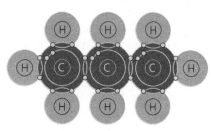

Molecular Diversity Arising from Variation in Carbon Skeletons

Carbon chains form the skeletons of most organic molecules. The skeletons vary in length and may be straight, branched, or arranged in closed rings (**Figure 3.4**). Some carbon skeletons have double bonds, which vary in number and location. Such variation in carbon skeletons is one important source of the molecular complexity and diversity that characterize living matter. In addition, atoms of other elements can be bonded to the skeletons at available sites.

Hydrocarbons

All of the molecules shown in Figures 3.2 and 3.4 are **hydrocarbons**, organic molecules consisting of only carbon and hydrogen. Atoms of hydrogen are attached to the carbon skeleton wherever electrons are available for covalent bonding. Hydrocarbons are the major components of petroleum, which is called a fossil fuel because it consists of the partially decomposed remains of organisms that lived millions of years ago. Although hydrocarbons are not prevalent in most living

▼ **Figure 3.4 Four ways that carbon skeletons can vary.**

(a) Length

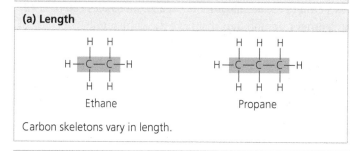

Ethane   Propane

Carbon skeletons vary in length.

(b) Branching

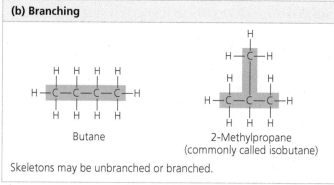

Butane   2-Methylpropane (commonly called isobutane)

Skeletons may be unbranched or branched.

(c) Double bond position

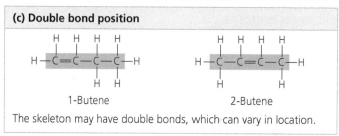

1-Butene   2-Butene

The skeleton may have double bonds, which can vary in location.

(d) Presence of rings

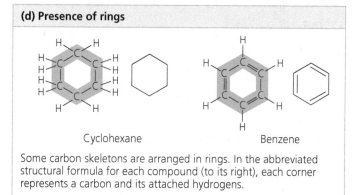

Cyclohexane   Benzene

Some carbon skeletons are arranged in rings. In the abbreviated structural formula for each compound (to its right), each corner represents a carbon and its attached hydrogens.

organisms, many of a cell's organic molecules have regions consisting of only carbon and hydrogen. For example, the molecules known as fats have long hydrocarbon tails attached to a nonhydrocarbon component (as you will see in Figure 3.13). Neither petroleum nor fat dissolves in water; both are hydrophobic compounds because the great majority of their bonds are relatively nonpolar carbon-to-hydrogen linkages. Another characteristic of hydrocarbons is that they can undergo reactions that release a relatively large amount of energy. The gasoline that fuels a car consists of hydrocarbons, and the hydrocarbon tails of fats serve as stored fuel for plant embryos (seeds) and animals.

Isomers

Variation in the architecture of organic molecules can be seen in **isomers**, compounds that have the same numbers of atoms of the same elements but different structures and hence different properties. We will examine three types of isomers: structural isomers, *cis-trans* isomers, and enantiomers.

Structural isomers differ in the covalent arrangements of their atoms. Compare, for example, the two five-carbon compounds in **Figure 3.5a.** Both have the molecular formula C_5H_{12}, but they differ in the covalent arrangement of their carbon skeletons. The skeleton is straight in one compound but branched in the other. The number of possible isomers increases tremendously as carbon skeletons increase in size.

▼ **Figure 3.5 Three types of isomers, compounds with the same molecular formula but different structures.**

(a) Structural isomers

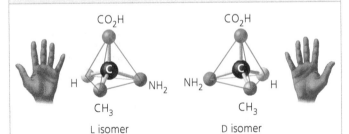

Pentane   2-Methylbutane

Structural isomers differ in covalent partners, as shown in this example of two isomers of C_5H_{12}.

(b) Cis-trans isomers

cis isomer: The two Xs are on the same side.

trans isomer: The two Xs are on opposite sides.

Cis-trans isomers differ in arrangement about a double bond. In these diagrams, X represents an atom or group of atoms attached to a double-bonded carbon.

(c) Enantiomers

CO₂H   CO₂H

H   NH₂   NH₂   H

CH₃   CH₃

L isomer   D isomer

Enantiomers differ in spatial arrangement around an asymmetric carbon, resulting in molecules that are mirror images, like left and right hands. The two isomers here are designated the L and D isomers from the Latin for "left" and "right" (*levo* and *dextro*). Enantiomers cannot be superimposed on each other.

DRAW IT *There are three structural isomers of C_5H_{12} (two of which are shown in Figure 3.5a); draw the one not shown in (a).*

There are only three forms of C_5H_{12} (two of which are shown in Figure 3.5a), but there are 18 variants of C_8H_{18} and 366,319 possible structural isomers of $C_{20}H_{42}$. Structural isomers may also differ in the location of double bonds.

In *cis-trans* **isomers**, carbons have covalent bonds to the same atoms, but these atoms differ in their spatial arrangements due to the inflexibility of double bonds. Single bonds allow the atoms they join to rotate freely about the bond axis without changing the compound. In contrast, double bonds do not permit such rotation. If a double bond joins two carbon atoms, and each C also has two different atoms (or groups of atoms) attached to it, then two distinct *cis-trans* isomers are possible. Consider a simple molecule with two double-bonded carbons, each of which has an H and an X attached to it **(Figure 3.5b)**. The arrangement with both Xs on the same side of the double bond is called a *cis isomer*, and that with the Xs on opposite sides is called a *trans isomer*. The subtle difference in shape between such isomers can dramatically affect the biological activities of organic molecules. For example, the biochemistry of vision involves a light-induced change of retinal, a chemical compound in the eye, from the *cis* isomer to the *trans* isomer (see Figure 38.26). Another example involves *trans* fats, which are discussed in later in this chapter.

Enantiomers are isomers that are mirror images of each other and that differ in shape due to the presence of an *asymmetric carbon*, one that is attached to four different atoms or groups of atoms. (See the middle carbon in the ball-and-stick models shown in **Figure 3.5c**.) The four groups can be arranged in space around the asymmetric carbon in two different ways that are mirror images. Enantiomers are, in a way, left-handed and right-handed versions of the molecule. Just as your right hand won't fit into a left-handed glove, a "right-handed" molecule won't fit into the same space as the "left-handed" version. Usually, only one isomer is biologically active because only that form can bind to specific molecules in an organism.

The concept of enantiomers is important in the pharmaceutical industry because the two enantiomers of a drug may not be equally effective, as is the case for both ibuprofen and the asthma medication albuterol. Methamphetamine also occurs in two enantiomers that have very different effects. One enantiomer is the highly addictive stimulant drug known as "crank," sold illegally in the street drug trade. The other has a much weaker effect and is the active ingredient in an over-the-counter vapor inhaler for treatment of nasal congestion. The differing effects of enantiomers in the body demonstrate that organisms are sensitive to even the most subtle variations in molecular architecture. Once again, we see that molecules have emergent properties that depend on the specific arrangement of their atoms.

The Chemical Groups Most Important to Life

The distinctive properties of an organic molecule depend not only on the arrangement of its carbon skeleton but also on the various chemical groups attached to that skeleton **(Figure 3.6)**.

▼ **Figure 3.6 Some biologically important chemical groups.**

Chemical Group	Compound Name	Examples
Hydroxyl group (—OH) —OH  (may be written HO—)	**Alcohol** (The specific name usually ends in *-ol*.)	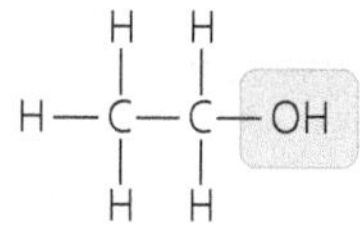 **Ethanol**, the alcohol present in alcoholic beverages
Carbonyl group ($>C=O$) 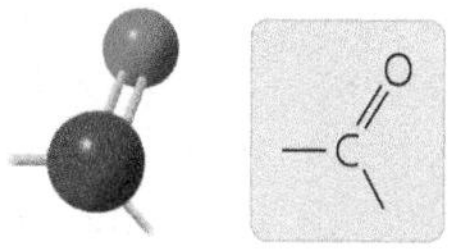	**Ketone** if the carbonyl group is within a carbon skeleton **Aldehyde** if the carbonyl group is at the end of a carbon skeleton	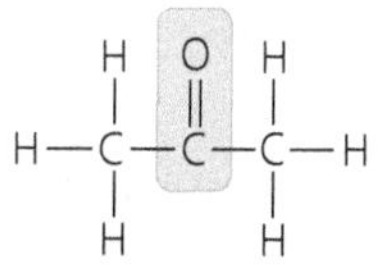 **Acetone**, the simplest ketone 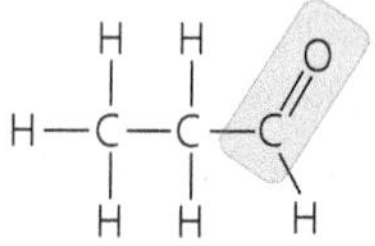 **Propanal**, an aldehyde
Carboxyl group (—COOH) 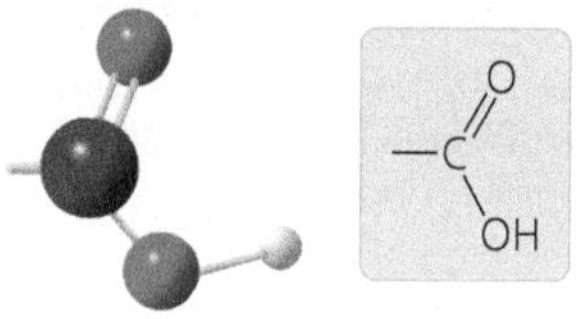	**Carboxylic acid**, or **organic acid**	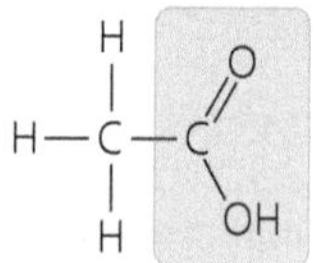 **Acetic acid**, which gives vinegar its sour taste 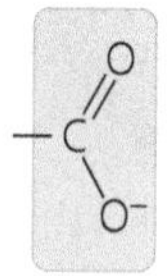 Ionized form of —COOH (carboxylate ion), found in cells
Amino group (—NH$_2$) 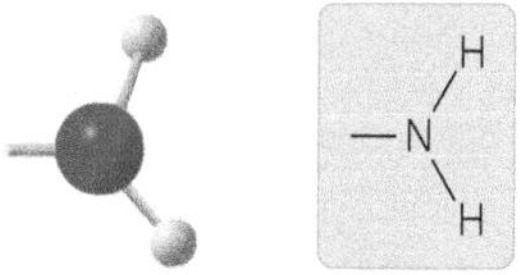	**Amine**	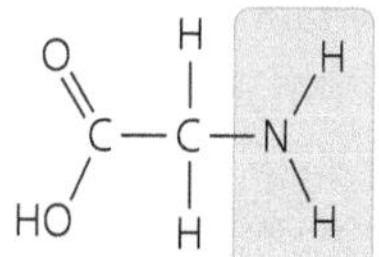 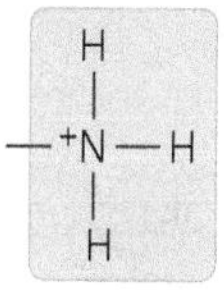 **Glycine**, an amino acid (note its carboxyl group) Ionized form of —NH$_2$, found in cells
Sulfhydryl group (—SH) —SH 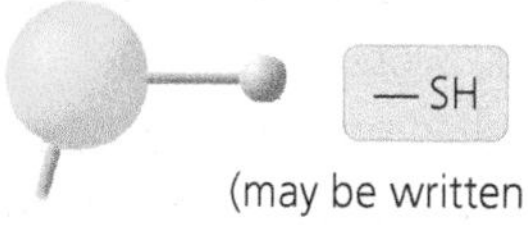 (may be written HS—)	**Thiol**	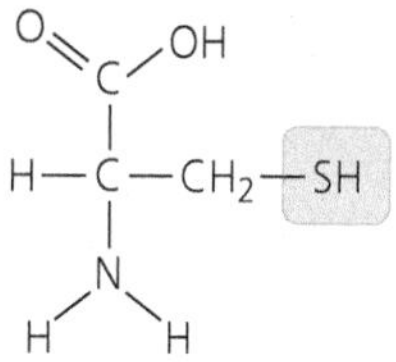 **Cysteine**, a sulfur-containing amino acid
Phosphate group (—OPO$_3^{2-}$) 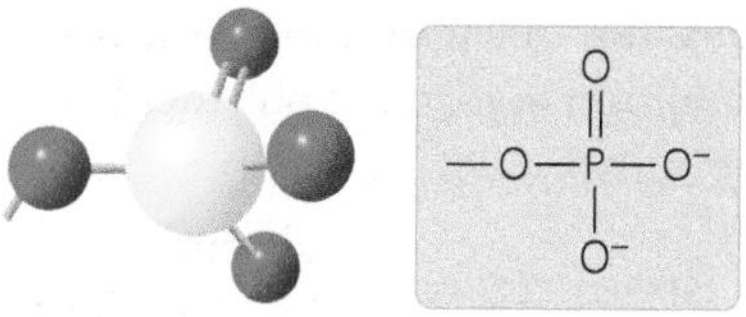	**Organic phosphate**	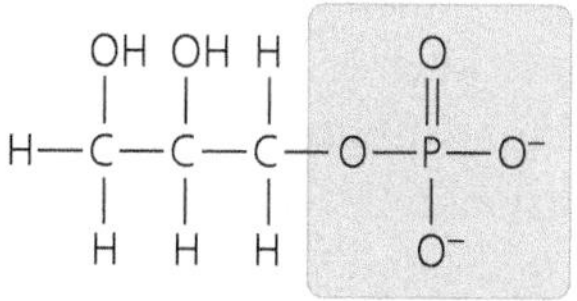 **Glycerol phosphate**, which takes part in many important chemical reactions in cells
Methyl group (—CH$_3$) 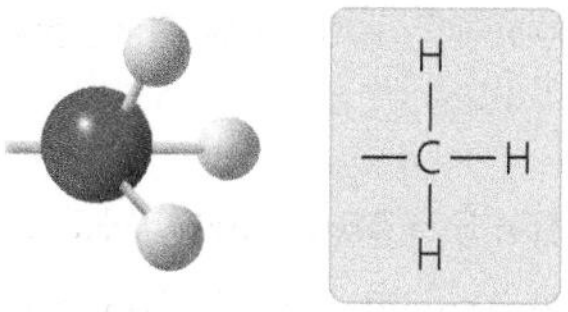	**Methylated compound**	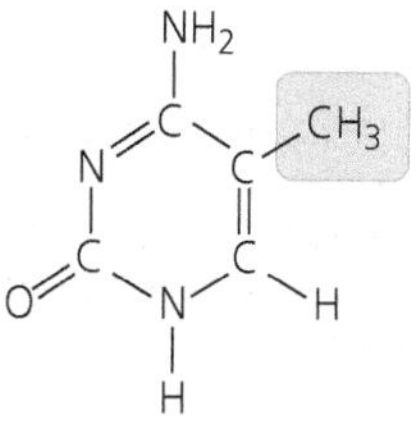 **5-Methylcytosine**, a component of DNA that has been modified by addition of a methyl group

We can think of hydrocarbons, the simplest organic molecules, as the underlying framework for more complex organic molecules. A number of chemical groups can replace one or more of the hydrogens bonded to the carbon skeleton of the hydrocarbon. The number and arrangement of chemical groups help give each organic molecule its unique properties.

In some cases, chemical groups contribute to function primarily by affecting the molecule's shape. This is true for the steroid sex hormones estradiol (a type of estrogen) and testosterone, which differ in attached chemical groups and act to produce the contrasting features of male and female vertebrates.

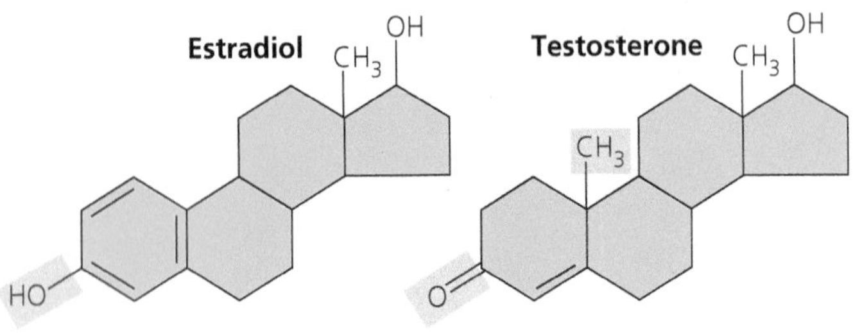

In other cases, the chemical groups affect molecular function by being directly involved in chemical reactions; these important chemical groups are known as **functional groups**. Each functional group participates in chemical reactions in a characteristic way.

The seven chemical groups most important in biological processes are the hydroxyl, carbonyl, carboxyl, amino, sulfhydryl, phosphate, and methyl groups (see Figure 3.6). The first six groups can act as functional groups; also, except for the sulfhydryl group, they are hydrophilic and thus increase the solubility of organic compounds in water. The last group, the methyl group, is not reactive, but instead often serves as a recognizable tag on biological molecules. Study Figure 3.6 to become familiar with these biologically important chemical groups. At normal cellular pH, the carboxyl group and amino group are ionized, as shown at the right.

ATP: An Important Source of Energy for Cellular Processes

The "Phosphate group" row in Figure 3.6 shows a simple example of an organic phosphate molecule. A more complicated organic phosphate, **adenosine triphosphate**, or **ATP**, is worth mentioning here because its function in the cell is so important. ATP consists of an organic molecule called adenosine attached to a string of three phosphate groups:

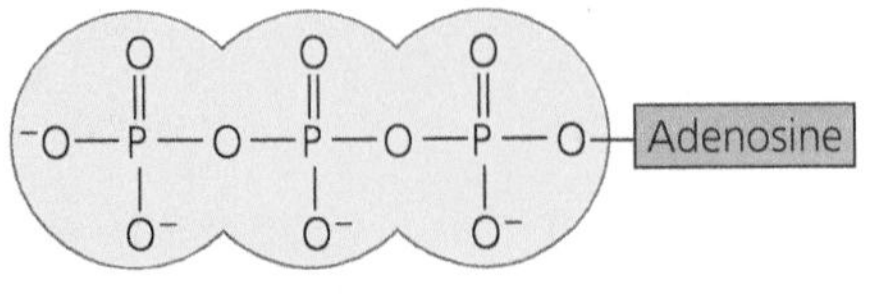

Where three phosphates are present in series, as in ATP, one phosphate may be split off as a result of a reaction with water.

This inorganic phosphate ion, $HOPO_3^{2-}$, is often abbreviated $\textcircled{P}_i$ in this book, and a phosphate group in an organic molecule is often written as $\textcircled{P}$. Having lost one phosphate, ATP becomes adenosine *di*phosphate, or ADP. Although ATP is sometimes said to store energy, it is more accurate to think of it as storing the potential to react with water. This reaction releases energy that can be used by the cell. (You will learn about this in more detail in Chapter 6.)

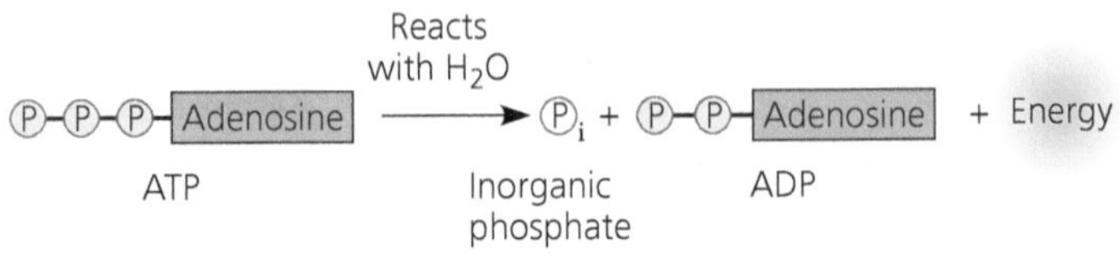

CONCEPT CHECK 3.1

1. How are gasoline and fat chemically similar?
2. Which molecules in Figure 3.4 are isomers? For each pair, identify the type of isomer.
3. What does the term *amino acid* signify about the structure of such a molecule?
4. **DRAW IT** Suppose you had an organic molecule such as cysteine (see Figure 3.6, sulfhydryl group example), and you chemically removed the —NH₂ group and replaced it with —COOH. Draw this structure. How would this change the chemical properties of the molecule? Is the central carbon asymmetric before the change? After?

For suggested answers, see Appendix A.

CONCEPT 3.2

Macromolecules are polymers, built from monomers

The macromolecules in three of the four classes of life's organic compounds—carbohydrates, proteins, and nucleic acids—are chain-like molecules called polymers (from the Greek *polys*, many, and *meros*, part). A **polymer** is a long molecule consisting of many similar or identical building blocks linked by covalent bonds, much as a train consists of a chain of cars. The repeating units that serve as the building blocks of a polymer are smaller molecules called **monomers** (from the Greek *monos*, single). In addition to forming polymers, some monomers have functions of their own.

The Synthesis and Breakdown of Polymers

Although each class of polymer is made up of a different type of monomer, the chemical mechanisms by which cells make and break down polymers are basically the same in all cases. In cells, these processes are facilitated by **enzymes**, specialized macromolecules (usually proteins) that speed up chemical reactions. Monomers are connected by a reaction in which two molecules are covalently bonded to each other, with the loss of a water molecule; this is known as a **dehydration reaction**

(Figure 3.7a). When a bond forms between two monomers, each monomer contributes part of the water molecule that is released during the reaction: One monomer provides a hydroxyl group (—OH), while the other provides a hydrogen (—H). This reaction is repeated as monomers are added to the chain one by one, making a polymer (also called polymerization).

Polymers are disassembled to monomers by **hydrolysis**, a process that is essentially the reverse of the dehydration reaction **(Figure 3.7b).** Hydrolysis means water breakage (from the Greek *hydro*, water, and *lysis*, break). The bond between the monomers is broken by the addition of a water molecule, with a hydrogen from water attaching to one monomer and the hydroxyl group attaching to the other. An example of hydrolysis working within our bodies is the process of digestion. The bulk of the organic material in our food is in the form of polymers that are much too large to enter our cells. Within the digestive tract, various enzymes attack the polymers, speeding up hydrolysis. Released monomers are then absorbed into the bloodstream for distribution to all body cells. Those cells can then use dehydration reactions to assemble the monomers into new, different polymers that can perform specific functions required by the cell.

The Diversity of Polymers

A cell has thousands of different macromolecules; the collection varies from one type of cell to another even in the same organism. The inherited differences between close relatives, such as human siblings, reflect small variations in polymers, particularly DNA and proteins. Molecular differences between unrelated individuals are more extensive, and those between species greater still. The diversity of macromolecules in the living world is vast, and the possible variety is effectively limitless.

What is the basis for such diversity in life's polymers? These molecules are constructed from only 40 to 50 common monomers and some others that occur rarely. Building a huge variety of polymers from such a limited number of monomers is analogous to constructing hundreds of thousands of words from only 26 letters of the alphabet. The key is arrangement—the particular linear sequence that the units follow. However, this analogy falls far short of describing the great diversity of macromolecules because most biological polymers have many more monomers than the number of letters in even the longest word. Proteins, for example, are built from 20 kinds of amino acids arranged in chains that are typically hundreds of amino acids long. The molecular logic of life is simple but elegant: Small molecules common to all organisms are ordered into unique macromolecules.

Despite this immense diversity, molecular structure and function can still be grouped roughly by class. Let's examine each of the four major classes of large biological molecules. For each class, the large molecules have emergent properties not found in their individual building blocks.

CONCEPT CHECK 3.2

1. How many molecules of water are needed to completely hydrolyze a polymer that is ten monomers long?
2. **WHAT IF?** Suppose you eat a serving of fish. What reactions must occur for the amino acid monomers in the protein of the fish to be converted to new proteins in your body?

   For suggested answers, see Appendix A.

CONCEPT 3.3

Carbohydrates serve as fuel and building material

Carbohydrates include both sugars and polymers of sugars. The simplest carbohydrates are the monosaccharides, or simple sugars; these are the monomers from which more complex carbohydrates are built. Disaccharides are double sugars, consisting of two monosaccharides joined by a covalent bond. Carbohydrates also include macromolecules called polysaccharides, polymers composed of many sugar building blocks joined together by dehydration reactions.

Sugars

Monosaccharides (from the Greek *monos*, single, and *sacchar*, sugar) generally have molecular formulas that are some multiple of the unit CH_2O. Glucose ($C_6H_{12}O_6$), the most common

---

▼ **Figure 3.7 The synthesis and breakdown of polymers.**

(a) Dehydration reaction: synthesizing a polymer

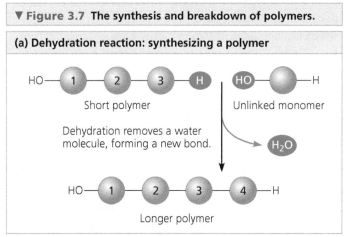

(b) Hydrolysis: breaking down a polymer

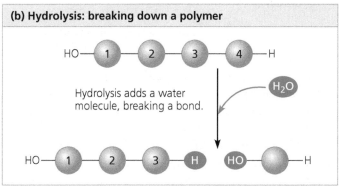

Triose: three-carbon sugar (C₃H₆O₃)	Pentose: five-carbon sugar (C₅H₁₀O₅)	Hexoses: six-carbon sugars (C₆H₁₂O₆)
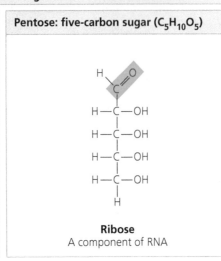		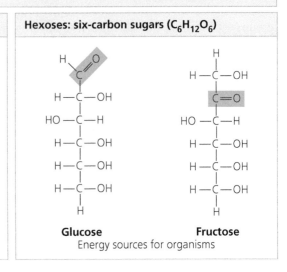
Glyceraldehyde An initial breakdown product of glucose in cells	**Ribose** A component of RNA	**Glucose** **Fructose** Energy sources for organisms

monosaccharide, is of central importance in the chemistry of life. In the structure of glucose, we can see the trademarks of a sugar: The molecule has a carbonyl group ($\rangle C{=}O$) and multiple hydroxyl groups (—OH) **(Figure 3.8)**. The carbonyl group can be on the end of the linear sugar molecule, as in glucose, or attached to an interior carbon, as in fructose. (Thus, sugars are either aldehydes or ketones; see Figure 3.6.) The carbon skeleton of a sugar molecule ranges from three to seven carbons long. Glucose, fructose, and other sugars that have six carbons are called hexoses. Trioses (three-carbon sugars) and pentoses (five-carbon sugars) are also common. Note that most names for sugars end in -ose.

Although it is convenient to draw glucose with a linear carbon skeleton, this representation is not completely accurate. In aqueous solutions, glucose molecules (as well as most other five- and six-carbon sugars) form rings, because they are the most stable form of these sugars under physiological conditions **(Figure 3.9)**.

Monosaccharides, particularly glucose, are major nutrients for cells. In the process known as cellular respiration, cells extract energy from glucose molecules by breaking them down in a series of reactions. Also, the carbon skeletons of sugars serve as raw material for the synthesis of other types of small organic molecules, such as amino acids. Sugar molecules that are not immediately used in these ways are generally incorporated as monomers into disaccharides or polysaccharides.

A **disaccharide** consists of two monosaccharides joined by a **glycosidic linkage**, a covalent bond formed between two monosaccharides by a dehydration reaction (*glyco* refers to carbohydrate). The most prevalent disaccharide is sucrose, which is table sugar. Its two monomers are glucose and fructose **(Figure 3.10)**. Plants generally transport carbohydrates from leaves to roots and other nonphotosynthetic organs in the form of sucrose. Some other disaccharides are lactose, the sugar present in milk, and maltose, used in making beer.

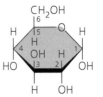

(a) Linear and ring forms. Chemical equilibrium between the linear and ring structures greatly favors the formation of rings. The carbons of the sugar are numbered 1 to 6, as shown. To form the glucose ring, carbon 1 (magenta) bonds to the oxygen (blue) attached to carbon 5.

(b) Abbreviated ring structure. Each unlabeled corner represents a carbon. The ring's thicker edge indicates that you are looking at the ring edge-on; the components attached to the ring lie above or below the plane of the ring.

▲ **Figure 3.9 Linear and ring forms of glucose.**

DRAW IT *Start with the linear form of fructose (see Figure 3.8) and draw the formation of the fructose ring in two steps, as shown in (a). First, number the carbons starting at the top of the linear structure. Then draw the molecule in a ringlike orientation, attaching carbon 5 via its oxygen to carbon 2. Compare the number of carbons in the fructose and glucose rings.*

synthesis. Sucrose is a disaccharide formed from glucose and fructose by a dehydration reaction. Notice that fructose, though a hexose like glucose, forms a five-sided ring.

DRAW IT *Number the carbons in each sugar (see Figure 3.9). How does the name of the linkage relate to the numbers?*

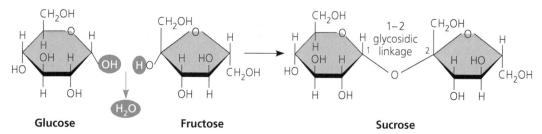

Glucose   Fructose   Sucrose

Polysaccharides

Polysaccharides are macromolecules, polymers with a few hundred to a few thousand monosaccharides joined by glycosidic linkages. Some polysaccharides serve as storage material, hydrolyzed as needed to provide sugar for cells. Other polysaccharides serve as building material for structures that protect the cell or the whole organism. The structure and function of a polysaccharide are determined by its sugar monomers and by the positions of its glycosidic linkages.

Storage Polysaccharides

Both plants and animals store sugars for later use in the form of storage polysaccharides **(Figure 3.11)**. Plants store **starch**, a polymer of glucose monomers, as granules within cells. Synthesizing starch enables the plant to stockpile surplus glucose. Because glucose is a major cellular fuel, starch represents stored energy. The sugar can later be withdrawn from this carbohydrate "bank" by hydrolysis, which breaks the bonds between the glucose monomers. Most animals, including

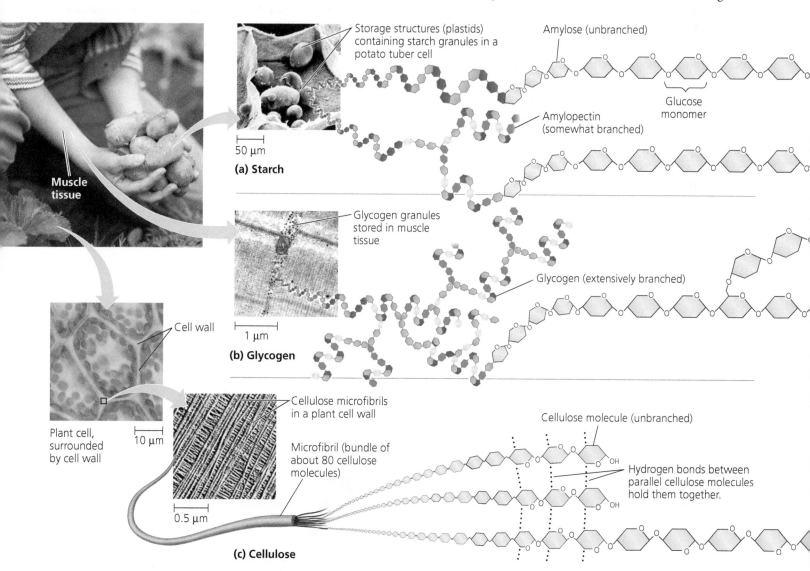

▲ **Figure 3.11 Polysaccharides of plants and animals. (a)** Starch stored in plant cells, **(b)** glycogen stored in muscle cells, and **(c)** structural cellulose fibers in plant cell walls are all polysaccharides composed entirely of glucose monomers (green hexagons). In starch and glycogen, the polymer chains tend to form helices in unbranched regions because of the angle of the 1–4 linkage between the glucose monomers. Cellulose, with a different kind of 1–4 linkage, is always unbranched.

humans, also have enzymes that can hydrolyze plant starch, making glucose available as a nutrient for cells. Potato tubers and grains—the fruits of wheat, maize (corn), rice, and other grasses—are the major sources of starch in the human diet.

Most of the glucose monomers in starch are joined by 1–4 linkages (number 1 carbon to number 4 carbon). The simplest form of starch, amylose, is unbranched, as shown in **Figure 3.11a**. Amylopectin, a more complex starch, is a branched polymer with 1–6 linkages at the branch points.

Animals store a polysaccharide called **glycogen**, a polymer of glucose that is like amylopectin but more extensively branched (see **Figure 3.11b**). Humans and other vertebrates store glycogen mainly in liver and muscle cells. Hydrolysis of glycogen in these cells releases glucose when the demand for sugar increases. This stored fuel cannot sustain an animal for long, however. In humans, for example, glycogen stores are depleted in about a day unless they are replenished by eating. This is an issue of concern in ultra-low-carbohydrate diets, which can result in weakness and fatigue.

Structural Polysaccharides

Organisms build strong materials from structural polysaccharides. The polysaccharide called **cellulose** is a major component of the tough walls that enclose plant cells (see **Figure 3.11c**). On a global scale, plants produce almost 10^{14} kg (100 billion tons) of cellulose per year; it is the most abundant organic compound on Earth. Like starch, cellulose is a polymer of glucose with 1–4 glycosidic linkages, but the linkages in these two polymers differ. The difference is based on the fact that there are actually two slightly different ring structures for glucose **(Figure 3.12a)**. When glucose forms a ring, the hydroxyl group attached to the number 1 carbon is positioned either below or above the plane of the ring. These two ring forms for glucose are called alpha (α) and beta (β), respectively. In starch, all the glucose monomers are in the α configuration **(Figure 3.12b)**, the arrangement we saw in Figure 3.9. In contrast, the glucose monomers of cellulose are all in the β configuration, making every glucose monomer "upside down" with respect to its neighbors **(Figure 3.12c)**.

The differing glycosidic linkages in starch and cellulose give the two molecules distinct three-dimensional shapes. Whereas certain starch molecules are largely helical, a cellulose molecule is straight. Cellulose is never branched, and some hydroxyl groups on its glucose monomers are free to hydrogen-bond with the hydroxyls of other cellulose molecules lying parallel to it. In plant cell walls, parallel cellulose molecules held together in this way are grouped into units called microfibrils (see Figure 3.11c). These cable-like microfibrils are a strong building material for plants and an important substance for humans because cellulose is the major constituent of paper and the only component of cotton.

Enzymes that digest starch by hydrolyzing its α linkages are unable to hydrolyze the β linkages of cellulose due to the different shapes of these two molecules. In fact, few organisms possess enzymes that can digest cellulose. Almost all animals, including humans, do not; the cellulose in our food passes through the digestive tract and is eliminated with the feces. Along the way, the cellulose abrades the wall of the digestive tract and stimulates the lining to secrete mucus, which aids in the smooth passage of food through the tract. Thus, although cellulose is not a nutrient for humans, it is an important part of a healthful diet. Most fruits, vegetables, and whole grains are rich in cellulose. On food packages, "insoluble fiber" refers mainly to cellulose.

Some microorganisms can digest cellulose, breaking it down into glucose monomers. A cow harbors cellulose-digesting

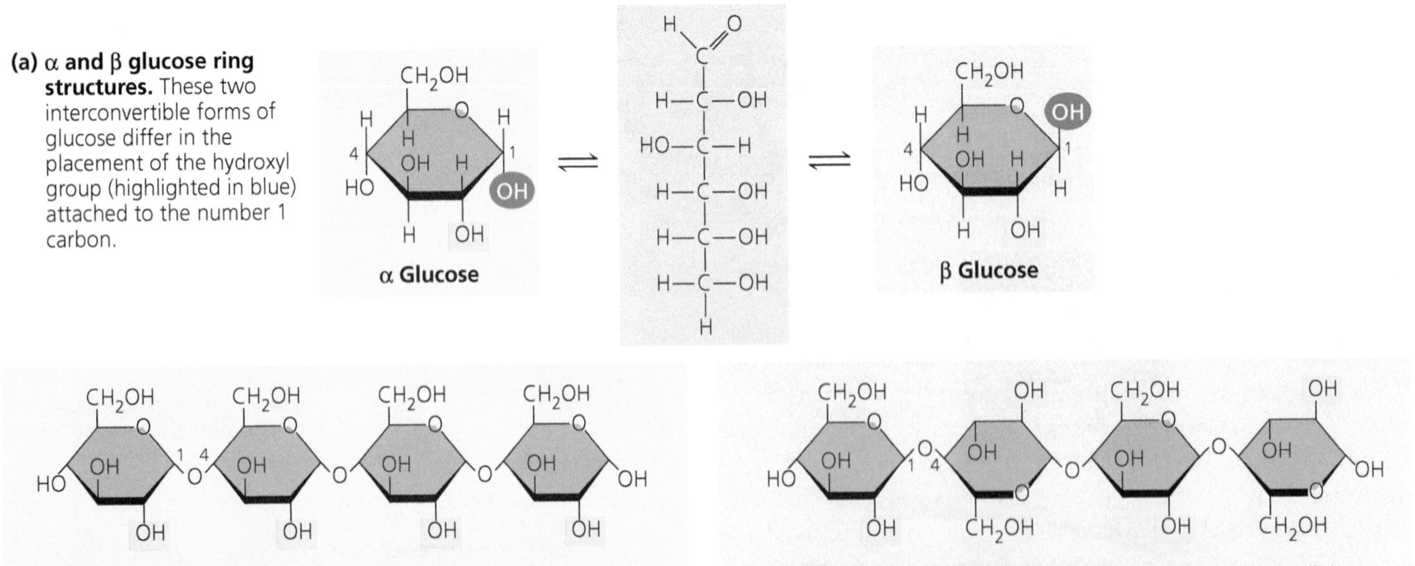

(a) **α and β glucose ring structures.** These two interconvertible forms of glucose differ in the placement of the hydroxyl group (highlighted in blue) attached to the number 1 carbon.

α Glucose

β Glucose

(b) **Starch: 1–4 linkage of α glucose monomers.** All monomers are in the same orientation. Compare the positions of the —OH groups highlighted in yellow with those in cellulose (c).

(c) **Cellulose: 1–4 linkage of β glucose monomers.** In cellulose, every β glucose monomer is upside down with respect to its neighbors. (See the highlighted —OH groups.)

▲ **Figure 3.12 Starch and cellulose structures.**

prokaryotes and protists in its gut. These microbes hydrolyze the cellulose of hay and grass and convert the glucose to other compounds that nourish the cow. Similarly, a termite, which is unable to digest cellulose by itself, has prokaryotes or protists living in its gut that can make a meal of wood. Some fungi can also digest cellulose in soil and elsewhere, thereby helping recycle chemical elements within Earth's ecosystems.

Another important structural polysaccharide is **chitin**, the carbohydrate used by arthropods (insects, spiders, crustaceans, and related animals) to build their exoskeletons—hard cases that surround the soft parts of these animals. Chitin is also found in many fungi, which use this polysaccharide as the building material for their cell walls. Chitin is similar to cellulose except that the glucose monomer of chitin has a nitrogen-containing attachment.

CONCEPT CHECK 3.3

1. Write the formula for a monosaccharide that has three carbons.
2. A dehydration reaction joins two glucose molecules to form maltose. The formula for glucose is $C_6H_{12}O_6$. What is the formula for maltose?
3. **WHAT IF?** After a cow is given antibiotics to treat an infection, a vet gives the animal a drink of "gut culture" containing various prokaryotes. Why is this necessary?

For suggested answers, see Appendix A.

CONCEPT 3.4

Lipids are a diverse group of hydrophobic molecules

Lipids are the one class of large biological molecules that does not include true polymers, and they are generally not big enough to be considered macromolecules. The compounds called **lipids** are grouped together because they share one important trait: They mix poorly, if at all, with water. The hydrophobic behavior of lipids is based on their molecular structure. Although they may have some polar bonds associated with oxygen, lipids consist mostly of hydrocarbon regions. Lipids are varied in form and function. They include waxes and certain pigments, but we will focus on the types of lipids that are most biologically important: fats, phospholipids, and steroids.

Fats

Although fats are not polymers, they are large molecules assembled from smaller molecules by dehydration reactions. A **fat** is constructed from two kinds of smaller molecules: glycerol and fatty acids (**Figure 3.13a**). Glycerol is an alcohol; each of its three carbons bears a hydroxyl group. A **fatty acid** has a long carbon skeleton, usually 16 or 18 carbon atoms in length. The carbon at one end of the skeleton is part of a carboxyl group, the functional group that gives these molecules the name fatty *acid*. The rest of the skeleton consists of a hydrocarbon chain. The relatively nonpolar C—H bonds in the

hydrocarbon chains of fatty acids are the reason fats are hydrophobic. Fats separate from water because the water molecules hydrogen-bond to one another and exclude the fats. This is the reason that vegetable oil (a liquid fat) separates from the aqueous vinegar solution in a bottle of salad dressing.

In making a fat, three fatty acid molecules are each joined to glycerol by an ester linkage, a bond between a hydroxyl group and a carboxyl group. The resulting fat, also called a **triacylglycerol**, thus consists of three fatty acids linked to one glycerol molecule. (Still another name for a fat is *triglyceride*, a word often found in the list of ingredients on packaged foods.) The fatty acids in a fat can be the same, or they can be of two or three different kinds, as in **Figure 3.13b**.

The terms *saturated fats* and *unsaturated fats* are commonly used in the context of nutrition. These terms refer to the structure of the hydrocarbon chains of the fatty acids. If there are no double bonds between carbon atoms composing a chain, then as many hydrogen atoms as possible are bonded to the carbon skeleton. Such a structure is said to be *saturated* with hydrogen, and the resulting fatty acid is called a **saturated fatty acid**. An **unsaturated fatty acid** has one or more double bonds, with one fewer hydrogen atom on each double-bonded carbon. Nearly every double bond in naturally occurring fatty acids is a *cis* double bond, which creates a kink

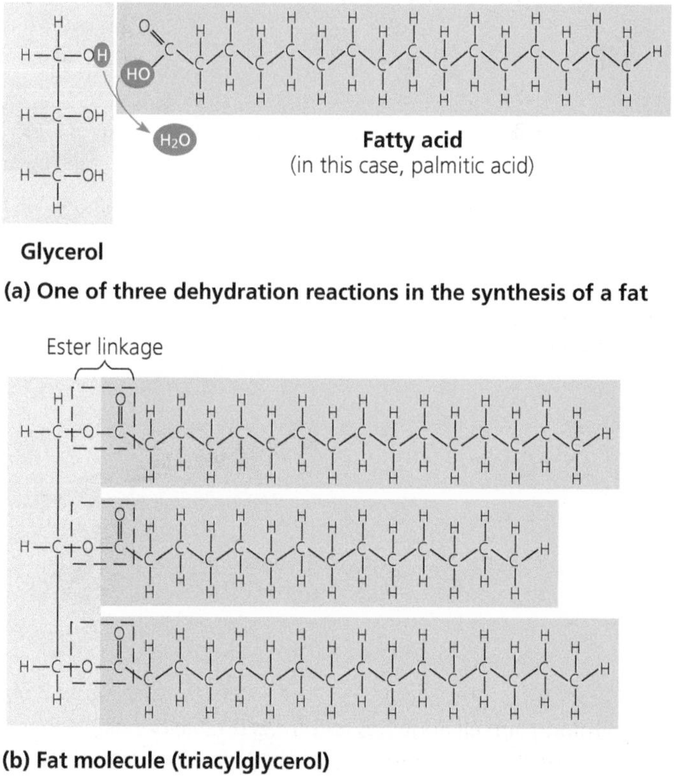

Glycerol

(a) One of three dehydration reactions in the synthesis of a fat

(b) Fat molecule (triacylglycerol)

▲ **Figure 3.13 The synthesis and structure of a fat, or triacylglycerol.** The molecular building blocks of a fat are one molecule of glycerol and three molecules of fatty acids. **(a)** One water molecule is removed for each fatty acid joined to the glycerol. **(b)** A fat molecule with three fatty acid units, two of them identical. The carbons of the fatty acids are arranged zigzag to suggest the actual orientations of the four single bonds extending from each carbon (see Figure 3.2a).

▼ Figure 3.14 Saturated and unsaturated fats and fatty acids.

(a) Saturated fat

At room temperature, the molecules of a saturated fat, such as the fat in butter, are packed closely together, forming a solid.

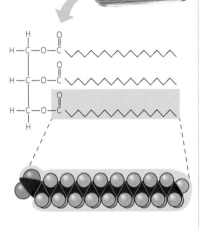

Structural formula of a saturated fat molecule (Each hydrocarbon chain is represented as a zigzag line, where each bend represents a carbon atom and hydrogens are not shown.)

Space-filling model of stearic acid, a saturated fatty acid (red = oxygen, black = carbon, gray = hydrogen)

(b) Unsaturated fat

At room temperature, the molecules of an unsaturated fat such as olive oil cannot pack together closely enough to solidify because of the kinks in some of their fatty acid hydrocarbon chains.

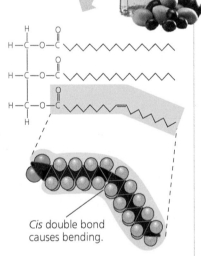

Structural formula of an unsaturated fat molecule

Space-filling model of oleic acid, an unsaturated fatty acid

Cis double bond causes bending.

---

are built of one or more types of unsaturated fatty acids. Usually liquid at room temperature, plant and fish fats are referred to as oils—olive oil and cod liver oil are examples **(Figure 3.14b)**. The kinks where the *cis* double bonds are located prevent the molecules from packing together closely enough to solidify at room temperature. The phrase "hydrogenated vegetable oils" on food labels means that unsaturated fats have been synthetically converted to saturated fats by adding hydrogen, allowing them to solidify. This process also produces unsaturated fats with *trans* double bonds, known as ***trans* fats**. It appears that *trans* fats can contribute to coronary heart disease (see Concept 34.4). Because *trans* fats are especially common in baked goods and processed foods, the U.S. Food and Drug Administration (FDA) requires nutritional labels to include information on *trans* fat content. The FDA has proposed a ban on *trans* fats in the U.S. food supply; some countries, such as Denmark and Switzerland, have already implemented restrictions on the level of *trans* fats in foods.

The major function of fats is energy storage. The hydrocarbon chains of fats are similar to gasoline molecules and just as rich in energy. A gram of fat stores more than twice as much energy as a gram of a polysaccharide, such as starch. Because plants are relatively immobile, they can function with bulky energy storage in the form of starch. (Vegetable oils are generally obtained from seeds, where more compact storage is an asset to the plant.) Animals, however, must carry their energy stores with them, so there is an advantage to having a more compact reservoir of fuel—fat.

Phospholipids

Cells could not exist without another type of lipid, called phospholipids. Phospholipids are essential for cells because they are major constituents of cell membranes. Their structure provides a classic example of how form fits function at the molecular level. As shown in **Figure 3.15**, a **phospholipid** is similar to a fat molecule but has only two fatty acids attached to glycerol rather than three. The third hydroxyl group of glycerol is joined to a phosphate group, which has a negative electrical charge in the cell. Additional small molecules, which are usually charged or polar, can be linked to the phosphate group to form a variety of phospholipids.

The two ends of a phospholipid exhibit different behavior toward water. The hydrocarbon tails are hydrophobic and are excluded from water. However, the phosphate group and its attachments form a hydrophilic head that has an affinity for water. When phospholipids are added to water, they self-assemble into double-layered structures called "bilayers," shielding their hydrophobic portions from water (see Figure 3.15d).

At the surface of a cell, phospholipids are arranged in a similar bilayer. The hydrophilic heads of the molecules are on the outside of the bilayer, in contact with the aqueous solutions inside and outside of the cell. The hydrophobic tails point toward the interior of the bilayer, away from the water. The phospholipid bilayer forms a boundary between the cell and its external environment; in fact, the existence of cells depends on the properties of phospholipids.

---

in the hydrocarbon chain wherever it occurs. (See Figure 3.5b to remind yourself about *cis* and *trans* double bonds.)

A fat made from saturated fatty acids is called a saturated fat. Most animal fats are saturated: The hydrocarbon chains of their fatty acids—the "tails" of the fat molecules—lack double bonds, and their flexibility allows the fat molecules to pack together tightly. Saturated animal fats—such as lard and butter—are solid at room temperature **(Figure 3.14a)**. In contrast, the fats of plants and fishes are generally unsaturated, meaning that they

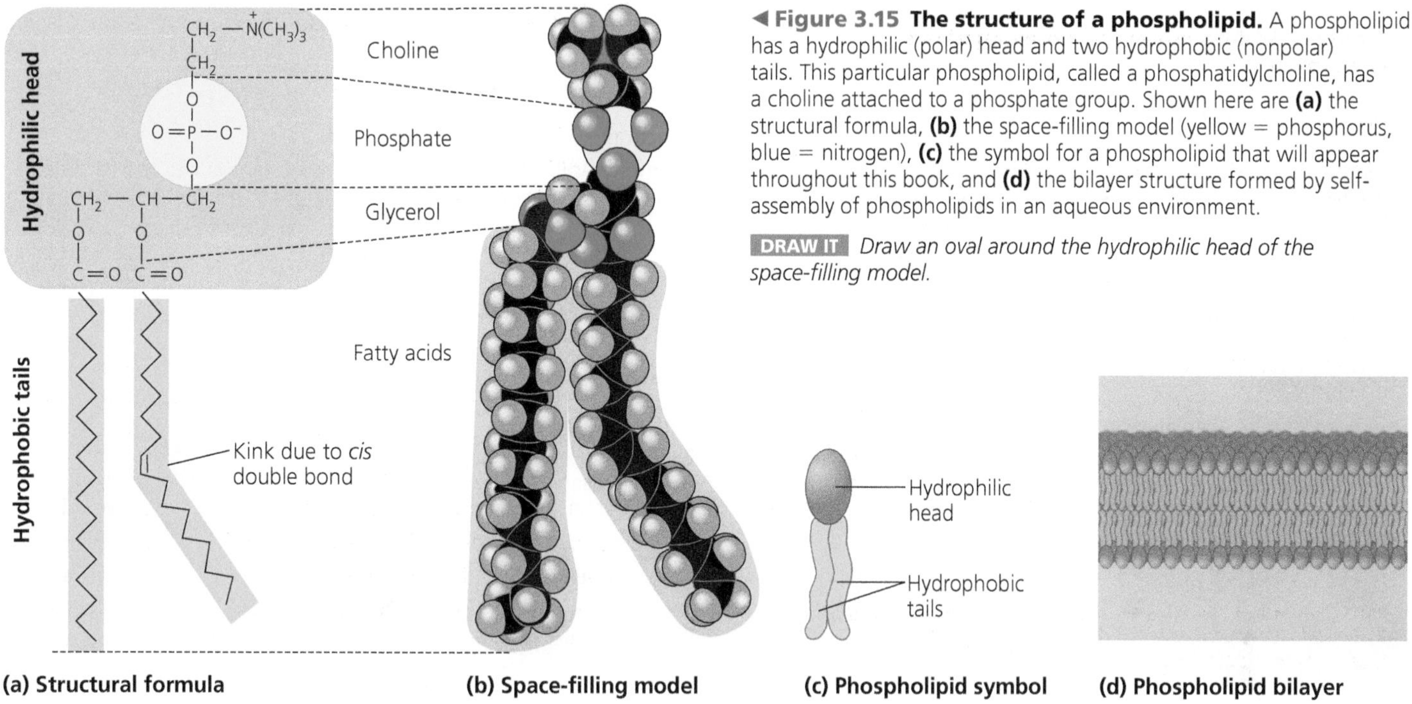

◀ **Figure 3.15 The structure of a phospholipid.** A phospholipid has a hydrophilic (polar) head and two hydrophobic (nonpolar) tails. This particular phospholipid, called a phosphatidylcholine, has a choline attached to a phosphate group. Shown here are **(a)** the structural formula, **(b)** the space-filling model (yellow = phosphorus, blue = nitrogen), **(c)** the symbol for a phospholipid that will appear throughout this book, and **(d)** the bilayer structure formed by self-assembly of phospholipids in an aqueous environment.

DRAW IT *Draw an oval around the hydrophilic head of the space-filling model.*

Steroids

Steroids are lipids characterized by a carbon skeleton consisting of four fused rings. Different steroids are distinguished by the particular chemical groups attached to this ensemble of rings. Shown in **Figure 3.16**, **cholesterol** is a crucial steroid in animals. It is a common component of animal cell membranes and is also the precursor from which other steroids are synthesized, such as the vertebrate sex hormones estrogen and testosterone (see Concept 3.1). In vertebrates, cholesterol is synthesized in the liver and is also obtained from the diet. A high level of cholesterol in the blood may contribute to atherosclerosis, although some researchers are questioning the roles of cholesterol and saturated fats in development of this condition.

▶ **Figure 3.16 Cholesterol, a steroid.**

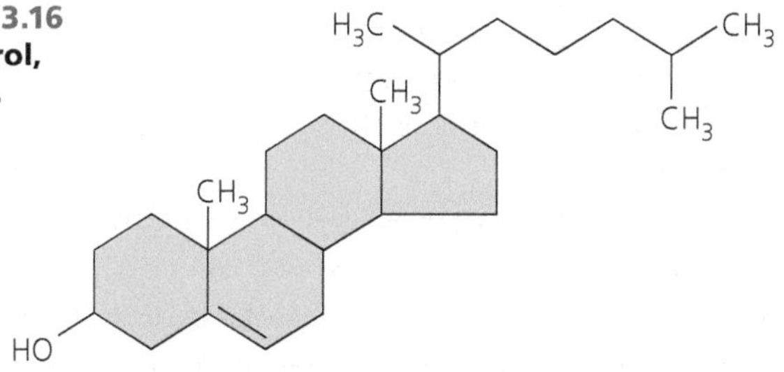

CONCEPT CHECK 3.4

1. Compare the structure of a fat (triglyceride) with that of a phospholipid.
2. Why are human sex hormones considered lipids?
3. **WHAT IF?** Suppose a membrane surrounded an oil droplet, as it does in the cells of plant seeds. Describe and explain the form it might take.

For suggested answers, see Appendix A.

CONCEPT 3.5

Proteins include a diversity of structures, resulting in a wide range of functions

Nearly every dynamic function of a living being depends on proteins. In fact, the importance of proteins is underscored by their name, which comes from the Greek word *proteios*, meaning "first," or "primary." Proteins account for more than 50% of the dry mass of most cells, and they are instrumental in almost everything organisms do. Some proteins speed up chemical reactions, while others play a role in defense, storage, transport, cellular communication, movement, or structural support. **Figure 3.17** shows examples of proteins with these functions (which you'll learn more about in later chapters).

Life would not be possible without enzymes, most of which are proteins. Enzymatic proteins regulate metabolism by acting as **catalysts**, chemical agents that selectively speed up chemical reactions without being consumed in the reaction. Because an enzyme can perform its function over and over again, these molecules can be thought of as workhorses that keep cells running by carrying out the processes of life.

A human has tens of thousands of different proteins, each with a specific structure and function; proteins, in fact, are the most structurally sophisticated molecules known. Consistent with their diverse functions, they vary extensively in structure, each type of protein having a unique three-dimensional shape.

Proteins are all constructed from the same set of 20 amino acids, linked in unbranched polymers. The bond between amino acids is called a peptide bond, so a polymer of amino

Figure 3.17 An overview of protein functions.

Enzymatic proteins

Function: Selective acceleration of chemical reactions

Example: Digestive enzymes catalyze the hydrolysis of bonds in food molecules.

Enzyme

Defensive proteins

Function: Protection against disease

Example: Antibodies inactivate and help destroy viruses and bacteria.

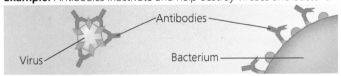

Antibodies

Virus

Bacterium

Storage proteins

Function: Storage of amino acids

Examples: Casein, the protein of milk, is the major source of amino acids for baby mammals. Plants have storage proteins in their seeds. Ovalbumin is the protein of egg white, used as an amino acid source for the developing embryo.

Ovalbumin   Amino acids for embryo

Transport proteins

Function: Transport of substances

Examples: Hemoglobin, the iron-containing protein of vertebrate blood, transports oxygen from the lungs to other parts of the body. Other proteins transport molecules across membranes, as shown here.

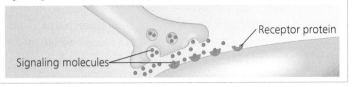

Transport protein

Cell membrane

Hormonal proteins

Function: Coordination of an organism's activities

Example: Insulin, a hormone secreted by the pancreas, causes other tissues to take up glucose, thus regulating blood sugar concentration.

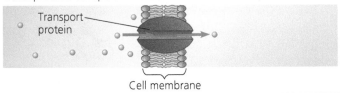

High blood sugar   Insulin secreted   Normal blood sugar

Receptor proteins

Function: Response of cell to chemical stimuli

Example: Receptors built into the membrane of a nerve cell detect signaling molecules released by other nerve cells.

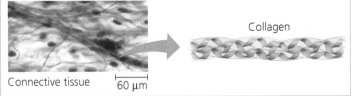

Receptor protein

Signaling molecules

Contractile and motor proteins

Function: Movement

Examples: Motor proteins are responsible for the undulations of cilia and flagella. Actin and myosin proteins are responsible for the contraction of muscles.

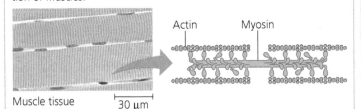

Actin   Myosin

Muscle tissue   30 μm

Structural proteins

Function: Support

Examples: Keratin is the protein of hair, horns, feathers, and other skin appendages. Insects and spiders use silk fibers to make their cocoons and webs, respectively. Collagen and elastin proteins provide a fibrous framework in animal connective tissues.

Collagen

Connective tissue   60 μm

---

acids is called a **polypeptide**. A **protein** is a biologically functional molecule made up of one or more polypeptides folded and coiled into a specific three-dimensional structure.

Amino Acid Monomers

All amino acids share a common structure. An **amino acid** is an organic molecule with both an amino group and a carboxyl group; the small figure shows the general formula for an amino acid. At the

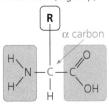

Side chain (R group)

R

α carbon

Amino group   Carboxyl group

center of the amino acid is a carbon atom called the *alpha* (α) *carbon*. Its four different partners are an amino group, a carboxyl group, a hydrogen atom, and a variable group symbolized by R. The R group, also called the side chain, differs with each amino acid **(Figure 3.18)**.

The 20 amino acids in Figure 3.18 are the ones cells use to build their proteins. Here the amino groups and carboxyl groups are all depicted in ionized form, the way they usually exist at the pH found in a cell. The

▼ **Figure 3.18 The 20 amino acids of proteins.** The amino acids are grouped here according to the properties of their side chains (R groups) and shown in their prevailing ionic forms at pH 7.2, the pH within a cell. The three-letter and one-letter abbreviations for the amino acids are in parentheses.

Nonpolar side chains; hydrophobic

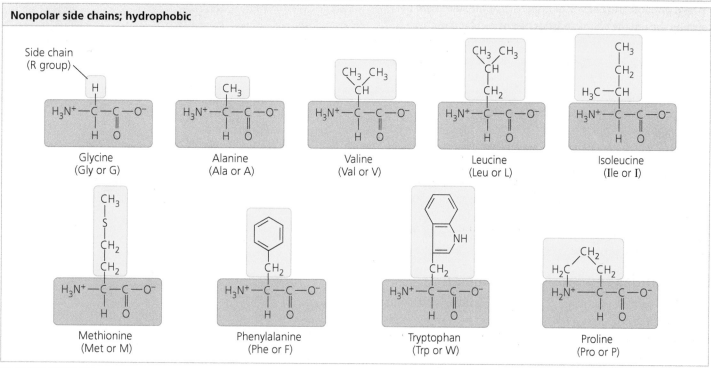

Glycine
(Gly or G)

Alanine
(Ala or A)

Valine
(Val or V)

Leucine
(Leu or L)

Isoleucine
(Ile or I)

Methionine
(Met or M)

Phenylalanine
(Phe or F)

Tryptophan
(Trp or W)

Proline
(Pro or P)

Polar side chains; hydrophilic

Since cysteine is only weakly polar, it is sometimes classified as a nonpolar amino acid.

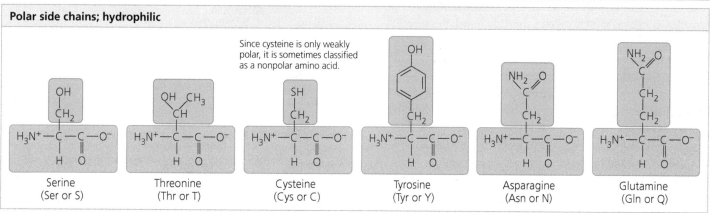

Serine
(Ser or S)

Threonine
(Thr or T)

Cysteine
(Cys or C)

Tyrosine
(Tyr or Y)

Asparagine
(Asn or N)

Glutamine
(Gln or Q)

Electrically charged side chains; hydrophilic

Basic (positively charged)

Acidic (negatively charged)

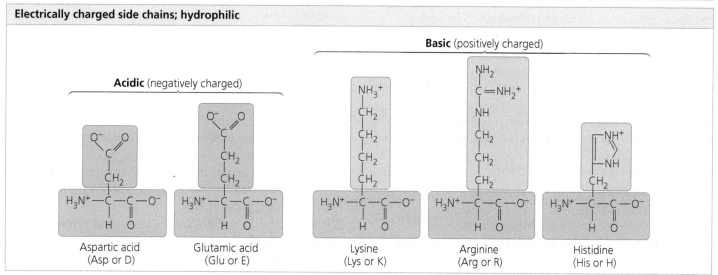

Aspartic acid
(Asp or D)

Glutamic acid
(Glu or E)

Lysine
(Lys or K)

Arginine
(Arg or R)

Histidine
(His or H)

side chain (R group) may be as simple as a hydrogen atom, as in the amino acid glycine, or it may be a carbon skeleton with various functional groups attached, as in glutamine.

The physical and chemical properties of the side chain determine the unique characteristics of a particular amino acid, thus affecting its functional role in a polypeptide. In Figure 3.18, the amino acids are grouped according to the properties of their side chains. One group consists of amino acids with nonpolar side chains, which are hydrophobic. Another group consists of amino acids with polar side chains, which are hydrophilic. Acidic amino acids are those with side chains that are generally negative in charge due to the presence of a carboxyl group, which is usually dissociated (ionized) at cellular pH. Basic amino acids have amino groups in their side chains that are generally positive in charge. (Notice that *all* amino acids have carboxyl groups and amino groups; the terms *acidic* and *basic* in this context refer only to groups in the side chains.) Because they are charged, acidic and basic side chains are also hydrophilic.

Polypeptides (Amino Acid Polymers)

Now that we have examined amino acids, let's see how they are linked to form polymers (**Figure 3.19**). When two amino acids are positioned so that the carboxyl group of one is adjacent to the amino group of the other, they can become joined by a dehydration reaction, with the removal of a water molecule. The resulting covalent bond is called a **peptide bond**. Repeated over and over, this process yields a polypeptide, a polymer of many amino acids linked by peptide bonds. You'll learn more about how cells synthesize polypeptides in Chapter 14.

The repeating sequence of atoms highlighted in purple in Figure 3.19 is called the polypeptide backbone. Extending from this backbone are the different side chains (R groups) of the amino acids. Polypeptides range in length from a few amino acids to a thousand or more. Each specific polypeptide has a unique linear sequence of amino acids. Note that one end of the polypeptide chain has a free amino group, while the opposite end has a free carboxyl group. Thus, a polypeptide of any length has a single amino end (N-terminus) and a single carboxyl end (C-terminus). In a polypeptide of any significant size, the side chains far outnumber the terminal groups, so the chemical nature of the molecule as a whole is determined by the kind and sequence of the side chains. The immense variety of polypeptides in nature illustrates an important concept introduced earlier—that cells can make many different polymers by linking a limited set of monomers into diverse sequences.

Protein Structure and Function

The specific activities of proteins result from their intricate three-dimensional architecture, the simplest level of which is the sequence of their amino acids. What can the amino acid sequence of a polypeptide tell us about the three-dimensional structure (commonly referred to simply as "the structure") of the protein and its function? The term *polypeptide* is not

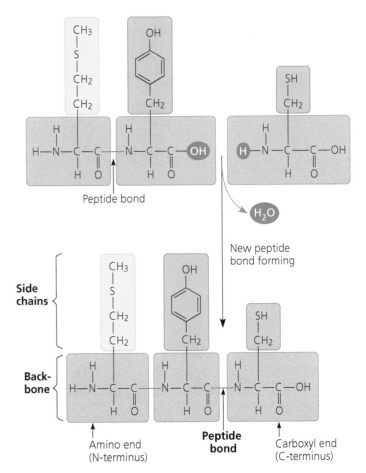

▲ **Figure 3.19 Making a polypeptide chain.** Peptide bonds are formed by dehydration reactions, which link the carboxyl group of one amino acid to the amino group of the next. The peptide bonds are formed one at a time, starting with the amino acid at the amino end (N-terminus). The polypeptide has a repetitive backbone (purple) from which the amino acid side chains (yellow and green) extend.

DRAW IT *At the top of the figure, circle and label the carboxyl and amino groups that will form the new peptide bond. Under each amino acid, write its three- and one-letter abbreviations (see Figure 3.18).*

synonymous with the term *protein*. Even for a protein consisting of a single polypeptide, the relationship is somewhat analogous to that between a long strand of yarn and a sweater of particular size and shape that can be knitted from the yarn. A functional protein is not *just* a polypeptide chain, but one or more polypeptides precisely twisted, folded, and coiled into a molecule of unique shape, which can be shown in several different types of models (**Figure 3.20**). And it is the amino acid sequence of each polypeptide that determines what three-dimensional structure the protein will have under normal cellular conditions.

When a cell synthesizes a polypeptide, the chain may fold spontaneously, assuming the functional structure for that protein. This folding is driven and reinforced by the formation of various bonds between parts of the chain, which in turn depends on the sequence of amino acids. Many proteins are roughly spherical (*globular proteins*), while others are shaped like long fibers (*fibrous proteins*). Even within these broad categories, countless variations exist.

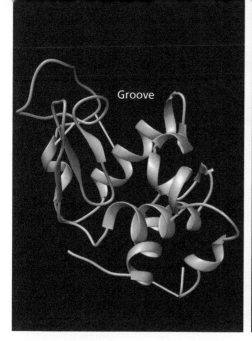

(a) A **ribbon model** shows how the single polypeptide chain folds and coils to form the functional protein. (The yellow lines represent disulfide bridges that stabilize the protein's shape.)

(b) A **space-filling model** shows more clearly the globular shape seen in many proteins, as well as the specific three-dimensional structure unique to lysozyme. The groove is the site that will bind to the target bacterial molecule.

(c) In this view, a ribbon model is superimposed on a **wireframe model**, which shows the backbone with the side chains extending from it. The yellow structure is the target molecule on the bacterial cell surface.

▲ **Figure 3.20 Structure of a protein, the enzyme lysozyme.** Present in our sweat, tears, and saliva, lysozyme is an enzyme that helps prevent infection by binding to and catalyzing the destruction of specific (target) molecules on the surface of many kinds of bacteria. The groove is the part of the protein that recognizes and binds to the target molecules on the surface of bacterial cell walls.

A protein's specific structure determines how it works. In almost every case, the function of a protein depends on its ability to recognize and bind to some other molecule. In an especially striking example of the marriage of form and function, **Figure 3.21** shows the exact match of shape between an antibody (a protein in the body) and the particular foreign substance on a flu virus that the antibody binds to and marks for destruction. (In Chapter 35, you'll learn more about how the immune system generates antibodies that match the shapes of specific foreign molecules so well.)

Another example of molecules with matching shapes is endorphin molecules (produced by the body) and morphine molecules (a manufactured drug), both of which fit into receptor molecules on the surface of brain cells in humans, producing euphoria and relieving pain. Morphine, heroin, and other opiate drugs are able to mimic endorphins because they all share a similar shape with endorphins and can thus fit into and bind to endorphin receptors. This fit is very specific, something like a lock and key (see Figure 2.14). The endorphin receptor, like other receptor molecules, is a protein. The function of a protein—for instance, the ability of a receptor protein to bind to a particular pain-relieving signaling molecule—is an emergent property resulting from exquisite molecular order.

Four Levels of Protein Structure

In spite of their great diversity, all proteins share three superimposed levels of structure, known as primary, secondary, and tertiary structure. A fourth level, quaternary structure, arises when a protein consists of two or more polypeptide chains. **Figure 3.22** describes these four levels of protein structure. Be sure to study this figure thoroughly before going on to the next section.

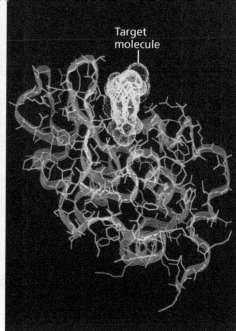

▲ **Figure 3.21 An antibody binding to a protein from a flu virus.** A technique called X-ray crystallography was used to generate a computer model of an antibody protein (blue and orange, left) bound to a flu virus protein (green and yellow, right). Computer software was then used to back the images away from each other, revealing the exact complementarity of shape between the two protein surfaces.

Primary Structure

Linear chain of amino acids

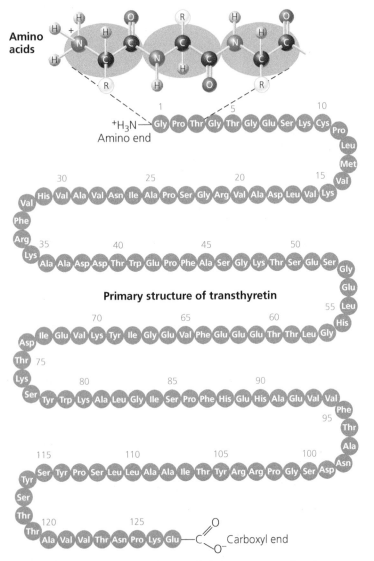

Amino acids

^+H_3N—Gly Pro Thr Gly Thr Gly Glu Ser Lys Cys
Amino end

Primary structure of transthyretin

Carboxyl end

Secondary Structure

Regions stabilized by hydrogen bonds between atoms of the polypeptide backbone

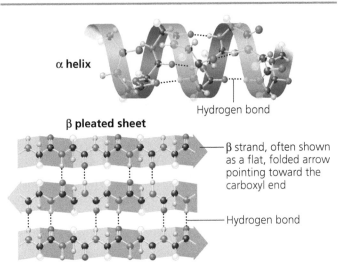

α helix

Hydrogen bond

β pleated sheet

β strand, often shown as a flat, folded arrow pointing toward the carboxyl end

Hydrogen bond

The **primary structure** of a protein is its sequence of amino acids. As an example, let's consider transthyretin, a globular blood protein that transports vitamin A and one of the thyroid hormones throughout the body. Transthyretin is made up of four identical polypeptide chains, each composed of 127 amino acids. Shown here is one of these chains unraveled for a closer look at its primary structure. Each of the 127 positions along the chain is occupied by one of the 20 amino acids, indicated here by its three-letter abbreviation.

The primary structure is like the order of letters in a very long word. If left to chance, there would be 20^{127} different ways of making a polypeptide chain 127 amino acids long. However, the precise primary structure of a protein is determined not by the random linking of amino acids, but by inherited genetic information. The primary structure in turn dictates secondary and tertiary structure, due to the chemical nature of the backbone and the side chains (R groups) of the amino acids along the polypeptide.

Most proteins have segments of their polypeptide chains repeatedly coiled or folded in patterns that contribute to the protein's overall shape. These coils and folds, collectively referred to as **secondary structure**, are the result of hydrogen bonds between the repeating constituents of the polypeptide backbone (not the amino acid side chains). Within the backbone, the oxygen atoms have a partial negative charge, and the hydrogen atoms attached to the nitrogens have a partial positive charge (see Figure 2.12); therefore, hydrogen bonds can form between these atoms. Individually, these hydrogen bonds are weak, but because they are repeated many times over a relatively long region of the polypeptide chain, they can support a particular shape for that part of the protein.

One such secondary structure is the **α helix**, a delicate coil held together by hydrogen bonding between every fourth amino acid, as shown here. Although each transthyretin polypeptide has only one α helix region (see the Tertiary Structure section), other globular proteins have multiple stretches of α helix separated by nonhelical regions (see hemoglobin in the Quaternary Structure section). Some fibrous proteins, such as α-keratin, the structural protein of hair, have the α helix formation over most of their length.

The other main type of secondary structure is the **β pleated sheet**. As shown here, in this structure two or more segments of the polypeptide chain lying side by side (called β strands) are connected by hydrogen bonds between parts of the two parallel segments of polypeptide backbone. β pleated sheets make up the core of many globular proteins, as is the case for transthyretin (see Tertiary Structure), and dominate some fibrous proteins, including the silk protein of a spider's web. The teamwork of so many hydrogen bonds makes each spider silk fiber stronger than a steel strand of the same weight.

▶ Spiders secrete silk fibers made of a structural protein containing β pleated sheets, which allow the spider web to stretch and recoil.

Tertiary Structure

Three-dimensional shape stabilized by interactions between side chains

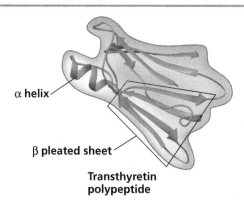

α helix

β pleated sheet

Transthyretin polypeptide

Superimposed on the patterns of secondary structure is a protein's tertiary structure, shown here in a ribbon model of the transthyretin polypeptide. While secondary structure involves interactions between backbone constituents, **tertiary structure** is the overall shape of a polypeptide resulting from interactions between the side chains (R groups) of the various amino acids. One type of interaction that contributes to tertiary structure is called—somewhat misleadingly—a **hydrophobic interaction**. As a polypeptide folds into its functional shape, amino acids with hydrophobic (nonpolar) side chains usually end up in clusters at the core of the protein, out of contact with water. Thus, a "hydrophobic interaction" is actually caused by the exclusion of nonpolar substances by water molecules. Once nonpolar amino acid side chains are close together, van der Waals interactions help hold them together. Meanwhile, hydrogen bonds between polar side chains and ionic bonds between positively and negatively charged side chains also help stabilize tertiary structure. These are all weak interactions in the aqueous cellular environment, but their cumulative effect helps give the protein a unique shape.

Covalent bonds called **disulfide bridges** may further reinforce the shape of a protein. Disulfide bridges form where two cysteine monomers, which have sulfhydryl groups (—SH) on their side chains (see Figure 3.6), are brought close together by the folding of the protein. The sulfur of one cysteine bonds to the sulfur of the second, and the disulfide bridge (—S—S—) rivets parts of the protein together (see yellow lines in Figure 3.20a). All of these different kinds of interactions can contribute to the tertiary structure of a protein, as shown here in a small part of a hypothetical protein:

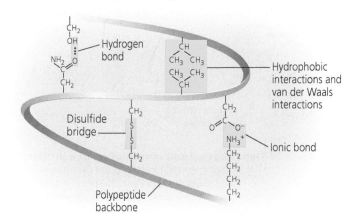

Hydrogen bond

Hydrophobic interactions and van der Waals interactions

Disulfide bridge

Ionic bond

Polypeptide backbone

Quaternary Structure

Association of two or more polypeptides (some proteins only)

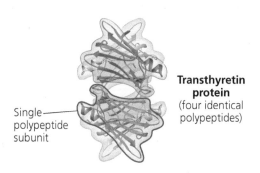

Single polypeptide subunit

Transthyretin protein (four identical polypeptides)

Some proteins consist of two or more polypeptide chains aggregated into one functional macromolecule. **Quaternary structure** is the overall protein structure that results from the aggregation of these polypeptide subunits. For example, shown here is the complete globular transthyretin protein, made up of its four polypeptides.

Another example is collagen, which is a fibrous protein that has three identical helical polypeptides intertwined into a larger triple helix, giving the long fibers great strength. This suits collagen fibers to their function as the girders of connective tissue in skin, bone, tendons, ligaments, and other body parts. (Collagen accounts for 40% of the protein in a human body.)

Collagen

Hemoglobin, the oxygen-binding protein of red blood cells, is another example of a globular protein with quaternary structure. It consists of four polypeptide subunits, two of one kind (α) and two of another kind (β). Both α and β subunits consist primarily of α-helical secondary structure. Each subunit has a nonpolypeptide component, called heme, with an iron atom that binds oxygen.

Heme

Iron

β subunit

α subunit

α subunit

β subunit

Hemoglobin

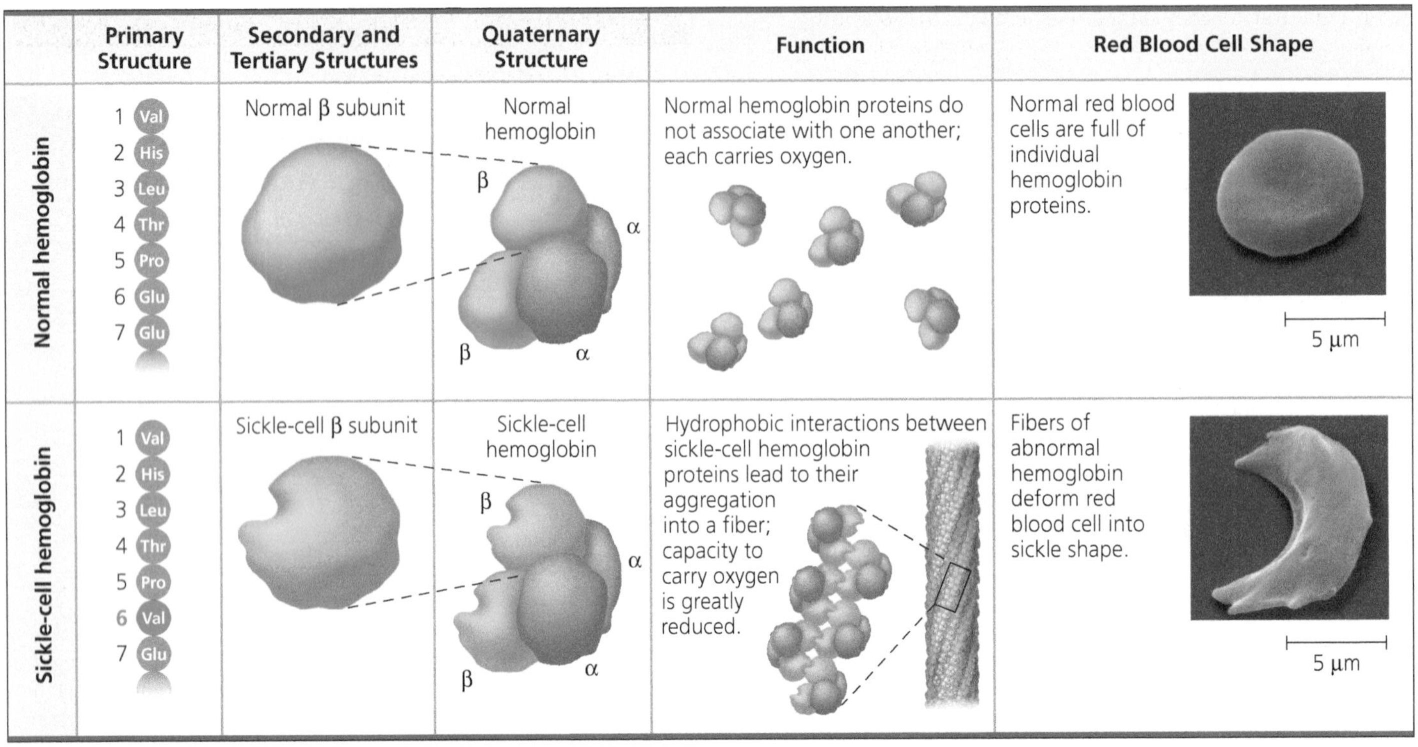

	Primary Structure	Secondary and Tertiary Structures	Quaternary Structure	Function	Red Blood Cell Shape
Normal hemoglobin	1 Val 2 His 3 Leu 4 Thr 5 Pro 6 Glu 7 Glu	Normal β subunit	Normal hemoglobin β α β α	Normal hemoglobin proteins do not associate with one another; each carries oxygen.	Normal red blood cells are full of individual hemoglobin proteins. 5 μm
Sickle-cell hemoglobin	1 Val 2 His 3 Leu 4 Thr 5 Pro 6 Val 7 Glu	Sickle-cell β subunit	Sickle-cell hemoglobin β α β α	Hydrophobic interactions between sickle-cell hemoglobin proteins lead to their aggregation into a fiber; capacity to carry oxygen is greatly reduced.	Fibers of abnormal hemoglobin deform red blood cell into sickle shape. 5 μm

▲ **Figure 3.23** A single amino acid substitution in a protein causes sickle-cell disease.

MAKE CONNECTIONS *Considering the chemical characteristics of the amino acids valine and glutamic acid (see Figure 3.18), propose a possible explanation for the dramatic effect on protein function that occurs when valine is substituted for glutamic acid.*

Sickle-Cell Disease: A Change in Primary Structure

Even a slight change in primary structure can affect a protein's shape and ability to function. For instance, **sickle-cell disease**, an inherited blood disorder, is caused by the substitution of one amino acid (valine) for the normal one (glutamic acid) at a particular position in the primary structure of hemoglobin, the protein that carries oxygen in red blood cells. Normal red blood cells are disk-shaped, but in sickle-cell disease, the abnormal hemoglobin molecules tend to aggregate into fibers, deforming some of the cells into a sickle shape **(Figure 3.23)**. A person with the disease has periodic "sickle-cell crises" when the angular cells clog tiny blood vessels, impeding blood flow. The toll taken on such patients is a dramatic example of how a simple change in protein structure can have devastating effects on protein function.

What Determines Protein Structure?

You've learned that a unique shape endows each protein with a specific function. But what are the key factors determining protein structure? You already know most of the answer: A polypeptide chain of a given amino acid sequence can be arranged into a three-dimensional shape determined by the interactions responsible for secondary and tertiary structure. This folding normally occurs as the protein is being synthesized in the crowded environment within a cell, aided by other proteins. However, protein structure also depends on the physical and chemical conditions of the protein's environment.

If the pH, salt concentration, temperature, or other aspects of its environment are altered, the weak chemical bonds and interactions within a protein may be destroyed, causing the protein to unravel and lose its native shape, a change called **denaturation (Figure 3.24)**. Because it is misshapen, the denatured protein is biologically inactive.

Most proteins become denatured if they are transferred from an aqueous environment to a nonpolar solvent, such as ether or chloroform; the polypeptide chain refolds so that its hydrophobic regions face outward toward the solvent.

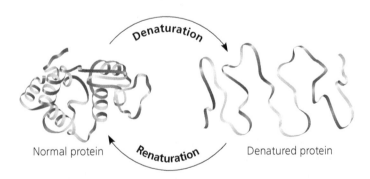

Normal protein   Denaturation   Renaturation   Denatured protein

▲ **Figure 3.24 Denaturation and renaturation of a protein.** High temperatures or various chemical treatments will denature a protein, causing it to lose its shape and hence its ability to function. If the denatured protein remains dissolved, it may renature when the chemical and physical aspects of its environment are restored to normal.

Other denaturation agents include chemicals that disrupt the hydrogen bonds, ionic bonds, and disulfide bridges that maintain a protein's shape. Denaturation can also result from excessive heat, which agitates the polypeptide chain enough to overpower the weak interactions that stabilize the structure. The white of an egg becomes opaque during cooking because the denatured proteins are insoluble and solidify. This also explains why excessively high fevers can be fatal: Proteins in the blood tend to denature at very high body temperatures.

When a protein in a test-tube solution has been denatured by heat or chemicals, it can sometimes return to its functional shape when the denaturing agent is removed. (Sometimes this is not possible: For example, a fried egg will not become liquefied when placed back into the refrigerator!) We can conclude that the information for building a specific shape is intrinsic to the protein's primary structure. The sequence of amino acids determines the protein's shape—where an α helix can form, where β pleated sheets can exist, where disulfide bridges are located, where ionic bonds can form, and so on. But how does protein folding occur in the cell?

Protein Folding in the Cell

Biochemists now know the amino acid sequence for nearly 50 million proteins, with about 1.7 million added each month, and the three-dimensional shape for more than 31,000. Researchers have tried to correlate the primary structure of many proteins with their three-dimensional structure to discover the rules of protein folding. Unfortunately, however, the protein-folding process is not that simple. Most proteins probably go through several intermediate structures on their way to a stable shape, and looking at the mature structure does not reveal the stages of folding required to achieve that form. However, biochemists have developed methods for tracking a protein through such stages. They are still working to develop computer programs that can predict the 3-D structure of a polypeptide from its primary structure alone.

Misfolding of polypeptides is a serious problem in cells. Many diseases, such as Alzheimer's, Parkinson's, and mad cow disease, are associated with an accumulation of misfolded proteins. In fact, misfolded versions of the transthyretin protein featured in Figure 3.22 have been implicated in several diseases, including one form of senile dementia.

Even when scientists have a correctly folded protein in hand, determining its exact three-dimensional structure is not simple, for a single protein molecule has thousands of atoms. The method most commonly used to determine the 3-D shape of a protein is **X-ray crystallography**, which depends on the diffraction of an X-ray beam by the atoms of a crystallized molecule. Using this technique, scientists can build a 3-D model that shows the exact position of every atom in a protein molecule **(Figure 3.25)**. Nuclear magnetic resonance (NMR) spectroscopy and bioinformatics (see Concept 1.1) are complementary approaches to understanding protein structure and function.

▼ Figure 3.25 Research Method

X-Ray Crystallography

Application Scientists use X-ray crystallography to determine the three-dimensional (3-D) structure of macromolecules such as nucleic acids and proteins. As an example, we show how this method was used to determine the 3-D shape of transthyretin, the blood transport protein whose levels of structure are described in Figure 3.22.

Technique Researchers aimed an X-ray beam through the crystallized protein. The atoms of the crystal diffracted (bent) the X-rays into an orderly array that a digital detector recorded as a pattern of spots called an X-ray diffraction pattern, an example of which is shown below.

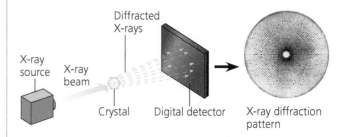

Results Using data from X-ray diffraction patterns, as well as the amino acid sequence determined by chemical methods, researchers built a 3-D model of the four-subunit transthyretin protein with the help of computer software.

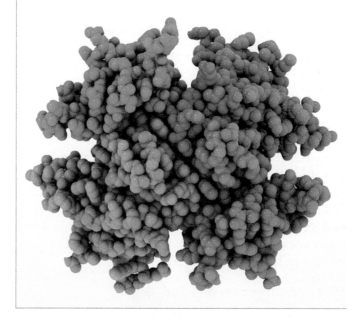

CONCEPT CHECK 3.5

1. Why does a denatured protein no longer function normally?
2. What parts of a polypeptide participate in the bonds that hold together secondary structure? Tertiary structure?
3. **WHAT IF?** Where would you expect a polypeptide region rich in the amino acids valine, leucine, and isoleucine to be located in a folded polypeptide? Explain.

For suggested answers, see Appendix A.

CONCEPT 3.6

Nucleic acids store, transmit, and help express hereditary information

If the primary structure of polypeptides determines a protein's shape, what determines primary structure? The amino acid sequence of a polypeptide is programmed by a discrete unit of inheritance known as a **gene**. Genes consist of DNA, which belongs to the class of compounds called nucleic acids. **Nucleic acids** are polymers made of monomers called nucleotides.

The Roles of Nucleic Acids

The two types of nucleic acids, **deoxyribonucleic acid (DNA)** and **ribonucleic acid (RNA)**, enable living organisms to reproduce their complex components from one generation to the next. Unique among molecules, DNA provides directions for its own replication. DNA also directs RNA synthesis and, through RNA, controls protein synthesis; this entire process is called **gene expression (Figure 3.26)**.

DNA is the genetic material that organisms inherit from their parents. Each chromosome contains one long DNA molecule, usually carrying several hundred or more genes. When a cell reproduces itself by dividing, its DNA molecules are copied and passed along from one generation of cells to the

next. Encoded in the structure of DNA is the information that programs all the cell's activities. The DNA, however, is not directly involved in running the operations of the cell, any more than computer software by itself can print a bank statement or read the bar code on a box of cereal. Just as a printer is needed to print out a statement and a scanner is needed to read a bar code, proteins are required to implement genetic programs. The molecular hardware of the cell—the tools for biological functions—consists mostly of proteins. For example, the oxygen carrier in red blood cells is the protein hemoglobin (see Figure 3.22), not the DNA that specifies its structure.

How does RNA, the other type of nucleic acid, fit into gene expression, the flow of genetic information from DNA to proteins? A given gene along a DNA molecule can direct synthesis of a type of RNA called *messenger RNA* (*mRNA*). The mRNA molecule interacts with the cell's protein-synthesizing machinery to direct production of a polypeptide, which folds into all or part of a protein. We can summarize the flow of genetic information as DNA → RNA → protein (see Figure 3.26). The sites of protein synthesis are cellular structures called ribosomes. In a eukaryotic cell, ribosomes are in the cytoplasm—the region between the nucleus and the cell's outer boundary, the plasma membrane—but DNA resides in the nucleus. Messenger RNA conveys genetic instructions for building proteins from the nucleus to the cytoplasm. Prokaryotic cells lack nuclei but still use mRNA to convey a message from the DNA to ribosomes and other cellular equipment that translate the coded information into amino acid sequences. Later in the book, you'll read about other functions of some recently discovered RNA molecules; the stretches of DNA that direct synthesis of these RNAs are also considered genes (see Concept 15.3).

The Components of Nucleic Acids

Nucleic acids are macromolecules that exist as polymers called **polynucleotides (Figure 3.27a)**. As indicated by the name, each polynucleotide consists of monomers called **nucleotides**. A nucleotide, in general, is composed of three parts: a nitrogen-containing (nitrogenous) base, a five-carbon sugar (a pentose), and one to three phosphate groups **(Figure 3.27b)**. The beginning monomer used to build a polynucleotide has three phosphate groups, but two are lost during the polymerization process. The portion of a nucleotide without any phosphate groups is called a *nucleoside*.

To understand the structure of a single nucleotide, let's first consider the nitrogenous bases **(Figure 3.27c)**. Each nitrogenous base has one or two rings that include nitrogen atoms. (They are called nitrogenous *bases* because the nitrogen atoms tend to take up H^+ from solution, thus acting as bases.) There are two families of nitrogenous bases: pyrimidines and purines. A **pyrimidine** has one six-membered ring of carbon and nitrogen atoms. The members of the pyrimidine family are cytosine (C), thymine (T), and uracil (U). **Purines** are larger, with a

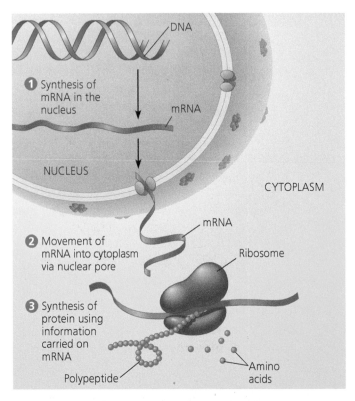

① Synthesis of mRNA in the nucleus

DNA

mRNA

NUCLEUS

CYTOPLASM

② Movement of mRNA into cytoplasm via nuclear pore

mRNA

Ribosome

③ Synthesis of protein using information carried on mRNA

Polypeptide

Amino acids

▲ **Figure 3.26 Gene expression: DNA → RNA → protein.** In a eukaryotic cell, DNA in the nucleus programs protein production in the cytoplasm by dictating synthesis of messenger RNA (mRNA).

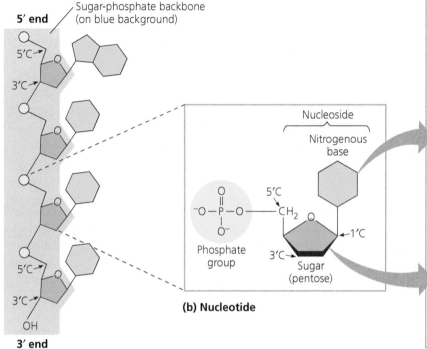

▼ **Figure 3.27 Components of nucleic acids. (a)** A polynucleotide has a sugar-phosphate backbone with variable appendages, the nitrogenous bases. **(b)** A nucleotide monomer includes a nitrogenous base, a sugar, and a phosphate group. Note that carbon numbers in the sugar include primes ('). **(c)** A nucleoside includes a nitrogenous base (purine or pyrimidine) and a five-carbon sugar (deoxyribose or ribose).

NITROGENOUS BASES

Pyrimidines

Cytosine (C)   Thymine (T, in DNA)   Uracil (U, in RNA)

Purines

Adenine (A)   Guanine (G)

SUGARS

Deoxyribose (in DNA)   Ribose (in RNA)

(c) Nucleoside components

5′ end

Sugar-phosphate backbone (on blue background)

5′C
3′C

OH

3′ end

(a) Polynucleotide, or nucleic acid

Nucleoside

Nitrogenous base

Phosphate group

Sugar (pentose)

(b) Nucleotide

six-membered ring fused to a five-membered ring. The purines are adenine (A) and guanine (G). The specific pyrimidines and purines differ in the chemical groups attached to the rings. Adenine, guanine, and cytosine are found in both DNA and RNA; thymine is found only in DNA and uracil only in RNA.

Now let's add the sugar to which the nitrogenous base is attached. In DNA the sugar is **deoxyribose**; in RNA it is **ribose** (see Figure 3.27c). The only difference between these two sugars is that deoxyribose lacks an oxygen atom on the second carbon in the ring, hence the name *deoxy*ribose.

So far, we have built a nucleoside (nitrogenous base plus sugar). To complete the construction of a nucleotide, we attach a phosphate group to the 5′ carbon of the sugar (the carbon numbers in the sugar include ′, the prime symbol; see Figure 3.27b). The molecule is now a nucleoside monophosphate, more often called a nucleotide.

Nucleotide Polymers

The linkage of nucleotides into a polynucleotide involves a dehydration reaction. (You will learn the details in Concept 13.2.) In the polynucleotide, adjacent nucleotides are joined by a phosphodiester linkage, which consists of a phosphate group that covalently links the sugars of two nucleotides. This

bonding results in a backbone with a repeating pattern of sugar-phosphate units called the *sugar-phosphate backbone* (see Figure 3.27a). (Note that the nitrogenous bases are not part of the backbone.) The two free ends of the polymer are distinctly different from each other. One end has a phosphate attached to a 5′ carbon, and the other end has a hydroxyl group on a 3′ carbon; we refer to these as the *5′ end* and the *3′ end*, respectively. We can say that a polynucleotide has a built-in directionality along its sugar-phosphate backbone, from 5′ to 3′, somewhat like a one-way street. All along this sugar-phosphate backbone are appendages consisting of the nitrogenous bases.

The sequence of bases along a DNA (or mRNA) polymer is unique for each gene and provides very specific information to the cell. Because genes are hundreds to thousands of nucleotides long, the number of possible base sequences is effectively limitless. A gene's meaning to the cell is encoded in its specific sequence of the four DNA bases. For example, the sequence 5′-AGGTAACTT-3′ means one thing, whereas the sequence 5′-CGCTTTAAC-3′ has a different meaning. (Entire genes, of course, are much longer.) The linear order of bases in a gene specifies the amino acid sequence—the primary structure— of a protein, which in turn specifies that protein's three-dimensional structure, thus enabling its function in the cell.

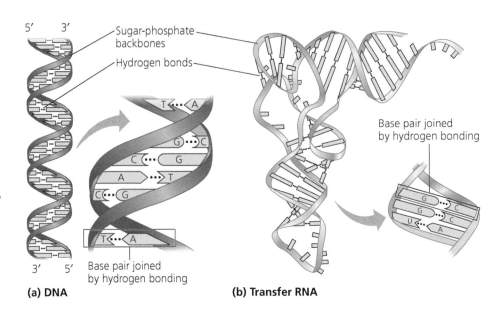

▶ **Figure 3.28 The structures of DNA and tRNA molecules. (a)** The DNA molecule is usually a double helix, with the sugar-phosphate backbones of the antiparallel polynucleotide strands (symbolized here by blue ribbons) on the outside of the helix. Hydrogen bonds between pairs of nitrogenous bases hold the two strands together. As illustrated here with symbolic shapes for the bases, adenine (A) can pair only with thymine (T), and guanine (G) can pair only with cytosine (C). Each DNA strand in this figure is the structural equivalent of the polynucleotide diagrammed in Figure 3.27a. **(b)** A tRNA molecule has a roughly L-shaped structure, due to complementary base pairing of antiparallel stretches of RNA. In RNA, A pairs with U.

(a) DNA

(b) Transfer RNA

The Structures of DNA and RNA Molecules

DNA molecules have two polynucleotides, or "strands," that wind around an imaginary axis, forming a **double helix (Figure 3.28a)**. The two sugar-phosphate backbones run in opposite 5′ → 3′ directions from each other; this arrangement is referred to as **antiparallel**, somewhat like a divided highway. The sugar-phosphate backbones are on the outside of the helix, and the nitrogenous bases are paired in the interior of the helix. The two strands are held together by hydrogen bonds between the paired bases (see Figure 3.28a). Most DNA molecules are very long, with thousands or even millions of base pairs. The one long DNA double helix in a eukaryotic chromosome includes many genes, each one a particular segment of the molecule.

In base pairing, only certain bases in the double helix are compatible with each other. Adenine (A) in one strand always pairs with thymine (T) in the other, and guanine (G) always pairs with cytosine (C). The two strands of the double helix are said to be *complementary*, each the predictable counterpart of the other. It is this feature of DNA that makes it possible to generate two identical copies of each DNA molecule in a cell that is preparing to divide. When the cell divides, the copies are distributed to the daughter cells, making them genetically identical to the parent cell. Thus, the structure of DNA accounts for its function of transmitting genetic information whenever a cell reproduces.

RNA molecules, by contrast, exist as single strands. Complementary base pairing can occur, however, between regions of two RNA molecules or even between two stretches of nucleotides in the *same* RNA molecule. In fact, base pairing within an RNA molecule allows it to take on the particular three-dimensional shape necessary for its function. Consider, for example, the type of RNA called *transfer RNA* (tRNA),

which brings amino acids to the ribosome during the synthesis of a polypeptide. A tRNA molecule is about 80 nucleotides in length. Its functional shape results from base pairing between nucleotides where complementary stretches of the molecule can run antiparallel to each other **(Figure 3.28b)**.

Note that in RNA, adenine (A) pairs with uracil (U); thymine (T) is not present in RNA. Another difference between RNA and DNA is that DNA almost always exists as a double helix, whereas RNA molecules are more variable in shape. RNAs are versatile molecules, and many biologists believe RNA may have preceded DNA as the carrier of genetic information in early forms of life (see Concept 24.1).

CONCEPT CHECK 3.6

1. **DRAW IT** Go to Figure 3.27a and, for the top three nucleotides, number all the carbons in the sugars (don't forget the primes), circle the nitrogenous bases, and star the phosphates.

2. **DRAW IT** In a DNA double helix, a region along one DNA strand has the following sequence of nitrogenous bases: 5′-TAGGCCT-3′. Copy this sequence, and write down its complementary strand, clearly indicating the 5′ and 3′ ends of the complementary strand.

For suggested answers, see Appendix A.

CONCEPT 3.7

Genomics and proteomics have transformed biological inquiry and applications

Experimental work in the first half of the 20th century established the role of DNA as the bearer of genetic information, passed from generation to generation, that specified the functioning of living cells and organisms. Once the structure of the DNA molecule was described in 1953, and the linear sequence of nucleotide bases was understood to specify the amino acid sequence of proteins, biologists sought to "decode" genes by learning their base sequences.

The first chemical techniques for *DNA sequencing*, or determining the sequence of nucleotides along a DNA strand, one by one, were developed in the 1970s. Researchers began to study gene sequences, gene by gene, and the more they learned, the more questions they had: How was expression of genes regulated? Genes and their protein products clearly interacted with each other, but how? What was the function, if any, of the DNA that is not part of genes? To fully understand the genetic functioning of a living organism, the entire sequence of the full complement of DNA, the organism's *genome*, would be most enlightening. In spite of the apparent impracticality of this idea, in the late 1980s several prominent biologists put forth an audacious proposal to launch a project that would sequence the entire human genome—all 3 billion bases of it! This endeavor began in 1990 and was effectively completed in the early 2000s.

An unplanned but profound side benefit of this project—the Human Genome Project—was the rapid development of faster and less expensive methods of sequencing. This trend has continued apace: The cost for sequencing 1 million bases in 2001, well over $5,000, has decreased to about $0.08 in 2014. And a human genome, the first of which took over 10 years to sequence, could be completed at today's pace in just a few days **(Figure 3.29)**. The number of genomes that have been fully sequenced has burgeoned, generating reams of data and prompting development of *bioinformatics*, the use of computer software and other computational tools that can handle and analyze these large data sets.

The reverberations of these developments have transformed the study of biology and related fields. Biologists often look at problems by analyzing large sets of genes or even comparing whole genomes of different species, an approach called **genomics**. A similar analysis of large sets of proteins, including their sequences, is called **proteomics**. (Protein sequences

▲ **Figure 3.29 Automatic DNA sequencing machines and abundant computing power enable rapid sequencing of genes and genomes.**

can be determined either by using biochemical techniques or by translating the DNA sequences that code for them.) These approaches permeate all fields of biology, some examples of which are shown in **Figure 3.30**.

DNA and Proteins as Tape Measures of Evolution

EVOLUTION We are accustomed to thinking of shared traits, such as hair and milk production in mammals, as evidence of shared ancestry. Because DNA carries heritable information in the form of genes, sequences of genes and their protein products document the hereditary background of an organism. The linear sequences of nucleotides in DNA molecules are passed from parents to offspring; these sequences determine the amino acid sequences of proteins. As a result, siblings have greater similarity in their DNA and proteins than do unrelated individuals of the same species.

Given our evolutionary view of life, we can extend this concept of "molecular genealogy" to relationships between species: We would expect two species that appear to be closely related based on anatomical evidence (and possibly fossil evidence) to also share a greater proportion of their DNA and protein sequences than do less closely related species. In fact, that is the case. An example is the comparison of the β polypeptide chain of human hemoglobin with the corresponding hemoglobin polypeptide in other vertebrates. In this chain of 146 amino acids, humans and gorillas differ in just 1 amino acid, while humans and frogs, more distantly related, differ in 67 amino acids. In the **Scientific Skills Exercise**, you can apply this sort of reasoning to additional species. The relative sequence similarity also holds true when comparing whole genomes: The human genome is 95–98% identical to that of the chimpanzee, but only roughly 85% identical to that of the mouse, a more distant evolutionary relative. Molecular biology has added a new tape measure to the toolkit biologists use to assess evolutionary kinship.

Perhaps the most significant impact of genomics and proteomics on the field of biology has been their contributions to our understanding of evolution. To quote one of the founders of modern evolutionary theory, Theodosius Dobzhansky, "Nothing in biology makes sense except in the light of evolution." In addition to confirming evidence for evolution from the study of fossils and characteristics of currently existing species, genomics has helped us tease out relationships among different groups of organisms that had not been resolved by previous types of evidence, and thus infer their evolutionary history.

CONCEPT CHECK 3.7

1. How would sequencing the entire genome of an organism help scientists to understand how that organism functioned?
2. Given the function of DNA, why would you expect two species with very similar traits to also have very similar genomes?

For suggested answers, see Appendix A.

Light Microscopy (LM)

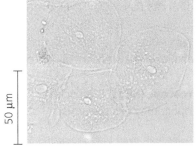

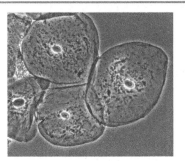

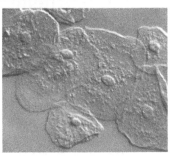

Brightfield (unstained specimen). Light passes directly through the specimen. Unless the cell is naturally pigmented or artificially stained, the image has little contrast.

Brightfield (stained specimen). Staining with various dyes enhances contrast. Most staining procedures require that cells be fixed (preserved), thereby killing them.

Phase-contrast. Variations in density within the specimen are amplified to enhance contrast in unstained cells; this is especially useful for examining living, unpigmented cells.

Differential-interference contrast (Nomarski). As in phase-contrast microscopy, optical modifications are used to exaggerate differences in density; the image appears almost 3-D.

The light micrographs above show human cheek epithelial cells; the scale bar pertains to all four micrographs.

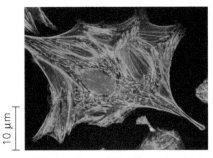

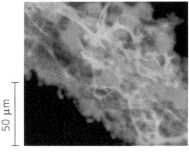

Fluorescence. The locations of specific molecules in the cell can be revealed by labeling the molecules with fluorescent dyes or antibodies; some cells have molecules that fluoresce on their own. Fluorescent substances absorb ultraviolet radiation and emit visible light. In this fluorescently labeled uterine cell, nuclear material is blue, organelles called mitochondria are orange, and the cell's "skeleton" is green.

Confocal. The left image is a standard fluorescence micrograph of fluorescently labeled nervous tissue (nerve cells are green, support cells are orange, and regions of overlap are yellow); the right image is a confocal image of the same tissue. Using a laser, this "optical sectioning" technique eliminates out-of-focus light from a thick sample, creating a single plane of fluorescence in the image. By capturing sharp images at many different planes, a 3-D reconstruction can be created. The standard image is blurry because out-of-focus light is not excluded.

Electron Microscopy (EM)

Scanning electron microscopy (SEM). Micrographs taken with a scanning electron microscope show a 3-D image of the surface of a specimen. This SEM shows the surface of a cell from a trachea (windpipe) covered with cilia. (Beating of the cilia helps move inhaled debris upward toward the throat.)

Electron micrographs are black and white but are often artificially colorized to highlight particular structures, as has been done with both electron micrographs (SEM and TEM) shown here.

> Abbreviations used in figure legends throughout this text:
> LM = Light Micrograph
> SEM = Scanning Electron Micrograph
> TEM = Transmission Electron Micrograph

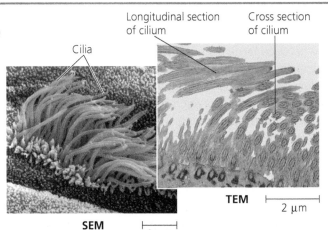

Transmission electron microscopy (TEM). A transmission electron microscope profiles a thin section of a specimen. This TEM shows a section through a tracheal cell, revealing its internal structure. In preparing the specimen, some cilia were cut along their lengths, creating longitudinal sections, while other cilia were cut straight across, creating cross sections.

(see Figure 4.3). The electron beam scans the surface of the sample, usually coated with a thin film of gold. The beam excites electrons on the surface, and these secondary electrons are detected by a device that translates the pattern of electrons into an electronic signal sent to a video screen. The result is an image of the specimen's surface that appears three-dimensional.

The **transmission electron microscope (TEM)** is used to study the internal structure of cells (see Figure 4.3). The TEM aims an electron beam through a very thin section of the specimen, much as a light microscope aims light through a sample on a slide. For the TEM, the specimen has been stained with atoms of heavy metals, which attach to certain cellular structures, thus enhancing the electron density of some parts of the cell more than others. The electrons passing through the specimen are scattered more in the denser regions, so fewer are transmitted. The image displays the pattern of transmitted electrons. Instead of using glass lenses, both the SEM and TEM use electromagnets as lenses to bend the paths of the electrons, ultimately focusing the image onto a monitor for viewing.

Electron microscopes have revealed many subcellular structures that were impossible to resolve with the light microscope. But the light microscope offers advantages, especially in studying living cells. A disadvantage of electron microscopy is that the methods used to prepare the specimen kill the cells. Specimen preparation for any type of microscopy can introduce artifacts, structural features seen in micrographs that do not exist in the living cell.

In the past several decades, light microscopy has been revitalized by major technical advances. Labeling individual cellular molecules or structures with fluorescent markers has made it possible to see such structures with increasing detail. In addition, confocal and other newer types of fluorescent light microscopy have produced sharper images of three-dimensional tissues and cells. Finally, a group of new techniques and labeling molecules developed in recent years have allowed researchers to "break" the resolution barrier and distinguish subcellular structures as small as 10–20 nm across. As this "super-resolution microscopy" becomes more widespread, the images we see of living cells are proving as awe-inspiring to us as van Leeuwenhoek's were to Robert Hooke 350 years ago.

Microscopes are the most important tools of *cytology*, the study of cell structure. Understanding the function of each structure, however, required the integration of cytology and *biochemistry*, the study of the chemical processes (metabolism) of cells.

Cell Fractionation

A useful technique for studying cell structure and function is **cell fractionation**. Broken-up cells are placed in a tube that is spun in a centrifuge. The resulting force causes the largest cell components to settle to the bottom of the tube, forming a pellet. The liquid above the pellet is poured into a new tube and centrifuged at a higher speed for a longer time. This process is repeated several times, resulting in a series of pellets that consist of nuclei, mitochondria (and chloroplasts if the cells are from a photosynthetic organism), pieces of membrane, and ribosomes, the smallest components.

Cell fractionation enables researchers to prepare specific cell components in bulk and identify their functions, a task not usually possible with intact cells. For example, in one of the cell fractions resulting from centrifugation, biochemical tests showed the presence of enzymes involved in cellular respiration, while electron microscopy revealed large numbers of the organelles called mitochondria. Together, these data helped biologists determine that mitochondria are the sites of cellular respiration. Biochemistry and cytology thus complement each other in correlating cell function with structure.

CONCEPT CHECK 4.1

1. How do stains used for light microscopy compare with those used for electron microscopy?
2. **WHAT IF?** Which type of microscope would you use to study (a) the changes in shape of a living white blood cell and (b) the details of surface texture of a hair?

For suggested answers, see Appendix A.

CONCEPT 4.2

Eukaryotic cells have internal membranes that compartmentalize their functions

Cells—the basic structural and functional units of every organism—are of two distinct types: prokaryotic and eukaryotic. Organisms of the domains Bacteria and Archaea consist of prokaryotic cells. Protists, fungi, animals, and plants all consist of eukaryotic cells. ("Protist" is an informal term referring to a group of mostly unicellular eukaryotes.)

Comparing Prokaryotic and Eukaryotic Cells

All cells share certain basic features: They are all bounded by a selective barrier, called the *plasma membrane*. Inside all cells is a semifluid, jellylike substance called **cytosol**, in which subcellular components are suspended. All cells contain *chromosomes*, which carry genes in the form of DNA. And all cells have *ribosomes*, tiny complexes that make proteins according to instructions from the genes.

A major difference between prokaryotic and eukaryotic cells is the location of their DNA. In a **eukaryotic cell**, most of the DNA is in an organelle called the *nucleus*, which is bounded by a double membrane (see Figure 4.7). In a **prokaryotic cell**, the DNA is concentrated in a region that is not membrane-enclosed, called the **nucleoid (Figure 4.4)**. *Eukaryotic* means "true nucleus" (from the Greek *eu*, true, and *karyon*, kernel, here referring to the nucleus), and *prokaryotic* means "before nucleus" (from the Greek *pro*, before), reflecting the earlier evolution of prokaryotic cells.

The interior of either type of cell is called the **cytoplasm**; in eukaryotic cells, this term refers only to the region between the nucleus and the plasma membrane. Within the cytoplasm of a eukaryotic cell, suspended in cytosol, are a variety of organelles of specialized form and function. These membrane-bounded structures are absent in prokaryotic cells, another distinction between prokaryotic and eukaryotic cells. However, in spite of the absence of organelles, the prokaryotic cytoplasm is not a formless soup. For example, some prokaryotes contain regions surrounded by proteins (not membranes), within which specific reactions take place.

Eukaryotic cells are generally much larger than prokaryotic cells (see Figure 4.2). Size is a general feature of cell structure that relates to function. The logistics of carrying out cellular metabolism sets limits on cell size. At the lower limit, the smallest cells known are bacteria called mycoplasmas, which have diameters between 0.1 and 1.0 μm. These are perhaps the smallest packages with enough DNA to program metabolism and enough enzymes and other cellular equipment to carry out the activities necessary for a cell to sustain itself and reproduce. Typical bacteria are 1–5 μm in diameter, about ten times the size of mycoplasmas. Eukaryotic cells are typically 10–100 μm in diameter.

Metabolic requirements also impose theoretical upper limits on the size that is practical for a single cell. At the boundary of every cell, the **plasma membrane** functions as a selective barrier that allows passage of enough oxygen, nutrients, and wastes to service the entire cell **(Figure 4.5)**. For each square micrometer of membrane, only a limited amount of a particular substance can cross per second, so the ratio of surface area to volume is critical. As a cell (or any other object) increases in size, its surface area grows proportionately less than its volume. (Area is proportional to a linear dimension squared, whereas volume is proportional to the linear dimension cubed.) Thus, a smaller object has a greater ratio of surface area to volume **(Figure 4.6)**. The **Scientific Skills Exercise** for this chapter gives you a chance to calculate the volumes and surface areas of two actual cells—a mature yeast cell and a cell budding from it. To see different ways organisms maximize the surface area of cells, see Make Connections Figure 26.14.

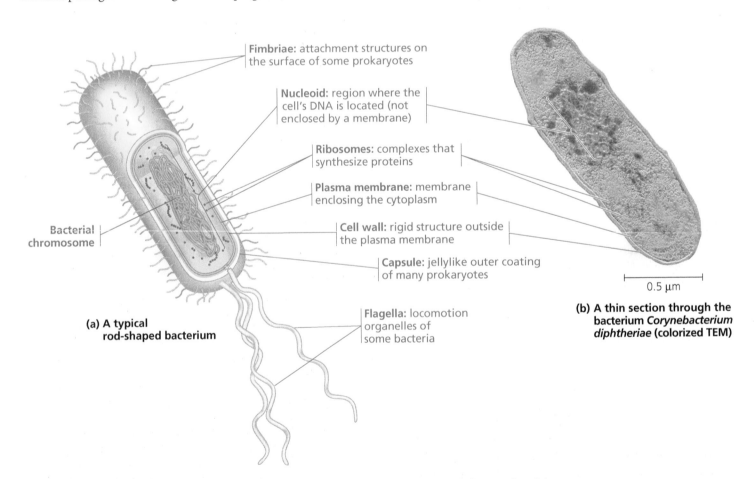

Fimbriae: attachment structures on the surface of some prokaryotes

Nucleoid: region where the cell's DNA is located (not enclosed by a membrane)

Ribosomes: complexes that synthesize proteins

Plasma membrane: membrane enclosing the cytoplasm

Bacterial chromosome

Cell wall: rigid structure outside the plasma membrane

Capsule: jellylike outer coating of many prokaryotes

Flagella: locomotion organelles of some bacteria

(a) A typical rod-shaped bacterium

0.5 μm

(b) A thin section through the bacterium *Corynebacterium diphtheriae* (colorized TEM)

▲ **Figure 4.4 A prokaryotic cell.** Lacking a true nucleus and the other membrane-enclosed organelles of the eukaryotic cell, the prokaryotic cell appears much simpler in internal structure. Prokaryotes include bacteria and archaea; the general cell structure of the two domains is quite similar.

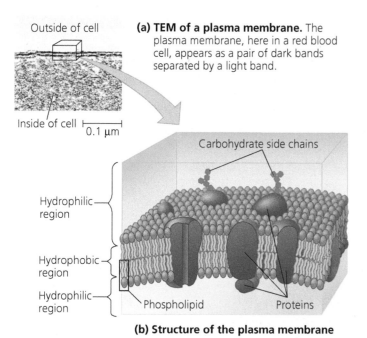

(a) TEM of a plasma membrane. The plasma membrane, here in a red blood cell, appears as a pair of dark bands separated by a light band.

Outside of cell

Inside of cell 0.1 μm

Carbohydrate side chains

Hydrophilic region

Hydrophobic region

Hydrophilic region

Phospholipid   Proteins

(b) Structure of the plasma membrane

▲ **Figure 4.5 The plasma membrane.** The plasma membrane and the membranes of organelles consist of a double layer (bilayer) of phospholipids with various proteins attached to or embedded in it. The hydrophobic parts of phospholipids and membrane proteins are found in the interior of the membrane, while the hydrophilic parts are in contact with aqueous solutions on either side. Carbohydrate side chains may be attached to proteins or lipids on the outer surface of the plasma membrane.

MAKE CONNECTIONS *Review Figure 3.15 and describe the characteristics of phospholipids that allow them to function as the major components of the plasma membrane.*

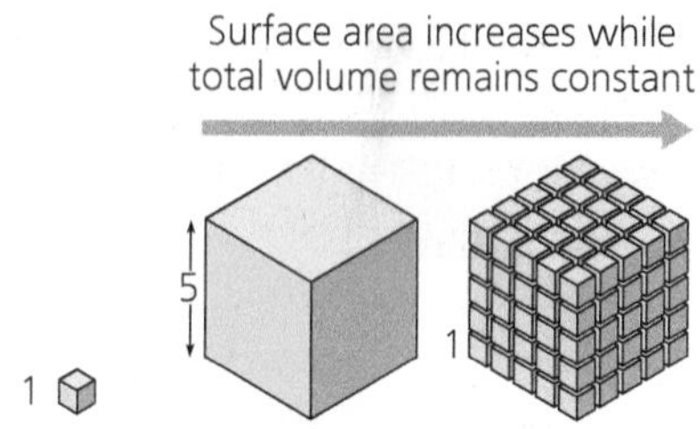

The need for a surface area sufficiently large to accommodate the volume helps explain the microscopic size of most cells and the narrow, elongated shapes of others, such as nerve cells. Larger organisms do not generally have *larger* cells than smaller organisms—they simply have *more* cells. A sufficiently high ratio of surface area to volume is especially important in cells that exchange a lot of material with their surroundings, such as intestinal cells. Such cells may have many long, thin projections from their surface called *microvilli*, which increase surface area without an appreciable increase in volume.

The evolutionary relationships between prokaryotic and eukaryotic cells will be discussed later in this chapter, and prokaryotic cells will be described in detail elsewhere (see Chapter 24). Most of the discussion of cell structure that follows in this chapter applies to eukaryotic cells.

A Panoramic View of the Eukaryotic Cell

In addition to the plasma membrane at its outer surface, a eukaryotic cell has extensive, elaborately arranged internal membranes that divide the cell into compartments—the organelles mentioned earlier. The cell's compartments provide different local environments that support specific metabolic functions,

Surface area increases while total volume remains constant

	1	5	1
Total surface area [sum of the surface areas (height × width) of all box sides × number of boxes]	6	150	750
Total volume [height × width × length × number of boxes]	1	125	125
Surface-to-volume (S-to-V) ratio [surface area ÷ volume]	6	1.2	6

▲ **Figure 4.6 Geometric relationships between surface area and volume.** In this diagram, cells are represented as boxes. Using arbitrary units of length, we can calculate the cell's surface area (in square units, or units²), volume (in cubic units, or units³), and ratio of surface area to volume. A high surface-to-volume ratio facilitates the exchange of materials between a cell and its environment.

so incompatible processes can go on simultaneously inside a single cell. The plasma membrane and organelle membranes also participate directly in the cell's metabolism, because many enzymes are built right into the membranes.

The basic fabric of most biological membranes is a double layer of phospholipids and other lipids. Embedded in this lipid bilayer or attached to its surfaces are diverse proteins (see Figure 4.5). However, each type of membrane has a unique composition of lipids and proteins suited to that membrane's specific functions. For example, enzymes embedded in the membranes of the organelles called mitochondria function in cellular respiration. Because membranes are so fundamental to the organization of the cell, Chapter 5 will discuss them in more detail.

Before continuing with this chapter, examine the eukaryotic cells in **Figure 4.7**. The generalized diagrams of an animal cell and a plant cell introduce the various organelles and show the key differences between animal and plant cells. The micrographs at the bottom of the figure give you a glimpse of cells from different types of eukaryotic organisms.

CONCEPT CHECK 4.2

1. Briefly describe the structure and function of the nucleus, the mitochondrion, the chloroplast, and the endoplasmic reticulum.
2. **WHAT IF?** Imagine an elongated cell (such as a nerve cell) that measures 125 × 1 × 1 arbitrary units. Predict how its surface-to-volume ratio would compare with those in Figure 4.6. Then calculate the ratio and check your prediction.

For suggested answers, see Appendix A.

Animal Cell (cutaway view of generalized cell)

Flagellum: motility structure present in some animal cells, composed of a cluster of microtubules within an extension of the plasma membrane

Centrosome: region where the cell's microtubules are initiated; contains a pair of centrioles

ENDOPLASMIC RETICULUM (ER): network of membranous sacs and tubes; active in membrane synthesis and other synthetic and metabolic processes; has rough (ribosome-studded) and smooth regions

Rough ER   Smooth ER

Nuclear envelope: double membrane enclosing the nucleus; perforated by pores; continuous with ER

Nucleolus: nonmembranous structure involved in production of ribosomes; a nucleus has one or more nucleoli

Chromatin: material consisting of DNA and proteins; visible in a dividing cell as individual condensed chromosomes

NUCLEUS

Plasma membrane: membrane enclosing the cell

CYTOSKELETON: reinforces cell's shape; functions in cell movement; components are made of protein. Includes:

Microfilaments

Intermediate filaments

Microtubules

Microvilli: projections that increase the cell's surface area

Ribosomes (small brown dots): complexes that make proteins; free in cytosol or bound to rough ER or nuclear envelope

Golgi apparatus: organelle active in synthesis, modification, sorting, and secretion of cell products

Peroxisome: organelle with various specialized metabolic functions; produces hydrogen peroxide as a by-product and then converts it to water

Lysosome: digestive organelle where macromolecules are hydrolyzed

Mitochondrion: organelle where cellular respiration occurs and most ATP is generated

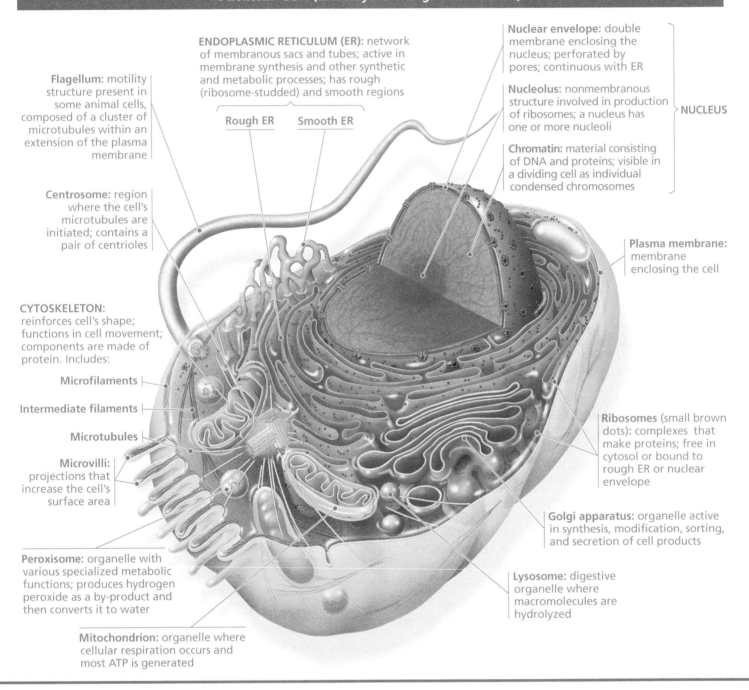

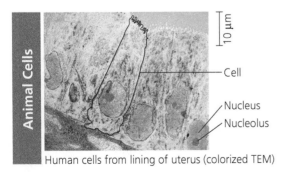

Animal Cells

10 μm

Cell

Nucleus

Nucleolus

Human cells from lining of uterus (colorized TEM)

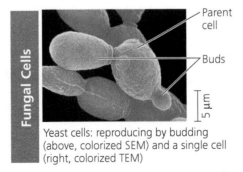

Fungal Cells

Parent cell

Buds

5 μm

Yeast cells: reproducing by budding (above, colorized SEM) and a single cell (right, colorized TEM)

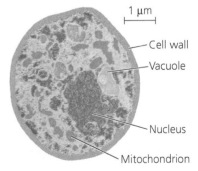

1 μm

Cell wall

Vacuole

Nucleus

Mitochondrion

Plant Cell (cutaway view of generalized cell)

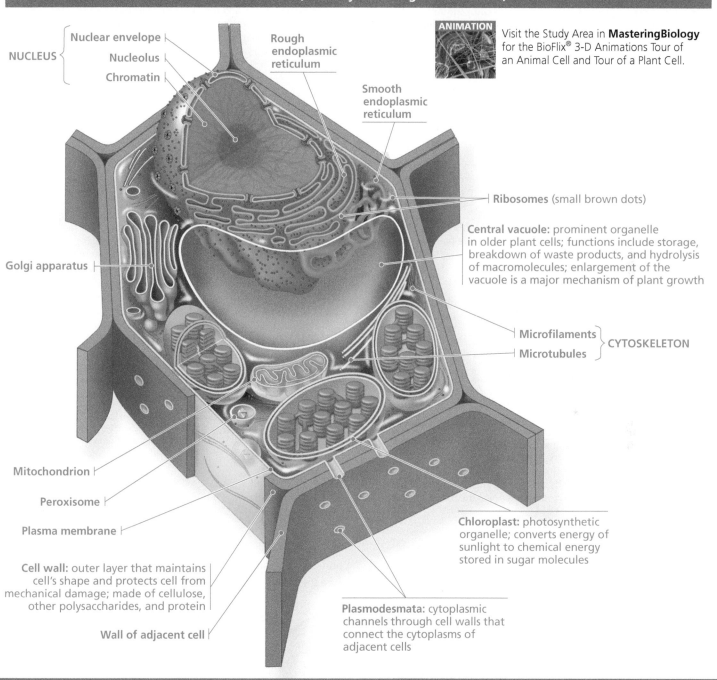

NUCLEUS
- Nuclear envelope
- Nucleolus
- Chromatin

Rough endoplasmic reticulum

Smooth endoplasmic reticulum

ANIMATION Visit the Study Area in **MasteringBiology** for the BioFlix® 3-D Animations Tour of an Animal Cell and Tour of a Plant Cell.

Ribosomes (small brown dots)

Central vacuole: prominent organelle in older plant cells; functions include storage, breakdown of waste products, and hydrolysis of macromolecules; enlargement of the vacuole is a major mechanism of plant growth

Golgi apparatus

Microfilaments
Microtubules } **CYTOSKELETON**

Mitochondrion

Peroxisome

Plasma membrane

Chloroplast: photosynthetic organelle; converts energy of sunlight to chemical energy stored in sugar molecules

Cell wall: outer layer that maintains cell's shape and protects cell from mechanical damage; made of cellulose, other polysaccharides, and protein

Wall of adjacent cell

Plasmodesmata: cytoplasmic channels through cell walls that connect the cytoplasms of adjacent cells

---

Plant Cells

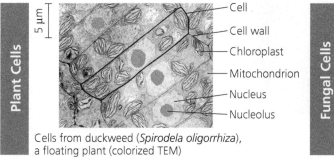

- Cell
- Cell wall
- Chloroplast
- Mitochondrion
- Nucleus
- Nucleolus

5 μm

Cells from duckweed (*Spirodela oligorrhiza*), a floating plant (colorized TEM)

Fungal Cells

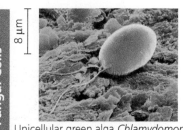

8 μm

Unicellular green alga *Chlamydomonas* (above, colorized SEM; right, colorized TEM)

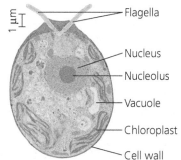

1 μm

- Flagella
- Nucleus
- Nucleolus
- Vacuole
- Chloroplast
- Cell wall

Using a Scale Bar to Calculate Volume and Surface Area of a Cell

How Much New Cytoplasm and Plasma Membrane Are Made by a Growing Yeast Cell? The unicellular yeast *Saccharomyces cerevisiae* divides by budding off a small new cell that then grows to full size (see the yeast cells at the bottom of Figure 4.7). During its growth, the new cell synthesizes new cytoplasm, which increases its volume, and new plasma membrane, which increases its surface area.

In this exercise, you will use a scale bar to determine the sizes of a mature parent yeast cell and a cell budding from it. You will then calculate the volume and surface area of each cell. You will use your calculations to determine how much cytoplasm and plasma membrane the new cell needs to synthesize to grow to full size.

How the Experiment Was Done Yeast cells were grown under conditions that promoted division by budding. The cells were then viewed with a differential interference contrast light microscope and photographed.

Data from the Experiment This light micrograph shows a budding yeast cell about to be released from the mature parent cell:

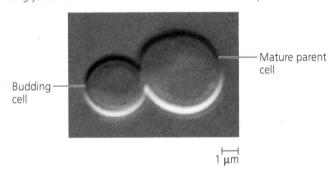

Budding cell

Mature parent cell

1 μm

INTERPRET THE DATA

1. Examine the micrograph of the yeast cells. The scale bar under the photo is labeled 1 μm. The scale bar works in the same way as a scale on a map, where, for example, 1 inch equals 1 mile. In this case the bar represents one thousandth of a millimeter. Using the scale bar as a basic unit, determine the diameter of the

mature parent cell and the new cell. Start by measuring the scale bar and the diameter of each cell. The units you use are irrelevant, but working in millimeters is convenient. Divide each diameter by the length of the scale bar and then multiply by the scale bar's length value to give you the diameter in micrometers.

2. The shape of a yeast cell can be approximated by a sphere. (a) Calculate the volume of each cell using the formula for the volume of a sphere:

$$V = \frac{4}{3}\pi r^3$$

Note that π (the Greek letter pi) is a constant with an approximate value of 3.14, *d* stands for diameter, and *r* stands for radius, which is half the diameter. (b) What volume of new cytoplasm will the new cell have to synthesize as it matures? To determine this, calculate the difference between the volume of the full-sized cell and the volume of the new cell.

3. As the new cell grows, its plasma membrane needs to expand to contain the increased volume of the cell. (a) Calculate the surface area of each cell using the formula for the surface area of a sphere: $A = 4\pi r^2$. (b) How much area of new plasma membrane will the new cell have to synthesize as it matures?

4. When the new cell matures, it will be approximately how many times greater in volume and how many times greater in surface area than its current size?

Micrograph from Kelly Tatchell, using yeast cells grown for experiments described in L. Kozubowski et al., Role of the septin ring in the asymmetric localization of proteins at the mother-bud neck in *Saccharomyces cerevisiae, Molecular Biology of the Cell* 16:3455–3466 (2005).

(MB) A version of this Scientific Skills Exercise can be assigned in MasteringBiology.

CONCEPT 4.3

The eukaryotic cell's genetic instructions are housed in the nucleus and carried out by the ribosomes

On the first stop of our detailed tour of the eukaryotic cell, let's look at two cellular components involved in the genetic control of the cell: the nucleus, which houses most of the cell's DNA, and the ribosomes, which use information from the DNA to make proteins.

The Nucleus: Information Central

The **nucleus** contains most of the genes in the eukaryotic cell. (Some genes are located in mitochondria

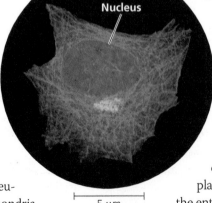

Nucleus

5 μm

and chloroplasts.) It is usually the most conspicuous organelle (see the purple structure in the cell in the fluorescence micrograph), averaging about 5 μm in diameter. The **nuclear envelope** encloses the nucleus **(Figure 4.8)**, separating its contents from the cytoplasm.

The nuclear envelope is a *double* membrane. The two membranes, each a lipid bilayer with associated proteins, are separated by a space of 20–40 nm. The envelope is perforated by pore structures that are about 100 nm in diameter. At the lip of each pore, the inner and outer membranes of the nuclear envelope are continuous. An intricate protein structure called a *pore complex* lines each pore and plays an important role in the cell by regulating the entry and exit of proteins and RNAs, as well as

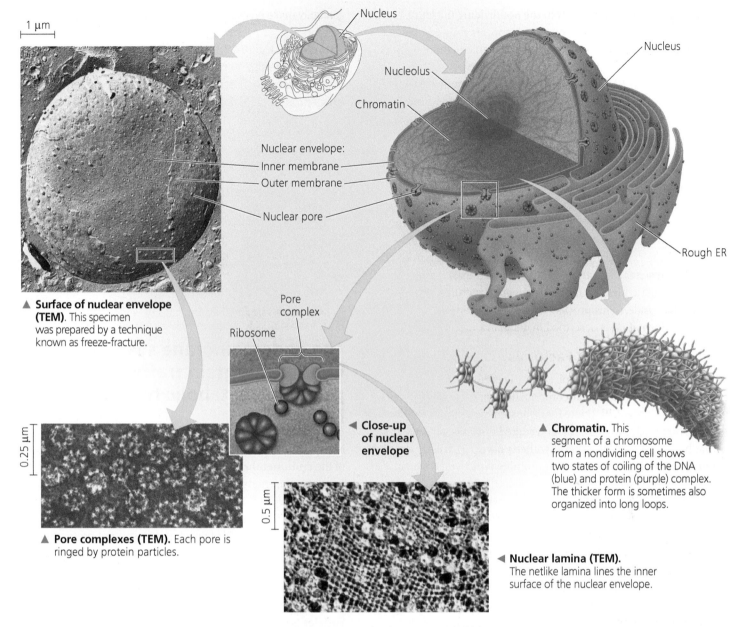

1 μm

Nucleus

Nucleolus

Chromatin

Nucleus

Nuclear envelope:
Inner membrane
Outer membrane

Nuclear pore

Rough ER

▲ **Surface of nuclear envelope (TEM).** This specimen was prepared by a technique known as freeze-fracture.

Pore complex

Ribosome

0.25 μm

◄ **Close-up of nuclear envelope**

▲ **Pore complexes (TEM).** Each pore is ringed by protein particles.

0.5 μm

▲ **Chromatin.** This segment of a chromosome from a nondividing cell shows two states of coiling of the DNA (blue) and protein (purple) complex. The thicker form is sometimes also organized into long loops.

◄ **Nuclear lamina (TEM).** The netlike lamina lines the inner surface of the nuclear envelope.

▲ **Figure 4.8 The nucleus and its envelope.** Within the nucleus are the chromosomes, which appear as a mass of chromatin (DNA and associated proteins), and one or more nucleoli (singular, *nucleolus*), which function in ribosome synthesis. The nuclear envelope, which consists of two membranes separated by a narrow space, is perforated with pores and lined by the nuclear lamina.

MAKE CONNECTIONS *Since the chromosomes contain the genetic material and reside in the nucleus, how does the rest of the cell get access to the information they carry? See Figure 3.26.*

large complexes of macromolecules. Except at the pores, the nuclear side of the envelope is lined by the **nuclear lamina**, a netlike array of protein filaments that maintains the shape of the nucleus by mechanically supporting the nuclear envelope.

Within the nucleus, the DNA is organized into discrete units called **chromosomes**, structures that carry the genetic information. Each chromosome contains one long DNA molecule associated with many proteins. Some of the proteins help coil the DNA molecule of each chromosome, reducing its length and allowing it to fit into the nucleus. The complex of DNA and proteins making up chromosomes is called

chromatin. When a cell is not dividing, stained chromatin appears as a diffuse mass in micrographs, and the chromosomes cannot be distinguished from one another, even though discrete chromosomes are present. As a cell prepares to divide, however, the chromosomes coil (condense) further, becoming thick enough to be distinguished under a microscope as separate structures. Each eukaryotic species has a characteristic number of chromosomes. For example, a typical human cell has 46 chromosomes in its nucleus; the exceptions are the sex cells (eggs and sperm), which have only 23 chromosomes in humans.

A prominent structure within the nondividing nucleus is the **nucleolus** (plural, *nucleoli*), which appears through the electron microscope as a mass of densely stained granules and fibers adjoining part of the chromatin. Here a type of RNA called *ribosomal RNA* (*rRNA*) is synthesized from instructions in the DNA. Also in the nucleolus, proteins imported from the cytoplasm are assembled with rRNA into large and small subunits of ribosomes. These subunits then exit the nucleus through the nuclear pores to the cytoplasm, where a large and a small subunit can assemble into a ribosome. Sometimes there are two or more nucleoli.

As we saw in Figure 3.26, the nucleus directs protein synthesis by synthesizing messenger RNA (mRNA) according to instructions provided by the DNA. The mRNA is then transported to the cytoplasm via the nuclear pores. Once an mRNA molecule reaches the cytoplasm, ribosomes translate the mRNA's genetic message into the primary structure of a specific polypeptide. (This process of transcribing and translating genetic information is described in detail in Chapter 14.)

Ribosomes: Protein Factories

Ribosomes, which are complexes made of ribosomal RNA and protein, are the cellular components that carry out protein synthesis **(Figure 4.9)**. (Note that ribosomes are not membrane bound and thus are not considered organelles.) Cells that have high rates of protein synthesis have particularly large numbers of ribosomes as well as prominent nucleoli—which makes sense, given the role of nucleoli in ribosome assembly. For example, a human pancreas cell, which makes many digestive enzymes, has a few million ribosomes.

Ribosomes build proteins in two cytoplasmic locales. At any given time, *free ribosomes* are suspended in the cytosol, while *bound ribosomes* are attached to the outside of the endoplasmic reticulum or nuclear envelope (see Figure 4.9). Bound and free ribosomes are structurally identical, and ribosomes can alternate between the two roles. Most of the proteins made on free ribosomes function within the cytosol; examples are enzymes that catalyze the first steps of sugar breakdown. Bound ribosomes

generally make proteins that are destined for insertion into membranes, for packaging within certain organelles such as lysosomes (see Figure 4.7), or for export from the cell (secretion). Cells that specialize in protein secretion—for instance, the cells of the pancreas that secrete digestive enzymes—frequently have a high proportion of bound ribosomes. (You will learn more about ribosome structure and function in Concept 14.4.)

CONCEPT CHECK 4.3

1. What role do ribosomes play in carrying out genetic instructions?
2. Describe the molecular composition of nucleoli, and explain their function.
3. **WHAT IF?** As a cell begins the process of dividing, its chromosomes become shorter, thicker, and individually visible in an LM. Explain what is happening at the molecular level.

For suggested answers, see Appendix A.

CONCEPT 4.4

The endomembrane system regulates protein traffic and performs metabolic functions in the cell

Many of the different membranes of the eukaryotic cell are part of the **endomembrane system**, which includes the nuclear envelope, the endoplasmic reticulum, the Golgi apparatus, lysosomes, various kinds of vesicles and vacuoles, and the plasma membrane. This system carries out a variety of tasks in the cell, including synthesis of proteins, transport of proteins into membranes and organelles or out of the cell, metabolism and movement of lipids, and detoxification of poisons. The membranes of this system are related either through direct physical continuity or by the transfer of membrane segments as tiny **vesicles** (sacs made of membrane). Despite these relationships, the various membranes are not identical in structure and function. Moreover, the thickness, molecular composition, and types

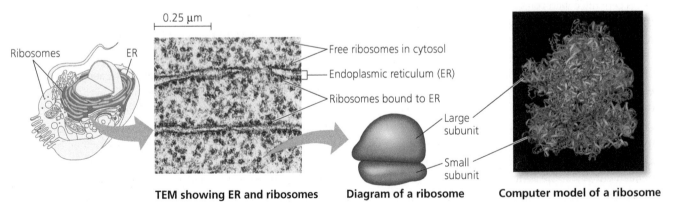

0.25 μm

Ribosomes   ER

Free ribosomes in cytosol

Endoplasmic reticulum (ER)

Ribosomes bound to ER

Large subunit

Small subunit

TEM showing ER and ribosomes   **Diagram of a ribosome**   **Computer model of a ribosome**

▲ **Figure 4.9 Ribosomes.** This electron micrograph of part of a pancreas cell shows both free and bound ribosomes. The simplified diagram and computer model show the two subunits of a ribosome.

DRAW IT *After you have read the section on ribosomes, circle a ribosome in the micrograph that might be making a protein that will be secreted.*

of chemical reactions carried out in a given membrane are not fixed, but may be modified several times during the membrane's life. Having already discussed the nuclear envelope, we will now focus on the endoplasmic reticulum and the other endomembranes to which the endoplasmic reticulum gives rise.

The Endoplasmic Reticulum: Biosynthetic Factory

The **endoplasmic reticulum (ER)** is such an extensive network of membranes that it accounts for more than half the total membrane in many eukaryotic cells. (The word *endoplasmic* means "within the cytoplasm," and *reticulum* is Latin for "little net.") The ER consists of a network of membranous tubules and sacs called cisternae (from the Latin *cisterna*, a reservoir for a liquid). The ER membrane separates the internal compartment of the ER, called the ER lumen (cavity) or cisternal space, from the cytosol. And because the ER membrane is continuous with the nuclear envelope, the space between the two membranes of the envelope is continuous with the lumen of the ER **(Figure 4.10)**.

There are two distinct, though connected, regions of the ER that differ in structure and function: smooth ER and rough ER. **Smooth ER** is so named because its outer surface lacks ribosomes. **Rough ER** is studded with ribosomes on the outer surface of the membrane and thus appears rough through the electron microscope. As already mentioned, ribosomes are also attached to the cytoplasmic side of the nuclear envelope's outer membrane, which is continuous with rough ER.

Functions of Smooth ER

The smooth ER functions in diverse metabolic processes, which vary with cell type. These processes include synthesis of lipids, metabolism of carbohydrates, detoxification of drugs and poisons, and storage of calcium ions.

Enzymes of the smooth ER are important in the synthesis of lipids, including oils, steroids, and new membrane phospholipids. Among the steroids produced by the smooth ER in animal cells are the sex hormones of vertebrates and the various steroid hormones secreted by the adrenal glands. The cells that synthesize and secrete these hormones—in the testes and ovaries, for example—are rich in smooth ER, a structural feature that fits the function of these cells.

Other enzymes of the smooth ER help detoxify drugs and poisons, especially in liver cells. Detoxification usually involves adding hydroxyl groups to drug molecules, making them more soluble and easier to flush from the body. The sedative phenobarbital and other barbiturates are examples of drugs metabolized in this manner by smooth ER in liver cells. In fact, barbiturates, alcohol, and many other drugs induce the proliferation of smooth ER and its associated detoxification enzymes, thus increasing the rate of detoxification. This, in turn, increases tolerance to the drugs, meaning that higher doses are required to achieve a particular effect, such as sedation. Also, because some of the detoxification enzymes have relatively broad action, the proliferation of smooth ER in response to

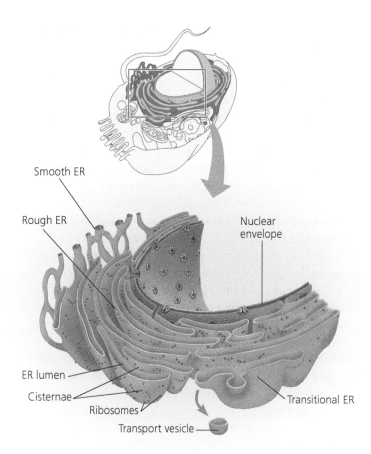

Smooth ER

Rough ER

Nuclear envelope

ER lumen

Cisternae

Ribosomes

Transitional ER

Transport vesicle

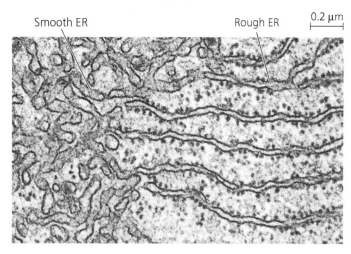

Smooth ER   Rough ER   0.2 μm

▲ **Figure 4.10 Endoplasmic reticulum (ER).** A membranous system of interconnected tubules and flattened sacs called cisternae, the ER is also continuous with the nuclear envelope, as shown in the cutaway diagram at the top. The membrane of the ER encloses a continuous compartment called the ER lumen (or cisternal space). Rough ER, which is studded on its outer surface with ribosomes, can be distinguished from smooth ER in the electron micrograph (TEM). Transport vesicles bud off from a region of the rough ER called transitional ER and travel to the Golgi apparatus and other destinations.

one drug can increase the need for higher dosages of other drugs as well. Barbiturate abuse, for example, can decrease the effectiveness of certain antibiotics and other useful drugs.

The smooth ER also stores calcium ions. In muscle cells, for example, the smooth ER membrane pumps calcium ions from the cytosol into the ER lumen. When a muscle cell is stimulated by a nerve impulse, calcium ions rush back across the ER membrane into the cytosol and trigger contraction of the muscle cell.

Functions of Rough ER

Many cells secrete proteins that are produced by ribosomes attached to rough ER. For example, certain pancreatic cells synthesize the protein insulin in the ER and secrete this hormone into the bloodstream. As a polypeptide chain grows from a bound ribosome, the chain is threaded into the ER lumen through a pore formed by a protein complex in the ER membrane. The new polypeptide folds into its functional shape as it enters the ER lumen. Most secretory proteins are **glycoproteins**, proteins with carbohydrates covalently bonded to them. The carbohydrates are attached to the proteins in the ER lumen by enzymes built into the ER membrane.

After secretory proteins are formed, the ER membrane keeps them separate from proteins that remain in the cytosol, which are produced by free ribosomes. Secretory proteins depart from the ER wrapped in the membranes of vesicles that bud like bubbles from a specialized region called transitional ER (see Figure 4.10). Vesicles in transit from one part of the cell to another are called **transport vesicles**; we will discuss their fate shortly.

In addition to making secretory proteins, rough ER is a membrane factory for the cell; it grows in place by adding membrane proteins and phospholipids to its own membrane. As polypeptides destined to be membrane proteins grow from the ribosomes, they are inserted into the ER membrane itself and anchored there by their hydrophobic portions. Like the smooth ER, the rough ER also makes membrane phospholipids; enzymes built into the ER membrane assemble phospholipids from precursors in the cytosol. The ER membrane expands, and portions of it are transferred in the form of transport vesicles to other components of the endomembrane system.

The Golgi Apparatus: Shipping and Receiving Center

After leaving the ER, many transport vesicles travel to the **Golgi apparatus**. We can think of the Golgi as a warehouse for receiving, sorting, shipping, and even some manufacturing. Here, products of the ER, such as proteins, are modified and stored and then sent to other destinations. Not surprisingly, the Golgi apparatus is especially extensive in cells specialized for secretion.

The Golgi apparatus consists of flattened membranous sacs—cisternae—looking like a stack of pita bread **(Figure 4.11)**. A cell may have many, even hundreds, of these stacks. The membrane of each cisterna in a stack separates its internal space from the cytosol. Vesicles concentrated in the vicinity of the Golgi apparatus are engaged in the transfer of material between parts of the Golgi and other structures.

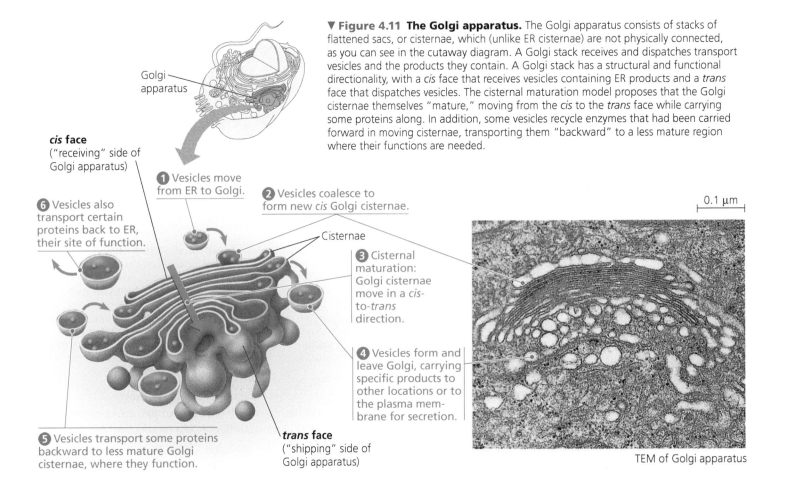

▼ **Figure 4.11 The Golgi apparatus.** The Golgi apparatus consists of stacks of flattened sacs, or cisternae, which (unlike ER cisternae) are not physically connected, as you can see in the cutaway diagram. A Golgi stack receives and dispatches transport vesicles and the products they contain. A Golgi stack has a structural and functional directionality, with a *cis* face that receives vesicles containing ER products and a *trans* face that dispatches vesicles. The cisternal maturation model proposes that the Golgi cisternae themselves "mature," moving from the *cis* to the *trans* face while carrying some proteins along. In addition, some vesicles recycle enzymes that had been carried forward in moving cisternae, transporting them "backward" to a less mature region where their functions are needed.

Golgi apparatus

cis face ("receiving" side of Golgi apparatus)

❻ Vesicles also transport certain proteins back to ER, their site of function.

❶ Vesicles move from ER to Golgi.

❷ Vesicles coalesce to form new *cis* Golgi cisternae.

Cisternae

❸ Cisternal maturation: Golgi cisternae move in a *cis*-to-*trans* direction.

❹ Vesicles form and leave Golgi, carrying specific products to other locations or to the plasma membrane for secretion.

❺ Vesicles transport some proteins backward to less mature Golgi cisternae, where they function.

trans face ("shipping" side of Golgi apparatus)

0.1 μm

TEM of Golgi apparatus

A Golgi stack has a distinct structural directionality, with the membranes of cisternae on opposite sides of the stack differing in thickness and molecular composition. The two sides of a Golgi stack are referred to as the *cis* face and the *trans* face; these act, respectively, as the receiving and shipping departments of the Golgi apparatus. The term *cis* means "on the same side," and the *cis* face is usually located near the ER. Transport vesicles move material from the ER to the Golgi apparatus. A vesicle that buds from the ER can add its membrane and the contents of its lumen to the *cis* face by fusing with a Golgi membrane. The *trans* face ("on the opposite side") gives rise to vesicles that pinch off and travel to other sites.

Products of the endoplasmic reticulum are usually modified during their transit from the *cis* region to the *trans* region of the Golgi apparatus. For example, glycoproteins formed in the ER have their carbohydrates modified, first in the ER itself, and then as they pass through the Golgi. The Golgi removes some sugar monomers and substitutes others, producing a large variety of carbohydrates. Membrane phospholipids may also be altered in the Golgi.

In addition to its finishing work, the Golgi apparatus also manufactures some macromolecules. Many polysaccharides secreted by cells are Golgi products. For example, pectins and certain other noncellulose polysaccharides are made in the Golgi of plant cells and then incorporated along with cellulose into their cell walls. Like secretory proteins, nonprotein Golgi products that will be secreted depart from the *trans* face of the Golgi inside transport vesicles that eventually fuse with the plasma membrane.

The Golgi manufactures and refines its products in stages, with different cisternae containing unique teams of enzymes. Until recently, biologists viewed the Golgi as a static structure, with products in various stages of processing transferred from one cisterna to the next by vesicles. While this may occur, research from several labs has given rise to a new model of the Golgi as a more dynamic structure. According to the *cisternal maturation model*, the cisternae of the Golgi actually progress forward from the *cis* to the *trans* face, carrying and modifying their cargo as they move. Figure 4.11 shows the details of this model.

Before a Golgi stack dispatches its products by budding vesicles from the *trans* face, it sorts these products and targets them for various parts of the cell. Molecular identification tags, such as phosphate groups added to the Golgi products, aid in sorting by acting like zip codes on mailing labels. Finally, transport vesicles budded from the Golgi may have external molecules on their membranes that recognize "docking sites" on the surface of specific organelles or on the plasma membrane, thus targeting the vesicles appropriately.

Lysosomes: Digestive Compartments

A **lysosome** is a membranous sac of hydrolytic enzymes that many eukaryotic cells use to digest (hydrolyze) macromolecules

(Figure 4.12). Lysosomal enzymes work best in the acidic environment found in lysosomes. If a lysosome breaks open or leaks its contents, the released enzymes are not very active because the cytosol has a near-neutral pH. However, excessive leakage from a large number of lysosomes can destroy a cell by self-digestion.

Hydrolytic enzymes and lysosomal membrane are made by rough ER and then transferred to the Golgi apparatus for further processing. At least some lysosomes probably arise by budding from the *trans* face of the Golgi apparatus (see Figure 4.11). How are the proteins of the inner surface of the lysosomal membrane and the digestive enzymes themselves spared from destruction? Apparently, the three-dimensional shapes of these lysosomal proteins protect vulnerable bonds from enzymatic attack.

Lysosomes carry out intracellular digestion in a variety of circumstances. Amoebas and many other unicellular eukaryotes eat by engulfing smaller organisms or food particles, a process called **phagocytosis** (from the Greek *phagein*, to eat, and *kytos*, vessel, referring here to the cell). The *food vacuole* formed in this way then fuses with a lysosome, whose enzymes digest the food (see Figure 4.12, bottom). Digestion products, including simple sugars, amino acids, and other monomers,

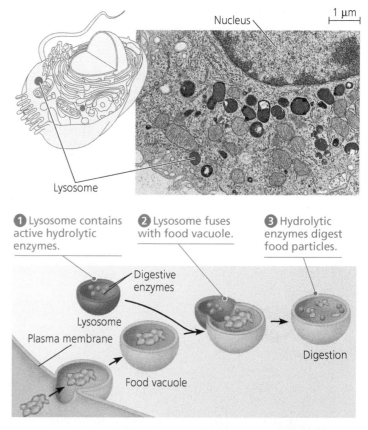

❶ Lysosome contains active hydrolytic enzymes.

❷ Lysosome fuses with food vacuole.

❸ Hydrolytic enzymes digest food particles.

▲ **Figure 4.12 Lysosomes: Phagocytosis.** In phagocytosis, lysosomes digest (hydrolyze) materials taken into the cell and recycle intracellular materials. *Top*: In this macrophage (a type of white blood cell) from a rat, the lysosomes are very dark because of a stain that reacts with one of the products of digestion inside the lysosome (TEM). Macrophages ingest bacteria and viruses and destroy them using lysosomes. *Bottom*: This diagram shows a lysosome fusing with a food vacuole during the process of phagocytosis by a unicellular eukaryote.

pass into the cytosol and become nutrients for the cell. Some human cells also carry out phagocytosis. Among them are macrophages, a type of white blood cell that helps defend the body by engulfing and destroying bacteria and other invaders (see Figure 4.12, top, and Figure 4.28).

Lysosomes also use their hydrolytic enzymes to recycle the cell's own organic material, a process called *autophagy*. During autophagy, a damaged organelle or small amount of cytosol becomes surrounded by a double membrane, and a lysosome fuses with the outer membrane of this vesicle **(Figure 4.13)**. The lysosomal enzymes dismantle the enclosed material, and the resulting small organic compounds are released to the cytosol for reuse. With the help of lysosomes, the cell continually renews itself. A human liver cell, for example, recycles half of its macromolecules each week.

The cells of people with inherited lysosomal storage diseases lack a functioning hydrolytic enzyme normally present in lysosomes. The lysosomes become engorged with indigestible material, which begins to interfere with other cellular activities. In Tay-Sachs disease, for example, a lipid-digesting enzyme is missing or inactive, and the brain becomes impaired by an accumulation of lipids in the cells. Fortunately, lysosomal storage diseases are rare in the general population.

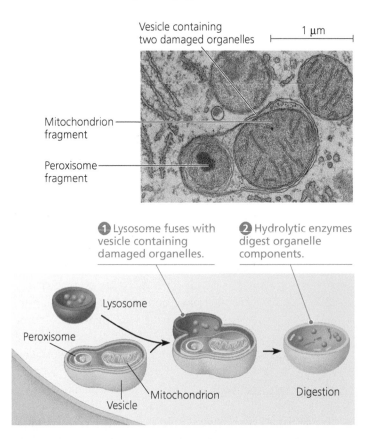

▲ **Figure 4.13 Lysosomes: Autophagy.** In autophagy, lysosomes recycle intracellular materials. *Top*: In the cytoplasm of this rat liver cell is a vesicle containing two disabled organelles; the vesicle will fuse with a lysosome in the process of autophagy (TEM). *Bottom*: This diagram shows fusion of such a vesicle with a lysosome and the subsequent digestion of the damaged organelles.

Vacuoles: Diverse Maintenance Compartments

Vacuoles are large vesicles derived from the endoplasmic reticulum and Golgi apparatus. Thus, vacuoles are an integral part of a cell's endomembrane system. Like all cellular membranes, the vacuolar membrane is selective in transporting solutes; as a result, the solution inside a vacuole differs in composition from the cytosol.

Vacuoles perform a variety of functions in different kinds of cells. **Food vacuoles**, formed by phagocytosis, have already been mentioned (see Figure 4.12). Many unicellular eukaryotes living in fresh water have **contractile vacuoles** that pump excess water out of the cell, thereby maintaining a suitable concentration of ions and molecules inside the cell (see Figure 5.12). In plants and fungi, certain vacuoles carry out enzymatic hydrolysis, a function shared by lysosomes in animal cells. (In fact, some biologists consider these hydrolytic vacuoles to be a type of lysosome.) In plants, small vacuoles can hold reserves of important organic compounds, such as the proteins stockpiled in the storage cells in seeds. Vacuoles may also help protect the plant against herbivores by storing compounds that are poisonous or unpalatable to animals. Some plant vacuoles contain pigments, such as the red and blue pigments of petals that help attract pollinating insects to flowers.

Mature plant cells generally contain a large **central vacuole** **(Figure 4.14)**, which develops by the coalescence of smaller vacuoles. The solution inside the central vacuole, called cell sap, is the plant cell's main repository of inorganic ions, including potassium and chloride. The central vacuole plays a major role in the growth of plant cells, which enlarge as the vacuole absorbs water, enabling the cell to become larger with a minimal investment in new cytoplasm. The cytosol often occupies only a thin layer between the central vacuole and the plasma

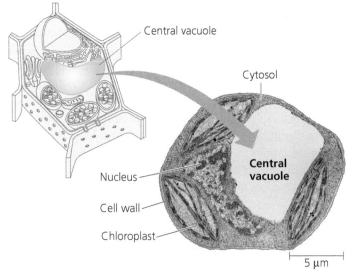

▲ **Figure 4.14 The plant cell vacuole.** The central vacuole is usually the largest compartment in a plant cell; the rest of the cytoplasm is often confined to a narrow zone between the vacuolar membrane and the plasma membrane (TEM).

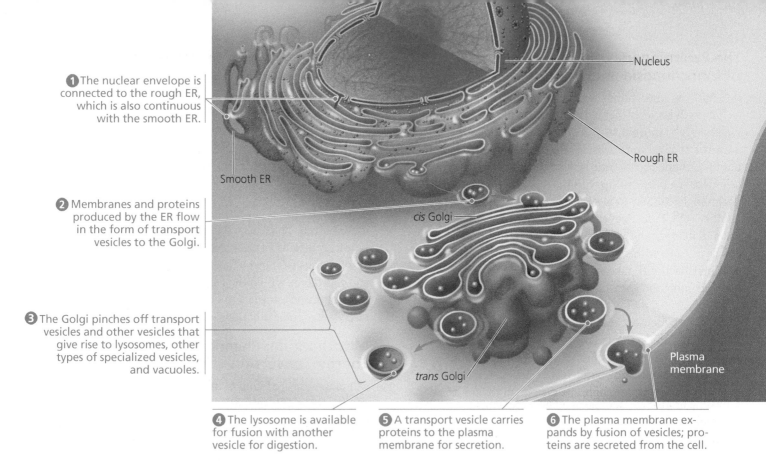

1 The nuclear envelope is connected to the rough ER, which is also continuous with the smooth ER.

Smooth ER

2 Membranes and proteins produced by the ER flow in the form of transport vesicles to the Golgi.

3 The Golgi pinches off transport vesicles and other vesicles that give rise to lysosomes, other types of specialized vesicles, and vacuoles.

Nucleus

Rough ER

cis Golgi

trans Golgi

Plasma membrane

4 The lysosome is available for fusion with another vesicle for digestion.

5 A transport vesicle carries proteins to the plasma membrane for secretion.

6 The plasma membrane expands by fusion of vesicles; proteins are secreted from the cell.

▲ **Figure 4.15 Review: relationships among organelles of the endomembrane system.** The red arrows show some of the migration pathways for membranes and the materials they enclose.

membrane, so the ratio of plasma membrane surface to cytosolic volume is sufficient, even for a large plant cell.

The Endomembrane System: *A Review*

Figure 4.15 reviews the endomembrane system, showing the flow of membrane lipids and proteins through the various organelles. As the membrane moves from the ER to the Golgi and then elsewhere, its molecular composition and metabolic functions are modified, along with those of its contents. The endomembrane system is a complex and dynamic player in the cell's compartmental organization.

We'll continue our tour of the cell with some organelles that are not closely related to the endomembrane system but play crucial roles in the energy transformations carried out by cells.

CONCEPT CHECK 4.4

1. Describe the structural and functional distinctions between rough and smooth ER.
2. Describe how transport vesicles integrate the endomembrane system.
3. **WHAT IF?** Imagine a protein that functions in the ER but requires modification in the Golgi apparatus before it can achieve that function. Describe the protein's path through the cell, starting with the mRNA molecule that specifies the protein.

For suggested answers, see Appendix A.

CONCEPT 4.5

Mitochondria and chloroplasts change energy from one form to another

Organisms transform the energy they acquire from their surroundings. In eukaryotic cells, mitochondria and chloroplasts are the organelles that convert energy to forms that cells can use for work. **Mitochondria** (singular, *mitochondrion*) are the sites of cellular respiration, the metabolic process that uses oxygen to drive the generation of ATP by extracting energy from sugars, fats, and other fuels. **Chloroplasts**, found in plants and algae, are the sites of photosynthesis. This process in chloroplasts converts solar energy to chemical energy by absorbing sunlight and using it to drive the synthesis of organic compounds such as sugars from carbon dioxide and water.

In addition to having related functions, mitochondria and chloroplasts share similar evolutionary origins, which we'll discuss briefly before describing their structures. In this section, we will also consider the peroxisome, an oxidative organelle. The evolutionary origin of the peroxisome, as well as its relation to other organelles, is still under debate.

The Evolutionary Origins of Mitochondria and Chloroplasts

EVOLUTION Mitochondria and chloroplasts display similarities with bacteria that led to the **endosymbiont theory**, illustrated in **Figure 4.16**. This theory states that an early ancestor of eukaryotic cells engulfed an oxygen-using non-photosynthetic prokaryotic cell. Eventually, the engulfed cell formed a relationship with the host cell in which it was enclosed, becoming an *endosymbiont* (a cell living within another cell). Indeed, over the course of evolution, the host cell and its endosymbiont merged into a single organism, a eukaryotic cell with a mitochondrion. At least one of these cells may have then taken up a photosynthetic prokaryote, becoming the ancestor of eukaryotic cells that contain chloroplasts.

This is a widely accepted theory, which we will discuss in detail in Concept 25.1. This theory is consistent with many structural features of mitochondria and chloroplasts. First, rather than being bounded by a single membrane like organelles of the endomembrane system, mitochondria and

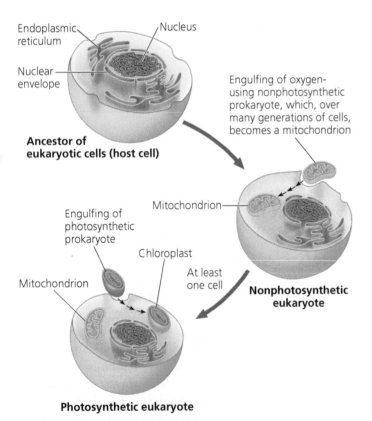

Ancestor of eukaryotic cells (host cell)

Endoplasmic reticulum

Nucleus

Nuclear envelope

Engulfing of oxygen-using nonphotosynthetic prokaryote, which, over many generations of cells, becomes a mitochondrion

Mitochondrion

Nonphotosynthetic eukaryote

Engulfing of photosynthetic prokaryote

Chloroplast

At least one cell

Mitochondrion

Photosynthetic eukaryote

▲ **Figure 4.16 The endosymbiont theory of the origins of mitochondria and chloroplasts in eukaryotic cells.** According to this theory, the proposed ancestors of mitochondria were oxygen-using nonphotosynthetic prokaryotes, while the proposed ancestors of chloroplasts were photosynthetic prokaryotes. The large arrows represent change over evolutionary time; the small arrows inside the cells show the process of the endosymbiont becoming an organelle, also over long periods of time.

typical chloroplasts have two membranes surrounding them. (Chloroplasts also have an internal system of membranous sacs.) There is evidence that the ancestral engulfed prokaryotes had two outer membranes, which became the double membranes of mitochondria and chloroplasts. Second, like prokaryotes, mitochondria and chloroplasts contain ribosomes, as well as multiple circular DNA molecules associated with their inner membranes. The DNA in these organelles programs the synthesis of some organelle proteins on ribosomes that have been synthesized and assembled there as well. Third, also consistent with their probable evolutionary origins as cells, mitochondria and chloroplasts are autonomous (somewhat independent) organelles that grow and reproduce within the cell. Next we focus on the structures of mitochondria and chloroplasts, while providing an overview of their functions.

Mitochondria: Chemical Energy Conversion

Mitochondria are found in nearly all eukaryotic cells, including those of plants, animals, fungi, and most unicellular eukaryotes. Some cells have a single large mitochondrion, but more often a cell has hundreds or even thousands of mitochondria; the number correlates with the cell's level of metabolic activity. For example, cells that move or contract have proportionally more mitochondria per volume than less active cells.

Each of the two membranes enclosing the mitochondrion is a phospholipid bilayer with a unique collection of embedded proteins **(Figure 4.17)**. The outer membrane is smooth, but the inner membrane is convoluted, with infoldings called **cristae**. The inner membrane divides the mitochondrion into two internal compartments. The first is the intermembrane space, the narrow region between the inner and outer membranes. The second compartment, the **mitochondrial matrix**, is enclosed by the inner membrane. The matrix contains many different enzymes as well as the mitochondrial DNA and ribosomes. Enzymes in the matrix catalyze some of the steps of cellular respiration. Other proteins that function in respiration, including the enzyme that makes ATP, are built into the inner membrane. As highly folded surfaces, the cristae give the inner mitochondrial membrane a large surface area, thus enhancing the productivity of cellular respiration. This is another example of structure fitting function. (Chapter 7 discusses cellular respiration in detail.)

Mitochondria are generally in the range of 1–10 μm long. Time-lapse films of living cells reveal mitochondria moving around, changing their shapes, and fusing or dividing in two, unlike the static structures seen in electron micrographs of dead cells. These studies helped biologists understand that mitochondria form a branched tubular network (see Figure 4.17b) in a dynamic state of flux.

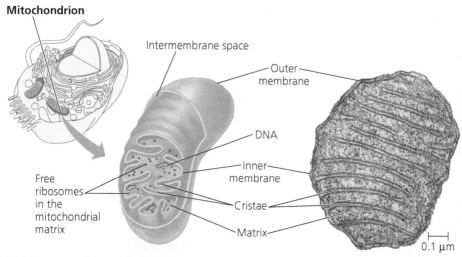

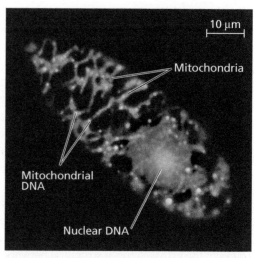

(a) Diagram and TEM of mitochondrion

(b) Network of mitochondria in *Euglena* (LM)

▲ **Figure 4.17 The mitochondrion, site of cellular respiration.** **(a)** The inner and outer membranes of the mitochondrion are evident in the drawing and electron micrograph (TEM). The cristae are infoldings of the inner membrane, which increase its surface area. The cutaway drawing shows the two compartments bounded by the membranes: the intermembrane space and the mitochondrial matrix. Many respiratory enzymes are found in the inner membrane and the matrix. Free ribosomes are also present in the matrix. The circular DNA molecules are associated with the inner mitochondrial membrane. **(b)** The light micrograph shows an entire unicellular eukaryote (*Euglena gracilis*) at a much lower magnification than the TEM. The mitochondrial matrix has been stained green. The mitochondria form a branched tubular network. The nuclear DNA is stained red; molecules of mitochondrial DNA appear as bright yellow spots.

Chloroplasts: Capture of Light Energy

Chloroplasts contain the green pigment chlorophyll, along with enzymes and other molecules that function in the photosynthetic production of sugar. These lens-shaped organelles, about 3–6 μm in length, are found in leaves and other green organs of plants and in algae **(Figure 4.18)**.

The contents of a chloroplast are partitioned from the cytosol by an envelope consisting of two membranes separated by a very narrow intermembrane space. Inside the chloroplast is another membranous system in the form of flattened, interconnected sacs called **thylakoids**. In some regions, thylakoids are stacked like poker chips; each stack is called a **granum**

▼ **Figure 4.18 The chloroplast, site of photosynthesis. (a)** Many plants have lens-shaped chloroplasts, as shown here in a diagram and a TEM. A chloroplast has three compartments: the intermembrane space, the stroma, and the thylakoid space. Free ribosomes are present in the stroma, as are copies of chloroplast DNA molecules. **(b)** This fluorescence micrograph, at much lower magnification than the TEM, shows a whole cell of the green alga *Spirogyra crassa*, which is named for its spiral chloroplasts. Under natural light the chloroplasts appear green, but under ultraviolet light they naturally fluoresce red, as shown here.

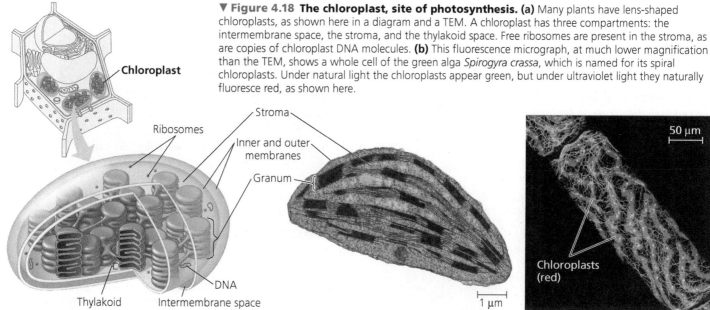

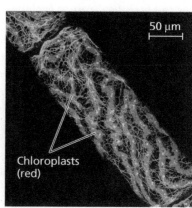

(a) Diagram and TEM of chloroplast

(b) Chloroplasts in an algal cell

(plural, *grana*). The fluid outside the thylakoids is the **stroma**, which contains the chloroplast DNA and ribosomes as well as many enzymes. The membranes of the chloroplast divide the chloroplast space into three compartments: the intermembrane space, the stroma, and the thylakoid space. This compartmental organization enables the chloroplast to convert light energy to chemical energy during photosynthesis. (You will learn more about photosynthesis in Chapter 8.)

As with mitochondria, the static and rigid appearance of chloroplasts in micrographs or schematic diagrams is not true to their dynamic behavior in the living cell. Their shape is changeable, and they grow and occasionally pinch in two, reproducing themselves. They are mobile and, as with mitochondria and other organelles, move around the cell along tracks of the cytoskeleton, a structural network we will consider in Concept 4.6.

The chloroplast is a specialized member of a family of closely related plant organelles called **plastids**. One type of plastid, the *amyloplast*, is a colorless organelle that stores starch (amylose), particularly in roots and tubers. Another is the *chromoplast*, which has pigments that give fruits and flowers their orange and yellow hues.

Peroxisomes: Oxidation

The **peroxisome** is a specialized metabolic compartment bounded by a single membrane (**Figure 4.19**). Peroxisomes contain enzymes that remove hydrogen atoms from certain molecules and transfer them to oxygen (O_2), producing hydrogen peroxide (H_2O_2). These reactions have many different functions. For example, peroxisomes in the liver detoxify alcohol and other harmful compounds by transferring hydrogen from the poisons to oxygen. The H_2O_2 formed by peroxisomes is itself toxic, but the organelle also contains an enzyme that converts H_2O_2 to water. This is an excellent example of how the cell's compartmental structure is crucial to its functions: The enzymes that produce H_2O_2 and those that dispose of this toxic compound are sequestered from other cellular components that could be damaged.

Peroxisomes grow larger by incorporating proteins made in the cytosol and ER, as well as lipids made in the ER and within the peroxisome itself. But how peroxisomes increase in number and how they arose in evolution are still open questions.

CONCEPT CHECK 4.5

1. Describe two characteristics shared by chloroplasts and mitochondria. Consider both function and membrane structure.
2. Do plant cells have mitochondria? Explain.
3. **WHAT IF?** A classmate proposes that mitochondria and chloroplasts should be classified in the endomembrane system. Argue against the proposal.

For suggested answers, see Appendix A.

CONCEPT 4.6

The cytoskeleton is a network of fibers that organizes structures and activities in the cell

In the early days of electron microscopy, biologists thought that the organelles of a eukaryotic cell floated freely in the cytosol. But improvements in both light microscopy and electron microscopy have revealed the **cytoskeleton**, a network of fibers extending throughout the cytoplasm (**Figure 4.20**). The cytoskeleton plays a major role in organizing the structures and activities of the cell.

Roles of the Cytoskeleton: Support and Motility

The most obvious function of the cytoskeleton is to give mechanical support to the cell and maintain its shape. This is especially important for animal cells, which lack walls. The remarkable strength and resilience of the cytoskeleton as a whole are based on its architecture. Like a dome tent, the cytoskeleton is stabilized by a balance between opposing forces exerted by its elements. And just as the skeleton of an animal helps fix the positions of other body parts, the cytoskeleton provides anchorage for many organelles and even cytosolic enzyme molecules. The cytoskeleton is more dynamic than an animal skeleton,

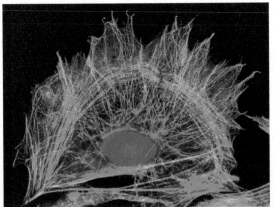

▲ **Figure 4.20 The cytoskeleton.** As shown in this fluorescence micrograph, the cytoskeleton extends throughout the cell. The cytoskeletal elements have been tagged with different fluorescent molecules: green for microtubules and reddish-orange for microfilaments. A third component of the cytoskeleton, intermediate filaments, is not evident here. (The blue color tags the DNA in the nucleus.)

▶ **Figure 4.19 A peroxisome.** Peroxisomes are roughly spherical and often have a granular or crystalline core that is thought to be a dense collection of enzyme molecules. Chloroplasts and mitochondria cooperate with peroxisomes in certain metabolic functions (TEM).

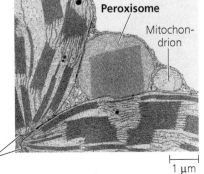

however. It can be quickly dismantled in one part of the cell and reassembled in a new location, changing the shape of the cell.

Some types of cell motility (movement) also involve the cytoskeleton. The term *cell motility* includes both changes in cell location and more limited movements of cell parts. Cell motility generally requires the interaction of the cytoskeleton with **motor proteins**. Examples of such cell motility abound. Cytoskeletal elements and motor proteins work together with plasma membrane molecules to allow whole cells to move along fibers outside the cell. Inside the cell, vesicles and other organelles often use motor protein "feet" to "walk" to their destinations along a track provided by the cytoskeleton. For instance, this is how vesicles containing neurotransmitter molecules migrate to the tips of axons, the long extensions of nerve cells that release these molecules as chemical signals to adjacent nerve cells **(Figure 4.21)**. The cytoskeleton also manipulates the plasma membrane, bending it inward to form food vacuoles or other phagocytic vesicles.

Components of the Cytoskeleton

Let's look more closely at the three main types of fibers that make up the cytoskeleton: *Microtubules* are the thickest, *microfilaments* (actin filaments) are the thinnest, and *intermediate filaments* are fibers with diameters in a middle range. **Table 4.1** summarizes the properties of these fibers.

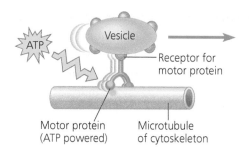

(a) Motor proteins that attach to receptors on vesicles can "walk" the vesicles along microtubules or, in some cases, along microfilaments.

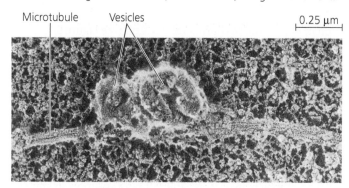

(b) Two vesicles containing neurotransmitters move along a microtubule toward the tip of a nerve cell extension called an axon (SEM).

▲ Figure 4.21 **Motor proteins and the cytoskeleton.**

Table 4.1 The Structure and Function of the Cytoskeleton			
Property	**Microtubules (Tubulin Polymers)**	**Microfilaments (Actin Filaments)**	**Intermediate Filaments**
Structure	Hollow tubes	Two intertwined strands of actin	Fibrous proteins coiled into cables
Diameter	25 nm with 15-nm lumen	7 nm	8–12 nm
Protein subunits	Tubulin, a dimer consisting of α-tubulin and β-tubulin	Actin	One of several different proteins (such as keratins)
Main functions	Maintenance of cell shape; cell motility; chromosome movements in cell division; organelle movements	Maintenance of cell shape; changes in cell shape; muscle contraction; cytoplasmic streaming (plant cells); cell motility; cell division (animal cells)	Maintenance of cell shape; anchorage of nucleus and certain other organelles; formation of nuclear lamina
Fluorescence micrographs of fibroblasts. Fibroblasts are a favorite cell type for cell biology studies because they spread out flat and their internal structures are easy to see. In each, the structure of interest has been tagged with fluorescent molecules. The DNA in the nucleus has also been tagged in the first micrograph (blue) and third micrograph (orange).	10 μm; Column of tubulin dimers; 25 nm; α β Tubulin dimer	10 μm; Actin subunit; 7 nm	5 μm; Keratin proteins; Fibrous subunit (keratins coiled together); 8–12 nm

Microtubules

All eukaryotic cells have **microtubules**, hollow rods constructed from a globular protein called tubulin. Each tubulin protein is a *dimer*, a molecule made up of two subunits. A tubulin dimer consists of two slightly different polypeptides, α-tubulin and β-tubulin. Microtubules grow in length by adding tubulin dimers; they can also be disassembled and their tubulin used to build microtubules elsewhere in the cell.

Microtubules shape and support the cell and serve as tracks along which organelles equipped with motor proteins can move (see Figure 4.21). Microtubules are also involved in the separation of chromosomes during cell division (see Figure 9.7).

Centrosomes and Centrioles In animal cells, microtubules grow out from a **centrosome**, a region that is often located near the nucleus and is considered a "microtubule-organizing center." These microtubules function as compression-resisting girders of the cytoskeleton. Within the centrosome is a pair of **centrioles**, each composed of nine sets of triplet microtubules arranged in a ring **(Figure 4.22)**. Although centrosomes with centrioles may help organize microtubule assembly in animal cells, many other eukaryotic cells lack centrosomes with centrioles and instead organize microtubules by other means.

Cilia and Flagella In eukaryotes, a specialized arrangement of microtubules is responsible for the beating of **flagella** (singular, *flagellum*) and **cilia** (singular, *cilium*), microtubule-containing extensions that project from some cells. (The bacterial flagellum, shown in Figure 4.4, has a completely different structure.) Many unicellular eukaryotes are propelled through water by cilia or flagella that act as locomotor appendages, and the sperm of animals, algae, and some plants have flagella. When cilia or flagella extend from cells that are held in place as part of a tissue layer, they can move fluid over the surface of the tissue. For example, the ciliated lining of the trachea (windpipe) sweeps mucus containing trapped debris out of the lungs (see the EMs in Figure 4.3). In a woman's reproductive tract, the cilia lining the oviducts help move an egg toward the uterus.

Motile cilia usually occur in large numbers on the cell surface. Flagella are usually limited to just one or a few per cell, and they are longer than cilia. Flagella and cilia also differ in their beating patterns. A flagellum has an undulating motion like the tail of a fish. In contrast, cilia have alternating power and recovery strokes, like the oars of a racing crew boat.

A cilium may also act as a signal-receiving antenna for the cell. Cilia that have this function are generally nonmotile, and there is only one per cell. (In fact, in vertebrate animals, it appears that almost all cells have such a cilium, which is called a *primary cilium*.) Membrane proteins on this kind of cilium transmit molecular signals from the cell's environment to its interior, triggering signaling pathways that may lead to changes in the cell's activities. Cilium-based signaling appears to be crucial to brain function and to embryonic development.

Though different in length, number per cell, and beating pattern, motile cilia and flagella share a common structure. Each motile cilium or flagellum has a group of microtubules sheathed in an extension of the plasma membrane **(Figure 4.23a)**. Nine doublets of microtubules are arranged in a ring with two single microtubules in its center **(Figure 4.23b)**. This arrangement, referred to as the "9 + 2" pattern, is found in nearly all eukaryotic flagella and motile cilia. (Nonmotile primary cilia have a "9 + 0" pattern, lacking the central pair of microtubules.) The microtubule assembly of a cilium or flagellum is anchored in the cell by a **basal body**, which is structurally similar to a centriole, with microtubule triplets in a "9 + 0" pattern **(Figure 4.23c)**. In fact, in many animals (including humans), the basal body of the fertilizing sperm's flagellum enters the egg and becomes a centriole.

How does the microtubule assembly produce the bending movements of flagella and motile cilia? Bending involves large motor proteins called **dyneins** (red in the diagram in Figure 4.23b) that are attached along each outer microtubule doublet. A typical dynein protein has two "feet" that "walk" along the microtubule of the adjacent doublet, using ATP for energy. One foot maintains contact, while the other releases and reattaches one step farther along the microtubule (see Figure 4.21). The outer doublets and two central microtubules are held together by flexible cross-linking proteins (blue in Figure 4.23b). If the doublets were not held in place, the walking action would make them slide past each other. Instead, the movements of the dynein feet cause the microtubules—and the organelle as a whole—to bend.

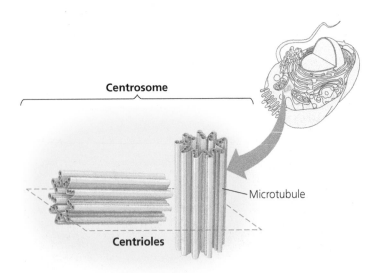

▲ Figure 4.22 Centrosome containing a pair of centrioles. Most animal cells have a centrosome, a region near the nucleus where the cell's microtubules are initiated. Within the centrosome is a pair of centrioles, each about 250 nm (0.25 μm) in diameter. The two centrioles are at right angles to each other, and each is made up of nine sets of three microtubules. The blue portions of the drawing represent nontubulin proteins that connect the microtubule triplets.

? *How many microtubules are in a centrosome? In the drawing, circle and label one microtubule and describe its structure. Circle and label a triplet.*

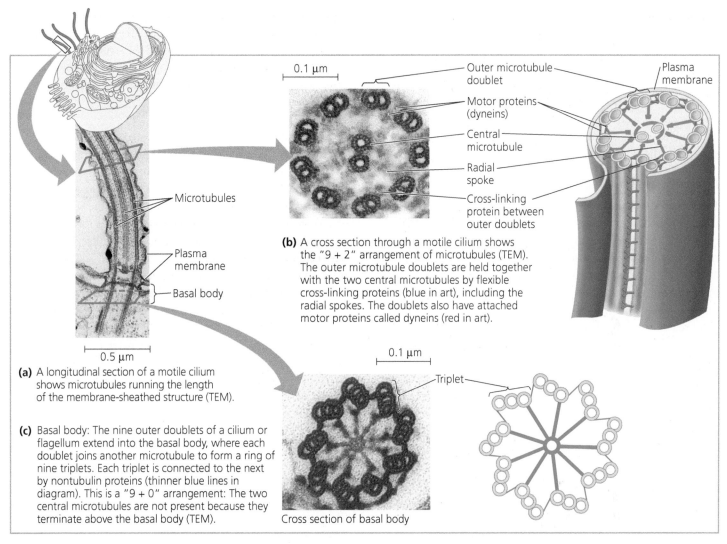

0.1 μm

Outer microtubule doublet

Motor proteins (dyneins)

Central microtubule

Radial spoke

Cross-linking protein between outer doublets

Plasma membrane

Microtubules

Plasma membrane

Basal body

0.5 μm

(b) A cross section through a motile cilium shows the "9 + 2" arrangement of microtubules (TEM). The outer microtubule doublets are held together with the two central microtubules by flexible cross-linking proteins (blue in art), including the radial spokes. The doublets also have attached motor proteins called dyneins (red in art).

(a) A longitudinal section of a motile cilium shows microtubules running the length of the membrane-sheathed structure (TEM).

(c) Basal body: The nine outer doublets of a cilium or flagellum extend into the basal body, where each doublet joins another microtubule to form a ring of nine triplets. Each triplet is connected to the next by nontubulin proteins (thinner blue lines in diagram). This is a "9 + 0" arrangement: The two central microtubules are not present because they terminate above the basal body (TEM).

0.1 μm

Triplet

Cross section of basal body

▲ **Figure 4.23 Structure of a flagellum or motile cilium.**

DRAW IT *In (a), circle and label the central pair of microtubules. Show where they terminate, and explain why they aren't seen in the cross section of the basal body in (c).*

Microfilaments (Actin Filaments)

Microfilaments are thin solid rods. They are also called actin filaments because they are built from molecules of **actin**, a globular protein. A microfilament is a twisted double chain of actin subunits (see Table 4.1). Besides occurring as linear filaments, microfilaments can form structural networks when certain proteins bind along the side of such a filament and allow a new filament to extend as a branch.

The structural role of microfilaments in the cytoskeleton is to bear tension (pulling forces). A three-dimensional network formed by microfilaments just inside the plasma membrane helps support the cell's shape. In some kinds of animal cells, such as nutrient-absorbing intestinal cells, bundles of micro-filaments make up the core of microvilli, delicate projections that increase the cell's surface area **(Figure 4.24)**.

Microfilaments are well known for their role in cell motility. Thousands of actin filaments and thicker filaments of a

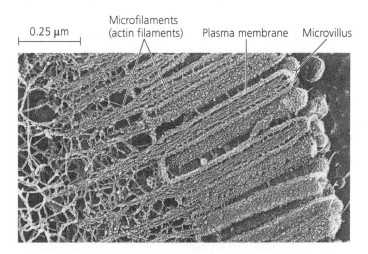

0.25 μm

Microfilaments (actin filaments)

Plasma membrane

Microvillus

▲ **Figure 4.24 A structural role of microfilaments.** The surface area of this intestinal cell is increased by its many microvilli (singular, *microvillus*), cellular extensions reinforced by bundles of microfilaments (TEM).

motor protein called **myosin** interact to cause contraction of muscle cells (described in detail in Concept 39.1). In the unicellular eukaryote *Amoeba* and some of our white blood cells, localized contractions brought about by actin and myosin are involved in the amoeboid (crawling) movement of the cells. In plant cells, actin-myosin interaction contributes to *cytoplasmic streaming*, a circular flow of cytoplasm within cells. This movement, which is especially common in large plant cells, speeds the distribution of materials within the cell.

Intermediate Filaments

Intermediate filaments are named for their diameter, which is larger than the diameter of microfilaments but smaller than that of microtubules (see Table 4.1). While microtubules and microfilaments are found in all eukaryotic cells, intermediate filaments are only found in the cells of some animals, including vertebrates. Specialized for bearing tension (like microfilaments), intermediate filaments are a diverse class of cytoskeletal elements. Each type is constructed from a particular molecular subunit belonging to a family of proteins whose members include the keratins in hair and nails.

Intermediate filaments are more permanent fixtures of cells than are microfilaments and microtubules, which are often disassembled and reassembled in various parts of a cell. Even after cells die, intermediate filament networks often persist; for example, the outer layer of our skin consists of dead skin cells full of keratin filaments. Intermediate filaments are especially sturdy and play an important role in reinforcing the shape of a cell and fixing the position of certain organelles. For instance, the nucleus typically sits within a cage made of intermediate filaments. Other intermediate filaments make up the nuclear lamina, which lines the interior of the nuclear envelope (see Figure 4.8). In general, the various kinds of intermediate filaments seem to function together as the permanent framework of the entire cell.

CONCEPT CHECK 4.6

1. How do cilia and flagella bend?
2. **WHAT IF?** Males afflicted with Kartagener's syndrome are sterile because of immotile sperm, and they tend to suffer from lung infections. This disorder has a genetic basis. Suggest what the underlying defect might be.

For suggested answers, see Appendix A.

CONCEPT 4.7

Extracellular components and connections between cells help coordinate cellular activities

Having crisscrossed the cell to explore its interior components, we complete our tour of the cell by returning to the surface of this microscopic world, where there are additional structures with important functions. The plasma membrane is usually regarded as the boundary of the living cell, but most cells synthesize and secrete materials extracellularly (to the outside of the cell). Although these materials and the structures they form are outside the cell, their study is important to cell biology because they are involved in a great many cellular functions.

Cell Walls of Plants

The **cell wall** is an extracellular structure of plant cells **(Figure 4.25)**. This is one of the features that distinguishes plant cells from animal cells (see Figure 4.7). The wall protects the plant cell, maintains its shape, and prevents excessive uptake of water. On the level of the whole plant, the strong walls of specialized cells hold the plant up against the force of gravity. Prokaryotes, fungi, and some unicellular eukaryotes also have cell walls, as you saw in Figures 4.4 and 4.7, but we will postpone discussion of them until Chapters 24–26.

Plant cell walls are much thicker than the plasma membrane, ranging from 0.1 μm to several micrometers. The exact chemical composition of the wall varies from species to species and even from one cell type to another in the same plant, but the basic design of the wall is consistent. Microfibrils made of the polysaccharide cellulose (see Figure 3.11) are synthesized by an enzyme called cellulose synthase and secreted to the extracellular space,

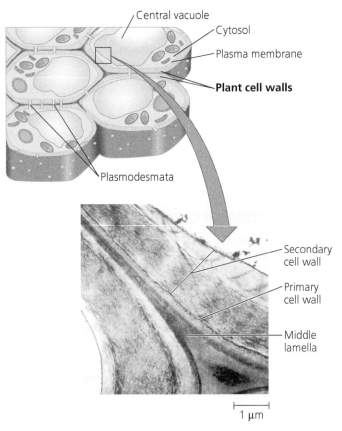

▲ **Figure 4.25 Plant cell walls.** The drawing shows several cells, each with a large vacuole, a nucleus, and several chloroplasts and mitochondria. The TEM shows the cell walls where two cells come together. The multilayered partition between plant cells consists of adjoining walls individually secreted by the cells. Plasmodesmata are channels through cell walls that connect the cytoplasm of adjacent plant cells.

where they become embedded in a matrix of other polysaccharides and proteins. This combination of materials, strong fibers in a "ground substance" (matrix), is the same basic architectural design found in steel-reinforced concrete and in fiberglass.

A young plant cell first secretes a relatively thin and flexible wall called the **primary cell wall** (see Figure 4.25). Between primary walls of adjacent cells is the **middle lamella**, a thin layer rich in sticky polysaccharides called pectins. The middle lamella glues adjacent cells together. (Pectin is used as a thickening agent in jams and jellies.) When the cell matures and stops growing, it strengthens its wall. Some plant cells do this simply by secreting hardening substances into the primary wall. Other cells add a **secondary cell wall** between the plasma membrane and the primary wall. The secondary wall, often deposited in several laminated layers, has a strong and durable matrix that affords the cell protection and support. Wood, for example, consists mainly of secondary walls. Plant cell walls are usually perforated by channels between adjacent cells called plasmodesmata, which will be discussed shortly.

The Extracellular Matrix (ECM) of Animal Cells

Although animal cells lack walls akin to those of plant cells, they do have an elaborate **extracellular matrix (ECM)**. The main ingredients of the ECM are glycoproteins and other carbohydrate-containing molecules secreted by the cells. (Recall that glycoproteins are proteins with covalently bonded carbohydrates.) The most abundant glycoprotein in the ECM of most animal cells is **collagen**, which forms strong fibers outside the cells (see Figure 3.22, carbohydrate not shown). In fact, collagen accounts for about 40% of the total protein in the human body. The collagen fibers are embedded in a network woven of secreted **proteoglycans (Figure 4.26)**. A proteoglycan molecule consists of a small core protein with many carbohydrate chains covalently attached; it may be up to 95% carbohydrate. Large proteoglycan complexes can form when hundreds of proteoglycan molecules become noncovalently attached to a single long polysaccharide molecule, as shown in Figure 4.26. Some cells are attached to the ECM by ECM glycoproteins such as **fibronectin**. Fibronectin and other ECM proteins bind to cell-surface receptor proteins called **integrins** that are built into the plasma membrane. Integrins span the membrane and bind on their cytoplasmic side to associated proteins attached to microfilaments of the cytoskeleton. The name *integrin* is based on the word *integrate*: Integrins are in a position to transmit signals between the ECM and the cytoskeleton and thus to integrate changes occurring outside and inside the cell.

Current research is revealing the influential role of the ECM in the lives of cells. By communicating with a cell through integrins, the ECM can regulate a cell's behavior. For example, some cells in a developing embryo migrate along specific pathways by matching the orientation of their microfilaments to the "grain" of fibers in the extracellular matrix. Researchers have also learned that the extracellular matrix around a cell can influence the activity of genes in the nucleus. Information about the ECM probably reaches the nucleus by a combination of mechanical and chemical signaling pathways. Mechanical signaling involves fibronectin, integrins, and microfilaments of the cytoskeleton. Changes in the cytoskeleton may in turn trigger chemical signaling pathways inside the cell, leading to changes in the set of proteins being made by the cell and therefore changes in the cell's function. In this way, the extracellular

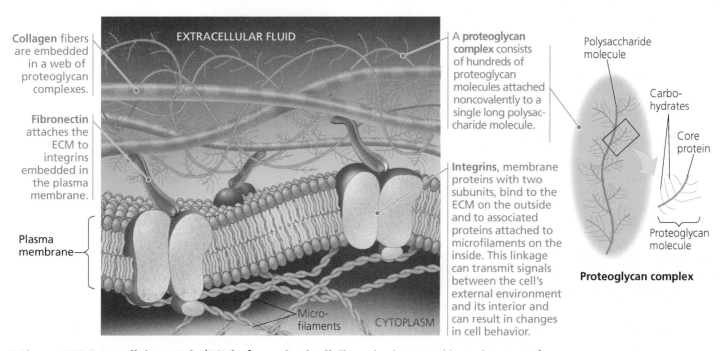

▲ **Figure 4.26 Extracellular matrix (ECM) of an animal cell.** The molecular composition and structure of the ECM vary from one cell type to another. In this example, three different types of ECM molecules are present: proteoglycans, collagen, and fibronectin.

matrix of a particular tissue may help coordinate the behavior of all the cells of that tissue. Direct connections between cells also function in this coordination, as we discuss next.

Cell Junctions

Neighboring cells in an animal or plant often adhere, interact, and communicate via sites of direct physical contact.

Plasmodesmata in Plant Cells

It might seem that the nonliving cell walls of plants would isolate plant cells from one another. But in fact, as shown in Figure 4.25, cell walls are perforated with **plasmodesmata** (singular, *plasmodesma*; from the Greek *desma*, bond), membrane-lined channels filled with cytosol. By joining adjacent cells, plasmodesmata unify most of a plant into one living continuum. The plasma membranes of adjacent cells line the channel of each plasmodesma and thus are continuous. Water and small solutes can pass freely from cell to cell, and experiments have shown that in some circumstances, certain proteins and RNA molecules can do this as well. The macromolecules transported to neighboring cells appear to reach the plasmodesmata by moving along fibers of the cytoskeleton.

Tight Junctions, Desmosomes, and Gap Junctions in Animal Cells

In animals, there are three main types of cell junctions: *tight junctions*, *desmosomes*, and *gap junctions* (**Figure 4.27**). All three types are especially common in epithelial tissue, which

---

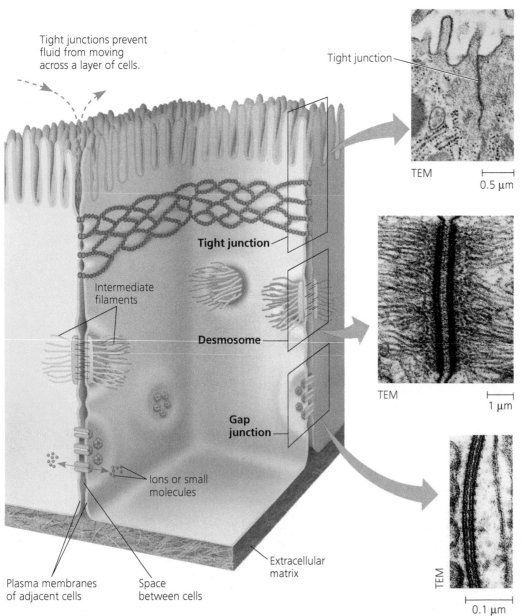

Tight junctions prevent fluid from moving across a layer of cells.

Tight junction

Tight junction

Intermediate filaments

Desmosome

Gap junction

Ions or small molecules

Plasma membranes of adjacent cells

Space between cells

Extracellular matrix

Tight Junctions

At **tight junctions**, the plasma membranes of neighboring cells are very tightly pressed against each other, bound together by specific proteins (purple). Forming continuous seals around the cells, tight junctions establish a barrier that prevents leakage of extracellular fluid across a layer of epithelial cells (see red dashed arrow). For example, tight junctions between skin cells make us watertight.

TEM   0.5 μm

Desmosomes

Desmosomes (one type of *anchoring junction*) function like rivets, fastening cells together into strong sheets. Intermediate filaments made of sturdy keratin proteins anchor desmosomes in the cytoplasm. Desmosomes attach muscle cells to each other in a muscle. Some "muscle tears" involve the rupture of desmosomes.

TEM   1 μm

Gap Junctions

Gap junctions (also called *communicating junctions*) provide cytoplasmic channels from one cell to an adjacent cell and in this way are similar in their function to the plasmodesmata in plants. Gap junctions consist of membrane proteins that surround a pore through which ions, sugars, amino acids, and other small molecules may pass. Gap junctions are necessary for communication between cells in many types of tissues, such as heart muscle, and in animal embryos.

TEM   0.1 μm

lines the external and internal surfaces of the body. Figure 4.27 uses epithelial cells of the intestinal lining to illustrate these junctions. (Gap junctions are most like the plasmodesmata of plants, although gap junction pores are not lined with membrane.)

CONCEPT CHECK 4.7

1. In what way are the cells of plants and animals structurally different from single-celled eukaryotes?
2. **WHAT IF?** If the plant cell wall or the animal extracellular matrix were impermeable, what effect would this have on cell function?
3. **MAKE CONNECTIONS** The polypeptide chain that makes up a tight junction weaves back and forth through the membrane four times, with two extracellular loops, and one loop plus short C-terminal and N-terminal tails in the cytoplasm. Looking at Figure 3.18, what would you predict about the amino acids making up the tight junction protein?

For suggested answers, see Appendix A.

The Cell: A Living Unit Greater Than the Sum of Its Parts

From our panoramic view of the cell's compartmental organization to our close-up inspection of each organelle's architecture, this tour of the cell has provided many opportunities to correlate structure with function. But even as we dissect the cell, remember that none of its components works alone. As an example of cellular integration, consider the microscopic scene in **Figure 4.28**. The large cell is a macrophage (see Figure 4.12). It helps defend the mammalian body against infections by ingesting bacteria (the smaller cells) into phagocytic vesicles. The macrophage crawls along a surface and reaches out to the bacteria with thin cell extensions called pseudopodia (specifically, filopodia). Actin filaments interact with other elements of the cytoskeleton in these movements. After the macrophage engulfs the bacteria, they are destroyed by lysosomes. The elaborate endomembrane system produces the lysosomes. The digestive enzymes of the lysosomes and the proteins of the cytoskeleton are all made on ribosomes. And the synthesis of these proteins is programmed by genetic messages dispatched from the DNA in the nucleus. All these processes require energy, which mitochondria supply in the form of ATP. To see how these processes work together in the living cell, see Make Connections Figure 8.20. Cellular functions arise from cellular order: The cell is a living unit greater than the sum of its parts.

10 μm

▲ **Figure 4.28 The emergence of cellular functions.** The ability of this macrophage (brown) to recognize, apprehend, and destroy *Staphylococcus* bacteria (orange) is a coordinated activity of the whole cell. Its cytoskeleton, lysosomes, and plasma membrane are among the components that function in phagocytosis (colorized SEM).

Go to **MasteringBiology®** for Assignments, the eText, and the Study Area with Animations, Activities, Vocab Self-Quiz, and Practice Tests.

4 Chapter Review

SUMMARY OF KEY CONCEPTS

VOCAB SELF-QUIZ

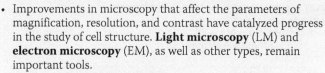

goo.gl/gbai8v

CONCEPT 4.1

Biologists use microscopes and the tools of biochemistry to study cells (pp. 73–75)

- Improvements in microscopy that affect the parameters of magnification, resolution, and contrast have catalyzed progress in the study of cell structure. **Light microscopy** (LM) and **electron microscopy** (EM), as well as other types, remain important tools.
- Cell biologists can obtain pellets enriched in particular cellular components by centrifuging disrupted cells at sequential speeds, a process known as **cell fractionation**. Larger cellular components are in the pellet after lower-speed centrifugation, and smaller components are in the pellet after higher-speed centrifugation.

? *How do microscopy and biochemistry complement each other to reveal cell structure and function?*

CONCEPT 4.2

Eukaryotic cells have internal membranes that compartmentalize their functions (pp. 75–80)

- All cells are bounded by a **plasma membrane**, a bilayer of phospholipids with their hydrophobic tails on in the interior of the membrane and their hydrophilic heads in contact with the aqueous solutions on either side.
- **Prokaryotic cells** lack nuclei and other membrane-enclosed **organelles**, while **eukaryotic cells** have internal membranes that compartmentalize cellular functions.
- The surface-to-volume ratio is an important parameter affecting cell size and shape.
- Plant and animal cells have most of the same organelles: a nucleus, endoplasmic reticulum, Golgi apparatus, and mitochondria. Some organelles are found only in plant or in animal cells. Chloroplasts are present only in cells of photosynthetic eukaryotes.

? *Explain how the compartmental organization of a eukaryotic cell contributes to its biochemical functioning.*

	Cell Component	Structure	Function
CONCEPT 4.3 **The eukaryotic cell's genetic instructions are housed in the nucleus and carried out by the ribosomes (pp. 80–82)** **?** *Describe the relationship between the nucleus and ribosomes.*	Nucleus (ER)	Surrounded by nuclear envelope (double membrane) perforated by nuclear pores; nuclear envelope continuous with endoplasmic reticulum (ER)	Houses chromosomes, which are made of chromatin (DNA and proteins); contains nucleoli, where ribosomal subunits are made; pores regulate entry and exit of materials
	Ribosome	Two subunits made of ribosomal RNA and proteins; can be free in cytosol or bound to ER	Protein synthesis
CONCEPT 4.4 **The endomembrane system regulates protein traffic and performs metabolic functions in the cell (pp. 82–87)** **?** *Describe the key role played by transport vesicles in the endomembrane system.*	Endoplasmic reticulum (Nuclear envelope)	Extensive network of membrane-bounded tubules and sacs; membrane separates lumen from cytosol; continuous with nuclear envelope	Smooth ER: synthesis of lipids, metabolism of carbohydrates, Ca^{2+} storage, detoxification of drugs and poisons Rough ER: aids in synthesis of secretory and other proteins from bound ribosomes; adds carbohydrates to proteins to make glycoproteins; produces new membrane
	Golgi apparatus	Stacks of flattened membranous sacs; has polarity (*cis* and *trans* faces)	Modification of proteins, carbohydrates on proteins, and phospholipids; synthesis of many polysaccharides; sorting of Golgi products, which are then released in vesicles
	Lysosome	Membranous sac of hydrolytic enzymes (in animal cells)	Breakdown of ingested substances, cell macromolecules, and damaged organelles for recycling
	Vacuole	Large membrane-bounded vesicle	Digestion, storage, waste disposal, water balance, plant cell growth and protection
CONCEPT 4.5 **Mitochondria and chloroplasts change energy from one form to another (pp. 87–90)** **?** *What is the endosymbiont theory?*	Mitochondrion	Bounded by double membrane; inner membrane has infoldings (cristae)	Cellular respiration
	Chloroplast	Typically two membranes around fluid stroma, which contains thylakoids stacked into grana (in cells of photosynthetic eukaryotes, including plants)	Photosynthesis
	Peroxisome	Specialized metabolic compartment bounded by a single membrane	Contains enzymes that transfer hydrogen atoms from certain molecules to oxygen, producing hydrogen peroxide (H_2O_2) as a by-product; H_2O_2 is converted to water by another enzyme

CONCEPT 4.6

The cytoskeleton is a network of fibers that organizes structures and activities in the cell (pp. 90–94)

- The **cytoskeleton** functions in structural support for the cell and in motility and signal transmission.
- **Microtubules** shape the cell, guide organelle movement, and separate chromosomes in dividing cells. **Cilia** and **flagella** are motile appendages containing microtubules. *Primary cilia* play sensory and signaling roles. **Microfilaments** are thin rods that function in muscle contraction, amoeboid movement, cytoplasmic streaming, and support of microvilli. **Intermediate filaments** support cell shape and fix organelles in place.

? *Describe the role of motor proteins inside the eukaryotic cell and in whole-cell movement.*

CONCEPT 4.7

Extracellular components and connections between cells help coordinate cellular activities (pp. 94–97)

- Plant **cell walls** are made of cellulose fibers embedded in other polysaccharides and proteins.
- Animal cells secrete glycoproteins and proteoglycans that form the **extracellular matrix (ECM)**, which functions in support, adhesion, movement, and regulation.
- Cell junctions connect neighboring cells in plants and animals. Plants have **plasmodesmata** that pass through adjoining cell walls. Animal cells have **tight junctions**, **desmosomes**, and **gap junctions**.

? *Compare the structure and functions of a plant cell wall and the extracellular matrix of an animal cell.*

TEST YOUR UNDERSTANDING

PRACTICE TEST
goo.gl/CRZjvS

Level 1: Knowledge/Comprehension

1. Which structure is *not* part of the endomembrane system?
   (A) nuclear envelope
   (B) chloroplast
   (C) Golgi apparatus
   (D) plasma membrane

2. Which structure is common to plant *and* animal cells?
   (A) chloroplast   (C) mitochondrion
   (B) wall made of cellulose   (D) centriole

3. Which of the following is present in a prokaryotic cell?
   (A) mitochondrion   (C) nuclear envelope
   (B) ribosome   (D) chloroplast

4. Which structure-function pair is *mismatched*?
   (A) microtubule; muscle contraction
   (B) ribosome; protein synthesis
   (C) Golgi; protein trafficking
   (D) nucleolus; production of ribosomal subunits

Level 2: Application/Analysis

5. Cyanide binds to at least one molecule involved in producing ATP. If a cell is exposed to cyanide, most of the cyanide will be found within the
   (A) mitochondria.   (C) peroxisomes.
   (B) ribosomes.   (D) lysosomes.

6. What is the most likely pathway taken by a newly synthesized protein that will be secreted by a cell?
   (A) ER → Golgi → nucleus
   (B) nucleus → ER → Golgi
   (C) ER → Golgi → vesicles that fuse with plasma membrane
   (D) ER → lysosomes → vesicles that fuse with plasma membrane

7. Which cell would be best for studying lysosomes?
   (A) muscle cell   (C) phagocytic white blood cell
   (B) nerve cell   (D) bacterial cell

8. **DRAW IT** From memory, draw two eukaryotic cells. Label the structures listed here and show any physical connections between the internal structures of each cell: nucleus, rough ER, smooth ER, mitochondrion, centrosome, chloroplast, vacuole, lysosome, microtubule, cell wall, ECM, microfilament, Golgi apparatus, intermediate filament, plasma membrane, peroxisome, ribosome, nucleolus, nuclear pore, vesicle, flagellum, microvilli, plasmodesma.

Level 3: Synthesis/Evaluation

9. **SCIENTIFIC INQUIRY**
   In studying micrographs of an unusual protist (single-celled eukaryote) that you found in a sample of pond water, you spot an organelle that you can't recognize. You successfully develop a method for growing this organism in liquid in the laboratory. Describe how you would go about finding out what this organelle is and what it does in the cell. Assume that you would make use of additional microscopy, cell fractionation, and biochemical tests.

10. **FOCUS ON EVOLUTION**
    Compare different aspects of cell structure. (a) What structures best reveal evolutionary unity? (b) Provide an example of diversity related to specialized modifications.

11. **FOCUS ON ORGANIZATION**
    Considering some of the characteristics that define life and drawing on your new knowledge of cellular structures and functions, write a short essay (100–150 words) that discusses this statement: Life is an emergent property that appears at the level of the cell. (Review the section on emergent properties in Concept 1.1.)

12. **SYNTHESIZE YOUR KNOWLEDGE**

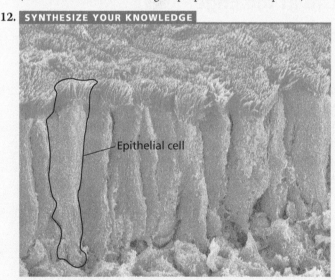

Epithelial cell

The cells in the SEM are epithelial cells from the small intestine. Discuss how their cellular structure contributes to their specialized functions of nutrient absorption and as a barrier between intestinal contents and the blood supply on the other side of the cell sheet.

For selected answers, see Appendix A.

5 Membrane Transport and Cell Signaling

KEY CONCEPTS

5.1 Cellular membranes are fluid mosaics of lipids and proteins

5.2 Membrane structure results in selective permeability

5.3 Passive transport is diffusion of a substance across a membrane with no energy investment

5.4 Active transport uses energy to move solutes against their gradients

5.5 Bulk transport across the plasma membrane occurs by exocytosis and endocytosis

5.6 The plasma membrane plays a key role in most cell signaling

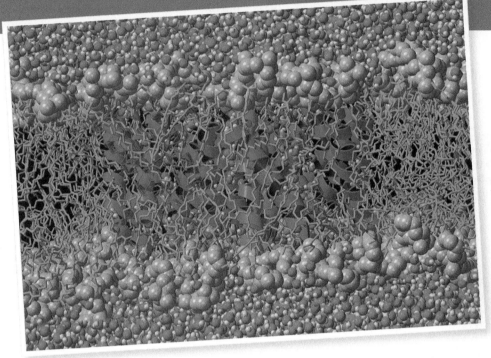

▲ **Figure 5.1** How do cell membrane proteins help regulate chemical traffic?

Life at the Edge

The plasma membrane is the edge of life, the boundary that separates the living cell from its surroundings. A remarkable film only about 8 nm thick—it would take over 8,000 plasma membranes to equal the thickness of a piece of paper—the plasma membrane controls traffic into and out of the cell it surrounds. Like all biological membranes, the plasma membrane exhibits **selective permeability**; that is, it allows some substances to cross it more easily than others. The resulting ability of the cell to discriminate in its chemical exchanges with its environment is fundamental to life.

Most of this chapter is devoted to how cellular membranes control the passage of substances through them. **Figure 5.1** shows a computer model of water molecules (red and gray) passing through a short section of a membrane, a phospholipid bilayer (phosphates are yellow, and hydrocarbon tails are green). The blue ribbons within the lipid bilayer represent helical regions of a membrane protein called an aquaporin. One molecule of this protein enables billions of water molecules to pass through the membrane every second, many more than could cross on their own. Found in many kinds of cells, aquaporins are but one example of how the plasma membrane and its proteins enable cells to survive and function.

To understand how membranes work, we'll begin by examining their molecular structure. Then we'll describe in some detail how plasma membranes control transport into and out of cells. Finally, we'll discuss cell signaling, emphasizing the role of the plasma membrane in cell communication.

CONCEPT 5.1

Cellular membranes are fluid mosaics of lipids and proteins

Figure 5.2 shows the currently accepted model of the arrangement of molecules in the plasma membrane. Lipids and proteins are the staple ingredients of membranes, although carbohydrates are also important. The most abundant lipids in most membranes are phospholipids. The ability of phospholipids to form membranes is inherent in their molecular structure. A phospholipid is an **amphipathic** molecule, meaning it has both a hydrophilic region and a hydrophobic region (see Figure 3.15). A phospholipid bilayer can exist as a stable boundary between two aqueous compartments because the molecular arrangement shelters the hydrophobic tails of the phospholipids from water while exposing the hydrophilic heads to water (**Figure 5.3**).

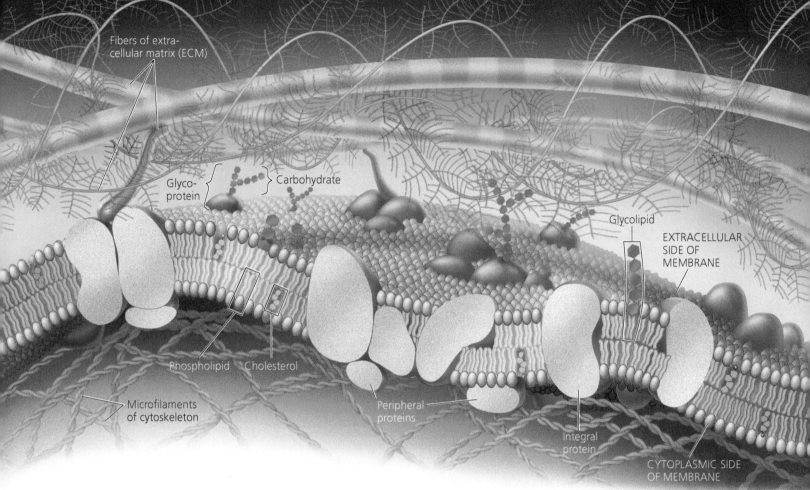

Fibers of extra-
cellular matrix (ECM)

Glyco-
protein

Carbohydrate

Glycolipid

EXTRACELLULAR
SIDE OF
MEMBRANE

Phospholipid   Cholesterol

Microfilaments
of cytoskeleton

Peripheral
proteins

Integral
protein

CYTOPLASMIC SIDE
OF MEMBRANE

▲ **Figure 5.2 Current model of an animal cell's plasma membrane (cutaway view).** Lipids are colored gray and gold, proteins purple, and carbohydrates green.

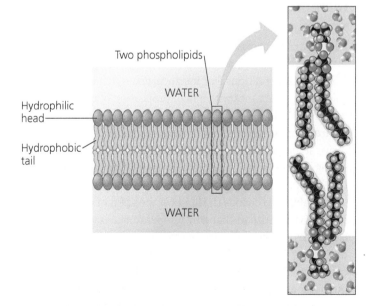

Two phospholipids

WATER

Hydrophilic
head

Hydrophobic
tail

WATER

▲ **Figure 5.3 Phospholipid bilayer (cross section).**

MAKE CONNECTIONS *Refer to Figure 3.15b, and then circle the hydrophilic and hydrophobic portions of the upper phospholipid on the right side of Figure 5.3. Explain what each portion contacts when the phospholipid is in the plasma membrane.*

Like membrane lipids, most membrane proteins are amphipathic. Such proteins can reside in the phospholipid bilayer with their hydrophilic regions protruding. This molecular orientation maximizes contact of the hydrophilic regions of a protein with water in the cytosol and extracellular fluid, while providing its hydrophobic parts with a nonaqueous environment.

In the **fluid mosaic model** in Figure 5.2, the membrane is a mosaic of protein molecules bobbing in a fluid bilayer of phospholipids. The proteins are not randomly distributed in the membrane, however. Groups of proteins are often associated in long-lasting, specialized patches, as are certain lipids. In some regions, the membrane may be much more packed with proteins than shown in Figure 5.2. Like all models, the fluid mosaic model is continually being refined as new research reveals more about membrane structure.

The Fluidity of Membranes

Membranes are not static sheets of molecules locked rigidly in place. A membrane is held together primarily by hydrophobic interactions, which are much weaker than covalent bonds (see Figure 3.22). Most of the lipids and some of the proteins can shift about laterally—that is, in the plane of the membrane—like partygoers elbowing their way through a crowded room.

The lateral movement of phospholipids within the membrane is rapid. Proteins are much larger than lipids and move more slowly, but some membrane proteins do drift, as shown

▼ Figure 5.4 Inquiry

Do membrane proteins move?

Experiment Larry Frye and Michael Edidin, at Johns Hopkins University, labeled the plasma membrane proteins of a mouse cell and a human cell with two different markers and fused the cells. Using a microscope, they observed the markers on the hybrid cell.

Results

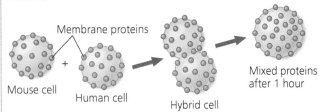

Membrane proteins

Mouse cell + Human cell → Hybrid cell → Mixed proteins after 1 hour

Conclusion The mixing of the mouse and human membrane proteins indicates that at least some membrane proteins move sideways within the plane of the plasma membrane.

Data from L. D. Frye and M. Edidin, The rapid intermixing of cell surface antigens after formation of mouse-human heterokaryons, *Journal of Cell Science* 7:319 (1970).

WHAT IF? Suppose the proteins did not mix in the hybrid cell, even many hours after fusion. Would you be able to conclude that proteins don't move within the membrane? What other explanation could there be?

▼ Figure 5.5 Factors that affect membrane fluidity.

(a) Unsaturated versus saturated hydrocarbon tails.

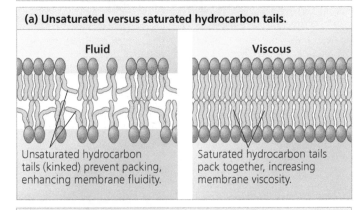

Fluid

Viscous

Unsaturated hydrocarbon tails (kinked) prevent packing, enhancing membrane fluidity.

Saturated hydrocarbon tails pack together, increasing membrane viscosity.

(b) Cholesterol within the animal cell membrane.

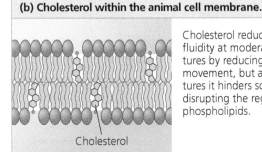

Cholesterol

Cholesterol reduces membrane fluidity at moderate temperatures by reducing phospholipid movement, but at low temperatures it hinders solidification by disrupting the regular packing of phospholipids.

---

in a classic experiment described in **Figure 5.4**. And some membrane proteins seem to move in a highly directed manner, perhaps driven along cytoskeletal fibers by motor proteins. However, many other membrane proteins seem to be held immobile by their attachment to the cytoskeleton or to the extracellular matrix (see Figure 5.2).

A membrane remains fluid as temperature decreases until the phospholipids settle into a closely packed arrangement and the membrane solidifies, much as bacon grease forms lard when it cools. The temperature at which a membrane solidifies depends on the types of lipids it is made of. The membrane remains fluid to a lower temperature if it is rich in phospholipids with unsaturated hydrocarbon tails (see Figures 3.14 and 3.15). Because of kinks in the tails where double bonds are located, unsaturated hydrocarbon tails cannot pack together as closely as saturated hydrocarbon tails, and this looseness makes the membrane more fluid **(Figure 5.5a)**.

The steroid cholesterol, which is wedged between phospholipid molecules in the plasma membranes of animal cells, has different effects on membrane fluidity at different temperatures **(Figure 5.5b)**. At relatively high temperatures—at 37°C, the body temperature of humans, for example—cholesterol makes the membrane less fluid by restraining phospholipid movement. However, because cholesterol also hinders the close packing of phospholipids, it lowers the temperature required for the membrane to solidify. Thus, cholesterol helps membranes resist changes in fluidity when the temperature changes.

Membranes must be fluid to work properly; they are usually about as fluid as salad oil. When a membrane solidifies, its permeability changes, and enzymatic proteins in the membrane may become inactive. However, membranes that are too fluid cannot support protein function either. Therefore, extreme environments pose a challenge for life, resulting in evolutionary adaptations that include differences in membrane lipid composition.

Evolution of Differences in Membrane Lipid Composition

EVOLUTION Variations in the cell membrane lipid compositions of many species appear to be evolutionary adaptations that maintain the appropriate membrane fluidity under specific environmental conditions. For instance, fishes that live in extreme cold have membranes with a high proportion of unsaturated hydrocarbon tails, enabling their membranes to remain fluid (see Figure 5.5a). At the other extreme, some bacteria and archaea thrive at temperatures greater than 90°C (194°F) in thermal hot springs and geysers. Their membranes include unusual lipids that help prevent excessive fluidity at such high temperatures.

The ability to change the lipid composition of cell membranes in response to changing temperatures has evolved in organisms that live where temperatures vary. In many plants that tolerate extreme cold, such as winter wheat, the percentage of unsaturated phospholipids increases in autumn, keeping the membranes from solidifying during winter. Some bacteria and archaea can also change the proportion of unsaturated phospholipids in their cell membranes, depending on the temperature at which they are growing. Overall, natural selection has apparently favored organisms whose mix of membrane lipids ensures an appropriate level of membrane fluidity for their environment.

Membrane Proteins and Their Functions

Now we return to the *mosaic* aspect of the fluid mosaic model. Somewhat like a tile mosaic, a membrane is a collage of different proteins embedded in the fluid matrix of the lipid bilayer (see Figure 5.2). More than 50 kinds of proteins have been found so far in the plasma membrane of red blood cells, for example. Phospholipids form the main fabric of the membrane, but proteins determine most of the membrane's functions. Different types of cells contain different sets of membrane proteins, and the various membranes within a cell each have a unique collection of proteins.

Notice in Figure 5.2 that there are two major populations of membrane proteins: integral proteins and peripheral proteins. **Integral proteins** penetrate the hydrophobic interior of the lipid bilayer. The majority are *transmembrane proteins*, which span the membrane; other integral proteins extend only partway into the hydrophobic interior. The hydrophobic regions of an integral protein consist of one or more stretches of nonpolar amino acids (see Figure 3.18), usually coiled into α helices **(Figure 5.6)**. The hydrophilic parts of the molecule are exposed to the aqueous solutions on either side of the membrane. Some proteins also have one or more hydrophilic channels that allow passage of hydrophilic substances (even water itself; see Figure 5.1). **Peripheral proteins** are not embedded in the lipid bilayer at all; they are loosely bound to the surface of the membrane, often to exposed parts of integral proteins (see Figure 5.2).

On the cytoplasmic side of the plasma membrane, some membrane proteins are held in place by attachment to the cytoskeleton. And on the extracellular side, certain membrane proteins are attached to fibers of the extracellular matrix (see Figure 4.26). These attachments combine to give animal cells a stronger framework than the plasma membrane alone could provide.

Figure 5.7 gives an overview of six major functions performed by proteins of the plasma membrane. A single cell may have membrane proteins carrying out several of these functions, and a single membrane protein may have multiple

(a) Transport. *Left:* A protein that spans the membrane may provide a hydrophilic channel across the membrane that is selective for a particular solute. *Right:* Other transport proteins shuttle a substance from one side to the other by changing shape. Some of these proteins hydrolyze ATP as an energy source to actively pump substances across the membrane.

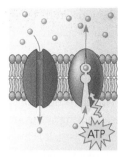

(b) Enzymatic activity. A protein built into the membrane may be an enzyme with its active site (where the target molecule binds) exposed to substances in the adjacent solution. In some cases, several enzymes in a membrane are organized as a team that carries out sequential steps of a metabolic pathway.

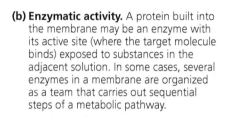
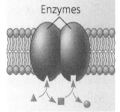

(c) Signal transduction. A membrane protein (receptor) may have a binding site with a specific shape that fits the shape of a chemical messenger, such as a hormone. The external messenger (signaling molecule) may cause the protein to change shape, allowing it to relay the message to the inside of the cell, usually by binding to a cytoplasmic protein.

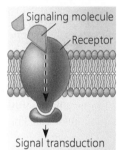

(d) Cell-cell recognition. Some glycoproteins serve as identification tags that are specifically recognized by membrane proteins of other cells. This type of cell-cell binding is usually short-lived compared to that shown in (e).

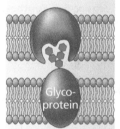
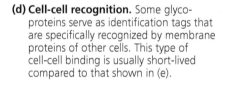

(e) Intercellular joining. Membrane proteins of adjacent cells may hook together in various kinds of junctions, such as gap junctions or tight junctions. This type of binding is more long-lasting than that shown in (d).

(f) Attachment to the cytoskeleton and extracellular matrix (ECM). Microfilaments or other elements of the cytoskeleton may be noncovalently bound to membrane proteins, a function that helps maintain cell shape and stabilizes the location of certain membrane proteins. Proteins that can bind to ECM molecules can coordinate extracellular and intracellular changes.

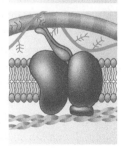

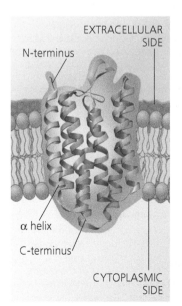

◀ **Figure 5.6 The structure of a transmembrane protein.** Bacteriorhodopsin (a bacterial transport protein) has a distinct orientation in the membrane, with its N-terminus outside the cell and its C-terminus inside. This ribbon model highlights the α-helical secondary structure of the hydrophobic parts, which lie mostly within the hydrophobic interior of the membrane. The protein includes seven transmembrane helices. The nonhelical hydrophilic segments are in contact with the aqueous solutions on the extracellular and cytoplasmic sides of the membrane.

EXTRACELLULAR SIDE
N-terminus
α helix
C-terminus
CYTOPLASMIC SIDE

▲ **Figure 5.7 Some functions of membrane proteins.** In many cases, a single protein performs multiple tasks.

? *Some transmembrane proteins can bind to a particular ECM molecule and, when bound, transmit a signal into the cell. Use the proteins shown in (c) and (f) to explain how this might occur.*

functions. In this way, the membrane is a functional mosaic as well as a structural one.

The Role of Membrane Carbohydrates in Cell-Cell Recognition

Cell-cell recognition, a cell's ability to distinguish one type of neighboring cell from another, is crucial to the functioning of an organism. It is important, for example, in the sorting of cells into tissues and organs in an animal embryo. It is also the basis for the rejection of foreign cells by the immune system, an important line of defense in vertebrate animals (see Concept 35.3). Cells recognize other cells by binding to molecules, often containing carbohydrates, on the extracellular surface of the plasma membrane (see Figure 5.7d).

Membrane carbohydrates are usually short, branched chains of fewer than 15 sugar units. Some are covalently bonded to lipids, forming molecules called **glycolipids**. (Recall that *glyco* refers to carbohydrate.) However, most are covalently bonded to proteins, which are thereby **glycoproteins**.

The carbohydrates on the extracellular side of the plasma membrane vary from species to species, among individuals of the same species, and even from one cell type to another in a single individual. The diversity of the molecules and their location on the cell's surface enable membrane carbohydrates to function as markers that distinguish one cell from another. For example, the four human blood types designated A, B, AB, and O reflect variation in the carbohydrate part of glycoproteins on the surface of red blood cells.

Synthesis and Sidedness of Membranes

Membranes have distinct inside and outside faces. The two lipid layers may differ in lipid composition, and each protein has directional orientation in the membrane (see Figure 5.6, for example). **Figure 5.8** shows how membrane sidedness arises: The asymmetric arrangement of proteins, lipids, and their associated carbohydrates in the plasma membrane is determined as the membrane is being built by the endoplasmic reticulum (ER) and Golgi apparatus.

CONCEPT CHECK 5.1

1. Plasma membrane proteins have carbohydrates attached to them in the ER and Golgi apparatus and then are transported in vesicles to the cell surface. On which side of the vesicle membrane are the carbohydrates?

2. **WHAT IF?** How would the membrane lipid composition of a native grass found in very warm soil around hot springs compare with that of a native grass found in cooler soil? Explain.

For suggested answers, see Appendix A.

▼ **Figure 5.8 Synthesis of membrane components and their orientation in the membrane.** The cytoplasmic (orange) face of the plasma membrane differs from the extracellular (aqua) face. The latter arises from the inside face of ER, Golgi, and vesicle membranes.

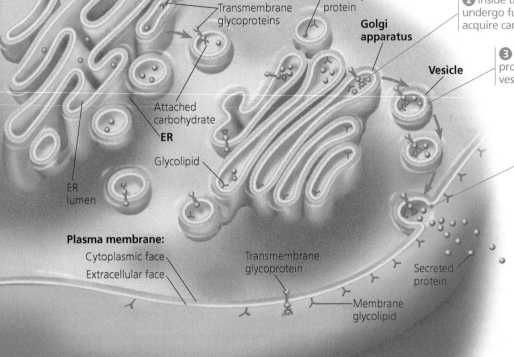

❶ Membrane proteins and lipids are synthesized in association with the endoplasmic reticulum (ER). In the ER, carbohydrates (green) are added to the transmembrane proteins (purple dumbbells), making them glycoproteins. The carbohydrate portions may then be modified.

❷ Inside the Golgi apparatus, the glycoproteins undergo further carbohydrate modification, and lipids acquire carbohydrates, becoming glycolipids.

❸ The glycoproteins, glycolipids, and secretory proteins (purple spheres) are transported in vesicles to the plasma membrane.

❹ As vesicles fuse with the plasma membrane, the outside face of the vesicle becomes continuous with the inside (cytoplasmic) face of the plasma membrane. This releases the secretory proteins from the cell, a process called *exocytosis*, and positions the carbohydrates of membrane glycoproteins and glycolipids on the outside (extracellular) face of the plasma membrane.

DRAW IT *Draw an integral membrane protein extending from partway through the ER membrane into the ER lumen. Next, draw the protein where it would be located in a series of numbered steps ending at the plasma membrane. Would the protein contact the cytoplasm or the extracellular fluid?*

CONCEPT 5.2

Membrane structure results in selective permeability

The biological membrane is an exquisite example of a supramolecular structure—many molecules ordered into a higher level of organization—with emergent properties beyond those of the individual molecules. We now focus on one of the most important of those properties: the ability to regulate transport across cellular boundaries, a function essential to the cell's existence. We will see once again that form fits function: The fluid mosaic model helps explain how membranes regulate the cell's molecular traffic.

A steady traffic of small molecules and ions moves across the plasma membrane in both directions. Consider the chemical exchanges between a muscle cell and the extracellular fluid that bathes it. Sugars, amino acids, and other nutrients enter the cell, and metabolic waste products leave it. The cell takes in O_2 for use in cellular respiration and expels CO_2. Also, the cell regulates its concentrations of inorganic ions, such as Na^+, K^+, Ca^{2+}, and Cl^-, by shuttling them one way or the other across the plasma membrane. In spite of heavy traffic through them, cell membranes are selectively permeable, and substances do not cross the barrier indiscriminately. The cell is able to take up some small molecules and ions and exclude others.

The Permeability of the Lipid Bilayer

Nonpolar molecules, such as hydrocarbons, CO_2, and O_2, are hydrophobic. They can therefore dissolve in the lipid bilayer of the membrane and cross it easily, without the aid of membrane proteins. However, the hydrophobic interior of the membrane impedes the direct passage through the membrane of ions and polar molecules, which are hydrophilic. Polar molecules such as glucose and other sugars pass only slowly through a lipid bilayer, and even water, a very small polar molecule, does not cross rapidly. A charged atom or molecule and its surrounding shell of water (see Figure 2.21) are even less likely to penetrate the hydrophobic interior of the membrane. Furthermore, the lipid bilayer is only one aspect of the gatekeeper system responsible for a cell's selective permeability. Proteins built into the membrane play key roles in regulating transport.

Transport Proteins

Specific ions and a variety of polar molecules can't move through cell membranes on their own. However, these hydrophilic substances can avoid contact with the lipid bilayer by passing through **transport proteins** that span the membrane.

Some transport proteins, called *channel proteins*, function by having a hydrophilic channel that certain molecules or atomic ions use as a tunnel through the membrane (see Figure 5.7a, left). For example, as you read earlier, the passage of water molecules through the plasma membrane of certain cells is greatly facilitated by channel proteins called

aquaporins (see Figure 5.1). Most aquaporin proteins consist of four identical subunits (see Figure 3.22). The polypeptide making up each subunit forms a channel that allows single-file passage of up to *3 billion* (3×10^9) water molecules per second, many more than would cross the membrane without aquaporin. Other transport proteins, called *carrier proteins*, hold onto their passengers and change shape in a way that shuttles them across the membrane (see Figure 5.7a, right).

A transport protein is specific for the substance it translocates (moves), allowing only a certain substance (or a small group of related substances) to cross the membrane. For example, a specific carrier protein in the plasma membrane of red blood cells transports glucose across the membrane 50,000 times faster than glucose can pass through on its own. This "glucose transporter" is so selective that it even rejects fructose, a structural isomer of glucose (see Figure 3.8).

Thus, the selective permeability of a membrane depends on both the discriminating barrier of the lipid bilayer and the specific transport proteins built into the membrane. But what establishes the *direction* of traffic across a membrane? At a given time, what determines whether a particular substance will enter the cell or leave the cell? And what mechanisms actually drive molecules across membranes? We will address these questions next as we explore two modes of membrane traffic: passive transport and active transport.

CONCEPT CHECK 5.2

1. What property allows O_2 and CO_2 to cross a lipid bilayer without the help of membrane proteins?
2. Why is a transport protein needed to move many water molecules rapidly across a membrane?
3. **MAKE CONNECTIONS** Aquaporins exclude passage of hydronium ions (H_3O^+), but some aquaporins allow passage of glycerol, a three-carbon alcohol (see Figure 3.13), as well as H_2O. Since H_3O^+ is closer in size to water than glycerol is, yet cannot pass through, what might be the basis of this selectivity?

For suggested answers, see Appendix A.

CONCEPT 5.3

Passive transport is diffusion of a substance across a membrane with no energy investment

Molecules have a type of energy called thermal energy, due to their constant motion (see Concept 2.5). One result of this motion is **diffusion**, the movement of particles of any substance so that they tend to spread out into the available space. Each molecule moves randomly, yet diffusion of a *population* of molecules may be directional. To understand this process, let's imagine a synthetic membrane separating pure water from

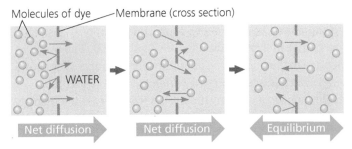

Molecules of dye — Membrane (cross section)

WATER

Net diffusion   Net diffusion   Equilibrium

(a) **Diffusion of one solute.** The membrane has pores large enough for molecules of dye to pass through. Random movement of dye molecules will cause some to pass through the pores; this will happen more often on the side with more dye molecules. The dye diffuses from where it is more concentrated to where it is less concentrated (called diffusing down a concentration gradient). This leads to a dynamic equilibrium: The solute molecules continue to cross the membrane, but at roughly equal rates in both directions.

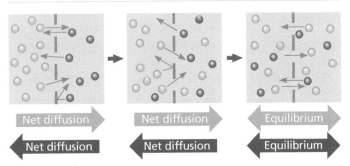

Net diffusion   Net diffusion   Equilibrium

Net diffusion   Net diffusion   Equilibrium

(b) **Diffusion of two solutes.** Solutions of two different dyes are separated by a membrane that is permeable to both. Each dye diffuses down its own concentration gradient. There will be a net diffusion of the purple dye toward the left, even though the *total* solute concentration was initially greater on the left side.

▲ **Figure 5.9 The diffusion of solutes across a synthetic membrane.** Each of the large arrows under the diagrams shows the net diffusion of the dye molecules of that color.

a solution of a dye in water. Study **Figure 5.9a** to appreciate how diffusion would result in both solutions having equal concentrations of the dye molecules. Once that point is reached, there will be a dynamic equilibrium, with roughly as many dye molecules crossing the membrane each second in one direction as in the other.

We can now state a simple rule of diffusion: In the absence of other forces, a substance will diffuse from where it is more concentrated to where it is less concentrated. Put another way, any substance will diffuse down its **concentration gradient**, the region along which the density of a substance increases or decreases (in this case, decreases). No work must be done to make this happen; diffusion is a spontaneous process, needing no input of energy. Note that each substance diffuses down its *own* concentration gradient, unaffected by the concentration gradients of other substances **(Figure 5.9b)**.

Much of the traffic across cell membranes occurs by diffusion. When a substance is more concentrated on one side of a membrane than on the other, there is a tendency for the substance to diffuse across the membrane down its concentration gradient (assuming that the membrane is permeable to that substance). One important example is the uptake of oxygen by a cell performing

cellular respiration. Dissolved oxygen diffuses into the cell across the plasma membrane. As long as cellular respiration consumes the O_2 as it enters, diffusion into the cell will continue because the concentration gradient favors movement in that direction.

The diffusion of a substance across a biological membrane is called **passive transport** because the cell does not have to expend energy to make it happen. The concentration gradient itself represents potential energy (see Concept 2.2 and Figure 6.5b) and drives diffusion. Remember, however, that membranes are selectively permeable and therefore have different effects on the rates of diffusion of various molecules. In the case of water, aquaporins allow water to diffuse very rapidly across the membranes of certain cells. As we'll see next, the movement of water across the plasma membrane has important consequences for cells.

Effects of Osmosis on Water Balance

To see how two solutions with different solute concentrations interact, picture a U-shaped glass tube with a selectively permeable artificial membrane separating two sugar solutions **(Figure 5.10)**. Pores in this synthetic membrane are too small

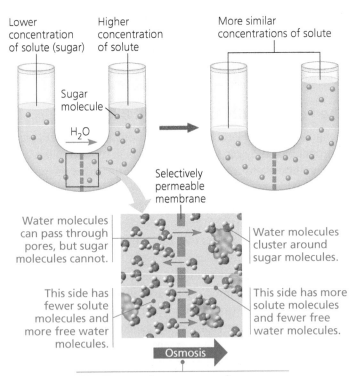

Lower concentration of solute (sugar)   Higher concentration of solute   More similar concentrations of solute

Sugar molecule

H_2O

Selectively permeable membrane

Water molecules can pass through pores, but sugar molecules cannot.   Water molecules cluster around sugar molecules.

This side has fewer solute molecules and more free water molecules.   This side has more solute molecules and fewer free water molecules.

Osmosis

Water moves from an area of higher to lower free water concentration (lower to higher solute concentration).

▲ **Figure 5.10 Osmosis.** Two sugar solutions of different concentrations are separated by a membrane that the solvent (water) can pass through but the solute (sugar) cannot. Water molecules move randomly and may cross in either direction, but overall, water diffuses from the solution with less concentrated solute to that with more concentrated solute. This passive transport of water, or osmosis, makes the sugar concentrations on both sides roughly equal.

WHAT IF? *If an orange dye capable of passing through the membrane was added to the left side of the tube above, how would it be distributed at the end of the experiment? (See Figure 5.9.) Would the final solution levels in the tube be affected?*

for sugar molecules to pass through but large enough for water molecules. However, tight clustering of water molecules around the hydrophilic solute molecules makes some of the water unavailable to cross the membrane. As a result, the solution with a higher solute concentration has a lower *free* water concentration. Water diffuses across the membrane from the region of higher free water concentration (lower solute concentration) to that of lower free water concentration (higher solute concentration) until the solute concentrations on both sides of the membrane are more nearly equal. The diffusion of free water across a selectively permeable membrane, whether artificial or cellular, is called **osmosis**. The movement of water across cell membranes and the balance of water between the cell and its environment are crucial to organisms. Let's now apply to living cells what we've learned about osmosis in this system to living cells.

(a) Animal cell. An animal cell fares best in an isotonic environment unless it has special adaptations that offset the osmotic uptake or loss of water.

(b) Plant cell. Plant cells are turgid (firm) and generally healthiest in a hypotonic environment, where the uptake of water is eventually balanced by the wall pushing back on the cell.

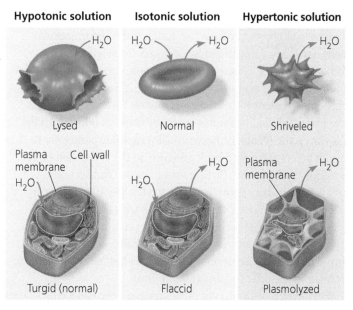

Hypotonic solution	Isotonic solution	Hypertonic solution

Lysed — Normal — Shriveled

Turgid (normal) — Flaccid — Plasmolyzed

▲ **Figure 5.11 The water balance of living cells.** How living cells react to changes in the solute concentration of their environment depends on whether or not they have cell walls. **(a)** Animal cells, such as this red blood cell, do not have cell walls. **(b)** Plant cells do. (Arrows indicate net water movement after the cells were first placed in these solutions.)

Water Balance of Cells Without Cell Walls

To explain the behavior of a cell in a solution, we must consider both solute concentration and membrane permeability. Both factors are taken into account in the concept of **tonicity**, the ability of a surrounding solution to cause a cell to gain or lose water. The tonicity of a solution depends in part on its concentration of solutes that cannot cross the membrane (nonpenetrating solutes) relative to that inside the cell. If there is a higher concentration of nonpenetrating solutes in the surrounding solution, water will tend to leave the cell, and vice versa.

If a cell without a cell wall, such as an animal cell, is immersed in an environment that is **isotonic** to the cell (*iso* means "same"), there will be no *net* movement of water across the plasma membrane. Water diffuses across the membrane, but at the same rate in both directions. In an isotonic environment, the volume of an animal cell is stable, as shown in the middle of **Figure 5.11a**.

Let's transfer the cell to a solution that is **hypertonic** to the cell (*hyper* means "more," in this case referring to nonpenetrating solutes). The cell will lose water, shrivel, and probably die (see Figure 5.11a, right). This is why an increase in the salinity (saltiness) of a lake can kill the animals there; if the lake water becomes hypertonic to the animals' cells, they might shrivel and die. However, taking up too much water can be just as hazardous as losing water. If we place the cell in a solution that is **hypotonic** to the cell (*hypo* means "less"), water will enter the cell faster than it leaves, and the cell will swell and lyse (burst) like an overfilled water balloon (see Figure 5.11a, left).

A cell without rigid cell walls can tolerate neither excessive uptake nor excessive loss of water. This problem of water balance is automatically solved if such a cell lives in isotonic surroundings. Seawater is isotonic to many marine invertebrates. The cells of most terrestrial (land-dwelling) animals are bathed in an extracellular fluid that is isotonic to the cells. In hypertonic or hypotonic environments, however, organisms that lack rigid cell walls must have other adaptations for **osmoregulation**, the control of solute concentrations and water balance. For example, the unicellular protist *Paramecium caudatum* lives in pond water, which is hypotonic to the cell. Water continually enters the cell. The *P. caudatum* cell doesn't burst because it is equipped with a contractile vacuole, an organelle that functions as a bilge pump to force water out of the cell as fast as it enters by osmosis **(Figure 5.12)**. We will examine other evolutionary adaptations for osmoregulation in Concept 32.4.

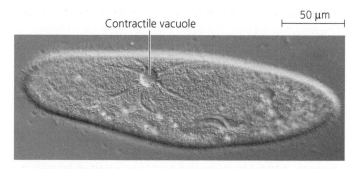

Contractile vacuole

50 μm

▲ **Figure 5.12 The contractile vacuole of *Paramecium caudatum*.** The vacuole collects fluid from a system of canals in the cytoplasm. When full, the vacuole and canals contract, expelling fluid from the cell (LM).

Water Balance of Cells with Cell Walls

The cells of plants, prokaryotes, fungi, and some unicellular eukaryotes are surrounded by cell walls (see Figure 4.25). When such a cell is immersed in a hypotonic solution—bathed in rainwater, for example—the cell wall helps maintain the cell's water balance. Consider a plant cell. Like an animal cell, the plant cell swells as water enters by osmosis **(Figure 5.11b)**. However, the relatively inelastic cell wall will expand only so much before it exerts a back pressure on the cell, called *turgor pressure*, that opposes further water uptake. At this point, the cell is **turgid** (very firm), which is the healthy state for most plant cells. Plants that are not woody, such as most house-plants, depend for mechanical support on cells kept turgid by a surrounding hypotonic solution. If a plant's cells and their surroundings are isotonic, there is no net tendency for water to enter, and the cells become **flaccid** (limp).

However, a cell wall is of no advantage if the cell is immersed in a hypertonic environment. In this case, a plant cell, like an animal cell, will lose water to its surroundings and shrink. As the plant cell shrivels, its plasma membrane pulls away from the cell wall at multiple places. This phenomenon, called **plasmolysis**, causes the plant to wilt and can lead to plant death. The walled cells of bacteria and fungi also plasmolyze in hypertonic environments.

Facilitated Diffusion: Passive Transport Aided by Proteins

Let's look more closely at how water and certain hydrophilic solutes cross a membrane. As mentioned earlier, many polar molecules and ions impeded by the lipid bilayer of the membrane diffuse passively with the help of transport proteins that span the membrane. This phenomenon is called **facilitated diffusion**. Cell biologists are still trying to learn exactly how various transport proteins facilitate diffusion. Most transport proteins are very specific: They transport some substances but not others.

As mentioned earlier, the two types of transport proteins are channel proteins and carrier proteins. Channel proteins simply provide corridors that allow specific molecules or ions to cross the membrane **(Figure 5.13a)**. The hydrophilic passageways provided by these proteins can allow water molecules or small ions to diffuse very quickly from one side of the membrane to the other. Aquaporins, the water channel proteins, facilitate the massive amounts of diffusion that occur in plant cells and in animal cells such as red blood cells. Certain kidney cells also have many aquaporin molecules, allowing them to reclaim water from urine before it is excreted. If the kidneys did not perform this function, you would excrete about 180 L of urine per day—and have to drink an equal volume of water!

Channel proteins that transport ions are called **ion channels**. Many ion channels function as **gated channels**, which open or close in response to a stimulus. For some gated channels, the stimulus is electrical. In a nerve cell, for example,

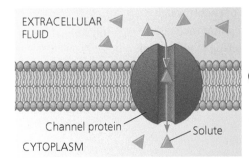

(a) A channel protein has a channel through which water molecules or a specific solute can pass.

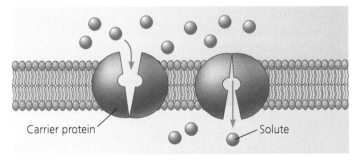

(b) A carrier protein alternates between two shapes, moving a solute across the membrane during the shape change.

▲ Figure 5.13 **Two types of transport proteins that carry out facilitated diffusion.** In both cases, the protein can transport the solute in either direction, but the net movement is down the concentration gradient of the solute.

an ion channel opens in response to an electrical stimulus, allowing a stream of potassium ions to leave the cell. This restores the cell's ability to fire again. Other gated channels open or close when a specific substance other than the one to be transported binds to the channel. These gated channels are also important in the functioning of the nervous system (as you'll learn in Concept 37.3).

Carrier proteins, such as the glucose transporter mentioned earlier, seem to undergo a subtle change in shape that somehow translocates the solute-binding site across the membrane **(Figure 5.13b)**. Such a change in shape may be triggered by the binding and release of the transported molecule. Like ion channels, carrier proteins involved in facilitated diffusion result in the net movement of a substance down its concentration gradient. No energy input is required: This is passive transport. The **Scientific Skills Exercise** gives you an opportunity to work with data from an experiment related to glucose transport.

CONCEPT CHECK 5.3

1. How do you think a cell performing cellular respiration rids itself of the resulting CO_2?
2. **WHAT IF?** If a *Paramecium caudatum* cell swims from a hypotonic to an isotonic environment, will its contractile vacuole become more active or less? Why?

For suggested answers, see Appendix A.

Interpreting a Scatter Plot with Two Sets of Data

▶ 15-day-old and 1-month-old guinea pigs

Is Glucose Uptake into Cells Affected by Age? Glucose, an important energy source for animals, is transported into cells by facilitated diffusion using protein carriers. In this exercise, you will interpret a graph with two sets of data from an experiment that examined glucose uptake over time in red blood cells from guinea pigs of different ages. You will determine if the age of the guinea pigs affected their cells' rate of glucose uptake.

How the Experiment Was Done Researchers incubated guinea pig red blood cells in a 300 mM (millimolar) radioactive glucose solution at pH 7.4 at 25°C. Every 10 or 15 minutes, they removed a sample of cells from the solution and measured the concentration of radioactive glucose inside those cells. The cells came from either a 15-day-old or 1-month-old guinea pig.

Data from the Experiment When you have multiple sets of data, it can be useful to plot them on the same graph for comparison. In the graph here, each set of dots (dots of the same color) forms a *scatter plot,* in which every data point represents two numerical values, one for each variable. For each data set, a curve that best fits the points has been drawn to make it easier to see the trends. (For additional information about graphs, see the Scientific Skills Review in Appendix F and in the Study Area in MasteringBiology.)

INTERPRET THE DATA

1. First make sure you understand the parts of the graph. (a) Which variable is the independent variable—the variable that was controlled by the researchers? (b) Which variable is the dependent variable—the variable that depended on the treatment and was measured by the researchers? (c) What do the red dots represent? (d) The blue dots?

2. From the data points on the graph, construct a table of the data. Put "Incubation Time (min)" in the left column of the table.

3. What does the graph show? Compare and contrast glucose uptake in red blood cells from a 15-day-old and a 1-month-old guinea pig.

Glucose Uptake over Time in Guinea Pig Red Blood Cells

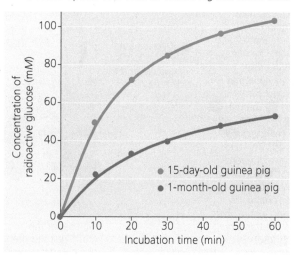

- 15-day-old guinea pig
- 1-month-old guinea pig

Data from T. Kondo and E. Beutler, Developmental changes in glucose transport of guinea pig erythrocytes, *Journal of Clinical Investigation* 65:1–4 (1980).

4. Develop a hypothesis to explain the difference between glucose uptake in red blood cells from a 15-day-old and a 1-month-old guinea pig. (Think about how glucose gets into cells.)

5. Design an experiment to test your hypothesis.

(MB) A version of this Scientific Skills Exercise can be assigned in MasteringBiology.

CONCEPT 5.4

Active transport uses energy to move solutes against their gradients

Despite the help of transport proteins, facilitated diffusion is considered passive transport because the solute is moving down its concentration gradient, a process that requires no energy. Facilitated diffusion speeds transport of a solute by providing efficient passage through the membrane, but it does not alter the direction of transport. Some other transport proteins, however, can move solutes against their concentration gradients, across the plasma membrane from the side where they are less concentrated (whether inside or outside) to the side where they are more concentrated.

The Need for Energy in Active Transport

To pump a solute across a membrane against its gradient requires work; the cell must expend energy. Therefore, this type of membrane traffic is called **active transport**. The transport proteins that move solutes against their concentration gradients are all carrier proteins rather than channel proteins. This makes sense because when channel proteins are open, they merely allow solutes to diffuse down their concentration gradients rather than picking them up and transporting them against their gradients. Active transport enables a cell to maintain internal concentrations of small solutes that differ from concentrations in its environment. For example, compared with its surroundings, an animal cell has a much higher concentration of potassium ions (K^+) and a much lower concentration of sodium ions (Na^+). The plasma membrane helps maintain these steep gradients by pumping Na^+ out of the cell and K^+ into the cell.

As in other types of cellular work, ATP supplies the energy for most active transport. One way ATP can power active transport is by transferring its terminal phosphate group directly to the transport protein. This can induce the protein to change its shape in a manner that translocates a solute bound to the protein across the membrane. One transport system

► Figure 5.14 **The sodium-potassium pump: a specific case of active transport.** This transport system pumps ions against steep concentration gradients: Sodium ion concentration ($[Na^+]$) is high outside the cell and low inside, while potassium ion concentration ($[K^+]$) is low outside the cell and high inside. The pump oscillates between two shapes in a cycle that moves 3 Na^+ out of the cell (steps ❶ through ❸) for every 2 K^+ pumped into the cell (steps ❹ through ❻). The two shapes have different binding affinities for Na^+ and K^+. ATP powers the shape change by transferring a phosphate group to the transport protein (phosphorylating the protein).

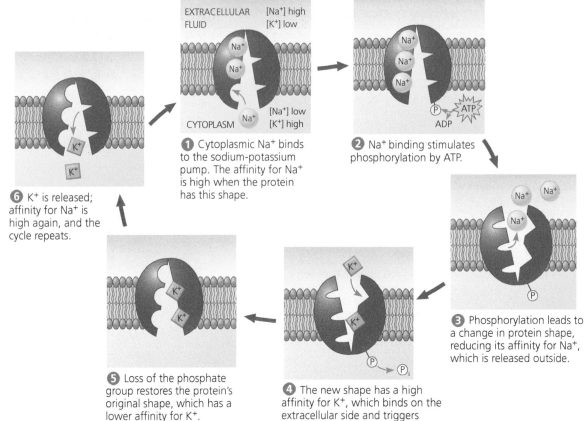

EXTRACELLULAR FLUID $[Na^+]$ high $[K^+]$ low

CYTOPLASM $[Na^+]$ low $[K^+]$ high

❶ Cytoplasmic Na^+ binds to the sodium-potassium pump. The affinity for Na^+ is high when the protein has this shape.

❷ Na^+ binding stimulates phosphorylation by ATP.

❸ Phosphorylation leads to a change in protein shape, reducing its affinity for Na^+, which is released outside.

❹ The new shape has a high affinity for K^+, which binds on the extracellular side and triggers release of the phosphate group.

❺ Loss of the phosphate group restores the protein's original shape, which has a lower affinity for K^+.

❻ K^+ is released; affinity for Na^+ is high again, and the cycle repeats.

that works this way is the **sodium-potassium pump**, which exchanges Na^+ for K^+ across the plasma membrane of animal cells **(Figure 5.14)**. The distinction between passive transport and active transport is reviewed in **Figure 5.15**.

How Ion Pumps Maintain Membrane Potential

All cells have voltages across their plasma membranes. Voltage is electrical potential energy—a separation of opposite charges. The cytoplasmic side of the membrane is negative in charge relative to the extracellular side because of an unequal distribution of anions and cations on the two sides. The voltage across a membrane, called a **membrane potential**, ranges from about −50 to −200 millivolts (mV). (The minus sign indicates that the inside of the cell is negative relative to the outside.)

The membrane potential acts like a battery, an energy source that affects the traffic of all charged substances across the membrane. Because the inside of the cell is negative compared with the outside, the membrane potential favors the passive transport of cations into the cell and anions out of the cell. Thus, *two* forces drive the diffusion of ions across a membrane: a chemical force (the ion's concentration gradient) and an electrical force (the effect of the membrane potential on the ion's movement). This combination of forces acting on an ion is called the **electrochemical gradient**.

▼ Figure 5.15 **Review: passive and active transport.**

Passive transport. Substances diffuse spontaneously down their concentration gradients, crossing a membrane with no expenditure of energy by the cell. The rate of diffusion can be greatly increased by transport proteins in the membrane.

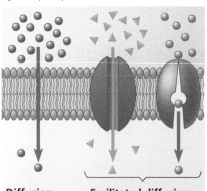

Diffusion. Hydrophobic molecules and (at a slow rate) very small uncharged polar molecules can diffuse through the lipid bilayer.

Facilitated diffusion. Many hydrophilic substances diffuse through membranes with the assistance of transport proteins, either channel proteins (left) or carrier proteins (right).

Active transport. Some transport proteins act as pumps, moving substances across a membrane against their concentration (or electrochemical) gradients. Energy for this work is usually supplied by ATP.

? *For each solute in the right panel, describe its direction of movement, and state whether it is moving with or against its concentration gradient.*

In the case of ions, then, we must refine our concept of passive transport: An ion diffuses not simply down its *concentration* gradient but, more exactly, down its *electrochemical* gradient. For example, the concentration of Na^+ inside a resting nerve cell is much lower than outside it. When the cell is stimulated, gated channels open that facilitate Na^+ diffusion. Sodium ions then "fall" down their electrochemical gradient, driven by the concentration gradient of Na^+ and by the attraction of these cations to the negative side (inside) of the membrane. In this example, both electrical and chemical contributions to the electrochemical gradient act in the same direction across the membrane, but this is not always so. In cases where electrical forces due to the membrane potential oppose the simple diffusion of an ion down its concentration gradient, active transport may be necessary. In Chapter 37, you'll learn about the importance of electrochemical gradients and membrane potentials in the transmission of nerve impulses.

Some membrane proteins that actively transport ions contribute to the membrane potential. An example is the sodium-potassium pump. Notice in Figure 5.14 that the pump does not translocate Na^+ and K^+ one for one, but pumps three sodium ions out of the cell for every two potassium ions it pumps into the cell. With each "crank" of the pump, there is a net transfer of one positive charge from the cytoplasm to the extracellular fluid, a process that stores energy as voltage. A transport protein that generates voltage across a membrane is called an **electrogenic pump**. The sodium-potassium pump appears to be the major electrogenic pump of animal cells. The main electrogenic pump of plants, fungi, and bacteria is a **proton pump**, which actively transports protons (hydrogen ions, H^+) out of the cell. The pumping of H^+ transfers positive charge from the cytoplasm to the extracellular solution **(Figure 5.16)**. By generating voltage across membranes, electrogenic pumps help store energy that can be tapped for cellular work. One important use of proton gradients in the cell is for ATP synthesis during cellular respiration (as you will see in Concept 7.4). Another is a type of membrane traffic called cotransport.

Cotransport: Coupled Transport by a Membrane Protein

A solute that exists in different concentrations across a membrane can do work as it moves across that membrane by diffusion down its concentration gradient. This is analogous to water that has been pumped uphill and performs work as it flows back down. In a mechanism called **cotransport**, a transport protein (a cotransporter) can couple the "downhill" diffusion of the solute to the "uphill" transport of a second substance against its own concentration (or electrochemical) gradient. For instance, a plant cell uses the gradient of H^+ generated by its ATP-powered proton pumps to drive the active transport of amino acids, sugars, and several other nutrients into the cell. In the example shown in **Figure 5.17**, a cotransporter couples the return of H^+ to the transport of sucrose into the cell. This protein can translocate sucrose into the cell against its concentration gradient, but only if the sucrose molecule travels in the company of an H^+. The H^+ uses the transport protein as an avenue to diffuse down its own electrochemical gradient, which is maintained by the proton pump. Plants use sucrose-H^+ cotransport to load sucrose produced by photosynthesis into cells in the veins of leaves. The vascular tissue of the plant can then distribute the sugar to nonphotosynthetic organs, such as roots.

What we know about cotransport proteins in animal cells has helped us find more effective treatments for diarrhea, a serious problem in developing countries. Normally, sodium in waste is reabsorbed in the colon, maintaining constant levels

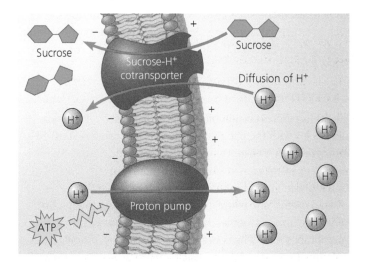

▲ **Figure 5.17 Cotransport: active transport driven by a concentration gradient.** A carrier protein, such as this sucrose-H^+ cotransporter in a plant cell (top), is able to use the diffusion of H^+ down its electrochemical gradient into the cell to drive the uptake of sucrose against its concentration gradient. (The cell wall is not shown.) Although not technically part of the cotransport process, an ATP-driven proton pump is shown here (bottom), which concentrates H^+ outside the cell. The resulting H^+ gradient represents potential energy that can be used for active transport—of sucrose, in this case. Thus, ATP indirectly provides the energy necessary for cotransport.

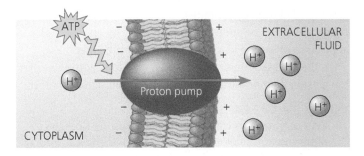

▲ **Figure 5.16 A proton pump.** Proton pumps are electrogenic pumps that store energy by generating voltage (charge separation) across membranes. A proton pump translocates positive charge in the form of hydrogen ions (that is, protons). The voltage and H^+ concentration gradient represent a dual energy source that can drive other processes, such as the uptake of nutrients. Most proton pumps are powered by ATP.

in the body, but diarrhea expels waste so rapidly that reabsorption is not possible, and sodium levels fall precipitously. To treat this life-threatening condition, patients are given a solution to drink containing high concentrations of salt (NaCl) and glucose. The solutes are taken up by sodium-glucose cotransporters on the surface of intestinal cells and passed through the cells into the blood. This simple treatment has lowered infant mortality worldwide.

CONCEPT 5.5

Bulk transport across the plasma membrane occurs by exocytosis and endocytosis

Water and small solutes enter and leave the cell by diffusing through the lipid bilayer of the plasma membrane or by being moved across the membrane by transport proteins. However, large molecules—such as proteins and polysaccharides, as well as larger particles—generally cross the membrane in bulk, packaged in vesicles. Like active transport, these processes require energy.

Exocytosis

The cell secretes certain biological molecules by the fusion of vesicles with the plasma membrane; this process is called **exocytosis**. A transport vesicle that has budded from the Golgi apparatus moves along microtubules of the cytoskeleton to the plasma membrane. When the vesicle membrane and plasma membrane come into contact, specific proteins rearrange the lipid molecules of the two bilayers so that the two membranes fuse. The contents of the vesicle then spill to the outside of the cell, and the vesicle membrane becomes part of the plasma membrane (see Figure 5.8, step 4).

Many secretory cells use exocytosis to export products. For example, the cells in the pancreas that make insulin secrete it into the extracellular fluid by exocytosis. In another example, nerve cells use exocytosis to release neurotransmitters that signal other neurons or muscle cells. When plant cells are making cell walls, exocytosis delivers proteins and carbohydrates from Golgi vesicles to the outside of the cell.

Endocytosis

In **endocytosis**, the cell takes in molecules and particulate matter by forming new vesicles from the plasma membrane. Although the proteins involved in the two processes are different, the events of endocytosis look like the reverse of exocytosis. First, a small area of the plasma membrane sinks inward to form a pocket. Then, as the pocket deepens, it pinches in, forming a vesicle containing material that had been outside the cell. Study **Figure 5.18** carefully to understand the three types of endocytosis: phagocytosis ("cellular eating"), pinocytosis ("cellular drinking"), and receptor-mediated endocytosis.

Human cells use receptor-mediated endocytosis to take in cholesterol for membrane synthesis and the synthesis of other steroids. Cholesterol travels in the blood in particles called low-density lipoproteins (LDLs), each a complex of lipids and a protein. LDLs bind to LDL receptors on plasma membranes and then enter the cells by endocytosis. In the inherited disease familial hypercholesterolemia, characterized by a very high level of cholesterol in the blood, LDLs cannot enter cells because the LDL receptor proteins are defective or missing:

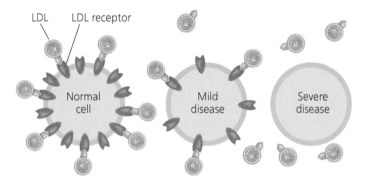

Consequently, cholesterol accumulates in the blood, where it contributes to early atherosclerosis, the buildup of lipid deposits within the walls of blood vessels. This buildup narrows the space in the vessels and impedes blood flow, potentially resulting in heart damage or stroke.

Endocytosis and exocytosis also provide mechanisms for rejuvenating or remodeling the plasma membrane. These processes occur continually in most eukaryotic cells, yet the amount of plasma membrane in a nongrowing cell remains fairly constant. The addition of membrane by one process appears to offset the loss of membrane by the other.

In the final section of this chapter, we'll look at the role of the plasma membrane and its proteins in cell signaling.

Phagocytosis

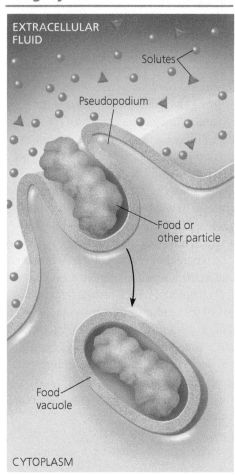

In **phagocytosis**, a cell engulfs a particle by extending pseudopodia (singular, *pseudopodium*) around it and packaging it within a membranous sac called a food vacuole. The particle will be digested after the food vacuole fuses with a lysosome containing hydrolytic enzymes (see Figure 4.12).

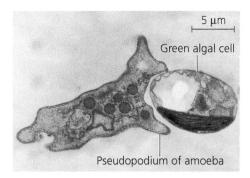

An amoeba engulfing a green algal cell via phagocytosis (TEM).

ANIMATION Visit the Study Area in **MasteringBiology** for the BioFlix® 3-D Animation on Membrane Transport.

Pinocytosis

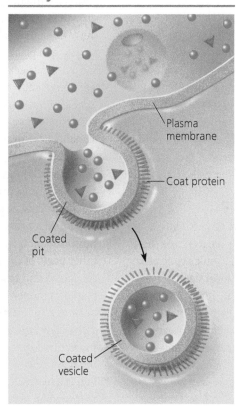

In **pinocytosis**, a cell continually "gulps" droplets of extracellular fluid into tiny vesicles, formed by infoldings of the plasma membrane. In this way, the cell obtains molecules dissolved in the droplets. Because any and all solutes are taken into the cell, pinocytosis as shown here is nonspecific for the substances it transports. In many cases, as above, the parts of the plasma membrane that form vesicles are lined on their cytoplasmic side by a fuzzy layer of coat protein; the "pits" and resulting vesicles are said to be "coated."

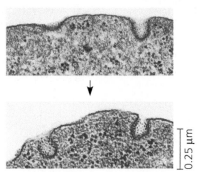

Pinocytotic vesicles forming (TEMs).

Receptor-Mediated Endocytosis

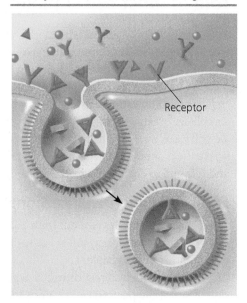

Receptor-mediated endocytosis is a specialized type of pinocytosis that enables the cell to acquire bulk quantities of specific substances, even though those substances may not be very concentrated in the extracellular fluid. Embedded in the plasma membrane are proteins with receptor sites exposed to the extracellular fluid. Specific solutes bind to the sites. The receptor proteins then cluster in coated pits, and each coated pit forms a vesicle containing the bound molecules. Notice that there are relatively more bound molecules (purple triangles) inside the vesicle, but other molecules (green balls) are also present. After the ingested material is liberated from the vesicle, the emptied receptors are recycled to the plasma membrane by the same vesicle (not shown).

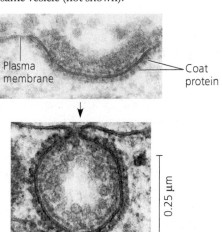

Top: A coated pit. *Bottom*: A coated vesicle forming during receptor-mediated endocytosis (TEMs).

The plasma membrane plays a key role in most cell signaling

In a multicellular organism, whether a human being or an oak tree, it is cell-to-cell communication that allows the trillions of cells of the body to coordinate their activities, and the communication process usually involves the cells' plasma membranes. In fact, communication between cells is also essential for many unicellular organisms, including prokaryotes. However, here we will focus on cell signaling in animals and plants. We'll describe the main mechanisms by which cells receive, process, and respond to chemical signals sent from other cells.

Local and Long-Distance Signaling

The signaling molecules sent out from cells are targeted for other cells that may or may not be immediately adjacent. As discussed earlier in this chapter and in Concept 4.7, eukaryotic cells may communicate by direct contact, a type of local signaling. Both animals and plants have cell junctions that, where present, directly connect the cytoplasms of adjacent cells; in animals, these are gap junctions (see Figure 4.27), and in plants, plasmodesmata (see Figure 4.25). In these cases, signaling substances dissolved in the cytosol can pass freely between adjacent cells. Also, animal cells may communicate via direct contact between membrane-bound cell-surface molecules in cell-cell recognition (see Figure 5.7d). This sort of local signaling is especially important in embryonic development and in the immune response.

In many other cases of local signaling, the signaling cell secretes messenger molecules. Some of these travel only short distances; such local regulators influence cells in the vicinity. One class of local regulators in animals, *growth factors*, are compounds that stimulate nearby target cells to grow and divide. Numerous cells can simultaneously receive and respond to the molecules of growth factor produced by a nearby cell. This type of local signaling in animals is called *paracrine signaling* **(Figure 5.19a)**. (Local signaling in plants is discussed in Concept 31.1.)

A more specialized type of local signaling called *synaptic signaling* occurs in the animal nervous system **(Figure 5.19b)**. An electrical signal moving along a nerve cell triggers the secretion of neurotransmitter molecules carrying a chemical signal. These molecules diffuse across the synapse, the narrow space between the nerve cell and its target cell (often another nerve cell), triggering a response in the target cell.

Both animals and plants use chemicals called **hormones** for long-distance signaling. In hormonal signaling in animals, also known as *endocrine signaling*, specialized cells release hormone molecules, which travel via the circulatory system to other parts of the body, where they reach target cells that can recognize and respond to the hormones **(Figure 5.19c)**. Most plant hormones (see Concept 31.1) reach distant targets via plant vascular tissues (xylem or phloem; see Concept 28.1), but some travel through the air as a gas. Hormones vary widely in molecular size and type, as do local regulators. For instance, the plant hormone ethylene, a gas that promotes fruit ripening, is a hydrocarbon of only six atoms (C_2H_4). In contrast, the mammalian hormone insulin, which regulates sugar levels in the blood, is a protein with thousands of atoms.

What happens when a cell encounters a secreted signaling molecule? We will now consider this question, beginning with a bit of historical background.

▼ **Figure 5.19 Local and long-distance cell signaling by secreted molecules in animals.** In both local and long-distance signaling, only specific target cells that can recognize a given signaling molecule will respond to it.

Local signaling

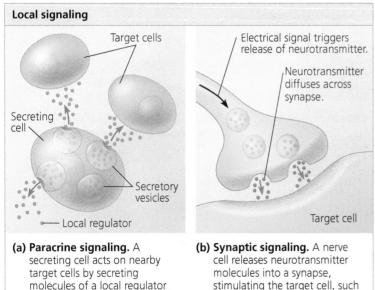

Long-distance signaling

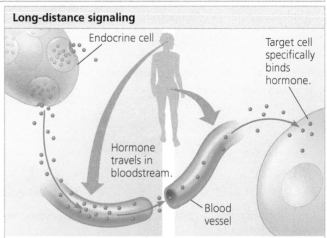

(a) Paracrine signaling. A secreting cell acts on nearby target cells by secreting molecules of a local regulator (a growth factor, for example).

(b) Synaptic signaling. A nerve cell releases neurotransmitter molecules into a synapse, stimulating the target cell, such as a muscle or nerve cell.

(c) Endocrine (hormonal) signaling. Specialized endocrine cells secrete hormones into body fluids, often blood. Hormones reach virtually all body cells, but are bound only by some cells.

The Three Stages of Cell Signaling: *A Preview*

Our current understanding of how chemical messengers act on cells had its origins in the pioneering work of the American Earl W. Sutherland about a half-century ago. He was investigating how the animal hormone epinephrine (also called adrenaline) triggers the "fight-or-flight" response in animals by stimulating the breakdown of the storage polysaccharide glycogen within liver cells and skeletal muscle cells. Glycogen breakdown releases the sugar glucose 1-phosphate, which the cell converts to glucose 6-phosphate. The liver or muscle cell can then use this compound, an early intermediate in glycolysis, for energy production. Alternatively, the compound can be stripped of phosphate and released from the cell into the blood as glucose, which can fuel cells throughout the body. Thus, one effect of epinephrine is the mobilization of fuel reserves, which can be used by an animal to either defend itself (fight) or escape whatever elicited a scare (flight), as this impala is doing. Sutherland's research team discovered that epinephrine stimulates glycogen breakdown by activating a cytosolic enzyme (glycogen phosphorylase) while never actually entering the glycogen-containing cells. This discovery provided two insights. First, epinephrine does not interact directly with glycogen phosphorylase; an intermediate step or series of steps must be occurring in the cell. Second, the plasma membrane must somehow be involved in transmitting the signal. Sutherland's research suggested that the process going on at the receiving end of a cell-to-cell message can be divided into three stages: reception, transduction, and response (**Figure 5.20**). ❶ **Reception** is the target cell's detection of a signaling molecule coming from outside the cell. A chemical signal is "detected" when the signaling molecule binds to a receptor protein located at the cell's surface or, in some cases, inside the cell. ❷ **Transduction** is a step or series of steps that converts the signal to a form that can bring about a specific cellular response. Transduction usually requires a sequence of changes in a series of different molecules—a **signal transduction pathway**. The molecules in the pathway are often called relay molecules. ❸ In the third stage of cell signaling, the transduced signal finally triggers a specific cellular **response**. The response may be almost any imaginable cellular activity, such as catalysis by an enzyme (for example, glycogen phosphorylase),

rearrangement of the cytoskeleton, or activation of specific genes in the nucleus. The cell-signaling process helps ensure that crucial activities like these occur in the right cells, at the right time, and in proper coordination with the activities of other cells of the organism. We'll now explore the mechanisms of cell signaling in more detail.

Reception, the Binding of a Signaling Molecule to a Receptor Protein

A radio station broadcasts its signal indiscriminately, but it can be picked up only by radios tuned to the right frequency; reception of the signal depends on the receiver. Similarly, in the case of epinephrine, the hormone encounters many types of cells as it circulates in the blood, but only certain target cells detect and react to the epinephrine molecule. A receptor protein on or in the target cell allows the cell to detect the signal and respond to it. The signaling molecule is complementary in shape to a specific site on the receptor and attaches there, like a key in a lock. The signaling molecule acts as a **ligand**, a molecule that specifically binds to another molecule, often a larger one. (LDLs, mentioned in Concept 5.5, act as ligands when they bind to their receptors, as do the molecules that bind to enzymes; see Figure 3.17.) Ligand binding generally causes a receptor protein to undergo a change in shape. For many receptors, this shape change directly activates the receptor, enabling it to interact with other cellular molecules.

Most signal receptors are plasma membrane proteins. Their ligands are water-soluble and generally too large to pass freely through the plasma membrane. Other signal receptors, however, are located inside the cell. We discuss both of these types next.

Receptors in the Plasma Membrane

Most water-soluble signaling molecules bind to specific sites on receptor proteins that span the cell's plasma membrane. Such a transmembrane receptor transmits information from the extracellular environment to the inside of the cell by

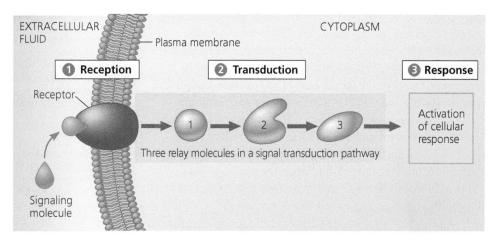

▲ **Figure 5.20 Overview of cell signaling.** From the perspective of the cell receiving the message, cell signaling can be divided into three stages: signal reception, signal transduction, and cellular response. When reception occurs at the plasma membrane, as shown here, the transduction stage is usually a pathway of several steps, with each specific relay molecule in the pathway bringing about a change in the next molecule. The final molecule in the pathway triggers the cell's response. The three stages are explained in more detail in the text.

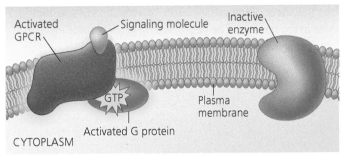

① When the appropriate signaling molecule binds to the extracellular side of the receptor, the receptor is activated and changes shape. Its cytoplasmic side then binds and activates a G protein. The activated G protein carries a GTP molecule.

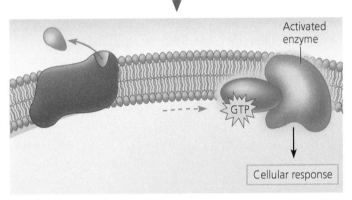

② The activated G protein leaves the receptor, diffuses along the membrane, and then binds to an enzyme, altering the enzyme's shape and activity. Once activated, the enzyme can trigger the next step leading to a cellular response. Binding of signaling molecules is reversible. The activating change in the GPCR, as well as the changes in the G protein and enzyme, are only temporary; these molecules soon become available for reuse.

▲ **Figure 5.21 A G protein-coupled receptor (GPCR) in action.**

changing shape when a specific ligand binds to it. We can see how transmembrane receptors work by looking at two major types: G protein-coupled receptors and ligand-gated ion channels. (A third type, not discussed here, is receptor tyrosine kinases, or RTKs. Abnormal functioning of some RTKs is associated with breast cancer; see Make Connections Figure 16.21.)

Figure 5.21 shows the functioning of a **G protein-coupled receptor (GPCR)**. A GPCR is a cell-surface transmembrane receptor that works with the help of a **G protein**, a protein that binds the energy-rich molecule GTP, which is similar to ATP (see end of Concept 3.1). Many signaling molecules—including epinephrine, other hormones, and neurotransmitters—use GPCRs. These receptors vary in the binding sites for their signaling molecules (ligands) and for different types of G proteins inside the cell. Nevertheless, GPCRs are all remarkably similar in structure, as are many G proteins, suggesting that these signaling systems evolved very early in the history of life.

The nearly 1,000 GPCRs examined to date make up the largest family of cell-surface receptors in mammals. GPCR pathways are extremely diverse in their functions, which

include roles in embryonic development and the senses of sight, smell, and taste. They are also involved in many human diseases. For example, cholera, pertussis (whooping cough), and botulism are caused by bacterial toxins that interfere with G protein function. Up to 60% of all medicines used today exert their effects by influencing G protein pathways.

A **ligand-gated ion channel** is a membrane receptor with a region that can act as a "gate" for ions when the receptor assumes a certain shape **(Figure 5.22)**. When a signaling molecule binds as a ligand to the receptor protein, the gate opens or closes, allowing or blocking the diffusion of specific ions, such as Na^+ or Ca^{2+}, through a channel in the protein. Like other membrane receptors, these proteins bind the ligand at a specific site on their extracellular side.

Ligand-gated ion channels are very important in the nervous system. For example, the neurotransmitter molecules released at a synapse between two nerve cells (see Figure 5.19b) bind as ligands to ion channels on the receiving cell, causing

① Here we show a ligand-gated ion channel receptor in which the gate remains closed until a ligand binds to the receptor.

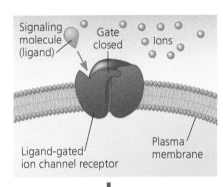

② When the ligand binds to the receptor and the gate opens, specific ions can flow through the channel and rapidly change the concentration of that particular ion inside the cell. This change may directly affect the activity of the cell in some way.

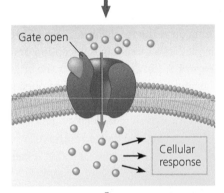

③ When the ligand dissociates from this receptor, the gate closes and ions no longer enter the cell.

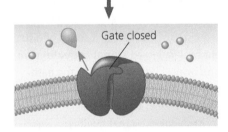

▲ **Figure 5.22 Ion channel receptor.** This is a ligand-gated ion channel, a type of receptor protein that regulates the passage of specific ions across the membrane. Whether the channel is open or closed depends on whether a specific ligand is bound to the protein.

the channels to open. The diffusion of ions through the open channels may trigger an electrical signal that propagates down the length of the receiving cell. (You'll learn more about ion channels in Chapter 37.)

Intracellular Receptors

Intracellular receptor proteins are found in either the cytoplasm or nucleus of target cells. To reach such a receptor, a signaling molecule passes through the target cell's plasma membrane. A number of important signaling molecules can do this because they are hydrophobic enough to cross the hydrophobic interior of the membrane. These hydrophobic chemical messengers include the steroid hormones and thyroid hormones of animals. In both animals and plants, another chemical signaling molecule with an intracellular receptor is nitric oxide (NO), a gas; its very small, hydrophobic molecules can easily pass between the membrane phospholipids.

The behavior of aldosterone is representative of steroid hormones. This hormone is secreted by cells of the adrenal gland, a gland that lies over the kidney. It then travels through the blood and enters cells all over the body. However, a response occurs only in kidney cells, which contain receptor molecules for aldosterone. In these cells, the hormone binds to the receptor protein, activating it **(Figure 5.23)**. With the hormone attached, the active form of the receptor protein then enters the nucleus and turns on specific genes that control water and sodium flow in kidney cells, ultimately affecting blood volume.

How does the activated hormone-receptor complex turn on genes? Recall that the genes in a cell's DNA function by being transcribed and processed into messenger RNA (mRNA), which leaves the nucleus and is translated into a specific protein by ribosomes in the cytoplasm (see Figure 3.26). Special proteins called *transcription factors* control which genes are turned on—that is, which genes are transcribed into mRNA—in a particular cell at a particular time. When the aldosterone receptor is activated, it acts as a transcription factor that turns on specific genes.

By acting as a transcription factor, the aldosterone receptor itself carries out the transduction part of the signaling pathway. Most other intracellular receptors function in the same way, although many of them, such as the thyroid hormone receptor, are already in the nucleus before the signaling molecule reaches them. Interestingly, many of these intracellular receptor proteins are structurally similar, suggesting an evolutionary kinship.

Transduction by Cascades of Molecular Interactions

When receptors for signaling molecules are plasma membrane proteins, like most of those we have discussed, the transduction stage of cell signaling is usually a multistep pathway involving many molecules. Steps often include activation of proteins by addition or removal of phosphate groups or release of other small molecules or ions that act as messengers. One benefit of multiple steps is the possibility of greatly amplifying a signal. If

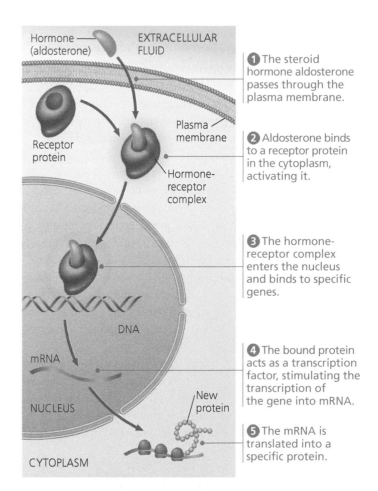

1 The steroid hormone aldosterone passes through the plasma membrane.

2 Aldosterone binds to a receptor protein in the cytoplasm, activating it.

3 The hormone-receptor complex enters the nucleus and binds to specific genes.

4 The bound protein acts as a transcription factor, stimulating the transcription of the gene into mRNA.

5 The mRNA is translated into a specific protein.

▲ **Figure 5.23 Steroid hormone interacting with an intracellular receptor.**

? *Why is a cell-surface receptor protein not required for this steroid hormone to enter the cell?*

each molecule in a pathway transmits the signal to numerous molecules at the next step in the series, the result is a geometric increase in the number of activated molecules by the end of the pathway. Moreover, multistep pathways provide more opportunities for coordination and control than do simpler systems.

The binding of a specific signaling molecule to a receptor in the plasma membrane triggers the first step in the chain of molecular interactions—the signal transduction pathway—that leads to a particular response within the cell. Like falling dominoes, the signal-activated receptor activates another molecule, which activates yet another molecule, and so on, until the protein that produces the final cellular response is activated. The molecules that relay a signal from receptor to response, which we call relay molecules in this book, are often proteins. The interaction of proteins is a major theme of cell signaling.

Keep in mind that the original signaling molecule is not physically passed along a signaling pathway; in most cases, it never even enters the cell. When we say that the signal is relayed along a pathway, we mean that certain information is passed on. At each step, the signal is transduced into a different form, commonly via a shape change in a protein. Very often, the shape change is brought about by phosphorylation, the addition of phosphate groups to a protein (see Figure 3.6).

Protein Phosphorylation and Dephosphorylation

The phosphorylation of proteins and its reverse, dephosphorylation, are a widespread cellular mechanism for regulating protein activity. An enzyme that transfers phosphate groups from ATP to a protein is known as a **protein kinase**. Such enzymes are widely involved in signaling pathways in animals, plants, and fungi.

Many of the relay molecules in signal transduction pathways are protein kinases, and they often act on other protein kinases in the pathway. A hypothetical pathway containing two different protein kinases that form a short **phosphorylation cascade** is depicted in **Figure 5.24**. The sequence shown is similar to many known pathways, although typically three protein kinases are involved. The signal is transmitted by a cascade of protein phosphorylations, each bringing with it a shape change. Each such shape change results from the interaction of the newly added phosphate groups with charged or polar amino acids (see Figure 3.18). The addition of phosphate groups often changes the form of a protein from inactive to active.

The importance of protein kinases can hardly be overstated. About 2% of our own genes are thought to code for protein kinases. A single cell may have hundreds of different kinds, each specific for a different protein. Together, they probably regulate a large proportion of the thousands of proteins in a cell. Among these are most of the proteins that, in turn, regulate cell division. Abnormal activity of such a kinase can cause abnormal cell division and contribute to the development of cancer.

Equally important in the phosphorylation cascade are the **protein phosphatases** (see Figure 5.24), enzymes that can rapidly remove phosphate groups from proteins, a process called dephosphorylation. By dephosphorylating and thus inactivating protein kinases, phosphatases provide the mechanism for turning off the signal transduction pathway when the initial signal is no longer present. Phosphatases also make the protein kinases available for reuse, enabling the cell to respond again to an extracellular signal. A phosphorylation-dephosphorylation system acts as a molecular switch in the cell, turning an activity on or off, or up or down, as required. At any given moment, the activity of a protein regulated by phosphorylation depends on the balance in the cell between active kinase molecules and active phosphatase molecules.

Small Molecules and Ions as Second Messengers

Not all components of signal transduction pathways are proteins. Many signaling pathways also involve small, nonprotein, water-soluble molecules or ions called **second messengers**. (The pathway's "first messenger" is considered to be the extracellular signaling molecule that binds to the membrane receptor.) Because they are small, second messengers can readily spread throughout the cell by diffusion. The two most common second messengers are cyclic AMP and calcium ions, Ca^{2+}. Here we'll limit our discussion to cyclic AMP.

In his research on epinephrine, Earl Sutherland discovered that the binding of epinephrine to the plasma membrane of a liver cell elevates the cytosolic concentration of **cyclic AMP** (**cAMP**; cyclic adenosine monophosphate). The binding of epinephrine to a G protein-coupled receptor leads, via a G protein, to activation of adenylyl cyclase, an enzyme embedded in the plasma membrane that converts ATP to cAMP (**Figure 5.25**). Each molecule of adenylyl cyclase can catalyze the synthesis of many molecules of cAMP. In this way, the normal cellular concentration of cAMP can be boosted 20-fold in a matter of seconds. The cAMP broadcasts the signal to the cytoplasm. It does not persist for long in the absence of the hormone because a different enzyme converts cAMP to AMP. Another surge of epinephrine is needed to boost the cytosolic concentration of cAMP again.

Subsequent research has revealed that epinephrine is only one of many

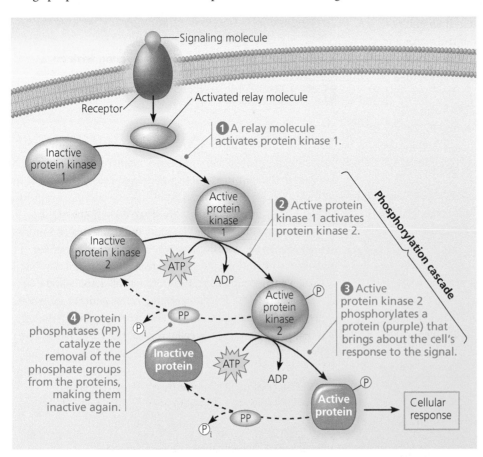

▲ **Figure 5.24 A phosphorylation cascade.** In a phosphorylation cascade, a series of different proteins in a pathway are phosphorylated in turn, each protein adding a phosphate group to the next one in line. Dephosphorylation by protein phosphatases (PP) can then return the protein to its inactive form.

? *Which protein is responsible for activation of protein kinase 2?*

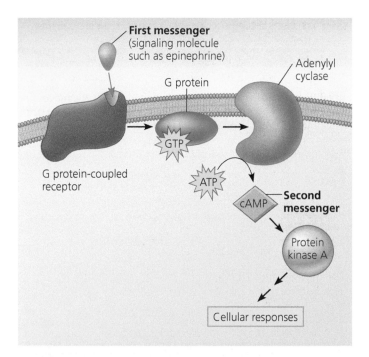

▲ **Figure 5.25 cAMP as a second messenger in a G protein signaling pathway.** The first messenger activates a G protein-coupled receptor, which activates a specific G protein. In turn, the G protein activates adenylyl cyclase, which catalyzes the conversion of ATP to cAMP. The cAMP then acts as a second messenger and activates another protein, usually protein kinase A, leading to cellular responses.

hormones and other signaling molecules that trigger the formation of cAMP. The immediate effect of cAMP is usually the activation of a protein kinase called *protein kinase A*. The activated protein kinase A then phosphorylates various other proteins.

Response: Regulation of Transcription or Cytoplasmic Activities

What is the nature of the final step in a signaling pathway—the *response* to an external signal? Ultimately, a signal transduction pathway leads to the regulation of one or more cellular activities. The response may occur in the nucleus of the cell or in the cytoplasm.

Many signaling pathways ultimately regulate protein synthesis, usually by turning specific genes on or off in the nucleus. Like an activated steroid receptor (see Figure 5.23), the final activated molecule in a signaling pathway may function as a transcription factor. **Figure 5.26** shows an example in which a signaling pathway activates a transcription factor that turns a gene on: The response to this growth factor signal is transcription, the synthesis of one or more specific mRNAs, which will be translated in the cytoplasm into specific proteins. In other cases, the transcription factor might regulate a gene by turning it off. Often a transcription factor regulates several different genes.

Sometimes a signaling pathway may regulate the *activity* of proteins rather than causing their *synthesis* by activating gene expression. This directly affects proteins that function

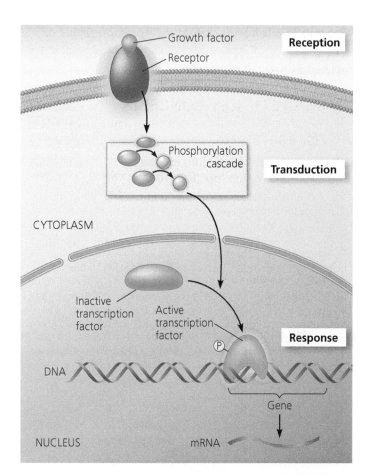

▲ **Figure 5.26 Nuclear response to a signal: the activation of a specific gene by a growth factor.** This diagram shows a typical signaling pathway that leads to the regulation of gene activity in the cell nucleus. The initial signaling molecule, a local regulator called a growth factor, triggers a phosphorylation cascade. (The ATP molecules and phosphate groups are not shown.) Once phosphorylated, the last kinase in the sequence enters the nucleus and activates a transcription factor, which stimulates transcription of a specific gene. The resulting mRNAs then direct the synthesis of a particular protein in the cytoplasm.

outside the nucleus. For example, a signal may cause the opening or closing of an ion channel in the plasma membrane or a change in cell metabolism. As we have discussed, the response of cells to the hormone epinephrine helps regulate cellular energy metabolism by affecting the activity of an enzyme: The final step in the signaling pathway that begins with epinephrine binding activates the enzyme that catalyzes the breakdown of glycogen.

CONCEPT CHECK 5.6

1. During an epinephrine-initiated signal in liver cells, in which of the three stages of cell signaling does glycogen phosphorylase act?
2. When a signal transduction pathway involves a phosphorylation cascade, what turns off the cell's response?
3. **WHAT IF?** How can a target cell's response to a single hormone molecule result in a response that affects a million other molecules?

For suggested answers, see Appendix A.

Go to **MasteringBiology**® for Assignments, the eText, and the Study Area with Animations, Activities, Vocab Self-Quiz, and Practice Tests.

SUMMARY OF KEY CONCEPTS

VOCAB SELF-QUIZ

goo.gl/gbai8v

CONCEPT 5.1

Cellular membranes are fluid mosaics of lipids and proteins (pp. 100–104)

- In the **fluid mosaic model**, **amphipathic** proteins are embedded in the phospholipid bilayer.
- Phospholipids and some proteins move laterally within the membrane. The unsaturated hydrocarbon tails of some phospholipids keep membranes fluid at lower temperatures, while cholesterol helps membranes resist changes in fluidity caused by temperature changes.
- Membrane proteins function in transport, enzymatic activity, attachment to the cytoskeleton and extracellular matrix, cell-cell recognition, intercellular joining, and signal transduction. Short chains of sugars linked to proteins (in **glycoproteins**) and lipids (in **glycolipids**) on the exterior side of the plasma membrane interact with surface molecules of other cells.
- Membrane proteins and lipids are synthesized in the ER and modified in the ER and Golgi apparatus. The inside and outside faces of membranes differ in molecular composition.

? *In what ways are membranes crucial to life?*

CONCEPT 5.2

Membrane structure results in selective permeability (p. 105)

- A cell must exchange molecules and ions with its surroundings, a process controlled by the **selective permeability** of the plasma membrane. Hydrophobic molecules are soluble in lipids and pass through membranes rapidly, whereas polar molecules and ions usually need specific **transport proteins**.

? *How do aquaporins affect the permeability of a membrane?*

CONCEPT 5.3

Passive transport is diffusion of a substance across a membrane with no energy investment (pp. 105–109)

- **Diffusion** is the spontaneous movement of a substance down its **concentration gradient**. Water diffuses out through the permeable membrane of a cell (**osmosis**) if the solution outside has a higher solute concentration than the cytosol (is **hypertonic**); water enters the cell if the solution has a lower solute concentration (is **hypotonic**). If the concentrations are equal (**isotonic**), no net osmosis occurs. Cell survival depends on balancing water uptake and loss.

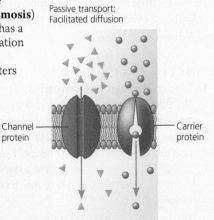
Passive transport: Facilitated diffusion

Channel protein

Carrier protein

- In **facilitated diffusion**, a transport protein speeds the movement of water or a solute across a membrane down its concentration gradient. **Ion channels** facilitate the diffusion of ions across a membrane. Carrier proteins can undergo changes in shape that translocate bound solutes across the membrane.

? *What happens to a cell placed in a hypertonic solution? Describe the free water concentration inside and out.*

CONCEPT 5.4

Active transport uses energy to move solutes against their gradients (pp. 109–112)

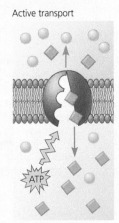
Active transport

- Specific membrane proteins use energy, usually in the form of ATP, to do the work of **active transport**.
- Ions can have both a concentration (chemical) gradient and an electrical gradient (voltage). These gradients combine in the **electrochemical gradient**, which determines the net direction of ionic diffusion.
- **Cotransport** of two solutes occurs when a membrane protein enables the "downhill" diffusion of one solute to drive the "uphill" transport of the other.

? *ATP is not directly involved in the functioning of a cotransporter. Why, then, is cotransport considered active transport?*

CONCEPT 5.5

Bulk transport across the plasma membrane occurs by exocytosis and endocytosis (pp. 112–113)

- Three main types of **endocytosis** are **phagocytosis**, **pinocytosis**, and **receptor-mediated endocytosis**.

? *Which type of endocytosis involves the binding of specific substances in the extracellular fluid to membrane proteins? What does this type of transport enable a cell to do?*

CONCEPT 5.6

The plasma membrane plays a key role in most cell signaling (pp. 114–119)

- Local signaling by animal cells involves direct contact or the secretion of growth factors and other signaling molecules. For long-distance signaling, animal and plant cells use **hormones**; animals also signal electrically.
- Signaling molecules that bind to membrane receptors trigger a three-stage cell-signaling pathway:

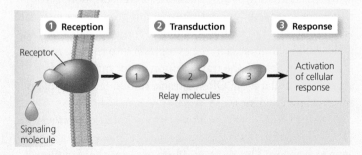

❶ Reception **❷ Transduction** **❸ Response**

Receptor

Relay molecules

Activation of cellular response

Signaling molecule

- In **reception**, a signaling molecule binds to a receptor protein, causing the protein to change shape. Two major types of membrane receptors are **G protein-coupled receptors (GPCRs)**, which work with the help of cytoplasmic **G proteins**, and **ligand-gated ion channels**, which open or close in response to binding by signaling molecules. Signaling molecules that are hydrophobic cross the plasma membrane and bind to receptors inside the cell.
- At each step in a **signal transduction pathway**, the signal is *transduced* into a different form, which commonly involves a change in a protein's shape. Many pathways include **phosphorylation cascades**, in which a series of **protein kinases** each add a phosphate group to the next one in line, activating it. The balance between phosphorylation and dephosphorylation, by **protein phosphatases**, regulates the activity of proteins in the pathway.
- **Second messengers**, such as the small molecule **cyclic AMP (cAMP)**, diffuse readily through the cytosol and thus help broadcast signals quickly. Many G proteins activate the enzyme that makes cAMP from ATP.
- The cell's **response** to a signal may be the regulation of transcription in the nucleus or of an activity in the cytoplasm.

? *What determines whether a cell responds to a hormone such as epinephrine? What determines how the cell responds?*

TEST YOUR UNDERSTANDING

PRACTICE TEST

goo.gl/CRZjvS

Level 1: Knowledge/Comprehension

1. In what way do the membranes of a eukaryotic cell vary?
   (A) Phospholipids are found only in certain membranes.
   (B) Certain proteins are unique to each kind of membrane.
   (C) Only certain membranes of the cell are selectively permeable.
   (D) Only certain membranes are constructed from amphipathic molecules.

2. Which of the following factors would tend to increase membrane fluidity?
   (A) a greater proportion of unsaturated phospholipids
   (B) a greater proportion of saturated phospholipids
   (C) a lower temperature
   (D) a relatively high protein content in the membrane

3. Phosphorylation cascades involving a series of protein kinases are useful for cellular signal transduction because
   (A) they are species specific.
   (B) they always lead to the same cellular response.
   (C) they amplify the original signal manyfold.
   (D) they counter the harmful effects of phosphatases.

4. Lipid-soluble signaling molecules, such as aldosterone, cross the membranes of all cells but affect only target cells because
   (A) only target cells retain the appropriate DNA segments.
   (B) intracellular receptors are present only in target cells.
   (C) only target cells have enzymes that break down aldosterone.
   (D) only in target cells is aldosterone able to initiate the phosphorylation cascade that turns genes on.

Level 2: Application/Analysis

5. Which of the following processes includes all the others?
   (A) osmosis
   (B) diffusion of a solute across a membrane
   (C) passive transport
   (D) transport of an ion down its electrochemical gradient

6. Based on Figure 5.17, which of these experimental treatments would increase the rate of sucrose transport into a plant cell?
   (A) decreasing extracellular sucrose concentration
   (B) decreasing extracellular pH
   (C) decreasing cytoplasmic pH
   (D) adding a substance that makes the membrane more permeable to hydrogen ions

Level 3: Synthesis/Evaluation

7. **SCIENTIFIC INQUIRY**
   An experiment is designed to study the mechanism of sucrose uptake by plant cells. Cells are immersed in a sucrose solution, and the pH of the solution is monitored. Samples of the cells are taken at intervals, and their sucrose concentration is measured. The pH is observed to decrease until it reaches a steady, slightly acidic level, and then sucrose uptake begins. (a) Evaluate these results and propose a hypothesis to explain them. (b) Predict what would happen if an inhibitor of ATP regeneration by the cell were added to the beaker once the pH was at a steady level? Explain your thinking.

8. **SCIENCE, TECHNOLOGY, AND SOCIETY**
   Extensive irrigation in arid regions causes salts to accumulate in the soil. (When water evaporates, salts that were dissolved in the water are left behind in the soil.) Based on what you have learned about water balance in plant cells, explain why increased soil salinity (saltiness) might be harmful to crops.

9. **FOCUS ON EVOLUTION**
   Paramecium and other unicellular eukaryotes that live in hypotonic environments have cell membranes that limit water uptake, while those living in isotonic environments have membranes that are more permeable to water. Describe what water regulation adaptations might have evolved in unicellular eukaryotes in hypertonic habitats such as the Great Salt Lake and in habitats with changing salt concentration.

10. **FOCUS ON INTERACTIONS**
    A human pancreatic cell obtains O_2—and necessary molecules such as glucose, amino acids, and cholesterol—from its environment, and it releases CO_2 as a waste product. In response to hormonal signals, the cell secretes digestive enzymes. It also regulates its ion concentrations by exchange with its environment. Based on what you have just learned about the structure and function of cellular membranes, write a short essay (100–150 words) to describe how such a cell accomplishes these interactions with its environment.

11. **SYNTHESIZE YOUR KNOWLEDGE**

In the supermarket, lettuce and other produce are often sprayed with water. Explain why this makes vegetables crisp.

For selected answers, see Appendix A.

KEY CONCEPTS

6.1 An organism's metabolism transforms matter and energy

6.2 The free-energy change of a reaction tells us whether or not the reaction occurs spontaneously

6.3 ATP powers cellular work by coupling exergonic reactions to endergonic reactions

6.4 Enzymes speed up metabolic reactions by lowering energy barriers

6.5 Regulation of enzyme activity helps control metabolism

▲ **Figure 6.1** What causes these breaking waves to glow?

The Energy of Life

The living cell is a chemical factory in miniature, where thousands of reactions occur within a microscopic space. Sugars can be converted to amino acids that are linked together into proteins when needed, and when food is digested, proteins are dismantled into amino acids that can be converted to sugars. The process called cellular respiration drives the cellular economy by extracting the energy stored in sugars and other fuels. Cells apply this energy to perform various types of work. In an exotic example, the ocean waves shown in **Figure 6.1** are brightly illuminated from within by free-floating single-celled marine organisms called dinoflagellates. These dinoflagellates convert the energy stored in certain organic molecules to light, a process called bioluminescence. Such metabolic activities are precisely coordinated and controlled in the cell. In its complexity, its efficiency, and its responsiveness to subtle changes, the cell is peerless as a chemical factory. The concepts of metabolism that you learn in this chapter will help you understand how matter and energy flow during life's processes and how that flow is regulated.

CONCEPT 6.1

An organism's metabolism transforms matter and energy

The totality of an organism's chemical reactions is called **metabolism** (from the Greek *metabole*, change). Metabolism is an emergent property of life that arises from orderly interactions between molecules.

Metabolic Pathways

We can picture a cell's metabolism as an elaborate road map of many chemical reactions, arranged as intersecting metabolic pathways. In a **metabolic pathway**, a specific molecule is altered in a series of defined steps, resulting in a product. Each step of the pathway is catalyzed by a specific enzyme:

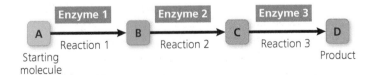

Analogous to the red, yellow, and green stoplights that control the flow of automobile traffic, mechanisms that regulate enzymes balance metabolic supply and demand.

Metabolism as a whole manages the material and energy resources of the cell. Some metabolic pathways release energy by breaking down complex molecules to simpler compounds. These degradative processes are called **catabolic pathways**, or breakdown pathways. A major pathway of catabolism is cellular respiration, in which the sugar glucose and other organic fuels are broken down in the presence of oxygen to carbon dioxide and water. Energy stored in the organic molecules becomes available to do the work of the cell, such as ciliary beating or membrane transport. **Anabolic pathways**, in contrast, consume energy to build complicated molecules from simpler ones; they are sometimes called biosynthetic pathways. Examples of anabolism are the synthesis of an amino acid from simpler molecules and the synthesis of a protein from amino acids. Catabolic and anabolic pathways are the "downhill" and "uphill" avenues of the metabolic landscape. Energy released from the downhill reactions of catabolic pathways can be stored and then used to drive the uphill reactions of anabolic pathways.

In this chapter, we will focus on mechanisms common to metabolic pathways. Because energy is fundamental to all metabolic processes, a basic knowledge of energy is necessary to understand how the living cell works. Although we will use some nonliving examples to study energy, the concepts demonstrated by these examples also apply to **bioenergetics**, the study of how energy flows through living organisms.

Forms of Energy

Energy is the capacity to cause change. In everyday life, energy is important because some forms of energy can be used to do work—that is, to move matter against opposing forces, such as gravity and friction. Put another way, energy is the ability to rearrange a collection of matter. For example, you expend energy to turn the pages of this book, and your cells expend energy in transporting certain substances across membranes. Energy exists in various forms, and the work of life depends on the ability of cells to transform energy from one form to another.

Energy can be associated with the relative motion of objects; this energy is called **kinetic energy**. Moving objects can perform work by imparting motion to other matter: Water gushing through a dam turns turbines, and the contraction of leg muscles pushes bicycle pedals. **Thermal energy** is kinetic energy associated with the random movement of atoms or molecules; thermal energy in transfer from one object to another is called **heat**. Light is also a type of energy that can be harnessed to perform work, such as powering photosynthesis in green plants.

An object not presently moving may still possess energy. Energy that is not kinetic is called **potential energy**; it is energy that matter possesses because of its location or structure. Water behind a dam, for instance, possesses energy because of its altitude above sea level. Molecules possess energy because of the arrangement of electrons in the bonds between their atoms. **Chemical energy** is a term used by biologists to refer to the potential energy available for release in a chemical reaction. Recall that catabolic pathways release energy by breaking down complex molecules. Biologists say that these complex molecules, such as glucose, are high in chemical energy. During a catabolic reaction, some bonds are broken and others are formed, releasing energy and resulting in lower-energy breakdown products. This transformation also occurs in the engine of a car when the hydrocarbons of gasoline react explosively with oxygen, releasing the energy that pushes the pistons and producing exhaust. Although less explosive, a similar reaction of food molecules with oxygen provides chemical energy in biological systems, producing carbon dioxide and water as waste products. Biochemical pathways, carried out in the context of cellular structures, enable cells to release chemical energy from food molecules and use the energy to power life processes.

How is energy converted from one form to another? Consider **Figure 6.2**. The young woman climbing the ladder to the diving platform is releasing chemical energy from the food she ate for lunch and using some of that energy to perform the work of climbing. The kinetic energy of muscle movement is thus being transformed into potential energy due to her increasing height above the water. The young man diving is converting his potential energy to kinetic energy, which is then transferred to the water as he enters it. A small amount of energy is lost as heat due to friction.

Now let's consider the original source of the organic food molecules that provided the necessary chemical energy for the diver to climb the steps. This chemical energy was itself derived from light energy absorbed by plants during photosynthesis. Organisms are energy transformers.

A diver has more potential energy on the platform than in the water.

Diving converts potential energy to kinetic energy.

Climbing up converts the kinetic energy of muscle movement to potential energy.

A diver has less potential energy in the water than on the platform.

▲ **Figure 6.2 Transformations between potential and kinetic energy.**

The Laws of Energy Transformation

The study of the energy transformations that occur in a collection of matter is called **thermodynamics**. Scientists use the word *system* to denote the matter under study; they refer to the rest of the universe—everything outside the system—as the *surroundings*. An *isolated system*, such as that approximated by liquid in a thermos bottle, is unable to exchange either energy or matter with its surroundings outside the thermos. In an *open system*, energy and matter can be transferred between the system and its surroundings. Organisms are open systems. They absorb energy—for instance, light energy or chemical energy in the form of organic molecules—and release heat and metabolic waste products, such as carbon dioxide, to the surroundings. Two laws of thermodynamics govern energy transformations in organisms and all other collections of matter.

The First Law of Thermodynamics

According to the **first law of thermodynamics**, the energy of the universe is constant: *Energy can be transferred and or transformed, but it cannot be created or destroyed.* The first law is also known as the *principle of conservation of energy*. The electric company does not make energy, but merely converts it to a form that is convenient for us to use. By converting sunlight to chemical energy, a plant acts as an energy transformer, not an energy producer.

The brown bear in **Figure 6.3a** will convert the chemical energy of the organic molecules in its food to kinetic and other forms of energy as it carries out biological processes. What happens to this energy after it has performed work? The second law of thermodynamics helps to answer this question.

The Second Law of Thermodynamics

If energy cannot be destroyed, why can't organisms simply recycle their energy over and over again? It turns out that during every energy transfer or transformation, some energy is converted to thermal energy and released as heat, becoming unavailable to do work. Only a small fraction of the chemical energy from the food in Figure 6.3a is transformed into the motion of the brown bear shown in **Figure 6.3b**; most is lost as heat, which dissipates rapidly through the surroundings.

A system can put thermal energy to work only when there is a temperature difference that results in the thermal energy flowing as heat from a warmer location to a cooler one. If temperature is uniform, as it is in a living cell, then the heat generated during a chemical reaction will simply warm a body of matter, such as the organism. (This can make a room crowded with people uncomfortably warm, as each person is carrying out a multitude of chemical reactions!)

A logical consequence of the loss of usable energy as heat to the surroundings is that each energy transfer or transformation makes the universe more disordered. Scientists use a quantity called **entropy** as a measure of disorder, or randomness. The more randomly arranged a collection of matter is, the greater its entropy. We can now state the **second law of thermodynamics**: *Every energy transfer or transformation increases the entropy of the universe.* Although order can increase locally, there is an unstoppable trend toward randomization of the universe as a whole.

In many cases, increased entropy is evident in the physical disintegration of a system's organized structure. For example, you can observe increasing entropy in the gradual decay of an unmaintained building. Much of the increasing entropy of the universe is less obvious, however, because it takes the form of increasing amounts of heat and less ordered forms of matter. As the bear in Figure 6.3b converts chemical energy to kinetic energy, it is also increasing the disorder of its surroundings by producing heat and small molecules, such as the CO_2 it exhales, that are the breakdown products of food.

The concept of entropy helps us understand why certain processes are energetically favorable and occur on their own. It turns out that if a given process, by itself, leads to an increase in entropy, that process can proceed without requiring

(a) First law of thermodynamics: Energy can be transferred or transformed but neither created nor destroyed. For example, chemical reactions in this brown bear will convert the chemical (potential) energy in the fish into the kinetic energy of running.

(b) Second law of thermodynamics: Every energy transfer or transformation increases the disorder (entropy) of the universe. For example, as the bear runs, disorder is increased around it by the release of heat and small molecules that are the by-products of metabolism. A brown bear can run at speeds up to 35 miles per hour (56 km/hr) —as fast as a racehorse.

▲ **Figure 6.3 The two laws of thermodynamics.**

an input of energy. Such a process is called a **spontaneous process**. Note that as we're using it here, the word *spontaneous* does not imply that the process would occur quickly; rather, the word signifies that it is energetically favorable. (In fact, it may be helpful for you to think of the phrase "energetically favorable" when you read the formal term "spontaneous.") Some spontaneous processes, such as an explosion, may be virtually instantaneous, while others, such as the rusting of an old car over time, are much slower.

A process that, on its own, leads to a decrease in entropy is said to be nonspontaneous: It will happen only if energy is supplied. We know from experience that certain events occur spontaneously and others do not. For instance, we know that water flows downhill spontaneously but moves uphill only with an input of energy, such as when a machine pumps the water against gravity. This understanding gives us another way to state the second law: *For a process to occur spontaneously, it must increase the entropy of the universe.*

Biological Order and Disorder

Living systems increase the entropy of their surroundings, as predicted by thermodynamic law. It is true that cells create ordered structures from less organized starting materials. For example, simpler molecules are ordered into the more complex structure of an amino acid, and amino acids are ordered into polypeptide chains. At the organismal level as well, complex and beautifully ordered structures result from biological processes that use simpler starting materials (**Figure 6.4**). On the other hand, an organism also takes in organized forms of matter and energy from the surroundings and replaces them with less ordered forms. For example, an animal obtains starch, proteins, and other complex molecules from the food it eats. As catabolic pathways break these molecules down, the animal releases carbon dioxide and water—small molecules that possess less chemical energy than the food did. The depletion of chemical energy is accounted for by heat

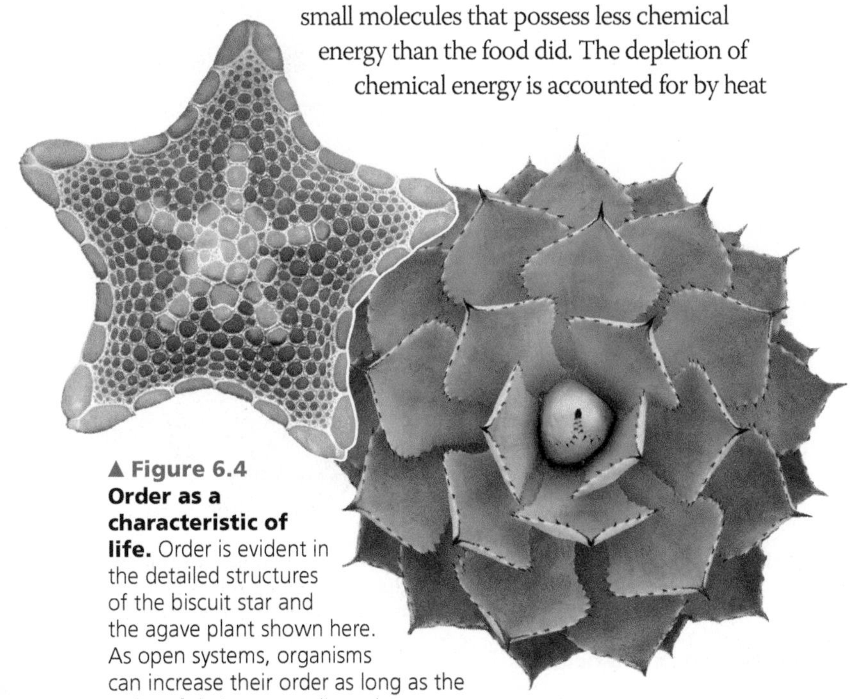

▲ **Figure 6.4 Order as a characteristic of life.** Order is evident in the detailed structures of the biscuit star and the agave plant shown here. As open systems, organisms can increase their order as long as the order of their surroundings decreases.

generated during metabolism. On a larger scale, energy flows into most ecosystems in the form of light and exits in the form of heat.

During the early history of life, complex organisms evolved from simpler ancestors. For instance, we can trace the ancestry of the plant kingdom from much simpler organisms called green algae to more complex flowering plants. However, this increase in organization over time in no way violates the second law. The entropy of a particular system, such as an organism, may actually decrease as long as the total entropy of the *universe*—the system plus its surroundings—increases. Thus, organisms are islands of low entropy in an increasingly random universe. The evolution of biological order is perfectly consistent with the laws of thermodynamics.

CONCEPT CHECK 6.1

1. **MAKE CONNECTIONS** How does the second law of thermodynamics help explain the diffusion of a substance across a membrane? (See Figure 5.9.)
2. Describe the forms of energy found in an apple as it grows on a tree, falls, and then is digested by someone who eats it.

For suggested answers, see Appendix A.

CONCEPT 6.2

The free-energy change of a reaction tells us whether or not the reaction occurs spontaneously

The laws of thermodynamics that we've just discussed apply to the universe as a whole. As biologists, we want to understand the chemical reactions of life—for example, which reactions occur spontaneously and which ones require some input of energy from outside. But how can we know this without assessing the energy and entropy changes in the entire universe for each separate reaction?

Free-Energy Change (ΔG), Stability, and Equilibrium

Recall that the universe is really equivalent to "the system" plus "the surroundings." In 1878, J. Willard Gibbs, a professor at Yale, defined a very useful function called the Gibbs free energy of a system (without considering its surroundings), symbolized by the letter G. We'll refer to the Gibbs free energy simply as free energy. **Free energy** is the portion of a system's energy that can perform work when temperature and pressure are uniform throughout the system, as in a living cell. Biologists find it most informative to focus on the *change* in free energy (ΔG) during the chemical reactions of life. ΔG represents the difference between the free energy of the final state and the free energy of the initial state:

$$\Delta G = G_{\text{final state}} - G_{\text{initial state}}$$

Using chemical methods, we can measure ΔG for any reaction. More than a century of experiments has shown that only reactions with a negative ΔG can occur with no input of energy, so the value of ΔG tells us whether a particular reaction is a spontaneous one. This principle is very important in the study of metabolism, where a major goal is to determine which reactions occur spontaneously and can be harnessed to supply energy for cellular work.

For a reaction to have a negative ΔG, the system must lose free energy during the change from initial state to final state. Because it has less free energy, the system in its final state is less likely to change and is therefore more stable than it was previously. We can think of free energy as a measure of a system's instability—its tendency to change to a more stable state. Unstable systems (higher G) tend to change in such a way that they become more stable (lower G), as shown in **Figure 6.5**.

Another term that describes a state of maximum stability is chemical *equilibrium*. At equilibrium, the forward and reverse reactions occur at the same rate, and there is no further net change in the relative concentration of products and reactants. For a system at equilibrium, G is at its lowest possible value in that system. We can think of the equilibrium state as a free-energy valley. Any change from the equilibrium position will have a positive ΔG and will not be spontaneous. For this reason, systems never spontaneously move away from equilibrium. Because a system at equilibrium cannot spontaneously change, it can do no work. *A process is spontaneous and can perform work only when it is moving toward equilibrium.*

Free Energy and Metabolism

We can now apply the free-energy concept more specifically to the chemistry of life's processes.

Exergonic and Endergonic Reactions in Metabolism

Based on their free-energy changes, chemical reactions can be classified as either exergonic ("energy outward") or endergonic ("energy inward"). An **exergonic reaction** proceeds with a net release of free energy **(Figure 6.6a)**. Because the chemical mixture loses free energy (G decreases), ΔG is negative for an exergonic reaction. Using ΔG as a standard for spontaneity, exergonic reactions are those that occur spontaneously. (Remember, the word *spontaneous* implies that it is energetically favorable, not that it will occur rapidly.) The magnitude of ΔG for an exergonic reaction represents the maximum amount of work the reaction can perform (some of the free energy is released as heat and cannot do work). The greater the decrease in free energy, the greater the amount of work that can be done.

Consider the overall reaction for cellular respiration:

$$C_6H_{12}O_6 + 6\,O_2 \rightarrow 6\,CO_2 + 6\,H_2O$$
$$\Delta G = -686 \text{ kcal/mol } (-2{,}870 \text{ kJ/mol})$$

686 kcal (2,870 kJ) of energy are made available for work for each mole (180 g) of glucose broken down by respiration under "standard conditions" (1 M of each reactant and product, 25°C, pH 7). Because energy must be conserved, the products of respiration store 686 kcal less free energy per mole than the reactants. The products are the "exhaust" of a process that tapped the free energy stored in the bonds of the sugar molecules.

It is important to realize that the breaking of bonds does not release energy; on the contrary, as you will soon see, it requires energy. The phrase "energy stored in bonds" is shorthand for the potential energy that can be released when new bonds are

- More free energy (higher G)
- Less stable
- Greater work capacity

In a **spontaneous change**
- The free energy of the system decreases ($\Delta G < 0$)
- The system becomes more stable
- The released free energy can be harnessed to do work

- Less free energy (lower G)
- More stable
- Less work capacity

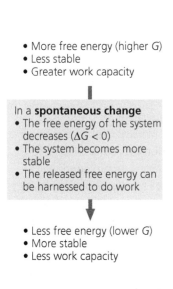

(a) Gravitational motion. Objects move spontaneously from a higher altitude to a lower one.

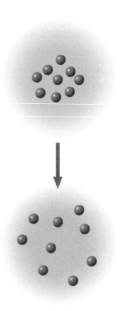

(b) Diffusion. Molecules in a drop of dye diffuse until they are randomly dispersed.

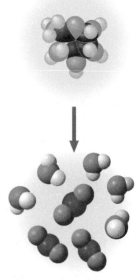

(c) Chemical reaction. In a cell, a glucose molecule is broken down into simpler molecules.

▲ **Figure 6.5 The relationship of free energy to stability, work capacity, and spontaneous change.** Unstable systems (top) are rich in free energy, G. They have a tendency to change spontaneously to a more stable state (bottom), and it is possible to harness this "downhill" change to perform work.

Figure 6.6 Free energy changes (ΔG) in exergonic and endergonic reactions.

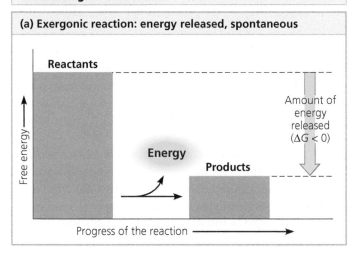

(a) Exergonic reaction: energy released, spontaneous

Reactants

Free energy →

Energy

Products

Amount of energy released ($\Delta G < 0$)

Progress of the reaction →

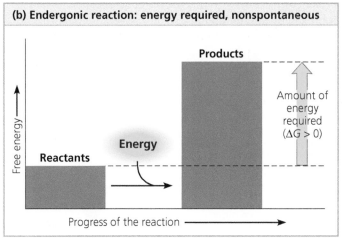

(b) Endergonic reaction: energy required, nonspontaneous

Products

Free energy →

Energy

Reactants

Amount of energy required ($\Delta G > 0$)

Progress of the reaction →

---

formed after the original bonds break, as long as the products are of lower free energy than the reactants.

An **endergonic reaction** is one that absorbs free energy from its surroundings **(Figure 6.6b)**. Because this kind of reaction essentially *stores* free energy in molecules (G increases), ΔG is positive. Such reactions are nonspontaneous, and the magnitude of ΔG is the quantity of energy required to drive the reaction. If a chemical process is exergonic (downhill), releasing energy in one direction, then the reverse process must be endergonic (uphill), using energy. A reversible process cannot be downhill in both directions. If $\Delta G = -686$ kcal/mol for respiration, which converts glucose and oxygen to carbon dioxide and water, then the reverse process—the conversion of carbon dioxide and water to glucose and oxygen—must be strongly endergonic, with $\Delta G = +686$ kcal/mol. Such a reaction would never happen by itself.

How, then, do plants make the sugar that organisms use for energy? Plants get the required energy—686 kcal to make a mole of glucose—from the environment by capturing light and converting its energy to chemical energy. Next, in a long series of exergonic steps, they gradually spend that chemical energy to assemble glucose molecules.

Equilibrium and Metabolism

Reactions in an isolated system eventually reach equilibrium and can then do no work, as illustrated by the isolated hydroelectric system in **Figure 6.7a**. The chemical reactions of metabolism are reversible, and they, too, would reach equilibrium if they occurred in the isolation of a test tube. Because systems at equilibrium are at a minimum of G and can do no work, a cell that has reached metabolic equilibrium is dead! The fact that metabolism as a whole is never at equilibrium is one of the defining features of life.

Like most systems, a living cell is not in equilibrium. The constant flow of materials in and out of the cell keeps the metabolic pathways from ever reaching equilibrium, and the cell continues to do work throughout its life. This principle is illustrated by the open (and more realistic) hydroelectric system in **Figure 6.7b**. However, unlike this simple single-step system,

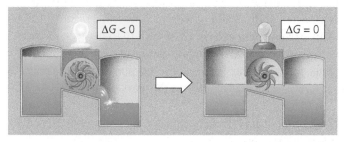

(a) An isolated hydroelectric system. Water flowing downhill turns a turbine that drives a generator providing electricity to a lightbulb, but only until the system reaches equilibrium.

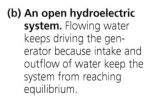

(b) An open hydroelectric system. Flowing water keeps driving the generator because intake and outflow of water keep the system from reaching equilibrium.

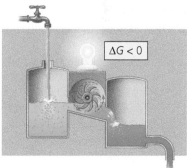

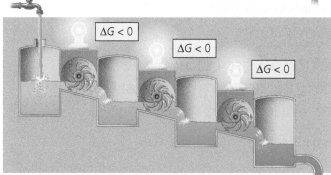

(c) A multistep open hydroelectric system. Cellular respiration is analogous to this system: Glucose is broken down in a series of exergonic reactions that power the work of the cell. The product of each reaction is used as the reactant for the next, so no reaction reaches equilibrium.

▲ Figure 6.7 **Equilibrium and work in isolated and open systems.**

a catabolic pathway in a cell releases free energy in a series of reactions. An example is cellular respiration, illustrated by the hydroelectric system analogy in **Figure 6.7c**. Some of the reversible reactions of respiration are constantly "pulled" in one direction—that is, they are kept out of equilibrium. The key to maintaining this lack of equilibrium is that the product of a reaction does not accumulate but instead becomes a reactant in the next step; finally, waste products are expelled from the cell. The overall sequence of reactions is kept going by the huge free-energy difference between glucose and oxygen at the top of the energy "hill" and carbon dioxide and water at the "downhill" end. As long as our cells have a steady supply of glucose or other fuels and oxygen and are able to expel waste products to the surroundings, their metabolic pathways never reach equilibrium and can continue to do the work of life.

We see once again how important it is to think of organisms as open systems. Sunlight provides a daily source of free energy for an ecosystem's plants and other photosynthetic organisms. Animals and other nonphotosynthetic organisms in an ecosystem must have a source of free energy in the form of the organic products of photosynthesis. Now that we have applied the free-energy concept to metabolism, we are ready to see how a cell actually performs the work of life.

CONCEPT CHECK 6.2

1. Cellular respiration uses glucose and oxygen, which have high levels of free energy, and releases CO_2 and water, which have low levels of free energy. Is cellular respiration spontaneous or not? Is it exergonic or endergonic? What happens to the energy released from glucose?

2. How do the processes of catabolism and anabolism relate to Figure 6.5c?

3. **WHAT IF?** Some nighttime partygoers wear glow-in-the-dark necklaces. The necklaces start glowing once they are "activated" by snapping the necklace in a way that allows two chemicals to react and emit light in the form of chemiluminescence. Is this chemical reaction exergonic or endergonic? Explain your answer.

For suggested answers, see Appendix A.

CONCEPT 6.3

ATP powers cellular work by coupling exergonic reactions to endergonic reactions

A cell does three main kinds of work:

- *Chemical work*, the pushing of endergonic reactions that would not occur spontaneously, such as the synthesis of polymers from monomers (chemical work will be discussed further in this chapter and in Chapters 7 and 8)
- *Transport work*, the pumping of substances across membranes against the direction of spontaneous movement (see Concept 5.4)

- *Mechanical work*, such as the beating of cilia (see Concept 4.6), the contraction of muscle cells, and the movement of chromosomes during cellular reproduction

A key feature in the way cells manage their energy resources to do this work is **energy coupling**, the use of an exergonic process to drive an endergonic one. ATP is responsible for mediating most energy coupling in cells, and in most cases it acts as the immediate source of energy that powers cellular work.

The Structure and Hydrolysis of ATP

ATP (adenosine triphosphate; see Concept 3.1) contains the sugar ribose, with the nitrogenous base adenine and a chain of three phosphate groups bonded to it **(Figure 6.8a)**. In addition to its role in energy coupling, ATP is also one of the nucleoside triphosphates used to make RNA (see Figure 3.27).

The bonds between the phosphate groups of ATP can be broken by hydrolysis. When the terminal phosphate bond is broken by the addition of a water molecule, a molecule of inorganic phosphate ($HOPO_3^{2-}$, which is abbreviated $\text{\textcircled{P}}_i$ throughout this book) leaves the ATP. In this way, adenosine

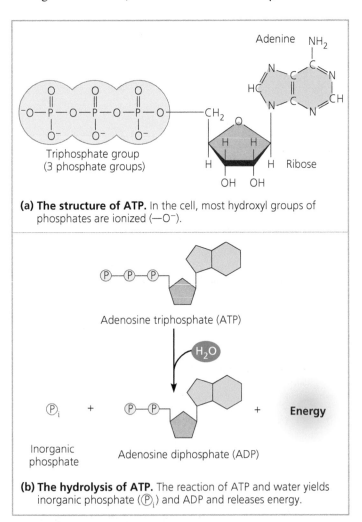

(a) The structure of ATP. In the cell, most hydroxyl groups of phosphates are ionized ($-O^-$).

(b) The hydrolysis of ATP. The reaction of ATP and water yields inorganic phosphate ($\text{\textcircled{P}}_i$) and ADP and releases energy.

▲ **Figure 6.8 The structure and hydrolysis of adenosine triphosphate (ATP).** Throughout this book, the chemical structure of the triphosphate group seen in (a) will be represented by the three joined yellow circles shown in (b).

*tri*phosphate becomes adenosine *di*phosphate, or ADP **(Figure 6.8b)**. The reaction is exergonic and releases 7.3 kcal of energy per mole of ATP hydrolyzed:

$$ATP + H_2O \rightarrow ADP + \textcircled{P}_i$$
$$\Delta G = -7.3 \text{ kcal/mol } (-30.5 \text{ kJ/mol})$$

This is the free-energy change measured under standard conditions. In the cell, conditions do not conform to standard conditions, primarily because reactant and product concentrations differ from 1 *M*. For example, when ATP hydrolysis occurs under cellular conditions, the actual ΔG is about −13 kcal/mol, 78% greater than the energy released by ATP hydrolysis under standard conditions.

Because their hydrolysis releases energy, the phosphate bonds of ATP are sometimes referred to as high-energy phosphate bonds, but the term is misleading. The phosphate bonds of ATP are not unusually strong bonds, as "high-energy" may imply; rather, the reactants (ATP and water) themselves have high energy relative to the energy of the products (ADP and $\textcircled{P}_i$). The release of energy during the hydrolysis of ATP comes from the chemical change to a state of lower free energy, not from the phosphate bonds themselves.

ATP is useful to the cell because the energy it releases on losing a phosphate group is somewhat greater than the energy most other molecules could deliver. But why does this hydrolysis release so much energy? If we reexamine the ATP molecule in Figure 6.8a, we can see that all three phosphate groups are negatively charged. These like charges are crowded together, and their mutual repulsion contributes to the instability of this region of the ATP molecule. The triphosphate tail of ATP is the chemical equivalent of a compressed spring.

How the Hydrolysis of ATP Performs Work

When ATP is hydrolyzed in a test tube, the release of free energy merely heats the surrounding water. In an organism, this same generation of heat can sometimes be beneficial. For instance, the process of shivering uses ATP hydrolysis during muscle contraction to warm the body. In most cases in the cell, however, the generation of heat alone would be an inefficient (and potentially dangerous) use of a valuable energy resource. Instead, the cell's proteins harness the energy released during ATP hydrolysis in several ways to perform the three types of cellular work—chemical, transport, and mechanical.

For example, with the help of specific enzymes, the cell is able to use the energy released by ATP hydrolysis directly to drive chemical reactions that, by themselves, are endergonic **(Figure 6.9)**. If the ΔG of an endergonic reaction is less than the amount of energy released by ATP hydrolysis, then the two reactions can be coupled so that, overall, the coupled reactions are exergonic. This usually involves phosphorylation, the transfer of a phosphate group from ATP to some other

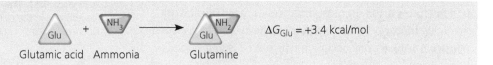

(a) Glutamic acid conversion to glutamine.
Glutamine synthesis from glutamic acid (Glu) by itself is endergonic (ΔG is positive), so it is not spontaneous.

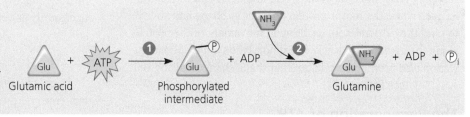

(b) Conversion reaction coupled with ATP hydrolysis. In the cell, glutamine synthesis occurs in two steps, coupled by a phosphorylated intermediate. **1** ATP phosphorylates glutamic acid, making it less stable. **2** Ammonia displaces the phosphate group, forming glutamine.

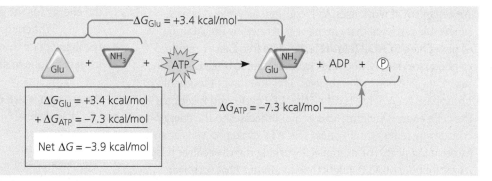

(c) Free-energy change for coupled reaction. ΔG for the glutamic acid conversion to glutamine (+3.4 kcal/mol) plus ΔG for ATP hydrolysis (−7.3 kcal/mol) gives the free-energy change for the overall reaction (−3.9 kcal/mol). Because the overall process is exergonic (net ΔG is negative), it occurs spontaneously.

▲ **Figure 6.9 How ATP drives chemical work: energy coupling using ATP hydrolysis.** In this example, the exergonic process of ATP hydrolysis is used to drive an endergonic process—the cellular synthesis of the amino acid glutamine from glutamic acid and ammonia.

MAKE CONNECTIONS *Explain why glutamine is drawn as a glutamic acid (Glu) with an amino group attached. (See Figure 3.18.)*

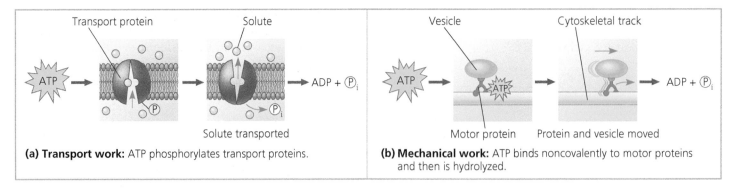

(a) **Transport work:** ATP phosphorylates transport proteins.

(b) **Mechanical work:** ATP binds noncovalently to motor proteins and then is hydrolyzed.

▲ **Figure 6.10 How ATP drives transport and mechanical work.** ATP hydrolysis causes changes in the shapes and binding affinities of proteins. This can occur either **(a)** directly, by phosphorylation, as shown for a membrane protein carrying out active transport of a solute (see also Figure 5.14), or **(b)** indirectly, via noncovalent binding of ATP and its hydrolytic products, as is the case for motor proteins that move vesicles (and other organelles) along cytoskeletal "tracks" in the cell (see also Figure 4.21).

molecule, such as the reactant (see Figure 6.9b). The recipient with the phosphate group covalently bonded to it is then called a **phosphorylated intermediate**. The key to coupling exergonic and endergonic reactions is the formation of this phosphorylated intermediate, which is more reactive (less stable) than the original unphosphorylated molecule.

Transport and mechanical work in the cell are also nearly always powered by the hydrolysis of ATP. In these cases, ATP hydrolysis leads to a change in a protein's shape and often its ability to bind another molecule. Sometimes this occurs via a phosphorylated intermediate, as seen for the transport protein in **Figure 6.10a**. In most instances of mechanical work involving motor proteins "walking" along cytoskeletal elements **(Figure 6.10b)**, a cycle occurs in which ATP is first bound noncovalently to the motor protein. Next, ATP is hydrolyzed, releasing ADP and P_i. Another ATP molecule can then bind. At each stage, the motor protein changes its shape and ability to bind the cytoskeleton, resulting in movement of the protein along the cytoskeletal track. Phosphorylation and dephosphorylation also promote crucial protein shape changes during cell signaling (see Figure 5.24).

The Regeneration of ATP

An organism at work uses ATP continuously, but ATP is a renewable resource that can be regenerated by the addition of phosphate to ADP **(Figure 6.11)**. The free energy required to phosphorylate ADP comes from exergonic breakdown reactions (catabolism) in the cell. This shuttling of inorganic phosphate and energy is called the ATP cycle, and it couples the cell's energy-yielding (exergonic) processes to the energy-consuming (endergonic) ones. The ATP cycle proceeds at an astonishing pace. For example, a working muscle cell recycles its entire pool of ATP in less than a minute. That turnover represents 10 million molecules of ATP consumed and regenerated per second per cell. If ATP could not be regenerated by the phosphorylation of ADP, humans would use up nearly their body weight in ATP each day.

ATP synthesis from ADP + P_i requires energy.

ATP hydrolysis to ADP + P_i yields energy.

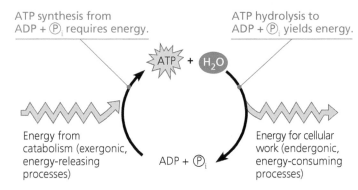

Energy from catabolism (exergonic, energy-releasing processes)

Energy for cellular work (endergonic, energy-consuming processes)

▲ **Figure 6.11 The ATP cycle.** Energy released by breakdown reactions (catabolism) in the cell is used to phosphorylate ADP, regenerating ATP. Chemical potential energy stored in ATP drives most cellular work.

Because both directions of a reversible process cannot be downhill, the regeneration of ATP from ADP and P_i is necessarily endergonic:

$$ADP + P_i \rightarrow ATP + H_2O$$
$$\Delta G = +7.3 \text{ kcal/mol } (+30.5 \text{ kJ/mol}) \text{ (standard conditions)}$$

Since ATP formation from ADP and P_i is not spontaneous, free energy must be spent to make it occur. Catabolic (exergonic) pathways, especially cellular respiration, provide the energy for the endergonic process of making ATP. Plants also use light energy to produce ATP. Thus, the ATP cycle is a revolving door through which energy passes during its transfer from catabolic to anabolic pathways.

CONCEPT CHECK 6.3

1. How does ATP typically transfer energy from exergonic to endergonic reactions in the cell?

2. Which of the following combinations has more free energy: glutamic acid + ammonia + ATP or glutamine + ADP + P_i? Explain your answer.

3. **MAKE CONNECTIONS** Does Figure 6.10a show passive or active transport? Explain. (See Concepts 5.3 and 5.4.)

For suggested answers, see Appendix A.

Enzymes speed up metabolic reactions by lowering energy barriers

The laws of thermodynamics tell us what will and will not happen under given conditions but say nothing about the *rate* of these processes. A spontaneous chemical reaction occurs without any requirement for outside energy, but it may occur so slowly that it is imperceptible. For example, even though the hydrolysis of sucrose (table sugar) to glucose and fructose is exergonic, occurring spontaneously with a release of free energy ($\Delta G = -7$ kcal/mol), a solution of sucrose dissolved in sterile water will sit for years at room temperature with no appreciable hydrolysis. However, if we add a small amount of the enzyme sucrase to the solution, then all the sucrose may be hydrolyzed within seconds, as shown here:

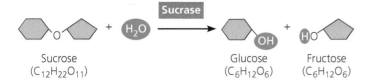

Sucrose
($C_{12}H_{22}O_{11}$)

Glucose
($C_6H_{12}O_6$)

Fructose
($C_6H_{12}O_6$)

How does the enzyme do this?

An **enzyme** is a macromolecule that acts as a **catalyst**, a chemical agent that speeds up a reaction without being consumed by the reaction. In this chapter, we are focusing on enzymes that are proteins. (Some RNA molecules, called ribozymes, can function as enzymes; these will be discussed in Concepts 14.3 and 24.1.) Without regulation by enzymes, chemical traffic through the pathways of metabolism would become terribly congested because many chemical reactions would take such a long time. In the next two sections, we will see why spontaneous reactions can be slow and how an enzyme changes the situation.

The Activation Energy Barrier

Every chemical reaction between molecules involves both bond breaking and bond forming. For example, the hydrolysis of sucrose involves breaking the bond between glucose and fructose and one of the bonds of a water molecule and then forming two new bonds, as shown above. Changing one molecule into another generally involves contorting the starting molecule into a highly unstable state before the reaction can proceed. This contortion can be compared to the bending of a metal key ring when you pry it open to add a new key. The key ring is highly unstable in its opened form but returns to a stable state once the key is threaded all the way onto the ring. To reach the contorted state where bonds can change, reactant molecules must absorb energy from their surroundings. When the new bonds of the product molecules form, energy is released as heat, and the molecules return to stable shapes with lower energy than the contorted state.

The initial investment of energy for starting a reaction—the energy required to contort the reactant molecules so the bonds can break—is known as the *free energy of activation*, or **activation energy**, abbreviated E_A in this book. We can think of activation energy as the amount of energy needed to push the reactants to the top of an energy barrier, or uphill, so that the "downhill" part of the reaction can begin. Activation energy is often supplied by heat in the form of thermal energy that the reactant molecules absorb from the surroundings. The absorption of thermal energy accelerates the reactant molecules, so they collide more often and more forcefully. It also agitates the atoms within the molecules, making the breakage of bonds more likely. When the molecules have absorbed enough energy for the bonds to break, the reactants are in an unstable condition known as the *transition state*.

Figure 6.12 graphs the energy changes for a hypothetical exergonic reaction that swaps portions of two reactant molecules:

$$AB + CD \rightarrow AC + BD$$
Reactants   Products

The activation of the reactants is represented by the uphill portion of the graph, in which the free-energy content of the reactant molecules is increasing. At the summit, when energy

The reactants AB and CD must absorb enough energy from the surroundings to reach the unstable transition state, where bonds can break.

After bonds have broken, new bonds form, releasing energy to the surroundings.

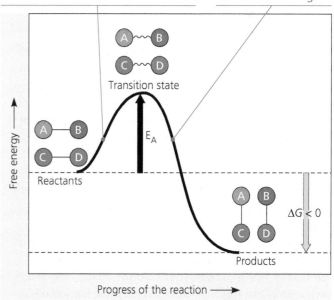

▲ **Figure 6.12 Energy profile of an exergonic reaction.** The "molecules" are hypothetical, with A, B, C, and D representing portions of the molecules. Thermodynamically, this is an exergonic reaction, with a negative ΔG, and the reaction occurs spontaneously. However, the activation energy (E_A) provides a barrier that determines the rate of the reaction.

DRAW IT *Graph the progress of an endergonic reaction in which EF and GH form products EG and FH, assuming that the reactants must pass through a transition state.*

equivalent to E_A has been absorbed, the reactants are in the transition state: They are activated, and their bonds can be broken. As the atoms then settle into their new, more stable bonding arrangements, energy is released to the surroundings. This corresponds to the downhill part of the curve, which shows the loss of free energy by the molecules. The overall decrease in free energy means that E_A is repaid with dividends, as the formation of new bonds releases more energy than was invested in the breaking of old bonds.

The reaction shown in Figure 6.12 is exergonic and occurs spontaneously ($\Delta G < 0$). However, the activation energy provides a barrier that determines the rate of the reaction. The reactants must absorb enough energy to reach the top of the activation energy barrier before the reaction can occur. For some reactions, E_A is modest enough that even at room temperature there is sufficient thermal energy for many of the reactant molecules to reach the transition state in a short time. In most cases, however, E_A is so high and the transition state is reached so rarely that the reaction will hardly proceed at all. In these cases, the reaction will occur at a noticeable rate only if energy is provided, usually as heat. For example, the reaction of gasoline and oxygen is exergonic and will occur spontaneously, but energy is required for the molecules to reach the transition state and react. Only when the spark plugs fire in an automobile engine can there be the explosive release of energy that pushes the pistons. Without a spark, a mixture of gasoline hydrocarbons and oxygen will not react because the E_A barrier is too high.

How Enzymes Speed Up Reactions

Proteins, DNA, and other complex cellular molecules are rich in free energy and have the potential to decompose spontaneously; that is, the laws of thermodynamics favor their breakdown. These molecules persist only because at temperatures typical for cells, few molecules can make it over the hump of activation energy. The barriers for selected reactions must occasionally be surmounted, however, for cells to carry out the processes needed for life. Heat can increase the rate of a reaction by allowing reactants to attain the transition state more often, but this would not work well in biological systems. First, high temperature denatures proteins and kills cells. Second, heat would speed up *all* reactions, not just those that are needed. Instead of heat, organisms carry out **catalysis**, a process by which a catalyst (for example, an enzyme) selectively speeds up a reaction without itself being consumed. (You learned about catalysts in Concept 3.5.)

An enzyme catalyzes a reaction by lowering the E_A barrier **(Figure 6.13)**, enabling the reactant molecules to absorb enough energy to reach the transition state even at moderate temperatures. An enzyme cannot change the ΔG for a reaction; it cannot make an endergonic reaction exergonic. Enzymes can only hasten reactions that would eventually occur anyway, but this enables the cell to have a dynamic metabolism, routing chemicals smoothly through metabolic pathways.

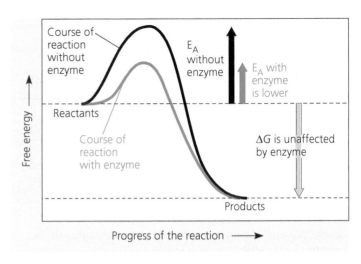

▲ **Figure 6.13 The effect of an enzyme on activation energy.** Without affecting the free-energy change (ΔG) for a reaction, an enzyme speeds the reaction by reducing its activation energy (E_A).

Also, enzymes are very specific for the reactions they catalyze, so they determine which chemical processes will be going on in the cell at any given time.

Substrate Specificity of Enzymes

The reactant an enzyme acts on is referred to as the enzyme's **substrate**. The enzyme binds to its substrate (or substrates, when there are two or more reactants), forming an **enzyme-substrate complex**. While enzyme and substrate are joined, the catalytic action of the enzyme converts the substrate to the product (or products) of the reaction. The overall process can be summarized as follows:

$$\text{Enzyme} + \text{Substrate(s)} \rightleftharpoons \text{Enzyme-substrate complex} \rightleftharpoons \text{Enzyme} + \text{Product(s)}$$

For example, the enzyme sucrase (most enzyme names end in *-ase*) catalyzes the hydrolysis of the disaccharide sucrose into its two monosaccharides, glucose and fructose (see the illustrated equation at the beginning of Concept 6.4):

$$\text{Sucrase} + \text{Sucrose} + H_2O \rightleftharpoons \text{Sucrase-sucrose-}H_2O \text{ complex} \rightleftharpoons \text{Sucrase} + \text{Glucose} + \text{Fructose}$$

The reaction catalyzed by each enzyme is very specific; an enzyme can recognize its specific substrate even among closely related compounds. For instance, sucrase will act only on sucrose and will not bind to other disaccharides, such as maltose. What accounts for this molecular recognition? Recall that most enzymes are proteins, and proteins are macromolecules with unique three-dimensional configurations. The specificity of an enzyme results from its shape, which is a consequence of its amino acid sequence.

Only a restricted region of the enzyme molecule actually binds to the substrate. This region, known as the **active site**, is typically a pocket or groove on the surface of the enzyme where catalysis occurs **(Figure 6.14a)**. Usually, the active site is formed by only a few of the enzyme's amino acids, with the rest of the protein molecule providing a framework that determines the shape of the active site. The specificity of an enzyme is attributed to a complementary fit between the shape of its active site and the shape of the substrate, like that seen in the binding of a signaling molecule to a receptor protein (see Concept 5.6).

An enzyme is not a stiff structure locked into a given shape. In fact, recent work by biochemists has shown that enzymes (and other proteins) seem to "dance" between subtly different shapes in a dynamic equilibrium, with slight differences in free energy for each "pose." The shape that best fits the substrate isn't necessarily the one with the lowest energy, but during the very short time the enzyme takes on this shape, its active site can bind to the substrate. The active site itself is also not a rigid receptacle for the substrate. As the substrate enters the active site, the enzyme changes shape slightly due to interactions between the substrate's chemical groups and chemical groups on the side chains of the amino acids that form the active site. This shape change makes the active site fit even more snugly around the substrate **(Figure 6.14b)**. This tightening of the binding after initial contact—called **induced fit**—is like a clasping handshake. Induced fit brings chemical groups of the active site into positions that enhance their ability to catalyze the chemical reaction.

Catalysis in the Enzyme's Active Site

In most enzymatic reactions, the substrate is held in the active site by so-called weak interactions, such as hydrogen bonds and ionic bonds. The R groups of a few of the amino acids that make up the active site catalyze the conversion of substrate to product, and the product departs from the active site. The enzyme is then free to take another substrate molecule into its active site. The entire cycle happens so fast that a single enzyme molecule typically acts on about 1,000 substrate molecules per second, and some enzymes are even faster. Enzymes, like other catalysts, emerge from the reaction in their original form. Therefore, very small amounts of enzyme can have a huge metabolic impact by functioning over and over again in catalytic cycles. **Figure 6.15** shows a catalytic cycle involving two substrates and two products.

Most metabolic reactions are reversible, and an enzyme can catalyze either the forward or the reverse reaction, depending on which direction has a negative ΔG. This in turn depends mainly on the relative concentrations of reactants and products. The net effect is always in the direction of equilibrium.

Enzymes use a variety of mechanisms that lower activation energy and speed up a reaction. First, in reactions involving

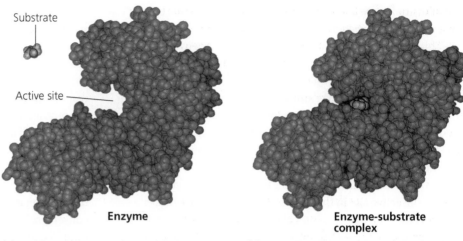

Substrate

Active site

Enzyme

Enzyme-substrate complex

(a) In this computer graphic model, the active site of this enzyme (hexokinase, shown in blue) forms a groove on its surface. Its substrate is glucose (red).

(b) When the substrate enters the active site, it forms weak bonds with the enzyme, inducing a change in the shape of the protein. This change allows additional weak bonds to form, causing the active site to enfold the substrate and hold it in place.

▲ **Figure 6.14 Induced fit between an enzyme and its substrate.**

two or more reactants, the active site provides a template on which the substrates can come together in the proper orientation for a reaction to occur between them (see Figure 6.15, step **2**). Second, as the active site of an enzyme clutches the bound substrates, the enzyme may stretch the substrate molecules toward their transition state form, stressing and bending critical chemical bonds that must be broken during the reaction. Because E_A is proportional to the difficulty of breaking the bonds, distorting the substrate helps it approach

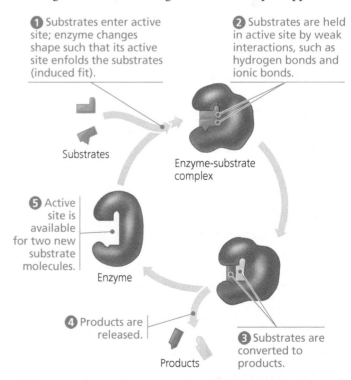

1 Substrates enter active site; enzyme changes shape such that its active site enfolds the substrates (induced fit).

2 Substrates are held in active site by weak interactions, such as hydrogen bonds and ionic bonds.

Substrates

Enzyme-substrate complex

5 Active site is available for two new substrate molecules.

Enzyme

4 Products are released.

Products

3 Substrates are converted to products.

▲ **Figure 6.15 The active site and catalytic cycle of an enzyme.** An enzyme can convert one or more reactant molecules to one or more product molecules. The enzyme shown here converts two substrate molecules to two product molecules.

the transition state and thus reduces the amount of free energy that must be absorbed to achieve that state.

Third, the active site may also provide a microenvironment that is more conducive to a particular type of reaction than the solution itself would be without the enzyme. For example, if the active site has amino acids with acidic R groups, the active site may be a pocket of low pH in an otherwise neutral cell. In such cases, an acidic amino acid may facilitate H^+ transfer to the substrate as a key step in catalyzing the reaction.

A fourth mechanism of catalysis is the direct participation of the active site in the chemical reaction. Sometimes this process even involves brief covalent bonding between the substrate and the side chain of an amino acid of the enzyme. Subsequent steps of the reaction restore the side chains to their original states, so that the active site is the same after the reaction as it was before.

The rate at which a particular amount of enzyme converts substrate to product is partly a function of the initial concentration of the substrate: The more substrate molecules that are available, the more frequently they access the active sites of the enzyme molecules. However, there is a limit to how fast the reaction can be pushed by adding more substrate to a fixed concentration of enzyme. At some point, the concentration of substrate will be high enough that all enzyme molecules will have their active sites engaged. As soon as the product exits an active site, another substrate molecule enters. At this substrate concentration, the enzyme is said to be *saturated*, and the rate of the reaction is determined by the speed at which the active site converts substrate to product. When an enzyme population is saturated, the only way to increase the rate of product formation is to add more enzyme. Cells often increase the rate of a reaction by producing more enzyme molecules. You can graph the progress of an enzymatic reaction in the **Scientific Skills Exercise**.

Scientific Skills Exercise

Making a Line Graph and Calculating a Slope

Does the Rate of Glucose 6-Phosphatase Activity Change over Time in Isolated Liver Cells? Glucose 6-phosphatase, which is found in mammalian liver cells, is a key enzyme in control of blood glucose levels. The enzyme catalyzes the breakdown of glucose 6-phosphate into glucose and inorganic phosphate (P_i). These products are transported out of liver cells into the blood, increasing blood glucose levels. In this exercise, you will graph data from a time-course experiment that measured P_i concentration in the buffer outside isolated liver cells, thus indirectly measuring glucose 6-phosphatase activity inside the cells.

How the Experiment Was Done Isolated rat liver cells were placed in a dish with buffer at physiological conditions (pH 7.4, 37°C). Glucose 6-phosphate (the substrate) was added to the dish, where it was taken up by the cells. Then a sample of buffer was removed every 5 minutes and the concentration of P_i determined.

Data from the Experiment

Time (min)	Concentration of P_i (µmol/mL)
0	0
5	10
10	90
15	180
20	270
25	330
30	355
35	355
40	355

Data from S. R. Commerford et al., Diets enriched in sucrose or fat increase gluconeogenesis and G-6-Pase but not basal glucose production in rats, *American Journal of Physiology—Endocrinology and Metabolism* 283:E545–E555 (2002).

INTERPRET THE DATA

1. To see patterns in the data from a time-course experiment like this, it is helpful to graph the data. First, determine which set of data goes on each axis. (a) What did the researchers intentionally vary in the experiment? This is the independent variable, which goes on the *x*-axis.

(b) What are the units (abbreviated) for the independent variable? Explain in words what the abbreviation stands for. (c) What was measured by the researchers? This is the dependent variable, which goes on the *y*-axis. (d) What does the units abbreviation stand for? Label each axis, including the units.

2. Next, you'll want to mark off the axes with just enough evenly spaced tick marks to accommodate the full set of data. Determine the range of data values for each axis. (a) What is the largest value to go on the *x*-axis? What is a reasonable spacing for the tick marks, and what should be the highest one? (b) What is the largest value to go on the *y*-axis? What is a reasonable spacing for the tick marks, and what should be the highest one?

3. Plot the data points on your graph. Match each *x*-value with its partner *y*-value and place a point on the graph at that coordinate. Draw a line that connects the points. (For additional information about graphs, see the Scientific Skills Review in Appendix F and in the Study Area in MasteringBiology.)

4. Examine your graph and look for patterns in the data. (a) Does the concentration of P_i increase evenly through the course of the experiment? To answer this question, describe the pattern you see in the graph. (b) What part of the graph shows the highest rate of enzyme activity? Consider that the rate of enzyme activity is related to the slope of the line, $\Delta y/\Delta x$ (the "rise" over the "run"), in µmol/(mL · min), with the steepest slope indicating the highest rate of enzyme activity. Calculate the rate of enzyme activity (slope) where the graph is steepest. (c) Can you think of a biological explanation for the pattern you see?

5. If your blood sugar level is low from skipping lunch, what reaction (discussed in this exercise) will occur in your liver cells? Write out the reaction and put the name of the enzyme over the reaction arrow. How will this reaction affect your blood sugar level?

(MB) A version of this Scientific Skills Exercise can be assigned in MasteringBiology.

Effects of Local Conditions on Enzyme Activity

The activity of an enzyme—how efficiently the enzyme functions—is affected by general environmental factors, such as temperature and pH. It can also be affected by chemicals that specifically influence that enzyme. In fact, researchers have learned much about enzyme function by employing such chemicals.

Effects of Temperature and pH

The three-dimensional structures of proteins are sensitive to their environment (see Concept 3.5). As a consequence, each enzyme works better under some conditions than under other conditions, because these *optimal conditions* favor the most active shape for the enzyme.

Temperature and pH are environmental factors important in the activity of an enzyme. Up to a point, the rate of an enzymatic reaction increases with increasing temperature, partly because substrates collide with active sites more frequently when the molecules move rapidly. Above that temperature, however, the speed of the enzymatic reaction drops sharply. The thermal agitation of the enzyme molecule disrupts the hydrogen bonds, ionic bonds, and other weak interactions that stabilize the active shape of the enzyme, and the protein molecule eventually denatures. Each enzyme has an optimal temperature at which its reaction rate is greatest. Without denaturing the enzyme, this temperature allows the greatest number of molecular collisions and the fastest conversion of the reactants to product molecules. Most human enzymes have optimal temperatures of about 35–40°C (close to human body temperature). The thermophilic bacteria that live in hot springs contain enzymes with optimal temperatures of 70°C or higher (**Figure 6.16a**).

Just as each enzyme has an optimal temperature, it also has a pH at which it is most active. The optimal pH values for most enzymes fall in the range of pH 6–8, but there are exceptions. For example, pepsin, a digestive enzyme in the human stomach, works best at pH 2. Such an acidic environment denatures most enzymes, but pepsin is adapted to maintain its functional three-dimensional structure in the acidic environment of the stomach. In contrast, trypsin, a digestive enzyme residing in the alkaline environment of the human intestine, has an optimal pH of 8 and would be denatured in the stomach (**Figure 6.16b**).

Cofactors

Many enzymes require nonprotein helpers for catalytic activity. These adjuncts, called **cofactors**, may be bound tightly to the enzyme as permanent residents, or they may bind loosely and reversibly along with the substrate. The cofactors of some enzymes are inorganic, such as the metal atoms zinc, iron, and copper in ionic form. If the cofactor is an organic molecule, it is referred to, more specifically, as a **coenzyme**. Most vitamins

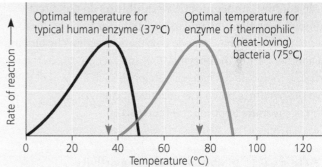

(a) The photo shows thermophilic cyanobacteria (green) thriving in the hot water of a Nevada geyser. The graph compares the optimal temperatures for an enzyme from the thermophilic bacterium *Thermus oshimai* (75°C) and human enzymes (body temperature, 37°C).

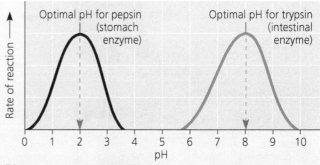

(b) Enzymes work best at different pHs, correlated with the conditions under which they function in the body.

▲ **Figure 6.16 Environmental factors affecting enzyme activity.** Each enzyme has an optimal **(a)** temperature and **(b)** pH that favor the most active shape of the protein molecule.

DRAW IT *Given that a mature lysosome has an internal pH of around 4.5, draw a curve in (b) showing what you would predict for a lysosomal enzyme, labeling its optimal pH.*

are important in nutrition because they act as coenzymes or raw materials from which coenzymes are made. Cofactors function in various ways, but in all cases where they are used, they perform a crucial chemical function in catalysis. You'll encounter examples of cofactors later in the book.

Enzyme Inhibitors

Certain chemicals selectively inhibit the action of specific enzymes. Sometimes the inhibitor attaches to the enzyme by covalent bonds, in which case the inhibition is usually irreversible. Many enzyme inhibitors, however, bind to the enzyme by weak interactions, and when this occurs, the inhibition is reversible. Some reversible inhibitors resemble the normal substrate molecule and compete for admission into the active site **(Figure 6.17a and b)**. These mimics, called **competitive inhibitors**, reduce the productivity of enzymes by blocking substrates from entering active sites. This kind of inhibition can be overcome by increasing the concentration of substrate so that as active sites become available, more substrate molecules than inhibitor molecules are around to gain entry to the sites.

In contrast, **noncompetitive inhibitors** do not directly compete with the substrate to bind to the enzyme at the active site. Instead, they impede enzymatic reactions by binding to another part of the enzyme. This interaction causes the enzyme molecule to change its shape in such a way that the active site becomes much less effective at catalyzing the conversion of substrate to product **(Figure 6.17c)**.

▼ Figure 6.17 **Inhibition of enzyme activity.**

(a) Normal binding

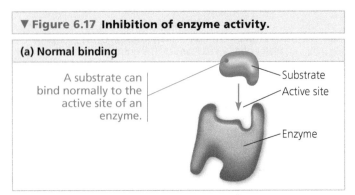

A substrate can bind normally to the active site of an enzyme.

Substrate
Active site
Enzyme

(b) Competitive inhibition

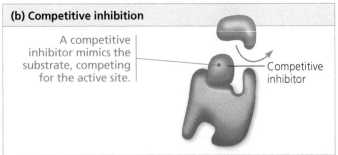

A competitive inhibitor mimics the substrate, competing for the active site.

Competitive inhibitor

(c) Noncompetitive inhibition

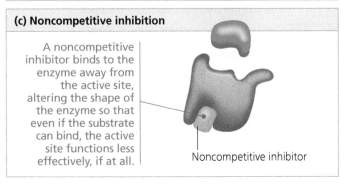

A noncompetitive inhibitor binds to the enzyme away from the active site, altering the shape of the enzyme so that even if the substrate can bind, the active site functions less effectively, if at all.

Noncompetitive inhibitor

Toxins and poisons are often irreversible enzyme inhibitors. An example is sarin, a nerve gas. Sarin was released by terrorists in the Tokyo subway in 1995, killing several people and injuring many others. This small molecule binds covalently to the R group on the amino acid serine, which is found in the active site of acetylcholinesterase, an enzyme important in the nervous system. Other examples include the pesticides DDT and parathion, inhibitors of key enzymes in the nervous system. Finally, many antibiotics are inhibitors of specific enzymes in bacteria. For instance, penicillin blocks the active site of an enzyme that many bacteria use to make cell walls.

Citing enzyme inhibitors that are metabolic poisons may give the impression that enzyme inhibition is generally abnormal and harmful. In fact, molecules naturally present in the cell often regulate enzyme activity by acting as inhibitors. Such regulation—selective inhibition—is essential to the control of cellular metabolism, as we will discuss in Concept 6.5.

The Evolution of Enzymes

EVOLUTION Thus far, biochemists have identified more than 4,000 different enzymes in various species, most likely a very small fraction of all enzymes. How did this grand profusion of enzymes arise? Recall that most enzymes are proteins, and proteins are encoded by genes. A permanent change in a gene, known as a *mutation*, can result in a protein with one or more changed amino acids. In the case of an enzyme, if the changed amino acids are in the active site or some other crucial region, the altered enzyme might have a novel activity or might bind to a different substrate. Under environmental conditions where the new function benefits the organism, natural selection would tend to favor the mutated form of the gene, causing it to persist in the population. This simplified model is generally accepted as the main way in which the multitude of different enzymes arose over the past few billion years of life's history.

CONCEPT CHECK 6.4

1. Many spontaneous reactions occur very slowly. Why don't all spontaneous reactions occur instantly?
2. Why do enzymes act only on very specific substrates?
3. **WHAT IF?** Malonate is an inhibitor of the enzyme succinate dehydrogenase. How would you determine whether malonate is a competitive or noncompetitive inhibitor?

For suggested answers, see Appendix A.

CONCEPT 6.5

Regulation of enzyme activity helps control metabolism

Chemical chaos would result if all of a cell's metabolic pathways were operating simultaneously. Intrinsic to life's processes is a cell's ability to tightly regulate its metabolic pathways by controlling when and where its various enzymes are active. It does this either by switching on and off the genes that encode specific enzymes (as we will discuss in Unit Two) or, as we discuss here, by regulating the activity of enzymes once they are made.

Allosteric Regulation of Enzymes

In many cases, the molecules that naturally regulate enzyme activity in a cell behave something like reversible noncompetitive inhibitors (see Figure 6.17c): These regulatory molecules change an enzyme's shape and the functioning of its active site by binding to a site elsewhere on the molecule, via noncovalent interactions. **Allosteric regulation** is the term used to describe any case in which a protein's function at one site is affected by the binding of a regulatory molecule to a separate site. It may result in either inhibition or stimulation of an enzyme's activity.

Allosteric Activation and Inhibition

Most enzymes known to be allosterically regulated are constructed from two or more subunits, each composed of a polypeptide chain with its own active site. The entire complex oscillates between two different shapes, one catalytically active and the other inactive **(Figure 6.18a)**. In the simplest kind of allosteric regulation, an activating or inhibiting regulatory molecule binds to a regulatory site (sometimes called an allosteric site), often located where subunits join. The binding of an *activator* to a regulatory site stabilizes the shape that has functional active sites, whereas the binding of an *inhibitor* stabilizes the inactive form of the enzyme. The subunits of an allosteric enzyme fit together in such a way that a shape change in one subunit is transmitted to all others. Through this interaction of subunits, a single activator or inhibitor molecule that binds to one regulatory site will affect the active sites of all subunits.

Fluctuating concentrations of regulators can cause a sophisticated pattern of response in the activity of cellular enzymes. The products of ATP hydrolysis (ADP and $\circled{P}_i$), for example, play a complex role in balancing the flow of traffic between anabolic and catabolic pathways by their effects on key enzymes. ATP binds to several catabolic enzymes allosterically, lowering their affinity for substrate and thus inhibiting their activity. ADP, however, functions as an activator of the same enzymes. This is logical because catabolism functions in regenerating ATP. If ATP production lags behind its use, ADP accumulates and activates the enzymes that speed up catabolism, producing more ATP. If the supply of ATP exceeds demand, then catabolism slows down as ATP molecules accumulate and bind to the same enzymes, inhibiting them. (You'll see examples of this type of regulation when you learn about cellular respiration in the next chapter.) ATP, ADP, and other related molecules also affect key enzymes in anabolic pathways. In this way, allosteric enzymes control the rates of important reactions in both sorts of metabolic pathways.

In another kind of allosteric activation, a *substrate* molecule binding to one active site in a multisubunit enzyme

▼ Figure 6.18 **Allosteric regulation of enzyme activity.**

(a) Allosteric activators and inhibitors

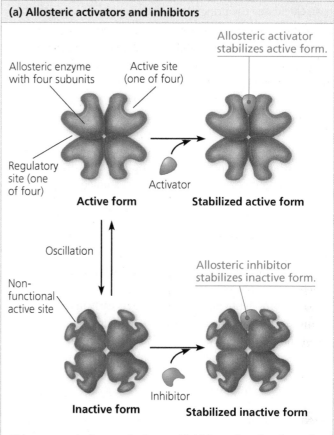

Allosteric enzyme with four subunits

Active site (one of four)

Allosteric activator stabilizes active form.

Regulatory site (one of four)

Activator

Active form   **Stabilized active form**

Oscillation

Non-functional active site

Allosteric inhibitor stabilizes inactive form.

Inhibitor

Inactive form   **Stabilized inactive form**

At low concentrations, activators and inhibitors dissociate from the enzyme. The enzyme can then oscillate again.

(b) Cooperativity: another type of allosteric activation

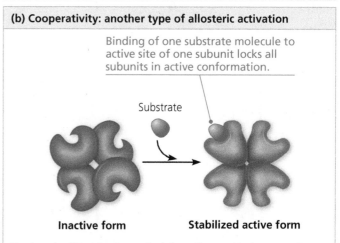

Binding of one substrate molecule to active site of one subunit locks all subunits in active conformation.

Substrate

Inactive form   **Stabilized active form**

The inactive form shown on the left oscillates with the active form when the active form is not stabilized by substrate.

triggers a shape change in all the subunits, thereby increasing catalytic activity at the other active sites **(Figure 6.18b)**. Called **cooperativity**, this mechanism amplifies the response of enzymes to substrates: One substrate molecule primes an enzyme to act on additional substrate molecules more readily. Cooperativity is considered allosteric regulation because binding of the substrate to one active site affects catalysis in another active site.

Although hemoglobin is not an enzyme (it carries O_2 rather than catalyzing a reaction), classic studies of hemoglobin have elucidated the principle of cooperativity. Hemoglobin is made up of four subunits, each with an oxygen-binding site (see Figure 3.22). The binding of an oxygen molecule to one binding site increases the affinity for oxygen of the remaining binding sites. Thus, where oxygen is at high levels, such as in the lungs or gills, hemoglobin's affinity for oxygen increases as more binding sites are filled. In oxygen-deprived tissues, however, the release of each oxygen molecule decreases the oxygen affinity of the other binding sites, resulting in the release of oxygen where it is most needed. Cooperativity works similarly in multisubunit enzymes that have been studied.

Feedback Inhibition

Earlier, we discussed the allosteric inhibition of an enzyme in an ATP-generating pathway by ATP itself. This is a common mode of metabolic control, called **feedback inhibition**, in which a metabolic pathway is halted by the inhibitory binding of its end product to an enzyme that acts early in the pathway. **Figure 6.19** shows an example of feedback inhibition operating on an anabolic pathway. Some cells use this five-step pathway to synthesize the amino acid isoleucine from threonine,

another amino acid. As isoleucine accumulates, it slows down its own synthesis by allosterically inhibiting the enzyme for the first step of the pathway. Feedback inhibition thereby prevents the cell from making more isoleucine than is necessary, and thus wasting chemical resources.

Organization of Enzymes Within the Cell

The cell is not just a bag of chemicals with thousands of different kinds of enzymes and substrates in a random mix. The cell is compartmentalized, and cellular structures help bring order to metabolic pathways. In some cases, a team of enzymes for several steps of a metabolic pathway is assembled into a multienzyme complex. The arrangement facilitates the sequence of reactions, with the product from the first enzyme becoming the substrate for an adjacent enzyme in the complex, and so on, until the end product is released. Some enzymes and enzyme complexes have fixed locations within the cell and act as structural components of particular membranes. Others are in solution within particular membrane-enclosed eukaryotic organelles, each with its own internal chemical environment. For example, in eukaryotic cells, the enzymes for cellular respiration reside in specific locations within mitochondria (**Figure 6.20**).

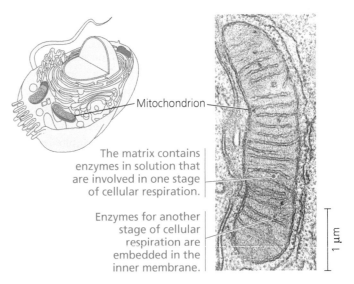

▲ Figure 6.20 **Organelles and structural order in metabolism.** Organelles such as the mitochondrion (TEM) contain enzymes that carry out specific functions, in this case cellular respiration.

In this chapter, you have learned that metabolism, the intersecting set of chemical pathways characteristic of life, is a choreographed interplay of thousands of different kinds of cellular molecules. In the next chapter, we'll explore cellular respiration, the major catabolic pathway that breaks down organic molecules, releasing energy that can be used for the crucial processes of life.

CONCEPT CHECK 6.5

1. How do an activator and an inhibitor have different effects on an allosterically regulated enzyme?

   For suggested answers, see Appendix A.

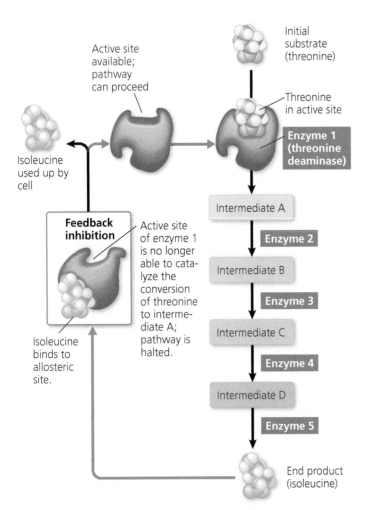

▲ Figure 6.19 **Feedback inhibition in isoleucine synthesis.**

Go to **MasteringBiology**® for Assignments, the eText, and the Study Area with Animations, Activities, Vocab Self-Quiz, and Practice Tests.

SUMMARY OF KEY CONCEPTS

VOCAB SELF-QUIZ

goo.gl/gbai8v

CONCEPT 6.1

An organism's metabolism transforms matter and energy (pp. 122–125)

- **Metabolism** is the collection of chemical reactions that occur in an organism. Enzymes catalyze reactions in intersecting **metabolic pathways**, which may be **catabolic** (breaking down molecules, releasing energy) or **anabolic** (building molecules, consuming energy).
- **Energy** is the capacity to cause change; some forms of energy do work by moving matter. **Kinetic energy** is associated with motion and includes **thermal energy**, associated with the random motion of atoms or molecules. **Heat** is thermal energy in transfer from one object to another. **Potential energy** is related to the location or structure of matter and includes **chemical energy** possessed by a molecule due to its structure.
- The **first law of thermodynamics**, conservation of energy, states that energy cannot be created or destroyed, only transferred or transformed. The **second law of thermodynamics** states that **spontaneous processes**, those requiring no outside input of energy, increase the **entropy** (disorder) of the universe.

? *Explain how the highly ordered structure of a cell does not conflict with the second law of thermodynamics.*

CONCEPT 6.2

The free-energy change of a reaction tells us whether or not the reaction occurs spontaneously (pp. 125–128)

- A living system's **free energy** is energy that can do work under cellular conditions. Organisms live at the expense of free energy. The change in free energy (ΔG) during a biological process tells us if the process is spontaneous. During a spontaneous process, free energy decreases and the stability of a system increases. At maximum stability, the system is at equilibrium and can do no work.
- In an **exergonic** (spontaneous) chemical reaction, the products have less free energy than the reactants ($-\Delta G$). **Endergonic** (nonspontaneous) reactions require an input of energy ($+\Delta G$). The addition of starting materials and the removal of end products prevent metabolism from reaching equilibrium.

? *Why are spontaneous reactions important in the metabolism of a cell?*

CONCEPT 6.3

ATP powers cellular work by coupling exergonic reactions to endergonic reactions (pp. 128–130)

- **ATP** is the cell's energy shuttle. Hydrolysis of its terminal phosphate yields ADP and Ⓟi and releases free energy.
- Through **energy coupling**, the exergonic process of ATP hydrolysis drives endergonic reactions by transfer of a phosphate group to specific reactants, forming a **phosphorylated intermediate** that is more reactive. ATP hydrolysis (sometimes with protein phosphorylation) also causes changes in the shape and binding affinities of transport and motor proteins.
- Catabolic pathways drive regeneration of ATP from ADP + Ⓟi.

? *Describe the ATP cycle: How is ATP used and regenerated in a cell?*

CONCEPT 6.4

Enzymes speed up metabolic reactions by lowering energy barriers (pp. 131–136)

- In a chemical reaction, the energy necessary to break the bonds of the reactants is the **activation energy**, E_A.
- **Enzymes** lower the E_A barrier:

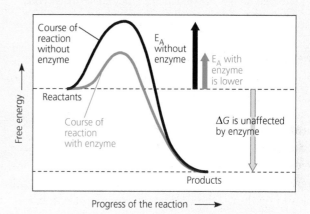

- Each type of enzyme has a unique **active site** that combines specifically with its **substrate(s)**, the reactant(s) on which it acts. It then changes shape, binding the substrate(s) more tightly (**induced fit**).
- The active site can lower an E_A barrier by orienting substrates correctly, straining their bonds, providing a favorable microenvironment, or even covalently bonding with the substrate.
- Each enzyme has an optimal temperature and pH. Inhibitors reduce enzyme function. A **competitive inhibitor** binds to the active site, whereas a **noncompetitive inhibitor** binds to a different site on the enzyme.
- Natural selection, acting on organisms with variant enzymes, is responsible for the diversity of enzymes found in organisms.

? *How do both activation energy barriers and enzymes help maintain the structural and metabolic order of life?*

CONCEPT 6.5

Regulation of enzyme activity helps control metabolism (pp. 136–138)

- Many enzymes are subject to **allosteric regulation**: Regulatory molecules, either activators or inhibitors, bind to specific regulatory sites, affecting the shape and function of the enzyme. In **cooperativity**, binding of one substrate molecule can stimulate binding or activity at other active sites. In **feedback inhibition**, the end product of a metabolic pathway allosterically inhibits the enzyme for a previous step in the pathway.
- Some enzymes are grouped into complexes, some are incorporated into membranes, and some are contained inside organelles, increasing the efficiency of metabolic processes.

? *What roles do allosteric regulation and feedback inhibition play in the metabolism of a cell?*

TEST YOUR UNDERSTANDING

PRACTICE TEST

goo.gl/CRZjvS

Level 1: Knowledge/Comprehension

1. Choose the pair of terms that correctly completes this sentence: Catabolism is to anabolism as _____ is to _____.
   (A) exergonic; spontaneous
   (B) exergonic; endergonic
   (C) free energy; entropy
   (D) work; energy

2. Most cells cannot harness heat to perform work because
   (A) heat does not involve a transfer of energy.
   (B) cells do not have much heat; they are relatively cool.
   (C) temperature is usually uniform throughout a cell.
   (D) heat can never be used to do work.

3. Which of the following metabolic processes can occur without a net influx of energy from some other process?
   (A) $ADP + \text{P}_i \rightarrow ATP + H_2O$
   (B) $C_6H_{12}O_6 + 6\,O_2 \rightarrow 6\,CO_2 + 6\,H_2O$
   (C) $6\,CO_2 + 6\,H_2O \rightarrow C_6H_{12}O_6 + 6\,O_2$
   (D) amino acids $\rightarrow$ protein

4. If an enzyme in solution is saturated with substrate, the most effective way to obtain a faster yield of products is to
   (A) add more of the enzyme.
   (B) heat the solution to 90°C.
   (C) add more substrate.
   (D) add an allosteric inhibitor.

5. Some bacteria are metabolically active in hot springs because
   (A) they are able to maintain a lower internal temperature.
   (B) high temperatures make catalysis unnecessary.
   (C) their enzymes have high optimal temperatures.
   (D) their enzymes are completely insensitive to temperature.

Level 2: Application/Analysis

6. If an enzyme is added to a solution where its substrate and product are in equilibrium, what will occur?
   (A) Additional product will be formed.
   (B) The reaction will change from endergonic to exergonic.
   (C) The free energy of the system will change.
   (D) Nothing; the reaction will stay at equilibrium.

Level 3: Synthesis/Evaluation

7. **DRAW IT** Using a series of arrows, draw the branched metabolic reaction pathway described by the following statements. Then answer the question at the end. Use red arrows and minus signs to indicate inhibition.

   L can form either M or N.
   M can form O.
   O can form either P or R.
   P can form Q.
   R can form S.
   O inhibits the reaction of L to form M.
   Q inhibits the reaction of O to form P.
   S inhibits the reaction of O to form R.

   Which reaction would prevail if both Q and S were present in the cell at high concentrations?

   (A) L → M
   (B) M → O
   (C) L → N
   (D) O → P

8. **SCIENTIFIC INQUIRY**
   DRAW IT A researcher has developed an assay to measure the activity of an important enzyme present in liver cells growing in culture. She adds the enzyme's substrate to a dish of cells and then measures the appearance of reaction products. The results are graphed as the amount of product on the y-axis versus time on the x-axis. The researcher notes four sections of the graph. For a short period of time, no products appear (section A). Then (section B) the reaction rate is quite high (the slope of the line is steep). Next, the reaction gradually slows down (section C). Finally, the graph line becomes flat (section D). Draw and label the graph, and propose a model to explain the molecular events occurring at each stage of this reaction profile.

9. **SCIENCE, TECHNOLOGY, AND SOCIETY**
   Organophosphates (organic compounds containing phosphate groups) are commonly used as insecticides to improve crop yield. Organophosphates typically interfere with nerve signal transmission by inhibiting the enzymes that degrade transmitter molecules. They affect humans and other vertebrates as well as insects. Thus, the use of organophosphate pesticides poses some health risks. On the other hand, these molecules break down rapidly upon exposure to air and sunlight. As a consumer, what level of risk are you willing to accept in exchange for an abundant and affordable food supply? Explain your thinking.

10. **FOCUS ON EVOLUTION**
    A recent revival of the antievolutionary "intelligent design" argument holds that biochemical pathways are too complex to have evolved, because all intermediate steps in a given pathway must be present to produce the final product. Critique this argument. How could you use the diversity of metabolic pathways that produce the same or similar products to support your case?

11. **FOCUS ON ENERGY AND MATTER**
    Life requires energy. In a short essay (100–150 words), describe the basic principles of bioenergetics in an animal cell. How is the flow and transformation of energy different in a photosynthesizing cell? Include the role of ATP and enzymes in your discussion.

12. **SYNTHESIZE YOUR KNOWLEDGE**

Explain what is happening in this photo in terms of kinetic energy and potential energy. Include the energy conversions that occur when the penguins eat fish and climb back up on the glacier. Describe the role of ATP and enzymes in the underlying molecular processes, including what happens to the free energy of some of the molecules involved.

For selected answers, see Appendix A.

Cellular Respiration and Fermentation

KEY CONCEPTS

7.1 Catabolic pathways yield energy by oxidizing organic fuels

7.2 Glycolysis harvests chemical energy by oxidizing glucose to pyruvate

7.3 After pyruvate is oxidized, the citric acid cycle completes the energy-yielding oxidation of organic molecules

7.4 During oxidative phosphorylation, chemiosmosis couples electron transport to ATP synthesis

7.5 Fermentation and anaerobic respiration enable cells to produce ATP without the use of oxygen

7.6 Glycolysis and the citric acid cycle connect to many other metabolic pathways

▲ **Figure 7.1** How do these leaves power the work of life for this giraffe?

Life Is Work

Living cells require transfusions of energy from outside sources to perform their many tasks—for example, assembling polymers, pumping substances across membranes, moving, and reproducing. The giraffe in **Figure 7.1** obtains energy for its cells by eating plants; some animals feed on other organisms that eat plants. The energy stored in the organic molecules of food ultimately comes from the sun. Energy flows into an ecosystem as sunlight and exits as heat; in contrast, the chemical elements essential to life are recycled **(Figure 7.2)**. Photosynthesis generates oxygen and organic molecules that are used by the mitochondria of eukaryotes (including plants and algae) as fuel for cellular respiration. Respiration breaks down this fuel, generating ATP. The waste products of this type of respiration, carbon dioxide and water, are the raw materials for photosynthesis.

In this chapter, we'll consider how cells harvest the chemical energy stored in organic molecules and use it to generate ATP, the molecule that drives most cellular work. After presenting some basics about respiration, we'll focus on three key pathways of respiration: glycolysis, the citric acid cycle, and oxidative phosphorylation. We'll also consider fermentation, a somewhat simpler pathway coupled to glycolysis that has deep evolutionary roots.

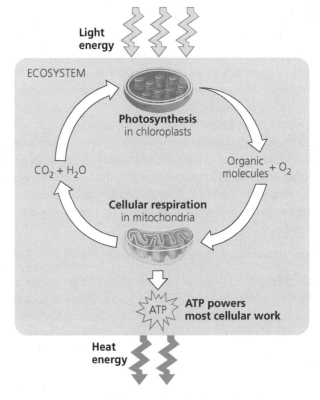

▲ **Figure 7.2 Energy flow and chemical recycling in ecosystems.** Energy flows into an ecosystem as sunlight and ultimately leaves as heat, while the chemical elements essential to life are recycled.

Catabolic pathways yield energy by oxidizing organic fuels

Metabolic pathways that release stored energy by breaking down complex molecules are called catabolic pathways (see Concept 6.1). Electron transfer plays a major role in these pathways. In this section, we'll consider these processes, which are central to cellular respiration.

Catabolic Pathways and Production of ATP

Organic compounds possess potential energy as a result of the arrangement of electrons in the bonds between their atoms. Compounds that can participate in exergonic reactions can act as fuels. Through the activity of enzymes, a cell systematically degrades complex organic molecules that are rich in potential energy to simpler waste products that have less energy. Some of the energy taken out of chemical storage can be used to do work; the rest is dissipated as heat.

One catabolic process, **fermentation**, is a partial degradation of sugars or other organic fuel that occurs without the use of oxygen. However, the most efficient catabolic pathway is **aerobic respiration**, in which oxygen is consumed as a reactant along with the organic fuel (*aerobic* is from the Greek *aer*, air, and *bios*, life). The cells of most eukaryotic and many prokaryotic organisms can carry out aerobic respiration. Some prokaryotes use substances other than oxygen as reactants in a similar process that harvests chemical energy without oxygen; this process is called *anaerobic respiration* (the prefix *an-* means "without"). Technically, the term **cellular respiration** includes both aerobic and anaerobic processes. However, it originated as a synonym for aerobic respiration because of the relationship of that process to organismal respiration, in which an animal breathes in oxygen. Thus, *cellular respiration* is often used to refer to the aerobic process, a practice we follow in most of this chapter.

Although very different in mechanism, aerobic respiration is in principle similar to the combustion of gasoline in an automobile engine after oxygen is mixed with the fuel (hydrocarbons). Food provides the fuel for respiration, and the exhaust is carbon dioxide and water. The overall process can be summarized as follows:

Organic compounds + Oxygen → Carbon dioxide + Water + Energy

Carbohydrates, fats, and proteins can all be processed and consumed as fuel. In animal diets, a major source of carbohydrates is starch, a storage polysaccharide that can be broken down into glucose ($C_6H_{12}O_6$) subunits. We will learn the steps of cellular respiration by tracking the degradation of the sugar glucose:

$$C_6H_{12}O_6 + 6\,O_2 \rightarrow 6\,CO_2 + 6\,H_2O + \text{Energy (ATP + heat)}$$

This breakdown of glucose is exergonic, having a free-energy change of −686 kcal (2,870 kJ) per mole of glucose

decomposed (ΔG = −686 kcal/mol). Recall that a negative ΔG indicates that the products of the chemical process store less energy than the reactants and that the reaction can happen spontaneously—in other words, without an input of energy.

Catabolic pathways do not directly move flagella, pump solutes across membranes, polymerize monomers, or perform other cellular work. Catabolism is linked to work by a chemical drive shaft—ATP (which you learned about in Concepts 3.1 and 6.3). To keep working, the cell must regenerate its supply of ATP from ADP and ⓟ_i (see Figure 6.11). To understand how cellular respiration accomplishes this, let's examine the fundamental chemical processes known as oxidation and reduction.

Redox Reactions: Oxidation and Reduction

How do the catabolic pathways that decompose glucose and other organic fuels yield energy? The answer is based on the transfer of electrons during the chemical reactions. The relocation of electrons releases energy stored in organic molecules, and this energy ultimately is used to synthesize ATP.

The Principle of Redox

In many chemical reactions, there is a transfer of one or more electrons (e^-) from one reactant to another. These electron transfers are called oxidation-reduction reactions, or **redox reactions** for short. In a redox reaction, the loss of electrons from one substance is called **oxidation**, and the addition of electrons to another substance is known as **reduction**. (Note that *adding* electrons is called *reduction*; adding negatively charged electrons to an atom *reduces* the amount of positive charge of that atom.) To take a simple, nonbiological example, consider the reaction between the elements sodium (Na) and chlorine (Cl) that forms table salt:

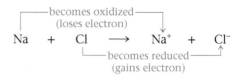

We could generalize a redox reaction this way:

$$\begin{array}{c} \overbrace{}^{\text{becomes oxidized}} \\ Xe^- \quad + \quad Y \quad \longrightarrow \quad X \quad + \quad Ye^- \\ \underbrace{}_{\text{becomes reduced}} \end{array}$$

In the generalized reaction, substance Xe^-, the electron donor, is called the **reducing agent**; it reduces Y, which accepts the donated electron. Substance Y, the electron acceptor, is the **oxidizing agent**; it oxidizes Xe^- by removing its electron. Because an electron transfer requires both an electron donor and an acceptor, oxidation and reduction always go hand in hand.

Not all redox reactions involve the complete transfer of electrons from one substance to another; some change the degree of electron sharing in covalent bonds. Methane combustion,

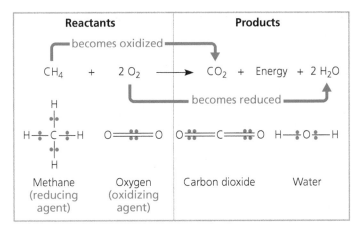

▲ **Figure 7.3 Methane combustion as an energy-yielding redox reaction.** The reaction releases energy to the surroundings because the electrons lose potential energy when they end up being shared unequally, spending more time near electronegative atoms such as oxygen.

shown in **Figure 7.3**, is an example. The covalent electrons in methane are shared nearly equally between the bonded atoms because carbon and hydrogen have about the same affinity for valence electrons; they are about equally electronegative. But when methane reacts with oxygen, forming carbon dioxide, electrons end up shared less equally between the carbon atom and its new covalent partners, the oxygen atoms, which are very electronegative. In effect, the carbon atom has partially "lost" its shared electrons; thus, methane has been oxidized.

Now let's examine the fate of the reactant O_2. The two atoms of the oxygen molecule (O_2) share their electrons equally. But when oxygen reacts with the hydrogen from methane, forming water, the electrons of the covalent bonds spend more time near the oxygen (see Figure 7.3). In effect, each oxygen atom has partially "gained" electrons, so the oxygen molecule has been reduced. Because oxygen is so electronegative, it is one of the most powerful of all oxidizing agents.

Energy must be added to pull an electron away from an atom, just as energy is required to push a ball uphill. The more electronegative the atom (the stronger its pull on electrons), the more energy is required to take an electron away from it. An electron loses potential energy when it shifts from a less electronegative atom toward a more electronegative one, just as a ball loses potential energy when it rolls downhill. A redox reaction that moves electrons closer to oxygen, such as the burning (oxidation) of methane, therefore releases chemical energy that can be put to work.

Oxidation of Organic Fuel Molecules During Cellular Respiration

The oxidation of methane by oxygen is the main combustion reaction that occurs at the burner of a gas stove. The combustion of gasoline in an automobile engine is also a redox reaction; the energy released pushes the pistons. But the energy-yielding redox process of greatest interest to biologists

is respiration: the oxidation of glucose and other molecules in food. Examine again the summary equation for cellular respiration, but this time think of it as a redox process:

$$C_6H_{12}O_6 + 6 O_2 \longrightarrow 6 CO_2 + 6 H_2O + \text{Energy}$$

As in the combustion of methane or gasoline, the fuel (glucose) is oxidized and oxygen is reduced. The electrons lose potential energy along the way, and energy is released.

In general, organic molecules that have an abundance of hydrogen are excellent fuels because their bonds are a source of "hilltop" electrons, whose energy may be released as these electrons "fall" down an energy gradient when they are transferred to oxygen. The summary equation for respiration indicates that hydrogen is transferred from glucose to oxygen. But the important point, not visible in the summary equation, is that the energy state of the electron changes as hydrogen (with its electron) is transferred to oxygen. In respiration, the oxidation of glucose transfers electrons to a lower energy state, liberating energy that becomes available for ATP synthesis.

The main energy-yielding foods, carbohydrates and fats, are reservoirs of electrons associated with hydrogen. Only the barrier of activation energy holds back the flood of electrons to a lower energy state (see Figure 6.12). Without this barrier, a food substance like glucose would combine almost instantaneously with O_2. If we supply the activation energy by igniting glucose, it burns in air, releasing 686 kcal (2,870 kJ) of heat per mole of glucose (about 180 g). Body temperature is not high enough to initiate burning, of course. Instead, if you swallow some glucose, enzymes in your cells will lower the barrier of activation energy, allowing the sugar to be oxidized in a series of steps.

Stepwise Energy Harvest via NAD⁺ and the Electron Transport Chain

If energy is released from a fuel all at once, it cannot be harnessed efficiently for constructive work. For example, if a gasoline tank explodes, it cannot drive a car very far. Cellular respiration does not oxidize glucose (or any other organic fuel) in a single explosive step, either. Rather, glucose is broken down in a series of steps, each one catalyzed by an enzyme. At key steps, electrons are stripped from the glucose. As is often the case in oxidation reactions, each electron travels with a proton—thus, as a hydrogen atom. The hydrogen atoms are not transferred directly to oxygen, but instead are usually passed first to an electron carrier, a coenzyme called **NAD⁺** (nicotinamide adenine dinucleotide, a derivative of the vitamin niacin). NAD⁺ is well suited as an electron carrier because it can cycle easily between oxidized (NAD⁺) and reduced (NADH) states. As an electron acceptor, NAD⁺ functions as an oxidizing agent during respiration.

How does NAD⁺ trap electrons from glucose and other organic molecules in food? Enzymes called dehydrogenases remove a pair of hydrogen atoms (2 electrons and 2 protons) from the

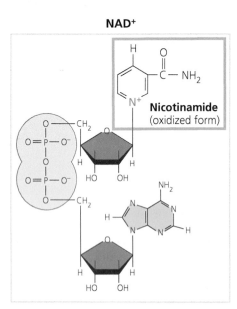

NAD⁺

Nicotinamide
(oxidized form)

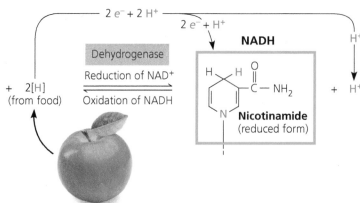

Dehydrogenase

Reduction of NAD⁺

Oxidation of NADH

NADH

Nicotinamide
(reduced form)

◄ **Figure 7.4 NAD⁺ as an electron shuttle.** The full name for NAD⁺, nicotinamide adenine dinucleotide, describes its structure: The molecule consists of two nucleotides joined together at their phosphate groups (shown in yellow). (Nicotinamide is a nitrogenous base, although not one that is present in DNA or RNA.) The enzymatic transfer of 2 electrons and 1 proton (H⁺) from an organic molecule in food to NAD⁺ reduces the NAD⁺ to NADH; the second proton (H⁺) is released. Most of the electrons removed from food are transferred initially to NAD⁺, forming NADH.

substrate (glucose, in this example), thereby oxidizing it. The enzyme delivers the 2 electrons along with 1 proton to its coenzyme, NAD⁺, forming NADH **(Figure 7.4)**. The other proton is released as a hydrogen ion (H⁺) into the surrounding solution:

$$H-\underset{|}{\overset{|}{C}}-OH + NAD^+ \xrightarrow{\text{Dehydrogenase}} \underset{|}{\overset{|}{C}}=O + NADH + H^+$$

By receiving 2 negatively charged electrons but only 1 positively charged proton, the nicotinamide portion of NAD⁺ has its charge neutralized when NAD⁺ is reduced to NADH. The name NADH shows the hydrogen that has been received in the reaction. NAD⁺ is the most versatile electron acceptor in cellular respiration and functions in several of the redox steps during the breakdown of glucose.

Electrons lose very little of their potential energy when they are transferred from glucose to NAD⁺. Each NADH molecule formed during respiration represents stored energy that can be tapped to make ATP when the electrons complete their "fall" down an energy gradient from NADH to oxygen.

How do electrons that are extracted from glucose and stored as potential energy in NADH finally reach oxygen? It will help to compare the redox chemistry of cellular respiration to a much simpler reaction: the reaction between hydrogen and oxygen to form water **(Figure 7.5a)**. Mix H₂ and O₂, provide a spark for activation energy, and the gases combine explosively. In fact, combustion of liquid

H₂ and O₂ is harnessed to help power the rocket engines that boost satellites into orbit and launch spacecraft. The explosion represents a release of energy as the electrons of hydrogen "fall" closer to the electronegative oxygen atoms. Cellular respiration also brings hydrogen and oxygen together to form water, but there are two important differences. First, in cellular respiration, the hydrogen that reacts with oxygen is derived from organic molecules rather than H₂. Second, instead of occurring in one explosive reaction, respiration uses an electron transport chain to break the fall of electrons

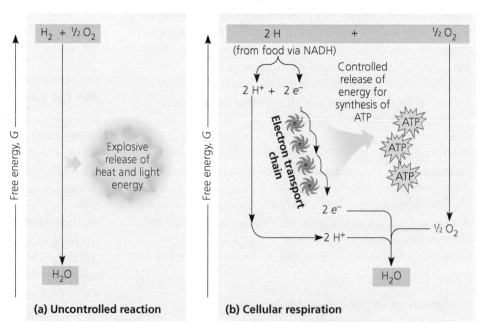

(a) Uncontrolled reaction

(b) Cellular respiration

▲ **Figure 7.5 An introduction to electron transport chains. (a)** The one-step exergonic reaction of hydrogen with oxygen to form water releases a large amount of energy in the form of heat and light: an explosion. **(b)** In cellular respiration, the same reaction occurs in stages: An electron transport chain breaks the "fall" of electrons in this reaction into a series of smaller steps and stores some of the released energy in a form that can be used to make ATP. (The rest of the energy is released as heat.)

to oxygen into several energy-releasing steps (**Figure 7.5b**). An **electron transport chain** consists of a number of molecules, mostly proteins, built into the inner membrane of the mitochondria of eukaryotic cells and the plasma membrane of aerobically respiring prokaryotes. Electrons removed from glucose are shuttled by NADH to the "top," higher-energy end of the chain. At the "bottom," lower-energy end, O_2 captures these electrons along with hydrogen nuclei (H^+), forming water.

Electron transfer from NADH to oxygen is an exergonic reaction with a free-energy change of −53 kcal/mol (−222 kJ/mol). Instead of this energy being released and wasted in a single explosive step, electrons cascade down the chain from one carrier molecule to the next in a series of redox reactions, losing a small amount of energy with each step until they finally reach oxygen, the terminal electron acceptor, which has a very great affinity for electrons. Each "downhill" carrier is more electronegative than, and thus capable of oxidizing, its "uphill" neighbor, with oxygen at the bottom of the chain. Therefore, the electrons transferred from glucose to NAD^+, forming NADH, will fall down an energy gradient in the electron transport chain to a far more stable location in the electronegative oxygen atom. Put another way, oxygen pulls electrons down the chain in an energy-yielding tumble analogous to gravity pulling objects downhill.

In summary, during cellular respiration, most electrons travel the following "downhill" route: glucose → NADH → electron transport chain → oxygen. Later in this chapter, you will learn more about how the cell uses the energy released from this exergonic electron fall to regenerate its supply of ATP. For now, having covered the basic redox mechanisms of cellular respiration, let's look at the entire process by which energy is harvested from organic fuels.

The Stages of Cellular Respiration: *A Preview*

The harvesting of energy from glucose by cellular respiration is a cumulative function of three metabolic stages. We list them here along with a color-coding scheme that we will use throughout the chapter to help you keep track of the big picture.

1. GLYCOLYSIS (color-coded blue throughout the chapter)
2. PYRUVATE OXIDATION and the CITRIC ACID CYCLE (color-coded orange)
3. OXIDATIVE PHOSPHORYLATION: Electron transport and chemiosmosis (color-coded purple)

Biochemists usually reserve the term *cellular respiration* for stages 2 and 3 together. In this text, however, we include glycolysis as a part of cellular respiration because most respiring cells deriving energy from glucose use glycolysis to produce the starting material for the citric acid cycle.

As diagrammed in **Figure 7.6**, glycolysis and pyruvate oxidation followed by the citric acid cycle are the catabolic pathways that break down glucose and other organic fuels. **Glycolysis**, which occurs in the cytosol, begins the degradation process by breaking glucose into two molecules of a compound called pyruvate. In eukaryotes, pyruvate enters the mitochondrion and is oxidized to a compound called acetyl CoA, which enters the **citric acid cycle** (also called the Krebs cycle). There, the breakdown of glucose to carbon dioxide is completed. (In prokaryotes, these processes take place in the cytosol.) Thus, the carbon dioxide produced by respiration represents fragments of oxidized organic molecules.

Some of the steps of glycolysis and the citric acid cycle are redox reactions in which dehydrogenases transfer electrons from substrates to NAD^+, forming NADH. In the third stage

▶ **Figure 7.6 An overview of cellular respiration.** During glycolysis, each glucose molecule is broken down into two molecules of pyruvate. In eukaryotic cells, as shown here, the pyruvate enters the mitochondrion. There it is oxidized to acetyl CoA, which will be further oxidized to CO_2 in the citric acid cycle. The electron carriers NADH and $FADH_2$ transfer electrons derived from glucose to electron transport chains. During oxidative phosphorylation, electron transport chains convert the chemical energy to a form used for ATP synthesis in the process called chemiosmosis. (During earlier steps of cellular respiration, smaller amounts of ATP are synthesized in a process called substrate-level phosphorylation.)

ANIMATION Visit the Study Area in **MasteringBiology** for the BioFlix® 3-D Animation on Cellular Respiration.

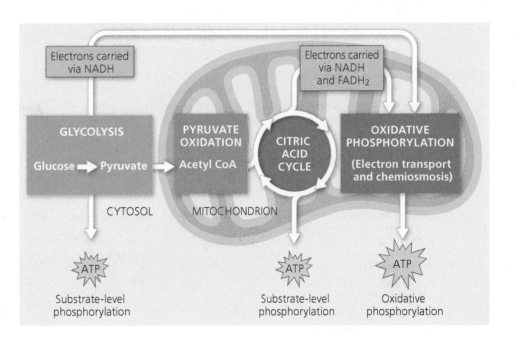

of respiration, the electron transport chain accepts electrons (most often via NADH) from the breakdown products of the first two stages and passes these electrons from one molecule to another. At the end of the chain, the electrons are combined with molecular oxygen and hydrogen ions (H^+), forming water (see Figure 7.5b). The energy released at each step of the chain is stored in a form the mitochondrion (or prokaryotic cell) can use to make ATP from ADP. This mode of ATP synthesis is called **oxidative phosphorylation** because it is powered by the redox reactions of the electron transport chain.

In eukaryotic cells, the inner membrane of the mitochondrion is the site of electron transport and chemiosmosis, the processes that together constitute oxidative phosphorylation. (In prokaryotes, these processes take place in the plasma membrane.) Oxidative phosphorylation accounts for almost 90% of the ATP generated by respiration. A smaller amount of ATP is formed directly in a few reactions of glycolysis and the citric acid cycle by a mechanism called **substrate-level phosphorylation (Figure 7.7)**. This mode of ATP synthesis occurs when an enzyme transfers a phosphate group from a substrate molecule to ADP, rather than adding an inorganic phosphate to ADP as in oxidative phosphorylation. "Substrate molecule" here refers to an organic molecule generated as an intermediate during the catabolism of glucose.

For each molecule of glucose degraded to carbon dioxide and water by respiration, the cell makes up to about 32 molecules of ATP, each with 7.3 kcal/mol of free energy. Respiration cashes in the large denomination of energy banked in a single molecule of glucose (686 kcal/mol) for the small change

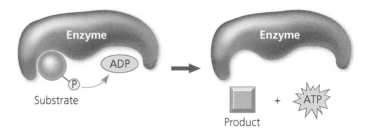

▲ **Figure 7.7 Substrate-level phosphorylation.** Some ATP is made by direct transfer of a phosphate group from an organic substrate to ADP by an enzyme. (For examples in glycolysis, see Figure 7.9, steps 7 and 10.)

MAKE CONNECTIONS *Review Figure 6.8. Do you think the potential energy is higher for the reactants or the products in the reaction shown above? Explain.*

of many molecules of ATP, which is more practical for the cell to spend on its work.

This preview has introduced you to how glycolysis, the citric acid cycle, and oxidative phosphorylation fit into the process of cellular respiration. We are now ready to take a closer look at each of these three stages of respiration.

CONCEPT CHECK 7.1

1. Compare and contrast aerobic and anaerobic respiration.
2. Name and describe the two ways in which ATP is made during cellular respiration. During what stage(s) in the process does each type occur?
3. **WHAT IF?** If the following redox reaction occurred, which compound would be oxidized? Which reduced?

$$C_4H_6O_5 + NAD^+ \rightarrow C_4H_4O_5 + NADH + H^+$$

For suggested answers, see Appendix A.

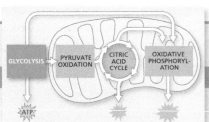

▼ **Figure 7.9 A closer look at glycolysis.** Note that glycolysis is a source of ATP and NADH.

GLYCOLYSIS: Energy Investment Phase

WHAT IF? *What would happen if you removed the dihydroxyacetone phosphate generated in step 4 as fast as it was produced?*

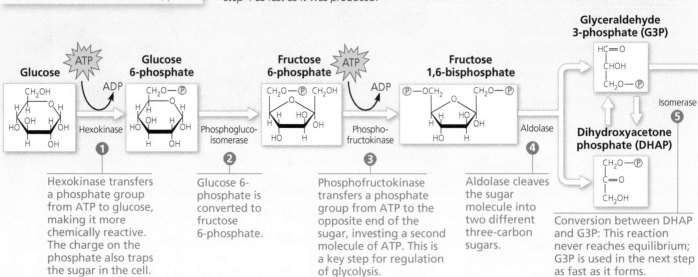

Glucose

Glucose 6-phosphate

Fructose 6-phosphate

Fructose 1,6-bisphosphate

Glyceraldehyde 3-phosphate (G3P)

Dihydroxyacetone phosphate (DHAP)

① Hexokinase transfers a phosphate group from ATP to glucose, making it more chemically reactive. The charge on the phosphate also traps the sugar in the cell.

② Glucose 6-phosphate is converted to fructose 6-phosphate.

③ Phosphofructokinase transfers a phosphate group from ATP to the opposite end of the sugar, investing a second molecule of ATP. This is a key step for regulation of glycolysis.

④ Aldolase cleaves the sugar molecule into two different three-carbon sugars.

⑤ Conversion between DHAP and G3P: This reaction never reaches equilibrium; G3P is used in the next step as fast as it forms.

CONCEPT 7.2

Glycolysis harvests chemical energy by oxidizing glucose to pyruvate

The word *glycolysis* means "sugar splitting," and that is exactly what happens during this pathway. Glucose, a six-carbon sugar, is split into two three-carbon sugars. These smaller sugars are then oxidized and their remaining atoms rearranged to form two molecules of pyruvate. (Pyruvate is the ionized form of pyruvic acid.)

As summarized in **Figure 7.8**, glycolysis can be divided into two phases: energy investment and energy payoff. During the energy investment phase, the cell actually spends ATP. This investment is repaid with interest during the energy payoff phase, when ATP is produced by substrate-level phosphorylation and NAD^+ is reduced to NADH by electrons released from the oxidation of glucose. The net energy yield from glycolysis, per glucose molecule, is 2 ATP plus 2 NADH.

Because glycolysis is a fundamental core process shared by bacteria, archaea, and eukaryotes alike, we will use it as an example of a biochemical pathway. The ten steps of the glycolytic pathway are shown in **Figure 7.9**.

All of the carbon originally present in glucose is accounted for in the two molecules of pyruvate; no carbon is released as CO_2 during glycolysis. Glycolysis occurs whether or not O_2 is present. However, if O_2 *is* present, the chemical energy stored in pyruvate and NADH can be extracted by pyruvate oxidation, the citric acid cycle, and oxidative phosphorylation.

▼ **Figure 7.8 The energy input and output of glycolysis.**

Energy Investment Phase

Glucose

2 ATP used ⟶ 2 ADP + 2 Ⓟ

Energy Payoff Phase

4 ADP + 4 Ⓟ ⟶ 4 ATP formed

2 NAD^+ + 4 e^- + 4 H^+ ⟶ 2 NADH + 2 H^+

⟶ 2 Pyruvate + 2 H_2O

Net

Glucose ⟶ 2 Pyruvate + 2 H_2O

4 ATP formed – 2 ATP used ⟶ 2 ATP

2 NAD^+ + 4 e^- + 4 H^+ ⟶ 2 NADH + 2 H^+

CONCEPT CHECK 7.2

1. During step 6 in Figure 7.9, which molecule acts as the oxidizing agent? The reducing agent?

   For suggested answers, see Appendix A.

The energy payoff phase occurs after glucose is split into two three-carbon sugars. Thus, the coefficient 2 precedes all molecules in this phase.

GLYCOLYSIS: Energy Payoff Phase

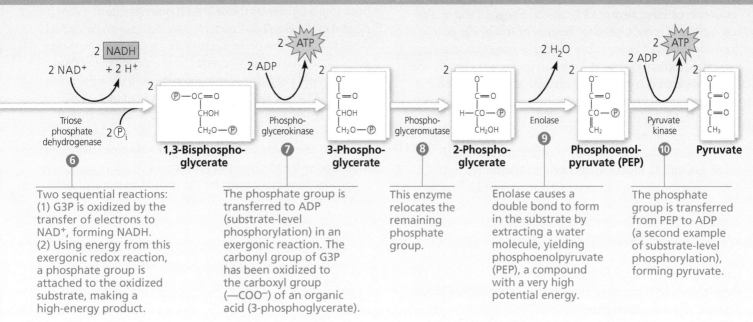

Two sequential reactions: (1) G3P is oxidized by the transfer of electrons to NAD^+, forming NADH. (2) Using energy from this exergonic redox reaction, a phosphate group is attached to the oxidized substrate, making a high-energy product.

The phosphate group is transferred to ADP (substrate-level phosphorylation) in an exergonic reaction. The carbonyl group of G3P has been oxidized to the carboxyl group (—COO⁻) of an organic acid (3-phosphoglycerate).

This enzyme relocates the remaining phosphate group.

Enolase causes a double bond to form in the substrate by extracting a water molecule, yielding phosphoenolpyruvate (PEP), a compound with a very high potential energy.

The phosphate group is transferred from PEP to ADP (a second example of substrate-level phosphorylation), forming pyruvate.

After pyruvate is oxidized, the citric acid cycle completes the energy-yielding oxidation of organic molecules

Glycolysis releases less than a quarter of the chemical energy in glucose that can be harvested by cells; most of the energy remains stockpiled in the two molecules of pyruvate. When O_2 is present, the pyruvate in eukaryotic cells enters a mitochondrion, where the oxidation of glucose is completed. (In aerobically respiring prokaryotic cells, this process occurs in the cytosol.)

Once inside the mitochondrion, pyruvate undergoes a series of enzymatic reactions that remove CO_2 and oxidizes the remaining fragment, forming NADH from NAD^+. The product is a highly reactive compound called acetyl coenzyme A, or **acetyl CoA**, which will feed its acetyl group into the citric acid cycle for further oxidation **(Figure 7.10)**.

The citric acid cycle (also known as the Krebs cycle) functions as a metabolic furnace that oxidizes organic fuel derived from pyruvate. Figure 7.10 summarizes the inputs and outputs as pyruvate is broken down to three CO_2 molecules, including the molecule of CO_2 released during the conversion of pyruvate to acetyl CoA. The cycle generates 1 ATP per turn by substrate-level phosphorylation, but most of the chemical energy is transferred to NAD^+ and a related electron carrier, the coenzyme FAD (flavin adenine dinucleotide, derived from riboflavin, a B vitamin), during the redox reactions. The reduced coenzymes, NADH and $FADH_2$, shuttle their cargo of high-energy electrons into the electron transport chain.

Now let's look at the citric acid cycle in more detail. The cycle has eight steps, each catalyzed by a specific enzyme. You can see in **Figure 7.11** that for each turn of the citric acid cycle, two carbons (red type) enter in the relatively reduced form of an acetyl group (step 1), and two different carbons (blue type) leave in the completely oxidized form of CO_2 molecules (steps 3 and 4). The acetyl group of acetyl CoA joins the cycle by combining with the compound oxaloacetate, forming citrate (step 1). (Citrate is the ionized form of citric acid, for which the cycle is named.) The next seven steps decompose the citrate back to oxaloacetate. It is this regeneration of oxaloacetate that makes the process a *cycle.*

Referring to Figure 7.11, we can tally the energy-rich molecules produced by the citric acid cycle. For each acetyl group entering the cycle, 3 NAD^+ are reduced to NADH (steps 3, 4, and 8). In step 6, electrons are transferred not to NAD^+, but to FAD, which accepts 2 electrons and 2 protons to become $FADH_2$. In many animal tissue cells, the reaction in step 5 produces a guanosine triphosphate (GTP) molecule by substrate-level phosphorylation, as shown in Figure 7.11. GTP is a molecule similar to ATP in its structure and cellular function. This GTP may be used to make an ATP molecule (as shown) or directly power work in the cell. In the cells of plants, bacteria, and some animal tissues, step 5 forms an ATP molecule directly by substrate-level phosphorylation. The output

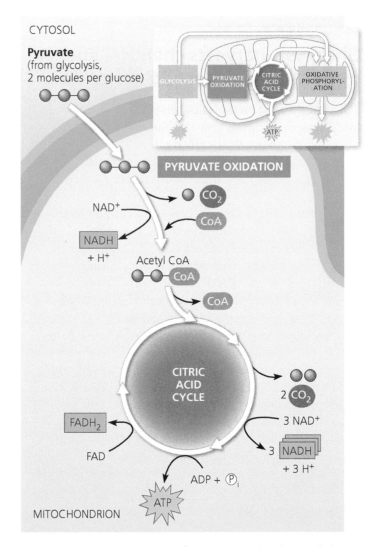

▲ **Figure 7.10 An overview of pyruvate oxidation and the citric acid cycle.** The inputs and outputs per pyruvate molecule are shown. To calculate on a per-glucose basis, multiply by 2, because each glucose molecule is split during glycolysis into two pyruvate molecules.

from step 5 represents the only ATP generated during the citric acid cycle. Recall that each glucose gives rise to two acetyl CoAs that enter the cycle. Because the numbers noted earlier are obtained from a single acetyl group entering the pathway, the total yield per glucose from the citric acid cycle turns out to be 6 NADHs, 2 $FADH_2$s, and the equivalent of 2 ATPs.

Most of the ATP produced by respiration results from oxidative phosphorylation, when the NADH and $FADH_2$ produced by the citric acid cycle relay the electrons extracted from food to the electron transport chain. In the process, they supply the necessary energy for the phosphorylation of ADP to ATP. We'll explore this process in the next section.

CONCEPT CHECK 7.3

1. Name the molecules that conserve most of the energy from redox reactions of the citric acid cycle. How is this energy converted to a form that can be used to make ATP?
2. What processes in your cells produce the CO_2 that you exhale?

For suggested answers, see Appendix A.

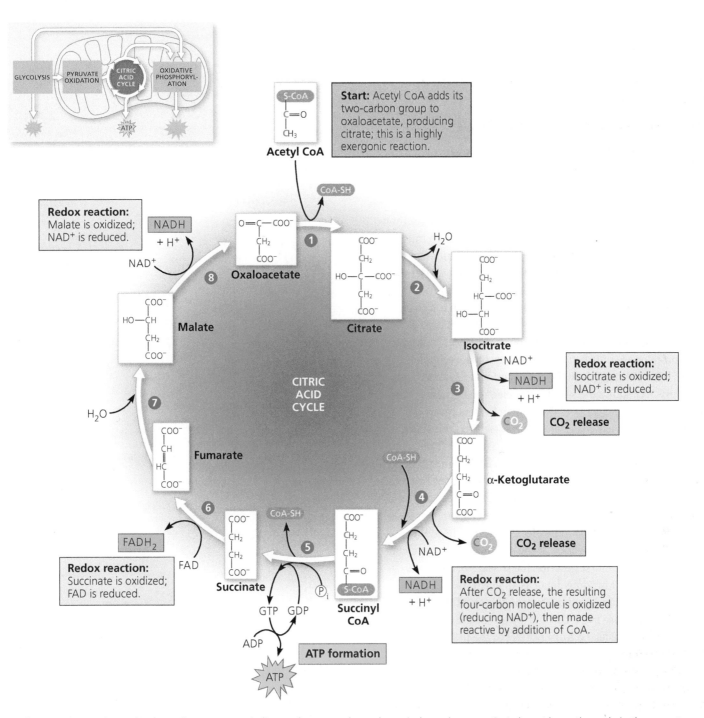

Start: Acetyl CoA adds its two-carbon group to oxaloacetate, producing citrate; this is a highly exergonic reaction.

Acetyl CoA

CoA-SH

Redox reaction: Malate is oxidized; NAD^+ is reduced.

NADH + H^+

NAD^+

⑧ **Oxaloacetate**

Malate

⑦

H_2O

Fumarate

⑥

FADH$_2$

FAD

Redox reaction: Succinate is oxidized; FAD is reduced.

Succinate

⑤

CoA-SH

GTP GDP

ADP

P_i

ATP formation

ATP

Citrate

①

②

H_2O

Isocitrate

CITRIC ACID CYCLE

NAD^+

NADH + H^+

③

CO_2

CO$_2$ release

Redox reaction: Isocitrate is oxidized; NAD^+ is reduced.

CoA-SH

④

NAD^+

CO_2

CO$_2$ release

α-Ketoglutarate

NADH + H^+

Succinyl CoA

Redox reaction: After CO_2 release, the resulting four-carbon molecule is oxidized (reducing NAD^+), then made reactive by addition of CoA.

▲ **Figure 7.11 A closer look at the citric acid cycle.** Key steps (redox reactions, CO_2 release, and ATP formation) are labeled. In the chemical structures, red type traces the fate of the two carbon atoms that enter the cycle via acetyl CoA (step 1), and blue type indicates the two carbons that exit the cycle as CO_2 in steps 3 and 4. (The red type goes only through step 5 because the succinate molecule is symmetrical; the two ends cannot be distinguished from each other.) Notice that the carbon atoms that enter the cycle from acetyl CoA do not leave the cycle in the same turn. They remain in the cycle, occupying a different location in the molecules on their next turn, after another acetyl group is added. Therefore, the oxaloacetate regenerated at step 8 is made up of different carbon atoms each time around.

CONCEPT 7.4

During oxidative phosphorylation, chemiosmosis couples electron transport to ATP synthesis

Our main objective in this chapter is to learn how cells harvest the energy of glucose and other nutrients in food to make ATP. But the metabolic components of respiration we have dissected so far, glycolysis and the citric acid cycle, produce only 4 ATP molecules per glucose molecule, all by substrate-level phosphorylation: 2 net ATP from glycolysis and 2 ATP from the citric acid cycle. At this point, molecules of NADH (and FADH$_2$) account for most of the energy extracted from each glucose molecule. These electron escorts link glycolysis and the citric acid cycle to the machinery of oxidative phosphorylation, which uses energy released by the electron transport chain to power ATP synthesis. In this section, you will learn first how the electron transport chain works and then how electron flow down the chain is coupled to ATP synthesis.

The Pathway of Electron Transport

The electron transport chain is a collection of molecules embedded in the inner membrane of the mitochondrion in eukaryotic cells. (In prokaryotes, these molecules reside in the plasma membrane.) The folding of the inner membrane to form cristae increases its surface area, providing space for thousands of copies of the electron transport chain in each mitochondrion. Once again, we see that structure fits function—the infolded membrane with its placement of electron carrier molecules in a row, one after the other, is well-suited for the series of sequential redox reactions that take place along the chain. Most components of the chain are proteins, which exist in multiprotein complexes numbered I through IV. Tightly bound to these proteins are *prosthetic groups*, nonprotein components essential for the catalytic functions of certain enzymes.

Figure 7.12 shows the sequence of electron carriers in the electron transport chain and the drop in free energy as electrons travel down the chain. During this electron transport, electron carriers alternate between reduced and oxidized states as they accept and then donate electrons. Each component of the chain becomes reduced when it accepts electrons from its "uphill" neighbor, which has a lower affinity for electrons (is less electronegative). It then returns to its oxidized form as it passes electrons to its "downhill," more electronegative neighbor.

Now let's take a closer look at the electron transport chain in Figure 7.12. We'll first describe the passage of electrons through complex I in some detail as an illustration of the general principles involved in electron transport. Electrons acquired from glucose by NAD^+ during glycolysis and the citric acid cycle are transferred from NADH to the first molecule of the electron transport chain in complex I. This molecule is a flavoprotein, so named because it has a prosthetic group called flavin mononucleotide (FMN). In the next redox reaction, the flavoprotein returns to its oxidized form as it passes electrons to an iron-sulfur protein (Fe · S in complex I), one of a family of proteins with both iron and sulfur tightly bound. The iron-sulfur protein then passes the electrons to a compound called ubiquinone (Q in Figure 7.12). This electron carrier is a small hydrophobic molecule, the only member of the electron transport chain that is not a protein. Ubiquinone is individually mobile within the membrane rather than residing in a particular complex. (Another name for ubiquinone is coenzyme Q, or CoQ; you may have seen it sold as a nutritional supplement.)

Most of the remaining electron carriers between ubiquinone and oxygen are proteins called **cytochromes**. Their prosthetic group, called a heme group, has an iron atom that accepts and donates electrons. (The heme group in a cytochrome is similar to the heme group in hemoglobin, the protein of red

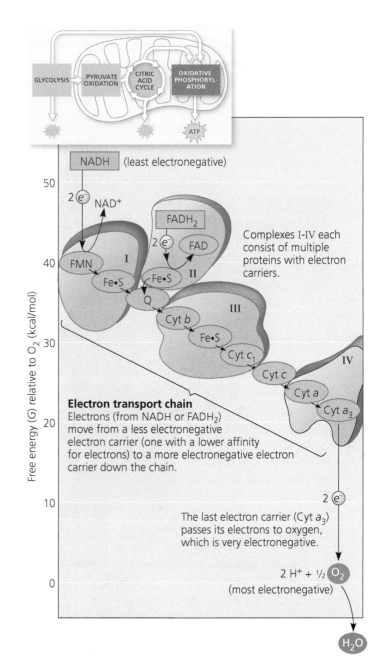

▲ **Figure 7.12 Free-energy change during electron transport.** The overall energy drop (ΔG) for electrons traveling from NADH to oxygen is 53 kcal/mol, but this "fall" is broken up into a series of smaller steps by the electron transport chain. (An oxygen atom is represented here as $\frac{1}{2} O_2$ to emphasize that the electron transport chain reduces molecular oxygen, O_2, not individual oxygen atoms.)

blood cells, except that the iron in hemoglobin carries oxygen, not electrons.) The electron transport chain has several types of cytochromes, each a different protein with a slightly different electron-carrying heme group. The last cytochrome of the chain, Cyt a_3, passes its electrons to oxygen, which is *very* electronegative. Each oxygen atom also picks up a pair of hydrogen ions (protons) from the aqueous solution, neutralizing the −2 charge of the added electrons and forming water.

Another source of electrons for the transport chain is $FADH_2$, the other reduced product of the citric acid cycle.

Notice in Figure 7.12 that $FADH_2$ adds its electrons to the electron transport chain from within complex II, at a lower energy level than NADH does. Consequently, although NADH and $FADH_2$ each donate an equivalent number of electrons (2) for oxygen reduction, the electron transport chain provides about one-third less energy for ATP synthesis when the electron donor is $FADH_2$ rather than NADH. We'll see why in the next section.

The electron transport chain makes no ATP directly. Instead, it eases the fall of electrons from food to oxygen, breaking a large free-energy drop into a series of smaller steps that release energy in manageable amounts. How does the mitochondrion (or the plasma membrane in prokaryotes) couple this electron transport and energy release to ATP synthesis? The answer is a mechanism called chemiosmosis.

Chemiosmosis: The Energy-Coupling Mechanism

Populating the inner membrane of the mitochondrion or the prokaryotic plasma membrane are many copies of a protein complex called **ATP synthase**, the enzyme that actually makes ATP from ADP and inorganic phosphate. ATP synthase works like an ion pump running in reverse. Ion pumps usually use ATP as an energy source to transport ions against their gradients. Enzymes can catalyze a reaction in either direction, depending on the ΔG for the reaction, which is affected by the local concentrations of reactants and products (see Concepts 6.2 and 6.3). Rather than hydrolyzing ATP to pump protons against their concentration gradient, under the conditions of cellular respiration ATP synthase uses the energy of an existing ion gradient to power ATP synthesis. The power source for ATP synthase is a difference in the concentration of H^+ on opposite sides of the inner mitochondrial membrane. (We can also think of this gradient as a difference in pH, since pH is a measure of H^+ concentration.) This process, in which energy stored in the form of a hydrogen ion gradient across a membrane is used to drive cellular work such as the synthesis of ATP, is called **chemiosmosis** (from the Greek *osmos*, push). We have previously used the word *osmosis* in discussing water transport, but here it refers to the flow of H^+ across a membrane.

From studying the structure of ATP synthase, scientists have learned how the flow of H^+ through this large enzyme powers ATP generation. ATP synthase is a multisubunit complex with four main parts, each made up of multiple polypeptides. Protons move one by one into binding sites on one of the parts (the rotor), causing it to spin in a way that catalyzes ATP production from ADP and inorganic phosphate **(Figure 7.13)**. The flow of protons thus behaves somewhat like a rushing stream that turns a waterwheel. ATP synthase is the smallest molecular rotary motor known in nature.

How does the inner mitochondrial membrane or the prokaryotic plasma membrane generate and maintain the H^+ gradient that drives ATP synthesis by the ATP synthase protein complex? Establishing the H^+ gradient across the inner

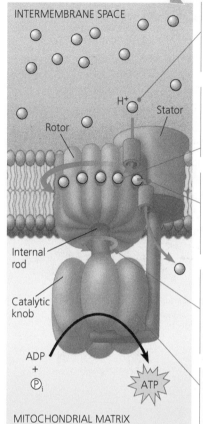

Intermembrane space — Mitochondrial matrix — Inner mitochondrial membrane

INTERMEMBRANE SPACE

1 H^+ ions flowing down their gradient enter a channel in a **stator**, which is anchored in the membrane.

2 H^+ ions enter binding sites within a **rotor**, changing the shape of each subunit so that the rotor spins within the membrane.

3 Each H^+ ion makes one complete turn before leaving the rotor and passing through a second channel in the stator into the mitochondrial matrix.

4 Spinning of the rotor causes an internal **rod** to spin as well. This rod extends like a stalk into the **knob** below it, which is held stationary by part of the stator.

5 Turning of the rod activates catalytic sites in the knob that produce ATP from ADP and $\textcircled{P}_i$.

H^+ Stator
Rotor
Internal rod
Catalytic knob
ADP + $\textcircled{P}_i$
ATP
MITOCHONDRIAL MATRIX

(a) The ATP synthase protein complex functions as a mill, powered by the flow of hydrogen ions.

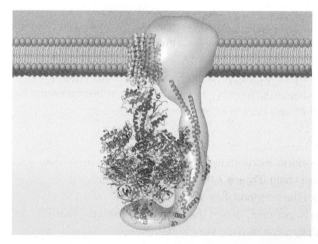

(b) This computer model shows the four parts of ATP synthase. Each part consists of a number of polypeptide subunits. The entire structure of the gray region has not yet been determined and is an area of active research.

▲ **Figure 7.13 ATP synthase, a molecular mill.** Multiple ATP synthases reside in eukaryotic mitochondrial and chloroplast membranes and in prokaryotic plasma membranes.

DRAW IT *Label the rotor, stator, internal rod, and catalytic knob in part (b), the computer model.*

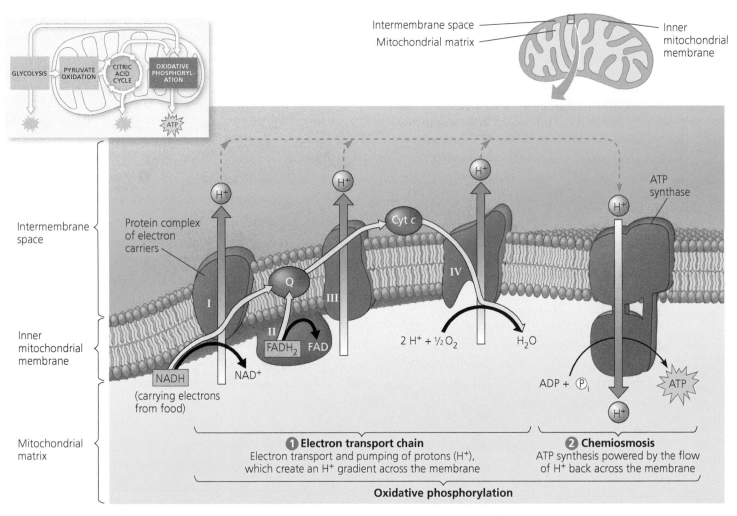

Intermembrane space

Mitochondrial matrix

Inner mitochondrial membrane

Intermembrane space

Inner mitochondrial membrane

Mitochondrial matrix

Protein complex of electron carriers

Cyt c

ATP synthase

H^+

H^+

H^+

H^+

I

Q

II

FADH$_2$ FAD

III

IV

$2 H^+ + \frac{1}{2} O_2$ H_2O

NADH

(carrying electrons from food)

NAD$^+$

ADP + ℗$_i$

ATP

H^+

❶ Electron transport chain
Electron transport and pumping of protons (H^+), which create an H^+ gradient across the membrane

❷ Chemiosmosis
ATP synthesis powered by the flow of H^+ back across the membrane

Oxidative phosphorylation

▲ **Figure 7.14 Chemiosmosis couples the electron transport chain to ATP synthesis.** ❶ NADH and FADH$_2$ shuttle high-energy electrons extracted from food during glycolysis and the citric acid cycle into an electron transport chain built into the inner mitochondrial membrane. The gold arrows trace the transport of electrons, which are finally passed to a terminal acceptor (O$_2$, in the case of aerobic respiration) at the "downhill" end of the chain, forming water. Most of the electron carriers of the chain are grouped into four complexes (I–IV). Two mobile carriers, ubiquinone (Q) and cytochrome c (Cyt c), move rapidly, ferrying electrons between the large complexes. As the complexes shuttle electrons, they pump protons from the mitochondrial matrix into the intermembrane space. FADH$_2$ deposits its electrons via complex II and so results in fewer protons being pumped into the intermembrane space than occurs with NADH. Chemical energy originally harvested from food is transformed into a proton-motive force, a gradient of H^+ across the membrane.

❷ During chemiosmosis, the protons flow back down their gradient via ATP synthase, which is built into the membrane nearby. The ATP synthase harnesses the proton-motive force to phosphorylate ADP, forming ATP. Together, electron transport and chemiosmosis make up oxidative phosphorylation.

WHAT IF? *If complex IV were nonfunctional, could chemiosmosis produce any ATP, and if so, how would the rate of synthesis differ?*

mitochondrial membrane is a major function of the electron transport chain **(Figure 7.14)**. The chain is an energy converter that uses the exergonic flow of electrons from NADH and FADH$_2$ to pump H^+ across the membrane, from the mitochondrial matrix into the intermembrane space. The H^+ has a tendency to move back across the membrane, diffusing down its gradient. And the ATP synthases are the only sites that provide a route through the membrane for H^+. As we described previously, the passage of H^+ through ATP synthase uses the exergonic flow of H^+ to drive the phosphorylation of ADP. Thus, the energy stored in an H^+ gradient across a membrane couples the redox reactions of the electron transport chain to ATP synthesis.

At this point, you may be wondering how the electron transport chain pumps hydrogen ions. Researchers have found that certain members of the electron transport chain accept and release protons (H^+) along with electrons. (The aqueous solutions inside and surrounding the cell are a ready source of H^+.) At certain steps along the chain, electron transfers cause H^+ to be taken up and released into the surrounding solution. In eukaryotic cells, the electron carriers are spatially arranged in the inner mitochondrial membrane in such a way that H^+ is accepted from the mitochondrial matrix and deposited in the intermembrane space (see Figure 7.14). The H^+ gradient that results is referred to as a **proton-motive force**, emphasizing the capacity of the gradient to perform work. The force drives H^+ back across the membrane through the H^+ channels provided by ATP synthases.

In general terms, *chemiosmosis is an energy-coupling mechanism that uses energy stored in the form of an H^+ gradient* *across a membrane to drive cellular work*. In mitochondria, the energy for gradient formation comes from exergonic redox reactions, and ATP synthesis is the work performed. But chemiosmosis also occurs elsewhere and in other variations. Chloroplasts use chemiosmosis to generate ATP during photosynthesis; in these organelles, light (rather than chemical energy) drives both electron flow down an electron transport chain and the resulting H^+ gradient formation. Prokaryotes, as already mentioned, generate H^+ gradients across their plasma membranes. They then tap the proton-motive force not only to make ATP inside the cell but also to rotate their flagella and to pump nutrients and waste products across the membrane. Because of its central importance to energy conversions in prokaryotes and eukaryotes, chemiosmosis has helped unify the study of bioenergetics. Peter Mitchell was awarded the Nobel Prize in 1978 for originally proposing the chemiosmotic model.

An Accounting of ATP Production by Cellular Respiration

In the last few sections, we have looked rather closely at the key processes of cellular respiration. Now let's take a step back and remind ourselves of its overall function: harvesting the energy of glucose for ATP synthesis.

During respiration, most energy flows in this sequence: glucose → NADH → electron transport chain → proton-motive force → ATP. We can do some bookkeeping to calculate the ATP profit when cellular respiration oxidizes a molecule of glucose to six molecules of carbon dioxide. The three main departments of this metabolic enterprise are glycolysis, the citric acid cycle, and the electron transport chain, which drives oxidative phosphorylation. **Figure 7.15** gives a detailed accounting of the ATP yield per glucose molecule oxidized. The tally adds the 4 ATP produced directly by substrate-level phosphorylation during glycolysis and the citric acid cycle to the many more molecules of ATP generated by oxidative phosphorylation. Each NADH that transfers a pair of electrons from glucose to the electron transport chain contributes enough to the proton-motive force to generate a maximum of about 3 ATP.

Why are the numbers in Figure 7.15 inexact? There are three reasons we cannot state an exact number of ATP molecules generated by the breakdown of one molecule of glucose. First, phosphorylation and the redox reactions are not directly coupled to each other, so the ratio of the number of NADH molecules to the number of ATP molecules is not a whole number. We know that 1 NADH results in 10 H^+ being transported out across the inner mitochondrial membrane, but the exact number of H^+ that must reenter the mitochondrial matrix via ATP synthase to generate 1 ATP has long been debated. Based on experimental data, however, most biochemists now agree that the most accurate number is 4 H^+. Therefore, a single molecule of NADH generates enough proton-motive

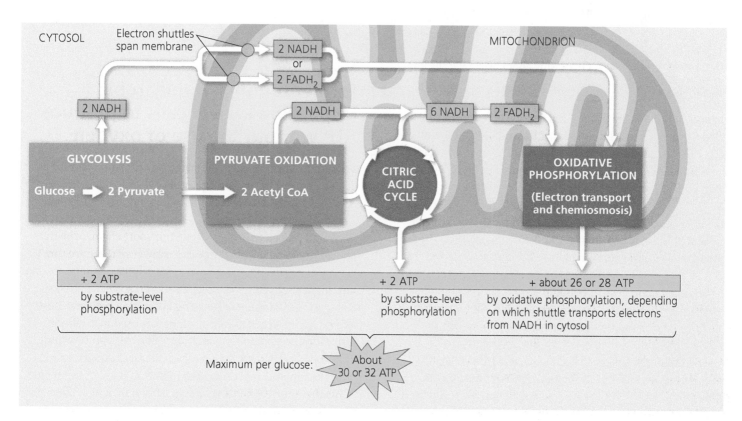

▲ **Figure 7.15 ATP yield per molecule of glucose at each stage of cellular respiration.**

❓ *Explain exactly how the total of 26 or 28 ATP (see the yellow bar) was calculated.*

force for the synthesis of 2.5 ATP. The citric acid cycle also supplies electrons to the electron transport chain via $FADH_2$, but since its electrons enter later in the chain, each molecule of this electron carrier is responsible for transport of only enough H^+ for the synthesis of 1.5 ATP. These numbers also take into account the slight energetic cost of moving the ATP formed in the mitochondrion out into the cytosol, where it will be used.

Second, the ATP yield varies slightly depending on the type of shuttle used to transport electrons from the cytosol into the mitochondrion. The mitochondrial inner membrane is impermeable to NADH, so NADH in the cytosol is segregated from the machinery of oxidative phosphorylation. The 2 electrons of NADH captured in glycolysis must be conveyed into the mitochondrion by one of several electron shuttle systems. Depending on the kind of shuttle in a particular cell type, the electrons are passed either to NAD^+ or to FAD in the mitochondrial matrix (see Figure 7.15). If the electrons are passed to FAD, as in brain cells, only about 1.5 ATP can result from each NADH that was originally generated in the cytosol. If the electrons are passed to mitochondrial NAD^+, as in liver cells and heart cells, the yield is about 2.5 ATP per NADH.

A third variable that reduces the yield of ATP is the use of the proton-motive force generated by the redox reactions of respiration to drive other kinds of work. For example, the proton-motive force powers the mitochondrion's uptake of pyruvate from the cytosol. However, if *all* the proton-motive force generated by the electron transport chain were used to drive ATP synthesis, one glucose molecule could generate a maximum of 28 ATP produced by oxidative phosphorylation plus 4 ATP (net) from substrate-level phosphorylation to give a total yield of about 32 ATP (or only about 30 ATP if the less efficient shuttle were functioning).

We can now roughly estimate the efficiency of respiration—that is, the percentage of chemical energy in glucose that has been transferred to ATP. Recall that the complete oxidation of a mole of glucose releases 686 kcal of energy under standard conditions ($\Delta G = -686$ kcal/mol). Phosphorylation of ADP to form ATP stores at least 7.3 kcal per mole of ATP. Therefore, the efficiency of respiration is 7.3 kcal per mole of ATP times 32 moles of ATP per mole of glucose divided by 686 kcal per mole of glucose, which equals 0.34. Thus, about 34% of the potential chemical energy in glucose has been transferred to ATP; the actual percentage is bound to vary as ΔG varies under different cellular conditions. Cellular respiration is remarkably efficient in its energy conversion. By comparison, the most efficient automobile converts only about 25% of the energy stored in gasoline to energy that moves the car.

The rest of the energy stored in glucose is lost as heat. We humans use some of this heat to maintain our relatively high body temperature (37°C), and we dissipate the rest through sweating and other cooling mechanisms.

Surprisingly, perhaps, it may be beneficial under certain conditions to reduce the efficiency of cellular respiration.

A remarkable adaptation is shown by hibernating mammals, which overwinter in a state of inactivity and lowered metabolism. Although their internal body temperature is lower than normal, it still must be kept significantly higher than the external air temperature. One type of tissue, called brown fat, is made up of cells packed full of mitochondria. The inner mitochondrial membrane contains a channel protein called the uncoupling protein, which allows protons to flow back down their concentration gradient without generating ATP. Activation of these proteins in hibernating mammals results in ongoing oxidation of stored fuel stores (fats), generating heat without any ATP production. In the absence of such an adaptation, the buildup of ATP would eventually cause cellular respiration to be shut down by regulatory mechanisms in the cell. In the **Scientific Skills Exercise**, you can work with data in a related but different case where a decrease in metabolic efficiency in cells is used to generate heat.

CONCEPT CHECK 7.4

1. What effect would an absence of O_2 have on the process shown in Figure 7.14?
2. **WHAT IF?** In the absence of O_2, as in question 1, what do you think would happen if you decreased the pH of the intermembrane space of the mitochondrion? Explain your answer.
3. **MAKE CONNECTIONS** Membranes must be fluid to function properly (as you learned in Concept 5.1). How does the operation of the electron transport chain support that assertion?

For suggested answers, see Appendix A.

CONCEPT 7.5

Fermentation and anaerobic respiration enable cells to produce ATP without the use of oxygen

Because most of the ATP generated by cellular respiration is due to the work of oxidative phosphorylation, our estimate of ATP yield from aerobic respiration depends on an adequate supply of oxygen to the cell. Without the electronegative oxygen to pull electrons down the transport chain, oxidative phosphorylation eventually ceases. However, there are two general mechanisms by which certain cells can oxidize organic fuel and generate ATP *without* the use of oxygen: anaerobic respiration and fermentation. The distinction between these two is that an electron transport chain is used in anaerobic respiration but not in fermentation. (The electron transport chain is also called the respiratory chain because of its role in both types of cellular respiration.)

We have mentioned anaerobic respiration, which takes place in some prokaryotic organisms living in environments lacking oxygen. These organisms have an electron transport chain but do not use oxygen as a final electron acceptor at the

Making a Bar Graph and Evaluating a Hypothesis

Does Thyroid Hormone Level Affect Oxygen Consumption in Cells? Some animals, such as mammals and birds, maintain a relatively constant body temperature, above that of their environment, by using heat produced as a by-product of metabolism. When the core temperature of these animals drops below an internal set point, their cells are triggered to reduce the efficiency of ATP production by the electron transport chains in mitochondria. At lower efficiency, extra fuel must be consumed to produce the same number of ATPs, generating additional heat. Because the response is moderated by the endocrine system, researchers hypothesized that thyroid hormone might trigger this cellular response. In this exercise, you will use a bar graph to visualize data from an experiment that compared the metabolic rates (by measuring oxygen consumption) in mitochondria of cells from animals with different levels of thyroid hormone.

How the Experiment Was Done Liver cells were isolated from sibling rats that had low, normal, or elevated thyroid hormone levels. The oxygen consumption rate due to activity of the mitochondrial electron transport chains of each type of cell was measured under controlled conditions.

Data from the Experiment

Thyroid Hormone Level	Oxygen Consumption Rate [nmol O_2/(min · mg cells)]
Low	4.3
Normal	4.8
Elevated	8.7

Data from M. E. Harper and M. D. Brand, The quantitative contributions of mitochondrial proton leak and ATP turnover reactions to the changed respiration rates of hepatocytes from rats of different thyroid status, *Journal of Biological Chemistry* 268:14850–14860 (1993).

INTERPRET THE DATA

1. To visualize any differences in oxygen consumption between cell types, it will be useful to graph the data in a bar graph. First, set up the axes. (a) What is the independent variable (intentionally varied by the researchers), which goes on the *x*-axis? List the categories along the *x*-axis; because they are discrete rather than continuous, you can list them in any order. (b) What is the dependent variable (measured by the researchers), which goes on the *y*-axis? (c) What units (abbreviated) should go on the *y*-axis? Label the *y*-axis, including the units specified in the data table. Determine the range of values of the data that will need to go on the *y*-axis. What is the largest value? Draw evenly spaced tick marks and label them, starting with 0 at the bottom.

2. Graph the data for each sample. Match each *x*-value with its *y*-value and place a mark on the graph at that coordinate, then draw a bar from the *x*-axis up to the correct height for each sample. Why is a bar graph more appropriate than a scatter plot or line graph? (For additional information about graphs, see the Scientific Skills Review in Appendix F and in the Study Area in MasteringBiology.)

3. Examine your graph and look for a pattern in the data. (a) Which cell type had the highest rate of oxygen consumption, and which had the lowest? (b) Does this support the researchers' hypothesis? Explain. (c) Based on what you know about mitochondrial electron transport and heat production, predict which rats had the highest, and which had the lowest, body temperature.

(MB) A version of this Scientific Skills Exercise can be assigned in MasteringBiology.

---

end of the chain. Oxygen performs this function very well because it is extremely electronegative, but other, less electronegative substances can also serve as final electron acceptors. Some "sulfate-reducing" marine bacteria, for instance, use the sulfate ion (SO_4^{2-}) at the end of their respiratory chain. Operation of the chain builds up a proton-motive force used to produce ATP, but H_2S (hydrogen sulfide) is made as a by-product rather than water. The rotten-egg odor you may have smelled while walking through a salt marsh or a mudflat signals the presence of sulfate-reducing bacteria.

Fermentation is a way of harvesting chemical energy without using either oxygen or any electron transport chain—in other words, without cellular respiration. How can food be oxidized without cellular respiration? Remember, oxidation simply refers to the loss of electrons to an electron acceptor, so it does not need to involve oxygen. Glycolysis oxidizes glucose to two molecules of pyruvate. The oxidizing agent of glycolysis is NAD^+, and neither oxygen nor any electron transfer chain is involved. Overall, glycolysis is exergonic, and some

of the energy made available is used to produce 2 ATP (net) by substrate-level phosphorylation. If oxygen *is* present, then additional ATP is made by oxidative phosphorylation when NADH passes electrons removed from glucose to the electron transport chain. But glycolysis generates 2 ATP whether oxygen is present or not—that is, whether conditions are aerobic or anaerobic.

As an alternative to respiratory oxidation of organic nutrients, fermentation is an extension of glycolysis that allows continuous generation of ATP by the substrate-level phosphorylation of glycolysis. For this to occur, there must be a sufficient supply of NAD^+ to accept electrons during the oxidation step of glycolysis. Without some mechanism to recycle NAD^+ from NADH, glycolysis would soon deplete the cell's pool of NAD^+ by reducing it all to NADH and would shut itself down for lack of an oxidizing agent. Under aerobic conditions, NAD^+ is recycled from NADH by the transfer of electrons to the electron transport chain. An anaerobic alternative is to transfer electrons from NADH to pyruvate, the end product of glycolysis.

Types of Fermentation

Fermentation consists of glycolysis plus reactions that regenerate NAD^+ by transferring electrons from NADH to pyruvate or derivatives of pyruvate. The NAD^+ can then be reused to oxidize sugar by glycolysis, which nets two molecules of ATP by substrate-level phosphorylation. There are many types of fermentation, differing in the end products formed from pyruvate. Two common types are alcohol fermentation and lactic acid fermentation, and both are harnessed by humans in food production.

In **alcohol fermentation (Figure 7.16a)**, pyruvate is converted to ethanol (ethyl alcohol) in two steps. The first step releases carbon dioxide from the pyruvate, which is converted to the two-carbon compound acetaldehyde. In the second step, acetaldehyde is reduced by NADH to ethanol. This regenerates the supply of NAD^+ needed for the continuation of glycolysis. Many bacteria carry out alcohol fermentation under anaerobic conditions. Yeast (a fungus) also carries out alcohol fermentation. For thousands of years, humans have used yeast in brewing, winemaking, and baking. The CO_2 bubbles generated by baker's yeast during alcohol fermentation allow bread to rise.

During **lactic acid fermentation (Figure 7.16b)**, pyruvate is reduced directly by NADH to form lactate as an end product, with no release of CO_2. (Lactate is the ionized form of lactic acid.) Lactic acid fermentation by certain fungi and bacteria is used in the dairy industry to make cheese and yogurt.

Human muscle cells make ATP by lactic acid fermentation when oxygen is scarce. This occurs during strenuous exercise, when sugar catabolism for ATP production outpaces the muscle's supply of oxygen from the blood. Under these conditions, the cells switch from aerobic respiration to fermentation. The lactate that accumulates was previously thought to cause the muscle fatigue and pain that occurs a day or so after intense exercise. However, evidence shows that within an hour, blood carries the excess lactate from the muscles to the liver, where it is converted back to pyruvate by liver cells. Because oxygen is available, this pyruvate can then enter the mitochondria in liver cells and complete cellular respiration. Next-day muscle soreness is more likely caused by trauma to small muscle fibers, which leads to inflammation and pain.

Comparing Fermentation with Anaerobic and Aerobic Respiration

Fermentation, anaerobic respiration, and aerobic respiration are three alternative cellular pathways for producing ATP by harvesting the chemical energy of food. All three use glycolysis to oxidize glucose and other organic fuels to pyruvate, with a net production of 2 ATP by substrate-level phosphorylation. And in all three pathways, NAD^+ is the oxidizing agent that accepts electrons from food during glycolysis.

A key difference is the contrasting mechanisms for oxidizing NADH back to NAD^+, which is required to sustain glycolysis. In fermentation, the final electron acceptor is an organic molecule such as pyruvate (lactic acid fermentation) or acetaldehyde (alcohol fermentation). In cellular respiration, by contrast, electrons carried by NADH are transferred to an electron transport chain, which regenerates the NAD^+ required for glycolysis.

Another major difference is the amount of ATP produced. Fermentation yields two molecules of ATP, produced by substrate-level phosphorylation. In the absence of an electron transport chain, the energy stored in pyruvate is unavailable. In cellular respiration, however, pyruvate is completely oxidized

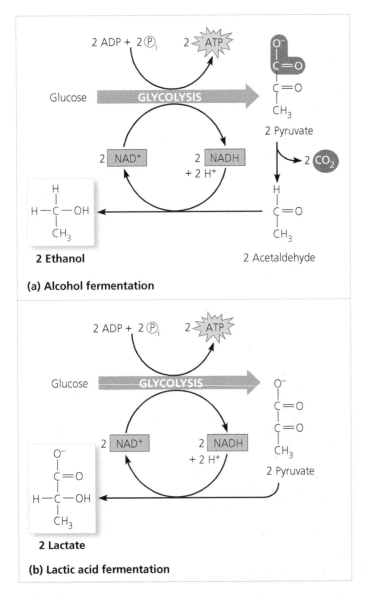

2 Ethanol

(a) Alcohol fermentation

2 Lactate

(b) Lactic acid fermentation

▲ **Figure 7.16 Fermentation.** In the absence of oxygen, many cells use fermentation to produce ATP by substrate-level phosphorylation. Pyruvate, the end product of glycolysis, serves as an electron acceptor for oxidizing NADH back to NAD^+, which can then be reused in glycolysis. Two of the common end products formed from fermentation are **(a)** ethanol and **(b)** lactate, the ionized form of lactic acid.

in the mitochondrion. Most of the chemical energy from this process is shuttled by NADH and $FADH_2$ in the form of electrons to the electron transport chain. There, the electrons move stepwise down a series of redox reactions to a final electron acceptor. (In aerobic respiration, the final electron acceptor is oxygen; in anaerobic respiration, the final acceptor is another molecule that is electronegative, although less so than oxygen.) Stepwise electron transport drives oxidative phosphorylation, yielding ATPs. Thus, cellular respiration harvests much more energy from each sugar molecule than fermentation can. In fact, aerobic respiration yields up to 32 molecules of ATP per glucose molecule—up to 16 times as much as does fermentation.

Some organisms, called **obligate anaerobes**, carry out only fermentation or anaerobic respiration. In fact, these organisms cannot survive in the presence of oxygen. A few cell types can carry out only aerobic oxidation of pyruvate, not fermentation. Other organisms, including yeasts and many bacteria, can make enough ATP to survive using either fermentation or respiration. Such species are called **facultative anaerobes**. On the cellular level, our muscle cells behave as facultative anaerobes. In such cells, pyruvate is a fork in the metabolic road that leads to two alternative catabolic routes (**Figure 7.17**). Under aerobic conditions, pyruvate can be converted to acetyl CoA, which enters the citric acid cycle. Under anaerobic conditions, lactic acid fermentation occurs: Pyruvate is diverted from the citric acid cycle, serving instead as an electron acceptor to

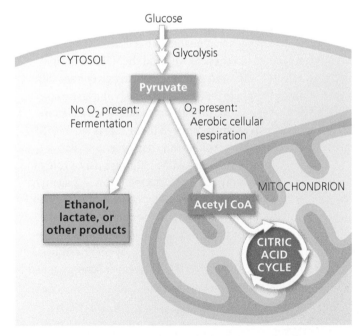

▲ **Figure 7.17 Pyruvate as a key juncture in catabolism.** Glycolysis is common to fermentation and cellular respiration. The end product of glycolysis, pyruvate, represents a fork in the catabolic pathways of glucose oxidation. In a facultative anaerobe or a muscle cell, which are capable of both aerobic cellular respiration and fermentation, pyruvate is committed to one of those two pathways, usually depending on whether or not oxygen is present.

recycle NAD^+. To make the same amount of ATP, a facultative anaerobe has to consume sugar at a much faster rate when fermenting than when respiring.

The Evolutionary Significance of Glycolysis

EVOLUTION The role of glycolysis in both fermentation and respiration has an evolutionary basis. Ancient prokaryotes are thought to have used glycolysis to make ATP long before oxygen was present in Earth's atmosphere. The oldest known fossils of bacteria date back 3.5 billion years, but appreciable quantities of oxygen probably did not begin to accumulate in the atmosphere until about 2.7 billion years ago, produced by photosynthesizing cyanobacteria. Therefore, early prokaryotes may have generated ATP exclusively from glycolysis. The fact that glycolysis is today the most widespread metabolic pathway among Earth's organisms suggests that it evolved very early in the history of life. The cytosolic location of glycolysis also implies great antiquity; the pathway does not require any of the membrane-enclosed organelles of the eukaryotic cell, which evolved approximately 1 billion years after the prokaryotic cell. Glycolysis is a metabolic heirloom from early cells that continues to function in fermentation and as the first stage in the breakdown of organic molecules by respiration.

CONCEPT CHECK 7.5

1. Consider the NADH formed during glycolysis. What is the final acceptor for its electrons during fermentation? What is the final acceptor for its electrons during aerobic respiration?
2. **WHAT IF?** A glucose-fed yeast cell is moved from an aerobic environment to an anaerobic one. How would its rate of glucose consumption change if ATP were to be generated at the same rate?

For suggested answers, see Appendix A.

CONCEPT 7.6

Glycolysis and the citric acid cycle connect to many other metabolic pathways

So far, we have treated the oxidative breakdown of glucose in isolation from the cell's overall metabolic economy. In this section, you will learn that glycolysis and the citric acid cycle are major intersections of the cell's catabolic (breakdown) and anabolic (biosynthetic) pathways.

The Versatility of Catabolism

Throughout this chapter, we have used glucose as an example of a fuel for cellular respiration. But free glucose molecules are not common in the diets of humans and other animals. We obtain most of our calories in the form of fats, proteins, and carbohydrates such as sucrose and other disaccharides, and

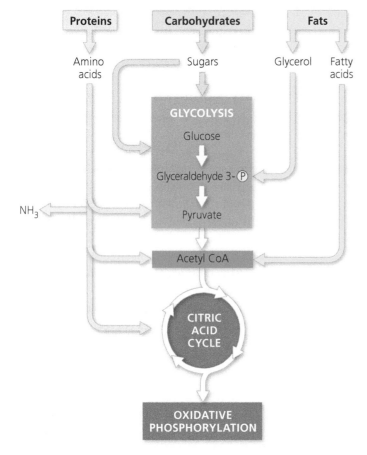

Proteins   Carbohydrates   Fats

Amino acids   Sugars   Glycerol   Fatty acids

GLYCOLYSIS

Glucose

Glyceraldehyde 3-(P)

Pyruvate

NH_3

Acetyl CoA

CITRIC ACID CYCLE

OXIDATIVE PHOSPHORYLATION

▲ **Figure 7.18 The catabolism of various molecules from food.** Carbohydrates, fats, and proteins can all be used as fuel for cellular respiration. Monomers of these molecules enter glycolysis or the citric acid cycle at various points. Glycolysis and the citric acid cycle are catabolic funnels through which electrons from all kinds of organic molecules flow on their exergonic fall to oxygen.

starch, a polysaccharide. All these organic molecules in food can be used by cellular respiration to make ATP (**Figure 7.18**).

Glycolysis can accept a wide range of carbohydrates for catabolism. In the digestive tract, starch is hydrolyzed to glucose, which is broken down in cells by glycolysis and the citric acid cycle. Similarly, glycogen, the polysaccharide that humans and many other animals store in their liver and muscle cells, can be hydrolyzed to glucose between meals as fuel for respiration. The digestion of disaccharides, including sucrose, provides glucose and other monosaccharides as fuel for respiration.

Proteins can also be used for fuel, but first they must be digested to their constituent amino acids. Many of the amino acids are used by the organism to build new proteins. Amino acids present in excess are converted by enzymes to intermediates of glycolysis and the citric acid cycle. Before amino acids can feed into glycolysis or the citric acid cycle, their amino groups must be removed, a process called *deamination*. The nitrogenous waste is excreted from the animal in the form of ammonia (NH_3), urea, or other waste products.

Catabolism can also harvest energy stored in fats obtained either from food or from fat cells. After fats are digested to glycerol and fatty acids, the glycerol is converted to glyceraldehyde 3-phosphate, an intermediate of glycolysis. Most

of the energy of a fat is stored in the fatty acids. A metabolic sequence called **beta oxidation** breaks the fatty acids down to two-carbon fragments, which enter the citric acid cycle as acetyl CoA. NADH and $FADH_2$ are also generated during beta oxidation, resulting in further ATP production. Fats make excellent fuels, largely due to their chemical structure and the high energy level of their electrons compared with those of carbohydrates. A gram of fat oxidized by respiration produces more than twice as much ATP as a gram of carbohydrate.

Biosynthesis (Anabolic Pathways)

Cells need substance as well as energy. Not all the organic molecules of food are destined to be oxidized as fuel to make ATP. In addition to calories, food must also provide the carbon skeletons that cells require to make their own molecules. Some organic monomers obtained from digestion can be used directly. For example, as previously mentioned, amino acids from the hydrolysis of proteins in food can be incorporated into the organism's own proteins. Often, however, the body needs specific molecules that are not present as such in food. Compounds formed as intermediates of glycolysis and the citric acid cycle can be diverted into anabolic pathways as precursors from which the cell can synthesize the molecules it requires. For example, humans can make about half of the 20 amino acids in proteins by modifying compounds siphoned away from the citric acid cycle; the rest are "essential amino acids" that must be obtained in the diet. Also, glucose can be made from pyruvate, and fatty acids can be synthesized from acetyl CoA. Of course, these anabolic, or biosynthetic, pathways do not generate ATP, but instead consume it.

In addition, glycolysis and the citric acid cycle function as metabolic interchanges that enable our cells to convert some kinds of molecules to others as we need them. For example, an intermediate compound generated during glycolysis, dihydroxyacetone phosphate (see Figure 7.9, step 5), can be converted to one of the major precursors of fats. If we eat more food than we need, we store fat even if our diet is fat-free. Metabolism is remarkably versatile and adaptable.

Cellular respiration and metabolic pathways play a role of central importance in organisms. Examine Figure 7.2 again to put cellular respiration into the broader context of energy flow and chemical cycling in ecosystems. The energy that keeps us alive is *released*, not *produced*, by cellular respiration. We are tapping energy that was stored in food by photosynthesis, which captures light and converts it to chemical energy, a process you will learn about in Chapter 8.

CONCEPT CHECK 7.6

1. **MAKE CONNECTIONS** Compare the structure of a fat (see Figure 3.13) with that of a carbohydrate (see Figure 3.8). What features of their structures make fat a much better fuel?

2. When might your body synthesize fat molecules?

3. **WHAT IF?** During intense exercise, can a muscle cell use fat as a concentrated source of chemical energy? Explain.

For suggested answers, see Appendix A.

7 Chapter Review

Go to **MasteringBiology**® for Assignments, the eText, and the Study Area with Animations, Activities, Vocab Self-Quiz, and Practice Tests.

SUMMARY OF KEY CONCEPTS

VOCAB SELF-QUIZ
goo.gl/gbai8v

CONCEPT 7.1

Catabolic pathways yield energy by oxidizing organic fuels (pp. 142–146)

• Cells break down glucose and other organic fuels to yield chemical energy in the form of ATP. **Fermentation** is a process that results in the partial degradation of glucose without the use of oxygen. **Cellular respiration** is a more complete breakdown of glucose; in **aerobic respiration**, oxygen is used as a reactant. The cell taps the energy stored in food molecules through **redox reactions**, in which one substance partially or totally shifts electrons to another. **Oxidation** is the loss of electrons from one substance, while **reduction** is the addition of electrons to the other.

• During aerobic respiration, glucose ($C_6H_{12}O_6$) is oxidized to CO_2, and O_2 is reduced to H_2O. Electrons lose potential energy during their transfer from glucose or other organic compounds to oxygen. Electrons are usually passed first to **NAD⁺**, reducing it to NADH, and then from NADH to an **electron transport chain**, which conducts them to O_2 in energy-releasing steps. The energy is used to make ATP.

• Aerobic respiration occurs in three stages: (1) **glycolysis**, (2) pyruvate oxidation and the **citric acid cycle**, and (3) **oxidative phosphorylation** (electron transport and chemiosmosis).

> ? *Describe the difference between the two processes in cellular respiration that produce ATP: oxidative phosphorylation and substrate-level phosphorylation.*

CONCEPT 7.2

Glycolysis harvests chemical energy by oxidizing glucose to pyruvate (pp. 146–147)

• Glycolysis ("splitting of sugar") is a series of reactions that breaks down glucose into two pyruvate molecules, which may go on to enter the citric acid cycle, and nets 2 ATP and 2 NADH per glucose molecule.

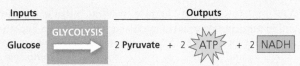

Inputs | **Outputs**
GLYCOLYSIS
Glucose → 2 **Pyruvate** + 2 ATP + 2 NADH

> ? *Which reactions are the source of energy for the formation of ATP and NADH in glycolysis?*

CONCEPT 7.3

After pyruvate is oxidized, the citric acid cycle completes the energy-yielding oxidation of organic molecules (pp. 148–149)

• In eukaryotic cells, pyruvate enters the mitochondrion and is oxidized to **acetyl CoA**, which is further oxidized in the citric acid cycle.

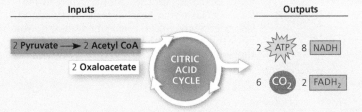

Inputs | **Outputs**
2 **Pyruvate** → 2 **Acetyl CoA** | 2 ATP 8 NADH
2 **Oxaloacetate** | CITRIC ACID CYCLE | 6 CO_2 2 FADH₂

> ? *What molecular products indicate the complete oxidation of glucose during cellular respiration?*

CONCEPT 7.4

During oxidative phosphorylation, chemiosmosis couples electron transport to ATP synthesis (pp. 149–154)

• NADH and FADH₂ transfer electrons to the electron transport chain. Electrons move down the chain, losing energy in several energy-releasing steps. Finally, electrons are passed to O_2, reducing it to H_2O.

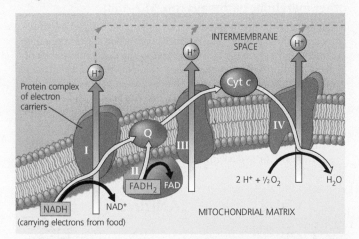

• Along the electron transport chain, electron transfer causes protein complexes to move H⁺ from the mitochondrial matrix (in eukaryotes) to the intermembrane space, storing energy as a **proton-motive force** (H⁺ gradient). As H⁺ diffuses back into the matrix through **ATP synthase**, its passage drives the phosphorylation of ADP, an energy-coupling mechanism called **chemiosmosis**.

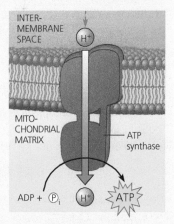

• About 34% of the energy stored in a glucose molecule is transferred to ATP during cellular respiration, producing a maximum of about 32 ATP.

> ? *Briefly explain the mechanism by which ATP synthase produces ATP. List three locations in which ATP synthases are found.*

CONCEPT 7.5

Fermentation and anaerobic respiration enable cells to produce ATP without the use of oxygen (pp. 154–157)

• Glycolysis nets 2 ATP by substrate-level phosphorylation, whether oxygen is present or not. Under anaerobic conditions, either anaerobic respiration or fermentation can take place. In anaerobic respiration, an electron transport chain is present with a final electron acceptor other than oxygen. In fermentation, the electrons from NADH are passed to pyruvate or a derivative of pyruvate, regenerating the NAD⁺ required to oxidize more glucose. Two common types of fermentation are **alcohol fermentation** and **lactic acid fermentation**.

- Fermentation, anaerobic respiration, and aerobic respiration all use glycolysis to oxidize glucose, but they differ in their final electron acceptor and whether an electron transport chain is used (respiration) or not (fermentation). Respiration yields more ATP; aerobic respiration, with O_2 as the final electron acceptor, yields about 16 times as much ATP as does fermentation.

- Glycolysis occurs in nearly all organisms and is thought to have evolved in ancient prokaryotes before there was O_2 in the atmosphere.

? *Which process yields more ATP, fermentation or anaerobic respiration? Explain.*

CONCEPT 7.6

Glycolysis and the citric acid cycle connect to many other metabolic pathways (pp. 157–158)

- Catabolic pathways funnel electrons from many kinds of organic molecules into cellular respiration. Many carbohydrates can enter glycolysis, most often after conversion to glucose. Amino acids of proteins must be deaminated before being oxidized. The fatty acids of fats undergo **beta oxidation** to two-carbon fragments and then enter the citric acid cycle as acetyl CoA. Anabolic pathways can use small molecules from food directly or build other substances using intermediates of glycolysis or the citric acid cycle.

? *Describe how the catabolic pathways of glycolysis and the citric acid cycle intersect with anabolic pathways in the metabolism of a cell.*

TEST YOUR UNDERSTANDING

PRACTICE TEST

Level 1: Knowledge/Comprehension

goo.gl/CRZjvS

1. The *immediate* energy source that drives ATP synthesis by ATP synthase during oxidative phosphorylation is the
   (A) oxidation of glucose and other organic compounds.
   (B) flow of electrons down the electron transport chain.
   (C) H^+ concentration gradient across the membrane holding ATP synthase.
   (D) transfer of phosphate to ADP.

2. Which metabolic pathway is common to both fermentation and cellular respiration of a glucose molecule?
   (A) the citric acid cycle
   (B) the electron transport chain
   (C) glycolysis
   (D) reduction of pyruvate to lactate

3. In mitochondria, exergonic redox reactions
   (A) are the source of energy driving prokaryotic ATP synthesis.
   (B) provide the energy that establishes the proton gradient.
   (C) reduce carbon atoms to carbon dioxide.
   (D) are coupled via phosphorylated intermediates to endergonic processes.

4. The final electron acceptor of the electron transport chain that functions in aerobic oxidative phosphorylation is
   (A) oxygen.   (C) NAD^+.
   (B) water.   (D) pyruvate.

Level 2: Application/Analysis

5. What is the oxidizing agent in the following reaction?

   Pyruvate + NADH + H^+ → Lactate + NAD^+

   (A) oxygen   (C) lactate
   (B) NADH   (D) pyruvate

6. When electrons flow along the electron transport chains of mitochondria, which of the following changes occurs?
   (A) The pH of the matrix increases.
   (B) ATP synthase pumps protons by active transport.
   (C) The electrons gain free energy.
   (D) NAD^+ is oxidized.

7. Most CO_2 from catabolism is released during
   (A) glycolysis.   (C) lactate fermentation.
   (B) the citric acid cycle.   (D) electron transport.

Level 3: Synthesis/Evaluation

8. **DRAW IT** The graph here shows the pH difference across the inner mitochondrial membrane over time in an actively respiring cell. At the time indicated by the vertical arrow, a metabolic poison is added that specifically and completely inhibits all function of mitochondrial ATP synthase. Draw what you would expect to see for the rest of the graphed line, and explain your graph.

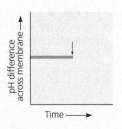

9. **INTERPRET THE DATA** Phosphofructokinase is an enzyme that acts on fructose 6-phosphate at an early step in glucose breakdown (step 3 in Figure 7.9). Negative regulation of this enzyme by ATP and positive regulation by AMP control whether the sugar will continue on in the glycolytic pathway. Considering this graph, under which condition is phosphofructokinase more active? Given this enzyme's role in glycolysis, explain why it makes sense that ATP and AMP have these effects.

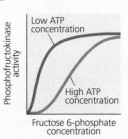

10. **SCIENTIFIC INQUIRY** In the 1930s, some physicians prescribed low doses of a compound called dinitrophenol (DNP) to help patients lose weight. This unsafe method was abandoned after some patients died. DNP uncouples the chemiosmotic machinery by making the lipid bilayer of the inner mitochondrial membrane leaky to H^+. Explain how this could cause weight loss and death.

11. **FOCUS ON EVOLUTION** ATP synthases are found in the prokaryotic plasma membrane and in mitochondria and chloroplasts. (a) Propose a hypothesis to account for an evolutionary relationship of these eukaryotic organelles and prokaryotes. (b) Explain how the amino acid sequences of the ATP synthases from the different sources might either support or fail to support your hypothesis.

12. **FOCUS ON ORGANIZATION** In a short essay (100–150 words), explain how oxidative phosphorylation—the production of ATP using energy derived from the redox reactions of a spatially organized electron transport chain followed by chemiosmosis—is an example of how new properties emerge at each level of the biological hierarchy.

13. **SYNTHESIZE YOUR KNOWLEDGE**

Coenzyme Q (CoQ) is sold as a nutritional supplement. One company uses this marketing slogan for CoQ: "Give your heart the fuel it craves most." Considering the role of coenzyme Q, how do you think this product might function as a nutritional supplement to benefit the heart? Is CoQ used as a "fuel" during cellular respiration?

For selected answers, see Appendix A.

KEY CONCEPTS

8.1 Photosynthesis converts light energy to the chemical energy of food

8.2 The light reactions convert solar energy to the chemical energy of ATP and NADPH

8.3 The Calvin cycle uses the chemical energy of ATP and NADPH to reduce CO_2 to sugar

▲ **Figure 8.1** How does sunlight help build the trunk, branches, and leaves of this broadleaf tree?

The Process That Feeds the Biosphere

Life on Earth is solar powered. The chloroplasts in plants and other photosynthetic organisms capture light energy that has traveled 150 million km from the sun and convert it to chemical energy that is stored in sugar and other organic molecules. This conversion process is called **photosynthesis**. Let's begin by placing photosynthesis in its ecological context.

Photosynthesis nourishes almost the entire living world directly or indirectly. An organism acquires the organic compounds it uses for energy and carbon skeletons by one of two major modes: autotrophic nutrition or heterotrophic nutrition. **Autotrophs** are "self-feeders" (*auto-* means "self," and *trophos* means "feeder"); they sustain themselves without eating anything derived from other living beings. Autotrophs produce their organic molecules from CO_2 and other inorganic raw materials obtained from the environment. They are the ultimate sources of organic compounds for all nonautotrophic

organisms, and for this reason, biologists refer to autotrophs as the *producers* of the biosphere.

Almost all plants are autotrophs; the only nutrients they require are water and minerals from the soil and carbon dioxide from the air. Specifically, plants are *photo*autotrophs, organisms that use light as a source of energy to synthesize organic substances **(Figure 8.1)**. Photosynthesis also occurs in algae, certain other unicellular eukaryotes, and some prokaryotes.

Heterotrophs are unable to make their own food; they live on compounds produced by other organisms (*hetero-* means "other"). Heterotrophs are the biosphere's *consumers*. This "other-feeding" is most obvious when an animal eats plants or other animals, but heterotrophic nutrition may be more subtle. Some heterotrophs decompose and feed on the remains of dead organisms and organic litter such as feces and fallen leaves; these types of organisms are known as decomposers. Most fungi and many types of prokaryotes get their nourishment this way. Almost all heterotrophs, including humans, are completely dependent, either directly or indirectly, on photoautotrophs for food—and also for oxygen, a by-product of photosynthesis.

In this chapter, you'll learn how photosynthesis works. A variety of photosynthetic organisms are shown in **Figure 8.2**, including both eukaryotes and prokaryotes. Our discussion here will focus mainly on plants. (Variations in autotrophic nutrition that occur in prokaryotes and algae will be described in Concepts 24.2 and 25.4.) After discussing the general principles of photosynthesis, we'll consider the two stages of photosynthesis: the light reactions, which capture solar energy and transform it into chemical energy; and the Calvin cycle, which uses that chemical energy to make the organic molecules of food. Finally, we'll consider some aspects of photosynthesis from an evolutionary perspective.

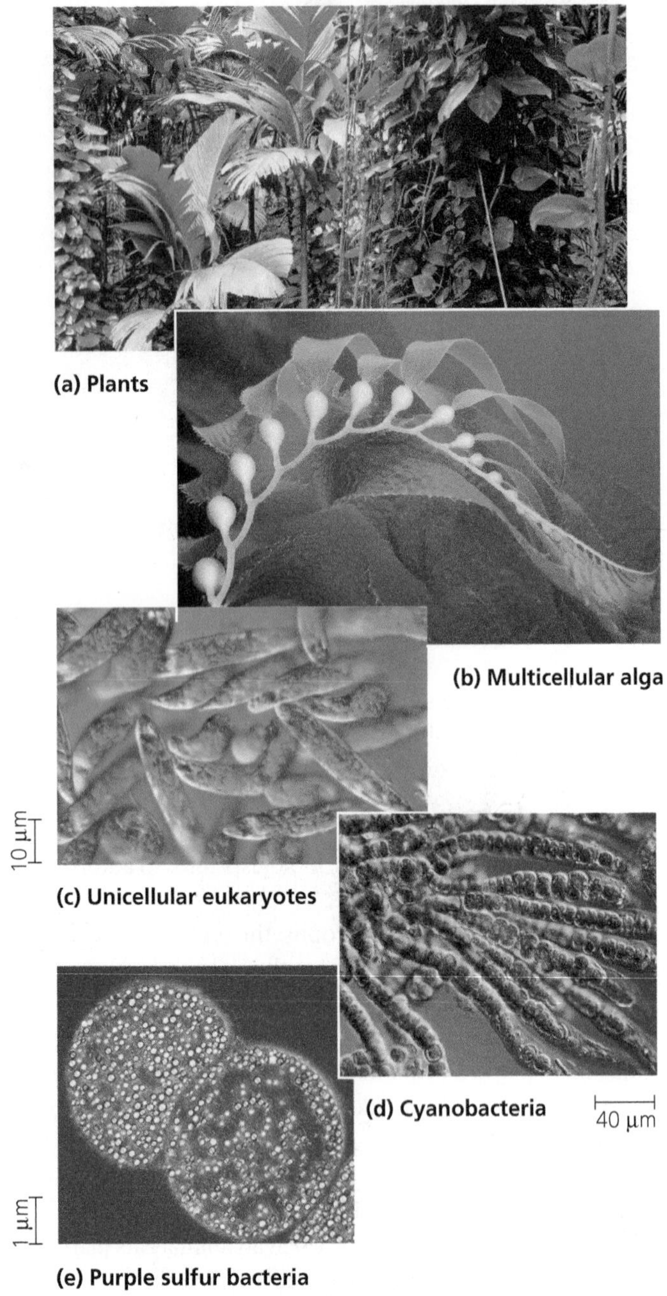

(a) Plants

(b) Multicellular alga

10 μm

(c) Unicellular eukaryotes

(d) Cyanobacteria   40 μm

1 μm

(e) Purple sulfur bacteria

▲ **Figure 8.2 Photoautotrophs.** These organisms use light energy to drive the synthesis of organic molecules from carbon dioxide and (in most cases) water. They feed themselves and the entire living world. **(a)** On land, plants are the predominant producers of food. In aquatic environments, photoautotrophs include unicellular and **(b)** multicellular algae, such as this kelp; **(c)** some non-algal unicellular eukaryotes, such as *Euglena*; **(d)** the prokaryotes called cyanobacteria; and **(e)** other photosynthetic prokaryotes, such as these purple sulfur bacteria, which produce sulfur (the yellow globules within the cells) (c–e, LMs).

CONCEPT 8.1

Photosynthesis converts light energy to the chemical energy of food

The remarkable ability of an organism to harness light energy and use it to drive the synthesis of organic compounds emerges from structural organization in the cell: Photosynthetic enzymes and other molecules are grouped together in a biological membrane, enabling the necessary series of chemical reactions to be carried out efficiently. The process of photosynthesis most likely originated in a group of bacteria that had infolded regions of the plasma membrane containing clusters of such molecules. In photosynthetic bacteria that exist today, infolded photosynthetic membranes function similarly to the internal membranes of the chloroplast, a eukaryotic organelle. According to the endosymbiont theory, the original chloroplast was a photosynthetic prokaryote that lived inside an ancestor of eukaryotic cells. (You learned about this theory in Concept 4.5, and it will be described more fully in Concept 25.1.) Chloroplasts are present in a variety of photosynthesizing organisms, but here we focus on chloroplasts in plants.

Chloroplasts: The Sites of Photosynthesis in Plants

All green parts of a plant, including green stems and unripened fruit, have chloroplasts, but the leaves are the major sites of photosynthesis in most plants **(Figure 8.3)**. There are about half a million chloroplasts in a chunk of leaf with a top surface area of 1 mm^2. Chloroplasts are found mainly in the cells of the **mesophyll**, the tissue in the interior of the leaf. Carbon dioxide enters the leaf, and oxygen exits, by way of microscopic pores called **stomata** (singular, *stoma*; from the Greek, meaning "mouth"). Water absorbed by the roots is delivered to the leaves in veins. Leaves also use veins to export sugar to roots and other nonphotosynthetic parts of the plant.

A typical mesophyll cell has about 30–40 chloroplasts, each measuring about 2–4 μm by 4–7 μm. A chloroplast has an envelope of two membranes surrounding a dense fluid called the **stroma**. Suspended within the stroma is a third membrane system, made up of sacs called **thylakoids**, which segregates the stroma from the *thylakoid space* inside these sacs. In some places, thylakoid sacs are stacked in columns called *grana* (singular, *granum*). **Chlorophyll**, the green pigment that gives leaves their color, resides in the thylakoid membranes of the chloroplast. (The internal photosynthetic membranes of some prokaryotes are also called thylakoid membranes; see Figure 24.11b.) It is the light energy absorbed by chlorophyll that drives the synthesis of organic molecules in the chloroplast. Now that we have looked at the sites of photosynthesis in plants, we are ready to look more closely at the process of photosynthesis.

Tracking Atoms Through Photosynthesis: *Scientific Inquiry*

Scientists have tried for centuries to piece together the process by which plants make food. Although some of the steps are still not completely understood, the overall photosynthetic equation has been known since the 1800s: In the presence of light, the green parts of plants produce organic compounds and oxygen from carbon dioxide and water. Using molecular formulas, we can summarize the complex series of chemical reactions in photosynthesis with this chemical equation:

$$6\ CO_2 + 12\ H_2O + \text{Light energy} \rightarrow C_6H_{12}O_6 + 6\ O_2 + 6\ H_2O$$

We use glucose ($C_6H_{12}O_6$) here to simplify the relationship between photosynthesis and respiration, but the direct product of photosynthesis is actually a three-carbon sugar that can be used to make glucose. Water appears on both sides of the equation because 12 molecules are consumed and 6 molecules are newly formed during photosynthesis. We can simplify the equation by indicating only the net consumption of water:

$$6\ CO_2 + 6\ H_2O + \text{Light energy} \rightarrow C_6H_{12}O_6 + 6\ O_2$$

Writing the equation in this form, we can see that the overall chemical change during photosynthesis is the reverse of the one that occurs during cellular respiration. Both of these metabolic processes occur in plant cells. However, as you will soon learn, chloroplasts do not synthesize sugars by simply reversing the steps of respiration.

Now let's divide the photosynthetic equation by 6 to put it in its simplest possible form:

$$CO_2 + H_2O \rightarrow [CH_2O] + O_2$$

Here, the brackets indicate that CH_2O is not an actual sugar but represents the general formula for a carbohydrate. In other words, we are imagining the synthesis of a sugar molecule one carbon at a time. Let's now use this simplified formula to see how researchers tracked the elements C, H, and O from the reactants of photosynthesis to the products.

The Splitting of Water

One of the first clues to the mechanism of photosynthesis came from the discovery that the O_2 given off by plants is

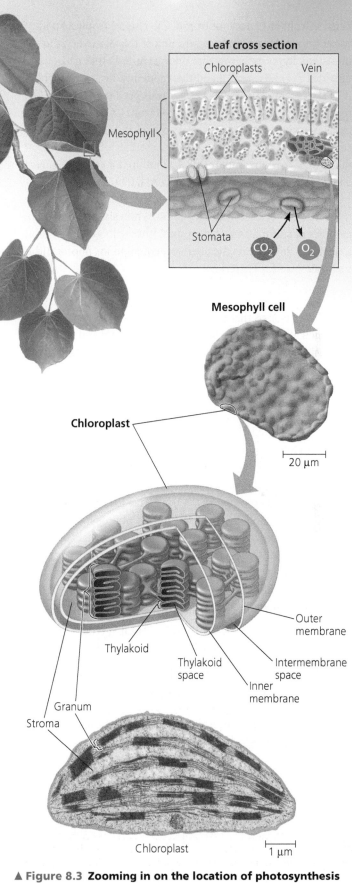

Leaf cross section

Chloroplasts

Vein

Mesophyll

Stomata

CO_2 O_2

Mesophyll cell

Chloroplast

20 μm

Outer membrane

Thylakoid

Thylakoid space

Intermembrane space

Inner membrane

Granum

Stroma

Chloroplast

1 μm

▲ **Figure 8.3 Zooming in on the location of photosynthesis in a plant.** Leaves are the major organs of photosynthesis in plants. These images take you into a leaf, then into a cell, and finally into a chloroplast, the organelle where photosynthesis occurs (middle, LM; bottom, TEM).

derived from H_2O and not from CO_2. The chloroplast splits water into hydrogen and oxygen. Before this discovery, the prevailing hypothesis was that photosynthesis split carbon dioxide ($CO_2 \rightarrow C + O_2$) and then added water to the carbon ($C + H_2O \rightarrow [CH_2O]$). This hypothesis predicted that the O_2 released during photosynthesis came from CO_2. This idea was challenged in the 1930s by C. B. van Niel, of Stanford University. Van Niel was investigating photosynthesis in bacteria that make their carbohydrate from CO_2 but do not release O_2. He concluded that, at least in these bacteria, CO_2 is not split into carbon and oxygen. One group of bacteria used hydrogen sulfide (H_2S) rather than water for photosynthesis, forming yellow globules of sulfur as a waste product (these globules are visible in Figure 8.2e). Here is the chemical equation for photosynthesis in these sulfur bacteria:

$$CO_2 + 2\,H_2S \rightarrow [CH_2O] + H_2O + 2\,S$$

Van Niel reasoned that the bacteria split H_2S and used the hydrogen atoms to make sugar. He then generalized that idea, proposing that all photosynthetic organisms require a hydrogen source but that the source varies:

Sulfur bacteria: $CO_2 + 2\,H_2S \rightarrow [CH_2O] + H_2O + 2\,S$
Plants: $CO_2 + 2\,H_2O \rightarrow [CH_2O] + H_2O + O_2$
General: $CO_2 + 2\,H_2X \rightarrow [CH_2O] + H_2O + 2\,X$

Thus, van Niel hypothesized that plants split H_2O as a source of electrons from hydrogen atoms, releasing O_2 as a by-product.

Nearly 20 years later, scientists confirmed van Niel's hypothesis by using oxygen-18 (^{18}O), a heavy isotope, as a tracer to follow the fate of oxygen atoms during photosynthesis. The experiments showed that the O_2 from plants was labeled with ^{18}O *only* if water was the source of the tracer (experiment 1). If the ^{18}O was introduced to the plant in the form of CO_2, the label did not turn up in the released O_2 (experiment 2). In the following summary, red denotes labeled atoms of oxygen (^{18}O):

Experiment 1: $CO_2 + 2\,H_2O \rightarrow [CH_2O] + H_2O + O_2$
Experiment 2: $CO_2 + 2\,H_2O \rightarrow [CH_2O] + H_2O + O_2$

A significant result of the shuffling of atoms during photosynthesis is the extraction of hydrogen from water and its incorporation into sugar. The waste product of photosynthesis, O_2, is released to the atmosphere. **Figure 8.4** shows the fates of all atoms in photosynthesis.

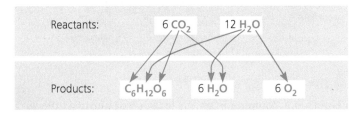

▲ Figure 8.4 Tracking atoms through photosynthesis. The atoms from CO_2 are shown in magenta, and the atoms from H_2O are shown in blue.

Photosynthesis as a Redox Process

Let's briefly compare photosynthesis with cellular respiration. Both processes involve redox reactions. During cellular respiration, energy is released from sugar when electrons associated with hydrogen are transported by carriers to oxygen, forming water as a by-product (see Concept 7.1). The electrons lose potential energy as they "fall" down the electron transport chain toward electronegative oxygen, and the mitochondrion harnesses that energy to synthesize ATP (see Figure 7.14). Photosynthesis reverses the direction of electron flow. Water is split, and electrons are transferred along with hydrogen ions from the water to carbon dioxide, reducing it to sugar.

$$\text{Energy} + 6\,CO_2 + 6\,H_2O \longrightarrow C_6H_{12}O_6 + 6\,O_2$$

becomes reduced

becomes oxidized

Because the electrons increase in potential energy as they move from water to sugar, this process requires energy—in other words, is endergonic. This energy boost is provided by light.

The Two Stages of Photosynthesis: A Preview

The equation for photosynthesis is a deceptively simple summary of a very complex process. Actually, photosynthesis is not a single process, but two processes, each with multiple steps. These two stages of photosynthesis are known as the **light reactions** (the *photo* part of photosynthesis) and the **Calvin cycle** (the *synthesis* part) **(Figure 8.5)**.

The light reactions are the steps of photosynthesis that convert solar energy to chemical energy. Water is split, providing a source of electrons and protons (hydrogen ions, H^+) and giving off O_2 as a by-product. Light absorbed by chlorophyll drives a transfer of the electrons and hydrogen ions from water to an acceptor called **NADP$^+$** (nicotinamide adenine dinucleotide phosphate), where they are temporarily stored. The electron acceptor $NADP^+$ is first cousin to NAD^+, which functions as an electron carrier in cellular respiration; the two molecules differ only by the presence of an extra phosphate group in the $NADP^+$ molecule. The light reactions use solar energy to reduce $NADP^+$ to **NADPH** by adding a pair of electrons along with an H^+. The light reactions also generate ATP, using chemiosmosis to power the addition of a phosphate group to ADP, a process called **photophosphorylation**. Thus, light energy is initially converted to chemical energy in the form of two compounds: NADPH and ATP. NADPH, a source of electrons, acts as "reducing power" that can be passed along to an electron acceptor, reducing it, while ATP is the versatile energy currency of cells. Notice that the light reactions produce no sugar; that happens in the second stage of photosynthesis, the Calvin cycle.

The Calvin cycle is named for Melvin Calvin, who, along with his colleagues, began to elucidate its steps in the late

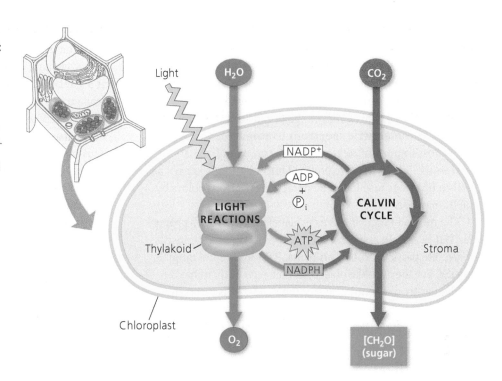

► **Figure 8.5 An overview of photosynthesis: cooperation of the light reactions and the Calvin cycle.** In the chloroplast, the thylakoid membranes (green) are the sites of the light reactions, whereas the Calvin cycle occurs in the stroma (gray). The light reactions use solar energy to make ATP and NADPH, which supply chemical energy and reducing power, respectively, to the Calvin cycle. The Calvin cycle incorporates CO_2 into organic molecules, which are converted to sugar. (Recall that most simple sugars have formulas that are some multiple of CH_2O.)

ANIMATION Visit the Study Area in **MasteringBiology** for the BioFlix® 3-D Animation on Photosynthesis.

1940s. The cycle begins by incorporating CO_2 from the air into organic molecules already present in the chloroplast. This initial incorporation of carbon into organic compounds is known as **carbon fixation**. The Calvin cycle then reduces the fixed carbon to carbohydrate by the addition of electrons. The reducing power is provided by NADPH, which acquired its cargo of electrons in the light reactions. To convert CO_2 to carbohydrate, the Calvin cycle also requires chemical energy in the form of ATP, which is also generated by the light reactions. Thus, it is the Calvin cycle that makes sugar, but it can do so only with the help of the NADPH and ATP produced by the light reactions. The metabolic steps of the Calvin cycle are sometimes referred to as the dark reactions, or light-independent reactions, because none of the steps requires light *directly*. Nevertheless, the Calvin cycle in most plants occurs during daylight, for only then can the light reactions provide the NADPH and ATP that the Calvin cycle requires. In essence, the chloroplast uses light energy to make sugar by coordinating the two stages of photosynthesis.

As Figure 8.5 indicates, the thylakoids of the chloroplast are the sites of the light reactions, while the Calvin cycle occurs in the stroma. On the outside of the thylakoids, molecules of $NADP^+$ and ADP pick up electrons and phosphate, respectively, and NADPH and ATP are then released to the stroma, where they play crucial roles in the Calvin cycle. The two stages of photosynthesis are treated in this figure as metabolic modules that take in ingredients and crank out products. In the next two sections, we'll look more closely at how the two stages work, beginning with the light reactions.

CONCEPT CHECK 8.1

1. How do the reactant molecules of photosynthesis reach the chloroplasts in leaves?
2. How did the use of an oxygen isotope help elucidate the chemistry of photosynthesis?
3. **WHAT IF?** The Calvin cycle requires ATP and NADPH, products of the light reactions. If a classmate asserted that the light reactions don't depend on the Calvin cycle and, with continual light, could just keep on producing ATP and NADPH, how would you respond?

For suggested answers, see Appendix A.

CONCEPT 8.2

The light reactions convert solar energy to the chemical energy of ATP and NADPH

Chloroplasts are chemical factories powered by the sun. Their thylakoids transform light energy into the chemical energy of ATP and NADPH. To understand this conversion better, we need to know about some important properties of light.

The Nature of Sunlight

Light is a form of energy known as electromagnetic energy, also called electromagnetic radiation. Electromagnetic energy travels in rhythmic waves analogous to those created by dropping a pebble into a pond. Electromagnetic waves, however, are disturbances of electric and magnetic fields rather than disturbances of a material medium such as water.

The distance between the crests of electromagnetic waves is called the **wavelength**. Wavelengths range from less than a nanometer (for gamma rays) to more than a kilometer (for radio waves). This entire range of radiation is known as the **electromagnetic spectrum (Figure 8.6)**. The segment most important to life is the narrow band from about 380 nm to 750 nm in wavelength. This radiation is known as **visible light** because it can be detected as various colors by the human eye.

The model of light as waves explains many of light's properties, but in certain respects light behaves as though it consists of discrete particles, called **photons**. Photons are not tangible objects, but they act like objects in that each of them has a fixed quantity of energy. The amount of energy is inversely related to the wavelength of the light: The shorter the wavelength, the greater the energy of each photon of that light. Thus, a photon of violet light packs nearly twice as much energy as a photon of red light (see Figure 8.6).

Although the sun radiates the full spectrum of electromagnetic energy, the atmosphere acts like a selective window, allowing visible light to pass through while screening out a substantial fraction of other radiation. The part of the spectrum we can see—visible light—is also the radiation that drives photosynthesis.

Photosynthetic Pigments: The Light Receptors

When light meets matter, it may be reflected, transmitted, or absorbed. Substances that absorb visible light are known as *pigments*. Different pigments absorb light of different wavelengths, and the wavelengths that are absorbed disappear. If a pigment is

illuminated with white light, the color we see is the color most reflected or transmitted by the pigment. (If a pigment absorbs all wavelengths, it appears black.) We see green when we look at a leaf because chlorophyll absorbs violet-blue and red light while transmitting and reflecting green light **(Figure 8.7)**. The ability of a pigment to absorb various wavelengths of light can be measured with an instrument called a **spectrophotometer**. This machine directs beams of light of different wavelengths through a solution of the pigment and measures the fraction of the light transmitted at each wavelength. A graph plotting a pigment's light absorption versus wavelength is called an **absorption spectrum (Figure 8.8)**.

The absorption spectra of chloroplast pigments provide clues to the relative effectiveness of different wavelengths for driving photosynthesis, since light can perform work in chloroplasts only if it is absorbed. **Figure 8.9a** shows the absorption spectra of three types of pigments in chloroplasts: **chlorophyll *a***, the key light-capturing pigment that participates directly in the light reactions; the accessory pigment **chlorophyll *b***; and a separate group of accessory pigments called carotenoids. The spectrum of chlorophyll *a* suggests that violet-blue and red light work best for photosynthesis, since they are absorbed, while green is the least effective color. This is confirmed by an **action spectrum** for photosynthesis **(Figure 8.9b)**, which profiles the relative effectiveness of different wavelengths of radiation in driving the process. An action spectrum is prepared by illuminating chloroplasts with light of different colors and then plotting wavelength against some measure of photosynthetic rate, such as CO_2 consumption or

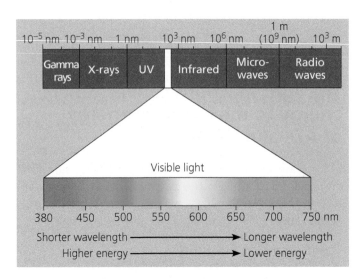

▲ **Figure 8.6 The electromagnetic spectrum.** White light is a mixture of all wavelengths of visible light. A prism can sort white light into its component colors by bending light of different wavelengths at different angles. (Droplets of water in the atmosphere can act as prisms, forming a rainbow.) Visible light drives photosynthesis.

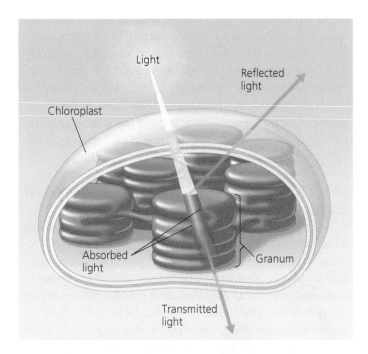

▲ **Figure 8.7 Why leaves are green: interaction of light with chloroplasts.** The chlorophyll molecules of chloroplasts absorb violet-blue and red light (the colors most effective in driving photosynthesis) and reflect or transmit green light. This is why leaves appear green.

Determining an Absorption Spectrum

Application An absorption spectrum is a visual representation of how well a particular pigment absorbs different wavelengths of visible light. Absorption spectra of various chloroplast pigments help scientists decipher the role of each pigment in a plant.

Technique A spectrophotometer measures the relative amounts of light of different wavelengths absorbed and transmitted by a pigment solution.

① White light is separated into colors (wavelengths) by a prism.

② One by one, the different colors of light are passed through the sample (chlorophyll in this example). Green light and blue light are shown here.

③ The transmitted light strikes a photoelectric tube, which converts the light energy to electricity.

④ The electric current is measured by a galvanometer. The meter indicates the fraction of light transmitted through the sample, from which we can determine the amount of light absorbed.

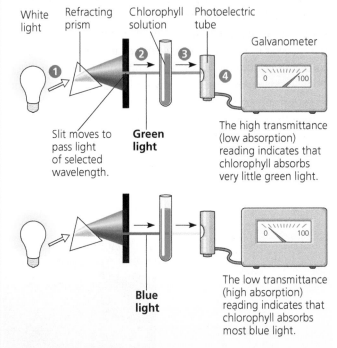

White light | Refracting prism | Chlorophyll solution | Photoelectric tube

Galvanometer

Slit moves to pass light of selected wavelength.

Green light

The high transmittance (low absorption) reading indicates that chlorophyll absorbs very little green light.

Blue light

The low transmittance (high absorption) reading indicates that chlorophyll absorbs most blue light.

Results See Figure 8.9a for absorption spectra of three types of chloroplast pigments.

O_2 release. The action spectrum for photosynthesis was first demonstrated by Theodor W. Engelmann, a German botanist, in 1883. Before equipment for measuring O_2 levels had even been invented, Engelmann performed a clever experiment in which he used bacteria to measure rates of photosynthesis in filamentous algae **(Figure 8.9c)**. His results are a striking match to the modern action spectrum shown in Figure 8.9b.

Notice by comparing Figure 8.9a and 8.9b that the action spectrum for photosynthesis is much broader than the absorption spectrum of chlorophyll *a*. The absorption spectrum of chlorophyll *a* alone underestimates the effectiveness of

Which wavelengths of light are most effective in driving photosynthesis?

Experiment Absorption and action spectra, along with a classic experiment by Theodor W. Engelmann, reveal which wavelengths of light are photosynthetically important.

Results

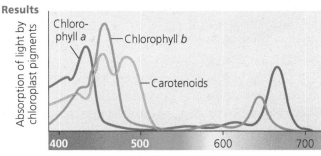

Wavelength of light (nm)

(a) Absorption spectra. The three curves show the wavelengths of light best absorbed by three types of chloroplast pigments.

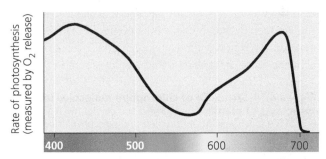

(b) Action spectrum. This graph plots the rate of photosynthesis versus wavelength. The resulting action spectrum resembles the absorption spectrum for chlorophyll *a* but does not match exactly (see part a). This is partly due to the absorption of light by accessory pigments such as chlorophyll *b* and carotenoids.

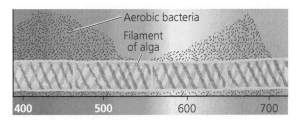

(c) Engelmann's experiment. In 1883, Theodor W. Engelmann illuminated a filamentous alga with light that had been passed through a prism, exposing different segments of the alga to different wavelengths. He used aerobic bacteria, which concentrate near an oxygen source, to determine which segments of the alga were releasing the most O_2 and thus photosynthesizing most. Bacteria congregated in greatest numbers around the parts of the alga illuminated with violet-blue or red light.

Conclusion Light in the violet-blue and red portions of the spectrum is most effective in driving photosynthesis.

Data from T. W. Engelmann, *Bacterium photometricum*. Ein Beitrag zur vergleichenden Physiologie des Licht-und Farbensinnes, *Archiv. für Physiologie* 30:95–124 (1883).

(**MB**) A related Experimental Inquiry Tutorial can be assigned in MasteringBiology.

INTERPRET THE DATA What wavelengths of light drive the highest rate of photosynthesis?

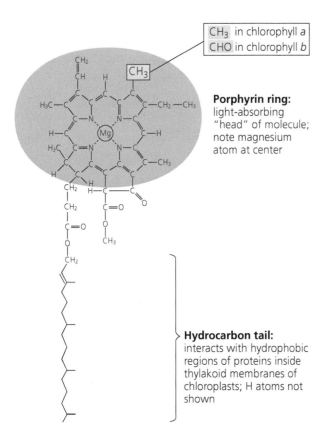

CH₃ in chlorophyll *a*
CHO in chlorophyll *b*

CH₃

Porphyrin ring: light-absorbing "head" of molecule; note magnesium atom at center

Hydrocarbon tail: interacts with hydrophobic regions of proteins inside thylakoid membranes of chloroplasts; H atoms not shown

▲ **Figure 8.10 Structure of chlorophyll molecules in chloroplasts of plants.** Chlorophyll *a* and chlorophyll *b* differ only in one of the functional groups bonded to the porphyrin ring. (Also see the space-filling model of chlorophyll in Figure 1.3.)

certain wavelengths in driving photosynthesis. This is partly because accessory pigments with different absorption spectra also present in chloroplasts—including chlorophyll *b* and carotenoids—broaden the spectrum of colors that can be used for photosynthesis. **Figure 8.10** shows the structure of chlorophyll *a* compared with that of chlorophyll *b*. A slight structural difference between them is enough to cause the two pigments to absorb at slightly different wavelengths in the red and blue parts of the spectrum (see Figure 8.9a). As a result, chlorophyll *a* appears blue green and chlorophyll *b* olive green under visible light.

Other accessory pigments include **carotenoids**, hydrocarbons that are various shades of yellow and orange because they absorb violet and blue-green light (see Figure 8.9a). Carotenoids may broaden the spectrum of colors that can drive photosynthesis. However, a more important function of at least some carotenoids seems to be *photoprotection*: These compounds absorb and dissipate

excessive light energy that would otherwise damage chlorophyll or interact with oxygen, forming reactive oxidative molecules that are dangerous to the cell. Interestingly, carotenoids similar to the photoprotective ones in chloroplasts have a photoprotective role in the human eye. (Carrots, known for aiding night vision, are rich in carotenoids.)

Excitation of Chlorophyll by Light

What exactly happens when chlorophyll and other pigments absorb light? The colors corresponding to the absorbed wavelengths disappear from the spectrum of the transmitted and reflected light, but energy cannot disappear. When a molecule absorbs a photon of light, one of the molecule's electrons is elevated to an electron shell where it has more potential energy (see Figure 2.5). When the electron is in its normal shell, the pigment molecule is said to be in its ground state. Absorption of a photon boosts an electron to a higher-energy electron shell, and the pigment molecule is then said to be in an excited state **(Figure 8.11a)**. The only photons absorbed are those whose energy is exactly equal to the energy difference between the ground state and an excited state, and this energy difference varies from one kind of molecule to another. Thus, a particular compound absorbs only photons corresponding to specific wavelengths, which is why each pigment has a unique absorption spectrum.

Once absorption of a photon raises an electron from the ground state to an excited state, the electron cannot stay there long. The excited state, like all high-energy states, is unstable. Generally, when isolated pigment molecules absorb light, their excited electrons drop back down to the ground-state electron shell in a billionth of a second, releasing their excess energy

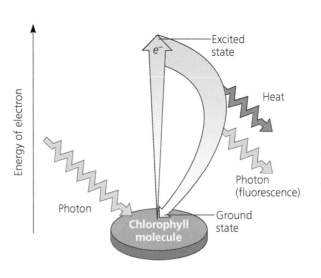

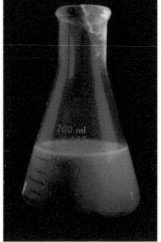

(a) Excitation of isolated chlorophyll molecule   **(b) Fluorescence**

▲ **Figure 8.11 Excitation of isolated chlorophyll by light. (a)** Absorption of a photon causes a transition of the chlorophyll molecule from its ground state to its excited state. The photon boosts an electron to an orbital where it has more potential energy. If the illuminated molecule exists in isolation, its excited electron immediately drops back down to the ground-state orbital, and its excess energy is given off as heat and fluorescence (light). **(b)** A chlorophyll solution excited with ultraviolet light fluoresces with a red-orange glow.

as heat. This conversion of light energy to heat is what makes the top of an automobile so hot on a sunny day. (White cars are coolest because their paint reflects all wavelengths of visible light.) In isolation, some pigments, including chlorophyll, emit light as well as heat after absorbing photons. As excited electrons fall back to the ground state, photons are given off, an afterglow called fluorescence. An illuminated solution of chlorophyll isolated from chloroplasts will fluoresce in the red-orange part of the spectrum and also give off heat. This is best seen by illuminating with ultraviolet light, which chlorophyll can also absorb (Figure 8.11b). Viewed under visible light, the fluorescence would be hard to see against the green of the solution.

A Photosystem: A Reaction-Center Complex Associated with Light-Harvesting Complexes

Chlorophyll molecules excited by the absorption of light energy produce very different results in an intact chloroplast than they do in isolation. In their native environment of the thylakoid membrane, chlorophyll molecules are organized along with other small organic molecules and proteins into complexes called photosystems.

A **photosystem** is composed of a **reaction-center complex** surrounded by several light-harvesting complexes (**Figure 8.12**). The reaction-center complex is an organized association of proteins holding a special pair of chlorophyll *a* molecules. Each **light-harvesting complex** consists of various pigment molecules (which may include chlorophyll *a*, chlorophyll *b*, and multiple carotenoids) bound to proteins. The number and variety of pigment molecules enable a photosystem to harvest light over a larger surface area and a larger portion of the spectrum than could any single pigment molecule alone. Together, these light-harvesting complexes act as an antenna for the reaction-center complex. When a pigment molecule absorbs a photon, the energy is transferred from pigment molecule to pigment molecule within a light-harvesting complex, somewhat like a human "wave" at a sports arena, until it is passed into the reaction-center complex. The reaction-center complex also contains a molecule capable of accepting electrons and becoming reduced; this is called the **primary electron acceptor**. The pair of chlorophyll *a* molecules in the reaction-center complex are special because their molecular environment—their location and the other molecules with which they are associated—enables them to use the energy from light not only to boost one of their electrons to a higher energy level, but also to transfer it to a different molecule—the primary electron acceptor.

The solar-powered transfer of an electron from the reaction-center chlorophyll *a* pair to the primary electron acceptor is one of the first steps of the light reactions. As soon as the chlorophyll electron is excited to a higher energy level, the primary electron acceptor captures it; this is a redox reaction. In the flask shown in Figure 8.11b, isolated chlorophyll fluoresces because there is no electron acceptor, so electrons

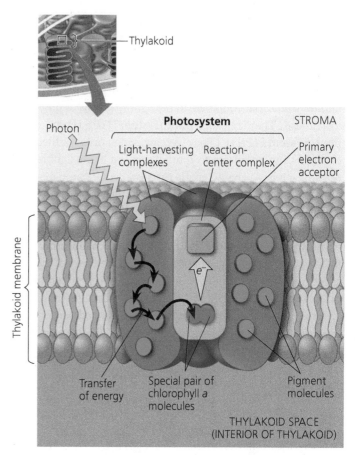

(a) **How a photosystem harvests light.** When a photon strikes a pigment molecule in a light-harvesting complex, the energy is passed from molecule to molecule until it reaches the reaction-center complex. Here, an excited electron from the special pair of chlorophyll *a* molecules is transferred to the primary electron acceptor.

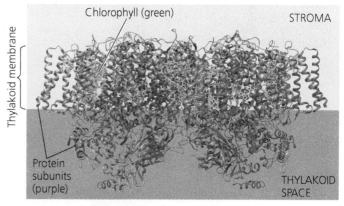

(b) **Structure of a photosystem.** This computer model, based on X-ray crystallography, shows two photosystem complexes side by side. Chlorophyll molecules (bright green ball-and-stick models within the membrane; the tails are not shown) are interspersed with protein subunits (purple ribbons; notice the many α helices spanning the membrane). For simplicity, a photosystem will be shown as a single complex in the rest of the chapter.

▲ **Figure 8.12 The structure and function of a photosystem.**

of photoexcited chlorophyll drop right back to the ground state. In the structured environment of a chloroplast, however, an electron acceptor is readily available, and the potential energy represented by the excited electron is not dissipated as light and heat. Thus, each photosystem—a reaction-center complex surrounded by light-harvesting complexes—functions in the chloroplast as a unit. It converts light energy to chemical energy, which will ultimately be used for the synthesis of sugar.

The thylakoid membrane is populated by two types of photosystems that cooperate in the light reactions of photosynthesis. They are called **photosystem II (PS II)** and **photosystem I (PS I)**. (They were named in order of their discovery, but photosystem II functions first in the light reactions.) Each has a characteristic reaction-center complex—a particular kind of primary electron acceptor next to a special pair of chlorophyll *a* molecules associated with specific proteins. The reaction-center chlorophyll *a* of photosystem II is known as P680 because this pigment is best at absorbing light having a wavelength of 680 nm (in the red part of the spectrum). The chlorophyll *a* at the reaction-center complex of photosystem I is called P700 because it most effectively absorbs light of wavelength 700 nm (in the far-red part of the spectrum). These two pigments, P680 and P700, are nearly identical chlorophyll *a* molecules. However, their association with different proteins in the thylakoid membrane affects the electron distribution in the two pigments and accounts for the slight differences in their light-absorbing properties. Now let's see how the two photosystems work together in using light energy to generate ATP and NADPH, the two main products of the light reactions.

Linear Electron Flow

Light drives the synthesis of ATP and NADPH by energizing the two photosystems embedded in the thylakoid membranes of chloroplasts. The key to this energy transformation is a flow of electrons through the photosystems and other molecular components built into the thylakoid membrane. This is called **linear electron flow**, and it occurs during the light reactions of photosynthesis, as shown in **Figure 8.13**. The numbered steps in the text correspond to those in the figure.

➊ A photon of light strikes one of the pigment molecules in a light-harvesting complex of PS II, boosting one of its electrons to a higher energy level. As this electron falls back to its ground state, an electron in a nearby pigment molecule is simultaneously raised to an excited state. The

▼ **Figure 8.13 How linear electron flow during the light reactions generates ATP and NADPH.** The gold arrows trace the current of light-driven electrons from water to NADPH.

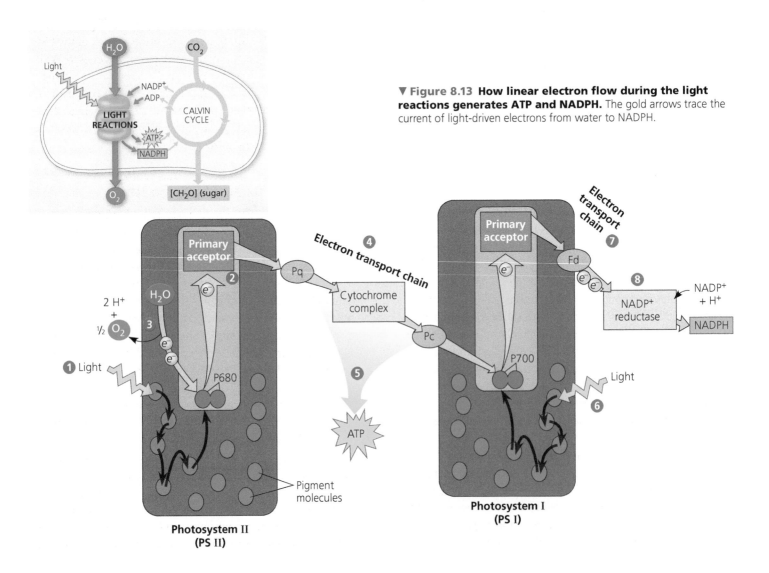

process continues, with the energy being relayed to other pigment molecules until it reaches the P680 pair of chlorophyll *a* molecules in the PS II reaction-center complex. It excites an electron in this pair of chlorophylls to a higher energy state.

❷ This electron is transferred from the excited P680 to the primary electron acceptor. We can refer to the resulting form of P680, missing an electron, as P680$^+$.

❸ An enzyme catalyzes the splitting of a water molecule into two electrons, two hydrogen ions (H$^+$), and an oxygen atom. The electrons are supplied one by one to the P680$^+$ pair, each electron replacing one transferred to the primary electron acceptor. (P680$^+$ is the strongest biological oxidizing agent known; its electron "hole" must be filled. This greatly facilitates the transfer of electrons from the split water molecule.) The H$^+$ are released into the thylakoid space. The oxygen atom immediately combines with an oxygen atom generated by the splitting of another water molecule, forming O$_2$.

❹ Each photoexcited electron passes from the primary electron acceptor of PS II to PS I via an electron transport chain, the components of which are similar to those of the electron transport chain that functions in cellular respiration. The electron transport chain between PS II and PS I is made up of the electron carrier plastoquinone (Pq), a cytochrome complex, and a protein called plastocyanin (Pc).

❺ The exergonic "fall" of electrons to a lower energy level provides energy for the synthesis of ATP. As electrons pass through the cytochrome complex, H$^+$ are pumped into the thylakoid space, contributing to the proton gradient that is then used in chemiosmosis, to be discussed shortly.

❻ Meanwhile, light energy has been transferred via light-harvesting complex pigments to the PS I reaction-center complex, exciting an electron of the P700 pair of chlorophyll *a* molecules located there. The photoexcited electron is then transferred to PS I's primary electron acceptor, creating an electron "hole" in the P700—which we now can call P700$^+$. In other words, P700$^+$ can now act as an electron acceptor, accepting an electron that reaches the bottom of the electron transport chain from PS II.

❼ Photoexcited electrons are passed in a series of redox reactions from the primary electron acceptor of PS I down a second electron transport chain through the protein ferredoxin (Fd). (This chain does not create a proton gradient and thus does not produce ATP.)

❽ The enzyme NADP$^+$ reductase catalyzes the transfer of electrons from Fd to NADP$^+$. Two electrons are required for its reduction to NADPH. This molecule is at a higher energy level than water, so its electrons are more readily available for the reactions of the Calvin cycle. This process also removes an H$^+$ from the stroma.

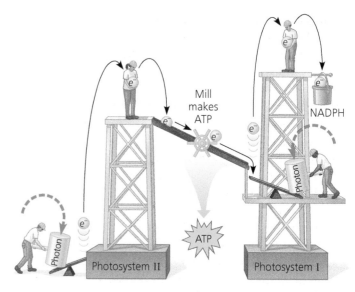

▲ **Figure 8.14 A mechanical analogy for linear electron flow during the light reactions.**

The energy changes of electrons during their linear flow through the light reactions are shown in a mechanical analogy in **Figure 8.14**. Although the scheme shown in Figures 8.13 and 8.14 may seem complicated, do not lose track of the big picture: The light reactions use solar power to generate ATP and NADPH, which provide chemical energy and reducing power, respectively, to the carbohydrate-synthesizing reactions of the Calvin cycle. Before we move on to the Calvin cycle, let's review chemiosmosis, the process that uses membranes to couple redox reactions to ATP production.

A Comparison of Chemiosmosis in Chloroplasts and Mitochondria

Chloroplasts and mitochondria generate ATP by the same basic mechanism: chemiosmosis (see Figure 7.14). An electron transport chain assembled in a membrane pumps protons (H$^+$) across the membrane as electrons are passed through a series of carriers that are progressively more electronegative. Thus, electron transport chains transform redox energy to a proton-motive force, potential energy stored in the form of an H$^+$ gradient across a membrane. An ATP synthase complex in the same membrane couples the diffusion of hydrogen ions down their gradient to the phosphorylation of ADP, forming ATP. Some of the electron carriers, including the iron-containing proteins called cytochromes, are very similar in chloroplasts and mitochondria. The ATP synthase complexes of the two organelles are also quite similar. But there are noteworthy differences between photophosphorylation in chloroplasts and oxidative phosphorylation in mitochondria. Both work by way of chemiosmosis, but in chloroplasts, the high-energy electrons dropped down the transport chain come from water, whereas in mitochondria, they are extracted from organic molecules (which are thus oxidized). Chloroplasts do

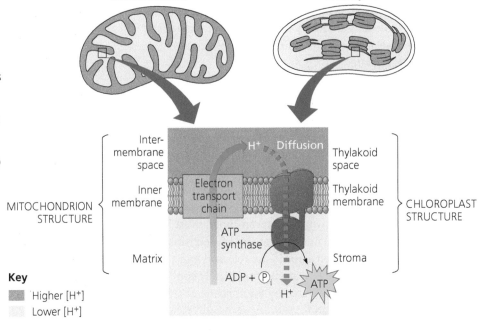

► **Figure 8.15 Comparison of chemiosmosis in mitochondria and chloroplasts.** In both kinds of organelles, electron transport chains pump protons (H^+) across a membrane from a region of low H^+ concentration (light gray in this diagram) to one of high H^+ concentration (dark gray). The protons then diffuse back across the membrane through ATP synthase, driving the synthesis of ATP.

MAKE CONNECTIONS *Describe how you would change the pH in order to artificially cause ATP synthesis (a) outside an isolated mitochondrion (assume H^+ can freely cross the outer membrane) and (b) in the stroma of a chloroplast. Explain.*

not need molecules from food to make ATP; their photosystems capture light energy and use it to drive the electrons from water to the top of the transport chain. In other words, mitochondria use chemiosmosis to transfer chemical energy from food molecules to ATP, whereas chloroplasts use it to transform light energy into chemical energy in ATP.

Although the spatial organization of chemiosmosis differs slightly between chloroplasts and mitochondria, it is easy to see similarities in the two **(Figure 8.15)**. The inner membrane of the mitochondrion pumps protons from the mitochondrial matrix out to the intermembrane space, which then serves as a reservoir of hydrogen ions. The thylakoid membrane of the chloroplast pumps protons from the stroma into the thylakoid space (interior of the thylakoid), which functions as the H^+ reservoir. If you imagine the cristae of mitochondria pinching off from the inner membrane, this may help you see how the thylakoid space and the intermembrane space are comparable spaces in the two organelles, while the mitochondrial matrix is analogous to the stroma of the chloroplast. In the mitochondrion, protons diffuse down their concentration gradient from the intermembrane space through ATP synthase to the matrix, driving ATP synthesis. In the chloroplast, ATP is synthesized as the hydrogen ions diffuse from the thylakoid space back to the stroma through ATP synthase complexes, whose catalytic knobs are on the stroma side of the membrane. Thus, ATP forms in the stroma, where it is used to help drive sugar synthesis during the Calvin cycle.

The proton (H^+) gradient, or pH gradient, across the thylakoid membrane is substantial. When chloroplasts in an experimental setting are illuminated, the pH in the thylakoid space drops to about 5 (the H^+ concentration increases), and the pH in the stroma increases to about 8 (the H^+ concentration decreases). This gradient of three pH units corresponds

to a thousandfold difference in H^+ concentration. If the lights are turned off, the pH gradient is abolished, but it can quickly be restored by turning the lights back on. Experiments such as this provided strong evidence in support of the chemiosmotic model.

Based on studies in several laboratories, **Figure 8.16** shows a current model for the organization of the light-reaction "machinery" within the thylakoid membrane. Each of the molecules and molecular complexes in the figure is present in numerous copies in each thylakoid. Notice that NADPH, like ATP, is produced on the side of the membrane facing the stroma, where the Calvin cycle reactions take place.

Let's summarize the light reactions. Electron flow pushes electrons from water, where they are at a low state of potential energy, ultimately to NADPH, where they are stored at a high state of potential energy. The light-driven electron flow also generates ATP. Thus, the equipment of the thylakoid membrane converts light energy to chemical energy stored in ATP and NADPH. (Oxygen is a by-product.) Let's now see how the Calvin cycle uses the products of the light reactions to synthesize sugar from CO_2.

CONCEPT CHECK 8.2

1. What color of light is *least* effective in driving photosynthesis? Explain.
2. In the light reactions, what is the initial electron donor? At the end of the light reactions, where are the electrons?
3. **WHAT IF?** In an experiment, isolated chloroplasts placed in an illuminated solution with the appropriate chemicals can carry out ATP synthesis. Predict what will happen to the rate of synthesis if a compound is added to the solution that makes membranes freely permeable to hydrogen ions.

For suggested answers, see Appendix A.

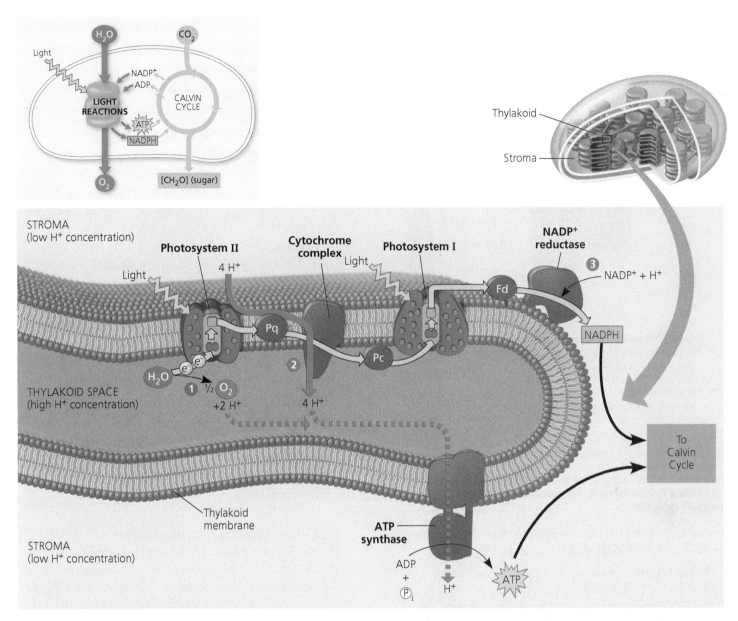

STROMA
(low H⁺ concentration)

Photosystem II

Light

4 H⁺

Cytochrome complex

Light

Photosystem I

NADP⁺ reductase

❸ NADP⁺ + H⁺

Fd

Pq

NADPH

THYLAKOID SPACE
(high H⁺ concentration)

H₂O

e⁻ e⁻

❶ ½ O₂

+2 H⁺

2

4 H⁺

Pc

Thylakoid membrane

STROMA
(low H⁺ concentration)

ATP synthase

ADP
+
℗ᵢ

H⁺

ATP

To Calvin Cycle

Thylakoid

Stroma

▲ **Figure 8.16 The light reactions and chemiosmosis: the current model of the organization of the thylakoid membrane.** The gold arrows track the linear electron flow outlined in Figure 8.13. At least three steps contribute to the H⁺ gradient across the thylakoid membrane: ❶ Water is split by photosystem II on the side of the membrane facing the thylakoid space; ❷ as plastoquinone (Pq) transfers electrons to the cytochrome complex, four protons are translocated across the membrane into the thylakoid space; and ❸ a hydrogen ion is removed from the stroma when it is taken up by NADP⁺. Notice that in step 2, hydrogen ions are being pumped from the stroma into the thylakoid space, as in Figure 8.15. The diffusion of H⁺ from the thylakoid space back to the stroma (along the H⁺ concentration gradient) powers the ATP synthase.

The Calvin cycle uses the chemical energy of ATP and NADPH to reduce CO₂ to sugar

The Calvin cycle is similar to the citric acid cycle in that a starting material is regenerated after some molecules enter and others exit the cycle. However, the citric acid cycle is catabolic, oxidizing acetyl CoA and using the energy to synthesize ATP, while the Calvin cycle is anabolic, building carbohydrates from smaller molecules and consuming energy. Carbon enters the Calvin cycle in CO₂ and leaves in sugar. The cycle spends ATP as an energy source and consumes NADPH as reducing power for adding high-energy electrons to make sugar.

As mentioned in Concept 8.1, the carbohydrate produced directly from the Calvin cycle is not glucose. It is actually a three-carbon sugar named **glyceraldehyde 3-phosphate (G3P)**. For net synthesis of one molecule of G3P, the cycle must take place three times, fixing three molecules of CO₂—one per turn of the cycle. (Recall that the term *carbon fixation* refers to the initial incorporation of CO₂ into organic material.) As we trace the steps of the Calvin cycle, keep in mind that we are following three molecules of CO₂ through the reactions.

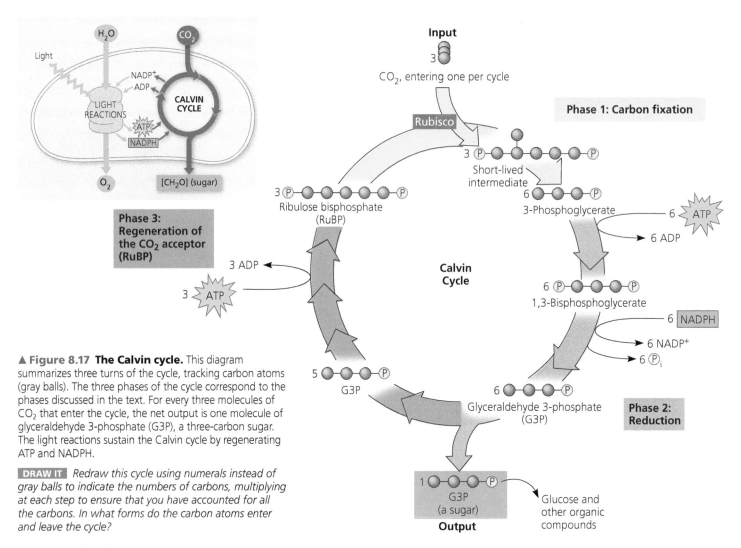

▲ Figure 8.17 The Calvin cycle. This diagram summarizes three turns of the cycle, tracking carbon atoms (gray balls). The three phases of the cycle correspond to the phases discussed in the text. For every three molecules of CO_2 that enter the cycle, the net output is one molecule of glyceraldehyde 3-phosphate (G3P), a three-carbon sugar. The light reactions sustain the Calvin cycle by regenerating ATP and NADPH.

DRAW IT *Redraw this cycle using numerals instead of gray balls to indicate the numbers of carbons, multiplying at each step to ensure that you have accounted for all the carbons. In what forms do the carbon atoms enter and leave the cycle?*

Figure 8.17 divides the Calvin cycle into three phases: carbon fixation, reduction, and regeneration of the CO_2 acceptor.

Phase 1: Carbon fixation. The Calvin cycle incorporates each CO_2 molecule, one at a time, by attaching it to a five-carbon sugar named ribulose bisphosphate (abbreviated RuBP). The enzyme that catalyzes this first step is RuBP carboxylase/oxygenase, or **rubisco**. (This is the most abundant protein in chloroplasts and is also thought to be the most abundant protein on Earth.) The product of the reaction is a six-carbon intermediate so unstable that it immediately splits in half, forming two molecules of 3-phosphoglycerate (for each CO_2 fixed).

Phase 2: Reduction. Each molecule of 3-phosphoglycerate receives an additional phosphate group from ATP, becoming 1,3-bisphosphoglycerate. Next, a pair of electrons donated from NADPH reduces 1,3-bisphosphoglycerate, which also loses a phosphate group, becoming G3P. Specifically, the electrons from NADPH reduce a carboyxl group on 1,3-bisphosphoglycerate to the aldehyde group of G3P, which stores more potential energy. G3P is a sugar—the same three-carbon sugar formed in glycolysis by the splitting of glucose (see Figure 7.9). Notice in Figure 8.17 that for every *three* molecules of CO_2 that enter the cycle, there are *six* molecules of G3P formed. But only one molecule of this three-carbon sugar can be counted as a net gain of carbohydrate, because the rest are required to complete the cycle. The cycle began with 15 carbons' worth of carbohydrate in the form of three molecules of the five-carbon sugar RuBP. Now there are 18 carbons' worth of carbohydrate in the form of six molecules of G3P. One molecule exits the cycle to be used by the plant cell, but the other five molecules must be recycled to regenerate the three molecules of RuBP.

Phase 3: Regeneration of the CO_2 acceptor (RuBP). In a complex series of reactions, the carbon skeletons of five molecules of G3P are rearranged by the last steps of the Calvin cycle into three molecules of RuBP. To accomplish this, the cycle spends three more ATPs. The RuBP is now prepared to receive CO_2 again, and the cycle continues.

For the net synthesis of one G3P molecule, the Calvin cycle consumes a total of nine molecules of ATP and six molecules of NADPH. The light reactions regenerate the ATP and NADPH. The G3P spun off from the Calvin cycle becomes the starting material for metabolic pathways that synthesize other organic compounds, including glucose (from two molecules of G3P) and other carbohydrates. Neither the light reactions nor the Calvin cycle alone can make sugar from CO_2. Photosynthesis is an emergent property of the intact chloroplast, which integrates the two stages of photosynthesis.

Evolution of Alternative Mechanisms of Carbon Fixation in Hot, Arid Climates

EVOLUTION Ever since plants first moved onto land about 475 million years ago, they have been adapting to the problem of dehydration. The solutions often involve trade-offs. An example is the balance between photosynthesis and the prevention of excessive water loss from the plant. The CO_2 required for photosynthesis enters a leaf (and the resulting O_2 exits) via stomata, the pores on the leaf surface (see Figure 8.3). However, stomata are also the main avenues of the evaporative loss of water from leaves and may be partially or fully closed on hot, dry days. This prevents water loss, but it also reduces CO_2 levels.

In most plants, initial fixation of carbon occurs via rubisco, the Calvin cycle enzyme that adds CO_2 to ribulose bisphosphate. Such plants are called **C_3 plants** because the first organic product of carbon fixation is a three-carbon compound, 3-phosphoglycerate (see Figure 8.17). C_3 plants include important agricultural plants such as rice, wheat, and soybeans. When their stomata close on hot, dry days, C_3 plants produce less sugar because the declining level of CO_2 in the leaf starves the Calvin cycle. In addition, rubisco is capable of binding O_2 in place of CO_2. As CO_2 becomes scarce and O_2 builds up, rubisco adds O_2 to the Calvin cycle instead of CO_2. The product splits, forming a two-carbon compound that leaves the chloroplast and is broken down in the cell, releasing CO_2. The process is called **photorespiration** because it occurs in the light (*photo*) and consumes O_2 while producing CO_2 (*respiration*). However, unlike normal cellular respiration, photorespiration uses ATP rather than generating it. And unlike photosynthesis, photorespiration produces no sugar. In fact, photorespiration *decreases* photosynthetic output by siphoning organic material from the Calvin cycle and releasing CO_2 that would otherwise be fixed.

According to one hypothesis, photorespiration is evolutionary baggage—a metabolic relic from a much earlier time when the atmosphere had less O_2 and more CO_2 than it does today. In the ancient atmosphere that prevailed when rubisco first evolved, the ability of the enzyme's active site to bind O_2 would have made little difference. The hypothesis suggests that modern rubisco retains some of its chance affinity for O_2, which is now so concentrated in the atmosphere that a certain amount of photorespiration is inevitable. There is also some evidence that photorespiration may provide protection against damaging products of the light reactions that build up when the Calvin cycle slows due to low CO_2.

In some plant species, alternate modes of carbon fixation have evolved that minimize photorespiration and optimize the Calvin cycle—even in hot, arid climates. The two most important of these photosynthetic adaptations are C_4 photosynthesis and crassulacean acid metabolism (CAM).

C_4 Plants

The **C_4 plants** are so named because they carry out a modified pathway for sugar synthesis that first fixes CO_2 into a four-carbon compound. When the weather is hot and dry, a C_4 plant partially closes its stomata, thus conserving water. Sugar continues to be made, however, through the function of two different types of photosynthetic cells: mesophyll cells and bundle-sheath cells **(Figure 8.18a)**. An enzyme in the mesophyll cells has a high affinity for CO_2 and can fix carbon even when the CO_2 concentration in the leaf is low. The resulting four-carbon compound then acts as a carbon shuttle; it moves into bundle-sheath cells, which are packed around the veins of the leaf, and releases CO_2. Thus, the CO_2 concentration in these cells remains high enough for the Calvin cycle to make sugars and avoid photorespiration. The C_4 pathway is believed to have evolved independently at least 45 times and is used by several thousand species in at least 19 plant families. Among the C_4 plants important to agriculture are sugarcane and corn (maize), members of the grass family. In the **Scientific Skills Exercise**, you will work with data to see how different concentrations of CO_2 affect growth in plants that use the C_4 pathway versus those that use the C_3 pathway.

CAM Plants

A second photosynthetic adaptation to arid conditions has evolved in pineapples, many cacti, and other succulent (water-storing) plants, such as aloe and jade plants **(Figure 8.18b)**. These

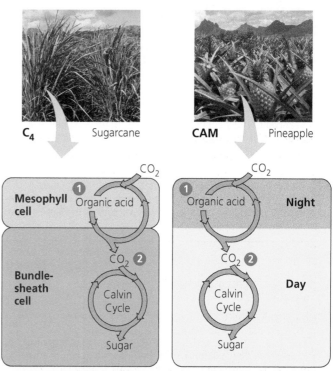

(a) **Spatial separation of steps.** In C_4 plants, carbon fixation and the Calvin cycle occur in different types of cells.

(b) **Temporal separation of steps.** In CAM plants, carbon fixation and the Calvin cycle occur in the same cell at different times.

▲ **Figure 8.18 C_4 and CAM photosynthesis compared.** Both adaptations are characterized by ❶ preliminary incorporation of CO_2 into organic acids, followed by ❷ transfer of CO_2 to the Calvin cycle. The C_4 and CAM pathways are two evolutionary solutions to the problem of maintaining photosynthesis with stomata partially or completely closed on hot, dry days.

plants open their stomata during the night and close them during the day, the reverse of how other plants behave. Closing stomata during the day helps desert plants conserve water, but it also prevents CO_2 from entering the leaves. During the night, when their stomata are open, these plants take up CO_2 and incorporate it into a variety of organic acids. This mode of carbon fixation is called **crassulacean acid metabolism (CAM)** after the plant family Crassulaceae, the succulents in which the process was first discovered. The mesophyll cells of **CAM plants** store the organic acids they make during the night in their vacuoles until morning, when the stomata close. During the day, when the light reactions can supply ATP and NADPH for the Calvin cycle, CO_2 is released from the organic acids made the night before to become incorporated into sugar in the chloroplasts.

Notice in Figure 8.18 that the CAM pathway is similar to the C_4 pathway in that carbon dioxide is first incorporated into organic intermediates before it enters the Calvin cycle. The difference is that in C_4 plants, the initial steps of carbon fixation are separated structurally from the Calvin cycle, whereas in CAM plants, the two steps occur within the same cell but at separate times. (Keep in mind that CAM, C_4, and C_3 plants all eventually use the Calvin cycle to make sugar from carbon dioxide.)

CONCEPT CHECK 8.3

1. **MAKE CONNECTIONS** How are the large numbers of ATP and NADPH molecules used during the Calvin cycle consistent with the high value of glucose as an energy source? (Compare Figures 7.15 and 8.17.)
2. **WHAT IF?** Explain why a poison that inhibits an enzyme of the Calvin cycle will also inhibit the light reactions.
3. Describe how photorespiration lowers photosynthetic output.

For suggested answers, see Appendix A.

The Importance of Photosynthesis: *A Review*

In this chapter, we have followed photosynthesis from photons to food. The light reactions capture solar energy and use it to make ATP and transfer electrons from water to $NADP^+$, forming NADPH. The Calvin cycle uses the ATP

Scientific Skills Exercise

Making Scatter Plots with Regression Lines

Does Atmospheric CO_2 Concentration Affect the Productivity of Agricultural Crops? Atmospheric concentration of CO_2 has been rising globally, and scientists wondered whether this would affect C_3 and C_4 plants differently. In this exercise, you will make a scatter plot to examine the relationship between CO_2 concentration and growth of corn (maize), a C_4 crop plant, and velvetleaf, a C_3 weed found in cornfields.

How the Experiment Was Done Researchers grew corn and velvetleaf plants under controlled conditions for 45 days, where all plants received the same amounts of water and light. The plants were divided into three groups, and each was exposed to a different concentration of CO_2 in the air: 350, 600, or 1,000 ppm (parts per million).

Data from the Experiment The table shows the dry mass (in grams) of corn and velvetleaf plants grown at the three concentrations of CO_2. The dry mass values are averages of the leaves, stems, and roots of eight plants.

	350 ppm CO_2	600 ppm CO_2	1,000 ppm CO_2
Average dry mass of one corn plant (g)	91	89	80
Average dry mass of one velvetleaf plant (g)	35	48	54

Data from D. T. Patterson and E. P. Flint, Potential effects of global atmospheric CO_2 enrichment on the growth and competitiveness of C_3 and C_4 weed and crop plants, *Weed Science* 28(1):71–75 (1980).

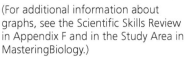
▶ Corn plant surrounded by invasive velvetleaf plants

(For additional information about graphs, see the Scientific Skills Review in Appendix F and in the Study Area in MasteringBiology.)

2. Draw a "best-fit" line for each set of points. A best-fit line does not necessarily pass through all or even most points. It is a straight line that passes as close as possible to all data points from that set. Drawing a best-fit line is a matter of judgment, so two people may draw slightly different lines. The line that fits best, a regression line, can be identified by squaring the distances of all points to any candidate line, then selecting the line that minimizes the sum of the squares. (See the graph in the Scientific Skills Exercise in Chapter 2 for an example of a linear regression line.) Using a spreadsheet program (such as Excel) or a graphing calculator, enter the data points for each data set and have the program draw the regression lines. Compare them with the lines you drew.

3. Describe the trends shown by the regression lines. (a) Compare the relationship between increasing concentration of CO_2 and the dry mass of corn with that of velvetleaf. (b) Since velvetleaf is a weed invasive to cornfields, predict how increased CO_2 concentration may affect interactions between the two species.

4. Based on the data in the scatter plot, estimate the percentage change in dry mass of corn and velvetleaf plants if atmospheric CO_2 concentration increased from 390 ppm (current levels) to 800 ppm. (a) What is the estimated dry mass of corn and velvetleaf plants at 390 ppm? 800 ppm? (b) To calculate the percentage change in mass for each plant, subtract the mass at 390 ppm from the mass at 800 ppm (change in mass), divide by the mass at 390 ppm (initial mass), and multiply by 100. What is the estimated percentage change in dry mass for corn? For velvetleaf? (c) Do these results support the conclusion from other experiments that C_3 plants grow better than C_4 plants under increased CO_2 concentration? Why or why not?

MB A version of this Scientific Skills Exercise can be assigned in MasteringBiology.

INTERPRET THE DATA

1. To explore the relationship between the two variables, it is useful to graph the data in a scatter plot and then draw a regression line. (a) First, place labels for the dependent and independent variables on the appropriate axes. Explain your choices. (b) Now plot the data points for corn and velvetleaf using different symbols for each set of data and add a key for the two symbols.

and NADPH to produce sugar from carbon dioxide. The energy that enters the chloroplasts as sunlight becomes stored as chemical energy in organic compounds. The entire process is reviewed visually in **Figure 8.19**, where photosynthesis is also shown in its natural context.

As for the fates of photosynthetic products, enzymes in the chloroplast and cytosol convert the G3P made in the Calvin cycle to many other organic compounds. In fact, the sugar made in the chloroplasts supplies the entire plant with chemical energy and carbon skeletons for the synthesis of all the major organic molecules of plant cells. About 50% of the organic material made by photosynthesis is consumed as fuel for cellular respiration in plant cell mitochondria.

Green cells are the only autotrophic parts of the plant. Other cells depend on organic molecules exported from leaves via veins (see Figure 8.19, top). In most plants, carbohydrate is transported out of the leaves to the rest of the plant as sucrose, a disaccharide. After arriving at nonphotosynthetic cells, the sucrose provides raw material for cellular respiration and many anabolic pathways that synthesize proteins, lipids, and other products. A considerable amount of sugar in the form of glucose is linked together to make the polysaccharide cellulose (see Figure 3.11c), especially in plant cells that are still growing and maturing. Cellulose, the main ingredient of cell walls, is the most abundant organic molecule in the plant—and probably on the surface of the planet.

Most plants and other photosynthesizers manage to make more organic material each day than they need to use as respiratory fuel and precursors for biosynthesis. They stockpile the extra sugar by synthesizing starch, storing some in the chloroplasts themselves and some in storage cells of roots, tubers, seeds, and fruits. In accounting for the consumption of the food molecules produced by photosynthesis, let's not forget that most plants lose leaves, roots, stems, fruits, and sometimes their entire bodies to heterotrophs, including humans.

On a global scale, photosynthesis is responsible for the oxygen in our atmosphere. Furthermore, while each chloroplast is minuscule, their collective food production is prodigious: Photosynthesis makes an estimated 150 billion metric tons of carbohydrate per year (a metric ton is 1,000 kg, about 1.1 tons). That's organic matter equivalent in mass to a stack of about 60 trillion biology textbooks! Such a stack would reach 17 times the distance from Earth to the sun! No chemical process is more important than photosynthesis to the welfare of life on Earth.

In Chapters 3 through 8, you have learned about many activities of cells. **Figure 8.20** integrates these in the context of a working plant cell. As you study the figure, reflect on how each process fits into the big picture: As the most basic unit of living organisms, a cell performs all functions characteristic of life.

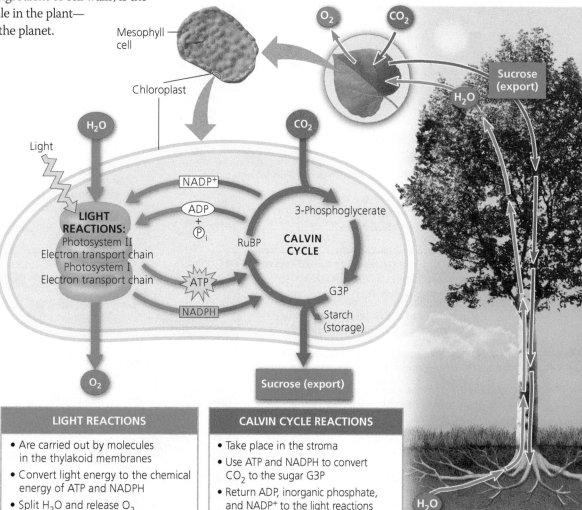

▶ **Figure 8.19 A review of photosynthesis.** This diagram shows the main reactants and products of photosynthesis as they move through the tissues of a tree (right) and a chloroplast (left).

MAKE CONNECTIONS *Can plants use the sugar they produce during photosynthesis to power the work of their cells? Explain. (See Figures 6.9, 6.10, and 7.6.)*

LIGHT REACTIONS
• Are carried out by molecules in the thylakoid membranes
• Convert light energy to the chemical energy of ATP and NADPH
• Split H_2O and release O_2

CALVIN CYCLE REACTIONS
• Take place in the stroma
• Use ATP and NADPH to convert CO_2 to the sugar G3P
• Return ADP, inorganic phosphate, and $NADP^+$ to the light reactions

MAKE CONNECTIONS

The Working Cell

This figure illustrates how a generalized plant cell functions, integrating the cellular activities you learned about in Chapters 3–8.

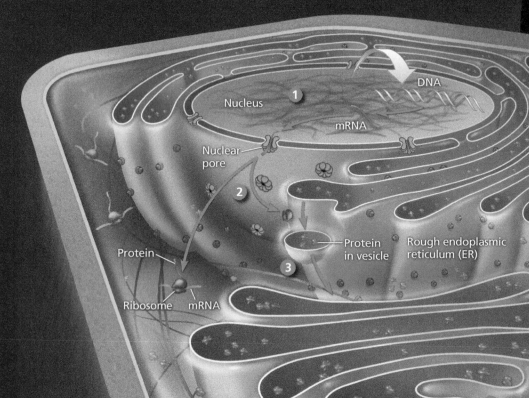

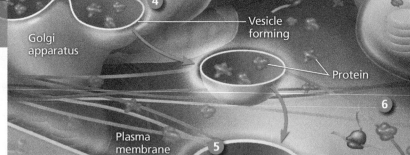

Flow of Genetic Information in the Cell: DNA → RNA → Protein (Chapters 3–5)

① In the nucleus, DNA serves as a template for the synthesis of mRNA, which moves to the cytoplasm. (See Figures 3.26 and 4.8.)

② mRNA attaches to a ribosome, which remains free in the cytosol or binds to the rough ER. Proteins are synthesized. (See Figures 3.26 and 4.9.)

③ Proteins and membrane produced by the rough ER flow in vesicles to the Golgi apparatus, where they are processed. (See Figures 4.15 and 5.8.)

④ Transport vesicles carrying proteins pinch off from the Golgi apparatus. (See Figure 4.15.)

⑤ Some vesicles merge with the plasma membrane, releasing proteins by exocytosis. (See Figure 5.8.)

⑥ Proteins synthesized on free ribosomes stay in the cell and perform specific functions; examples include the enzymes that catalyze the reactions of cellular respiration and photosynthesis. (See Figures 7.7, 7.9, and 8.17.)

Energy Transformations in the Cell: Photosynthesis and Cellular Respiration (Chapters 6–8)

7 In chloroplasts, the process of photosynthesis uses the energy of light to convert CO_2 and H_2O to organic molecules, with O_2 as a by-product. (See Figure 8.19.)

8 In mitochondria, organic molecules are broken down by cellular respiration, capturing energy in molecules of ATP, which are used to power the work of the cell, such as protein synthesis and active transport. CO_2 and H_2O are by-products. (See Figures 6.8–6.10, 7.2, and 7.15.)

Vacuole

Movement Across Cell Membranes (Chapter 5)

9 Water diffuses into and out of the cell directly through the plasma membrane and by facilitated diffusion through aquaporins. (See Figure 5.1.)

10 By passive transport, the CO_2 used in photosynthesis diffuses into the cell and the O_2 formed as a by-product of photosynthesis diffuses out of the cell. Both solutes move down their concentration gradients. (See Figures 5.9 and 8.19.)

11 In active transport, energy (usually supplied by ATP) is used to transport a solute against its concentration gradient. (See Figure 5.15.)

Exocytosis (shown in step 5) and endocytosis move larger materials out of and into the cell. (See Figures 5.8 and 5.18.)

7 Photosynthesis in chloroplast

CO_2

H_2O

Organic molecules

O_2

8 Cellular respiration in mitochondrion

ATP

ATP

ATP

ATP

Transport pump

11

10

9

O_2

CO_2

H_2O

MAKE CONNECTIONS *The first enzyme that functions in glycolysis is hexokinase. In this plant cell, describe the entire process by which this enzyme is produced and where it functions, specifying the locations for each step. (See Figures 3.22, 3.26, and 7.9.)*

ANIMATION Visit the Study Area in **MasteringBiology** for BioFlix® 3-D Animations in Chapters 4, 5, 7, and 8.

Go to **MasteringBiology**® for Assignments, the eText, and the Study Area with Animations, Activities, Vocab Self-Quiz, and Practice Tests.

SUMMARY OF KEY CONCEPTS

VOCAB
SELF-QUIZ

goo.gl/gbai8v

CONCEPT 8.1

Photosynthesis converts light energy to the chemical energy of food (pp. 162–165)

- In eukaryotes that are **autotrophs**, photosynthesis occurs in **chloroplasts**, organelles containing **thylakoids**. Stacks of thylakoids form grana. **Photosynthesis** is summarized as

$$6\ CO_2 + 12\ H_2O + \text{Light energy} \rightarrow C_6H_{12}O_6 + 6\ O_2 + 6\ H_2O.$$

- Chloroplasts split water into hydrogen and oxygen, incorporating the electrons of hydrogen into sugar molecules. Photosynthesis is a redox process: H_2O is oxidized, and CO_2 is reduced. The **light reactions** in the thylakoid membranes split water, releasing O_2, producing ATP, and forming **NADPH**. The **Calvin cycle** in the **stroma** forms sugars from CO_2, using ATP for energy and NADPH for reducing power.

? *Compare the roles of CO_2 and H_2O in respiration and photosynthesis.*

CONCEPT 8.2

The light reactions convert solar energy to the chemical energy of ATP and NADPH (pp. 165–173)

- Light is a form of electromagnetic energy. The colors we see as **visible light** include those **wavelengths** that drive photosynthesis. A pigment absorbs light of specific wavelengths; **chlorophyll *a*** is the main photosynthetic pigment in plants. Other accessory pigments absorb different wavelengths of light and pass the energy on to chlorophyll *a*.
- A pigment goes from a ground state to an excited state when a **photon** of light boosts one of the pigment's electrons to a higher-energy electron shell. Electrons from isolated pigments tend to fall back to the ground state, giving off heat and/or light.
- A **photosystem** is composed of a **reaction-center complex** surrounded by **light-harvesting complexes** that funnel the energy of photons to the reaction-center complex. When a special pair of reaction-center chlorophyll *a* molecules absorbs energy, one of its electrons is boosted to a higher energy level and transferred to the **primary electron acceptor**. **Photosystem II** contains P680 chlorophyll *a* molecules in the reaction-center complex; **photosystem I** contains P700 molecules.
- **Linear electron flow** during the light reactions uses both photosystems and produces NADPH, ATP, and oxygen:

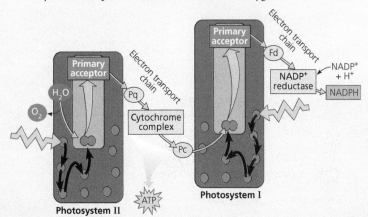

- During chemiosmosis in both mitochondria and chloroplasts, electron transport chains generate an H^+ (proton) gradient across a membrane. ATP synthase uses this proton-motive force to synthesize ATP.

? *The absorption spectrum of chlorophyll* a *differs from the action spectrum of photosynthesis. Explain this observation.*

CONCEPT 8.3

The Calvin cycle uses the chemical energy of ATP and NADPH to reduce CO_2 to sugar (pp. 173–177)

- The Calvin cycle occurs in the stroma, using electrons from NADPH and energy from ATP. One molecule of **G3P** exits the cycle per three CO_2 molecules fixed and is converted to glucose and other organic molecules.

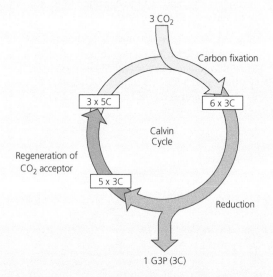

- On hot, dry days, **C_3 plants** close their stomata, conserving water but keeping CO_2 out and O_2 in. Under these conditions, **photorespiration** can occur: **Rubisco** binds O_2 instead of CO_2, leading to consumption of ATP and release of CO_2 without the production of sugar. Photorespiration may be an evolutionary relic and it may also play a protective role.
- **C_4 plants** are adapted to hot, dry climates. Even with their stomata partially or completely closed, they minimize the cost of photorespiration by incorporating CO_2 into four-carbon compounds in mesophyll cells. These compounds are exported to bundle-sheath cells, where they release carbon dioxide for use in the Calvin cycle.
- **CAM plants** are also adapted to hot, dry climates. They open their stomata at night, incorporating CO_2 into organic acids, which are stored in mesophyll cells. During the day, the stomata close, and the CO_2 is released from the organic acids for use in the Calvin cycle.
- Organic compounds produced by photosynthesis provide the energy and building material for Earth's ecosystems.

DRAW IT *On the diagram above, draw where ATP and NADPH are used and where rubisco functions. Describe these steps.*

TEST YOUR UNDERSTANDING

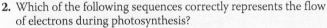

PRACTICE TEST

goo.gl/CRZjvS

Level 1: Knowledge/Comprehension

1. The light reactions of photosynthesis supply the Calvin cycle with
   (A) light energy.
   (B) CO_2 and ATP.
   (C) O_2 and NADPH.
   (D) ATP and NADPH.

2. Which of the following sequences correctly represents the flow of electrons during photosynthesis?
   (A) NADPH → O_2 → CO_2
   (B) H_2O → NADPH → Calvin cycle
   (C) H_2O → photosystem I → photosystem II
   (D) NADPH → electron transport chain → O_2

3. How is photosynthesis similar in C_4 plants and CAM plants?
   (A) In both cases, electron transport is not used.
   (B) Both types of plants make sugar without the Calvin cycle.
   (C) In both cases, rubisco is not used to fix carbon initially.
   (D) Both types of plants make most of their sugar in the dark.

4. Which of the following statements is a correct distinction between autotrophs and heterotrophs?
   (A) Autotrophs, but not heterotrophs, can nourish themselves beginning with CO_2 and other nutrients that are inorganic.
   (B) Only heterotrophs require chemical compounds from the environment.
   (C) Cellular respiration is unique to heterotrophs.
   (D) Only heterotrophs have mitochondria.

5. Which of the following does *not* occur during the Calvin cycle?
   (A) carbon fixation
   (B) oxidation of NADPH
   (C) release of oxygen
   (D) regeneration of the CO_2 acceptor

Level 2: Application/Analysis

6. In mechanism, photophosphorylation is most similar to
   (A) substrate-level phosphorylation in glycolysis.
   (B) oxidative phosphorylation in cellular respiration.
   (C) carbon fixation.
   (D) reduction of $NADP^+$.

7. Which process is most directly driven by light energy?
   (A) creation of a pH gradient by pumping protons across the thylakoid membrane
   (B) reduction of $NADP^+$ molecules
   (C) removal of electrons from chlorophyll molecules
   (D) ATP synthesis

8. To synthesize one glucose molecule, the Calvin cycle uses _____ molecules of CO_2, _____ molecules of ATP, and _____ molecules of NADPH.

Level 3: Synthesis/Evaluation

9. **SCIENCE, TECHNOLOGY, AND SOCIETY**
   Scientific evidence indicates that the CO_2 added to the air by the burning of wood and fossil fuels is contributing to global warming, a rise in global temperature. Tropical rain forests are estimated to be responsible for approximately 20% of global photosynthesis, yet the consumption of large amounts of CO_2 by living trees is thought to make little or no *net* contribution to reduction of global warming. Explain why might this be the case. (*Hint*: What processes in both living and dead trees produce CO_2?)

10. **SCIENTIFIC INQUIRY**
    DRAW IT The following diagram represents an experiment with isolated thylakoids. The thylakoids were first made acidic by soaking them in a solution at pH 4. After the thylakoid space reached pH 4, the thylakoids were transferred to a basic solution at pH 8. The thylakoids then made ATP in the dark. (See Concept 2.5 to review pH.)

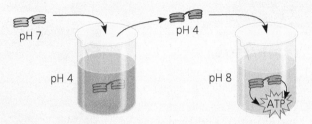

Draw an enlargement of part of the thylakoid membrane in the beaker with the solution at pH 8. Draw ATP synthase. Label the areas of high H^+ concentration and low H^+ concentration. Show the direction protons flow through the enzyme, and show the reaction where ATP is synthesized. Would ATP end up in the thylakoid or outside of it? Explain why the thylakoids in the experiment were able to make ATP in the dark.

11. **FOCUS ON EVOLUTION**
    Consider the endosymbiont theory (see Figure 4.16) and the fact that chloroplasts contain DNA molecules and ribosomes (see Figure 4.18). Chloroplasts, plant cell nuclei, and photosynthetic prokaryotes all have genes that code for ribosomal RNAs. Would you expect the DNA sequences of ribosomal RNA genes in chloroplasts to be more similar to those in plant cell nuclei or currently living photosynthetic prokaryotes? Explain. If sequencing studies show that your hypothesis is correct, what does this tell us about the evolution of photosynthesis?

12. **FOCUS ON EVOLUTION**
    Photorespiration can decrease soybeans' photosynthetic output by about 50%. Would you expect this figure to be higher or lower in wild relatives of soybeans? Explain.

13. **FOCUS ON ENERGY AND MATTER**
    Life is solar powered. Almost all the producers of the biosphere depend on energy from the sun to produce the organic molecules that supply the energy and carbon skeletons needed for life. In a short essay (100–150 words), describe how the process of photosynthesis in the chloroplasts of plants transforms the energy of sunlight into the chemical energy of sugar molecules.

14. **SYNTHESIZE YOUR KNOWLEDGE**

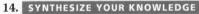

"Watermelon snow" in Antarctica is caused by a species of photosynthetic green algae that thrives in subzero temperatures (*Chlamydomonas nivalis*). These algae are also found in high-altitude year-round snowfields. In both locations, UV light levels tend to be high. Based on what you learned in this chapter, propose an explanation for why this photosynthetic alga appears reddish-pink.

For selected answers, see Appendix A.

KEY CONCEPTS

9.1 Most cell division results in genetically identical daughter cells

9.2 The mitotic phase alternates with interphase in the cell cycle

9.3 The eukaryotic cell cycle is regulated by a molecular control system

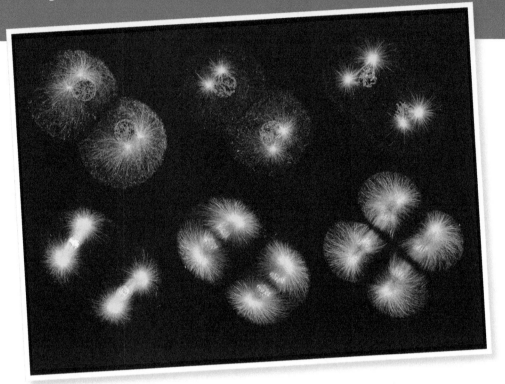

▲ **Figure 9.1** How do dividing cells distribute chromosomes to daughter cells?

The Key Roles of Cell Division

The ability of organisms to produce more of their own kind is the one characteristic that best distinguishes living things from nonliving matter. This unique capacity to procreate, like all biological functions, has a cellular basis. In 1855, Rudolf Virchow, a German physician, put it this way: "Where a cell exists, there must have been a preexisting cell, just as the animal arises only from an animal and the plant only from a plant." He summarized this concept with the Latin axiom "*Omnis cellula e cellula*," meaning "Every cell from a cell." The continuity of life is based on the reproduction of cells, or **cell division**. The series of confocal fluorescence micrographs in **Figure 9.1**, starting at the upper left and reading across both rows left to right, follows the events of cell division as the cells of a two-celled embryo become four.

Cell division plays several important roles in life. The division of one prokaryotic cell reproduces an entire organism. The same is true of a unicellular eukaryote **(Figure 9.2a)**. Cell division also enables multicellular eukaryotes to develop from a single cell, like the fertilized egg that gave rise to the two-celled embryo in **Figure 9.2b**. And after such an organism is fully grown, cell division continues to function in renewal and repair, replacing cells that die from accidents or normal wear and tear. For example, dividing cells in your bone marrow continuously make new blood cells **(Figure 9.2c)**.

The cell division process is an integral part of the **cell cycle**, the life of a cell from the time it is first formed during division of a parent cell until its own division into two daughter cells. (Biologists use the words *daughter* or *sister* in relation to cells, but this is not meant to imply gender.) Passing identical genetic material to cellular offspring is a crucial function of cell division. In this chapter, you'll learn how this process occurs. After studying the mechanics of cell division in eukaryotes and bacteria, you'll learn about the molecular control system that regulates progress through the eukaryotic cell cycle and what happens when the control system malfunctions. Because a breakdown in cell cycle control plays a major role in cancer development, this aspect of cell biology is an active area of research.

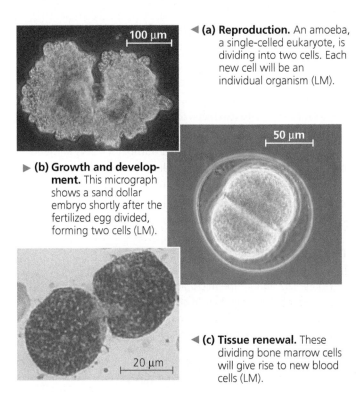

◀ **(a) Reproduction.** An amoeba, a single-celled eukaryote, is dividing into two cells. Each new cell will be an individual organism (LM).

▶ **(b) Growth and development.** This micrograph shows a sand dollar embryo shortly after the fertilized egg divided, forming two cells (LM).

◀ **(c) Tissue renewal.** These dividing bone marrow cells will give rise to new blood cells (LM).

▲ **Figure 9.2 The functions of cell division.**

Most cell division results in genetically identical daughter cells

The reproduction of a cell, with all its complexity, cannot occur by a mere pinching in half; a cell is not like a soap bubble that simply enlarges and splits in two. In both prokaryotes and eukaryotes, most cell division involves the distribution of identical genetic material—DNA—to two daughter cells. (The exception is meiosis, the special type of eukaryotic cell division that can produce sperm and eggs.) What is most remarkable about cell division is the fidelity with which the DNA is passed from one generation of cells to the next. A dividing cell replicates its DNA, allocates the two copies to opposite ends of the cell, and only then splits into daughter cells.

Cellular Organization of the Genetic Material

A cell's endowment of DNA, its genetic information, is called its **genome**. Although a prokaryotic genome is often a single DNA molecule, eukaryotic genomes usually consist of a number of DNA molecules. The overall length of DNA in a eukaryotic cell is enormous. A typical human cell, for example, has about 2 m of DNA—a length about 250,000 times greater than the cell's diameter. Before the cell can divide to form genetically identical daughter cells, all of this DNA must be copied, or replicated, and then the two copies must be separated so that each daughter cell ends up with a complete genome.

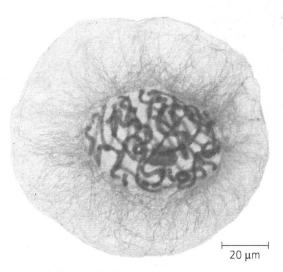

▲ **Figure 9.3 Eukaryotic chromosomes.** Chromosomes (stained purple) are visible within the nucleus of this cell from an African blood lily. The thinner red threads in the surrounding cytoplasm are the cytoskeleton. The cell is preparing to divide (LM).

The replication and distribution of so much DNA is manageable because the DNA molecules are packaged into structures called **chromosomes** (from the Greek *chroma*, color, and *soma*, body), so named because they take up certain dyes used in microscopy **(Figure 9.3)**. Each eukaryotic chromosome consists of one very long, linear DNA molecule associated with many proteins (see Figure 4.8). The DNA molecule carries several hundred to a few thousand genes, the units of information that specify an organism's inherited traits. The associated proteins maintain the structure of the chromosome and help control the activity of the genes. Together, the entire complex of DNA and proteins that is the building material of chromosomes is referred to as **chromatin**. As you will soon see, the chromatin of a chromosome varies in its degree of condensation during the process of cell division.

Every eukaryotic species has a characteristic number of chromosomes in each cell's nucleus. For example, the nuclei of human **somatic cells** (all body cells except the reproductive cells) each contain 46 chromosomes, made up of two sets of 23, one set inherited from each parent. Reproductive cells, or **gametes**—sperm and eggs—have half as many chromosomes as somatic cells, or one set of 23 chromosomes in humans. The number of chromosomes in somatic cells varies widely among species: 18 in cabbage plants, 48 in chimpanzees, 56 in elephants, 90 in hedgehogs, and 148 in one species of alga. We'll now consider how these chromosomes behave during cell division.

Distribution of Chromosomes During Eukaryotic Cell Division

When a cell is not dividing, and even as it replicates its DNA in preparation for cell division, each chromosome is in the form of a long, thin chromatin fiber. After DNA replication, however, the chromosomes condense as a part of cell division: Each chromatin fiber becomes densely coiled and folded,

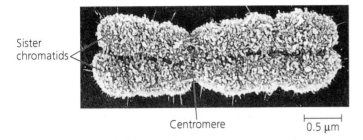

Sister chromatids

Centromere

0.5 µm

▲ **Figure 9.4 A highly condensed, duplicated human chromosome (SEM).**

DRAW IT *Circle one sister chromatid of the chromosome in this micrograph.*

making the chromosomes much shorter and so thick that we can see them with a light microscope.

Each duplicated chromosome has two **sister chromatids**, which are joined copies of the original chromosome **(Figure 9.4)**. The two chromatids, each containing an identical DNA molecule, are initially attached all along their lengths by protein complexes called *cohesins*; this attachment is known as *sister chromatid cohesion*. Each sister chromatid has a **centromere**, a region of the chromosomal DNA where the chromatid is attached most closely to its sister chromatid. This attachment is mediated by proteins bound to the centromeric DNA sequences and gives the condensed, duplicated chromosome a narrow "waist." The part of a chromatid to either side of the centromere is referred to as an *arm* of the chromatid. (An uncondensed, unduplicated chromosome has a single centromere and two arms.)

Later in the cell division process, the two sister chromatids of each duplicated chromosome separate and move into two new nuclei, one forming at each end of the cell. Once the sister chromatids separate, they are no longer called sister chromatids but are considered individual chromosomes; this step essentially doubles the number of chromosomes in the cell. Thus, each new nucleus receives a collection of chromosomes identical to that of the parent cell **(Figure 9.5)**. **Mitosis**, the division of the genetic material in the nucleus, is usually followed immediately by **cytokinesis**, the division of the cytoplasm. One cell has become two, each the genetic equivalent of the parent cell.

From a fertilized egg, mitosis and cytokinesis produced the 200 trillion somatic cells that now make up your body, and the same processes continue to generate new cells to replace dead and damaged ones. In contrast,

you produce gametes—eggs or sperm—by a variation of cell division called *meiosis*, which yields daughter cells with only one set of chromosomes, half as many chromosomes as the parent cell. Meiosis in humans occurs only in special cells in the ovaries or testes (the gonads). Generating gametes, meiosis reduces the chromosome number from 46 (two sets) to 23 (one set). Fertilization fuses two gametes together and returns the chromosome number to 46 (two sets). Mitosis then conserves that number in every somatic cell nucleus of the new human individual. In Chapter 10, we'll examine the role of meiosis in reproduction and inheritance in more detail. In the remainder of this chapter, we focus on mitosis and the rest of the cell cycle in eukaryotes.

CONCEPT CHECK 9.1

1. How many chromosomes are drawn in each part of Figure 9.5? (Ignore the micrograph in part 2.)

2. **WHAT IF?** A chicken has 78 chromosomes in its somatic cells. How many chromosomes did the chicken inherit from each parent? How many chromosomes are in each of the chicken's gametes? How many chromosomes will be in each somatic cell of the chicken's offspring?

For suggested answers, see Appendix A.

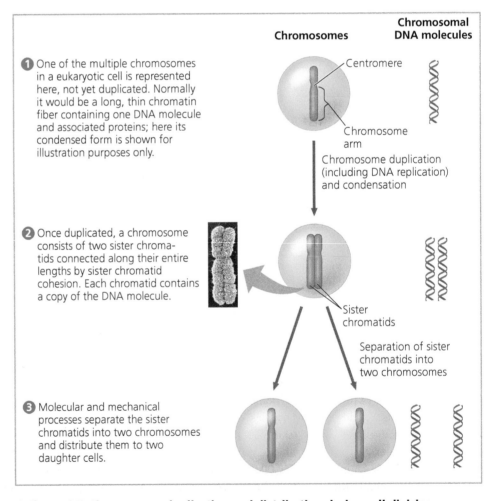

① One of the multiple chromosomes in a eukaryotic cell is represented here, not yet duplicated. Normally it would be a long, thin chromatin fiber containing one DNA molecule and associated proteins; here its condensed form is shown for illustration purposes only.

② Once duplicated, a chromosome consists of two sister chromatids connected along their entire lengths by sister chromatid cohesion. Each chromatid contains a copy of the DNA molecule.

③ Molecular and mechanical processes separate the sister chromatids into two chromosomes and distribute them to two daughter cells.

Chromosomes

Chromosomal DNA molecules

Centromere

Chromosome arm

Chromosome duplication (including DNA replication) and condensation

Sister chromatids

Separation of sister chromatids into two chromosomes

▲ **Figure 9.5 Chromosome duplication and distribution during cell division.**

? *How many chromatid arms does the chromosome in step ② have? Identify the point in the figure where one chromosome becomes two.*

CONCEPT 9.2

The mitotic phase alternates with interphase in the cell cycle

In 1882, a German anatomist named Walther Flemming developed dyes that allowed him to observe, for the first time, the behavior of chromosomes during mitosis and cytokinesis. (In fact, Flemming coined the terms *mitosis* and *chromatin*.) It appeared to Flemming that during the period between one cell division and the next, the cell was simply growing larger. But we now know that many critical events occur during this stage in the life of a cell.

Phases of the Cell Cycle

Mitosis is just one part of the cell cycle **(Figure 9.6)**. In fact, the **mitotic (M) phase**, which includes both mitosis and cytokinesis, is usually the shortest part of the cell cycle. The mitotic phase alternates with a much longer stage called **interphase**, which often accounts for about 90% of the cycle. Interphase can be divided into subphases: the **G_1 phase** ("first gap"), the **S phase** ("synthesis"), and the **G_2 phase** ("second gap"). The G phases were misnamed as "gaps" when they were first observed because the cells appeared inactive, but we now know that intense metabolic activity and growth occur throughout interphase. During all three subphases of interphase, in fact, a cell grows by producing proteins and cytoplasmic organelles such as mitochondria and endoplasmic reticulum. Duplication of the chromosomes, crucial for eventual division of the cell, occurs entirely during the S phase. (We will describe synthesis of DNA in Concept 13.2.) Thus, a cell grows (G_1), continues to grow as it copies its chromosomes (S), grows more as it completes preparations for cell division (G_2), and divides (M). The daughter cells may then repeat the cycle.

A particular human cell might undergo one division in 24 hours. Of this time, the M phase would occupy less than 1 hour, while the S phase might occupy about 10–12 hours, or about half the cycle. The rest of the time would be apportioned between the G_1 and G_2 phases. The G_2 phase usually takes 4–6 hours; in our example, G_1 would occupy about 5–6 hours. G_1 is the most variable in length in different types of cells. Some cells in a multicellular organism divide very infrequently or not at all. These cells spend their time in G_1 (or a related phase called G_0) doing their job in the organism—a nerve cell carries impulses, for example.

Mitosis is conventionally broken down into five stages: **prophase**, **prometaphase**, **metaphase**, **anaphase**, and **telophase**. Overlapping with the latter stages of mitosis, cytokinesis completes the mitotic phase. **Figure 9.7** describes these stages in an animal cell. Study this figure thoroughly before progressing to the next two sections, which examine mitosis and cytokinesis more closely.

The Mitotic Spindle: *A Closer Look*

Many of the events of mitosis depend on the **mitotic spindle**, which begins to form in the cytoplasm during prophase. This structure consists of fibers made of microtubules and associated proteins. While the mitotic spindle assembles, the other microtubules of the cytoskeleton partially disassemble, providing the material used to construct the spindle. The spindle microtubules elongate (polymerize) by incorporating more subunits of the protein tubulin (see Table 4.1) and shorten (depolymerize) by losing subunits.

In animal cells, the assembly of spindle microtubules starts at the **centrosome**, a subcellular region containing material that functions throughout the cell cycle to organize the cell's microtubules. (It is also a type of *microtubule-organizing center*.) A pair of centrioles is located at the center of the centrosome, but they are not essential for cell division: If the centrioles are destroyed with a laser microbeam, a spindle nevertheless forms during mitosis. In fact, centrioles are not even present in plant cells, which do form mitotic spindles.

During interphase in animal cells, the single centrosome duplicates, forming two centrosomes, which remain together near the nucleus (see Figure 9.7). The two centrosomes move apart during prophase and prometaphase of mitosis as spindle microtubules grow out from them. By the end of prometaphase, the two centrosomes, one at each pole of the spindle, are at opposite ends of the cell. An **aster**, a radial array of short microtubules, extends from each centrosome. The spindle includes the centrosomes, the spindle microtubules, and the asters.

Each of the two sister chromatids of a duplicated chromosome has a **kinetochore**, a structure made up of proteins that have assembled on specific sections of chromosomal DNA at each centromere. The chromosome's two kinetochores face in opposite directions. During prometaphase, some of the spindle microtubules attach to the kinetochores; these are called kinetochore microtubules. (The number of microtubules attached to a kinetochore varies among species, from one microtubule in yeast cells to 40 or so in some mammalian cells.)

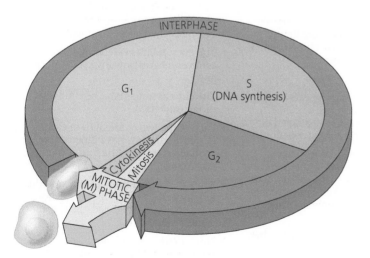

▲ **Figure 9.6 The cell cycle.** In a dividing cell, the mitotic (M) phase alternates with interphase, a growth period. The first part of interphase (G_1) is followed by the S phase, when the chromosomes duplicate; G_2 is the last part of interphase. In the M phase, mitosis distributes the daughter chromosomes to daughter nuclei, and cytokinesis divides the cytoplasm, producing two daughter cells.

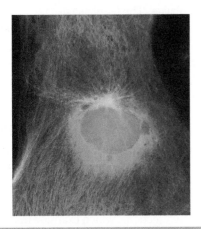

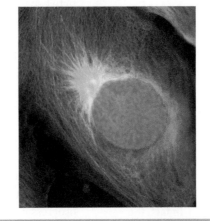

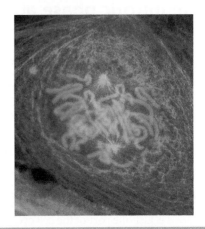

G₂ of Interphase

Prophase

Prometaphase

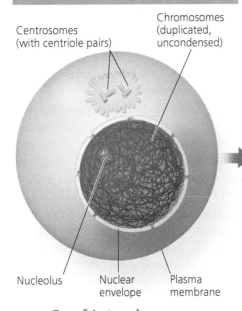

Centrosomes (with centriole pairs)

Chromosomes (duplicated, uncondensed)

Nucleolus   Nuclear envelope   Plasma membrane

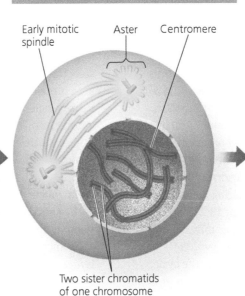

Early mitotic spindle   Aster   Centromere

Two sister chromatids of one chromosome

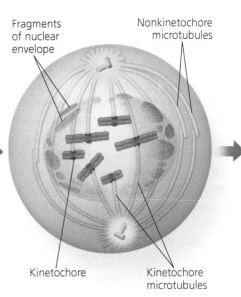

Fragments of nuclear envelope   Nonkinetochore microtubules

Kinetochore   Kinetochore microtubules

G₂ of Interphase

- A nuclear envelope encloses the nucleus.
- The nucleus contains one or more nucleoli (singular, *nucleolus*).
- Two centrosomes have formed by duplication of a single centrosome. Centrosomes are regions in animal cells that organize the microtubules of the spindle. Each centrosome contains two centrioles.
- Chromosomes, duplicated during S phase, cannot be seen individually because they have not yet condensed.

The fluorescence micrographs show dividing lung cells from a newt; this species has 22 chromosomes. Chromosomes appear blue, microtubules green, and intermediate filaments red. For simplicity, the drawings show only 6 chromosomes.

Prophase

- The chromatin fibers become more tightly coiled, condensing into discrete chromosomes observable with a light microscope.
- The nucleoli disappear.
- Each duplicated chromosome appears as two identical sister chromatids joined at their centromeres and, in some species, all along their arms by cohesins (sister chromatid cohesion).
- The mitotic spindle (named for its shape) begins to form. It is composed of the centrosomes and the microtubules that extend from them. The radial arrays of shorter microtubules that extend from the centrosomes are called asters ("stars").
- The centrosomes move away from each other, propelled partly by the lengthening microtubules between them.

Prometaphase

- The nuclear envelope fragments.
- The microtubules extending from each centrosome can now invade the nuclear area.
- The chromosomes have become even more condensed.
- Each of the two chromatids of each chromosome now has a kinetochore, a specialized protein structure at the centromere.
- Some of the microtubules attach to the kinetochores, becoming "kinetochore microtubules," which jerk the chromosomes back and forth.
- Nonkinetochore microtubules interact with those from the opposite pole of the spindle.

[?] *How many molecules of DNA are in the prometaphase drawing? How many molecules per chromosome? How many double helices are there per chromosome? Per chromatid?*

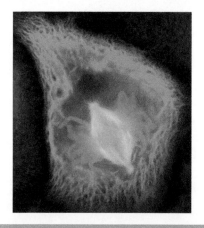
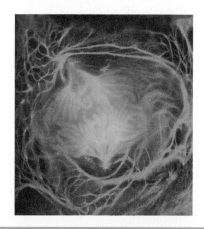
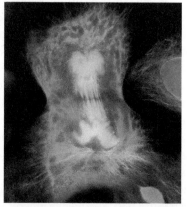

| **Metaphase** | **Anaphase** | **Telophase and Cytokinesis** |

10 µm

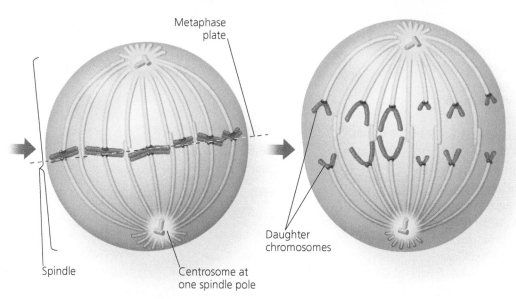
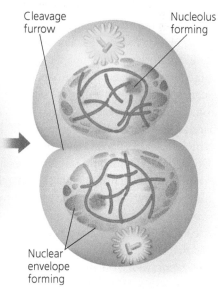

Metaphase plate

Spindle

Centrosome at one spindle pole

Daughter chromosomes

Cleavage furrow

Nucleolus forming

Nuclear envelope forming

Metaphase

- The centrosomes are now at opposite poles of the cell.

- The chromosomes have all arrived at the *metaphase plate*, a plane that is equidistant between the spindle's two poles. The chromosomes' centromeres lie at the metaphase plate.

- For each chromosome, the kinetochores of the sister chromatids are attached to kinetochore microtubules coming from opposite poles.

Anaphase

- Anaphase is the shortest stage of mitosis, often lasting only a few minutes.

- Anaphase begins when the cohesin proteins are cleaved. This allows the two sister chromatids of each pair to part suddenly. Each chromatid thus becomes a full-fledged chromosome.

- The two liberated daughter chromosomes begin moving toward opposite ends of the cell as their kinetochore microtubules shorten. Because these microtubules are attached at the centromere region, the chromosomes move centromere first (at about 1 µm/min).

- The cell elongates as the nonkinetochore microtubules lengthen.

- By the end of anaphase, the two ends of the cell have equivalent—and complete—collections of chromosomes.

Telophase

- Two daughter nuclei form in the cell. Nuclear envelopes arise from the fragments of the parent cell's nuclear envelope and other portions of the endomembrane system.

- Nucleoli reappear.

- The chromosomes become less condensed.

- Any remaining spindle microtubules are depolymerized.

- Mitosis, the division of one nucleus into two genetically identical nuclei, is now complete.

Cytokinesis

- The division of the cytoplasm is usually well under way by late telophase, so the two daughter cells appear shortly after the end of mitosis.

- In animal cells, cytokinesis involves the formation of a cleavage furrow, which pinches the cell in two.

ANIMATION Visit the Study Area in **MasteringBiology** for the BioFlix® 3-D Animation on Mitosis.

The kinetochore acts as a coupling device that attaches the motor of the spindle to the cargo that it moves—the chromosome. When one of a chromosome's kinetochores is "captured" by microtubules, the chromosome begins to move toward the pole from which those microtubules extend. However, this movement is checked as soon as microtubules from the opposite pole attach to the kinetochore on the other chromatid. What happens next is like a tug-of-war that ends in a draw. The chromosome moves first in one direction and then in the other, back and forth, finally settling midway between the two ends of the cell. At metaphase, the centromeres of all the duplicated chromosomes are on a plane midway between the spindle's two poles. This plane is called the **metaphase plate**, which is an imaginary plate rather than an actual cellular structure **(Figure 9.8)**. Meanwhile, microtubules that do not attach to kinetochores have been elongating, and by metaphase they overlap and interact with other nonkinetochore microtubules from the opposite pole of the spindle. By metaphase, the microtubules of the asters have also grown and are in contact with the plasma membrane. The spindle is now complete.

The structure of the completed spindle correlates well with its function during anaphase. Anaphase begins suddenly when the cohesins holding together the sister chromatids of each chromosome are cleaved by an enzyme called *separase*. Once separated, the chromatids become full-fledged chromosomes that move toward opposite ends of the cell.

How do the kinetochore microtubules function in this poleward movement of chromosomes? Apparently, two mechanisms are in play, both involving motor proteins. (To review how motor proteins move an object along a microtubule, see Figure 4.21.) Results of a cleverly designed experiment suggested that motor proteins on the kinetochores "walk" the chromosomes along the microtubules, which depolymerize at their kinetochore ends after the motor proteins have passed **(Figure 9.9)**. (This is referred to as the "Pac-man" mechanism because of its resemblance to the arcade game character that moves by eating all the dots in its path.) However, other researchers, working with different cell types or cells from other species, have shown that chromosomes are "reeled in" by motor proteins at the spindle poles and that the microtubules depolymerize after they pass by these motor proteins. The general consensus now is that both mechanisms are used and that their relative contributions vary among cell types.

In a dividing animal cell, the nonkinetochore microtubules are responsible for elongating the whole cell during anaphase. Nonkinetochore microtubules from opposite poles overlap each other extensively during metaphase (see Figure 9.8). During anaphase, the region of overlap is reduced as motor proteins attached to the microtubules walk them away from one another, using energy from ATP. As the microtubules push apart from each other, their spindle poles are pushed apart, elongating the cell. At the same time, the microtubules lengthen somewhat by the addition of tubulin subunits to their overlapping ends. As a result, the microtubules continue to overlap.

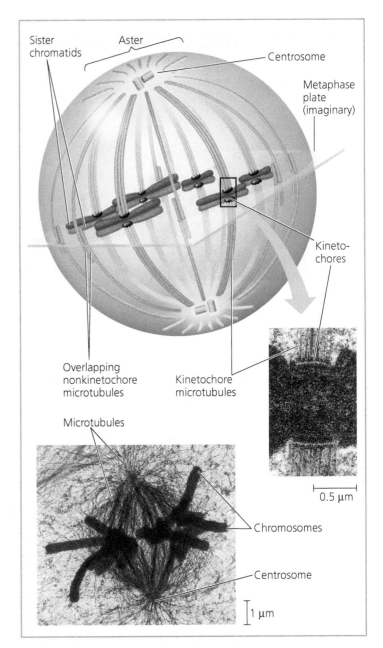

▲ **Figure 9.8 The mitotic spindle at metaphase.** The kinetochores of each chromosome's two sister chromatids face in opposite directions. Here, each kinetochore is attached to a cluster of kinetochore microtubules extending from the nearest centrosome. Nonkinetochore microtubules overlap at the metaphase plate (TEMs).

DRAW IT *On the lower micrograph, draw a line indicating the position of the metaphase plate. Circle an aster. Draw arrows indicating the directions of chromosome movement once anaphase begins.*

At the end of anaphase, duplicate groups of chromosomes have arrived at opposite ends of the elongated parent cell. Nuclei re-form during telophase. Cytokinesis generally begins during anaphase or telophase, and the spindle eventually disassembles by depolymerization of microtubules.

Cytokinesis: *A Closer Look*

In animal cells, cytokinesis occurs by a process known as **cleavage**. The first sign of cleavage is the appearance of a **cleavage furrow**, a shallow groove in the cell surface near the old metaphase plate **(Figure 9.10a)**. On the cytoplasmic side

At which end do kinetochore microtubules shorten during anaphase?

Experiment Gary Borisy and colleagues at the University of Wisconsin wanted to determine whether kinetochore microtubules depolymerize at the kinetochore end or the pole end as chromosomes move toward the poles during mitosis. First they labeled the microtubules of a pig kidney cell in early anaphase with a yellow fluorescent dye. (Nonkinetochore microtubules are not shown.)

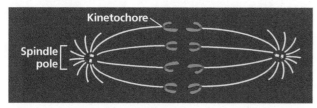

Then they marked a region of the kinetochore microtubules between one spindle pole and the chromosomes by using a laser to eliminate the fluorescence from that region, while leaving the microtubules intact (see below). As anaphase proceeded, they monitored the changes in microtubule length on either side of the mark.

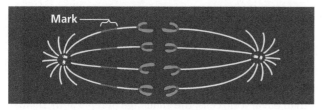

Results As the chromosomes moved poleward, the microtubule segments on the kinetochore side of the mark shortened, while those on the spindle pole side stayed the same length.

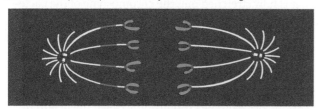

Conclusion During anaphase in this cell type, chromosome movement is correlated with kinetochore microtubules shortening at their kinetochore ends and not at their spindle pole ends. This experiment supports the hypothesis that during anaphase, a chromosome is walked along a microtubule as the microtubule depolymerizes at its kinetochore end, releasing tubulin subunits.

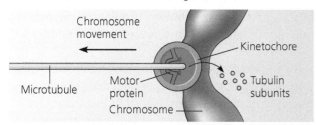

Data from G. J. Gorbsky, P. J. Sammak, and G. G. Borisy, Chromosomes move poleward in anaphase along stationary microtubules that coordinately disassemble from their kinetochore ends, *Journal of Cell Biology* 104:9–18 (1987).

WHAT IF? If this experiment had been done on a cell type in which "reeling in" at the poles was the main cause of chromosome movement, how would the mark have moved relative to the poles? How would the microtubule segment lengths have changed?

(a) Cleavage of an animal cell (SEM)

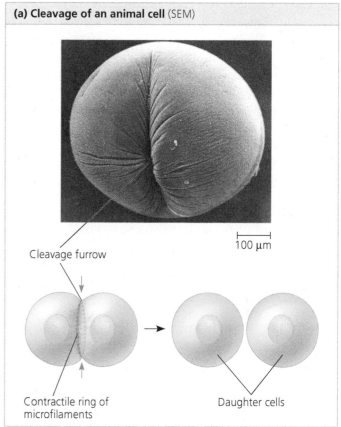

100 μm

Cleavage furrow

Contractile ring of microfilaments

Daughter cells

(b) Cell plate formation in a plant cell (TEM)

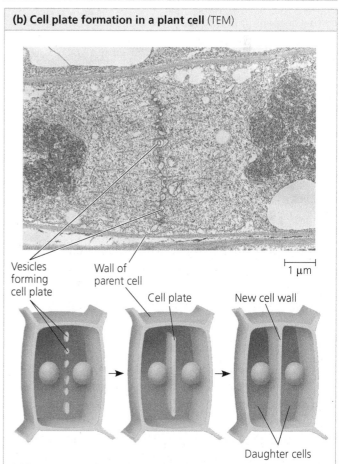

1 μm

Vesicles forming cell plate

Wall of parent cell

Cell plate

New cell wall

Daughter cells

Nucleus
Nucleolus
Chromosomes condensing
Chromosomes
Cell plate
10 μm

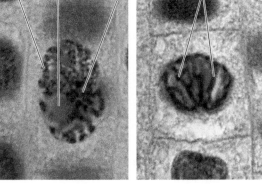
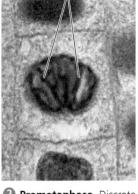

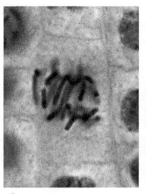
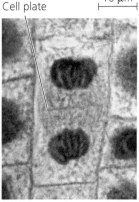

1 Prophase. The chromosomes are condensing and the nucleolus is beginning to disappear. Although not yet visible in the micrograph, the mitotic spindle is starting to form.

2 Prometaphase. Discrete chromosomes are now visible; each consists of two aligned, identical sister chromatids. Later in prometaphase, the nuclear envelope will fragment.

3 Metaphase. The spindle is complete, and the chromosomes, attached to microtubules at their kinetochores, are all at the metaphase plate.

4 Anaphase. The chromatids of each chromosome have separated, and the daughter chromosomes are moving to the ends of the cell as their kinetochore microtubules shorten.

5 Telophase. Daughter nuclei are forming. Meanwhile, cytokinesis has started: The cell plate, which will divide the cytoplasm in two, is growing toward the perimeter of the parent cell.

▲ **Figure 9.11 Mitosis in a plant cell.** These light micrographs show mitosis in cells of an onion root.

of the furrow is a contractile ring of actin microfilaments associated with molecules of the protein myosin. The actin microfilaments interact with the myosin molecules, causing the ring to contract. The contraction of the dividing cell's ring of microfilaments is like the pulling of a drawstring. The cleavage furrow deepens until the parent cell is pinched in two, producing two completely separated cells, each with its own nucleus and its own share of cytosol, organelles, and other subcellular structures.

Cytokinesis in plant cells, which have cell walls, is markedly different. There is no cleavage furrow. Instead, during telophase, vesicles derived from the Golgi apparatus move along microtubules to the middle of the cell, where they coalesce, producing a **cell plate (Figure 9.10b)**. Cell wall materials carried in the vesicles collect inside the cell plate as it grows. The cell plate enlarges until its surrounding membrane fuses with the plasma membrane along the perimeter of the cell. Two daughter cells result, each with its own plasma membrane. Meanwhile, a new cell wall arising from the contents of the cell plate has formed between the daughter cells.

Figure 9.11 is a series of micrographs of a dividing plant cell. Examining this figure will help you review mitosis and cytokinesis.

Binary Fission in Bacteria

Prokaryotes (bacteria and archaea) undergo a type of reproduction in which the cell grows to roughly double its size and then divides to form two cells. The term **binary fission**, meaning "division in half," refers to this process and to the asexual reproduction of single-celled eukaryotes, such as the amoeba in Figure 9.2a. However, the process in eukaryotes involves mitosis, while that in prokaryotes does not.

In bacteria, most genes are carried on a single bacterial chromosome that consists of a circular DNA molecule and associated proteins. Although bacteria are smaller and simpler than eukaryotic cells, the challenge of replicating their genomes in an orderly fashion and distributing the copies equally to two daughter cells is still formidable. For example, when it is fully stretched out, the chromosome of the bacterium *Escherichia coli* is about 500 times as long as the cell. For such a long chromosome to fit within the cell, it must be highly coiled and folded.

In *E. coli*, the process of cell division is initiated when the DNA of the bacterial chromosome begins to replicate at a specific place on the chromosome called the **origin of replication**, producing two origins. As the chromosome continues to replicate, one origin moves rapidly toward the opposite end of the cell **(Figure 9.12)**. While the chromosome is replicating, the cell elongates. When replication is complete and the bacterium has reached about twice its initial size, its plasma membrane pinches inward, dividing the parent *E. coli* cell into two daughter cells. In this way, each cell inherits a complete genome.

Using the techniques of modern DNA technology to tag the origins of replication with molecules that glow green in fluorescence microscopy (see Figure 4.3), researchers have directly observed the movement of bacterial chromosomes. This movement is reminiscent of the poleward movements of the centromere regions of eukaryotic chromosomes during anaphase of mitosis, but bacteria don't have visible mitotic spindles or even microtubules. In most bacterial species studied, the two origins of replication end up at opposite ends of the cell or in some other very specific location, possibly anchored there by one or more proteins. How bacterial

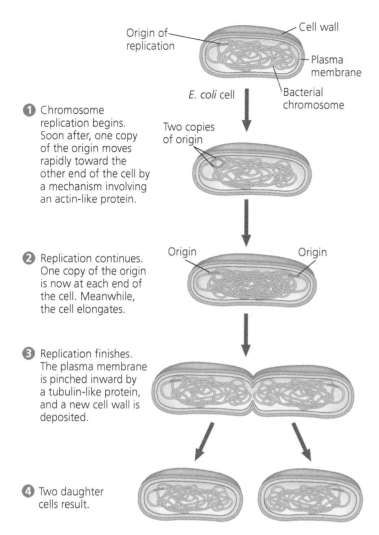

① Chromosome replication begins. Soon after, one copy of the origin moves rapidly toward the other end of the cell by a mechanism involving an actin-like protein.

Origin of replication
Cell wall
Plasma membrane
Bacterial chromosome
E. coli cell

Two copies of origin

② Replication continues. One copy of the origin is now at each end of the cell. Meanwhile, the cell elongates.

Origin
Origin

③ Replication finishes. The plasma membrane is pinched inward by a tubulin-like protein, and a new cell wall is deposited.

④ Two daughter cells result.

▲ Figure 9.12 **Bacterial cell division by binary fission.** The bacterium *E. coli*, shown here, has a single, circular chromosome.

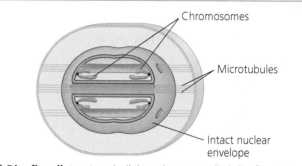
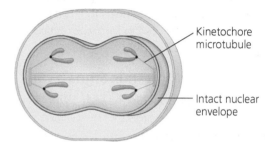

Chromosomes
Microtubules
Intact nuclear envelope

(a) Dinoflagellates. In unicellular eukaryotes called dinoflagellates, the chromosomes attach to the nuclear envelope, which remains intact during cell division. Microtubules pass through the nucleus inside cytoplasmic tunnels, reinforcing the spatial orientation of the nucleus, which then divides in a process reminiscent of bacterial binary fission.

Kinetochore microtubule
Intact nuclear envelope

(b) Diatoms and some yeasts. In two other groups of unicellular eukaryotes, diatoms and some yeasts, the nuclear envelope also remains intact during cell division. In these organisms, the microtubules form a spindle *within* the nucleus. Microtubules separate the chromosomes, and the nucleus splits into two daughter nuclei.

▲ Figure 9.13 **Mechanisms of cell division.** Some unicellular eukaryotes existing today have mechanisms of cell division that may resemble intermediate steps in the evolution of mitosis.

chromosomes move and how their specific location is established and maintained are active areas of research. Several proteins have been identified that play important roles. Polymerization of one protein resembling eukaryotic actin apparently functions in bacterial chromosome movement during cell division, and another protein that is related to tubulin helps pinch the plasma membrane inward, separating the two bacterial daughter cells.

The Evolution of Mitosis

EVOLUTION Given that prokaryotes preceded eukaryotes on Earth by more than a billion years, we might hypothesize that mitosis evolved from simpler prokaryotic mechanisms of cell reproduction. The fact that some of the proteins involved in bacterial binary fission are related to eukaryotic proteins that function in mitosis supports that hypothesis.

As eukaryotes with nuclear envelopes and larger genomes evolved, the ancestral process of binary fission, seen today in bacteria, somehow gave rise to mitosis. Variations on cell division exist in different groups. These variant processes may be similar to mechanisms used by ancestral species and thus

may resemble steps in the evolution of mitosis from a binary fission-like process carried out by very early bacteria. Possible intermediate stages are suggested by two unusual types of nuclear division found today in certain unicellular eukaryotes—dinoflagellates, diatoms, and some yeasts **(Figure 9.13)**. These are thought to be cases where ancestral mechanisms have remained relatively unchanged over evolutionary time. In both types, the nuclear envelope remains intact, in contrast to what happens in most eukaryotic cells.

CONCEPT CHECK 9.2

1. How many chromosomes are shown in the drawing in Figure 9.8? Are they duplicated? How many chromatids are shown?
2. Compare cytokinesis in animal cells and plant cells.
3. During which stages of the cell cycle does a chromosome consist of two identical chromatids?
4. Compare the roles of tubulin and actin during eukaryotic cell division with the roles of tubulin-like and actin-like proteins during bacterial binary fission.

For suggested answers, see Appendix A.

CONCEPT 9.3

The eukaryotic cell cycle is regulated by a molecular control system

The timing and rate of cell division in different parts of a plant or animal are crucial to normal growth, development, and maintenance. The frequency of cell division varies with the type of cell. For example, human skin cells divide frequently throughout life, whereas liver cells maintain the ability to divide but keep it in reserve until an appropriate need arises—say, to repair a wound. Some of the most specialized cells, such as fully formed nerve cells and muscle cells, do not divide at all in a mature human. These cell cycle differences result from regulation at the molecular level. The mechanisms of this regulation are of great interest, not only to understand the life cycles of normal cells but also to learn how cancer cells manage to escape the usual controls.

Evidence for Cytoplasmic Signals

What controls the cell cycle? In the early 1970s, a variety of experiments led to the hypothesis that the cell cycle is driven by specific signaling molecules present in the cytoplasm. Some of the first strong evidence for this hypothesis came from experiments with mammalian cells grown in culture (**Figure 9.14**). In these experiments, two cells in different phases of the cell cycle were fused to form a single cell with two nuclei. If one of the original cells was in the S phase and the other was in G_1, the G_1 nucleus immediately entered the S phase, as though stimulated by signaling molecules present in the cytoplasm of the first cell. Similarly, if a cell undergoing mitosis (M phase) was fused with another cell in any stage of its cell cycle, even G_1, the second nucleus immediately entered mitosis, with condensation of the chromatin and formation of a mitotic spindle.

Checkpoints of the Cell Cycle Control System

The experiment shown in Figure 9.14 and other experiments on animal cells and yeasts demonstrated that the sequential events of the cell cycle are directed by a distinct **cell cycle control system**, a cyclically operating set of molecules in the cell that both triggers and coordinates key events in the cell cycle. The cell cycle control system has been compared to the control device of a washing machine (**Figure 9.15**). Like the washer's timing device, the cell cycle control system proceeds on its own, according to a built-in clock. However, just as a washer's cycle is subject to both internal control (such as the sensor that detects when the tub is filled with water) and external adjustment (such as starting the machine), the cell cycle is regulated at certain checkpoints by both internal and external signals.

A **checkpoint** in the cell cycle is a control point where stop and go-ahead signals can regulate the cycle. (The signals are transmitted within the cell by the kinds of signal transduction pathways discussed in Concept 5.6.) Animal cells generally have built-in stop signals that halt the cell cycle at checkpoints

Do molecular signals in the cytoplasm regulate the cell cycle?

Experiment Researchers at the University of Colorado wondered whether a cell's progression through the cell cycle is controlled by cytoplasmic molecules. They induced cultured mammalian cells at different phases of the cell cycle to fuse. Two experiments are shown.

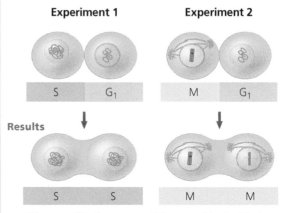

When a cell in the S phase was fused with a cell in G_1, the G_1 nucleus immediately entered the S phase—DNA was synthesized.

When a cell in the M phase was fused with a cell in G_1, the G_1 nucleus immediately began mitosis—a spindle formed and the chromosomes condensed, even though the chromosomes had not been duplicated.

Conclusion The results of fusing a G_1 cell with a cell in the S or M phase of the cell cycle suggest that molecules present in the cytoplasm during the S or M phase control the progression to those phases.

Data from R. T. Johnson and P. N. Rao, Mammalian cell fusion: Induction of premature chromosome condensation in interphase nuclei, *Nature* 226:717–722 (1970).

WHAT IF? If the progression of phases did not depend on cytoplasmic molecules and each phase began when the previous one was complete, how would the results have differed?

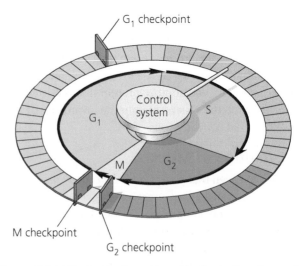

▲ **Figure 9.15 Mechanical analogy for the cell cycle control system.** In this diagram of the cell cycle, the flat "stepping stones" around the perimeter represent sequential events. Like the control device of an automatic washer, the cell cycle control system proceeds on its own, driven by a built-in clock. However, the system is subject to internal and external regulation at various checkpoints; three important checkpoints are shown (red).

until overridden by go-ahead signals. Many signals registered at checkpoints come from cellular surveillance mechanisms inside the cell. These signals report whether crucial cellular processes that should have occurred by that point have in fact been completed correctly and thus whether or not the cell cycle should proceed. Checkpoints also register signals from outside the cell, as we'll discuss later. Three important checkpoints are those in the G_1, G_2, and M phases (red gates in Figure 9.15).

For many cells, the G_1 checkpoint—dubbed the "restriction point" in mammalian cells—seems to be the most important. If a cell receives a go-ahead signal at the G_1 checkpoint, it will usually complete the G_1, S, G_2, and M phases and divide. If it does not receive a go-ahead signal at that point, it may exit the cycle, switching into a nondividing state called the **G_0 phase (Figure 9.16a)**. Most cells of the human body are actually in the G_0 phase. As mentioned earlier, mature nerve cells and muscle cells never divide. Other cells, such as liver cells, can be "called back" from the G_0 phase to the cell cycle by external cues, such as growth factors released during injury.

The cell cycle is regulated at the molecular level by a set of regulatory proteins and protein complexes, including proteins called *cyclins*, and other proteins interacting with cyclins that are kinases (enzymes that activate or inactivate other proteins by phosphorylating them; see Figure 5.24). To understand how a cell progresses through the cycle, let's consider the checkpoint signals that can make the cell cycle clock pause or continue.

Biologists are currently working out the pathways that link signals originating inside and outside the cell with the responses by cyclins, kinases, and other proteins. An example of an internal signal occurs at the third important checkpoint, the M phase checkpoint **(Figure 9.16b)**. Anaphase, the separation of sister chromatids, does not begin until all the chromosomes are properly attached to the spindle at the metaphase plate. Researchers have learned that as long as some kinetochores are unattached to spindle microtubules, the sister chromatids remain together, delaying anaphase. Only when the kinetochores of all the chromosomes are properly attached to the spindle does the appropriate regulatory protein complex become activated. Once activated, the complex sets off a chain

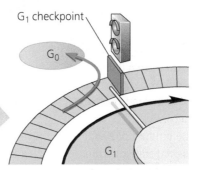

In the absence of a go-ahead signal, a cell exits the cell cycle and enters G_0, a nondividing state.

(a) G_1 checkpoint

If a cell receives a go-ahead signal, the cell continues on in the cell cycle.

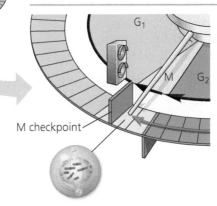

A cell in mitosis receives a stop signal when any of its chromosomes are not attached to spindle fibers.

(b) M checkpoint

When all chromosomes are attached to spindle fibers from both poles, a go-ahead signal allows the cell to proceed into anaphase.

▲ **Figure 9.16 Two important checkpoints.** At certain checkpoints in the cell cycle (red gates), cells do different things depending on the signals they receive. Events of the **(a)** G_1 and **(b)** M checkpoints are shown. In part (b), the G_2 checkpoint has already been passed by the cell.

WHAT IF? *What might be the result if the cell ignored either checkpoint and progressed through the cell cycle?*

of molecular events that activates the enzyme separase, which cleaves the cohesins, allowing the sister chromatids to separate. This mechanism ensures that daughter cells do not end up with missing or extra chromosomes.

Studies using animal cells in culture have led to the identification of many external factors, both chemical and physical, that can influence cell division. For example, cells fail to divide if an essential nutrient is lacking in the culture medium. (This is analogous to trying to run a washing machine without the water supply hooked up; an internal sensor won't allow the machine to continue past the point where water is needed.) And even if all other conditions are favorable, most types of mammalian cells divide in culture only if the growth medium includes specific growth factors. As mentioned in Concept 5.6, a **growth factor** is a protein released by certain cells that stimulates other cells to divide. Different cell types respond specifically to different growth factors or combinations of growth factors.

Consider, for example, *platelet-derived growth factor (PDGF)*, which is made by blood cell fragments called platelets. The experiment illustrated in **Figure 9.17** demonstrates that PDGF is required for the division of cultured fibroblasts, a type of connective tissue cell. Fibroblasts have PDGF receptors on their plasma membranes. The binding of PDGF molecules to these receptors triggers a signal transduction pathway that allows the cells to pass the G_1 checkpoint and divide. PDGF stimulates fibroblast division not only in the artificial conditions of cell culture, but also in an animal's body. When an injury occurs, platelets release PDGF in the vicinity. The resulting proliferation of fibroblasts helps heal the wound.

The effect of an external physical factor on cell division is clearly seen in **density-dependent inhibition**, a phenomenon in which crowded cells stop dividing (**Figure 9.18a**). As first observed many years ago, cultured cells normally divide until they form a single layer of cells on the inner surface of a culture flask, at which point the cells stop dividing. If some cells are removed, those bordering the open space begin dividing again and continue until the vacancy is filled. Follow-up studies revealed that the binding of a cell-surface protein to its counterpart on an adjoining cell sends a signal to both cells that inhibits cell division, preventing the cells from moving forward in the cell cycle. Growth factors also have a

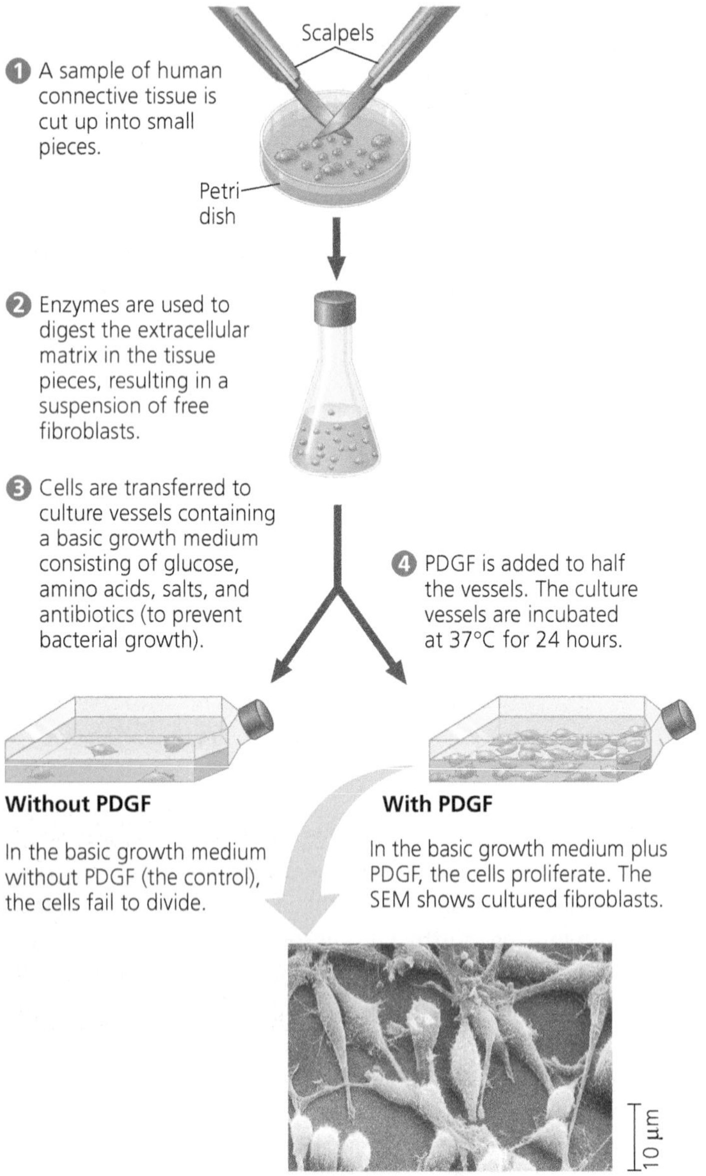

❶ A sample of human connective tissue is cut up into small pieces.

Scalpels

Petri dish

❷ Enzymes are used to digest the extracellular matrix in the tissue pieces, resulting in a suspension of free fibroblasts.

❸ Cells are transferred to culture vessels containing a basic growth medium consisting of glucose, amino acids, salts, and antibiotics (to prevent bacterial growth).

❹ PDGF is added to half the vessels. The culture vessels are incubated at 37°C for 24 hours.

Without PDGF

In the basic growth medium without PDGF (the control), the cells fail to divide.

With PDGF

In the basic growth medium plus PDGF, the cells proliferate. The SEM shows cultured fibroblasts.

10 μm

▲ Figure 9.17 **The effect of platelet-derived growth factor (PDGF) on cell division.**

MAKE CONNECTIONS *PDGF signals cells by binding to a cell-surface receptor that then becomes phosphorylated, activating it so that it sends a signal. If you added a chemical that blocked phosphorylation, how would the results differ? (See Figure 5.24.)*

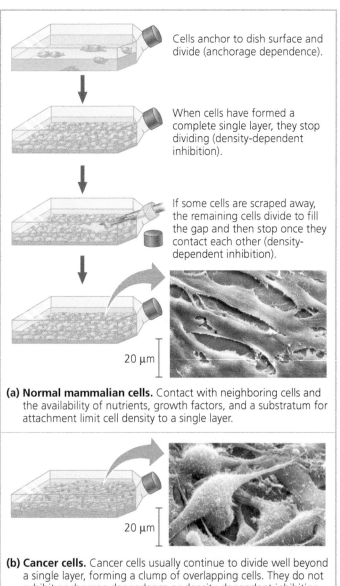

Cells anchor to dish surface and divide (anchorage dependence).

When cells have formed a complete single layer, they stop dividing (density-dependent inhibition).

If some cells are scraped away, the remaining cells divide to fill the gap and then stop once they contact each other (density-dependent inhibition).

20 μm

(a) **Normal mammalian cells.** Contact with neighboring cells and the availability of nutrients, growth factors, and a substratum for attachment limit cell density to a single layer.

20 μm

(b) **Cancer cells.** Cancer cells usually continue to divide well beyond a single layer, forming a clump of overlapping cells. They do not exhibit anchorage dependence or density-dependent inhibition.

▲ Figure 9.18 **Density-dependent inhibition and anchorage dependence of cell division.** Individual cells are shown disproportionately large in the drawings.

role in determining the density that cells attain before ceasing division.

Most animal cells also exhibit **anchorage dependence** (see Figure 9.18a). To divide, they must be attached to a substratum, such as the inside of a culture flask or the extracellular matrix of a tissue. Experiments suggest that like cell density, anchorage is signaled to the cell cycle control system via pathways involving plasma membrane proteins and elements of the cytoskeleton linked to them.

Density-dependent inhibition and anchorage dependence appear to function not only in cell culture but also in the body's tissues, checking the growth of cells at some optimal density and location during embryonic development and throughout an organism's life. Cancer cells, which we discuss next, exhibit neither density-dependent inhibition nor anchorage dependence (**Figure 9.18b**).

Loss of Cell Cycle Controls in Cancer Cells

Cancer cells do not heed the normal signals that regulate the cell cycle. In culture, they do not stop dividing when growth factors are depleted. A logical hypothesis is that cancer cells do not need growth factors in their culture medium to grow and divide. They may make a required growth factor themselves, or they may have an abnormality in the signaling pathway that conveys the growth factor's signal to the cell cycle control system even in the absence of that factor. Another possibility is an abnormal cell cycle control system. In these scenarios, the underlying basis of the abnormality is almost always a change in one or more genes (for example, a mutation) that alters the function of their protein products, resulting in faulty cell cycle control.

There are other important differences between normal cells and cancer cells that reflect derangements of the cell cycle. If and when they stop dividing, cancer cells do so at random points in the cycle, rather than at the normal checkpoints. Moreover, cancer cells can go on dividing indefinitely in culture if they are given a continual supply of nutrients; in essence, they are "immortal." A striking example is a cell line that has been reproducing in culture since 1951. Cells of this line are called HeLa cells because their original source was a tumor removed from a woman named *H*enrietta *La*cks. Cells in culture that acquire the ability to divide indefinitely are said to have undergone a process called **transformation**, causing them to behave (in cell division, at least) like cancer cells. By contrast, nearly all normal, nontransformed mammalian cells growing in culture divide only about 20 to 50 times before they stop dividing, age, and die. Finally, cancer cells evade the normal controls that trigger a cell to undergo a type of programmed cell death called *apoptosis* when something is wrong—for example, when an irreparable mistake has occurred during DNA replication preceding mitosis.

The abnormal behavior of cancer cells can be catastrophic when it occurs in the body. The problem begins when a single cell in a tissue undergoes the first changes of the multistep process that converts a normal cell to a cancer cell. Such a cell often has altered proteins on its surface, and the body's immune system normally recognizes the cell as an insurgent—and destroys it. However, if the cell evades destruction, it may proliferate and form a tumor, a mass of abnormal cells within otherwise normal tissue. The abnormal cells may remain at the original site if they have too few genetic and cellular changes to survive at another site. In that case, the tumor is called a **benign tumor**. Most benign tumors do not cause serious problems and can be removed by surgery. In contrast, a **malignant tumor** includes cells whose genetic and cellular changes enable them to spread to new tissues and impair the functions of one or more organs; based on their ability to divide indefinitely in culture, these cells are also considered *transformed* cells. An individual with a malignant tumor is said to have cancer; **Figure 9.19** shows the development of breast cancer.

The changes that have occurred in cells of malignant tumors show up in many ways besides excessive proliferation. These

▼ **Figure 9.19 The growth and metastasis of a malignant breast tumor.** A series of genetic and cellular changes contribute to a tumor becoming malignant (cancerous). The cells of malignant tumors grow in an uncontrolled way and can spread to neighboring tissues and, via lymph and blood vessels, to other parts of the body (metastasis).

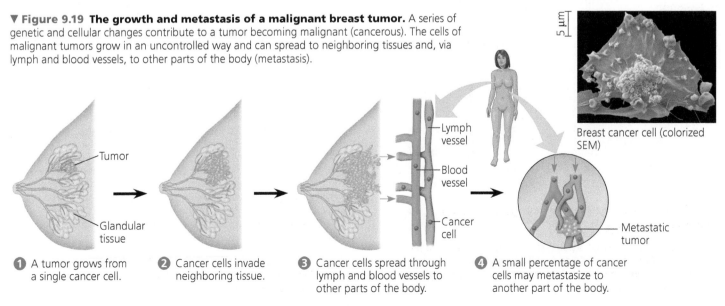

Breast cancer cell (colorized SEM)

5 μm

❶ A tumor grows from a single cancer cell.

Tumor

Glandular tissue

❷ Cancer cells invade neighboring tissue.

❸ Cancer cells spread through lymph and blood vessels to other parts of the body.

Lymph vessel

Blood vessel

Cancer cell

❹ A small percentage of cancer cells may metastasize to another part of the body.

Metastatic tumor

cells may have unusual numbers of chromosomes, though whether this is a cause or an effect of transformation is an ongoing topic of debate. Their metabolism may be altered, and they may cease to function in any constructive way. Abnormal changes on the cell surface cause cancer cells to lose attachments to neighboring cells and the extracellular matrix, allowing them to spread into nearby tissues. Cancer cells may also secrete signaling molecules that cause blood vessels to grow toward the tumor. A few tumor cells may separate from the original tumor, enter blood vessels and lymph vessels, and travel to other parts of the body. There, they may proliferate and form a new tumor. This spread of cancer cells to locations distant from their original site is called **metastasis** (see Figure 9.19).

A tumor that appears to be localized may be treated with high-energy radiation, which damages DNA in cancer cells much more than DNA in normal cells, apparently because the majority of cancer cells have lost the ability to repair such damage. To treat known or suspected metastatic tumors, chemotherapy is used, in which drugs that are toxic to actively dividing cells are administered through the circulatory system. As you might expect, chemotherapeutic drugs interfere with specific steps in the cell cycle. For example, the drug Taxol freezes the mitotic spindle by preventing microtubule depolymerization, which stops actively dividing cells from proceeding past metaphase and leads to their destruction. The side effects of chemotherapy are due to the drugs' effects on normal cells that divide often. For example, nausea results from chemotherapy's effects on intestinal cells, hair loss from effects on hair follicle cells, and susceptibility to infection from effects on immune system cells. You'll work with data from an experiment involving a potential chemotherapeutic agent in the **Scientific Skills Exercise**.

Scientific Skills Exercise

Interpreting Histograms

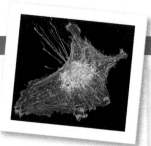

▶ Human glioblastoma cell

At What Phase Is the Cell Cycle Arrested by an Inhibitor? Many medical treatments are aimed at stopping cancer cell proliferation by blocking the cell cycle of cancerous tumor cells. One potential treatment is a cell cycle inhibitor derived from human umbilical cord stem cells. In this exercise, you will compare two histograms to determine where in the cell cycle the inhibitor blocks the division of cancer cells.

How the Experiment Was Done In the treated sample, human glioblastoma (brain cancer) cells were grown in tissue culture in the presence of the inhibitor, while control sample cells were grown in its absence. After 72 hours of growth, the two cell samples were harvested. To get a "snapshot" of the phase of the cell cycle each cell was in at that time, the samples were treated with a fluorescent chemical that binds to DNA and then run through a flow cytometer, an instrument that records the fluorescence level of each cell. Computer software then graphed the number of cells in each sample with a particular fluorescence level, as shown below.

Data from the Experiment

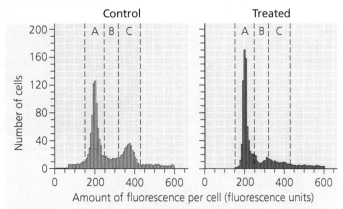

Data from K. K. Velpula et al., Regulation of glioblastoma progression by cord blood stem cells is mediated by downregulation of cyclin D1, *PLoS ONE* 6(3): e18017 (2011). doi:10.1371/journal.pone.0018017

The data are plotted in a type of graph called a histogram, which groups the values for a numeric variable on the *x*-axis into intervals.

A histogram allows you to see how all the experimental subjects (cells, in this case) are distributed along a continuous variable (amount of fluorescence). In these histograms, the bars are so narrow that the data appear to follow a curve for which you can detect peaks and dips. Each narrow bar represents the number of cells observed to have a level of fluorescence in the range of that interval. This in turn indicates the relative amount of DNA in those cells. Overall, comparing the two histograms allows you to see how the DNA content of this cell population is altered by the treatment.

INTERPRET THE DATA

1. Study the data in the histograms. (a) Which axis indirectly shows the relative amount of DNA per cell? Explain your answer. (b) In the control sample, compare the first peak in the histogram (in region A) to the second peak (in region C). Which peak shows the population of cells with the higher amount of DNA per cell? Explain. (For additional information about graphs, see the Scientific Skills Review in Appendix F and in the Study Area in MasteringBiology.)

2. (a) In the control sample histogram, identify the phase of the cell cycle (G$_1$, S, or G$_2$) of the population of cells in each region delineated by vertical lines. Label the histogram with these phases and explain your answer. (b) Does the S phase population of cells show a distinct peak in the histogram? Why or why not?

3. The histogram representing the treated sample shows the effect of growing the cancer cells alongside human umbilical cord stem cells that produce the potential inhibitor. (a) Label the histogram with the cell cycle phases. Which phase of the cell cycle has the greatest number of cells in the treated sample? Explain. (b) Compare the distribution of cells among G$_1$, S, and G$_2$ phases in the control and treated samples. What does this tell you about the cells in the treated sample? (c) Based on what you learned in Concept 9.3, propose a mechanism by which the stem cell–derived inhibitor might arrest the cancer cell cycle at this stage. (More than one answer is possible.)

MB) A version of this Scientific Skills Exercise can be assigned in MasteringBiology.

Over the past several decades, researchers have produced a flood of valuable information about cell-signaling pathways and how their malfunction contributes to the development of cancer through effects on the cell cycle. Coupled with new molecular techniques, such as the ability to rapidly sequence the DNA of cells in a particular tumor, medical treatments for cancer are beginning to become more "personalized" to a particular patient's tumor (see Figure 16.21).

For example, the cells of roughly 20% of breast cancer tumors show abnormally high amounts of a cell-surface receptor tyrosine kinase called HER2, and many show an increase in the number of estrogen receptor (ER) molecules, intracellular receptors that can trigger cell division. Based on lab findings, a physician can prescribe chemotherapy with a molecule that blocks the function of the specific protein (Herceptin for HER2 and tamoxifen for ERs). Treatment using these agents, when appropriate, has led to increased survival rates and fewer cancer recurrences.

CONCEPT CHECK 9.3

1. In Figure 9.14, why do the nuclei resulting from experiment 2 contain different amounts of DNA?
2. What phase are most of your body cells in?
3. Compare and contrast a benign tumor and a malignant tumor.
4. **WHAT IF?** What would happen if you performed the experiment in Figure 9.17 with cancer cells?

For suggested answers, see Appendix A.

9 Chapter Review

Go to **MasteringBiology**® for Assignments, the eText, and the Study Area with Animations, Activities, Vocab Self-Quiz, and Practice Tests.

SUMMARY OF KEY CONCEPTS

VOCAB SELF-QUIZ

goo.gl/gbai8v

- Unicellular organisms reproduce by **cell division**; multicellular organisms depend on cell division for their development from a fertilized egg and for growth and repair. Cell division is part of the **cell cycle**, an ordered sequence of events in the life of a cell.

CONCEPT 9.1

Most cell division results in genetically identical daughter cells (pp. 183–184)

- The genetic material (DNA) of a cell—its **genome**—is partitioned among **chromosomes**. Each eukaryotic chromosome consists of one DNA molecule associated with many proteins. Together, the complex of DNA and associated proteins is called **chromatin**. The chromatin of a chromosome exists in different states of condensation at different times. In animals, **gametes** have one set of chromosomes, and **somatic cells** have two sets.
- Cells replicate their genetic material before they divide, each daughter cell receiving a copy of the DNA. Prior to cell division, chromosomes are duplicated. Each one then consists of two identical **sister chromatids** joined along their lengths by sister chromatid cohesion and held most tightly together at a constricted region at the **centromeres**. When this cohesion is broken, the chromatids separate during cell division, becoming the chromosomes of the daughter cells. Eukaryotic cell division consists of **mitosis** (division of the nucleus) and **cytokinesis** (division of the cytoplasm).

? *Differentiate between these terms: chromosome, chromatin, and chromatid.*

CONCEPT 9.2

The mitotic phase alternates with interphase in the cell cycle (pp. 185–191)

- Between divisions, a cell is in **interphase**: the G_1, S, and G_2 **phases**. The cell grows throughout interphase, with DNA being replicated only during the synthesis (S) phase. Mitosis and cytokinesis make up the **mitotic (M) phase** of the cell cycle.

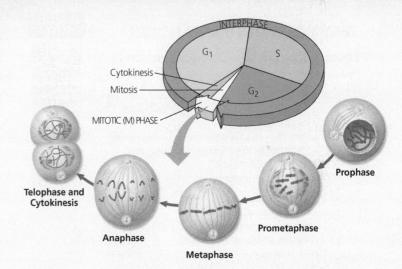

INTERPHASE

G_1

S

G_2

Cytokinesis

Mitosis

MITOTIC (M) PHASE

Telophase and Cytokinesis

Anaphase

Metaphase

Prometaphase

Prophase

- The **mitotic spindle**, made up of microtubules, controls chromosome movement during mitosis. In animal cells, the mitotic spindle arises from the **centrosomes** and includes spindle microtubules and **asters**. Some spindle microtubules attach to the **kinetochores** of chromosomes and move the chromosomes to the **metaphase plate**. After sister chromatids separate, motor proteins move them along kinetochore microtubules toward opposite ends of the cell. The cell elongates when motor proteins push nonkinetochore microtubules from opposite poles away from each other.
- Mitosis is usually followed by cytokinesis. Animal cells carry out cytokinesis by **cleavage**, and plant cells form a **cell plate**.
- During **binary fission** in bacteria, the chromosome replicates and the daughter chromosomes actively move apart. Some of the proteins involved in bacterial binary fission are related to eukaryotic actin and tubulin. Since prokaryotes preceded eukaryotes by more than a billion years, it is likely that mitosis evolved from prokaryotic cell division.

? *In which of the three subphases of interphase and the stages of mitosis do chromosomes exist as single DNA molecules?*

The eukaryotic cell cycle is regulated by a molecular control system (pp. 192–197)

- Signaling molecules present in the cytoplasm regulate progress through the cell cycle.
- The **cell cycle control system** is molecularly based; key regulatory proteins are cyclins and kinases. The cell cycle clock has specific **checkpoints** where the cell cycle stops until a go-ahead signal is received; important checkpoints occur in the G_1, G_2, and M phases. Cell culture has enabled researchers to study the molecular details of cell division. Both internal signals and external signals control the cell cycle checkpoints via signal transduction pathways. Most cells exhibit **density-dependent inhibition** of cell division as well as **anchorage dependence**.
- Cancer cells elude normal cell cycle regulation and divide unchecked, forming tumors. **Malignant tumors** invade nearby tissues and can undergo **metastasis**, exporting cancer cells to other sites, where they may form secondary tumors. Recent cell cycle and cell-signaling research, and new techniques for sequencing DNA, have led to improved cancer treatments.

? *Explain the significance of the G_1 and M checkpoints and the go-ahead signals involved in the cell cycle control system.*

TEST YOUR UNDERSTANDING

PRACTICE TEST

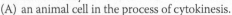

goo.gl/CRZjvS

Level 1: Knowledge/Comprehension

1. Through a microscope, you can see a cell plate beginning to develop across the middle of a cell and nuclei forming on either side of the cell plate. This cell is most likely
   (A) an animal cell in the process of cytokinesis.
   (B) a plant cell in the process of cytokinesis.
   (C) a bacterial cell dividing.
   (D) a plant cell in metaphase.

2. In the cells of some organisms, mitosis occurs without cytokinesis. This will result in
   (A) cells with more than one nucleus.
   (B) cells that are unusually small.
   (C) cells lacking nuclei.
   (D) cell cycles lacking an S phase.

3. Which of the following does *not* occur during mitosis?
   (A) condensation of the chromosomes
   (B) replication of the DNA
   (C) separation of sister chromatids
   (D) spindle formation

Level 2: Application/Analysis

4. A particular cell has half as much DNA as some other cells in a mitotically active tissue. The cell in question is most likely in
   (A) G_1.   (C) prophase.
   (B) G_2.   (D) metaphase.

5. The drug cytochalasin B blocks the function of actin. Which of the following aspects of the animal cell cycle would be most disrupted by cytochalasin B?
   (A) spindle formation
   (B) spindle attachment to kinetochores
   (C) cell elongation during anaphase
   (D) cleavage furrow formation and cytokinesis

6. **DRAW IT** Draw one eukaryotic chromosome as it would appear during interphase, during each of the stages of mitosis, and during cytokinesis. Also draw and label the nuclear envelope and any microtubules attached to the chromosome(s).

7. The light micrograph shows dividing cells near the tip of an onion root. Identify a cell in each of the following stages: prophase, prometaphase, metaphase, anaphase, and telophase. Describe the major events occurring at each stage.

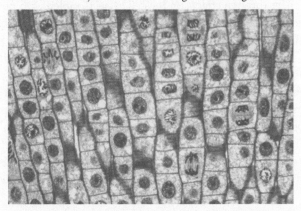

Level 3: Synthesis/Evaluation

8. **SCIENTIFIC INQUIRY**
   Although both ends of a microtubule can gain or lose subunits, one end (called the plus end) polymerizes and depolymerizes at a higher rate than the other end (the minus end). For spindle microtubules, the plus ends are in the center of the spindle, and the minus ends are at the poles. Motor proteins that move along microtubules specialize in walking either toward the plus end or toward the minus end; the two types are called plus end directed and minus end directed motor proteins, respectively. Given what you know about chromosome movement and spindle changes during anaphase, predict which type of motor proteins would be present on (a) kinetochore microtubules and (b) nonkinetochore microtubules.

9. **FOCUS ON EVOLUTION**
   The result of mitosis is that the daughter cells end up with the same number of chromosomes that the parent cell had. Another way to maintain the number of chromosomes would be to carry out cell division first and then duplicate the chromosomes in each daughter cell. Assess whether this would be an equally good way of organizing the cell cycle. Explain why evolution has not led to this alternative.

10. **FOCUS ON INFORMATION**
    The continuity of life is based on heritable information in the form of DNA. In a short essay (100–150 words), explain how the process of mitosis faithfully parcels out exact copies of this heritable information in the production of genetically identical daughter cells.

11. **SYNTHESIZE YOUR KNOWLEDGE**

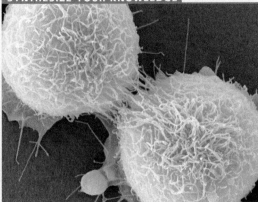

Shown here are two HeLa cancer cells that are just completing cytokinesis. Explain how the cell division of cancer cells like these is misregulated. What genetic and other changes might have caused these cells to escape normal cell cycle regulation?

For selected answers, see Appendix A.

Unit 2 Genetics

10 Meiosis and Sexual Life Cycles

Sexually reproducing species alternate fertilization with **meiosis**, accurately passing on genetic information while generating genetic diversity.

11 Mendel and the Gene Idea

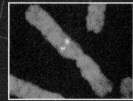

Although unaware of meiosis, Mendel did experiments that enabled him to describe the behavior of **genes**.

12 The Chromosomal Basis of Inheritance

Genes are located on **chromosomes**, and chromosomal behavior underlies genetic inheritance.

13 The Molecular Basis of Inheritance

The nucleotide sequence of the DNA in chromosomes provides the **molecular basis for inheritance**.

14 Gene Expression: From Gene to Protein

An organism's characteristics emerge from **gene expression**, the process in which information in **genes** is transcribed into **RNAs** that can be translated into **proteins**.

15 Regulation of Gene Expression

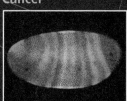

An organism's different cell types and responses to its environment depend on **regulation of gene expression**.

16 Development, Stem Cells, and Cancer

Coordinated gene regulation underlies **embryonic development**, while misregulation can contribute to **cancer**.

17 Viruses

Our understanding of gene expression is informed by studying **viruses**, protein-coated packets of genetic information that hijack cellular resources and replicate themselves.

18 Genomes and Their Evolution

The **evolution of genomes** is the basis of life's diversity.

Chemistry and Cells

Ecology

Animals

Plants

History of Life

Evolution

Genetics

10 Meiosis and Sexual Life Cycles
11 Mendel and the Gene Idea
12 The Chromosomal Basis of Inheritance
13 The Molecular Basis of Inheritance
14 Gene Expression: From Gene to Protein
15 Regulation of Gene Expression
16 Development, Stem Cells, and Cancer
17 Viruses
18 Genomes and Their Evolution

CHAPTER

10 Meiosis and Sexual Life Cycles

KEY CONCEPTS

10.1 Offspring acquire genes from parents by inheriting chromosomes

10.2 Fertilization and meiosis alternate in sexual life cycles

10.3 Meiosis reduces the number of chromosome sets from diploid to haploid

10.4 Genetic variation produced in sexual life cycles contributes to evolution

▲ **Figure 10.1** What accounts for family resemblance?

Variations on a Theme

Most people who send out birth announcements mention the sex of the baby, but they don't feel the need to specify that their offspring is a human being! One of the characteristics of life is the ability of organisms to reproduce their own kind—elephants produce little elephants, and oak trees generate oak saplings. Exceptions to this rule show up only as sensational but highly suspect stories in tabloid newspapers.

Another rule often taken for granted is that offspring resemble their parents more than they do unrelated individuals. If you examine the family members shown in **Figure 10.1**, you can pick out some similar features among them. The transmission of traits from one generation to the next is called inheritance, or **heredity** (from the Latin *heres*, heir). However, sons and daughters are not identical copies of either parent or of their siblings. Along with inherited similarity, there is also **variation**. Farmers have exploited the principles of heredity and variation for thousands of years, breeding plants and animals for desired traits. But what are the biological mechanisms leading to the hereditary similarity and variation that we call a "family resemblance"? A detailed answer to this question eluded biologists until the advance of genetics in the 20th century.

Genetics is the scientific study of heredity and inherited variation. In this unit, you'll learn about genetics at multiple levels, from organisms to cells to molecules. On the practical side, you'll see how genetics continues to revolutionize medicine, and you'll be asked to consider some social and ethical questions raised by our ability to manipulate DNA, the genetic material. At the end of the unit, you'll be able to stand back and consider the whole genome, an organism's entire complement of DNA. Rapid acquisition and analysis of the genome sequences of many species, including our own, have taught us a great deal about evolution on the molecular level—in other words, evolution of the genome itself. In fact, genetic methods and discoveries are catalyzing progress in all areas of biology, from cell biology to physiology, developmental biology, behavior, and even ecology.

We begin our study of genetics in this chapter by examining how chromosomes pass from parents to offspring in sexually reproducing organisms. The processes of meiosis (a special type of cell division) and fertilization (the fusion of sperm and egg) maintain a species' chromosome count during the sexual life cycle. We'll describe the cellular mechanics of meiosis and explain how this process differs from mitosis. Finally, we'll consider how both meiosis and fertilization contribute to genetic variation, such as the variation obvious in the family shown in Figure 10.1.

Offspring acquire genes from parents by inheriting chromosomes

Family friends may tell you that you have your mother's nose or your father's eyes. Of course, parents do not, in any literal sense, give their children a nose, eyes, hair, or any other traits. What, then, *is* actually inherited?

Inheritance of Genes

Parents endow their offspring with coded information in the form of hereditary units called **genes**. The genes we inherit from our mothers and fathers are our genetic link to our parents, and they account for family resemblances such as shared eye color or freckles. Our genes program specific traits that emerge as we develop from fertilized eggs into adults.

The genetic program is written in the language of DNA, the polymer of four different nucleotides (see Concepts 1.1 and 3.6). Inherited information is passed on in the form of each gene's specific sequence of DNA nucleotides, much as printed information is communicated in the form of meaningful sequences of letters. In both cases, the language is symbolic. Just as your brain translates the word *apple* into a mental image of the fruit, cells translate genes into freckles and other features. Most genes program cells to synthesize specific enzymes and other proteins, whose cumulative action produces an organism's inherited traits. The programming of these traits in the form of DNA is one of the unifying themes of biology.

The transmission of hereditary traits has its molecular basis in the replication of DNA, which produces copies of genes that can be passed from parents to offspring. In animals and plants, reproductive cells called **gametes** are the vehicles that transmit genes from one generation to the next. During fertilization, male and female gametes (sperm and eggs) unite, passing on genes of both parents to their offspring.

Except for small amounts of DNA in mitochondria and chloroplasts, the DNA of a eukaryotic cell is packaged into chromosomes within the nucleus. Every species has a characteristic number of chromosomes. For example, humans have 46 chromosomes in their **somatic cells**—all the cells of the body except the gametes and their precursors. Each chromosome consists of a single long DNA molecule elaborately coiled in association with various proteins. One chromosome includes several hundred to a few thousand genes, each of which is a specific sequence of nucleotides within the DNA molecule. A gene's specific location along the length of a chromosome is called the gene's **locus** (plural, *loci*; from the Latin, meaning "place"). Our genetic endowment (our genome) consists of the genes and other DNA that make up the chromosomes we inherited from our parents.

Comparison of Asexual and Sexual Reproduction

Only organisms that reproduce asexually have offspring that are exact genetic copies of themselves. In **asexual reproduction**, a single individual is the sole parent and passes copies of all its genes to its offspring without the fusion of gametes. For example, single-celled eukaryotic organisms can reproduce asexually by mitotic cell division, in which DNA is copied and allocated equally to two daughter cells. The genomes of the offspring are virtually exact copies of the parent's genome. Some multicellular organisms are also capable of reproducing asexually **(Figure 10.2)**. Because the cells of the offspring arise via mitosis in the parent, the offspring is usually genetically identical to its parent. An individual that reproduces asexually gives rise to a **clone**, a group of genetically identical individuals. Genetic differences occasionally arise in asexually reproducing organisms as a result of changes in the DNA called mutations, which we will discuss in Chapter 14.

In **sexual reproduction**, two parents give rise to offspring that have unique combinations of genes inherited from the two parents. In contrast to a clone, offspring of sexual reproduction vary genetically from their siblings and both parents: They are variations on a common theme of family resemblance, not exact replicas. Genetic variation like that shown in Figure 10.1 is an important consequence of sexual reproduction. What mechanisms generate this genetic variation? The key is the behavior of chromosomes during the sexual life cycle.

(a) Hydra **(b) Redwoods**

▲ **Figure 10.2 Asexual reproduction in two multicellular organisms. (a)** This relatively simple animal, a hydra, reproduces by budding. The bud, a localized mass of mitotically dividing cells, develops into a small hydra, which detaches from the parent (LM). **(b)** All the trees in this circle of redwoods arose asexually from a single parent tree, whose stump is in the center of the circle.

CONCEPT CHECK 10.1

1. **MAKE CONNECTIONS** Using what you know of gene expression in a cell, explain what causes traits of parents (such as hair color) to show up in their offspring. (See Concept 3.6.)

2. How does an asexually reproducing eukaryotic organism produce offspring that are genetically identical to each other and to their parent?

3. **WHAT IF?** A horticulturalist breeds orchids, trying to obtain a plant with a unique combination of desirable traits. After many years, she finally succeeds. To produce more plants like this one, should she crossbreed it with another plant or clone it? Why?

For suggested answers, see Appendix A.

CONCEPT 10.2

Fertilization and meiosis alternate in sexual life cycles

A **life cycle** is the generation-to-generation sequence of stages in the reproductive history of an organism, from conception to production of its own offspring. In this section, we use humans as an example to track the behavior of chromosomes through the sexual life cycle. We begin by considering the chromosome count in human somatic cells and gametes. We will then explore how the behavior of chromosomes relates to the human life cycle and other types of sexual life cycles.

Sets of Chromosomes in Human Cells

In humans, each somatic cell has 46 chromosomes. During mitosis, the chromosomes become condensed enough to be visible under a light microscope. At this point, they can be distinguished from one another by their size, the position of their centromeres, and the pattern of colored bands produced by certain chromatin-binding stains.

Careful examination of a micrograph of the 46 human chromosomes from a single cell in mitosis reveals that there are two chromosomes of each of 23 types. This becomes clear when images of the chromosomes are arranged in pairs, starting with the longest chromosomes. The resulting ordered display is called a **karyotype (Figure 10.3)**. The two chromosomes of a pair have the same length, centromere position, and staining pattern: These are called **homologous chromosomes** (or **homologs**, for short) or a **homologous pair**. Both chromosomes of each pair carry genes controlling the same inherited characters. For example, if a gene for eye color is situated at a particular locus on a certain chromosome, its homologous chromosome will also have a version of the eye color gene at the equivalent locus.

The two chromosomes referred to as X and Y are an important exception to the general pattern of homologous chromosomes in human somatic cells. Human females have a homologous pair of X chromosomes (XX), but males have one X and one Y chromosome (XY; see Figure 10.3). Only

▼ Figure 10.3 Research Method

Preparing a Karyotype

Application A karyotype is a display of condensed chromosomes arranged in pairs. Karyotyping can be used to screen for defective chromosomes or abnormal numbers of chromosomes associated with certain congenital disorders, such as Down syndrome.

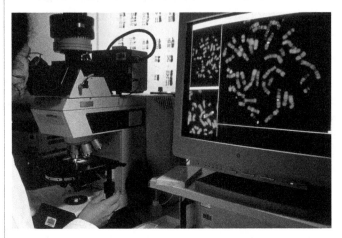

Technique Karyotypes are prepared from isolated somatic cells, which are treated with a drug to stimulate mitosis and then grown in culture for several days. Cells arrested when chromosomes are most highly condensed—in metaphase—are stained and then viewed with a microscope equipped with a digital camera. An image of the chromosomes is displayed on a computer monitor, and digital software is used to arrange them in pairs according to their appearance.

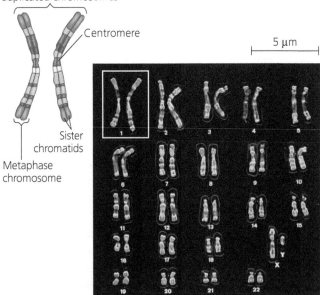

Results This karyotype shows the chromosomes from a human male, digitally colored to emphasize the chromosome banding patterns. The size of the chromosome, position of the centromere, and pattern of stained bands help identify specific chromosomes. Although difficult to discern in the karyotype, each metaphase chromosome consists of two closely attached sister chromatids (see the diagram of the boxed pair of homologous duplicated chromosomes).

small parts of the X and Y are homologous. Most of the genes carried on the X chromosome do not have counterparts on the tiny Y, and the Y chromosome has genes lacking on the X. Because they determine an individual's sex, the X and Y chromosomes are called **sex chromosomes**. The other chromosomes are called **autosomes**.

The occurrence of pairs of homologous chromosomes in each human somatic cell is a consequence of our sexual origins. We inherit one chromosome of each pair from each parent. Thus, the 46 chromosomes in our somatic cells are actually two sets of 23 chromosomes—a maternal set (from our mother) and a paternal set (from our father). The number of chromosomes in a single set is represented by n. Any cell with two chromosome sets is called a **diploid cell** and has a diploid number of chromosomes, abbreviated $2n$. For humans, the diploid number is 46 ($2n = 46$), the number of chromosomes in our somatic cells. In a cell in which DNA synthesis has occurred, all the chromosomes are duplicated, and therefore each consists of two identical sister chromatids, associated closely at the centromere and along the arms. (Even though the chromosomes are duplicated, we still say the cell is diploid, or $2n$, because it has only two sets of information.) **Figure 10.4** helps clarify the various terms that we use to describe duplicated chromosomes in a diploid cell.

Unlike somatic cells, gametes contain a single set of chromosomes. Such cells are called **haploid cells**, and each has a haploid number of chromosomes (n). For humans, the haploid number is 23 ($n = 23$). The set of 23 consists of the 22 autosomes plus a single sex chromosome. An unfertilized egg contains an X chromosome, but a sperm may contain an X or a Y chromosome.

Each sexually reproducing species has a characteristic diploid and haploid number. For example, the fruit fly *Drosophila melanogaster* has a diploid number ($2n$) of 8 and a haploid number (n) of 4, while for dogs, $2n$ is 78 and n is 39.

Now let's consider chromosome behavior during sexual life cycles. We'll use the human life cycle as an example.

Behavior of Chromosome Sets in the Human Life Cycle

The human life cycle begins when a haploid sperm from the father fuses with a haploid egg from the mother (**Figure 10.5**). This union of gametes, culminating in fusion of their nuclei, is called **fertilization**. The resulting fertilized egg, or **zygote**, is diploid because it contains two haploid sets of chromosomes bearing genes representing the maternal and paternal family lines. As a human develops into a sexually mature adult, mitosis of the zygote and its descendant cells generates all the somatic cells of the body. Both chromosome sets in the zygote and all the genes they carry are passed with precision to the somatic cells.

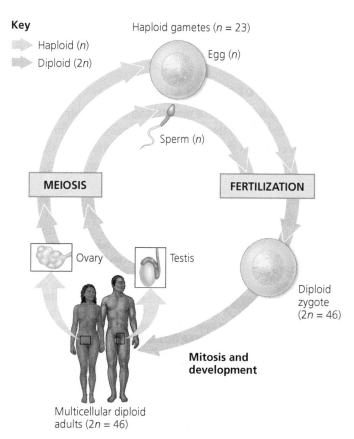

▲ **Figure 10.5 The human life cycle.** In each generation, the number of chromosome sets doubles at fertilization but is halved during meiosis. For humans, the number of chromosomes in a haploid cell is 23, consisting of one set ($n = 23$); the number of chromosomes in the diploid zygote and all somatic cells arising from it is 46, consisting of two sets ($2n = 46$).

This figure introduces a color code that will be used for other life cycles later in this book. The aqua arrows identify haploid stages of a life cycle, and the tan arrows identify diploid stages.

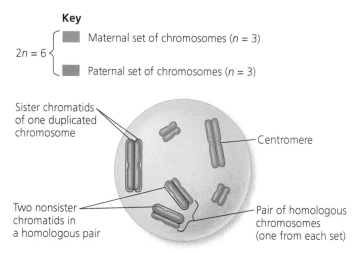

▲ **Figure 10.4 Describing chromosomes.** A cell from an organism with a diploid number of 6 ($2n = 6$) is depicted here following chromosome duplication and condensation. Each of the six duplicated chromosomes consists of two sister chromatids associated closely along their lengths. Each homologous pair is composed of one chromosome from the maternal set (red) and one from the paternal set (blue). Each set is made up of three chromosomes in this example (long, medium, and short). Together, one maternal and one paternal chromatid in a pair of homologous chromosomes are called nonsister chromatids.

? *How many sets of chromosomes are present in this diagram? How many pairs of homologs are present?*

MEIOSIS I: Separates homologous chromosomes

Prophase I	Metaphase I	Anaphase I	Telophase I and Cytokinesis

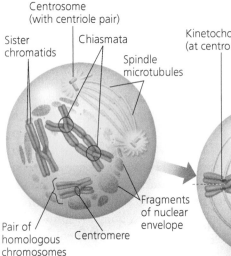

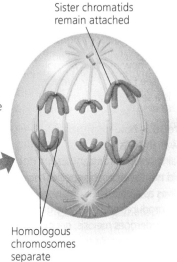

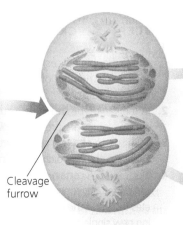

Duplicated homologous chromosomes (red and blue) pair up and exchange segments; 2n = 6 in this example.

Chromosomes line up by homologous pairs.

Each pair of homologous chromosomes separates.

Two haploid cells form; each chromosome still consists of two sister chromatids.

Prophase I

- Centrosome movement, spindle formation, and nuclear envelope breakdown occur as in mitosis. Chromosomes condense progressively throughout prophase I.

- During early prophase I, before the stage shown above, each chromosome pairs with its homolog, aligned gene by gene, and **crossing over** occurs: The DNA molecules of nonsister chromatids are broken (by proteins) and are rejoined to each other.

- At the stage shown above, each homologous pair has one or more X-shaped regions called **chiasmata** (singular, *chiasma*), where crossovers have occurred.

- Later in prophase I, after the stage shown above, microtubules from one pole or the other attach to the kinetochores, one at the centromere of each homolog. (Each homolog acts as if it has a single kinetochore.) Microtubules move the homologous pairs toward the metaphase plate (see the metaphase I diagram).

Metaphase I

- Pairs of homologous chromosomes are now arranged at the metaphase plate, with one chromosome of each pair facing each pole.

- Both chromatids of one homolog are attached to kinetochore microtubules from one pole; the chromatids of the other homolog are attached to microtubules from the opposite pole.

Anaphase I

- Breakdown of proteins that are responsible for sister chromatid cohesion along chromatid arms allows homologs to separate.

- The homologs move toward opposite poles, guided by the spindle apparatus.

- Sister chromatid cohesion persists at the centromere, causing chromatids to move as a unit toward the same pole.

Telophase I and Cytokinesis

- When telophase I begins, each half of the cell has a complete haploid set of duplicated chromosomes. Each chromosome is composed of two sister chromatids; one or both chromatids include regions of nonsister chromatid DNA.

- Cytokinesis (division of the cytoplasm) usually occurs simultaneously with telophase I, forming two haploid daughter cells.

- In animal cells like these, a cleavage furrow forms. (In plant cells, a cell plate forms.)

- In some species, chromosomes decondense and nuclear envelopes form.

- No chromosome duplication occurs between meiosis I and meiosis II.

MEIOSIS II: Separates sister chromatids

Prophase II	Metaphase II	Anaphase II	Telophase II and Cytokinesis

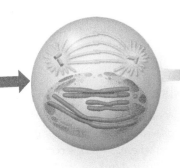 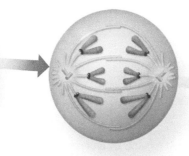 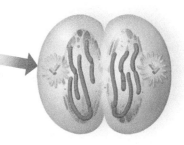

During another round of cell division, the sister chromatids finally separate; four haploid daughter cells result, containing unduplicated chromosomes.

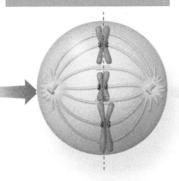 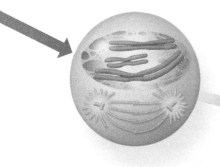 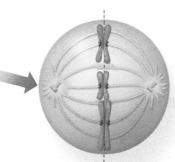 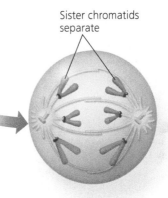

Sister chromatids separate

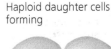 Haploid daughter cells forming

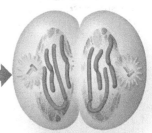

Prophase II

- A spindle apparatus forms.

- In late prophase II (not shown here), chromosomes, each still composed of two chromatids associated at the centromere, are moved by microtubules toward the metaphase II plate.

Metaphase II

- The chromosomes are positioned at the metaphase plate as in mitosis.

- Because of crossing over in meiosis I, the two sister chromatids of each chromosome are not genetically identical.

- The kinetochores of sister chromatids are attached to microtubules extending from opposite poles.

Anaphase II

- Breakdown of proteins holding the sister chromatids together at the centromere allows the chromatids to separate. The chromatids move toward opposite poles as individual chromosomes.

Telophase II and Cytokinesis

- Nuclei form, the chromosomes begin decondensing, and cytokinesis occurs.

- The meiotic division of one parent cell produces four daughter cells, each with a haploid set of (unduplicated) chromosomes.

- The four daughter cells are genetically distinct from one another and from the parent cell.

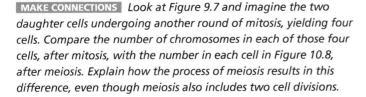 **MAKE CONNECTIONS** *Look at Figure 9.7 and imagine the two daughter cells undergoing another round of mitosis, yielding four cells. Compare the number of chromosomes in each of those four cells, after mitosis, with the number in each cell in Figure 10.8, after meiosis. Explain how the process of meiosis results in this difference, even though meiosis also includes two cell divisions.*

 ANIMATION Visit the Study Area in **MasteringBiology** for the BioFlix® 3-D Animation on Meiosis.

Crossing Over and Synapsis During Prophase I

Prophase I of meiosis is a very busy time. The prophase I cell shown in Figure 10.8 is at a point fairly late in prophase I, when pairing of homologous chromosomes, crossing over, and chromosome condensation have already taken place. The sequence of events leading up to that point is shown in more detail in **Figure 10.9**.

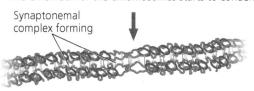

DNA breaks   Centromere   DNA breaks

Cohesins

Pair of homologous chromosomes:

Paternal sister chromatids

Maternal sister chromatids

1 After interphase, the chromosomes have been duplicated, and sister chromatids are held together by proteins called cohesins (purple). Each pair of homologs associate along their length. The DNA molecules of two nonsister chromatids are broken at precisely corresponding points. The chromatin of the chromosomes starts to condense.

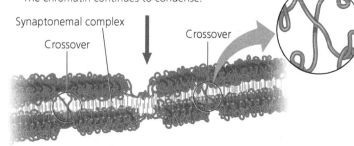

Synaptonemal complex forming

2 A zipper-like protein complex, the synaptonemal complex (green), begins to form, attaching one homolog to the other. The chromatin continues to condense.

Synaptonemal complex

Crossover   Crossover

3 The synaptonemal complex is fully formed; the two homologs are said to be in synapsis. During synapsis, the DNA breaks are closed up when each broken end is joined to the corresponding segment of the nonsister chromatid, producing crossovers.

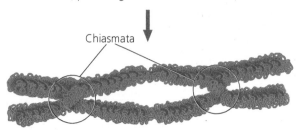

Chiasmata

4 After the synaptonemal complex disassembles, the homologs move slightly apart from each other but remain attached because of sister chromatid cohesion, even though some of the DNA may no longer be attached to its original chromosome. The points of attachment where crossovers have occurred show up as chiasmata. The chromosomes continue to condense as they move toward the metaphase plate.

▲ **Figure 10.9 Crossing over and synapsis in prophase I.**

As shown in this figure, the two members of a homologous pair associate along their length, aligned allele by allele. The DNA molecules of a maternal and a paternal chromatid are broken at precisely matching points. A zipper-like structure called the **synaptonemal complex** forms, and during this attachment (**synapsis**), the DNA breaks are closed up so that a paternal chromatid is joined to a piece of maternal chromatid beyond the crossover point, and vice versa. At least one crossover per chromosome must occur, in conjunction with sister chromatid cohesion, in order for the homologous pair to stay together as it moves to the metaphase I plate.

A Comparison of Mitosis and Meiosis

Figure 10.10 summarizes the key differences between meiosis and mitosis in diploid cells. Meiosis reduces the number of chromosome sets from two to one, whereas mitosis conserves the number. Meiosis produces cells that differ genetically from the parent cell and from each other, whereas mitosis produces daughter cells that are genetically identical to the parent cell.

Three events unique to meiosis occur during meiosis I:

1. **Synapsis and crossing over.** During prophase I, duplicated homologs pair up, and crossing over occurs as described previously and in Figure 10.9.
2. **Alignment of homologous pairs at the metaphase plate.** At metaphase I of meiosis, pairs of homologs are positioned at the metaphase plate, rather than individual chromosomes as in metaphase of mitosis.
3. **Separation of homologs.** At anaphase I of meiosis, the duplicated chromosomes of each homologous pair move toward opposite poles, but the sister chromatids of each duplicated chromosome remain attached. In anaphase of mitosis, by contrast, sister chromatids separate.

Sister chromatids stay together due to sister chromatid cohesion, mediated by cohesion proteins. In mitosis, this attachment lasts until the end of metaphase, when enzymes cleave the cohesins, freeing the sister chromatids to move to opposite poles of the cell. In meiosis, sister chromatid cohesion is released in two steps, one at the start of anaphase I and one at anaphase II. In metaphase I, the two homologs of each pair are held together by cohesion between sister chromatid arms in regions beyond points of crossing over, where stretches of sister chromatids now belong to different chromosomes. The combination of crossing over and sister chromatid cohesion along the arms results in the formation of a chiasma. Chiasmata hold homologs together as the spindle forms for the first meiotic division. At the onset of anaphase I, the release of cohesion along sister chromatid arms allows homologs to separate. At anaphase II, the release of sister chromatid cohesion at the centromeres allows the sister chromatids to separate. Thus, sister chromatid cohesion and crossing over, acting together, play an essential role in the lining up of chromosomes by homologous pairs at metaphase I.

Meiosis I reduces the number of chromosome sets per cell from two (diploid) to one set (haploid). During the second

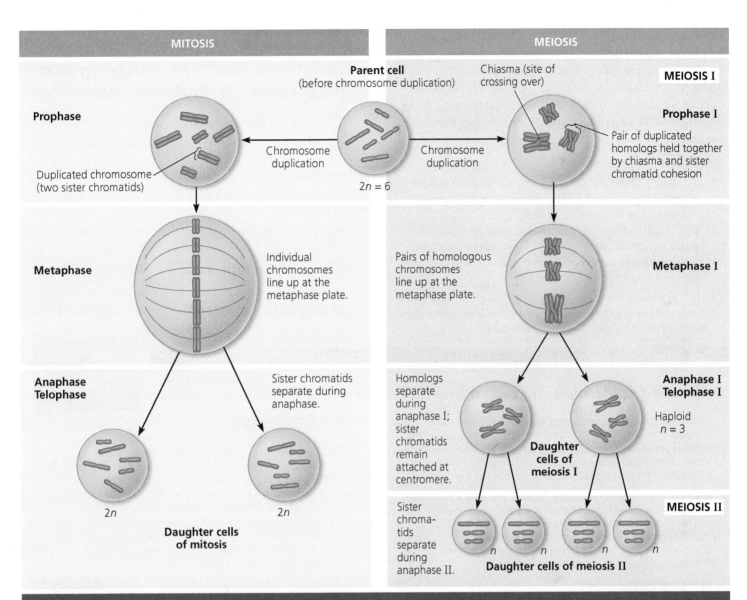

MITOSIS		MEIOSIS	

Prophase — Duplicated chromosome (two sister chromatids)

Parent cell (before chromosome duplication)

Chromosome duplication ← $2n = 6$ → Chromosome duplication

MEIOSIS I

Chiasma (site of crossing over)

Prophase I — Pair of duplicated homologs held together by chiasma and sister chromatid cohesion

Metaphase — Individual chromosomes line up at the metaphase plate.

Pairs of homologous chromosomes line up at the metaphase plate. — **Metaphase I**

Anaphase Telophase — Sister chromatids separate during anaphase.

Homologs separate during anaphase I; sister chromatids remain attached at centromere.

Daughter cells of meiosis I

Anaphase I Telophase I — Haploid $n = 3$

$2n$ $2n$

Daughter cells of mitosis

Sister chromatids separate during anaphase II.

MEIOSIS II

n n n n

Daughter cells of meiosis II

SUMMARY

Property	Mitosis (occurs in both diploid and haploid cells)	Meiosis (can only occur in diploid cells)
DNA replication	Occurs during interphase before mitosis begins	Occurs during interphase before meiosis I begins
Number of divisions	One, including prophase, prometaphase, metaphase, anaphase, and telophase	Two, each including prophase, metaphase, anaphase, and telophase
Synapsis of homologous chromosomes	Does not occur	Occurs during prophase I along with crossing over between nonsister chromatids; resulting chiasmata hold pairs together due to sister chromatid cohesion
Number of daughter cells and genetic composition	Two, each genetically identical to the parent cell, with the same number of chromosomes	Four, each haploid (n); genetically different from the parent cell and from each other
Role in the animal or plant body	Enables multicellular animal or plant (gametophyte or sporophyte) to arise from a single cell; produces cells for growth, repair, and, in some species, asexual reproduction; produces gametes in the gametophyte plant	Produces gametes (in animals) or spores (in the sporophyte plant); reduces number of chromosome sets by half and introduces genetic variability among the gametes or spores

▲ **Figure 10.10 A comparison of mitosis and meiosis.**

DRAW IT *Could any other combinations of chromosomes be generated during meiosis II from the specific cells shown in telophase I? Explain. (Hint: Draw the cells as they would appear in metaphase II.)*

meiotic division, meiosis II, the sister chromatids separate, producing haploid daughter cells. The mechanisms for separating sister chromatids in meiosis II and mitosis are virtually identical. The molecular basis of chromosome behavior during meiosis continues to be a focus of intense research. In the **Scientific Skills Exercise**, you can work with data that tracks the amount of DNA in cells during meiosis.

CONCEPT CHECK 10.3

1. **MAKE CONNECTIONS** Compare the chromosomes in a cell at metaphase of mitosis with those in a cell at metaphase of meiosis II. (See Figures 9.7 and 10.8.)

2. **WHAT IF?** After the synaptonemal complex disappears, how would any pair of homologous chromosomes be associated if crossing over did not occur? What effect might this have on gamete formation?

For suggested answers, see Appendix A.

CONCEPT 10.4

Genetic variation produced in sexual life cycles contributes to evolution

How do we account for the genetic variation of the family members in Figure 10.1? As you'll learn more about in later chapters, mutations are the original source of genetic diversity. These changes in an organism's DNA create the different versions of genes known as alleles. Once these differences arise, reshuffling of the alleles during sexual reproduction produces the variation that results in each member of a sexually reproducing population having a unique combination of traits.

Origins of Genetic Variation Among Offspring

In species that reproduce sexually, the behavior of chromosomes during meiosis and fertilization is responsible for most

---

Scientific Skills Exercise

Making a Line Graph and Converting Between Units of Data

▶ Budding yeast

How Does DNA Content Change as Budding Yeast Cells Proceed Through Meiosis? When nutrients are low, cells of the budding yeast (*Saccharomyces cerevisiae*) exit the mitotic cell cycle and enter meiosis. In this exercise you will track the DNA content of a population of yeast cells as they progress through meiosis.

How the Experiment Was Done Researchers grew a culture of yeast cells in a nutrient-rich medium and then transferred the cells to a nutrient-poor medium to induce meiosis. At different times after induction, the DNA content per cell was measured in a sample of the cells, and the average DNA content per cell was recorded in femtograms (fg; 1 femtogram = 1×10^{-15} gram).

Data from the Experiment

Time After Induction (hours)	Average Amount of DNA per Cell (fg)
0.0	24.0
1.0	24.0
2.0	40.0
3.0	47.0
4.0	47.5
5.0	48.0
6.0	48.0
7.0	47.5
7.5	25.0
8.0	24.0
9.0	23.5
9.5	14.0
10.0	13.0
11.0	12.5
12.0	12.0
13.0	12.5
14.0	12.0

INTERPRET THE DATA

1. First, set up your graph. (a) Place the labels for the independent and dependent variables on the appropriate axes, followed by units of measurement in parentheses. Explain your choices. (b) Add tick marks and values for each axis. Explain your choices. (For additional information about graphs, see the Scientific Skills Review in Appendix F and in the Study Area in MasteringBiology.)

2. Because the variable on the *x*-axis varies continuously, it makes sense to plot the data on a line graph. (a) Plot each data point from the table onto the graph. (b) Connect the data points with line segments.

3. Most of the yeast cells in the culture were in G_1 of the cell cycle before being moved to the nutrient-poor medium. (a) How many femtograms of DNA are there in each yeast cell in G_1? Estimate this value from the data in your graph. (b) How many femtograms of DNA should be present in each cell in G_2? (See Concept 9.2 and Figure 9.6.) At the end of meiosis I (MI)? At the end of meiosis II (MII)? (See Figure 10.7.) (c) Using these values as a guideline, distinguish the different phases by inserting vertical dashed lines in the graph between phases and label each phase (G_1, S, G_2, MI, MII). You can figure out where to put the dividing lines based on what you know about the DNA content of each phase (see Figure 10.7). (d) Think carefully about the point where the line at the highest value begins to slope downward. What specific point of meiosis does this "corner" represent? What stage(s) correspond to the downward sloping line?

4. Given the fact that 1 fg of DNA = 9.78×10^5 base pairs (on average), you can convert the amount of DNA per cell to the length of DNA in numbers of base pairs. (a) Calculate the number of base pairs of DNA in the haploid yeast genome. Express your answer in millions of base pairs (Mb), a standard unit for expressing genome size. Show your work. (b) How many base pairs per minute were synthesized during the S phase of these yeast cells?

MB A version of this Scientific Skills Exercise can be assigned in MasteringBiology.

Further Reading G. Simchen, Commitment to meiosis: What determines the mode of division in budding yeast? *BioEssays* 31:169–177 (2009). doi:10.1002/bies.200800124

of the variation that arises in each generation. Three mechanisms contribute to the genetic variation arising from sexual reproduction: independent assortment of chromosomes, crossing over, and random fertilization.

Independent Assortment of Chromosomes

One aspect of sexual reproduction that generates genetic variation is the random orientation of pairs of homologous chromosomes at metaphase of meiosis I. At metaphase I, the homologous pairs, each consisting of one maternal and one paternal chromosome, are situated at the metaphase plate. (Note that the terms *maternal* and *paternal* refer, respectively, to whether the chromosome in question was contributed by the mother or the father of the individual whose cells are undergoing meiosis.) Each pair may orient with either its maternal or paternal homolog closer to a given pole—its orientation is as random as the flip of a coin. Thus, there is a 50% chance that a given daughter cell of meiosis I will get the maternal chromosome of a certain homologous pair and a 50% chance that it will get the paternal chromosome.

Because each pair of homologous chromosomes is positioned independently of the other pairs at metaphase I, the first meiotic division results in each pair sorting its maternal and paternal homologs into daughter cells independently of every other pair. This is called *independent assortment*. Each daughter cell represents one outcome of all possible combinations of maternal and paternal chromosomes. As shown in **Figure 10.11**, the number of combinations possible for daughter cells formed by meiosis of a diploid cell with two pairs of homologous chromosomes ($n = 2$) is four: two possible arrangements for the first pair times two possible arrangements for the second pair. Note that only two of the four combinations of daughter cells shown in the figure would result from meiosis of a *single* diploid cell, because a single parent cell would have one or the other possible chromosomal arrangement at metaphase I, but not both. However, the population of daughter cells resulting from meiosis of a large number of diploid cells contains all four types in approximately equal numbers. In the case of $n = 3$, eight combinations of chromosomes are possible for daughter cells. More generally, the number of possible combinations when chromosomes sort independently during meiosis is 2^n, where n is the haploid number of the organism.

In the case of humans ($n = 23$), the number of possible combinations of maternal and paternal chromosomes in the resulting gametes is 2^{23}, or about 8.4 million. Each gamete that you produce in your lifetime contains one of roughly 8.4 million possible combinations of chromosomes.

Crossing Over

As a consequence of the independent assortment of chromosomes during meiosis, each of us produces a collection of gametes differing greatly in their combinations of the chromosomes we inherited from our two parents. Figure 10.11 suggests that each chromosome in a gamete is exclusively maternal or paternal in origin. In fact, this is *not* the case because crossing over produces **recombinant chromosomes**, individual chromosomes that carry genes (DNA) from two different parents. In meiosis in humans, an average of one to three crossover events occur per chromosome pair, depending on the size of the chromosomes and the position of their centromeres. As you learned in Figure 10.9, crossing over produces chromosomes with new combinations of maternal and paternal alleles. At metaphase II, chromosomes that contain one or more recombinant chromatids can be oriented in two nonequivalent ways with respect to other chromosomes because their sister chromatids are no longer identical. The possible arrangements of nonidentical sister chromatids during meiosis II increase the number of genetic types of daughter cells that can result from meiosis.

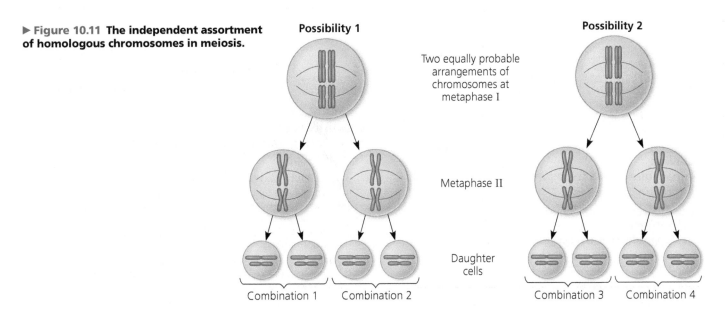

▶ **Figure 10.11 The independent assortment of homologous chromosomes in meiosis.**

Possibility 1

Possibility 2

Two equally probable arrangements of chromosomes at metaphase I

Metaphase II

Daughter cells

Combination 1   Combination 2   Combination 3   Combination 4

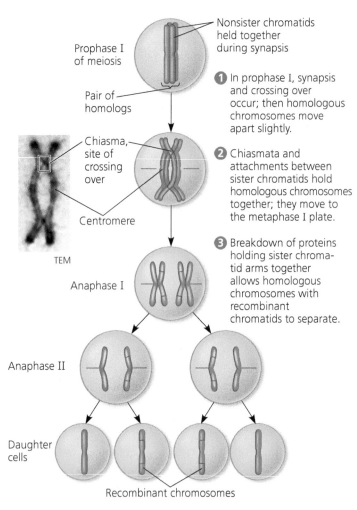

- Prophase I of meiosis
- Nonsister chromatids held together during synapsis
- Pair of homologs
- Chiasma, site of crossing over
- Centromere
- TEM
- Anaphase I
- Anaphase II
- Daughter cells
- Recombinant chromosomes

❶ In prophase I, synapsis and crossing over occur; then homologous chromosomes move apart slightly.

❷ Chiasmata and attachments between sister chromatids hold homologous chromosomes together; they move to the metaphase I plate.

❸ Breakdown of proteins holding sister chromatid arms together allows homologous chromosomes with recombinant chromatids to separate.

▲ Figure 10.12 **The results of crossing over during meiosis.**

Figure 10.12 provides an overview of how crossing over increases genetic variation by producing recombinant chromosomes that include DNA from two parents. You'll learn more about crossing over in Chapter 12.

Random Fertilization

The random nature of fertilization adds to the genetic variation arising from meiosis. In humans, each male and female gamete represents one of about 8.4 million (2^{23}) possible chromosome combinations due to independent assortment. The fusion of a male gamete with a female gamete during fertilization will produce a zygote with any of about 70 trillion ($2^{23} \times 2^{23}$) diploid combinations. With the variation from crossing over, the number of possibilities is astronomical. You really *are* unique.

The Evolutionary Significance of Genetic Variation Within Populations

EVOLUTION How does the genetic variation in a population relate to evolution? A population evolves through differential reproductive success of its members. On average, those best suited to the environment leave more offspring, thereby transmitting their genes. Thus, natural selection leads to an increase in genetic variations favored by the environment. As the environment changes, the population may survive if some members can cope with the new conditions. Mutations, the original source of different alleles, are mixed and matched during meiosis. New combinations of alleles may work better than those that previously prevailed.

We have seen how sexual reproduction greatly increases the genetic variation present in a population. Although Darwin realized that heritable variation makes evolution possible, he could not explain why offspring resemble—but are not identical to—their parents. Ironically, Gregor Mendel, a contemporary of Darwin, published a theory of inheritance that helps explain genetic variation, but his discoveries had no impact on biologists until 1900, more than 15 years after Darwin (1809–1882) and Mendel (1822–1884) had died. In the next chapter, you'll learn how Mendel discovered the basic rules governing the inheritance of traits.

CONCEPT CHECK 10.4

1. What is the source of variation among alleles of a gene?
2. **WHAT IF?** If maternal and paternal chromatids have the identical two alleles for every gene, will crossing over lead to genetic variation?

For suggested answers, see Appendix A.

Go to **MasteringBiology®** for Assignments, the eText, and the Study Area with Animations, Activities, Vocab Self-Quiz, and Practice Tests.

10 Chapter Review

SUMMARY OF KEY CONCEPTS

VOCAB SELF-QUIZ

goo.gl/gbai8v

CONCEPT 10.1

Offspring acquire genes from parents by inheriting chromosomes (pp. 201–202)

- Each **gene** in an organism's DNA exists at a specific **locus** on a certain chromosome.
- In **asexual reproduction**, a single parent produces genetically identical offspring by mitosis. **Sexual reproduction** combines genes from two parents, leading to genetically diverse offspring.

? *Explain why human offspring resemble their parents but are not identical to them.*

CONCEPT 10.2

Fertilization and meiosis alternate in sexual life cycles (pp. 202–205)

- Normal human **somatic cells** are **diploid**. They have 46 chromosomes made up of two sets of 23 chromosomes, one set from each parent. Human diploid cells have 22 homologous pairs of **autosomes** and one pair of **sex chromosomes**; the latter determines whether the person is female (XX) or male (XY).
- In humans, ovaries and testes produce haploid gametes by **meiosis**, each gamete containing a single set of 23 chromosomes ($n = 23$). During **fertilization**, an egg and sperm unite, forming a diploid ($2n = 46$) single-celled **zygote**, which develops into a multicellular organism by mitosis.

- Sexual **life cycles** differ in the timing of meiosis relative to fertilization and in the point(s) of the cycle at which a multicellular organism is produced by mitosis.

    ? *Compare the life cycles of animals and plants, mentioning their similarities and differences.*

CONCEPT 10.3

Meiosis reduces the number of chromosome sets from diploid to haploid (pp. 205–210)

- **Meiosis I** and **meiosis II** produce four haploid daughter cells. The number of chromosome sets is reduced from two (diploid) to one (haploid) during meiosis I.
- Meiosis is distinguished from mitosis by three events of meiosis I:

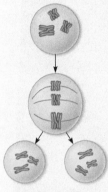

Prophase I: Each pair of homologous chromosomes undergoes **synapsis** and **crossing over** between nonsister chromatids with the subsequent appearance of **chiasmata**.

Metaphase I: Chromosomes line up as homologous pairs on the metaphase plate.

Anaphase I: Homologs separate from each other; sister chromatids remain joined at the centromere.

- Meiosis II separates the sister chromatids.
- Sister chromatid cohesion and crossing over allow chiasmata to hold homologs together until anaphase I. Cohesins are cleaved along the arms at anaphase I, allowing homologs to separate, and at the centromeres in anaphase II, releasing sister chromatids.

    ? *In prophase I, homologous chromosomes pair up and undergo crossing over. Can this also occur during prophase II? Explain.*

CONCEPT 10.4

Genetic variation produced in sexual life cycles contributes to evolution (pp. 210–212)

- Three events in sexual reproduction contribute to genetic variation in a population: independent assortment of chromosomes during meiosis, crossing over during meiosis I, and random fertilization of egg cells by sperm. During crossing over, DNA of nonsister chromatids in a homologous pair is broken and rejoined.
- Genetic variation is the raw material for evolution by natural selection. Mutations are the original source of this variation; recombination of variant genes generates additional diversity.

    ? *Explain how three processes unique to sexual reproduction generate a great deal of genetic variation.*

TEST YOUR UNDERSTANDING

PRACTICE TEST

goo.gl/CRZjvS

Level 1: Knowledge/Comprehension

1. A human cell containing 22 autosomes and a Y chromosome is
    (A) a sperm.
    (B) an egg.
    (C) a zygote.
    (D) a somatic cell of a male.

2. Homologous chromosomes move toward opposite poles of a dividing cell during
    (A) mitosis.
    (B) meiosis I.
    (C) meiosis II.
    (D) fertilization.

Level 2: Application/Analysis

3. If the DNA content of a diploid cell in the G_1 phase of the cell cycle is represented by x, then the DNA content of the same cell at metaphase of meiosis I would be
    (A) $0.25x$.
    (B) $0.5x$.
    (C) x.
    (D) $2x$.

4. If we continued to follow the cell lineage from question 3, the DNA content of a cell at metaphase of meiosis II would be
    (A) $0.25x$.
    (B) $0.5x$.
    (C) x.
    (D) $2x$.

5. **DRAW IT** The diagram shows a cell in meiosis. (a) Label the appropriate structures with these terms: chromosome (label as duplicated or unduplicated), centromere, kinetochore, sister chromatids, nonsister chromatids, homologous pair (use a bracket when labeling), homolog (label each one), chiasma, sister chromatid cohesion, gene loci, alleles of the F gene, alleles of the H gene. (b) Identify the stage of meiosis shown. (c) Describe the makeup of a haploid set and a diploid set.

Level 3: Synthesis/Evaluation

6. Explain how you can tell that the cell in question 5 is undergoing meiosis, not mitosis.

7. **SCIENTIFIC INQUIRY**
    The diagram in question 5 represents a meiotic cell. Assume the freckles gene is at the locus marked F, and the hair-color gene is located at the locus marked H, both on the long chromosome. The person from whom this cell was taken has inherited different alleles for each gene ("freckles" and "black hair" from one parent and "no freckles" and "blond hair" from the other). Predict allele combinations in the gametes resulting from this meiotic event. List other possible combinations of these alleles in this person's gametes.

8. **FOCUS ON EVOLUTION**
    Many species can reproduce either asexually or sexually. What might be the evolutionary significance of the switch from asexual to sexual reproduction that occurs in some organisms when the environment becomes unfavorable?

9. **FOCUS ON INFORMATION**
    The continuity of life is based on heritable information in the form of DNA. In a short essay (100–150 words), explain how chromosome behavior during sexual reproduction in animals ensures perpetuation of parental traits in offspring and, at the same time, genetic variation among offspring.

10. **SYNTHESIZE YOUR KNOWLEDGE**

The Cavendish banana, the world's most popular fruit, is threatened by extinction due to a fungus. This banana variety is "triploid" ($3n$, with three sets of chromosomes) and can only reproduce through cloning by cultivators. Explain how the triploid number accounts for its inability to form normal gametes. Discuss how the absence of sexual reproduction might make this species vulnerable to infection.

For selected answers, see Appendix A.

11 Mendel and the Gene Idea

KEY CONCEPTS

11.1 Mendel used the scientific approach to identify two laws of inheritance

11.2 Probability laws govern Mendelian inheritance

11.3 Inheritance patterns are often more complex than predicted by simple Mendelian genetics

11.4 Many human traits follow Mendelian patterns of inheritance

▲ **Figure 11.1** What principles of inheritance did Gregor Mendel discover by breeding pea plants?

Drawing from the Deck of Genes

The crowd at a soccer match displays the marvelous variety and diversity of humankind. Brown, blue, or gray eyes; black, brown, or blond hair—these are just a few examples of heritable variations among individuals in a population. What principles account for the transmission of such traits from parents to offspring?

The explanation of heredity most widely in favor during the 1800s was the "blending" hypothesis: the idea that genetic material contributed by the two parents mixes, just as blue and yellow paints blend to make green. This hypothesis predicts that over many generations a freely mating population will give rise to a uniform population of individuals—something we don't see. The blending hypothesis also fails to explain how traits can reappear after skipping a generation.

An alternative to the blending model is a "particulate" hypothesis of inheritance: the gene idea. In this model, parents pass on discrete heritable units—genes—that retain their separate identities in offspring. An organism's collection of genes is more like a deck of cards than a bucket of paint. Like cards, genes can be shuffled and passed along, generation after generation, in undiluted form.

Modern genetics had its genesis in an abbey garden, where a monk named Gregor Mendel documented a particulate mechanism for inheritance using pea plants **(Figure 11.1)**. Mendel developed his theory of inheritance several decades before chromosomes were observed under the microscope and the significance of their behavior during mitosis or meiosis was understood. In this chapter, we'll step into Mendel's garden to re-create his experiments and explain how he arrived at his theory of inheritance. We'll also explore inheritance patterns more complex than those observed by Mendel in garden peas. Finally, we'll see how the Mendelian model applies to the inheritance of human variations, including hereditary disorders such as sickle-cell disease.

Mendel used the scientific approach to identify two laws of inheritance

Mendel discovered the basic principles of heredity by breeding garden peas in carefully planned experiments. As we retrace his work, you'll recognize the key elements of the scientific process that were introduced in Chapter 1.

Mendel's Experimental, Quantitative Approach

One reason Mendel probably chose to work with peas is that they are available in many varieties. For example, one variety has purple flowers, while another variety has white flowers. A heritable feature that varies among individuals, such as flower color, is called a **character**. Each variant for a character, such as purple or white color for flowers, is called a **trait**.

Mendel could strictly control mating between plants. Each pea flower has both pollen-producing organs (stamens) and an egg-bearing organ (carpel). In nature, pea plants usually self-fertilize: Pollen grains from the stamens land on the carpel of the same flower, and sperm released from the pollen grains fertilize eggs present in the carpel. To achieve cross-pollination of two plants, Mendel removed the immature stamens of a plant before they produced pollen and then dusted pollen from another plant onto the altered flowers **(Figure 11.2)**. Each resulting zygote then developed into a plant embryo encased in a seed (pea). His method allowed Mendel to always be sure of the parentage of new seeds.

Mendel chose to track only those characters that occurred in two distinct, alternative forms, such as purple or white flower color. He also made sure that he started his experiments with varieties that, over many generations of self-pollination, had produced only the same variety as the parent plant. Such plants are said to be **true-breeding**. For example, a plant with purple flowers is true-breeding if the seeds produced by self-pollination in successive generations all give rise to plants that also have purple flowers.

In a typical breeding experiment, Mendel cross-pollinated two contrasting, true-breeding pea varieties—for example, purple-flowered plants and white-flowered plants (see Figure 11.2). This mating, or *crossing*, of two true-breeding varieties is called **hybridization**. The true-breeding parents are referred to as the **P generation** (parental generation), and their hybrid offspring are the **F₁ generation** (first filial generation, the word *filial* from the Latin word for "son"). Allowing these F₁ hybrids to self-pollinate (or to cross-pollinate with other F₁ hybrids) produces an **F₂ generation** (second filial generation). Mendel usually followed traits for at least the P, F₁, and F₂ generations. Had Mendel stopped his experiments with the F₁ generation, the basic patterns of inheritance would have eluded him. Mendel's quantitative analysis of the F₂ plants from thousands of genetic crosses like these allowed him to

---

▼ Figure 11.2 Research Method

Crossing Pea Plants

Application By crossing (mating) two true-breeding varieties of an organism, scientists can study patterns of inheritance. In this example, Mendel crossed pea plants that varied in flower color.

Technique

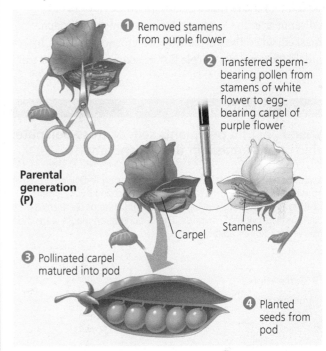

❶ Removed stamens from purple flower

❷ Transferred sperm-bearing pollen from stamens of white flower to egg-bearing carpel of purple flower

Parental generation (P)

Carpel

Stamens

❸ Pollinated carpel matured into pod

❹ Planted seeds from pod

Results When pollen from a white flower was transferred to a purple flower, the first-generation hybrids all had purple flowers. The result was the same for the reciprocal cross, which involved the transfer of pollen from purple flowers to white flowers.

First filial generation offspring (F₁)

❺ Examined offspring: all purple flowers

---

deduce two fundamental principles of heredity, now called the law of segregation and the law of independent assortment.

The Law of Segregation

If the blending model of inheritance were correct, the F₁ hybrids from a cross between purple-flowered and white-flowered pea plants would have pale purple flowers, a trait intermediate between those of the P generation. Notice in Figure 11.2 that the experiment produced a very different result: All the F₁ offspring had flowers of the same color as the purple-flowered parents. What happened to the white-flowered plants' genetic contribution to the hybrids? If it were lost, then the F₁ plants could produce only purple-flowered offspring in the F_2 generation. But when Mendel allowed the F_1 plants to self-pollinate and planted their seeds, the white-flower trait reappeared in the F_2 generation.

Mendel used very large sample sizes and kept accurate records of his results: 705 of the F_2 plants had purple flowers, and 224 had white flowers. These data fit a ratio of approximately three purple to one white (Figure 11.3). Mendel reasoned that the heritable factor for white flowers did not disappear in the F_1 plants, but was somehow hidden, or masked, when the purple-flower factor was present. In Mendel's terminology, purple flower color is a *dominant* trait,

and white flower color is a *recessive* trait. The reappearance of white-flowered plants in the F_2 generation was evidence that the heritable factor causing white flowers had not been diluted or destroyed by coexisting with the purple-flower factor in the F_1 hybrids.

Mendel observed the same pattern of inheritance in six other characters, each represented by two distinctly different traits (Table 11.1). For example, when Mendel crossed a true-breeding variety that produced smooth, round pea seeds with one that produced wrinkled seeds, all the F_1 hybrids produced round seeds; this is the dominant trait for seed shape. In the F_2 generation, approximately 75% of the seeds were round and 25% were wrinkled—a 3:1 ratio, as in Figure 11.3. Now let's see how Mendel deduced the law of segregation from his experimental results. In the discussion that follows, we will use modern terms instead of some of the terms used by Mendel. (For example, we'll use "gene" instead of Mendel's "heritable factor.")

▼ Figure 11.3 Inquiry

When F_1 hybrid pea plants self- or cross-pollinate, which traits appear in the F_2 generation?

Experiment Mendel crossed true-breeding purple-flowered plants and white-flowered plants (crosses are symbolized by ✕). The resulting F_1 hybrids were allowed to self-pollinate or were cross-pollinated with other F_1 hybrids. The F_2 generation plants were then observed for flower color.

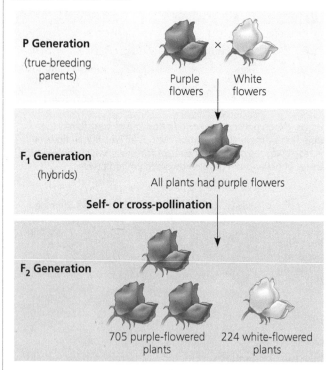

P Generation
(true-breeding parents)

Purple flowers   White flowers

F_1 Generation
(hybrids)

All plants had purple flowers

Self- or cross-pollination

F_2 Generation

705 purple-flowered plants   224 white-flowered plants

Results Both purple-flowered and white-flowered plants appeared in the F_2 generation, in a ratio of approximately 3:1.

Conclusion The "heritable factor" for the recessive trait (white flowers) had not been destroyed, deleted, or "blended" in the F_1 generation but was merely masked by the presence of the factor for purple flowers, which is the dominant trait.

Data from G. Mendel, Experiments in plant hybridization, *Proceedings of the Natural History Society of Brünn* 4:3–47 (1866).

WHAT IF? If you mated two purple-flowered plants from the P generation, what ratio of traits would you expect to observe in the offspring? Explain.

Table 11.1 The Results of Mendel's F_1 Crosses for Seven Characters in Pea Plants

Character	Dominant Trait	✕	Recessive Trait	F_2 Generation Dominant: Recessive	Ratio
Flower color	Purple	✕	White	705:224	3.15:1
Seed color	Yellow	✕	Green	6,022:2,001	3.01:1
Seed shape	Round	✕	Wrinkled	5,474:1,850	2.96:1
Pod shape	Inflated	✕	Constricted	882:299	2.95:1
Pod color	Green	✕	Yellow	428:152	2.82:1
Flower position	Axial	✕	Terminal	651:207	3.14:1
Stem length	Tall	✕	Dwarf	787:277	2.84:1

Mendel's Model

Mendel developed a model to explain the 3:1 inheritance pattern that he consistently observed among the F_2 offspring in his pea experiments. We describe four related concepts making up this model, the fourth of which is the law of segregation.

First, *alternative versions of genes account for variations in inherited characters.* The gene for flower color in pea plants, for example, exists in two versions, one for purple flowers and the other for white flowers. These alternative versions of a gene are called **alleles**. Today, we can relate this concept to chromosomes and DNA. As shown in **Figure 11.4**, each gene is a sequence of nucleotides at a specific place, or locus, along a particular chromosome. The DNA at that locus, however, can vary slightly in its nucleotide sequence. This variation in information content can affect the function of the encoded protein and thus an inherited character of the organism. The purple-flower allele and the white-flower allele are two DNA sequence variations possible at the flower-color locus on one of a pea plant's chromosomes. The purple-flower allele sequence allows synthesis of purple pigment, and the white-flower allele sequence does not.

Second, *for each character, an organism inherits two copies (that is, two alleles) of a gene, one from each parent.* Remarkably, Mendel made this deduction without knowing about the role, or even the existence, of chromosomes. Each somatic cell in a diploid organism has two sets of chromosomes, one set inherited from each parent (see Figure 10.4). Thus, a genetic locus is actually represented twice in a diploid cell, once on each homolog of a specific pair of chromosomes. The two alleles at a particular locus may be identical, as in the true-breeding plants of Mendel's P generation, or the alleles may differ, as in the F_1 hybrids (see Figure 11.4).

Third, *if the two alleles at a locus differ, then one, the* **dominant allele**, *determines the organism's appearance; the other, the* **recessive allele**, *has no noticeable effect on the organism's appearance.* Accordingly, Mendel's F_1 plants had purple flowers because the allele for that trait is dominant and the allele for white flowers is recessive.

The fourth and final part of Mendel's model, the **law of segregation**, states that *the two alleles for a heritable character segregate (separate from each other) during gamete formation and end up in different gametes.* Thus, an egg or a sperm gets only one of the two alleles that are present in the somatic cells of the organism making the gamete. In terms of chromosomes, this segregation corresponds to the distribution of copies of the two members of a pair of homologous chromosomes to different gametes in meiosis (see Figure 10.7). Note that if an organism has identical alleles for a particular character—that is, the organism is true-breeding for that character—then that allele is present in all gametes. But if different alleles are present, as in the F_1 hybrids, then 50% of the gametes receive the dominant allele and 50% receive the recessive allele.

Does Mendel's segregation model account for the 3:1 ratio he observed in the F_2 generation of his numerous crosses? For the flower-color character, the model predicts that the two different alleles present in an F_1 individual will segregate into gametes such that half the gametes will have the purple-flower allele and half will have the white-flower allele. During self-pollination, gametes of each class unite randomly. An egg with a purple-flower allele has an equal chance of being fertilized by a sperm with a purple-flower allele or one with a white-flower allele. Since the same is true for an egg with a white-flower allele, there are four equally likely combinations of sperm

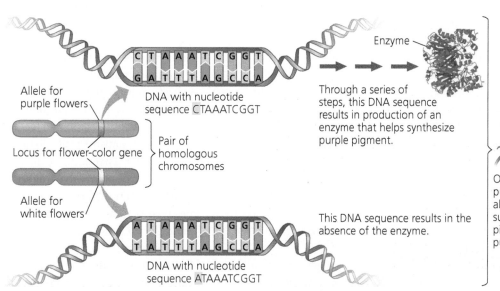

► Figure 11.4 **Alleles, alternative versions of a gene.** This diagram shows a pair of homologous chromosomes in an F_1 hybrid pea plant, with the actual DNA sequence from the flower color allele of each chromosome. The paternally inherited chromosome (blue) has an allele for purple flowers, which codes for a protein that indirectly controls synthesis of purple pigment. The maternally inherited chromosome (red) has an allele for white flowers, which results in no functional protein being made.

Allele for purple flowers

DNA with nucleotide sequence CTAAATCGGT

Enzyme

Through a series of steps, this DNA sequence results in production of an enzyme that helps synthesize purple pigment.

Locus for flower-color gene

Pair of homologous chromosomes

Allele for white flowers

DNA with nucleotide sequence ATAAATCGGT

This DNA sequence results in the absence of the enzyme.

One purple-flower allele results in sufficient pigment for purple flowers.

▶ **Figure 11.5 Mendel's law of segregation.** This diagram shows the genetic makeup of the generations in Figure 11.3. It illustrates Mendel's model for inheritance of the alleles of a single gene. Each plant has two alleles for the gene controlling flower color, one allele inherited from each of the plant's parents. To construct a Punnett square that predicts the F₂ generation offspring, we list all the possible gametes from one parent (here, the F₁ female) along the left side of the square and all the possible gametes from the other parent (here, the F₁ male) along the top. The boxes represent the offspring resulting from all the possible unions of male and female gametes.

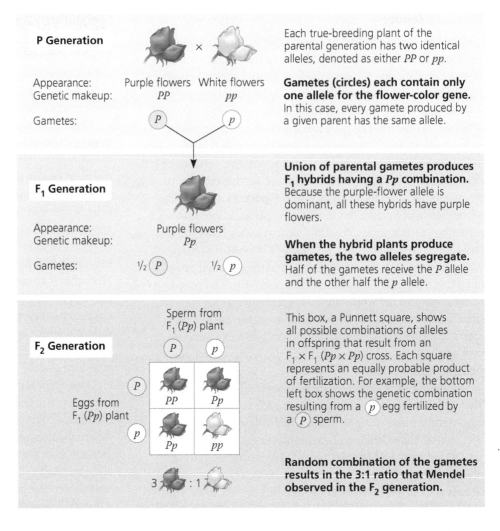

Each true-breeding plant of the parental generation has two identical alleles, denoted as either PP or pp.

Gametes (circles) each contain only one allele for the flower-color gene. In this case, every gamete produced by a given parent has the same allele.

Union of parental gametes produces F₁ hybrids having a Pp combination. Because the purple-flower allele is dominant, all these hybrids have purple flowers.

When the hybrid plants produce gametes, the two alleles segregate. Half of the gametes receive the P allele and the other half the p allele.

This box, a Punnett square, shows all possible combinations of alleles in offspring that result from an F₁ × F₁ ($Pp × Pp$) cross. Each square represents an equally probable product of fertilization. For example, the bottom left box shows the genetic combination resulting from a p egg fertilized by a P sperm.

Random combination of the gametes results in the 3:1 ratio that Mendel observed in the F₂ generation.

and egg. **Figure 11.5** illustrates these combinations using a **Punnett square**, a handy diagrammatic device for predicting the allele composition of all offspring resulting from a cross between individuals of known genetic makeup. Notice that we use a capital letter to symbolize a dominant allele and a lower-case letter for a recessive allele. In our example, P is the purple-flower allele, and p is the white-flower allele; the gene itself is sometimes referred to as the P/p gene.

In the F₂ offspring, what color will the flowers be? One-fourth of the plants have inherited two purple-flower alleles; these plants will have purple flowers. One-half of the F₂ offspring have inherited one purple-flower allele and one white-flower allele; these plants will also have purple flowers, the dominant trait. Finally, one-fourth of the F₂ plants have inherited two white-flower alleles and will express the recessive trait. Thus, Mendel's model accounts for the 3:1 ratio of traits that he observed in the F₂ generation.

Useful Genetic Vocabulary

An organism that has a pair of identical alleles for a gene encoding a character is called a **homozygote** and is said to be **homozygous** for that gene. In the parental generation in Figure 11.5, the purple-flowered pea plant is homozygous for the dominant allele (PP), while the white-flowered plant is homozygous for the recessive allele (pp). Homozygous plants "breed true" because all of their gametes contain the same allele—either P or p in this example. If we cross dominant homozygotes with recessive homozygotes, every offspring will have two different alleles—Pp in the case of the F₁ hybrids of our flower-color experiment (see Figure 11.5). An organism that has two different alleles for a gene is called a **heterozygote** and is said to be **heterozygous** for that gene. Unlike homozygotes, heterozygotes produce gametes with different alleles, so they are not true-breeding. For example, P- and p-containing gametes are both produced by our F₁ hybrids. Self-pollination of the F₁ hybrids thus produces both purple-flowered and white-flowered offspring.

Because of the different effects of dominant and recessive alleles, an organism's traits do not always reveal its genetic composition. Therefore, we distinguish between an organism's appearance or observable traits, called its **phenotype**, and its genetic makeup, its **genotype**. In the case of flower color in pea plants, PP and Pp plants have the same phenotype (purple) but different genotypes. **Figure 11.6** reviews these terms. Note that the term *phenotype* refers to physiological traits as well as traits that relate directly to appearance. For example, one pea variety lacks the normal ability to self-pollinate, which is a phenotypic trait (non-self-pollination).

Phenotype		Genotype	

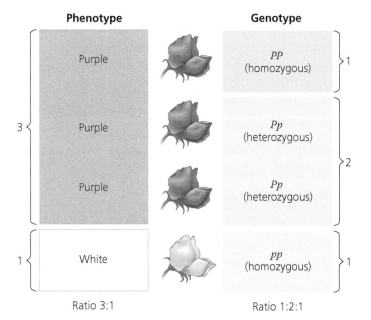

Ratio 3:1   Ratio 1:2:1

▲ **Figure 11.6 Phenotype versus genotype.** Grouping F₂ offspring from a cross for flower color according to phenotype results in the typical 3:1 phenotypic ratio. In terms of genotype, however, there are actually two categories of purple-flowered plants, *PP* (homozygous) and *Pp* (heterozygous), giving a 1:2:1 genotypic ratio.

The Testcross

Given a purple-flowered pea plant, we cannot tell if it is homozygous (*PP*) or heterozygous (*Pp*) because both genotypes result in the same purple phenotype. To determine the genotype, we can cross this plant with a white-flowered plant (*pp*), which will make only gametes with the recessive allele (*p*). The allele in the gamete contributed by the mystery plant will therefore determine the appearance of the offspring **(Figure 11.7)**. If all the offspring of the cross have purple flowers, then the purple-flowered mystery plant must be homozygous for the dominant allele, because a *PP* × *pp* cross produces all *Pp* offspring. But if both the purple and the white phenotypes appear among the offspring, then the purple-flowered parent must be heterozygous. The offspring of a *Pp* × *pp* cross will be expected to have a 1:1 phenotypic ratio. Breeding an organism of unknown genotype with a recessive homozygote is called a **testcross** because it can reveal the genotype of that organism. The testcross was devised by Mendel and continues to be used by geneticists.

The Law of Independent Assortment

Mendel derived the law of segregation from experiments in which he followed only a *single* character, such as flower color. All the F₁ progeny produced in his crosses of true-breeding parents were **monohybrids**, meaning that they were heterozygous for the one particular character being followed in the cross. We refer to a cross between such heterozygotes as a **monohybrid cross**.

Mendel identified his second law of inheritance by following *two* characters at the same time, such as seed color and

The Testcross

Application An organism that exhibits a dominant trait, such as purple flowers in pea plants, can be either homozygous for the dominant allele or heterozygous. To determine the organism's genotype, geneticists can perform a testcross.

Technique In a testcross, the individual with the unknown genotype is crossed with a homozygous individual expressing the recessive trait (white flowers in this example), and Punnett squares are used to predict the possible outcomes.

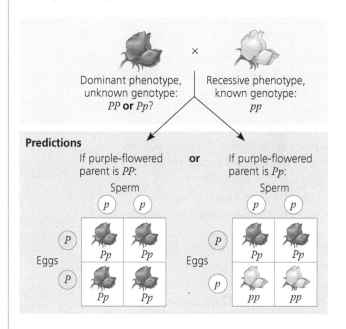

Results Matching the results to either prediction identifies the unknown parental genotype (either *PP* or *Pp* in this example). In this testcross, we transferred pollen from a white-flowered plant to the carpels of a purple-flowered plant; the opposite (reciprocal) cross would have led to the same results.

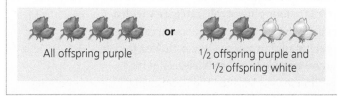

All offspring purple   or   ½ offspring purple and ½ offspring white

seed shape. Seeds (peas) may be either yellow or green. They also may be either round (smooth) or wrinkled. From single-character crosses, Mendel knew that the allele for yellow seeds (*Y*) is dominant and the allele for green seeds (*y*) is recessive. For the seed-shape character, the allele for round (*R*) is dominant, and the allele for wrinkled (*r*) is recessive.

Imagine crossing two true-breeding pea varieties that differ in *both* of these characters—a cross between a plant with yellow round seeds (*YYRR*) and a plant with green wrinkled seeds (*yyrr*). The F₁ plants will be **dihybrids**, individuals heterozygous for the two characters being followed in the cross (*YyRr*). But are these two characters transmitted from parents to offspring as a package? That is, will the *Y* and *R* alleles always stay together, generation after generation? Or are seed color and seed shape inherited independently? **Figure 11.8** shows how a **dihybrid cross**, a cross between F_1 dihybrids, can determine which of these two hypotheses is correct.

The F_1 plants, of genotype *YyRr*, exhibit both dominant phenotypes, yellow seeds with round shapes, no matter which hypothesis is correct. The key step in the experiment is to see what happens when F_1 plants self-pollinate and produce F_2 offspring. If the hybrids must transmit their alleles in the same combinations in which the alleles were inherited from the P generation, then the F_1 hybrids will produce only two classes of gametes: *YR* and *yr*. This "dependent assortment" hypothesis predicts that the phenotypic ratio of the F_2 generation will be 3:1, just as in a monohybrid cross (see Figure 11.8, left side).

The alternative hypothesis is that the two pairs of alleles segregate independently of each other. In other words, genes are packaged into gametes in all possible allelic combinations, as long as each gamete has one allele for each gene. In our example, an F_1 plant will produce four classes of gametes in equal quantities: *YR*, *Yr*, *yR*, and *yr*. If sperm of the four classes fertilize eggs of the four classes, there will be 16 (4 × 4) equally probable ways in which the alleles can combine in the F_2 generation, as shown in Figure 11.8, right side. These combinations result in four phenotypic categories with a ratio of 9:3:3:1 (nine yellow round to three green round to three yellow wrinkled to one green wrinkled). When Mendel did the experiment and classified the F_2 offspring, his results were close to the predicted 9:3:3:1 phenotypic ratio, supporting the hypothesis that the alleles for one gene—controlling seed color, for example—segregate into gametes independently of the alleles of any other gene, such as seed shape.

Mendel tested his seven pea characters in various dihybrid combinations and always observed a 9:3:3:1 phenotypic ratio in the F_2 generation. Is this consistent with the 3:1 phenotypic ratio seen for the monohybrid cross shown in Figure 11.5? If you calculate the ratio of yellow and green peas, ignoring shape, you will see that the color

Do the alleles for one character segregate into gametes dependently or independently of the alleles for a different character?

Experiment To follow the characters of seed color and seed shape through the F_2 generation, Mendel crossed a true-breeding plant with yellow round seeds with a true-breeding plant with green wrinkled seeds, producing dihybrid F_1 plants. Self-pollination of the F_1 dihybrids produced the F_2 generation. The two hypotheses (dependent and independent "assortment" of the two genes) predict different phenotypic ratios.

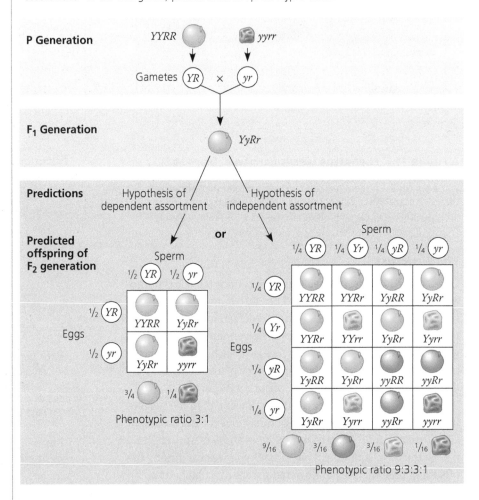

Results

315 ●   108 ●   101 🟫   32 🟫   Phenotypic ratio approximately 9:3:3:1

Conclusion Only the hypothesis of independent assortment predicts two of the observed phenotypes: green round seeds and yellow wrinkled seeds (see the right-hand Punnett square). The alleles for each gene segregate independently of those of the other, and the two genes are said to assort independently.

Data from G. Mendel, Experiments in plant hybridization, *Proceedings of the Natural History Society of Brünn* 4:3–47 (1866).

WHAT IF? Suppose Mendel had transferred pollen from an F_1 plant to the carpel of a plant that was homozygous recessive for both genes. Set up the cross and draw Punnett squares that predict the offspring for both hypotheses. Would this cross have supported the hypothesis of independent assortment equally well?

alleles segregate as if this were a monohybrid cross (3:1). The results of Mendel's dihybrid experiments are the basis for what we now call the **law of independent assortment**, which states that *two or more genes assort independently—that is, each pair of alleles segregates independently of any other pair during gamete formation.*

This law applies only to genes (allele pairs) located on different chromosomes—that is, on chromosomes that are not homologous—or very far apart on the same chromosome. (The latter case will be explained in Chapter 12, along with the more complex inheritance patterns of genes located near each other, which tend to be inherited together.) All the pea characters Mendel chose for analysis were controlled by genes on different chromosomes or far apart on the same chromosome; this greatly simplified the interpretation of his multicharacter pea crosses. All the examples we consider in the rest of this chapter involve genes located on different chromosomes.

CONCEPT CHECK 11.1

1. **DRAW IT** Pea plants heterozygous for flower position and stem length (*AaTt*) are allowed to self-pollinate, and 400 of the resulting seeds are planted. Draw a Punnett square for this cross. How many offspring would be predicted to have terminal flowers and be dwarf? (See Table 11.1.)

2. List all gametes that could be made by a pea plant heterozygous for seed color, seed shape, and pod shape (*YyRrIi*; see Table 11.1). How large a Punnett square is needed to predict the offspring of a self-pollination of this "trihybrid"?

3. **MAKE CONNECTIONS** In some pea plant crosses, the plants are self-pollinated. Explain whether self-pollination is considered asexual or sexual reproduction (refer to Concept 10.1).

For suggested answers, see Appendix A.

CONCEPT 11.2

Probability laws govern Mendelian inheritance

Mendel's laws of segregation and independent assortment reflect the same rules of probability that apply to tossing coins, rolling dice, and drawing cards from a deck. The probability scale ranges from 0 to 1. An event that is certain to occur has a probability of 1, while an event that is certain *not* to occur has a probability of 0. With a coin that has heads on both sides, the probability of tossing heads is 1, and the probability of tossing tails is 0. With a normal coin, the chance of tossing heads is ½, and the chance of tossing tails is ½. The probability of drawing the ace of spades from a 52-card deck is $\frac{1}{52}$. The probabilities of all possible outcomes for an event must add up to 1. With a deck of cards, the chance of picking a card other than the ace of spades is $\frac{51}{52}$.

Tossing a coin illustrates an important lesson about probability. For every toss, the probability of heads is ½. The outcome of any particular toss is unaffected by what has happened on previous trials. We refer to phenomena such as coin tosses as independent events. Each toss of a coin, whether done sequentially with one coin or simultaneously with many, is independent of every other toss. And like two separate coin tosses, the alleles of one gene segregate into gametes independently of another gene's alleles (the law of independent assortment). We'll now look at two basic rules of probability that help us predict the outcome of the fusion of such gametes in simple monohybrid crosses and more complicated crosses as well.

The Multiplication and Addition Rules Applied to Monohybrid Crosses

How do we determine the probability that two or more independent events will occur together in some specific combination? For example, what is the chance that two coins tossed simultaneously will both land heads up? The **multiplication rule** states that to determine this probability, we multiply the probability of one event (one coin coming up heads) by the probability of the other event (the other coin coming up heads). By the multiplication rule, then, the probability that both coins will land heads up is ½ × ½ = ¼.

We can apply the same reasoning to an F_1 monohybrid cross (**Figure 11.9**). With seed shape in pea plants as the heritable character, the genotype of F_1 plants is *Rr*. Segregation in a heterozygous plant is like flipping a coin in terms of calculating

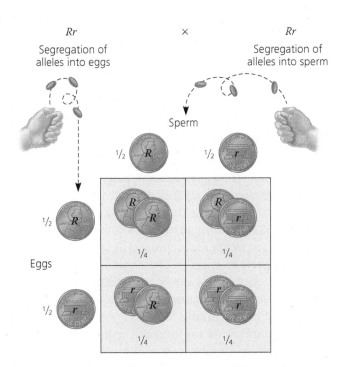

▲ **Figure 11.9 Segregation of alleles and fertilization as chance events.** When a heterozygote (*Rr*) forms gametes, whether a particular gamete ends up with an *R* or an *r* is like the toss of a coin. We can determine the probability for any genotype among the offspring of two heterozygotes by multiplying together the individual probabilities of an egg and sperm having a particular allele (*R* or *r* in this example).

the probability of each outcome: Each egg produced has a ½ chance of carrying the dominant allele (R) and a ½ chance of carrying the recessive allele (r). The same odds apply to each sperm cell produced. For a particular F_2 plant to have wrinkled seeds, the recessive trait, both the egg and the sperm that come together must carry the r allele. The probability that an r allele will be present in both gametes at fertilization is found by multiplying ½ (the probability that the egg will have an r) × ½ (the probability that the sperm will have an r). Thus, the multiplication rule tells us that the probability of an F_2 plant having wrinkled seeds (rr) is ¼ (see Figure 11.9). Likewise, the probability of an F_2 plant carrying both dominant alleles for seed shape (RR) is ¼.

To figure out the probability that an F_2 plant from a monohybrid cross will be heterozygous rather than homozygous, we need to invoke a second rule. Notice in Figure 11.9 that the dominant allele can come from the egg and the recessive allele from the sperm, or vice versa. That is, F_1 gametes can combine to produce Rr offspring in two *mutually exclusive* ways: For any particular heterozygous F_2 plant, the dominant allele can come from the egg *or* the sperm, but not from both. According to the **addition rule**, the probability that any one of two or more mutually exclusive events will occur is calculated by adding their individual probabilities. As we have just seen, the multiplication rule gives us the individual probabilities that we will now add together. The probability for one possible way of obtaining an F_2 heterozygote—the dominant allele from the egg and the recessive allele from the sperm—is ¼. The probability for the other possible way—the recessive allele from the egg and the dominant allele from the sperm—is also ¼ (see Figure 11.9). Using the rule of addition, then, we can calculate the probability of an F_2 heterozygote as ¼ + ¼ = ½.

Solving Complex Genetics Problems with the Rules of Probability

We can also apply the rules of probability to predict the outcome of crosses involving multiple characters. Recall that each allelic pair segregates independently during gamete formation (the law of independent assortment). Thus, a dihybrid or other multicharacter cross is equivalent to two or more independent monohybrid crosses occurring simultaneously. By applying what we have learned about monohybrid crosses, we can determine the probability of specific genotypes occurring in the F_2 generation without having to construct unwieldy Punnett squares.

Consider the dihybrid cross between $YyRr$ heterozygotes shown in Figure 11.8. We will focus first on the seed-color character. For a monohybrid cross of Yy plants, we can use a simple Punnett square to determine that the probabilities of the offspring genotypes are ¼ for YY, ½ for Yy, and ¼ for yy. We can draw a second Punnett square to determine that the same probabilities apply to the offspring genotypes for seed shape: ¼ RR, ½ Rr, and ¼ rr. Knowing these probabilities, we can simply use the multiplication rule to determine the probability of each of the genotypes in the F_2 generation. To give two examples, the

calculations for finding the probabilities of two of the possible F_2 genotypes ($YYRR$ and $YyRR$) are shown below:

Probability of $YYRR$ = ¼ (probability of YY) × ¼ (RR) = ¹⁄₁₆

Probability of $YyRR$ =   ½ (Yy) × ¼ (RR) = ⅛

The $YYRR$ genotype corresponds to the upper left box in the larger Punnett square in Figure 11.8 (one box = ¹⁄₁₆). Looking closely at the larger Punnett square in Figure 11.8, you will see that 2 of the 16 boxes (⅛) correspond to the $YyRR$ genotype.

Now let's see how we can combine the multiplication and addition rules to solve even more complex problems in Mendelian genetics. Imagine a cross of two pea varieties in which we track the inheritance of three characters. Let's cross a trihybrid with purple flowers and yellow round seeds (heterozygous for all three genes) with a plant with purple flowers and green wrinkled seeds (heterozygous for flower color but homozygous recessive for the other two characters). Using Mendelian symbols, our cross is $PpYyRr \times Ppyyrr$. What fraction of offspring from this cross is predicted to exhibit the recessive phenotypes for *at least two* of the three characters?

To answer this question, we can start by listing all genotypes we could get that fulfill this condition: $ppyyRr$, $ppYyrr$, $Ppyyrr$, $PPyyrr$, and $ppyyrr$. (Because the condition is *at least two* recessive traits, it includes the last genotype, which shows all three recessive traits.) Next, we calculate the probability for each of these genotypes resulting from our $PpYyRr \times Ppyyrr$ cross by multiplying together the individual probabilities for the allele pairs, just as we did in our dihybrid example. Note that in a cross involving heterozygous and homozygous allele pairs (for example, $Yy \times yy$), the probability of heterozygous offspring is ½ and the probability of homozygous offspring is ½. Finally, we use the addition rule to add the probabilities for all the different genotypes that fulfill the condition of at least two recessive traits, as shown below:

$ppyyRr$	¼ (probability of pp) × ½ (yy) × ½ (Rr)	= ¹⁄₁₆
$ppYyrr$	¼ × ½ × ½	= ¹⁄₁₆
$Ppyyrr$	½ × ½ × ½	= ²⁄₁₆
$PPyyrr$	¼ × ½ × ½	= ¹⁄₁₆
$ppyyrr$	¼ × ½ × ½	= ¹⁄₁₆
Chance of *at least two* recessive traits		= ⁶⁄₁₆ or ⅜

In time, you'll be able to solve genetics problems faster by using the rules of probability than by filling in Punnett squares.

We cannot predict with certainty the exact numbers of progeny of different genotypes resulting from a genetic cross. But the rules of probability give us the *likelihood* of various outcomes. Usually, the larger the sample size, the closer the results will conform to our predictions. The reason Mendel counted so many offspring from his crosses is that he understood this statistical feature of inheritance and had a keen sense of the rules of chance.

1. For any gene with a dominant allele *A* and recessive allele *a*, what proportions of the offspring from an *AA* × *Aa* cross are expected to be homozygous dominant, homozygous recessive, and heterozygous?

2. Two organisms, with genotypes *BbDD* and *BBDd*, are mated. Assuming independent assortment of the *B/b* and *D/d* genes, write the genotypes of all possible offspring from this cross and use the rules of probability to calculate the chance of each genotype occurring.

3. **WHAT IF?** Three characters (flower color, seed color, and pod shape) are considered in a cross between two pea plants: *PpYyIi* × *ppYyii*. What fraction of offspring is predicted to be homozygous recessive for at least two of the three characters?

For suggested answers, see Appendix A.

CONCEPT 11.3

Inheritance patterns are often more complex than predicted by simple Mendelian genetics

In the 20th century, geneticists extended Mendelian principles not only to diverse organisms but also to patterns of inheritance more complex than those described by Mendel. For the work that led to his two laws of inheritance, Mendel chose pea plant characters that turn out to have a relatively simple genetic basis: Each character is determined by one gene, for which there are only two alleles, one completely dominant and the other completely recessive. (There is one exception: Mendel's pod-shape character is actually determined by two genes.) Few heritable characters are determined so simply, and the relationship between genotype and phenotype is rarely so straightforward. Mendel himself realized that he could not explain the more complicated patterns he observed in crosses involving other pea characters or other plant species. This does not diminish the utility of Mendelian genetics, however, because the basic principles of segregation and independent assortment apply even to more complex patterns of inheritance. In this section, we'll extend Mendelian genetics to hereditary patterns that were not reported by Mendel.

Extending Mendelian Genetics for a Single Gene

The inheritance of characters determined by a single gene deviates from simple Mendelian patterns when alleles are not completely dominant or recessive, when a particular gene has more than two alleles, or when a single gene produces multiple phenotypes. We'll describe examples of each of these situations in this section.

Degrees of Dominance

Alleles can show different degrees of dominance and recessiveness in relation to each other. In Mendel's classic pea crosses,

the F_1 offspring always looked like one of the two parental varieties because one allele in a pair showed **complete dominance** over the other. In such situations, the phenotypes of the heterozygote and the dominant homozygote are indistinguishable.

For some genes, however, neither allele is completely dominant, and the F_1 hybrids have a phenotype somewhere between those of the two parental varieties. This phenomenon, called **incomplete dominance**, is seen when red snapdragons are crossed with white snapdragons: All the F_1 hybrids have pink flowers **(Figure 11.10)**. This third, intermediate phenotype results from flowers of the heterozygotes having less red pigment than the red homozygotes. (This is unlike the case of Mendel's pea plants, where the *Pp* heterozygotes make enough pigment for the flowers to be purple, indistinguishable from those of *PP* plants.)

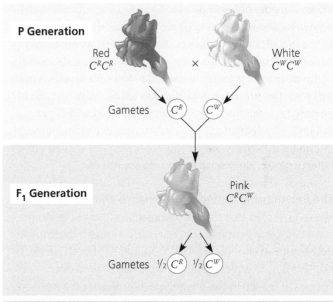
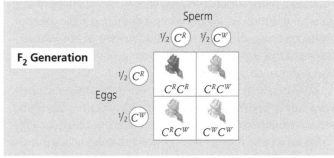

▲ **Figure 11.10 Incomplete dominance in snapdragon color.** When red snapdragons are crossed with white ones, the F_1 hybrids have pink flowers. Segregation of alleles into gametes of the F_1 plants results in an F_2 generation with a 1:2:1 ratio for both genotype and phenotype. Neither allele is dominant, so rather than using upper- and lowercase letters, we use the letter *C* with a superscript to indicate an allele for flower color: C^R for red and C^W for white.

❓ *Suppose a classmate argues that this figure supports the blending hypothesis for inheritance. What might your classmate say, and how would you respond?*

At first glance, incomplete dominance of either allele seems to provide evidence for the blending hypothesis of inheritance, which would predict that the red or white trait could never reappear among offspring of the pink hybrids. In fact, interbreeding F_1 hybrids produces F_2 offspring with a phenotypic ratio of one red to two pink to one white. (Because heterozygotes have a separate phenotype, the genotypic and phenotypic ratios for the F_2 generation are the same, 1:2:1.) The segregation of the red-flower and white-flower alleles in the gametes produced by the pink-flowered plants confirms that the alleles for flower color are heritable factors that maintain their identity in the hybrids; that is, inheritance is particulate.

Another variation on dominance relationships between alleles is called **codominance**; in this variation, the two alleles each affect the phenotype in separate, distinguishable ways. For example, the human MN blood group is determined by codominant alleles for two specific molecules located on the surface of red blood cells, the M and N molecules. A single gene locus, at which two allelic variations are possible, determines the phenotype of this blood group. Individuals homozygous for the *M* allele (*MM*) have red blood cells with only M molecules; individuals homozygous for the *N* allele (*NN*) have red blood cells with only N molecules. But *both* M and N molecules are present on the red blood cells of individuals heterozygous for the *M* and *N* alleles (*MN*). Note that the MN phenotype is *not* intermediate between the M and N phenotypes, which distinguishes codominance from incomplete dominance. Rather, *both* M and N phenotypes are exhibited by heterozygotes, since both molecules are present.

The Relationship Between Dominance and Phenotype - We've now seen that the relative effects of two alleles range from complete dominance of one allele, through incomplete dominance of either allele, to codominance of both alleles. It is important to understand that an allele is called *dominant* because it is seen in the phenotype, not because it somehow subdues a recessive allele. Alleles are simply variations in a gene's nucleotide sequence. When a dominant allele coexists with a recessive allele in a heterozygote, they do not actually interact at all. It is in the pathway from genotype to phenotype that dominance and recessiveness come into play.

To illustrate the relationship between dominance and phenotype, we can use one of the characters Mendel studied—round versus wrinkled pea seed shape. The dominant allele (round) codes for an enzyme that helps convert an unbranched form of starch to a branched form in the seed. The recessive allele (wrinkled) codes for a defective form of this enzyme, leading to an accumulation of unbranched starch, which causes excess water to enter the seed by osmosis. Later, when the seed dries, it wrinkles. If a dominant allele is present, no excess water enters the seed and it does not wrinkle when it dries. One dominant allele results in enough of the enzyme to synthesize adequate amounts of branched starch, which means that dominant homozygotes and heterozygotes have the same phenotype: round seeds.

A closer look at the relationship between dominance and phenotype reveals an intriguing fact: For any character, the observed dominant/recessive relationship of alleles depends on the level at which we examine the phenotype. **Tay-Sachs disease**, an inherited disorder in humans, provides an example. The brain cells of a child with Tay-Sachs disease cannot metabolize certain lipids because a crucial enzyme does not work properly. As these lipids accumulate in brain cells, the child begins to suffer seizures, blindness, and degeneration of motor and mental performance and dies within a few years.

Only children who inherit two copies of the Tay-Sachs allele (homozygotes) have the disease. Thus, at the *organismal* level, the Tay-Sachs allele qualifies as recessive. However, the activity level of the lipid-metabolizing enzyme in heterozygotes is intermediate between the activity level in individuals homozygous for the normal allele and the activity level in individuals with Tay-Sachs disease. (The term *normal* is used in the genetic sense to refer to the allele coding for the enzyme that functions properly.) The intermediate phenotype observed at the *biochemical* level is characteristic of incomplete dominance of either allele. Fortunately, the heterozygote condition does not lead to disease symptoms, apparently because half the normal enzyme activity is sufficient to prevent lipid accumulation in the brain. Extending our analysis to yet another level, we find that heterozygous individuals produce equal numbers of normal and dysfunctional enzyme molecules. Thus, at the *molecular* level, the normal allele and the Tay-Sachs allele are codominant. As you can see, whether alleles appear to be completely dominant, incompletely dominant, or codominant depends on the level at which the phenotype is analyzed.

Frequency of Dominant Alleles While you might assume that the dominant allele for a particular character would be more common in a population than the recessive one, this is not always so. For example, about one baby out of 400 in the United States is born with extra digits (fingers or toes), a condition known as polydactyly. Some cases are caused by the presence of a dominant allele. The low frequency of polydactyly indicates that the recessive allele, which results in five digits per appendage when homozygous, is far more prevalent than the dominant allele in the population.

Multiple Alleles

Only two alleles exist for each of the seven pea characters that Mendel studied, but most genes exist in more than two allelic forms. The ABO blood groups in humans, for instance, are determined by that person's two alleles of the blood group gene; there are three possible alleles: I^A, I^B, and i. A person's blood group may be one of four types: A, B, AB, or O. These letters refer to two carbohydrates—A and B—that are found on the surface of red blood cells. An individual's blood cells may have carbohydrate A (type A blood), carbohydrate B (type B), both (type AB), or neither (type O), as shown schematically in **Figure 11.11**. Matching compatible blood groups is critical for safe blood transfusions.

(a) **The three alleles for the ABO blood groups and their carbohydrates.** Each allele codes for an enzyme that may add a specific carbohydrate (designated by the superscript on the allele and shown as a triangle or circle) to red blood cells.			
Allele	I^A	I^B	i
Carbohydrate	A △	B ○	none

(b) **Blood group genotypes and phenotypes.** There are six possible genotypes, resulting in four different phenotypes.				
Genotype	$I^A I^A$ or $I^A i$	$I^B I^B$ or $I^B i$	$I^A I^B$	ii
Red blood cell appearance	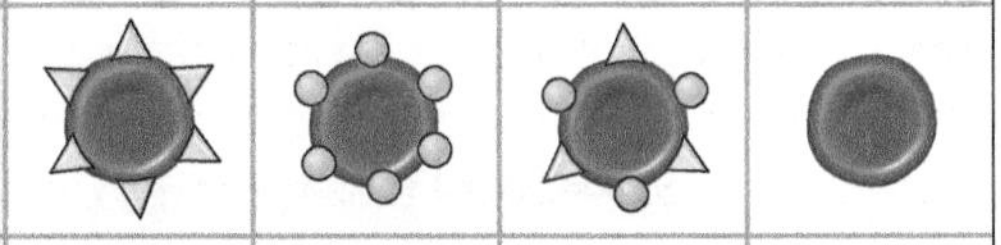			
Phenotype (blood group)	A	B	AB	O

▲ **Figure 11.11 Multiple alleles for the ABO blood groups.** The four blood groups result from different combinations of three alleles.

? *Based on the surface carbohydrate phenotype in (b), what are the dominance relationships among the alleles?*

Pleiotropy

So far, we have treated Mendelian inheritance as though each gene affects only one phenotypic character. Most genes, however, have multiple phenotypic effects, a property called **pleiotropy** (from the Greek *pleion*, more). In humans, for example, pleiotropic alleles are responsible for the multiple symptoms associated with certain hereditary diseases, such as cystic fibrosis and sickle-cell disease, discussed later in this chapter. In the garden pea, the gene that determines flower color also affects the color of the coating on the outer surface of the seed, which can be gray or white. Given the intricate molecular and cellular interactions responsible for an organism's development and physiology, it isn't surprising that a single gene can affect a number of characters.

Extending Mendelian Genetics for Two or More Genes

Dominance relationships, multiple alleles, and pleiotropy all have to do with the effects of the alleles of a single gene. We now consider two situations in which two or more genes are involved in determining a particular phenotype. In the first case, one gene affects the phenotype of another because the two gene products interact, whereas in the second case, multiple genes independently affect a single trait.

Epistasis

In **epistasis** (from the Greek for "standing upon"), the phenotypic expression of a gene at one locus alters that of a gene at a second locus. An example will help clarify this concept. In Labrador retrievers (commonly called Labs), black coat color

is dominant to brown. Let's designate *B* and *b* as the two alleles for this character. For a Lab to have brown fur, its genotype must be *bb*; these dogs are called chocolate Labs. But there is more to the story. A second gene determines whether or not pigment will be deposited in the hair. The dominant allele, symbolized by *E*, results in the deposition of either black or brown pigment, depending on the genotype at the first locus. But if the Lab is homozygous recessive for the second locus (*ee*), then the coat is yellow, regardless of the genotype at the black/brown locus. In this case, the gene for pigment deposition (*E/e*) is said to be epistatic to the gene that codes for black or brown pigment (*B/b*).

What happens if we mate black Labs that are heterozygous for both genes (*BbEe*)? Although the two genes affect the same phenotypic character (coat color), they follow the law of independent assortment. Thus, our breeding experiment represents an F_1 dihybrid cross, like those that produced a 9:3:3:1 ratio in Mendel's experiments. We can use a Punnett square to represent the genotypes of the F_2 offspring **(Figure 11.12)**. As a result of epistasis, the phenotypic ratio among the F_2 offspring is 9 black to 3 chocolate to 4 yellow Labs. Other types of epistatic interactions produce different ratios, but all are modified versions of 9:3:3:1.

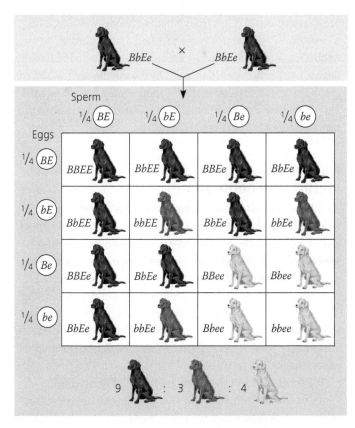

▲ **Figure 11.12 An example of epistasis.** This Punnett square illustrates the genotypes and phenotypes predicted for offspring of matings between two black Labrador retrievers of genotype *BbEe*. The *E/e* gene, which is epistatic to the *B/b* gene coding for hair pigment, controls whether or not pigment of any color will be deposited in the hair.

Polygenic Inheritance

Mendel studied characters that could be classified on an either-or basis, such as purple versus white flower color. But many characters, such as human skin color and height, are not one of two discrete characters, but instead vary in the population in gradations along a continuum. These are called **quantitative characters**. Quantitative variation usually indicates **polygenic inheritance**, an additive effect of two or more genes on a single phenotypic character. (In a way, this is the converse of pleiotropy, where a single gene affects several phenotypic characters.) Height is a good example of polygenic inheritance: Genomic studies have identified at least 180 gene variations that affect height.

Skin pigmentation in humans is also controlled by many separately inherited genes. Here, we'll simplify the story in order to understand the concept of polygenic inheritance. Let's consider three genes, with a dark-skin allele for each gene (*A*, *B*, or *C*) contributing one "unit" of darkness (also a simplification) to the phenotype and being incompletely dominant to the other, light-skin allele (*a*, *b*, or *c*). In our model, an *AABBCC* person would be very dark, whereas an *aabbcc* individual would be very light. An *AaBbCc* person would have skin of an intermediate shade. Because the alleles have a cumulative effect, the genotypes *AaBbCc* and *AABbcc* would make the same genetic contribution (three units) to skin darkness. There are seven skin-color phenotypes that could result from a mating between *AaBbCc* heterozygotes, as shown in **Figure 11.13**. In a large number of such matings, the majority of offspring would be expected to have intermediate phenotypes (skin color in the middle range). You can graph the predictions from the Punnett square in the **Scientific Skills Exercise**. Environmental factors, such as exposure to the sun, also affect the skin-color phenotype.

Nature and Nurture: The Environmental Impact on Phenotype

Another departure from simple Mendelian genetics arises when the phenotype for a character depends on environment as well as genotype. A single tree, locked into its inherited genotype, has leaves that vary in size, shape, and greenness, depending on their exposure to wind and sun. In humans, nutrition influences height, exercise alters build, sun-tanning darkens the skin, and experience improves performance on intelligence tests. Even identical twins, who are genetic equals, accumulate phenotypic differences as a result of their unique experiences.

Whether human characters are more influenced by genes or the environment—in everyday terms, nature versus nurture—is a debate that we will not attempt to settle here. We can say, however, that a genotype generally is not associated with a rigidly defined phenotype, but rather with a range of phenotypic possibilities due to environmental influences. For some characters, such as the ABO blood group system, the range is extremely narrow; that is, a given genotype mandates

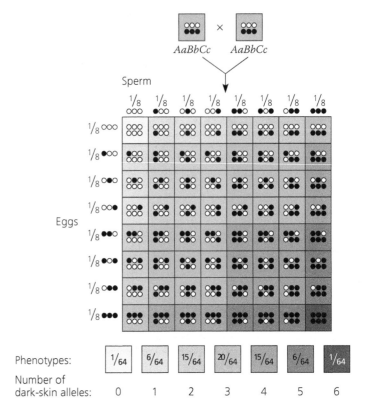

▲ **Figure 11.13 A simplified model for polygenic inheritance of skin color.** In this model, three separately inherited genes affect skin color. The heterozygous individuals (*AaBbCc*) represented by the two rectangles at the top of this figure each carry three dark-skin alleles (black circles, representing *A*, *B*, or *C*) and three light-skin alleles (white circles, representing *a*, *b*, or *c*). The Punnett square shows all the possible genetic combinations in gametes and offspring of many hypothetical matings between these heterozygotes. The results are summarized by the phenotypic frequencies (fractions) under the Punnett square. (The phenotypic ratio of the skin colors shown in the boxes is 1:6:15:20:15:6:1.)

a very specific phenotype. Other characters, such as a person's blood count of red and white cells, vary quite a bit, depending on such factors as the altitude, the customary level of physical activity, and the presence of infectious agents.

Generally, the phenotypic range is broadest for polygenic characters. Environment contributes to the quantitative nature of these characters, as we have seen in the continuous variation of skin color. Geneticists refer to such characters as **multifactorial**, meaning that many factors, both genetic and environmental, collectively influence phenotype.

A Mendelian View of Heredity and Variation

We have now broadened our view of Mendelian inheritance by exploring degrees of dominance as well as multiple alleles, pleiotropy, epistasis, polygenic inheritance, and the phenotypic impact of the environment. How can we integrate these refinements into a comprehensive theory of Mendelian genetics? The key is to make the transition from the reductionist emphasis on single genes and phenotypic characters to the emergent properties of the organism as a whole, one of the themes of this book.

Making a Histogram and Analyzing a Distribution Pattern

What Is the Distribution of Phenotypes Among Offspring of Two Parents Who Are Both Heterozygous for Three Additive Genes? Human skin color is a polygenic trait that is determined by the additive effects of many different genes. In this exercise, you will work with a simplified model of skin-color genetics where only three genes are assumed to affect the darkness of skin color and where each gene has two alleles—dark or light (see Figure 11.13). In this model, each dark allele contributes equally to the darkness of skin color, and each pair of alleles segregates independently of each other pair. Using a type of graph called a histogram, you will determine the distribution of phenotypes of offspring with different numbers of dark-skin alleles. (For additional information about graphs, see the Scientific Skills Review in Appendix F and in the Study Area in MasteringBiology.)

How This Model Is Analyzed To predict the phenotypes of the offspring of parents heterozygous for the three genes in our simplified model, we can use the Punnett square in Figure 11.13. The heterozygous individuals (*AaBbCc*) represented by the two rectangles at the top of that figure each carry three dark-skin alleles (black circles, which represent *A*, *B*, or *C*) and three light-skin alleles (white circles, which represent *a*, *b*, or *c*). The Punnett square shows all the possible genetic combinations in gametes and in offspring of a large number of hypothetical matings between these heterozygotes.

Predictions from the Punnett Square If we assume that each square in the Punnett square represents one offspring of the heterozygous *AaBbCc* parents, then the squares below show the possible phenotypes. Below the squares are the predicted phenotypic frequencies of individuals with the same number of dark-skin alleles.

Phenotypes:	$^1/_{64}$	$^6/_{64}$	$^{15}/_{64}$	$^{20}/_{64}$	$^{15}/_{64}$	$^6/_{64}$	$^1/_{64}$
Number of dark-skin alleles:	0	1	2	3	4	5	6

INTERPRET THE DATA

1. A histogram is a bar graph that shows the distribution of numeric data (here, the number of dark skin alleles). To make a histogram of the allele distribution, put skin color (as the number of dark-skin alleles) along the *x*-axis and number of offspring (out of 64) with each phenotype on the *y*-axis. There are no gaps in our allele data, so draw the bars with no space between them.

2. You can see that the skin-color phenotypes are not distributed uniformly. (a) Which phenotype has the highest frequency? Draw a vertical dashed line through that bar. (b) Distributions of values like this one tend to show one of several common patterns. Sketch a rough curve that approximates the values and look at its shape. Is it symmetrically distributed around a central peak value (a "normal distribution," sometimes called a bell curve); is it skewed to one end of the *x*-axis or the other (a "skewed distribution"); or does it show two apparent groups of frequencies (a "bimodal distribution")? Explain the reason for the curve's shape. (It will help to read the text description that supports Figure 11.13.)

(MB) A version of this Scientific Skills Exercise can be assigned in MasteringBiology.

Further Reading R. A. Sturm, A golden age of human pigmentation genetics, *Trends in Genetics* 22:464–468 (2006).

The term *phenotype* can refer not only to specific characters, such as flower color and blood group, but also to an organism in its entirety—*all* aspects of its physical appearance, internal anatomy, physiology, and behavior. Similarly, the term *genotype* can refer to an organism's entire genetic makeup, not just its alleles for a single genetic locus. In most cases, a gene's impact on phenotype is affected by other genes and by the environment. In this integrated view of heredity and variation, an organism's phenotype reflects its overall genotype and unique environmental history.

Considering all that can occur in the pathway from genotype to phenotype, it is indeed impressive that Mendel could uncover the fundamental principles governing the transmission of individual genes from parents to offspring. Mendel's laws of segregation and independent assortment explain heritable variations in terms of alternative forms of genes (hereditary "particles," now known as the alleles of genes) that are passed along, generation after generation, according to simple rules of probability. This theory of inheritance is equally valid for peas, flies, fishes, birds, and human beings—indeed, for any organism with a sexual life cycle. Furthermore, by extending the principles of

segregation and independent assortment to help explain such hereditary patterns as epistasis and quantitative characters, we begin to see how broadly Mendelian genetics applies. From Mendel's abbey garden came a theory of particulate inheritance that anchors modern genetics. In the last section of this chapter, we'll apply Mendelian genetics to human inheritance, with emphasis on the transmission of hereditary diseases.

CONCEPT CHECK 11.3

1. *Incomplete dominance* and *epistasis* are both terms that define genetic relationships. What is the most basic distinction between these terms?

2. If a man with type AB blood marries a woman with type O, what blood types would you expect in their children? What fraction would you expect of each type?

3. **WHAT IF?** A rooster with gray feathers and a hen of the same phenotype produce 15 gray, 6 black, and 8 white chicks. What is the simplest explanation for the inheritance of these colors in chickens? What phenotypes would you expect in the offspring of a cross between a gray rooster and a black hen?

For suggested answers, see Appendix A.

Many human traits follow Mendelian patterns of inheritance

Peas are convenient subjects for genetic research, but humans are not. The human generation span is long—about 20 years—and human parents produce many fewer offspring than peas and most other species. Even more important, it wouldn't be ethical to ask pairs of humans to breed so that the phenotypes of their offspring could be analyzed! In spite of these constraints, the study of human genetics continues, spurred on by our desire to understand our own inheritance. New molecular biological techniques have led to many breakthrough discoveries, but basic Mendelian genetics endures as the foundation of human genetics.

Pedigree Analysis

Unable to manipulate the matings of people, geneticists instead analyze the results of matings that have already occurred. They do so by collecting information about a family's history for a particular trait and assembling this information into a family tree describing the traits of parents and children across the generations—a family **pedigree**.

Figure 11.14a shows a three-generation pedigree that traces the occurrence of a pointed contour of the hairline on the forehead. This trait, called a widow's peak, is due to a dominant allele, W. Because the widow's-peak allele is dominant, all individuals who lack a widow's peak must be homozygous recessive (ww). The two grandparents with widow's peaks must have the Ww genotype, since some of their offspring are homozygous recessive. The offspring in the second generation who *do* have widow's peaks must also be heterozygous, because they are the products of $Ww \times ww$ matings. The third generation in this pedigree consists of two sisters. The one who has a widow's peak could be either homozygous (WW) or heterozygous (Ww), given what we know about the genotypes of her parents (both Ww).

Figure 11.14b is a pedigree of the same family, but this time we focus on a recessive trait, the inability of individuals to taste a chemical called PTC (phenylthiocarbamide). Compounds similar to PTC are found in broccoli, brussels sprouts, and related vegetables and account for the bitter taste some people report when eating these foods. We'll use t for the recessive allele and T for the dominant allele, which results in the ability to taste PTC. As you work your way through the pedigree, notice once again that you can apply what you have learned about Mendelian inheritance to understand the genotypes shown for the family members.

An important application of a pedigree is to help us calculate the probability that a future child will have a particular genotype and phenotype. Suppose that the couple represented in the second generation of Figure 11.14 decides to have one

Key

☐ Male   ▪ Male with the trait   ☐—○ Mating

○ Female   ● Female with the trait   Offspring, in birth order (first-born on left)

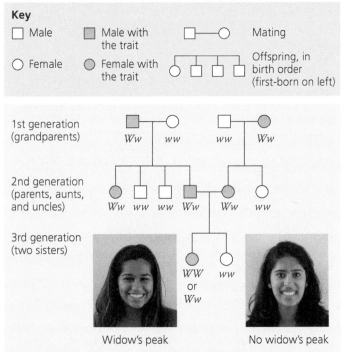

(a) Is a widow's peak a dominant or recessive trait?
Tips for pedigree analysis: Notice in the third generation that the second-born daughter lacks a widow's peak, although both of her parents had the trait. Such a pattern indicates that the trait is due to a dominant allele. If it were due to a *recessive* allele, and both parents had the recessive phenotype (straight hairline), *all* of their offspring would also have the recessive phenotype.

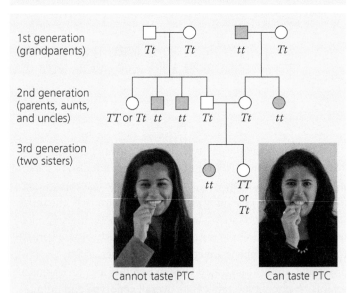

(b) Is the inability to taste a chemical called PTC a dominant or recessive trait?
Tips for pedigree analysis: Notice that the first-born daughter in the third generation has the trait (is unable to taste PTC), although both parents lack that trait (they *can* taste PTC). Such a pattern is explained if the non-taster phenotype is due to a recessive allele. (If it were due to a *dominant* allele, then at least one parent would also have had the trait.)

▲ **Figure 11.14 Pedigree analysis.** Each pedigree traces a trait through three generations of the same family. The two traits have different inheritance patterns. For the sake of understanding genetic principles, each trait is shown as being determined by two alleles of a single gene. This is a simplification because other genes may also affect each of these characters.

more child. What is the probability that the child will have a widow's peak? This is equivalent to a Mendelian F_1 monohybrid cross ($Ww \times Ww$), and therefore the probability that a child will inherit a dominant allele and have a widow's peak is ¾ (¼ WW + ½ Ww). What is the probability that the child will be unable to taste PTC? We can also treat this as a monohybrid cross ($Tt \times Tt$), but this time we want to know the chance that the offspring will be homozygous recessive (tt). The probability is ¼. Finally, what is the chance the child will have a widow's peak *and* be unable to taste PTC? Assuming that the genes for these two characters are on different chromosomes, the two pairs of alleles will assort independently in this dihybrid cross ($WwTt \times WwTt$). Thus, we can use the multiplication rule: ¾ (chance of widow's peak) × ¼ (chance of inability to taste PTC) = ³⁄₁₆ (chance of widow's peak and inability to taste PTC).

Pedigrees are a more serious matter when the alleles in question cause disabling or deadly diseases instead of an innocuous human variation, such as hairline configuration or ability to taste an innocuous chemical. However, for disorders inherited as simple Mendelian traits, the same techniques of pedigree analysis apply.

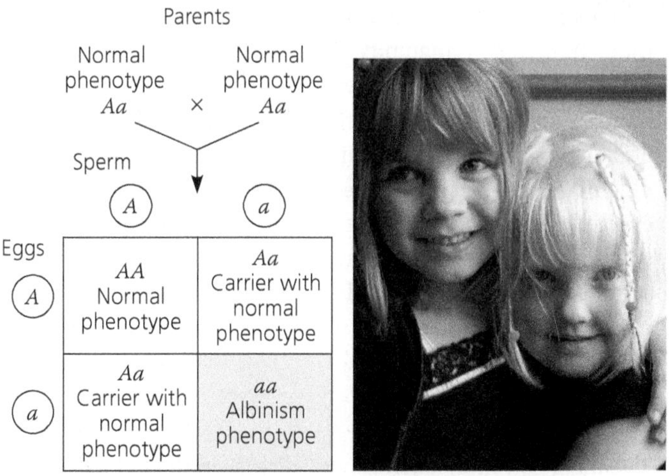

Recessively Inherited Disorders

Thousands of genetic disorders are known to be inherited as simple recessive traits. These disorders range in severity from relatively mild, such as albinism (lack of pigmentation, which results in susceptibility to skin cancers and vision problems), to life-threatening, such as cystic fibrosis.

The Behavior of Recessive Alleles

How can we account for the behavior of alleles that cause recessively inherited disorders? Recall that genes code for proteins of specific function. An allele that causes a genetic disorder (let's call it allele *a*) codes for either a malfunctioning protein or no protein at all. In the case of disorders classified as recessive, heterozygotes (Aa) typically have the normal phenotype because one copy of the normal allele (A) produces a sufficient amount of the specific protein. Thus, a recessively inherited disorder shows up only in the homozygous individuals (aa) who inherit a recessive allele from each parent. Although phenotypically normal with regard to the disorder, heterozygotes may transmit the recessive allele to their offspring and thus are called **carriers**. **Figure 11.15** illustrates these ideas using albinism as an example.

Most people who have recessive disorders are born to parents who are carriers of the disorder but have a normal phenotype, as is the case shown in the Punnett square in Figure 11.15. A mating between two carriers corresponds to a Mendelian F_1 monohybrid cross, so the predicted genotypic ratio for offspring is 1 AA : 2 Aa : 1 aa. Thus, each child has a ¼ chance of inheriting a double dose of the recessive allele; in the case of albinism, such a child will have albinism. From the genotypic ratio, we also can see that out of three offspring

▲ **Figure 11.15 Albinism: a recessive trait.** One of the two sisters shown here has normal coloration; the other has albinism. Most recessive homozygotes are born to parents who are carriers of the disorder but themselves have a normal phenotype, the case shown in the Punnett square.

? *What is the probability that the sister with normal coloration is a carrier of the albinism allele?*

with the normal phenotype (one AA plus two Aa), two are predicted to be heterozygous carriers, a ⅔ chance. Recessive homozygotes could also result from $Aa \times aa$ and $aa \times aa$ matings, but if the disorder is lethal before reproductive age or results in sterility (neither of which is true for albinism), no aa individuals will reproduce. Even if recessive homozygotes are able to reproduce, this will occur relatively rarely because such individuals account for a much smaller percentage of the population than heterozygous carriers.

In general, genetic disorders are not evenly distributed among all groups of people. For example, the incidence of Tay-Sachs disease, which we described earlier in this chapter, is disproportionately high among Ashkenazic Jews, Jewish people whose ancestors lived in central Europe. In that population, Tay-Sachs disease occurs in one out of 3,600 births, an incidence about 100 times greater than that among non-Jews or Mediterranean (Sephardic) Jews. This uneven distribution results from the different genetic histories of the world's peoples during less technological times, when populations were more geographically (and hence genetically) isolated.

When a disease-causing recessive allele is rare, it is relatively unlikely that two carriers of the same harmful allele will meet and mate. The probability of passing on recessive traits increases greatly, however, if the man and woman are close relatives (for example, siblings or first cousins). This is because people with recent common ancestors are more likely to carry the same recessive alleles than are unrelated people. Thus, these consanguineous ("same blood") matings, indicated in pedigrees by double lines, are more likely to produce offspring homozygous for recessive traits—including harmful ones. Such effects can be observed in many types of domesticated and zoo animals that have become inbred.

There is debate among geneticists about exactly how much human consanguinity increases the risk of inherited diseases. Many harmful alleles have such severe effects that a homozygous embryo spontaneously aborts long before birth. Still, most societies and cultures have laws or taboos forbidding marriages between close relatives. These rules may have evolved out of empirical observation that in most populations, stillbirths and birth defects are more common when parents are closely related. Social and economic factors have also influenced the development of customs and laws against consanguineous marriages.

Cystic Fibrosis

The most common lethal genetic disease in the United States is **cystic fibrosis**, which strikes one out of every 2,500 people of European descent but is much rarer in other groups. Among people of European descent, one out of 25 (4%) are carriers of the cystic fibrosis allele. The normal allele for this gene codes for a membrane protein that functions in the transport of chloride ions between certain cells and the extracellular fluid. These chloride transport channels are defective or absent in the plasma membranes of children who inherit two recessive alleles for cystic fibrosis. The result is an abnormally high concentration of extracellular chloride, which causes the mucus that coats certain cells to become thicker and stickier than normal. The mucus builds up in the pancreas, lungs, digestive tract, and other organs, leading to multiple (pleiotropic) effects, including poor absorption of nutrients from the intestines, chronic bronchitis, and recurrent bacterial infections.

Untreated, cystic fibrosis can cause death by the age of 5. Daily doses of antibiotics to stop infection, gentle pounding on the chest to clear mucus from clogged airways, and other therapies can prolong life. In the United States, more than half of those with cystic fibrosis now survive into their 30s and beyond.

Sickle-Cell Disease: A Genetic Disorder with Evolutionary Implications

EVOLUTION The most common inherited disorder among people of African descent is **sickle-cell disease**, which affects one out of 400 African-Americans. Sickle-cell disease is caused by the substitution of a single amino acid in the hemoglobin protein of red blood cells; in homozygous individuals, all hemoglobin is of the sickle-cell (abnormal) variety. When the oxygen content of an affected individual's blood is low (at high altitudes or under physical stress, for instance), the sickle-cell hemoglobin molecules aggregate into long rods that deform the red cells into a sickle shape (see Figure 3.23). Sickled cells may clump and clog small blood vessels, often leading to other symptoms throughout the body, including physical weakness, pain, organ damage, and even stroke and paralysis. Regular blood transfusions can ward off brain damage in children with sickle-cell disease, and new drugs can help prevent or treat other problems. There is currently no widely available cure, but the disease is the target of ongoing gene therapy research.

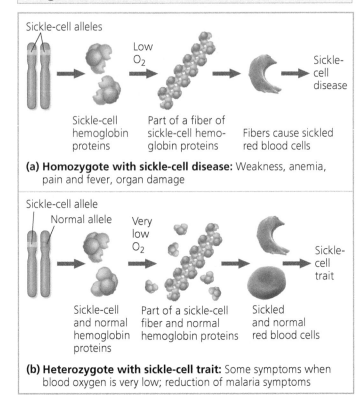

▼ **Figure 11.16 Sickle-cell disease and sickle-cell trait.**

Sickle-cell alleles

Low O₂

Sickle-cell hemoglobin proteins

Part of a fiber of sickle-cell hemoglobin proteins

Fibers cause sickled red blood cells

Sickle-cell disease

(a) Homozygote with sickle-cell disease: Weakness, anemia, pain and fever, organ damage

Sickle-cell allele
Normal allele

Very low O₂

Sickle-cell and normal hemoglobin proteins

Part of a sickle-cell fiber and normal hemoglobin proteins

Sickled and normal red blood cells

Sickle-cell trait

(b) Heterozygote with sickle-cell trait: Some symptoms when blood oxygen is very low; reduction of malaria symptoms

Although two sickle-cell alleles are necessary for an individual to manifest full-blown sickle-cell disease, the presence of one sickle-cell allele can affect the phenotype. Thus, at the organismal level, the normal allele is incompletely dominant to the sickle-cell allele **(Figure 11.16)**. At the molecular level, the two alleles are codominant; both normal and abnormal (sickle-cell) hemoglobins are made in heterozygotes (carriers), who are said to have *sickle-cell trait*. Heterozygotes are usually healthy but may suffer some symptoms during long periods of reduced blood oxygen.

About one out of ten African-Americans have sickle-cell trait, an unusually high frequency of heterozygotes for an allele with severe detrimental effects in homozygotes. Why haven't evolutionary processes resulted in the disappearance of the allele among this population? One explanation is that having a single copy of the sickle-cell allele reduces the frequency and severity of malaria attacks, especially among young children. The malaria parasite spends part of its life cycle in red blood cells (see Figure 25.26), and the presence of even heterozygous amounts of sickle-cell hemoglobin results in lower parasite densities and hence reduced malaria symptoms. Thus, in tropical Africa, where infection with the malaria parasite is common, the sickle-cell allele confers an advantage to heterozygotes even though it is harmful in the homozygous state. (The balance between these two effects will be discussed in Chapter 21; see Make Connections Figure 21.15.) The relatively high frequency of African-Americans with sickle-cell trait is a vestige of their African ancestry.

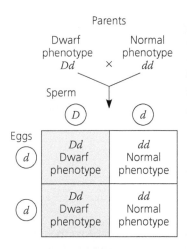

▲ **Figure 11.17 Achondroplasia: a dominant trait.** Dr. Michael C. Ain has achondroplasia, a form of dwarfism caused by a dominant allele. This has inspired his work: He is a specialist in the repair of bone defects caused by achondroplasia and other disorders. The dominant allele (*D*) might have arisen as a mutation in the egg or sperm of a parent or could have been inherited from an affected parent, as shown for an affected father in the Punnett square.

Dominantly Inherited Disorders

Although many harmful alleles are recessive, a number of human disorders are due to dominant alleles. One example is *achondroplasia*, a form of dwarfism that occurs in one of every 25,000 people. Heterozygous individuals have the dwarf phenotype **(Figure 11.17)**. Therefore, all people who do not have achondroplasia—99.99% of the population—are homozygous for the recessive allele. Like the presence of extra fingers or toes mentioned earlier, achondroplasia is a trait for which the recessive allele is much more prevalent than the corresponding dominant allele.

Unlike achondroplasia, which is relatively harmless, some dominant alleles cause lethal diseases. Those that do are much less common than recessive alleles that have lethal effects. A lethal recessive allele is only lethal when homozygous; it can be passed from one generation to the next by heterozygous carriers because the carriers themselves have normal phenotypes. A lethal dominant allele, however, often causes the death of afflicted individuals before they can mature and reproduce, and in this case the allele is not passed on to future generations.

A lethal dominant allele may be passed on, though, if the lethal disease symptoms first appear after reproductive age. In these cases, the individual may already have transmitted the allele to his or her children. For example, a degenerative disease of the nervous system called **Huntington's disease** is caused by a lethal dominant allele that has no obvious phenotypic effect until the individual is about 35 to 45 years old. Once the deterioration of the nervous system begins, it is irreversible and inevitably fatal. As with other dominant traits, a child born to a parent with the Huntington's disease allele has a 50% chance of inheriting the allele and the disorder (see the Punnett square in Figure 11.17). In the United States, this devastating disease afflicts about one in 10,000 people.

At one time, the onset of symptoms was the only way to know if a person had inherited the Huntington's allele, but this is no longer the case. By analyzing DNA samples from a large family with a high incidence of the disorder, geneticists tracked the Huntington's allele to a locus near the tip of chromosome 4, and the gene was sequenced in 1993. This information led to the development of a test that could detect the presence of the Huntington's allele in an individual's genome. The availability of this test poses an agonizing dilemma for those with a family history of Huntington's disease. Some individuals may want to be tested for this disease, whereas others may decide it would be too stressful to find out.

Multifactorial Disorders

The hereditary diseases we have discussed so far are sometimes described as simple Mendelian disorders because they result from abnormality of one or both alleles at a single genetic locus. Many more people are susceptible to diseases that have a multifactorial basis—a genetic component plus a significant environmental influence. Heart disease, diabetes, cancer, alcoholism, certain mental illnesses such as schizophrenia and bipolar disorder, and many other diseases are multifactorial. In these cases, the hereditary component is polygenic. For example, many genes affect cardiovascular health, making some of us more prone than others to heart attacks and strokes. No matter what our genotype, however, our lifestyle has a tremendous effect on phenotype for cardiovascular health and other multifactorial characters. Exercise, a healthful diet, abstinence from smoking, and an ability to handle stressful situations all reduce our risk of heart disease and some types of cancer.

Genetic Counseling Based on Mendelian Genetics

Avoiding simple Mendelian disorders is possible when the risk of a particular genetic disorder can be assessed before a child is conceived or during the early stages of the pregnancy. Many hospitals have genetic counselors who can provide information to prospective parents concerned about a family history for a specific disease.

Consider the case of a hypothetical couple, John and Carol. Each had a brother who died from the same recessively inherited lethal disease. Before conceiving their first child, John and Carol seek genetic counseling to determine the risk of having a child with the disease. From the information about their brothers, we know that both parents of John and both parents of Carol must have been carriers of the recessive allele. Thus, John and Carol are both products of $Aa \times Aa$ crosses, where *a* symbolizes the allele that causes this particular disease. We also know that John and Carol are not homozygous recessive (*aa*), because they do not have the disease. Therefore, their genotypes are either *AA* or *Aa*.

Given a genotypic ratio of 1 *AA* : 2 *Aa* : 1 *aa* for offspring of an $Aa \times Aa$ cross, John and Carol each have a ⅔ chance of being carriers (*Aa*). According to the rule of multiplication, the overall probability of their firstborn having the disorder is ⅔ (the chance that John is a carrier) times ⅔ (the chance that Carol is a carrier) times ¼ (the chance of two carriers having a child with the disease), which equals ⅑. Suppose that Carol and John decide to have a child—after all, there is an ⅛ chance that their baby will not have the disorder. If, despite these odds, their child is born with the disease, then we would know that *both* John and Carol are, in fact, carriers (*Aa* genotype). If both John and Carol are carriers, there is a ¼ chance that any subsequent child this couple has will have the disease. The probability is higher for subsequent children because the diagnosis of the disease in the first child established that both parents are carriers, not because the genotype of the first child affects in any way that of future children.

When we use Mendel's laws to predict possible outcomes of matings, it is important to remember that each child represents an independent event in the sense that its genotype is unaffected by the genotypes of older siblings. Suppose that John and Carol have three more children, and *all three* have the hypothetical hereditary disease. There is only one chance in 64 (¼ × ¼ × ¼) that such an outcome will occur. Despite this run of misfortune, the chance that still another child of this couple will have the disease remains ¼.

Genetic counseling like this relies on the Mendelian model of inheritance. We owe the "gene idea"—the concept of heritable factors transmitted according to simple rules of chance—to the elegant quantitative experiments of Gregor Mendel. The importance of his discoveries was overlooked by most biologists until early in the 20th century, decades after he reported his findings. In the next chapter, you'll learn how Mendel's laws have their physical basis in the behavior of chromosomes during sexual life cycles and how the synthesis of Mendelian genetics and a chromosome theory of inheritance catalyzed progress in genetics.

CONCEPT CHECK 11.4

1. Beth and Tom each have a sibling with cystic fibrosis, but neither Beth nor Tom nor any of their parents have the disease. Calculate the probability that if this couple has a child, the child will have cystic fibrosis. What would be the probability if a test revealed that Tom is a carrier but Beth is not? Explain your answers.
2. **MAKE CONNECTIONS** In Table 11.1, note the phenotypic ratio of the dominant to recessive trait in the F_2 generation for the monohybrid cross involving flower color. Then determine the phenotypic ratio for the offspring of the second-generation couple in Figure 11.14b. What accounts for the difference in the two ratios?

For suggested answers, see Appendix A.

---

11 Chapter Review

Go to **MasteringBiology®** for Assignments, the eText, and the Study Area with Animations, Activities, Vocab Self-Quiz, and Practice Tests.

SUMMARY OF KEY CONCEPTS

VOCAB SELF-QUIZ

goo.gl/gbai8v

CONCEPT 11.1

Mendel used the scientific approach to identify two laws of inheritance (pp. 215–221)

- Gregor Mendel formulated a theory of inheritance based on experiments with garden peas, proposing that parents pass on to their offspring discrete genes that retain their identity through generations. This theory includes two "laws."
- The **law of segregation** states that genes have alternative forms, or **alleles**. In a diploid organism, the two alleles of a gene segregate (separate) during meiosis and gamete formation; each sperm or egg carries only one allele of each pair. This law explains the 3:1 ratio of F_2 phenotypes observed when **monohybrids** self-pollinate. Each organism inherits one allele for each gene from each parent. In **heterozygotes**, the two alleles are different: expression of the **dominant allele** masks the phenotypic effect of the **recessive**

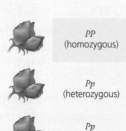

PP (homozygous)

Pp (heterozygous)

Pp (heterozygous)

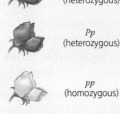

pp (homozygous)

allele. **Homozygotes** have identical alleles of a given gene and are **true-breeding**.
- The **law of independent assortment** states that the pair of alleles for a given gene segregates into gametes independently of the pair of alleles for any other gene. In a cross between **dihybrids** (individuals heterozygous for two genes), the offspring have four phenotypes in a 9:3:3:1 ratio.

? *When Mendel did crosses of true-breeding purple- and white-flowered pea plants, the white-flowered trait disappeared from the F_1 generation but reappeared in the F_2 generation. Use genetic terms to explain why that happened.*

CONCEPT 11.2

Probability laws govern Mendelian inheritance (pp. 221–223)

- The **multiplication rule** states that the probability of two or more events occurring together is equal to the product of the individual probabilities of the independent single events. The **addition rule** states that the probability of an event that can occur in two or more independent, mutually exclusive ways is the sum of the individual probabilities.
- The rules of probability can be used to solve complex genetics problems. A dihybrid or other multicharacter cross is equivalent to two or more independent monohybrid crosses occurring simultaneously. In calculating the chances of the various offspring

genotypes from such crosses, each character is first considered separately and then the individual probabilities are multiplied.

DRAW IT *Redraw the Punnett square on the right side of Figure 11.8 as two smaller monohybrid Punnett squares, one for each gene. Below each square, list the fractions of each phenotype produced. Use the rule of multiplication to compute the overall fraction of each possible dihybrid phenotype. What is the phenotypic ratio?*

CONCEPT 11.3

Inheritance patterns are often more complex than predicted by simple Mendelian genetics (pp. 223–227)

- Extensions of Mendelian genetics for a single gene:

Relationship among alleles of a single gene	Description	Example
Complete dominance of one allele	Heterozygous phenotype same as that of homozygous dominant	PP Pp
Incomplete dominance of either allele	Heterozygous phenotype intermediate between the two homozygous phenotypes	$C^R C^R$ $C^R C^W$ $C^W C^W$
Codominance	Both phenotypes expressed in heterozygotes	$I^A I^B$
Multiple alleles	In the population, some genes have more than two alleles	ABO blood group alleles I^A, I^B, i
Pleiotropy	One gene affects multiple phenotypic characters	Sickle-cell disease

- Extensions of Mendelian genetics for two or more genes:

Relationship among two or more genes	Description	Example
Epistasis	The phenotypic expression of one gene affects the expression of another gene	$BbEe$ × $BbEe$ 9 : 3 : 4
Polygenic inheritance	A single phenotypic character is affected by two or more genes	$AaBbCc$ × $AaBbCc$

- The expression of a genotype can be affected by environmental influences. Polygenic characters that are also influenced by the environment are called **multifactorial** characters.

- An organism's overall phenotype reflects its overall genotype and unique environmental history. Even in more complex inheritance patterns, Mendel's fundamental laws still apply.

? *Which genetic relationships listed in the first column of the two tables are demonstrated by the inheritance pattern of the ABO blood group alleles? For each genetic relationship, explain why this inheritance pattern is or is not an example.*

CONCEPT 11.4

Many human traits follow Mendelian patterns of inheritance (pp. 228–232)

- Analysis of family **pedigrees** can be used to deduce the possible genotypes of individuals and make predictions about future offspring. Such predictions are statistical probabilities rather than certainties.

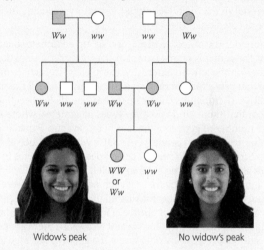

Widow's peak   No widow's peak

- Many genetic disorders are inherited as simple recessive traits. Most affected (homozygous recessive) individuals are children of phenotypically normal, heterozygous **carriers**.

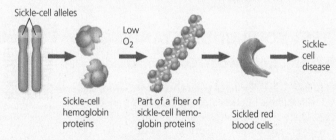

Sickle-cell alleles

Sickle-cell hemoglobin proteins   Low O_2 Part of a fiber of sickle-cell hemoglobin proteins   Sickled red blood cells   Sickle-cell disease

- The sickle-cell allele has probably persisted for evolutionary reasons: Heterozygotes have an advantage because one copy of the sickle-cell allele reduces both the frequency and severity of malaria attacks.
- Lethal dominant alleles are eliminated from the population if affected people die before reproducing. Nonlethal dominant alleles and lethal alleles that are expressed relatively late in life are inherited in a Mendelian way.
- Many human diseases are multifactorial—that is, they have both genetic and environmental components and do not follow simple Mendelian inheritance patterns.
- Using family histories, genetic counselors help couples determine the probability of their children having genetic disorders.

? *Both members of a couple know that they are carriers of the cystic fibrosis allele. None of their three children has cystic fibrosis, but any one of them might be a carrier. The couple would like to have a fourth child but are worried that he or she would very likely have the disease, since the first three do not. What would you tell the couple? Would it remove some more uncertainty in their prediction if they could find out whether the three children are carriers?*

TIPS FOR GENETICS PROBLEMS

1. Write down symbols for the alleles. (These may be given in the problem.) When represented by single letters, the dominant allele is uppercase and the recessive allele is lowercase.

2. Write down the possible genotypes, as determined by the phenotype.
   a. If the phenotype is that of the dominant trait (for example, purple flowers), then the genotype is either homozygous dominant or heterozygous (*PP* or *Pp*, in this example).
   b. If the phenotype is that of the recessive trait, the genotype must be homozygous recessive (for example, *pp*).
   c. If the problem says "true-breeding," the genotype is homozygous.

3. Determine what the problem is asking. If asked to do a cross, write it out in the form [genotype] × [genotype], using the alleles you've decided on.

4. To figure out the outcome of a cross, set up a Punnett square.
   a. Put the gametes of one parent at the top and those of the other on the left. To determine the allele(s) in each gamete for a given genotype, set up a systematic way to list all the possibilities. (Remember, each gamete has one allele of each gene.) Note that there are 2^n possible types of gametes, where *n* is the number of gene loci that are heterozygous. For example, an individual with genotype *AaBbCc* would produce $2^3 = 8$ types of gametes. Write the genotypes of the gametes in circles above the columns and to the left of the rows.
   b. Fill in the Punnett square as if each possible sperm were fertilizing each possible egg, making all of the possible offspring. In a cross of *AaBbCc* × *AaBbCc*, for example, the Punnett square would have 8 columns and 8 rows, so there are 64 different offspring; you would know the genotype of each and thus the phenotype. Count genotypes and phenotypes to obtain the genotypic and phenotypic ratios. Because the Punnett square is so large, this method is not the most efficient. Instead, see tip 5.

5. You can use the rules of probability if the Punnett square would be too big. (For example, see the question at the end of the summary for Concept 11.2 and question 7.) You can consider each gene separately (see the section Solving Complex Genetics Problems with the Rules of Probability in Concept 11.2).

6. If the problem gives you the phenotypic ratios of offspring but not the genotypes of the parents in a given cross, the phenotypes can help you deduce the parents' unknown genotypes.
   a. For example, if ½ of the offspring have the recessive phenotype and ½ the dominant, you know that the cross was between a heterozygote and a homozygous recessive.
   b. If the ratio is 3:1, the cross was between two heterozygotes.
   c. If two genes are involved and you see a 9:3:3:1 ratio in the offspring, you know that each parent is heterozygous for both genes. *Caution*: Don't assume that the reported numbers will exactly equal the predicted ratios. For example, if there are 13 offspring with the dominant trait and 11 with the recessive, assume that the ratio is one dominant to one recessive.

7. For pedigree problems, use the tips in Figure 11.14 and below to determine what kind of trait is involved.
   a. If parents without the trait have offspring with the trait, the trait must be recessive and both of the parents must be carriers.
   b. If the trait is seen in every generation, it is most likely dominant (see the next possibility, though).
   c. If both parents have the trait, then in order for it to be recessive, all offspring must show the trait.
   d. To determine the likely genotype of a certain individual in a pedigree, first label the genotypes of all the family members you can. Even if some of the genotypes are incomplete, label what you do know. For example, if an individual has the dominant phenotype, the genotype must be *AA* or *Aa*; you can write this as *A–*. Try different possibilities to see which fits the results. Use the rules of probability to calculate the probability of each possible genotype being the correct one.

TEST YOUR UNDERSTANDING

PRACTICE TEST
goo.gl/CRZjvS

Level 1: Knowledge/Comprehension

1. **DRAW IT** Two pea plants heterozygous for the characters of pod color and pod shape are crossed. Draw a Punnett square to determine the phenotypic ratios of the offspring.

2. A man with type A blood marries a woman with type B blood. Their child has type O blood. What are the genotypes of these three individuals? What genotypes, and in what frequencies, would you expect in future offspring from this marriage?

3. A man has six fingers on each hand and six toes on each foot. His wife and their daughter have the normal number of digits. Remember that extra digits is a dominant trait. What fraction of this couple's children would be expected to have extra digits?

4. **DRAW IT** A pea plant heterozygous for inflated pods (*Ii*) is crossed with a plant homozygous for constricted pods (*ii*). Draw a Punnett square for this cross to predict genotypic and phenotypic ratios. Assume that pollen comes from the *ii* plant.

Level 2: Application/Analysis

5. Flower position, stem length, and seed shape are three characters that Mendel studied. Each is controlled by an independently assorting gene and has dominant and recessive expression as indicated in Table 11.1. If a plant that is heterozygous for all three characters is allowed to self-fertilize, what proportion of the offspring would you expect to be as follows? (*Note*: Use the rules of probability instead of a huge Punnett square.)
   (a) homozygous for the three dominant traits
   (b) homozygous for the three recessive traits
   (c) heterozygous for all three characters
   (d) homozygous for axial and tall, heterozygous for seed shape

6. Hemochromatosis is an inherited disease caused by a recessive allele. If a woman and her husband, who are both carriers, have three children, what is the probability of each of the following?
   (a) All three children are of normal phenotype.
   (b) One or more of the three children have the disease.
   (c) All three children have the disease.
   (d) At least one child is phenotypically normal.

   (*Note*: It will help to remember that the probabilities of all possible outcomes always add up to 1.)

7. The genotype of F_1 individuals in a tetrahybrid cross is *AaBbCcDd*. Assuming independent assortment of these four genes, what are the probabilities that F_2 offspring will have the following genotypes?
   (a) *aabbccdd*
   (b) *AaBbCcDd*
   (c) *AABBCCDD*
   (d) *AaBBccDd*
   (e) *AaBBCCdd*

8. What is the probability that each of the following pairs of parents will produce the indicated offspring? (Assume independent assortment of all gene pairs.)
   (a) *AABBCC × aabbcc → AaBbCc*
   (b) *AABbCc × AaBbCc → AAbbCC*
   (c) *AaBbCc × AaBbCc → AaBbCc*
   (d) *aaBbCC × AABbcc → AaBbCc*

9. Karen and Steve each have a sibling with sickle-cell disease. Neither Karen nor Steve nor any of their parents have the disease, and none of them have been tested to see if they have the sickle-cell trait. Based on this incomplete information, calculate the probability that if this couple has a child, the child will have sickle-cell disease.

10. In 1981, a stray black cat with unusual rounded, curled-back ears was adopted by a family in California. Hundreds of descendants of the cat have since been born, and cat fanciers hope to develop the curl cat into a show breed. Suppose you owned the first curl cat and wanted  to develop a true-breeding variety. How would you determine whether the curl allele is dominant or recessive? How would you obtain true-breeding curl cats? How could you be sure they are true-breeding?

11. In tigers, a recessive allele that is pleiotropic causes an absence of fur pigmentation (a white tiger) and a cross-eyed condition. If two phenotypically normal tigers that are heterozygous at this locus are mated, what percentage of their offspring will be cross-eyed? What percentage of cross-eyed tigers will be white?

12. In maize (corn) plants, a dominant allele *I* inhibits kernel color, while the recessive allele *i* permits color when homozygous. At a different locus, the dominant allele *P* causes purple kernel color, while the homozygous recessive genotype *pp* causes red kernels. If plants heterozygous at both loci are crossed, what will be the phenotypic ratio of the offspring?

13. The pedigree below traces the inheritance of alkaptonuria, a biochemical disorder. Affected individuals, indicated here by the colored circles and squares, are unable to metabolize a substance called alkapton, which colors the urine and stains body tissues. Does alkaptonuria appear to be caused by a dominant allele or by a recessive allele? Fill in the genotypes of the individuals whose genotypes can be deduced. What genotypes are possible for each of the other individuals?

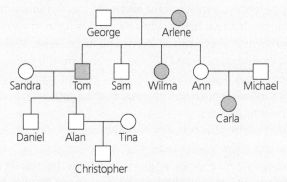

14. Imagine that you are a genetic counselor, and a couple planning to start a family comes to you for information. Charles was married once before, and he and his first wife had a child with cystic fibrosis. The brother of his current wife, Elaine, died of cystic fibrosis. What is the probability that Charles and Elaine will have a baby with cystic fibrosis? (Neither Charles, nor Elaine, nor their parents have cystic fibrosis.)

Level 3: Synthesis/Evaluation

15. FOCUS ON EVOLUTION
Over the past half century, there has been a trend in the United States and other developed countries for people to marry and start families later in life than did their parents and grandparents. Describe what effects this trend might have on the incidence (frequency) of late-acting dominant lethal alleles in the population.

16. SCIENTIFIC INQUIRY
You are handed a mystery pea plant with tall stems and axial flowers and asked to determine its genotype as quickly as possible. You know that the allele for tall stems (*T*) is dominant to that for dwarf stems (*t*) and that the allele for axial flowers (*A*) is dominant to that for terminal flowers (*a*).

(a) Identify ALL the possible genotypes for your mystery plant.
(b) Describe the ONE cross you would do, out in your garden, to determine the exact genotype of your mystery plant.
(c) While waiting for the results of your cross, you predict the results for each possible genotype listed in part a. Explain how you do this and why this is not called "performing a cross."
(d) Explain how the results of your cross and your predictions will help you learn the genotype of your mystery plant.

17. FOCUS ON INFORMATION
The continuity of life is based on heritable information in the form of DNA. In a short essay (100–150 words), explain how the passage of genes from parents to offspring, in the form of particular alleles, ensures perpetuation of parental traits in offspring and, at the same time, genetic variation among offspring. Use genetic terms in your explanation.

18. SYNTHESIZE YOUR KNOWLEDGE

Just for fun, imagine that "shirt-striping" is a phenotypic character caused by a single gene. Make up a genetic explanation for the appearance of the family in the above photograph, consistent with their "shirt phenotypes." Include in your answer the presumed allele combinations for "shirt-striping" in each family member. What is the inheritance pattern shown by the child?

For selected answers, see Appendix A.

12 The Chromosomal Basis of Inheritance

KEY CONCEPTS

12.1 Morgan showed that Mendelian inheritance has its physical basis in the behavior of chromosomes: *scientific inquiry*

12.2 Sex-linked genes exhibit unique patterns of inheritance

12.3 Linked genes tend to be inherited together because they are located near each other on the same chromosome

12.4 Alterations of chromosome number or structure cause some genetic disorders

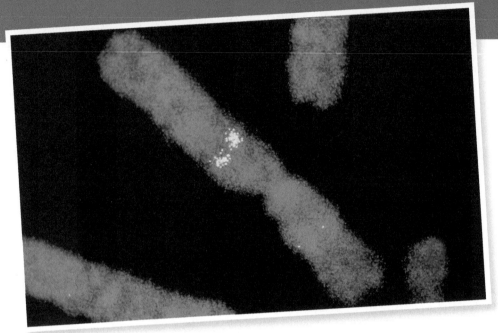

▲ **Figure 12.1** Where in the cell are Mendel's hereditary factors located?

Locating Genes Along Chromosomes

Today, we know that genes—Mendel's "factors"—are segments of DNA located along chromosomes. We can see the location of a particular gene by tagging chromosomes with a fluorescent dye that highlights that gene. For example, the two yellow regions in **Figure 12.1** mark a specific gene on human chromosome 6. (The chromosome has duplicated, so the allele on that chromosome is present as two copies, one per sister chromatid.) However, Gregor Mendel's "hereditary factors" were purely an abstract concept when he proposed their existence in 1860. At that time, no cellular structures had been identified that could house these imaginary units, and most biologists were skeptical about Mendel's proposed laws of inheritance.

Using improved techniques of microscopy, cytologists worked out the process of mitosis in 1875 and meiosis in the 1890s. Cytology and genetics converged as biologists began to see parallels between the behavior of Mendel's proposed hereditary factors during sexual life cycles and the behavior of chromosomes. As shown in **Figure 12.2**, chromosomes and genes are both present in pairs in diploid cells; homologous chromosomes separate and alleles segregate during the process of meiosis. After meiosis, fertilization restores the paired condition for both chromosomes and genes. Around

1902, Walter S. Sutton, Theodor Boveri, and others noted these parallels and began to develop the **chromosome theory of inheritance**. According to this theory, Mendelian genes have specific loci (positions) along chromosomes, and it is the chromosomes that undergo segregation and independent assortment.

As you can see in Figure 12.2, the separation of homologs during anaphase I accounts for the segregation of the two alleles of a gene into separate gametes, and the random arrangement of chromosome pairs at metaphase I accounts for independent assortment of the alleles for two or more genes located on different homologous pairs. This figure traces the same dihybrid pea cross you learned about in Figure 11.8. By carefully studying Figure 12.2, you can see how the behavior of chromosomes during meiosis in the F_1 generation and subsequent random fertilization give rise to the F_2 phenotypic ratio observed by Mendel.

In correlating the behavior of chromosomes with that of genes, this chapter will extend what you learned in the past two chapters. After describing evidence from the fruit fly that strongly supported the chromosome theory, we'll explore the chromosomal basis for the transmission of genes from parents to offspring, including what happens when two genes are linked on the same chromosome. Finally, we'll discuss some important exceptions to the standard mode of inheritance.

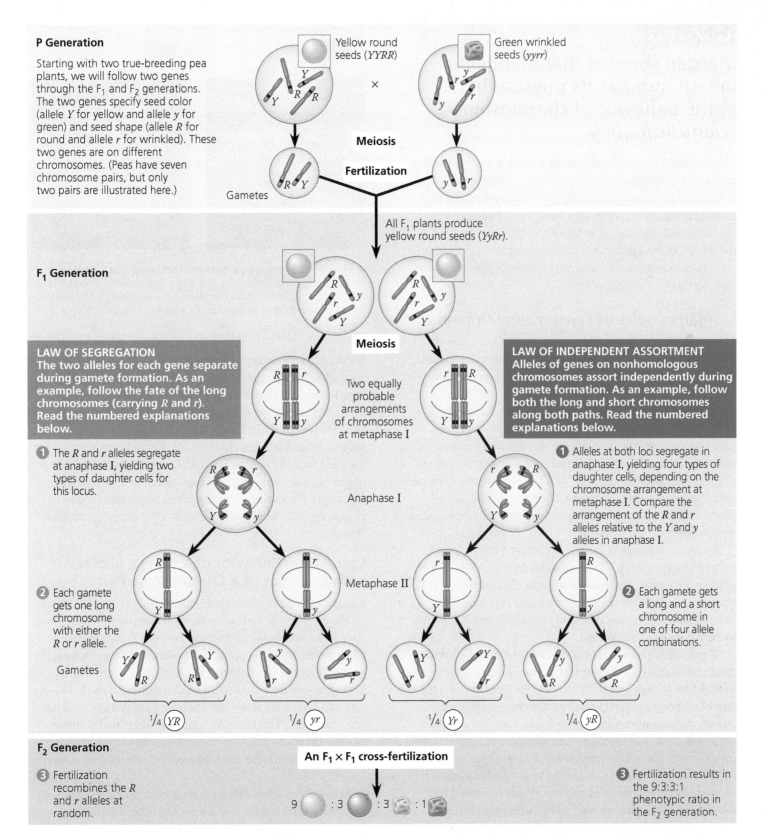

P Generation

Starting with two true-breeding pea plants, we will follow two genes through the F_1 and F_2 generations. The two genes specify seed color (allele Y for yellow and allele y for green) and seed shape (allele R for round and allele r for wrinkled). These two genes are on different chromosomes. (Peas have seven chromosome pairs, but only two pairs are illustrated here.)

Yellow round seeds ($YYRR$)

Green wrinkled seeds ($yyrr$)

Meiosis

Fertilization

Gametes

All F_1 plants produce yellow round seeds ($YyRr$).

F_1 Generation

Meiosis

LAW OF SEGREGATION
The two alleles for each gene separate during gamete formation. As an example, follow the fate of the long chromosomes (carrying R and r). Read the numbered explanations below.

LAW OF INDEPENDENT ASSORTMENT
Alleles of genes on nonhomologous chromosomes assort independently during gamete formation. As an example, follow both the long and short chromosomes along both paths. Read the numbered explanations below.

Two equally probable arrangements of chromosomes at metaphase I

❶ The R and r alleles segregate at anaphase I, yielding two types of daughter cells for this locus.

Anaphase I

❶ Alleles at both loci segregate in anaphase I, yielding four types of daughter cells, depending on the chromosome arrangement at metaphase I. Compare the arrangement of the R and r alleles relative to the Y and y alleles in anaphase I.

❷ Each gamete gets one long chromosome with either the R or r allele.

Metaphase II

❷ Each gamete gets a long and a short chromosome in one of four allele combinations.

Gametes

¼ YR ¼ yr ¼ Yr ¼ yR

F_2 Generation

An $F_1 \times F_1$ cross-fertilization

❸ Fertilization recombines the R and r alleles at random.

9 : 3 : 3 : 1

❸ Fertilization results in the 9:3:3:1 phenotypic ratio in the F_2 generation.

▲ **Figure 12.2 The chromosomal basis of Mendel's laws.** Here we correlate the results of one of Mendel's dihybrid crosses (see Figure 11.8) with the behavior of chromosomes during meiosis (see Figure 10.8). The arrangement of chromosomes at metaphase I of meiosis and their movement during anaphase I account for, respectively, the independent assortment and segregation of the alleles for seed color and shape. Each cell that undergoes meiosis in an F_1 plant produces two kinds of gametes. If we count the results for all cells, however, each F_1 plant produces equal numbers of all four kinds of gametes because the alternative chromosome arrangements at metaphase I are equally likely.

? *If you crossed an F_1 plant with a plant that was homozygous recessive for both genes* ($yyrr$), *how would the phenotypic ratio of the offspring compare with the 9:3:3:1 ratio seen here?*

Morgan showed that Mendelian inheritance has its physical basis in the behavior of chromosomes: *scientific inquiry*

The first solid evidence associating a specific gene with a specific chromosome came early in the 1900s from the work of Thomas Hunt Morgan, an experimental embryologist at Columbia University. Although Morgan was initially skeptical about both Mendelian genetics and the chromosome theory, his early experiments provided convincing evidence that chromosomes are indeed the location of Mendel's heritable factors.

Morgan's Choice of Experimental Organism

Many times in the history of biology, important discoveries have come to those insightful or lucky enough to choose an experimental organism suitable for the research problem being tackled. Mendel chose the garden pea because a number of distinct varieties were available. For his work, Morgan selected a species of fruit fly, *Drosophila melanogaster*, a common insect that feeds on the fungi growing on fruit. Fruit flies are prolific breeders; a single mating will produce hundreds of offspring, and a new generation can be bred every two weeks. Morgan's laboratory began using this convenient organism for genetic studies in 1907 and soon became known as "the fly room."

Another advantage of the fruit fly is that it has only four pairs of chromosomes, which are easily distinguishable with a light microscope. There are three pairs of autosomes and one pair of sex chromosomes. Female fruit flies have a pair of homologous X chromosomes, and males have one X chromosome and one Y chromosome.

While Mendel could readily obtain different pea varieties from seed suppliers, Morgan was probably the first person to want different varieties of the fruit fly. He faced the tedious task of carrying out many matings and then microscopically inspecting large numbers of offspring in search of naturally occurring variant individuals. After many months of this, he complained, "Two years' work wasted. I have been breeding those flies for all that time and I've got nothing out of it." Morgan persisted, however, and was finally rewarded with the discovery of a single male fly with white eyes instead of the usual red. The phenotype for a character most commonly observed in natural populations, such as red eyes in *Drosophila*, is called the **wild type** (Figure 12.3). Traits that are alternatives to the wild type, such as white eyes in *Drosophila*, are called *mutant phenotypes* because they are due to alleles assumed to have originated as changes, or mutations, in the wild-type allele.

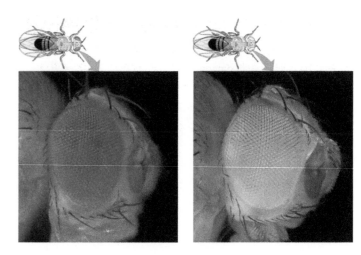

▲ Figure 12.3 **Morgan's first mutant.** Wild-type *Drosophila* flies have red eyes (left). Among his flies, Morgan discovered a mutant male with white eyes (right). This variation made it possible for Morgan to trace a gene for eye color to a specific chromosome (LMs).

Morgan and his students invented a notation for symbolizing alleles in *Drosophila* that is still widely used for fruit flies. For a given character in flies, the gene takes its symbol from the first mutant (non-wild type) discovered. Thus, the allele for white eyes in *Drosophila* is symbolized by *w*. The superscript + identifies the allele for the wild-type trait: w^+ for the allele for red eyes, for example. Over the years, a variety of gene notation systems have been developed for different organisms. For example, human genes are usually written in all capitals, such as *HTT* for the gene involved in Huntington's disease.

Correlating Behavior of a Gene's Alleles with Behavior of a Chromosome Pair

Morgan mated his white-eyed male fly with a red-eyed female. All the F_1 offspring had red eyes, suggesting that the wild-type allele is dominant. When Morgan bred the F_1 flies to each other, he observed the classical 3:1 phenotypic ratio among the F_2 offspring. However, there was a surprising additional result: The white-eye trait showed up only in males. All the F_2 females had red eyes, while half the males had red eyes and half had white eyes. Therefore, Morgan concluded that somehow a fly's eye color was linked to its sex. (If the eye-color gene were unrelated to sex, half of the white-eyed flies would have been female.)

Recall that a female fly has two X chromosomes (XX), while a male fly has an X and a Y (XY). The correlation between the trait of white eye color and the male sex of the affected F_2 flies suggested to Morgan that the gene involved in his white-eyed mutant was located exclusively on the X chromosome, with no corresponding allele present on the Y chromosome. His reasoning can be followed in **Figure 12.4**. For a male, a single copy of the mutant allele would confer white eyes; since a male has only one

▼ Figure 12.4 Inquiry

In a cross between a wild-type female fruit fly and a mutant white-eyed male, what color eyes will the F₁ and F₂ offspring have?

Experiment Thomas Hunt Morgan wanted to analyze the behavior of two alleles of a fruit fly eye-color gene. In crosses similar to those done by Mendel with pea plants, Morgan and his colleagues mated a wild-type (red-eyed) female with a mutant white-eyed male.

Morgan then bred an F₁ red-eyed female to an F₁ red-eyed male to produce the F₂ generation.

Results The F₂ generation showed a typical Mendelian ratio of 3 red-eyed flies to 1 white-eyed fly. However, all white-eyed flies were males; no females displayed the white-eye trait.

Conclusion All F₁ offspring had red eyes, so the mutant white-eye trait (w) must be recessive to the wild-type red-eye trait (w⁺). Since the recessive trait—white eyes—was expressed only in males in the F₂ generation, Morgan deduced that this eye-color gene is located on the X chromosome and that there is no corresponding locus on the Y chromosome.

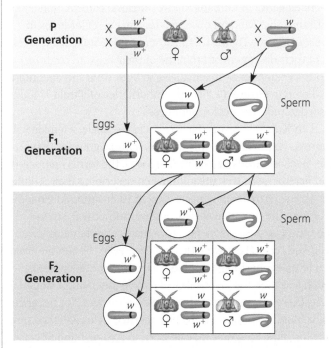

Data from T. H. Morgan, Sex-limited inheritance in *Drosophila, Science* 32:120–122 (1910).

(MB) A related Experimental Inquiry Tutorial can be assigned in MasteringBiology.

WHAT IF? Suppose this eye-color gene were located on an autosome. Predict the phenotypes (including gender) of the F₂ flies in this hypothetical cross. (*Hint*: Draw a Punnett square.)

X chromosome, there can be no wild-type allele (w^+) present to mask the recessive allele. However, a female could have white eyes only if both her X chromosomes carried the recessive mutant allele (w). This was impossible for the F₂ females in Morgan's experiment because all the F₁ fathers had red eyes, so each F₂ female received a w^+ allele on the X chromosome inherited from her father.

Morgan's finding of the correlation between a particular trait and an individual's sex provided support for the chromosome theory of inheritance, namely, that a specific gene is carried on a specific chromosome (in this case, an eye-color gene on the X chromosome). In addition, Morgan's work indicated that genes located on a sex chromosome exhibit unique inheritance patterns, which we'll discuss in the next section. Recognizing the importance of Morgan's early work, many bright students were attracted to his fly room.

CONCEPT CHECK 12.1

1. Which one of Mendel's laws relates to the inheritance of alleles for a single character? Which law relates to the inheritance of alleles for two characters in a dihybrid cross?
2. **MAKE CONNECTIONS** Review the description of meiosis (see Figure 10.8) and Mendel's laws of segregation and independent assortment (see Concept 11.1). What is the physical basis for each of Mendel's laws?
3. **WHAT IF?** Propose a possible reason that the first naturally occurring mutant fruit fly Morgan saw involved a gene on a sex chromosome and was found in a male.

For suggested answers, see Appendix A.

CONCEPT 12.2

Sex-linked genes exhibit unique patterns of inheritance

As you just learned, Morgan's discovery of a trait (white eyes) that correlated with the sex of flies was a key episode in the development of the chromosome theory of inheritance. Because the identity of the sex chromosomes in an individual could be inferred by observing the sex of the fly, the behavior of the two members of the pair of sex chromosomes could be correlated with the behavior of the two alleles of the eye-color gene. In this section, we'll take a closer look at the role of sex chromosomes in inheritance.

The Chromosomal Basis of Sex

Whether we are anatomically male or female may be one of our more obvious phenotypic characters. Although the anatomical and physiological differences between women and men are numerous, the chromosomal basis for determining sex is rather simple. Humans and other mammals have two types of sex chromosomes, designated X and Y. The Y chromosome is much smaller than the X chromosome

(Figure 12.5). A person who inherits two X chromosomes, one from each parent, usually develops as a female; a male inherits one X chromosome and one Y chromosome (Figure 12.6). Short segments at either end of the Y chromosome are the only regions that are homologous with regions on the X. These homologous regions allow the X and Y chromosomes in males to pair and behave like homologous chromosomes during meiosis in the testes.

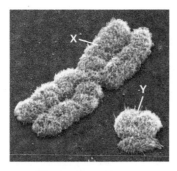

▲ Figure 12.5 **Human sex chromosomes.**

In mammalian testes and ovaries, the two sex chromosomes segregate during meiosis. Each egg receives one X chromosome. In contrast, sperm fall into two categories: Half the sperm cells a male produces receive an X chromosome, and half receive a Y chromosome. We can trace the sex of each offspring to the events of conception: If a sperm cell bearing an X chromosome fertilizes an egg, the zygote is XX, a female; if a sperm cell containing a Y chromosome fertilizes an egg, the zygote is XY, a male (see Figure 12.6). Thus, sex determination is a matter of chance—a fifty-fifty chance. In *Drosophila*, while males are also XY, sex depends not on the presence of the Y, but on the ratio between the number of X chromosomes and the number of autosome sets. There are other chromosomal systems as well, besides the X-Y system, for determining sex.

In humans, the anatomical signs of sex begin to emerge when the embryo is about 2 months old. Before then, the rudiments of the gonads are generic—they can develop into either testes or ovaries, depending on whether or not a Y chromosome is present. In 1990, a British research team identified a gene on the Y chromosome required for the development of testes. They named the gene *SRY*, for <u>s</u>ex-determining <u>r</u>egion

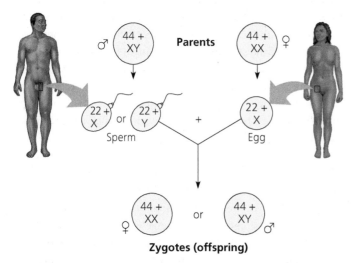

▲ Figure 12.6 **The mammalian X-Y chromosomal system of sex determination.** In mammals, the sex of an offspring depends on whether the sperm cell contains an X chromosome or a Y. (All eggs have an X.) Numerals indicate the number of autosomes.

of <u>Y</u>. In the absence of *SRY*, the gonads develop into ovaries. The biochemical, physiological, and anatomical features that distinguish males and females are complex, and many genes are involved in their development. In fact, *SRY* codes for a protein that regulates other genes.

Researchers have sequenced the human Y chromosome and have identified 78 genes that code for about 25 proteins (some genes are duplicates). About half of these genes are expressed only in the testis, and some are required for normal testicular functioning and the production of normal sperm. A gene located on either sex chromosome is called a **sex-linked gene**; those located on the Y chromosome are called *Y-linked genes*. The Y chromosome is passed along virtually intact from a father to all his sons. Because there are so few Y-linked genes, very few disorders are transferred from father to son on the Y chromosome. A rare example is that in the absence of certain Y-linked genes, an XY individual is male but does not produce normal sperm.

The human X chromosome contains approximately 1,100 genes, which are called **X-linked genes**. The fact that males and females inherit a different number of X chromosomes leads to a pattern of inheritance different from that produced by genes located on autosomes.

Inheritance of X-Linked Genes

While most Y-linked genes help determine sex, the X chromosomes have genes for many characters unrelated to sex. X-linked genes in humans follow the same pattern of inheritance that Morgan observed for the eye-color locus in *Drosophila* (see Figure 12.4). Fathers pass X-linked alleles to all of their daughters but to none of their sons. In contrast, mothers can pass X-linked alleles to both sons and daughters, as shown in **Figure 12.7** for the inheritance of a mild X-linked disorder, red-green color blindness.

If an X-linked trait is due to a recessive allele, a female will express the phenotype only if she is homozygous for that allele. Because males have only one locus, the terms *homozygous* and *heterozygous* lack meaning when describing their X-linked genes; the term *hemizygous* is used in such cases. Any male receiving the recessive allele from his mother will express the trait. For this reason, far more males than females have X-linked recessive disorders. However, even though the chance of a female inheriting a double dose of the mutant allele is much less than the probability of a male inheriting a single dose, there *are* females with X-linked disorders. For instance, color blindness is almost always inherited as an X-linked trait. A color-blind daughter may be born to a color-blind father whose mate is a carrier (see Figure 12.7c). Because the X-linked allele for color blindness is relatively rare, however, the probability that such a man and woman will mate is low.

A number of human X-linked disorders are much more serious than color blindness, such as **Duchenne muscular dystrophy**, which affects about one out of 3,500 males born in the United States. The disease is characterized by a progressive weakening of the muscles and loss of coordination. Affected

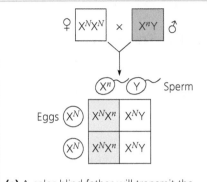

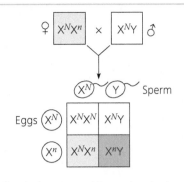

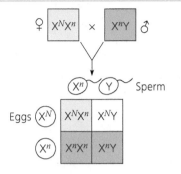

(a) A color-blind father will transmit the mutant allele to all daughters but to no sons. When the mother is a dominant homozygote, the daughters will have the normal phenotype but will be carriers of the mutation.

(b) If a carrier mates with a male who has normal color vision, there is a 50% chance that each daughter will be a carrier like her mother and a 50% chance that each son will have the disorder.

(c) If a carrier mates with a color-blind male, there is a 50% chance that each child born to them will have the disorder, regardless of sex. Daughters who have normal color vision will be carriers, whereas males who have normal color vision will be free of the recessive allele.

▲ **Figure 12.7 The transmission of X-linked recessive traits.** In this diagram, red-green color blindness is used as an example. The superscript N represents the dominant allele for normal color vision carried on the X chromosome, while n represents the recessive allele, which has a mutation causing color blindness. White boxes indicate unaffected individuals, light orange boxes indicate carriers, and dark orange boxes indicate color-blind individuals.

? *If a color-blind woman married a man who had normal color vision, what would be the probable phenotypes of their children?*

individuals rarely live past their early 20s. Researchers have traced the disorder to the absence of a key muscle protein called dystrophin and have mapped the gene for this protein to a specific locus on the X chromosome.

Hemophilia is an X-linked recessive disorder defined by the absence of one or more of the proteins required for blood clotting. When a person with hemophilia is injured, bleeding is prolonged because a firm clot is slow to form. Small cuts in the skin are usually not a problem, but bleeding in the muscles or joints can be painful and can lead to serious damage. In the 1800s, hemophilia was widespread among the royal families of Europe. Queen Victoria of England is known to have passed the allele to several of her descendants. Subsequent intermarriage with royal family members of other nations, such as Spain and Russia, further spread this X-linked trait, and its incidence is well documented in royal pedigrees. A few years ago, new genomic techniques allowed sequencing of DNA from tiny amounts isolated from the buried remains of royal family members. The genetic basis of the mutation, and how it resulted in a nonfunctional blood-clotting factor, is now understood. Today, people with hemophilia are treated as needed with intravenous injections of the protein that is missing.

X Inactivation in Female Mammals

Female mammals, including human females, inherit two X chromosomes—twice the number inherited by males—so you may wonder if females make twice as much of the proteins encoded by X-linked genes. In fact, almost all of one X chromosome in each cell in female mammals becomes inactivated during early embryonic development. As a result, the cells of females and males have the same effective dose (one active

copy) of most X-linked genes. The inactive X in each cell of a female condenses into a compact object called a **Barr body** (discovered by Canadian anatomist Murray Barr), which lies along the inside of the nuclear envelope. Most of the genes of the X chromosome that forms the Barr body are not expressed. In the ovaries, however, Barr-body chromosomes are reactivated in the cells that give rise to eggs, resulting in every female gamete (egg) having an active X after meiosis.

British geneticist Mary Lyon demonstrated that the selection of which X chromosome will form the Barr body occurs randomly and independently in each embryonic cell present at the time of X inactivation. As a consequence, females consist of a *mosaic* of two types of cells: those with the active X derived from the father and those with the active X derived from the mother. After an X chromosome is inactivated in a particular cell, all mitotic descendants of that cell have the same inactive X. Thus, if a female is heterozygous for a sex-linked trait, about half of her cells will express one allele, while the others will express the alternate allele. **Figure 12.8** shows how this mosaicism results in the patchy coloration of a tortoiseshell cat. In humans, mosaicism can be observed in a recessive X-linked mutation that prevents the development of sweat glands. A woman who is heterozygous for this trait has patches of normal skin and patches of skin lacking sweat glands.

Inactivation of an X chromosome involves modification of the DNA and proteins bound to it called histones, including attachment of methyl groups ($—CH_3$) to DNA nucleotides. (The regulatory role of DNA methylation is discussed further in Concept 15.2.) A particular region of each X chromosome contains several genes involved in the inactivation process. The two regions, one on each X chromosome, associate briefly with

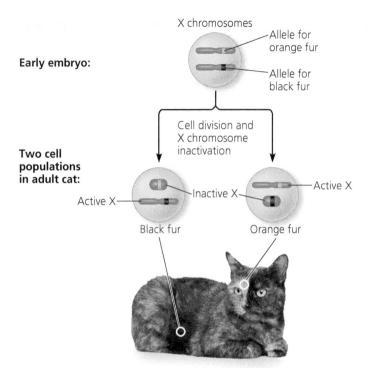

Early embryo:

X chromosomes
- Allele for orange fur
- Allele for black fur

Cell division and X chromosome inactivation

Two cell populations in adult cat:

Active X — Inactive X — Active X

Black fur   Orange fur

▲ **Figure 12.8 X inactivation and the tortoiseshell cat.** The tortoiseshell gene is on the X chromosome, and the tortoiseshell phenotype requires the presence of two different alleles, one for orange fur and one for black fur. Normally, only females can have both alleles, because only they have two X chromosomes. If a female cat is heterozygous for the tortoiseshell gene, she is tortoiseshell. Orange patches are formed by populations of cells in which the X chromosome with the orange allele is active; black patches have cells in which the X chromosome with the black allele is active. ("Calico" cats also have white areas, which are determined by yet another gene.)

each other in each cell at an early stage of embryonic development. Then one of the genes, called *XIST* (for <u>X</u>-<u>i</u>nactive <u>s</u>pecific <u>t</u>ranscript), becomes active *only* on the chromosome that will become the Barr body. Multiple copies of the RNA product of this gene apparently attach to the X chromosome on which they are made, eventually almost covering it. Interaction of this RNA with the chromosome initiates X inactivation, and the RNA products of nearby genes help to regulate the process.

CONCEPT CHECK 12.2

1. A white-eyed female *Drosophila* is mated with a red-eyed (wild-type) male, the reciprocal cross of the one shown in Figure 12.4. What phenotypes and genotypes do you predict for the offspring?

2. Neither Tim nor Rhoda has Duchenne muscular dystrophy, but their firstborn son does have it. What is the probability that a second child of this couple will have the disease? What is the probability if the second child is a boy? A girl?

3. **MAKE CONNECTIONS** Consider what you learned about dominant and recessive alleles in Concept 11.1. If a disorder were caused by a dominant X-linked allele, how would the inheritance pattern differ from what we see for recessive X-linked disorders?

For suggested answers, see Appendix A.

Linked genes tend to be inherited together because they are located near each other on the same chromosome

The number of genes in a cell is far greater than the number of chromosomes; in fact, each chromosome (except the Y) has hundreds or thousands of genes. Genes located near each other on the same chromosome tend to be inherited together in genetic crosses; such genes are said to be genetically linked and are called **linked genes**. (Note the distinction between the terms *sex-linked gene*, referring to a single gene on a sex chromosome, and *linked genes*, referring to two or more genes on the same chromosome that tend to be inherited together.) When geneticists follow linked genes in breeding experiments, the results deviate from those expected from Mendel's law of independent assortment.

How Linkage Affects Inheritance

To see how linkage between genes affects the inheritance of two different characters, let's examine another of Morgan's *Drosophila* experiments. In this case, the characters are body color and wing size, each with two different phenotypes. Wild-type flies have gray bodies and normal-sized wings. In addition to these flies, Morgan had managed to obtain, through breeding, doubly mutant flies with black bodies and wings much smaller than normal, called vestigial wings. The mutant alleles are recessive to the wild-type alleles, and neither gene is on a sex chromosome. In his investigation of these two genes, Morgan carried out the crosses shown in **Figure 12.9**. The first was a P generation cross to generate F_1 dihybrid flies, and the second was a testcross.

The resulting flies had a much higher proportion of the combinations of traits seen in the P generation flies (called parental phenotypes) than would be expected if the two genes assorted independently. Morgan thus concluded that body color and wing size are usually inherited together in specific (parental) combinations because the genes for these characters are near each other on the same chromosome:

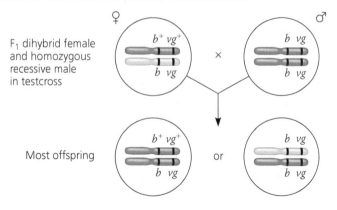

F_1 dihybrid female and homozygous recessive male in testcross

$b^+ \; vg^+$
$b \; vg$
×
$b \; vg$
$b \; vg$

Most offspring

$b^+ \; vg^+$
$b \; vg$
or
$b \; vg$
$b \; vg$

How does linkage between two genes affect inheritance of characters?

Experiment Morgan wanted to know whether the genes for body color and wing size are genetically linked and, if so, how this affects their inheritance. The alleles for body color are b^+ (gray) and b (black), and those for wing size are vg^+ (normal) and vg (vestigial).

Morgan mated true-breeding P (parental) generation flies—wild-type flies with black, vestigial-winged flies—to produce heterozygous F_1 dihybrids ($b^+ b$ $vg^+ vg$), all of which are wild-type in appearance.

He then mated wild-type F_1 dihybrid females with homozygous recessive males. This testcross will reveal the genotype of the eggs made by the dihybrid female.

The male's sperm contributes only recessive alleles, so the phenotype of the offspring reflects the genotype of the female's eggs.

Note: Although only females (with pointed abdomens) are shown, half the offspring in each class would be males (with rounded abdomens).

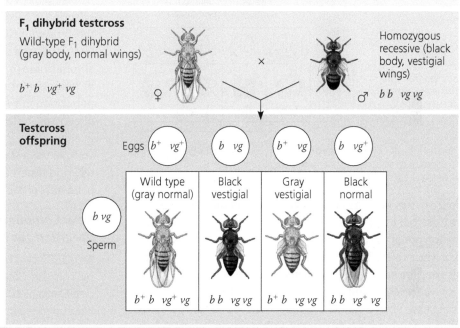

P Generation (homozygous)

Wild type (gray body, normal wings)

$b^+ b^+$ $vg^+ vg^+$

Double mutant (black body, vestigial wings)

$b b$ $vg vg$

F_1 dihybrid testcross

Wild-type F_1 dihybrid (gray body, normal wings)

$b^+ b$ $vg^+ vg$ ♀

Homozygous recessive (black body, vestigial wings)

♂ $b b$ $vg vg$

Testcross offspring

Eggs: $b^+\ vg^+$ | $b\ vg$ | $b^+\ vg$ | $b\ vg^+$

Sperm: $b\ vg$

Wild type (gray normal)	Black vestigial	Gray vestigial	Black normal
$b^+ b$ $vg^+ vg$	$b b$ $vg vg$	$b^+ b$ $vg vg$	$b b$ $vg^+ vg$

PREDICTED RATIOS

Predicted ratio if genes are located on different chromosomes:	1 :	1 :	1 :	1
Predicted ratio if genes are located on the same chromosome *and* parental alleles are always inherited together:	1 :	1 :	0 :	0
Data from Morgan's experiment:	965 :	944 :	206 :	185

Results

Conclusion Since most offspring had a parental (P generation) phenotype, Morgan concluded that the genes for body color and wing size are genetically linked on the same chromosome. However, the production of a relatively small number of offspring with nonparental phenotypes indicated that some mechanism occasionally breaks the linkage between specific alleles of genes on the same chromosome.

Data from T. H. Morgan and C. J. Lynch, The linkage of two factors in *Drosophila* that are not sex-linked, *Biological Bulletin* 23:174–182 (1912).

WHAT IF? If the parental (P generation) flies had been true-breeding for gray body with vestigial wings and black body with normal wings, which phenotypic class(es) would be largest among the testcross offspring?

However, as Figure 12.9 shows, both of the combinations of traits not seen in the P generation (called nonparental phenotypes) were also produced in Morgan's experiments, suggesting that the body-color and wing-size alleles are not always linked genetically. To understand this conclusion, we need to further explore **genetic recombination**, the production of offspring with combinations of traits that differ from those found in either P generation parent.

Genetic Recombination and Linkage

Meiosis and random fertilization generate genetic variation among offspring of sexually reproducing organisms due to independent assortment of chromosomes and crossing over in meiosis I and the possibility of any sperm fertilizing any egg (see Concept 10.4). Here we'll examine the chromosomal basis of recombination of alleles in relation to the genetic findings of Mendel and Morgan.

Recombination of Unlinked Genes: Independent Assortment of Chromosomes

Mendel learned from crosses in which he followed two characters that some offspring have combinations of traits that do not match those of either parent. For example, consider a cross of a dihybrid pea plant with yellow round seeds, heterozygous for both seed color and seed shape (*YyRr*), with a plant homozygous for both recessive alleles (with green wrinkled seeds, *yyrr*). (This cross acts as a testcross because the results will reveal the genotypes of the gametes made in the dihybrid *YyRr* plant.) Let's represent the cross by the following Punnett square:

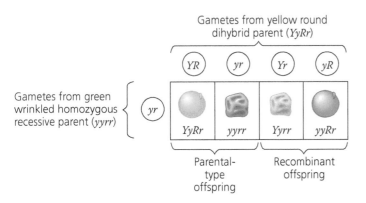

Gametes from yellow round dihybrid parent (*YyRr*)

Gametes from green wrinkled homozygous recessive parent (*yyrr*)

Parental-type offspring

Recombinant offspring

Notice in this Punnett square that one-half of the offspring are expected to inherit a phenotype that matches either of the phenotypes of the P (parental) generation originally crossed to produce the F$_1$ dihybrid (see Figure 12.2). These matching offspring are called **parental types**. But two nonparental phenotypes are also found among the offspring. Because these offspring have new combinations of seed shape and color, they are called **recombinant types**, or **recombinants** for short. When 50% of all offspring are recombinants, as in this example, geneticists say that there is a 50% frequency of recombination. The predicted phenotypic ratios among the offspring are similar to what Mendel actually found in his *YyRr* × *yyrr* crosses.

A 50% frequency of recombination in such testcrosses is observed for any two genes that are located on different chromosomes and thus cannot be linked. The physical basis of recombination between unlinked genes is the random orientation of homologous chromosomes at metaphase I of meiosis, which leads to the independent assortment of the two unlinked genes (see Figure 10.11 and the question in the Figure 12.2 legend).

Recombination of Linked Genes: Crossing Over

Now let's explain the results of the *Drosophila* testcross in Figure 12.9. Recall that most of the offspring from the testcross for body color and wing size had parental phenotypes. That suggested that the two genes were on the same chromosome, since the occurrence of parental types with a frequency greater than 50% indicates that the genes are linked. About 17% of offspring, however, were recombinants.

Seeing these results, Morgan proposed that some process must occasionally break the physical connection between specific alleles of genes on the same chromosome. Later experiments showed that this process, now called **crossing over**, accounts for the recombination of linked genes. In crossing over, which occurs while replicated homologous chromosomes are paired during prophase of meiosis I, a set of proteins orchestrates an exchange of corresponding segments of one maternal and one paternal chromatid (see Figure 10.12). In effect, when a single crossover occurs, end portions of two nonsister chromatids trade places.

Figure 12.10 shows how crossing over in a dihybrid female fly resulted in recombinant eggs and ultimately recombinant offspring in Morgan's testcross. Most of the eggs had a chromosome with either the $b^+ vg^+$ or b vg parental genotype for body color and wing size, but some eggs had a recombinant chromosome ($b^+ vg$ or b vg^+). Fertilization of all classes of eggs by homozygous recessive sperm (b vg) produced an offspring population in which 17% exhibited a nonparental, recombinant phenotype, reflecting combinations of alleles not seen before in either P generation parent. In the **Scientific Skills Exercise**, you can use a statistical test to analyze the results from an F$_1$ dihybrid testcross and see whether the two genes assort independently or are linked.

New Combinations of Alleles: Variation for Natural Selection

EVOLUTION The physical behavior of chromosomes during meiosis contributes to the generation of variation in offspring (see Concept 10.4). Each pair of homologous chromosomes lines up independently of other pairs during metaphase I, and crossing over prior to that, during prophase I, can mix and match parts of maternal and paternal homologs. Mendel's elegant experiments show that the behavior of the abstract entities known as genes—or, more concretely, alleles of genes—also leads to variation in offspring (see Concept 11.1). Now, putting these different ideas together, you can see that the recombinant chromosomes resulting from crossing over may bring alleles together in new combinations, and the subsequent events of meiosis distribute to gametes the recombinant chromosomes in a multitude of combinations, such as the new variants seen in Figures 12.9 and 12.10. Random fertilization then increases even further the number of variant allele combinations that can be created.

This abundance of genetic variation provides the raw material on which natural selection works. If the traits conferred by particular combinations of alleles are better suited for a given environment, organisms possessing those genotypes will be expected to thrive and leave more offspring, ensuring the continuation of their genetic complement. In the next generation, of course, the alleles will be shuffled anew. Ultimately, the interplay between environment and genotype will determine which genetic combinations persist over time.

▶ **Figure 12.10 Chromosomal basis for recombination of linked genes.** In these diagrams recreating the testcross in Figure 12.9, we track chromosomes as well as genes. The maternal chromosomes (present in the wild-type F_1 dihybrid) are color-coded red and pink to distinguish one homolog from the other before any meiotic crossing over has occurred. Because crossing over between the b^+/b and vg^+/vg loci occurs in some, but not all, egg-producing cells, more eggs with parental-type chromosomes than with recombinant ones are produced in the mating females. Fertilization of the eggs by sperm of genotype $b\ vg$ gives rise to some recombinant offspring. The recombination frequency is the percentage of recombinant flies in the total pool of offspring.

DRAW IT *Suppose, as in the question at the bottom of Figure 12.9, the parental (P generation) flies were true-breeding for gray body with vestigial wings and black body with normal wings. Draw the chromosomes in each of the four possible kinds of eggs from an F_1 female, and label each chromosome as "parental" or "recombinant."*

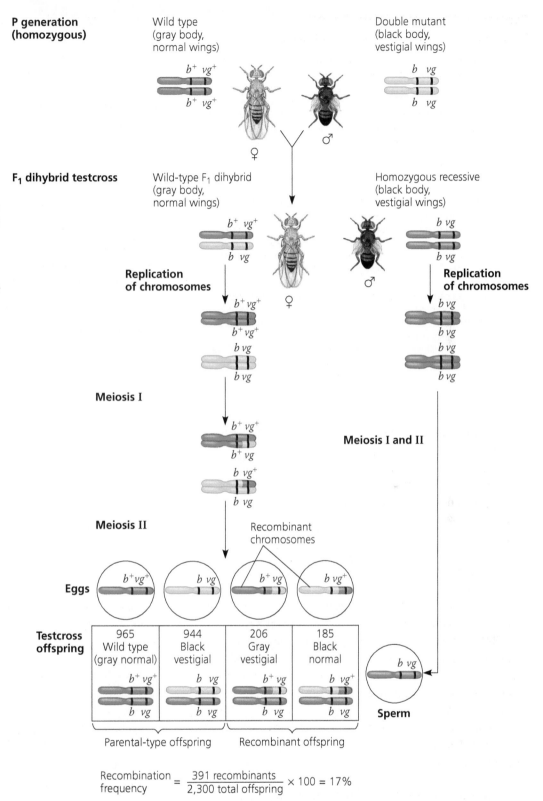

$$\text{Recombination frequency} = \frac{391\ \text{recombinants}}{2{,}300\ \text{total offspring}} \times 100 = 17\%$$

Mapping the Distance Between Genes Using Recombination Data: *Scientific Inquiry*

The discovery of linked genes and recombination due to crossing over motivated one of Morgan's students, Alfred H. Sturtevant, to work out a method for constructing a **genetic map**, an ordered list of the genetic loci along a particular chromosome.

Sturtevant hypothesized that the percentage of recombinant offspring, the *recombination frequency*, calculated from experiments like the one in Figures 12.9 and 12.10, depends on the distance between genes on a chromosome. He assumed that crossing over is a random event, with the chance of crossing over approximately equal at all

Using the Chi-Square (χ^2) Test

Are Two Genes Linked or Unlinked? Genes that are in close proximity on the same chromosome will result in the linked alleles being inherited together more often than not. But how can you tell if certain alleles are inherited together due to linkage or whether they just happen to assort together? In this exercise, you will use a simple statistical test, the chi-square (χ^2) test, to analyze phenotypes of F_1 testcross progeny in order to see whether two genes are linked or unlinked.

How These Experiments Are Done If genes are unlinked and assorting independently, the phenotypic ratio of offspring from an F_1 testcross is expected to be 1:1:1:1 (see Figure 12.9). If the two genes are linked, however, the observed phenotypic ratio of the offspring will not match that ratio. Given that random fluctuations in the data do occur, how much must the observed numbers deviate from the expected numbers for us to conclude that the genes are not assorting independently but may instead be linked? To answer this question, scientists use a statistical test. This test, called a chi-square (χ^2) test, compares an observed data set with an expected data set predicted by a hypothesis (here, that the genes are unlinked) and measures the discrepancy between the two, thus determining the "goodness of fit." If the discrepancy between the observed and expected data sets is so large that it is unlikely to have occurred by random fluctuation, we say there is statistically significant evidence against the hypothesis (or, more specifically, evidence for the genes being linked). If the discrepancy is small, then our observations are well explained by random variation alone. In this case, we say that the observed data are consistent with our hypothesis, or that the discrepancy is statistically insignificant. Note, however, that consistency with our hypothesis is not the same as proof of our hypothesis. Also, the size of the experimental data set is important: With small data sets like this one, even if the genes are linked, discrepancies might be small by chance alone if the linkage is weak. (For simplicity, we overlook the effect of sample size here.)

Data from the Simulated Experiment In cosmos plants, purple stem (A) is dominant to green stem (a), and short petals (B) is dominant to long petals (b). In a simulated cross, $AABB$ plants were crossed with $aabb$ plants to generate F_1 dihybrids ($AaBb$), which were then testcrossed ($AaBb \times aabb$). A total of 900 offspring plants were scored for stem color and flower petal length.

Offspring from testcross of $AaBb$ (F_1) × $aabb$	Purple stem/short petals (A–B–)	Green stem/short petals (aaB–)	Purple stem/long petals (A–bb)	Green stem/long petals ($aabb$)
Expected ratio if the genes are unlinked	1	1	1	1
Expected number of offspring (of 900)				
Observed number of offspring (of 900)	220	210	231	239

INTERPRET THE DATA

1. The results in the data table are from a simulated F_1 dihybrid testcross. The hypothesis that the two genes are unlinked predicts that the offspring phenotypic ratio will be 1:1:1:1. Using this ratio, calculate the expected number of each phenotype out of the 900 total offspring, and enter the values in that data table.

2. The goodness of fit is measured by χ^2. This statistic measures the amounts by which the observed values differ from their respective predictions to indicate how closely the two sets of values match. The formula for calculating this value is

$$\chi^2 = \Sigma \frac{(o - e)^2}{e}$$

where o = observed and e = expected. Calculate the χ^2 value for the data using the table below. Fill out that table, carrying out the operations indicated in the top row. Then add up the entries in the last column to find the χ^2 value.

Testcross offspring	Expected (e)	Observed (o)	Deviation (o − e)	(o − e)²	(o − e)²/e
(A–B–)		220			
(aaB–)		210			
(A–bb)		231			
($aabb$)		239			
				χ^2 =	Sum

3. The χ^2 value means nothing on its own—it is used to find the probability that, assuming the hypothesis is true, the observed data set could have resulted from random fluctuations. A low probability suggests that the observed data are not consistent with the hypothesis, and thus the hypothesis should be rejected. A standard cutoff point used by biologists is a probability of 0.05 (5%). If the probability corresponding to the χ^2 value is 0.05 or less, the differences between observed and expected values are considered statistically significant and the hypothesis (that the genes are unlinked) should be rejected. If the probability is above 0.05, the results are not statistically significant; the observed data are consistent with the hypothesis. To find the probability, locate your χ^2 value in the χ^2 Distribution Table in Appendix F. The "degrees of freedom" (df) of your data set is the number of categories (here, 4 phenotypes) minus 1, so df = 3. (a) Determine which values on the df = 3 line of the table your calculated χ^2 value lies between. (b) The column headings for these values show the probability range for your χ^2 number. Based on whether there are nonsignificant ($p > 0.05$) or significant ($p \leq 0.05$) differences between the observed and expected values, are the data consistent with the hypothesis that the two genes are unlinked and assorting independently, or is there enough evidence to reject this hypothesis?

(MB) A version of this Scientific Skills Exercise can be assigned in MasteringBiology.

points along a chromosome. Based on these assumptions, Sturtevant predicted that *the farther apart two genes are, the higher the probability that a crossover will occur between them and therefore the higher the recombination frequency.*

His reasoning was simple: The greater the distance between two genes, the more points there are between them where crossing over can occur. Using recombination data from various fruit fly crosses, Sturtevant proceeded to assign relative

Constructing a Linkage Map

Application A linkage map shows the relative locations of genes along a chromosome.

Technique A linkage map is based on the assumption that the probability of a crossover between two genetic loci is proportional to the distance separating the loci. The recombination frequencies used to construct a linkage map for a particular chromosome are obtained from experimental crosses, such as the cross depicted in Figures 12.9 and 12.10. The distances between genes are expressed as map units, with one map unit equivalent to a 1% recombination frequency. Genes are arranged on the chromosome in the order that best fits the data.

Results In this example, the observed recombination frequencies between three *Drosophila* gene pairs (*b* and *cn*, 9%; *cn* and *vg*, 9.5%; and *b* and *vg*, 17%) best fit a linear order in which *cn* is positioned about halfway between the other two genes:

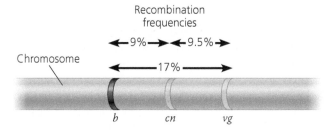

The *b-vg* recombination frequency (17%) is slightly less than the sum of the *b-cn* and *cn-vg* frequencies (9 + 9.5 = 18.5%) because of the few times that one crossover occurs between *b* and *cn* and another crossover occurs between *cn* and *vg*. The second crossover would "cancel out" the first, reducing the observed *b-vg* recombination frequency while contributing to the frequency between each of the closer pairs of genes. The value of 18.5% (18.5 map units) is closer to the actual distance between the genes. In practice, a geneticist would add the smaller distances in constructing a map.

positions to genes on the same chromosomes—that is, to *map* genes.

A genetic map based on recombination frequencies is called a **linkage map**. **Figure 12.11** shows Sturtevant's linkage map of three genes: the body-color (*b*) and wing-size (*vg*) genes depicted in Figure 12.10 and a third gene, called cinnabar (*cn*). Cinnabar is one of many *Drosophila* genes affecting eye color. Cinnabar eyes, a mutant phenotype, are a brighter red than the wild-type color. The recombination frequency between *cn* and *b* is 9%; that between *cn* and *vg*, 9.5%; and that between *b* and *vg*, 17%. In other words, crossovers between *cn* and *b* and between *cn* and *vg* are about half as frequent as crossovers between *b* and *vg*. Only a map that locates *cn* about midway between *b* and *vg* is consistent with these data, as you can prove to yourself by drawing alternative maps. Sturtevant expressed the distances between genes in **map units**, defining one map unit as equivalent to a 1% recombination frequency.

In practice, the interpretation of recombination data is more complicated than this example suggests. Some genes on a chromosome are so far from each other that a crossover between them is virtually certain. The observed frequency of

recombination in crosses involving two such genes can have a maximum value of 50%, a result indistinguishable from that for genes on different chromosomes. In this case, the physical connection between genes on the same chromosome is not reflected in the results of genetic crosses. Despite being on the same chromosome and thus being *physically connected*, the genes are *genetically unlinked*; alleles of such genes assort independently, as if they were on different chromosomes. In fact, at least two of the genes for pea characters that Mendel studied are now known to be on the same chromosome, but the distance between them is so great that linkage is not observed in genetic crosses. Consequently, the two genes behaved as if they were on different chromosomes in Mendel's experiments. Genes located far apart on a chromosome are mapped by adding the recombination frequencies from crosses involving closer pairs of genes lying between the two distant genes.

Using recombination data, Sturtevant and his colleagues were able to map numerous *Drosophila* genes in linear arrays. They found that the genes clustered into four groups of linked genes (*linkage groups*). Light microscopy had revealed four pairs of chromosomes in *Drosophila*, so the linkage map provided additional evidence that genes are located on chromosomes. Each chromosome has a linear array of specific genes, each gene with its own locus (**Figure 12.12**).

Because a linkage map is based strictly on recombination frequencies, it gives only an approximate picture of a chromosome. The frequency of crossing over is not actually uniform

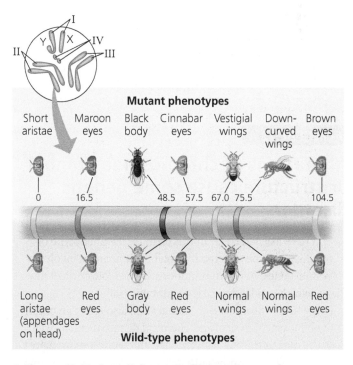

▲ **Figure 12.12 A partial genetic (linkage) map of a *Drosophila* chromosome.** This simplified map shows just seven of the genes that have been mapped on *Drosophila* chromosome 2. (DNA sequencing has revealed over 9,000 genes on that chromosome.) The number at each gene locus indicates the number of map units between that locus and the locus for arista length (left). Notice that more than one gene can affect a given phenotypic character, such as eye color.

over the length of a chromosome, as Sturtevant assumed, and therefore map units do not correspond to actual physical distances (in nanometers, for instance). A linkage map does portray the order of genes along a chromosome, but it does not accurately portray the precise locations of those genes. Other methods enable geneticists to construct **cytogenetic maps** of chromosomes, which locate genes with respect to chromosomal features, such as stained bands, that can be seen in the microscope. Technical advances over the last two decades have enormously increased the rate and affordability of DNA sequencing. Today, most researchers sequence whole genomes to map the locations of genes of a given species. The entire nucleotide sequence is the ultimate physical map of a chromosome, revealing the physical distances between gene loci in DNA nucleotides (see Concept 18.1). Comparing a linkage map with such a physical map or with a cytogenetic map of the same chromosome, we find that the linear order of genes is identical in all the maps, but the spacing between genes is not.

CONCEPT CHECK 12.3

1. When two genes are located on the same chromosome, what is the physical basis for the production of recombinant offspring in a testcross between a dihybrid parent and a double-mutant (recessive) parent?
2. For each type of offspring of the testcross in Figure 12.9, explain the relationship between its phenotype and the alleles contributed by the female parent. (It will be useful to draw out the chromosomes of each fly and follow the alleles throughout the cross.)
3. **WHAT IF?** Genes *A*, *B*, and *C* are located on the same chromosome. Testcrosses show that the recombination frequency between *A* and *B* is 28% and that between *A* and *C* is 12%. Can you determine the linear order of these genes? Explain.

For suggested answers, see Appendix A.

CONCEPT 12.4

Alterations of chromosome number or structure cause some genetic disorders

As you have learned so far in this chapter, the phenotype of an organism can be affected by small-scale changes involving individual genes. Random mutations are the source of all new alleles, which can lead to new phenotypic traits.

Large-scale chromosomal changes can also affect an organism's phenotype. Physical and chemical disturbances, as well as errors during meiosis, can damage chromosomes in major ways or alter their number in a cell. Large-scale chromosomal alterations in humans and other mammals often lead to spontaneous abortion (miscarriage) of a fetus, and individuals born with these types of genetic defects commonly exhibit various developmental disorders. Plants appear to tolerate such genetic defects better than animals do.

Abnormal Chromosome Number

Ideally, the meiotic spindle distributes chromosomes to daughter cells without error. But there is an occasional mishap, called a **nondisjunction**, in which the members of a pair of homologous chromosomes do not move apart properly during meiosis I or sister chromatids fail to separate during meiosis II **(Figure 12.13)**. In nondisjunction, one gamete receives two of the same type of chromosome and another gamete receives no copy. The other chromosomes are usually distributed normally.

If either of the aberrant gametes unites with a normal one at fertilization, the zygote will also have an abnormal number of a particular chromosome, a condition known as **aneuploidy**. Fertilization involving a gamete that has no copy of a particular chromosome will lead to a missing chromosome in the zygote (so that the cell has $2n - 1$ chromosomes); the aneuploid zygote is said to be **monosomic** for that chromosome. If a chromosome is present in triplicate in the zygote (so that the cell has $2n + 1$ chromosomes), the aneuploid cell is **trisomic** for that chromosome. Mitosis will subsequently transmit the anomaly to all embryonic cells. Monosomy and trisomy are estimated to occur in between 10 and 25% of human conceptions and are the main reason for pregnancy loss. If the organism survives, it usually has a set of traits caused by the abnormal dose of the genes associated with the extra or missing chromosome. Down syndrome is an example of trisomy in humans that will be discussed later. Nondisjunction can also occur during mitosis. If such an error takes place early

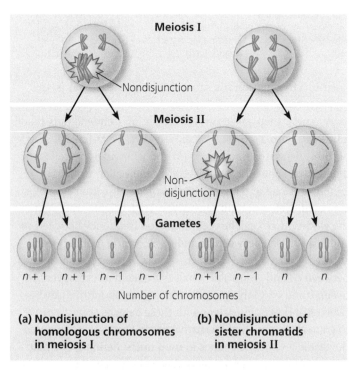

Meiosis I

Nondisjunction

Meiosis II

Nondisjunction

Gametes

$n + 1$ $n + 1$ $n - 1$ $n - 1$ $n + 1$ $n - 1$ n n

Number of chromosomes

(a) Nondisjunction of homologous chromosomes in meiosis I

(b) Nondisjunction of sister chromatids in meiosis II

▲ **Figure 12.13 Meiotic nondisjunction.** Gametes with an abnormal chromosome number can arise by nondisjunction in either meiosis I or meiosis II. For simplicity, the figure does not show the spores formed by meiosis in plants. Ultimately, spores form gametes that have the defects shown. (See Figure 10.6.)

in embryonic development, then the aneuploid condition is passed along by mitosis to a large number of cells and is likely to have a substantial effect on the organism.

Some organisms have more than two complete chromosome sets in all somatic cells. The general term for this chromosomal alteration is **polyploidy**; the specific terms *triploidy* ($3n$) and *tetraploidy* ($4n$) indicate three and four chromosomal sets, respectively. One way a triploid cell may arise is by the fertilization of an abnormal diploid egg produced by nondisjunction of all its chromosomes. Tetraploidy could result from the failure of a $2n$ zygote to divide after replicating its chromosomes. Subsequent normal mitotic divisions would then produce a $4n$ embryo.

Polyploidy is fairly common in plants; the spontaneous origin of polyploid individuals plays an important role in the evolution of plants (see Figure 22.9 and the associated text). Many of the plant species we eat are polyploid; for example, bananas are triploid, wheat is hexaploid ($6n$), and strawberries are octoploid ($8n$).

Alterations of Chromosome Structure

Errors in meiosis or damaging agents such as radiation can cause breakage of a chromosome, which can lead to four types of changes in chromosome structure (**Figure 12.14**). A **deletion** occurs when a chromosomal fragment is lost. The affected chromosome is then missing certain genes. The "deleted" fragment may become attached as an extra segment to a sister chromatid, producing a **duplication** of a portion of that chromosome. Alternatively, a detached fragment could attach to a nonsister chromatid of a homologous chromosome. In that case, though, the "duplicated" segments might not be identical because the homologs could carry different alleles of certain genes. A chromosomal fragment may also reattach to the original chromosome but in the reverse orientation, producing an **inversion**. A fourth possible result of chromosomal breakage is for the fragment to join a nonhomologous chromosome, a rearrangement called a **translocation**.

Deletions and duplications are especially likely to occur during meiosis. In crossing over, nonsister chromatids sometimes exchange unequal-sized segments of DNA, so that one partner gives up more genes than it receives. The products of such an unequal crossover are one chromosome with a deletion and one chromosome with a duplication.

A diploid embryo that is homozygous for a large deletion (or has a single X chromosome with a large deletion, in a male) is usually missing a number of essential genes, a condition that is typically lethal. Duplications and translocations also tend to be harmful. In reciprocal translocations, in which segments are exchanged between nonhomologous chromosomes, and in inversions, the balance of genes is not abnormal—all genes are present in their normal doses. Nevertheless, translocations and inversions can alter phenotype because a gene's expression can be influenced by its location among neighboring genes, which can have devastating effects.

▼ **Figure 12.14 Alterations of chromosome structure.** Red arrows indicate breakage points. Dark purple highlights the chromosomal parts affected by the rearrangements.

(a) Deletion

A **deletion** removes a chromosomal segment.

(b) Duplication

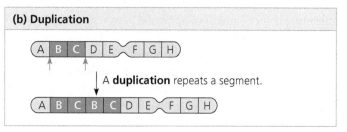

A **duplication** repeats a segment.

(c) Inversion

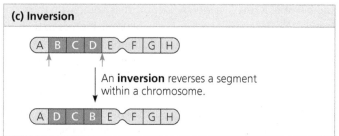

An **inversion** reverses a segment within a chromosome.

(d) Translocation

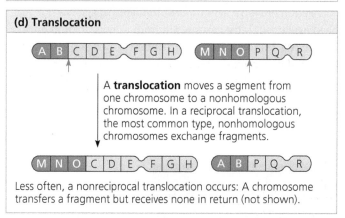

A **translocation** moves a segment from one chromosome to a nonhomologous chromosome. In a reciprocal translocation, the most common type, nonhomologous chromosomes exchange fragments.

Less often, a nonreciprocal translocation occurs: A chromosome transfers a fragment but receives none in return (not shown).

Human Disorders Due to Chromosomal Alterations

Alterations of chromosome number and structure are associated with a number of serious human disorders. As described earlier, nondisjunction in meiosis results in aneuploidy in gametes and any resulting zygotes. Although the frequency of aneuploid zygotes may be quite high in humans, most of these chromosomal alterations are so disastrous to development that the affected embryos are spontaneously aborted long before birth. However, some types of aneuploidy appear to upset the genetic balance less than others, where individuals with certain aneuploid conditions can survive to birth and beyond. These individuals have a set of traits—a *syndrome*—characteristic of the type of aneuploidy. Genetic disorders caused by aneuploidy can be diagnosed before birth by genetic testing of the fetus.

Down Syndrome (Trisomy 21)

One aneuploid condition, **Down syndrome**, affects approximately one out of every 830 children born in the United States (**Figure 12.15**). Down syndrome is usually the result of an extra chromosome 21, so that each body cell has a total of 47 chromosomes. Because the cells are trisomic for chromosome 21, Down syndrome is often called *trisomy 21*. Down syndrome includes characteristic facial features, short stature, correctable heart defects, and developmental delays. Individuals with Down syndrome have an increased chance of developing leukemia and Alzheimer's disease but have a lower rate of high blood pressure, atherosclerosis (hardening of the arteries), stroke, and many types of solid tumors. Although people with Down syndrome, on average, have a life span shorter than normal, most, with proper medical treatment, live to middle age and beyond. Many live independently or at home with their families, are employed, and are valuable contributors to their communities. Almost all males and about half of females with Down syndrome are sexually underdeveloped and sterile.

The frequency of Down syndrome increases with the age of the mother. While the disorder occurs in just 0.04% of children born to women under age 30, the risk climbs to 0.92% for mothers at age 40 and is even higher for older mothers. The correlation of Down syndrome with maternal age has not yet been explained. Most cases result from nondisjunction during meiosis I, and some research points to an age-dependent abnormality in meiosis. Medical experts recommend that prenatal screening for trisomies in the embryo be offered to all pregnant women, due to its low risk and useful results. A law passed in 2008 stipulates that medical practitioners give accurate, up-to-date information about any prenatal or postnatal diagnosis received by parents and that they connect parents with appropriate support services.

Aneuploidy of Sex Chromosomes

Aneuploid conditions involving sex chromosomes appear to upset the genetic balance less than those involving autosomes. This may be because the Y chromosome carries relatively few genes. Also, extra copies of the X chromosome simply become inactivated as Barr bodies in somatic cells.

An extra X chromosome in a male, producing an XXY genotype, occurs approximately once in every 500 to 1,000 live male births. People with this disorder, called *Klinefelter syndrome*, have male sex organs, but the testes are abnormally small and the man is sterile. Even though the extra X is inactivated, some breast enlargement and other female body characteristics are common. Affected individuals may have subnormal intelligence. About one of every 1,000 males is born with an extra Y chromosome (XYY). These males undergo normal sexual development and do not exhibit any well-defined syndrome.

Females with trisomy X (XXX), which occurs once in approximately 1,000 live female births, are healthy and have no unusual physical features other than being slightly taller than average. Triple-X females are at risk for learning disabilities but are fertile. Monosomy X, called *Turner syndrome*, occurs about once in every 2,500 female births and is the only known viable monosomy in humans. Although these X0 individuals are phenotypically female, they are sterile because their sex organs do not mature. When provided with estrogen replacement therapy, girls with Turner syndrome do develop secondary sex characteristics. Most have normal intelligence.

Disorders Caused by Structurally Altered Chromosomes

Many deletions in human chromosomes, even in a heterozygous state, cause severe problems. One such syndrome, known as *cri du chat* ("cry of the cat"), results from a specific deletion in chromosome 5. A child born with this deletion is severely intellectually disabled, has a small head with unusual facial features, and has a cry that sounds like the mewing of a distressed cat. Such individuals usually die in infancy or early childhood.

Chromosomal translocations can also occur during mitosis; some have been implicated in certain cancers, including *chronic myelogenous leukemia* (CML). This disease occurs when a reciprocal translocation happens during mitosis of pre-white blood cells. The exchange of a large portion of chromosome 22 with a small fragment from a tip of chromosome 9 produces a much shortened, easily recognized chromosome 22, called the *Philadelphia chromosome* (**Figure 12.16**). Such an exchange causes cancer by creating a new "fused" gene that leads to uncontrolled cell cycle progression. (The mechanism of gene activation will be discussed in Concept 16.3.)

▲ **Figure 12.15 Down syndrome.** The karyotype shows trisomy 21, the most common cause of Down syndrome. The child exhibits the facial features characteristic of this disorder.

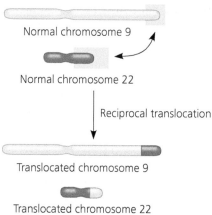

▲ **Figure 12.16 Translocation associated with chronic myelogenous leukemia (CML).** The cancerous cells in nearly all CML patients contain an abnormally short chromosome 22, the so-called Philadelphia chromosome, and an abnormally long chromosome 9. These altered chromosomes result from the reciprocal translocation shown here, which presumably occurred in a single white blood cell precursor undergoing mitosis and was then passed along to all descendant cells.

CONCEPT CHECK 12.4

1. About 5% of individuals with Down syndrome have a chromosomal translocation in which a third copy of chromosome 21 is attached to chromosome 14. If this translocation occurred in a parent's gonad, how could it lead to Down syndrome in a child?

2. **WHAT IF?** The ABO blood type locus has been mapped on chromosome 9. A father who has type AB blood and a mother who has type O blood have a child with trisomy 9 and type A blood. Using this information, can you tell in which parent the nondisjunction occurred? Explain your answer.

3. **MAKE CONNECTIONS** The gene that is activated on the Philadelphia chromosome codes for an intracellular kinase. Review the discussion of cell cycle control and cancer in Concept 9.3, and explain how the activation of this gene could contribute to the development of cancer.

4. Women born with an extra X chromosome (XXX) are generally healthy and indistinguishable in appearance from XX women. What is a likely explanation for this finding? How could you test this explanation?

For suggested answers, see Appendix A.

Go to **MasteringBiology**® for Assignments, the eText, and the Study Area with Animations, Activities, Vocab Self-Quiz, and Practice Tests.

12 Chapter Review

SUMMARY OF KEY CONCEPTS

VOCAB SELF-QUIZ

goo.gl/gbai8v

CONCEPT 12.1

Morgan showed that Mendelian inheritance has its physical basis in the behavior of chromosomes: *scientific inquiry* (pp. 238–239)

- Morgan's work with an eye-color gene in *Drosophila* led to the **chromosome theory of inheritance**, which states that genes are located on chromosomes and that the behavior of chromosomes during meiosis accounts for Mendel's laws.
- Morgan's discovery that transmission of the X chromosome in *Drosophila* correlates with inheritance of an eye-color trait was the first solid evidence indicating that a specific gene is associated with a specific chromosome.

  ❓ *What characteristic of the sex chromosomes allowed Morgan to correlate their behavior with that of the alleles of the eye-color gene?*

CONCEPT 12.2

Sex-linked genes exhibit unique patterns of inheritance (pp. 239–242)

- Sex is often chromosomally based. Humans and other mammals have an X-Y system in which sex is determined by whether a Y chromosome is present.
- The sex chromosomes carry **sex-linked genes**, virtually all of which are on the X chromosome (X-linked). Any male who inherits a recessive X-linked allele (from his mother) will express the trait, such as color blindness.
- In mammalian females, one of the two X chromosomes in each cell is randomly inactivated during early embryonic development, becoming highly condensed into a **Barr body**.

  ❓ *Why are males affected by X-linked disorders much more often than females?*

CONCEPT 12.3

Linked genes tend to be inherited together because they are located near each other on the same chromosome (pp. 242–248)

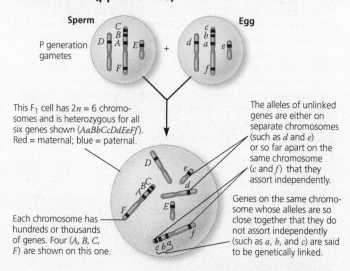

This F₁ cell has $2n = 6$ chromosomes and is heterozygous for all six genes shown (*AaBbCcDdEeFf*). Red = maternal; blue = paternal.

Each chromosome has hundreds or thousands of genes. Four (*A, B, C, F*) are shown on this one.

The alleles of unlinked genes are either on separate chromosomes (such as *d* and *e*) or so far apart on the same chromosome (*c* and *f*) that they assort independently.

Genes on the same chromosome whose alleles are so close together that they do not assort independently (such as *a*, *b*, and *c*) are said to be genetically linked.

- An F₁ testcross yields **parental types** with the same combination of traits as those in the P generation parents and **recombinant types** with new combinations of traits. Unlinked genes exhibit a 50% frequency of recombination in the gametes. For genetically **linked genes**, **crossing over** accounts for the observed recombinants, always less than 50%.
- Recombination frequencies observed in genetic crosses allow construction of a **linkage map** (a type of **genetic map**).

  ❓ *Why are specific alleles of two distant genes more likely to show recombination than those of two closer genes?*

Alterations of chromosome number or structure cause some genetic disorders (pp. 248–251)

- **Aneuploidy**, an abnormal chromosome number, results from **nondisjunction** during meiosis. When a normal gamete unites with one containing two copies or no copies of a particular chromosome, the resulting zygote and its descendant cells either have one extra copy of that chromosome (**trisomy**, $2n + 1$) or are missing a copy (**monosomy**, $2n - 1$). **Polyploidy** (extra sets of chromosomes) can result from complete nondisjunction.

- Chromosome breakage can result in alterations of chromosome structure: **deletions**, **duplications**, **inversions**, and **translocations**.

? *Why are inversions and reciprocal translocations less likely to be lethal than are aneuploidy, duplications, and deletions?*

TEST YOUR UNDERSTANDING

PRACTICE TEST

Level 1: Knowledge/Comprehension

goo.gl/CRZjvS

1. A man with hemophilia (a recessive, sex-linked condition) has a daughter without the condition, who marries a man who does not have hemophilia. What is the probability that their daughter will have the condition? Their son? If they have four sons, that all will be affected?

2. Pseudohypertrophic muscular dystrophy is an inherited disorder that causes gradual deterioration of the muscles. It is seen almost exclusively in boys born to apparently unaffected parents and usually results in death in the early teens. Is this disorder caused by a dominant or a recessive allele? Is its inheritance sex-linked or autosomal? How do you know? Explain why this disorder is almost never seen in girls.

3. A space probe discovers a planet inhabited by creatures that reproduce with the same hereditary patterns seen in humans. Three phenotypic characters are height (T = tall, t = dwarf), head appendages (A = antennae, a = no antennae), and nose morphology (S = upturned snout, s = downturned snout). Since the creatures are not "intelligent," Earth scientists are able to do some controlled breeding experiments using various heterozygotes in testcrosses. For tall heterozygotes with antennae, the offspring are tall-antennae, 46; dwarf-antennae, 7; dwarf-no antennae, 42; tall-no antennae, 5. For heterozygotes with antennae and an upturned snout, the offspring are antennae-upturned snout, 47; antennae-downturned snout, 2; no antennae-downturned snout, 48; no antennae-upturned snout, 3. Calculate the recombination frequencies for both experiments.

Level 2: Application/Analysis

4. Using the information from problem 3, scientists do a further testcross using a heterozygote for height and nose morphology. The offspring are tall-upturned snout, 40; dwarf-upturned snout, 9; dwarf-downturned snout, 42; tall-downturned snout, 9. Calculate the recombination frequency from these data; then use your answer from problem 3 to determine the correct order of the three linked genes.

5. A man with red-green color blindness (a recessive, sex-linked condition) marries a woman with normal vision whose father was color-blind. What is the probability that they will have a color-blind daughter? That their first son will be color-blind? (Note the different wording in the two questions.)

6. You design *Drosophila* crosses to provide recombination data for gene *a*, which is located on the chromosome shown in Figure 12.12. Gene *a* has recombination frequencies of 14% with the vestigial-wing locus and 26% with the brown-eye locus. Approximately where is gene *a* located along the chromosome?

7. A wild-type fruit fly (heterozygous for gray body color and red eyes) is mated with a black fruit fly with purple eyes. The offspring are wild-type, 721; black-purple, 751; gray-purple, 49; black-red, 45. What is the recombination frequency between these genes for body color and eye color? Using information from Figure 12.9, what fruit flies (genotypes and phenotypes) would you mate to determine the sequence of the body-color, wing-size, and eye-color genes on the chromosome?

8. Assume that genes *A* and *B* are 50 map units apart on the same chromosome. An animal heterozygous at both loci is crossed with one that is homozygous recessive at both loci. What percentage of the offspring will show recombinant phenotypes? Without knowing that these genes are on the same chromosome, how would you interpret the results of this cross?

9. Two genes of a flower, one controlling blue (*B*) versus white (*b*) petals and the other controlling round (*R*) versus oval (*r*) stamens, are linked and are 10 map units apart. You cross a homozygous blue-oval plant with a homozygous white-round plant. The resulting F_1 progeny are crossed with homozygous white-oval plants, and 1,000 F_2 progeny are obtained. How many F_2 plants of each of the four phenotypes do you expect?

Level 3: Synthesis/Evaluation

10. **SCIENTIFIC INQUIRY**

    DRAW IT Assume you are mapping genes *A*, *B*, *C*, and *D* in *Drosophila*. You know that these genes are linked on the same chromosome, and you determine the recombination frequencies between each pair of genes to be as follows: *A* and *B*, 8%; *A* and *C*, 28%; *A* and *D*, 25%; *B* and *C*, 20%, *B* and *D*, 33%.
    (a) Describe how you determined the recombination frequency for each pair of genes.
    (b) Draw a chromosome map based on your data.

11. **FOCUS ON EVOLUTION**
    Crossing over is thought to be evolutionarily advantageous because it continually shuffles genetic alleles into novel combinations. Until recently, it was thought that Y-linked genes might degenerate because they lack homologous genes on the X chromosome with which to recombine. However, when the Y chromosome was sequenced, eight large regions were found to be internally homologous to each other, and quite a few of the 78 genes represent duplicates. Explain how this might be beneficial.

12. **FOCUS ON INFORMATION**
    The continuity of life is based on heritable information in the form of DNA. In a short essay (100–150 words), relate the structure and behavior of chromosomes to inheritance in both asexually and sexually reproducing species.

13. **SYNTHESIZE YOUR KNOWLEDGE**

    Butterflies have an X-Y sex determination system that is different from that of flies or humans. Female butterflies may be either XY or XO, while butterflies with two or more X chromosomes are males. This photograph shows a tiger swallowtail *gynandromorph*, an individual that is half male (left side) and half female (right side). Given that the first division of the zygote divides the embryo into the future right and left halves of the butterfly, propose a hypothesis that explains how nondisjunction during the first mitosis might have produced this unusual-looking butterfly.

For selected answers, see Appendix A.

13 The Molecular Basis of Inheritance

KEY CONCEPTS

13.1 DNA is the genetic material

13.2 Many proteins work together in DNA replication and repair

13.3 A chromosome consists of a DNA molecule packed together with proteins

13.4 Understanding DNA structure and replication makes genetic engineering possible

▲ **Figure 13.1** What is the structure of DNA?

Life's Operating Instructions

The elegant double-helical structure of deoxyribonucleic acid, or DNA, has become an icon of modern biology (**Figure 13.1**). James Watson and Francis Crick shook the scientific world in April 1953 with their DNA model, which they constructed from sheet metal and wire (**Figure 13.2**). Gregor Mendel's heritable factors and Thomas Hunt Morgan's genes on chromosomes are, in fact, composed of DNA. Chemically speaking, your genetic endowment is the DNA you inherited from your parents. DNA, the substance of inheritance, is the most celebrated molecule of our time.

Of all nature's molecules, nucleic acids are unique in their ability to direct their own replication from monomers. Indeed, the resemblance of offspring to their parents has its basis in the accurate replication of DNA and its transmission from one generation to the next. Hereditary information in DNA directs the development of your biochemical, anatomical, physiological, and, to some extent, behavioral traits. In this chapter, you'll discover how biologists deduced that DNA is the genetic material and how Watson and Crick worked out its structure. You'll also learn how a molecule of DNA is copied during **DNA replication** and how cells repair their DNA. Next, you'll see how DNA is packaged together with proteins in a chromosome. Finally, you'll explore how an understanding of DNA-related processes has allowed scientists to directly manipulate genes for practical purposes.

◄ **Figure 13.2** James Watson (left) and Francis Crick with their DNA model.

DNA is the genetic material

Today, even schoolchildren have heard of DNA, and scientists routinely manipulate DNA in the laboratory, often to change the heritable traits of cells in their experiments. Early in the 20th century, however, identifying the molecules of inheritance loomed as a major challenge to biologists.

The Search for the Genetic Material: *Scientific Inquiry*

Once T. H. Morgan's group showed that genes exist as parts of chromosomes (described in Concept 12.1), the two chemical components of chromosomes—DNA and protein—emerged as the leading candidates for the genetic material. Until the 1940s, the case for proteins seemed stronger: Biochemists had identified proteins as a class of macromolecules with great heterogeneity and specificity of function, essential requirements for the hereditary material. Moreover, little was known about nucleic acids, whose physical and chemical properties seemed far too uniform to account for the multitude of specific inherited traits exhibited by every organism. This view gradually changed as the role of DNA in heredity was worked out in studies of bacteria and the viruses that infect them, systems far simpler than fruit flies or humans. Let's trace the search for the genetic material in some detail as a case study in scientific inquiry.

Evidence That DNA Can Transform Bacteria

In 1928, a British medical officer named Frederick Griffith was trying to develop a vaccine against pneumonia. He was studying *Streptococcus pneumoniae*, a bacterium that causes pneumonia in mammals. Griffith had two strains (varieties) of the bacterium, one pathogenic (disease-causing) and one nonpathogenic (harmless). He was surprised to find that when he killed the pathogenic bacteria with heat and then mixed the cell remains with living bacteria of the nonpathogenic strain, some of the living cells became pathogenic **(Figure 13.3)**. Furthermore, this newly acquired trait of pathogenicity was inherited by all the descendants of the transformed bacteria. Apparently, some chemical component of the dead pathogenic cells caused this heritable change, although the identity of the substance was not known. Griffith called the phenomenon **transformation**, now defined as a change in genotype and phenotype due to the assimilation of external DNA by a cell. Later work by Oswald Avery and others identified the transforming substance as DNA.

Scientists remained skeptical, however, since many still viewed proteins as better candidates for the genetic material. Also, many biologists were not convinced that bacterial genes would be similar in composition and function to those of more complex organisms. But the major reason for the continued doubt was that so little was known about DNA.

▼ **Figure 13.3** Inquiry

Can a genetic trait be transferred between different bacterial strains?

Experiment Frederick Griffith studied two strains of the bacterium *Streptococcus pneumoniae*. The S (smooth) strain can cause pneumonia in mice; it is pathogenic because the cells have an outer capsule that protects them from an animal's immune system. Cells of the R (rough) strain lack a capsule and are nonpathogenic. To test for the trait of pathogenicity, Griffith injected mice with the two strains:

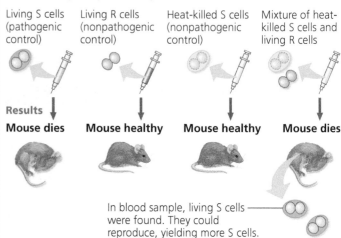

Living S cells (pathogenic control)   Living R cells (nonpathogenic control)   Heat-killed S cells (nonpathogenic control)   Mixture of heat-killed S cells and living R cells

Results

Mouse dies   Mouse healthy   Mouse healthy   Mouse dies

In blood sample, living S cells were found. They could reproduce, yielding more S cells.

Conclusion The living R bacteria had been transformed into pathogenic S bacteria by an unknown, heritable substance from the dead S cells that enabled the R cells to make capsules.

Data from F. Griffith, The significance of pneumococcal types, *Journal of Hygiene* 27:113–159 (1928).

WHAT IF? How did this experiment rule out the possibility that the R cells simply used the dead S cells' capsules to become pathogenic?

Evidence That Viral DNA Can Program Cells

Additional evidence that DNA was the genetic material came from studies of viruses that infect bacteria. These viruses are called **bacteriophages** (meaning "bacteria-eaters"), or **phages** for short. Viruses are much simpler than cells. A **virus** is little more than DNA (or sometimes RNA) enclosed by a protective coat, which is often simply protein **(Figure 13.4)**. To produce

▶ **Figure 13.4 A virus infecting a bacterial cell.** A phage called T2 attaches to a host cell and injects its genetic material through the plasma membrane while the head and tail parts remain on the outer bacterial surface (colorized TEM).

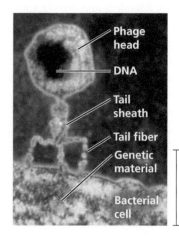

Phage head

DNA

Tail sheath

Tail fiber

Genetic material

Bacterial cell

100 nm

more viruses, a virus must infect a cell and take over the cell's metabolic machinery.

Phages have been widely used as tools by researchers in molecular genetics. In 1952, Alfred Hershey and Martha Chase performed experiments showing that DNA is the genetic material of a phage known as T2. This is one of many phages that infect *Escherichia coli* (*E. coli*), a bacterium that normally lives in the intestines of mammals and is a model organism for molecular biologists. At that time, biologists already knew that T2, like many other phages, was composed almost entirely of DNA and protein. They also knew that the T2 phage could quickly turn an *E. coli* cell into a T2-producing factory that released many copies of new phages when the cell ruptured. Somehow,

T2 could reprogram its host cell to produce viruses. But which viral component—protein or DNA—was responsible?

Hershey and Chase answered this question by devising an experiment showing that only one of the two components of T2 actually enters the *E. coli* cell during infection (Figure 13.5). In their experiment, they used a radioactive isotope of sulfur to tag protein in one batch of T2 and a radioactive isotope of phosphorus to tag DNA in a second batch. Because protein, but not DNA, contains sulfur, radioactive sulfur atoms were incorporated only into the protein of the phage. In a similar way, the atoms of radioactive phosphorus labeled only the DNA, not the protein, because nearly all the phage's phosphorus is in its DNA. In the experiment, separate samples

▼ Figure 13.5   Inquiry

Is protein or DNA the genetic material of phage T2?

Experiment Alfred Hershey and Martha Chase used radioactive sulfur and phosphorus to trace the fates of protein and DNA, respectively, of T2 phages that infected bacterial cells. They wanted to see which of these molecules entered the cells and could reprogram them to make more phages.

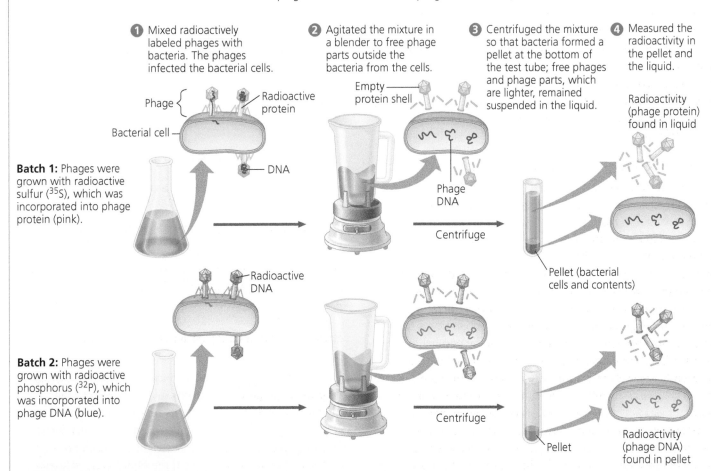

Results When proteins were labeled (batch 1), radioactivity remained outside the cells, but when DNA was labeled (batch 2), radioactivity was found inside the cells. Cells containing radioactive phage DNA released new phages with some radioactive phosphorus.

Conclusion Phage DNA entered bacterial cells, but phage proteins did not. Hershey and Chase concluded that DNA, not protein, functions as the genetic material of phage T2.

Data from A. D. Hershey and M. Chase, Independent functions of viral protein and nucleic acid in growth of bacteriophage, *Journal of General Physiology* 36:39–56 (1952).

WHAT IF? How would the results have differed if proteins carried the genetic information?

of nonradioactive *E. coli* cells were infected with the protein-labeled and DNA-labeled batches of T2. The researchers then tested the two samples shortly after the onset of infection to see which type of molecule—protein or DNA—had entered the bacterial cells and would therefore have been capable of reprogramming them.

Hershey and Chase found that the phage DNA entered the host cells, but the phage protein did not. Moreover, when these bacteria were returned to a culture medium and the infection ran its course, the *E. coli* released phages that contained some radioactive phosphorus. This result further showed that the DNA inside the cell played an ongoing role during the infection process.

Hershey and Chase concluded that the DNA injected by the phage must be the molecule carrying the genetic information that makes the cells produce new viral DNA and proteins. The Hershey-Chase experiment was a landmark study because it provided powerful evidence that nucleic acids, rather than proteins, are the hereditary material, at least for certain viruses.

Additional Evidence That DNA Is the Genetic Material

Further evidence that DNA is the genetic material came from the laboratory of biochemist Erwin Chargaff. It was already known that DNA is a polymer of nucleotides, each consisting of three components: a nitrogenous (nitrogen-containing) base, a pentose sugar called deoxyribose, and a phosphate group **(Figure 13.6)**. The base can be adenine (A), thymine (T), guanine (G), or cytosine (C). Chargaff analyzed the base composition of DNA from a number of different organisms. In 1950, he reported that the base composition of DNA varies from one species to another. For example, 32.8% of sea urchin DNA nucleotides have the base A, whereas only 24.7% of the DNA nucleotides from the bacterium *E. coli* have an A. This evidence of molecular diversity among species, which had been presumed absent from DNA, made DNA a more credible candidate for the genetic material.

Chargaff also noticed a peculiar regularity in the ratios of nucleotide bases. In the DNA of each species he studied, the number of adenines approximately equaled the number of thymines, and the number of guanines approximately equaled the number of cytosines. In sea urchin DNA, for example, the four bases are present in these percentages: A = 32.8% and T = 32.1%; G = 17.7% and C = 17.3%. (The percentages are not exactly the same because of limitations in Chargaff's techniques.)

These two findings became known as *Chargaff's rules*: (1) DNA base composition varies between species, and (2) for each species, the percentages of A and T bases are roughly equal, as are those of G and C bases. In the **Scientific Skills Exercise**, you can use Chargaff's rules to predict unknown percentages of nucleotide bases. The basis for these rules remained unexplained until the discovery of the double helix.

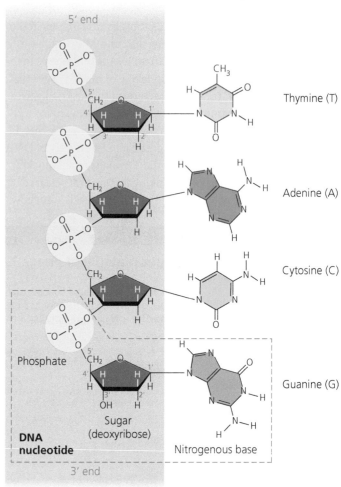

▲ **Figure 13.6 The structure of a DNA strand.** Each DNA nucleotide monomer consists of a nitrogenous base (T, A, C, or G), the sugar deoxyribose (blue), and a phosphate group (yellow). The phosphate group of one nucleotide is attached to the sugar of the next by a covalent bond, forming a "backbone" of alternating phosphates and sugars from which the bases project. The polynucleotide strand has directionality, from the 5′ end (with the phosphate group) to the 3′ end (with the —OH group of the sugar). 5′ and 3′ refer to the numbers assigned to the carbons in the sugar ring.

Building a Structural Model of DNA: *Scientific Inquiry*

Once most biologists were convinced that DNA was the genetic material, the challenge was to determine how the structure of DNA could account for its role in inheritance. By the early 1950s, the arrangement of covalent bonds in a nucleic acid polymer was well established (see Figure 13.6), and researchers focused on discovering the three-dimensional structure of DNA. Among the scientists working on the problem were Linus Pauling, at the California Institute of Technology, and Maurice Wilkins and Rosalind Franklin, at King's College in London. First to come up with the complete answer, however, were two scientists who were relatively unknown at the time—the American James Watson and the Englishman Francis Crick.

Working with Data in a Table

Given the Percentage Composition of One Nucleotide in a Genome, Can We Predict the Percentages of the Other Three Nucleotides? Even before the structure of DNA was elucidated, Erwin Chargaff and his coworkers noticed a pattern in the base composition of nucleotides from different species: The percentage of adenine (A) bases roughly equaled that of thymine (T) bases, and the percentage of cytosine (C) bases roughly equaled that of guanine (G) bases. Further, the percentage of each pair (A/T or C/G) varied from species to species. We now know that the 1:1 A/T and C/G ratios are due to complementary base pairing between A and T and between C and G in the DNA double helix, and interspecies differences are due to the unique sequences of bases along a DNA strand. In this exercise, you will apply Chargaff's rules to predict the composition of bases in a genome.

How the Experiments Were Done In Chargaff's experiments, DNA was extracted from the given organism, hydrolyzed to break apart the individual nucleotides, and then analyzed chemically. These experiments provided approximate values for each type of nucleotide. (Today, whole-genome sequencing allows base composition analysis to be done more precisely directly from the sequence data.)

Data from the Experiments Tables are useful for organizing sets of data representing a common set of values (here, percentages of A, G, C, and T) for a number of different samples (in this case, from different species). You can apply the patterns that you see in the known data to predict unknown values. In the table, complete base distribution data are given for sea urchin DNA and salmon DNA; you will use Chargaff's rules to fill in the rest of the table with predicted values.

▶ Sea urchin

Source of DNA	Base Percentage			
	Adenine	Guanine	Cytosine	Thymine
Sea urchin	32.8	17.7	17.3	32.1
Salmon	29.7	20.8	20.4	29.1
Wheat	28.1	21.8	22.7	
E. coli	24.7	26.0		
Human	30.4			30.1
Ox	29.0			
Average %				

Data from several papers by Chargaff, for example, E. Chargaff et al., Composition of the desoxypentose nucleic acids of four genera of sea-urchin, *Journal of Biological Chemistry* 195:155–160 (1952).

INTERPRET THE DATA

1. Explain how the sea urchin and salmon data demonstrate both of Chargaff's rules.

2. Using Chargaff's rules, fill in the table with your predictions of the missing percentages of bases, starting with the wheat genome and proceeding through *E. coli*, human, and ox. Show how you arrived at your answers.

3. If Chargaff's rule—that the amount of A equals the amount of T and the amount of C equals the amount of G—is valid, then hypothetically we could extrapolate this to the combined DNA of all species on Earth (like one huge Earth genome). To see whether the data in the table support this hypothesis, calculate the average percentage for each base in your completed table by averaging the values in each column. Does Chargaff's equivalence rule still hold true?

(MB) A version of this Scientific Skills Exercise can be assigned in MasteringBiology.

The brief but celebrated partnership that solved the puzzle of DNA structure began soon after Watson journeyed to Cambridge University, where Crick was studying protein structure with a technique called X-ray crystallography (see Figure 3.25). While visiting the laboratory of Maurice Wilkins, Watson saw an X-ray diffraction image of DNA produced by Wilkins's accomplished colleague Rosalind Franklin **(Figure 13.7a)**. Images produced by X-ray crystallography are not actually pictures of molecules. The spots and smudges in **Figure 13.7b** were produced by X-rays that were diffracted (deflected) as they passed through aligned fibers of purified DNA. Watson was familiar with the type of X-ray diffraction pattern that helical molecules produce, and an examination of the photo that Wilkins showed him confirmed that DNA was helical in shape. The photo also augmented earlier data obtained by Franklin and others suggesting the width of the helix and the spacing of the nitrogenous bases along it. The pattern in this photo implied that the helix was made up of two strands, contrary to a three-stranded model that Linus Pauling had

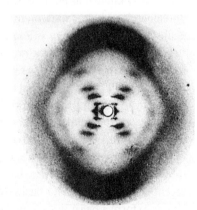

(a) Rosalind Franklin   **(b) Franklin's X-ray diffraction photograph of DNA**

▲ **Figure 13.7 Rosalind Franklin and her X-ray diffraction photo of DNA.** Franklin, a very accomplished X-ray crystallographer, conducted critical experiments resulting in the photo that allowed Watson and Crick to deduce the double-helical structure of DNA.

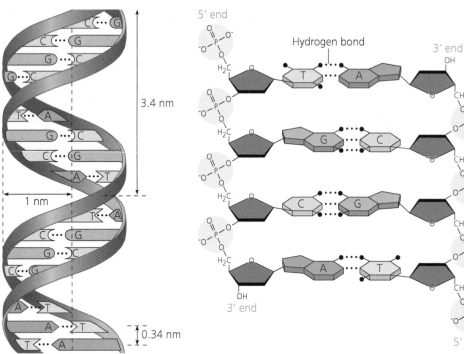
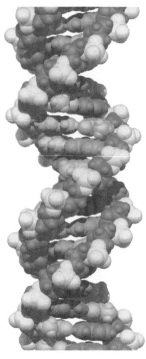

(a) Key features of DNA structure. The "ribbons" in this diagram represent the sugar-phosphate backbones of the two DNA strands. The helix is "right-handed," curving up to the right in the front. The two strands are held together by hydrogen bonds (dotted lines) between the nitrogenous bases, which are paired in the interior of the double helix.

(b) Partial chemical structure. For clarity, the two DNA strands are shown untwisted in this partial chemical structure. Strong covalent sugar-phosphate bonds link the nucleotides of each strand, while weaker hydrogen bonds between the bases hold one strand to the other. Notice that the strands are antiparallel, meaning that they are oriented in opposite directions, like the lanes of a divided street. From top to bottom, the left strand is oriented in the 5′ to 3′ direction, and the right strand in the 3′ to 5′ direction (see also Figure 13.6).

(c) Space-filling model. This space-filling model generated by a computer shows that the base pairs are tightly stacked. Van der Waals interactions between the stacked pairs play a major role in holding the molecule together.

▲ **Figure 13.8 The structure of the double helix.**

proposed a short time earlier. The presence of two strands accounts for the now-familiar term **double helix (Figure 13.8).**

Watson and Crick began building models of a double helix that would conform to the X-ray measurements and what was then known about the chemistry of DNA, including Chargaff's rules. They knew that Franklin had concluded that the sugar-phosphate backbones were on the outside of the DNA molecule. This arrangement was appealing because it put the negatively charged phosphate groups facing the aqueous surroundings, while the relatively hydrophobic nitrogenous bases were hidden in the interior. Watson constructed such a model (see Figure 13.2). In this model, the two sugar-phosphate backbones are **antiparallel**—that is, their subunits run in opposite directions (see Figure 13.8b). You can imagine the overall arrangement as a rope ladder with rigid rungs. The side ropes represent the sugar-phosphate backbones, and the rungs represent pairs of nitrogenous bases. Now imagine twisting the ladder to form a helix. Franklin's X-ray data indicated that the helix makes one full turn every 3.4 nm along its length. With the bases stacked just 0.34 nm apart, there are ten "rungs" of base pairs in each full turn of the helix.

The nitrogenous bases of the double helix are paired in specific combinations: adenine (A) with thymine (T), and guanine (G) with cytosine (C). It was mainly by trial and error that

Watson and Crick arrived at this key feature of DNA. At first, Watson imagined that the bases paired like with like—for example, A with A and C with C. But this model did not fit the X-ray data, which suggested that the double helix had a uniform diameter. Why is this requirement inconsistent with like-with-like pairing of bases? Adenine and guanine are purines, nitrogenous bases with two organic rings, while cytosine and thymine are nitrogenous bases called pyrimidines, which have a single ring. Pairing a purine with a pyrimidine is the only combination that results in a uniform diameter for the double helix **(Figure 13.9).**

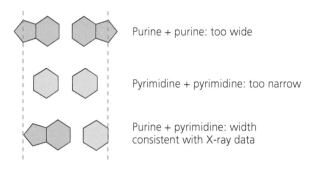

▲ **Figure 13.9 Possible base pairings in the DNA double helix.** Purines (A and G) are about twice as wide as pyrimidines (C and T). A purine-purine pair is too wide and a pyrimidine-pyrimidine pair is too narrow to account for the 2-nm diameter of the double helix, while a purine-pyrimidine pair fits the data well.

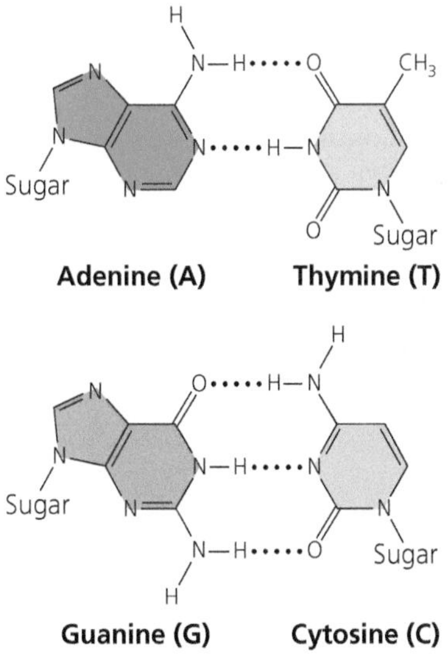

▶ **Figure 13.10 Base pairing in DNA.** The pairs of nitrogenous bases in a DNA double helix are held together by hydrogen bonds, shown here as black dotted lines.

Adenine (A) **Thymine (T)**

Guanine (G) **Cytosine (C)**

Watson and Crick reasoned that there must be additional specificity of pairing dictated by the structure of the bases. Each base has chemical side groups that can form hydrogen bonds with its appropriate partner: Adenine can form two hydrogen bonds with thymine and only thymine; guanine forms three hydrogen bonds with cytosine and only cytosine. In shorthand, A pairs with T, and G pairs with C **(Figure 13.10)**.

The Watson-Crick model took into account Chargaff's ratios and ultimately explained them. Wherever one strand of a DNA molecule has an A, the partner strand has a T. Similarly, a G in one strand is always paired with a C in the complementary strand. Therefore, in the DNA of any organism, the amount of adenine equals the amount of thymine, and the amount of guanine equals the amount of cytosine. (Modern DNA sequencing techniques have confirmed that the amounts are exactly equal.) Although the base-pairing rules dictate the combinations of nitrogenous bases that form the "rungs" of the double helix, they do not restrict the sequence of nucleotides *along* each DNA strand. The linear sequence of the four bases

can be varied in countless ways, and each gene has a unique order, or base sequence.

In April 1953, Watson and Crick surprised the scientific world with a succinct, one-page paper that reported their molecular model for DNA: the double helix, which has since become the symbol of molecular biology. Watson and Crick, along with Maurice Wilkins, were awarded the Nobel Prize in 1962 for this work. (Sadly, Rosalind Franklin had died at the age of 38 in 1958 and was thus ineligible for the prize.) The beauty of the double helix model was that the structure of DNA suggested the basic mechanism of its replication.

CONCEPT CHECK 13.1

1. Given a polynucleotide sequence such as GAATTC, explain what further information you would need in order to identify which end is the 5′ end. (See Figure 13.6.)

2. **WHAT IF?** Griffith did not expect transformation to occur in his experiment. What results was he expecting? Explain.

For suggested answers, see Appendix A.

CONCEPT 13.2

Many proteins work together in DNA replication and repair

The relationship between structure and function is manifest in the double helix. The idea that there is specific pairing of nitrogenous bases in DNA was the flash of inspiration that led Watson and Crick to the double helix. At the same time, they saw the functional significance of the base-pairing rules. They ended their classic paper with this wry statement: "It has not escaped our notice that the specific pairing we have postulated immediately suggests a possible copying mechanism for the genetic material." In this section, you'll learn about the basic principle of DNA replication **(Figure 13.11)**, as well as some important details of the process.

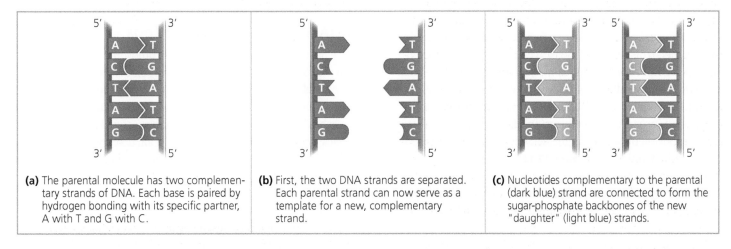

(a) The parental molecule has two complementary strands of DNA. Each base is paired by hydrogen bonding with its specific partner, A with T and G with C.

(b) First, the two DNA strands are separated. Each parental strand can now serve as a template for a new, complementary strand.

(c) Nucleotides complementary to the parental (dark blue) strand are connected to form the sugar-phosphate backbones of the new "daughter" (light blue) strands.

▲ **Figure 13.11 A model for DNA replication: the basic concept.** In this simplified illustration, a short segment of DNA has been untwisted. Simple shapes symbolize the four kinds of bases. Dark blue represents DNA strands present in the parental molecule; light blue represents newly synthesized DNA.

The Basic Principle: Base Pairing to a Template Strand

In a second paper, Watson and Crick stated their hypothesis for how DNA replicates:

> Now our model for deoxyribonucleic acid is, in effect, a pair of templates, each of which is complementary to the other. We imagine that prior to duplication the hydrogen bonds are broken, and the two chains unwind and separate. Each chain then acts as a template for the formation on to itself of a new companion chain, so that eventually we shall have two pairs of chains, where we only had one before. Moreover, the sequence of the pairs of bases will have been duplicated exactly.*

Figure 13.11 illustrates Watson and Crick's basic idea. To make it easier to follow, we show only a short section of double helix, in untwisted form. Notice that if you cover one of the two DNA strands of Figure 13.11a, you can still determine its linear sequence of nucleotides by referring to the uncovered strand and applying the base-pairing rules. The two strands are complementary; each stores the information necessary to reconstruct the other. When a cell copies a DNA molecule, each strand serves as a template for ordering nucleotides into a new, complementary strand. Nucleotides line up along the template strand according to the base-pairing rules and are linked to form the new strands. Where there was one double-stranded DNA molecule at the beginning of the process, there are soon two, each an exact replica of the "parental" molecule.

This model of DNA replication remained untested for several years following publication of the DNA structure. The requisite experiments were simple in concept but difficult to perform. Watson and Crick's model predicts that when a double helix replicates, each of the two daughter molecules will have one old strand, from the parental molecule, and one newly made strand. This **semiconservative model** can be distinguished from a conservative model of replication, in which the two parental strands somehow come back together after the process (that is, the parental molecule is conserved). In yet a third model, called the dispersive model, all four strands of DNA following replication have a mixture of old and new DNA. These three models are shown in **Figure 13.12**. Although mechanisms for conservative or dispersive DNA replication are not easy to come up with, these models remained possibilities until they could be ruled out. After two years of preliminary work at the California Institute of Technology in the late 1950s, Matthew Meselson and Franklin Stahl devised a clever experiment that distinguished between the three models, described in detail in **Figure 13.13**. Their results supported the semiconservative model of DNA replication, predicted by Watson and Crick, and their experiment is widely recognized among biologists as a classic example of elegant design.

*J. D. Watson and F. H. C. Crick, Genetical implications of the structure of deoxyribonucleic acid, *Nature* 171:964–967 (1953).

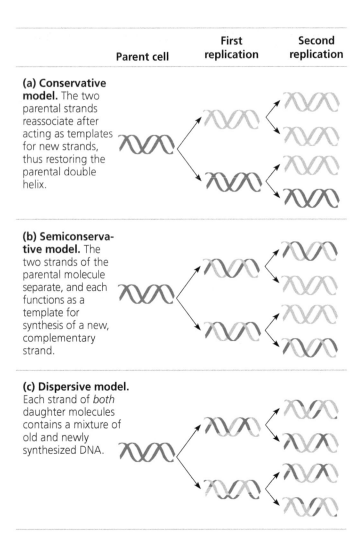

| | Parent cell | First replication | Second replication |

(a) Conservative model. The two parental strands reassociate after acting as templates for new strands, thus restoring the parental double helix.

(b) Semiconservative model. The two strands of the parental molecule separate, and each functions as a template for synthesis of a new, complementary strand.

(c) Dispersive model. Each strand of *both* daughter molecules contains a mixture of old and newly synthesized DNA.

▲ **Figure 13.12 Three alternative models of DNA replication.** Each segment of double helix symbolizes the DNA within a cell. Beginning with a parent cell, we follow the DNA for two more generations of cells—two rounds of DNA replication. Parental DNA is dark blue; newly made DNA is light blue.

The basic principle of DNA replication is conceptually simple. However, the actual process involves some complicated biochemical gymnastics, as we will now see.

DNA Replication: *A Closer Look*

The bacterium *E. coli* has a single chromosome of about 4.6 million nucleotide pairs. In a favorable environment, an *E. coli* cell can copy all this DNA and divide to form two genetically identical daughter cells in less than an hour. Each of *your* cells has 46 DNA molecules in its nucleus, one long double-helical molecule per chromosome. In all, that represents about 6 billion nucleotide pairs, or over a thousand times more DNA than is found in most bacterial cells. If we were to print the one-letter symbols for these bases (A, G, C, and T) the size of the type you are now reading, the 6 billion nucleotide pairs of information in a diploid human cell would fill about 1,400 biology textbooks. Yet it takes one of your cells just a few hours to copy all of this DNA. This replication of an enormous amount

Does DNA replication follow the conservative, semiconservative, or dispersive model?

Experiment Matthew Meselson and Franklin Stahl cultured *E. coli* for several generations in a medium containing nucleotide precursors labeled with a heavy isotope of nitrogen, ^{15}N. They then transferred the bacteria to a medium with only ^{14}N, a lighter isotope. They took one sample after the first DNA replication and another after the second replication. They extracted DNA from the bacteria in the samples and then centrifuged each DNA sample to separate DNA of different densities.

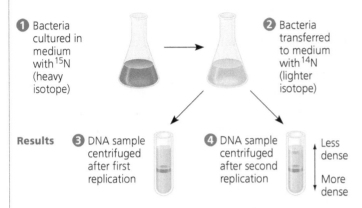

1 Bacteria cultured in medium with ^{15}N (heavy isotope)

2 Bacteria transferred to medium with ^{14}N (lighter isotope)

Results **3** DNA sample centrifuged after first replication

4 DNA sample centrifuged after second replication

Less dense

More dense

Conclusion Meselson and Stahl compared their results to those predicted by each of the three models in Figure 13.12, as shown below. The first replication in the ^{14}N medium produced a band of hybrid (^{15}N - ^{14}N) DNA. This result eliminated the conservative model. The second replication produced both light and hybrid DNA, a result that refuted the dispersive model and supported the semiconservative model. They therefore concluded that DNA replication is semiconservative.

Predictions:	First replication	Second replication
Conservative model		
Semiconservative model		
Dispersive model		

Data from M. Meselson and F. W. Stahl, The replication of DNA in *Escherichia coli*, *Proceedings of the National Academy of Sciences USA* 44:671–682 (1958).

Inquiry in Action Read and analyze the original paper in *Inquiry in Action: Interpreting Scientific Papers*.

MB A related Experimental Inquiry Tutorial can be assigned in MasteringBiology.

WHAT IF? If Meselson and Stahl had first grown the cells in ^{14}N-containing medium and then moved them into ^{15}N-containing medium before taking samples, what would have been the result?

of genetic information is achieved with very few errors—only about one per 10 billion nucleotides. The copying of DNA is remarkable in its speed and accuracy.

More than a dozen enzymes and other proteins participate in DNA replication. Much more is known about how this "replication machine" works in bacteria (such as *E. coli*) than in eukaryotes, and we will describe the basic steps of the process for *E. coli*, except where otherwise noted. What scientists have learned about eukaryotic DNA replication suggests, however, that most of the process is fundamentally similar for prokaryotes and eukaryotes.

Getting Started

The replication of chromosomal DNA begins at particular sites called **origins of replication**, short stretches of DNA that have a specific sequence of nucleotides. Proteins that initiate DNA replication recognize this sequence and attach to the DNA, separating the two strands and opening up a replication "bubble." At each end of a bubble is a **replication fork**, a Y-shaped region where the parental strands of DNA are being unwound. Several kinds of proteins participate in the unwinding (**Figure 13.14**). **Helicases** are enzymes that untwist the double helix at the replication forks, separating the two parental strands and making them available as template strands. After the parental strands separate, **single-strand binding proteins** bind to the unpaired DNA strands, keeping them from re-pairing. The untwisting of the double helix causes tighter twisting and strain ahead of the replication fork. **Topoisomerase** helps relieve this strain by breaking, swiveling, and rejoining DNA strands.

The *E. coli* chromosome, like many other bacterial chromosomes, is circular and has a single origin of replication, forming

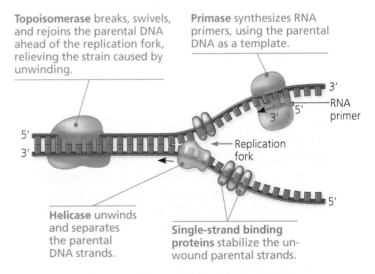

Topoisomerase breaks, swivels, and rejoins the parental DNA ahead of the replication fork, relieving the strain caused by unwinding.

Primase synthesizes RNA primers, using the parental DNA as a template.

RNA primer

Replication fork

Helicase unwinds and separates the parental DNA strands.

Single-strand binding proteins stabilize the unwound parental strands.

▲ **Figure 13.14 Some of the proteins involved in the initiation of DNA replication.** The same proteins function at both replication forks in a replication bubble. For simplicity, only the left-hand fork is shown, and the DNA bases are drawn much larger in relation to the proteins than they are in reality.

one replication bubble (Figure 13.15a). Replication of DNA then proceeds in both directions until the entire molecule is copied. In contrast to a bacterial chromosome, a eukaryotic chromosome may have hundreds or even a few thousand replication origins. Multiple replication bubbles form and eventually fuse, thus speeding up the copying of the very long DNA molecules (Figure 13.15b). As in bacteria, eukaryotic DNA replication proceeds in both directions from each origin.

Synthesizing a New DNA Strand

Within a bubble, the unwound sections of parental DNA strands are available to serve as templates for the synthesis of new complementary DNA strands. However, the enzymes that synthesize DNA cannot *initiate* the synthesis of a polynucleotide; they can only add nucleotides to the end of an already existing chain that is base-paired with the template strand. The initial nucleotide chain that is produced during DNA synthesis is actually a short stretch of RNA, not DNA. This RNA chain is called a **primer** and is synthesized by the enzyme **primase** (see Figure 13.14). Primase starts a complementary RNA chain with a single RNA nucleotide and adds RNA nucleotides one at a time, using the parental DNA strand as a template. The completed primer, generally 5–10 nucleotides long, is thus base-paired to the template strand. The new DNA strand will start from the 3′ end of the RNA primer.

Enzymes called **DNA polymerases** catalyze the synthesis of new DNA by adding nucleotides at the 3′ end of a preexisting chain. In *E. coli*, there are several DNA polymerases, but two appear to play the major roles in DNA replication: DNA polymerase III and DNA polymerase I. The situation in eukaryotes is more complicated, with at least 11 different DNA polymerases discovered so far, but the general principles are the same.

Most DNA polymerases require a primer and a DNA template strand along which complementary DNA nucleotides are lined up. In *E. coli*, DNA polymerase III (abbreviated DNA pol III) adds a DNA nucleotide to the RNA primer and then

▼ **Figure 13.15 Origins of replication in *E. coli* and eukaryotes.** The red arrows indicate the movement of the replication forks and thus the overall directions of DNA replication within each bubble.

(a) Origin of replication in an *E. coli* cell

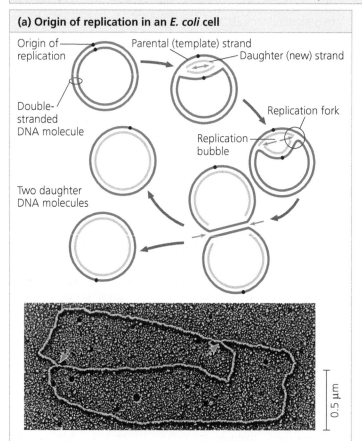

The circular chromosome of *E. coli* and other bacteria has only one origin of replication. The parental strands separate there, forming a replication bubble with two forks (red arrows). Replication proceeds in both directions until the forks meet on the other side, resulting in two daughter DNA molecules. The TEM shows a bacterial chromosome with a replication bubble.

(b) Origins of replication in a eukaryotic cell

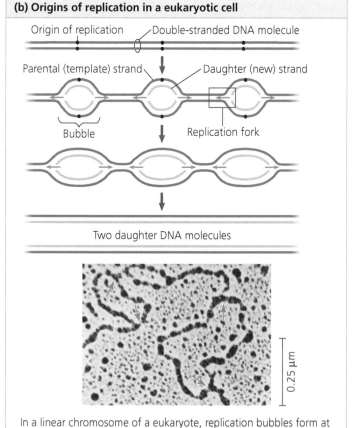

In a linear chromosome of a eukaryote, replication bubbles form at many sites along the giant DNA molecule. The bubbles expand as replication proceeds in both directions (red arrows). Eventually, the bubbles fuse and synthesis of the daughter strands is complete. The TEM shows three replication bubbles along the DNA of a cultured Chinese hamster cell.

DRAW IT *In the TEM above, add arrows for the third bubble.*

continues adding DNA nucleotides, complementary to the parental DNA template strand, to the growing end of the new DNA strand. The rate of elongation is about 500 nucleotides per second in bacteria and 50 per second in human cells.

Each nucleotide to be added to a growing DNA strand consists of a sugar attached to a base and to three phosphate groups. You have already encountered such a molecule—ATP (adenosine triphosphate; see Figure 6.8). The only difference between the ATP of energy metabolism and dATP, the adenine nucleotide used to make DNA, is the sugar component, which is deoxyribose in the building block of DNA but ribose in ATP. Like ATP, the nucleotides used for DNA synthesis are chemically reactive, partly because their triphosphate tails have an unstable cluster of negative charge. As each monomer joins the growing end of a DNA strand in a dehydration reaction (see Figure 3.7a) catalyzed by DNA polymerase, two phosphate groups are lost as a molecule of pyrophosphate (P—P_i). Subsequent hydrolysis of the pyrophosphate to two molecules of inorganic phosphate (P_i) is a coupled exergonic reaction that helps drive the polymerization reaction (**Figure 13.16**).

Antiparallel Elongation

As we have noted previously, the two ends of a DNA strand are different, giving each strand directionality, like a one-way street (see Figure 13.6). In addition, the two strands of DNA in a double helix are antiparallel, meaning that they are oriented in opposite directions to each other, like the two sides of a divided street (see Figure 13.16). Therefore, the two new strands formed during DNA replication must also be antiparallel to their template strands.

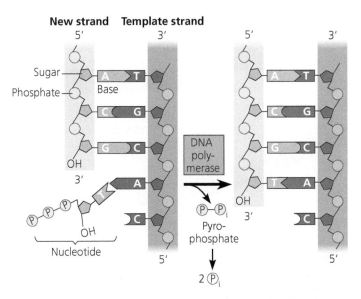

▲ **Figure 13.16 Addition of a nucleotide to a DNA strand.** DNA polymerase catalyzes the addition of a nucleotide to the 3′ end of a growing DNA strand, with the release of two phosphates.

? Use this diagram to explain what we mean when we say that each DNA strand has directionality.

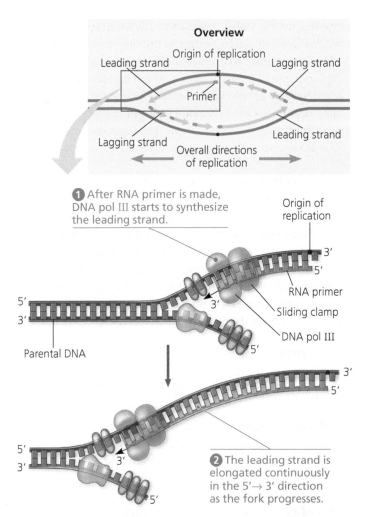

❶ After RNA primer is made, DNA pol III starts to synthesize the leading strand.

❷ The leading strand is elongated continuously in the 5′→ 3′ direction as the fork progresses.

▲ **Figure 13.17 Synthesis of the leading strand during DNA replication.** This diagram focuses on the left replication fork shown in the overview box. DNA polymerase III (DNA pol III), shaped like a cupped hand, is shown closely associated with a protein called the "sliding clamp" that encircles the newly synthesized double helix like a doughnut. The sliding clamp moves DNA pol III along the DNA template strand.

How does the antiparallel arrangement of the double helix affect replication? Because of their structure, DNA polymerases can add nucleotides only to the free 3′ end of a primer or growing DNA strand, never to the 5′ end (see Figure 13.16). Thus, a new DNA strand can elongate only in the 5′ → 3′ direction. With this in mind, let's examine one of the two replication forks in a bubble (**Figure 13.17**). Along one template strand, DNA polymerase III can synthesize a complementary strand continuously by elongating the new DNA in the mandatory 5′ → 3′ direction. DNA pol III remains in the replication fork on that template strand and continuously adds nucleotides to the new complementary strand as the fork progresses. The DNA strand made by this mechanism is called the **leading strand**. Only one primer is required for DNA pol III to synthesize the entire leading strand.

To elongate the other new strand of DNA in the mandatory 5′ → 3′ direction, DNA pol III must work along the other template strand in the direction *away from* the replication fork. The DNA strand elongating in this direction is called the **lagging strand**. In contrast to the leading strand, which elongates continuously, the lagging strand is synthesized discontinuously, as a series of segments. These segments of the lagging strand are called **Okazaki fragments**, after the Japanese scientist who discovered them. The fragments are about 1,000–2,000 nucleotides long in *E. coli* and 100–200 nucleotides long in eukaryotes.

Figure 13.18 illustrates the steps in the synthesis of the lagging strand at one fork. Whereas only one primer is required on the leading strand, each Okazaki fragment on the lagging strand must be primed separately (steps ❶ and ❹). After DNA pol III forms an Okazaki fragment (steps ❷ to ❹), another DNA polymerase, DNA polymerase I (DNA pol I), replaces the RNA nucleotides of the adjacent primer with DNA nucleotides (step ❺). But DNA pol I cannot join the final nucleotide of this replacement DNA segment to the first DNA nucleotide of the adjacent Okazaki fragment. Another enzyme, **DNA ligase**, accomplishes this task, joining the sugar-phosphate backbones of all the Okazaki fragments into a continuous DNA strand (step ❻).

Synthesis of the leading strand and synthesis of the lagging strand occur concurrently and at the same rate. The lagging strand is so named because its synthesis is delayed slightly relative to synthesis of the leading strand; each new fragment of the lagging strand cannot be started until enough template has been exposed at the replication fork.

Figure 13.19 summarizes DNA replication. Please study it carefully before proceeding.

The DNA Replication Complex

It is traditional—and convenient—to represent DNA polymerase molecules as locomotives moving along a DNA railroad track, but such a model is inaccurate in two important ways. First, the various proteins that participate in DNA replication actually form a single large complex, a "DNA replication machine." Many protein-protein interactions facilitate the efficiency of this complex. For example, by interacting with other proteins at the fork, primase apparently acts as a molecular brake, slowing progress of the replication fork and coordinating the placement of primers and the rates of replication on the leading and lagging strands. Second, the DNA replication complex may not move along the DNA; rather, the DNA may move through the complex during the replication process. In eukaryotic cells, multiple copies of the complex, perhaps grouped into "factories," may be anchored to the nuclear matrix, a framework of fibers extending through the interior of the nucleus. Experimental evidence supports a model in which two DNA polymerase molecules, one on each template strand, "reel in" the parental DNA and extrude newly made daughter DNA molecules. In this so-called trombone model, the lagging strand is also looped back through the complex **(Figure 13.20)**.

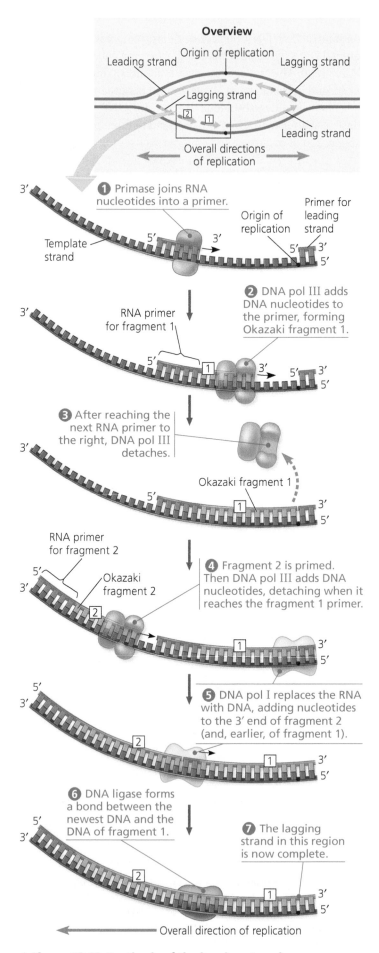

▲ **Figure 13.18 Synthesis of the lagging strand.**

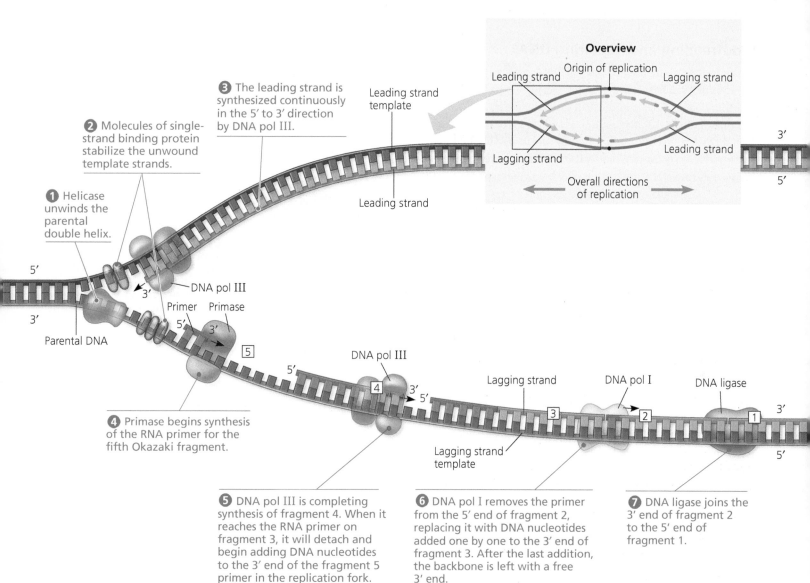

2 Molecules of single-strand binding protein stabilize the unwound template strands.

1 Helicase unwinds the parental double helix.

3 The leading strand is synthesized continuously in the 5′ to 3′ direction by DNA pol III.

Leading strand template

Leading strand

Overview

Leading strand   Origin of replication   Lagging strand

Lagging strand   Leading strand

Overall directions of replication

3′
5′

5′
3′

Parental DNA

DNA pol III

Primer   Primase

5′   3′

5   DNA pol III

4

5′

3′
5′

DNA pol III

Lagging strand

DNA pol I

DNA ligase

3   2   1   3′

4 Primase begins synthesis of the RNA primer for the fifth Okazaki fragment.

Lagging strand template

5′

5 DNA pol III is completing synthesis of fragment 4. When it reaches the RNA primer on fragment 3, it will detach and begin adding DNA nucleotides to the 3′ end of the fragment 5 primer in the replication fork.

6 DNA pol I removes the primer from the 5′ end of fragment 2, replacing it with DNA nucleotides added one by one to the 3′ end of fragment 3. After the last addition, the backbone is left with a free 3′ end.

7 DNA ligase joins the 3′ end of fragment 2 to the 5′ end of fragment 1.

▲ **Figure 13.19 A summary of bacterial DNA replication.** The detailed diagram shows the left-hand replication fork of the replication bubble in the overview (upper right). Viewing each daughter strand in its entirety in the overview, you can see that half of it is made continuously as the leading strand, while the other half (on the other side of the origin) is synthesized in fragments as the lagging strand.

DRAW IT *Draw a diagram showing the right-hand fork of the bubble in Figure 13.19. Number the Okazaki fragments and label all 5′ and 3′ ends.*

▶ **Figure 13.20 The "trombone" model of the DNA replication complex.** Two DNA polymerase III molecules work together in a complex, one on each template strand. The lagging strand template DNA loops through the complex, resembling the slide of a trombone.

DRAW IT *Draw a line tracing the lagging strand template along the entire stretch of DNA shown here.*

 ANIMATION Visit the Study Area in **MasteringBiology** for the BioFlix® 3-D Animation on DNA Replication.

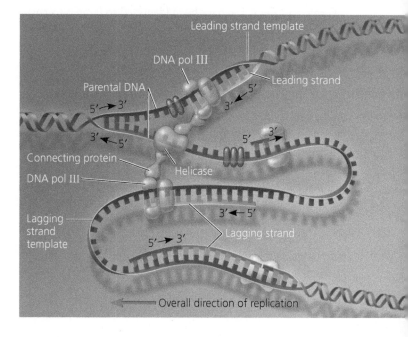

Leading strand template

DNA pol III

Leading strand

Parental DNA

5′   3′
3′

3′   5′

5′

3′

5′

Connecting protein

DNA pol III

Helicase

3′   5′

Lagging strand template

Lagging strand

5′   3′

Overall direction of replication

Proofreading and Repairing DNA

We cannot attribute the accuracy of DNA replication solely to the specificity of base pairing. Initial pairing errors between incoming nucleotides and those in the template strand occur at a rate of one in 10^5 nucleotides. However, errors in the completed DNA molecule amount to only one in 10^{10} (10 billion) nucleotides, an error rate that is 100,000 times lower. This is because during DNA replication, DNA polymerases proofread each nucleotide against its template as soon as it is added to the growing strand. Upon finding an incorrectly paired nucleotide, the polymerase removes the nucleotide and then resumes synthesis. (This action is similar to fixing a texting error by deleting the wrong letter and then entering the correct letter.)

Mismatched nucleotides sometimes do evade proofreading by a DNA polymerase. In **mismatch repair**, other enzymes remove and replace incorrectly paired nucleotides resulting from replication errors. Researchers highlighted the importance of such repair enzymes when they found that a hereditary defect in one of them is associated with a form of colon cancer. Apparently, this defect allows cancer-causing errors to accumulate in the DNA faster than normal.

Incorrectly paired or altered nucleotides can also arise after replication. In fact, maintenance of the genetic information encoded in DNA requires frequent repair of various kinds of damage to existing DNA. DNA molecules are constantly subjected to potentially harmful chemical and physical agents, such as cigarette smoke and X-rays (as we'll discuss in Concept 14.5). In addition, DNA bases often undergo spontaneous chemical changes under normal cellular conditions. However, these changes in DNA are usually corrected before they become permanent changes—*mutations*—perpetuated through successive replications. Each cell continuously monitors and repairs its genetic material. Because repair of damaged DNA is so important to the survival of an organism, it is no surprise that many different DNA repair enzymes have evolved. Almost 100 are known in *E. coli*, and about 130 have been identified so far in humans.

Most cellular systems for repairing incorrectly paired nucleotides, whether they are due to DNA damage or to replication errors, use a mechanism that takes advantage of the base-paired structure of DNA. In many cases, a segment of the strand containing the damage is cut out (excised) by a DNA-cutting enzyme—a **nuclease**—and the resulting gap is then filled in with nucleotides, using the undamaged strand as a template. The enzymes involved in filling the gap are a DNA polymerase and DNA ligase. One such DNA repair system is called **nucleotide excision repair** (**Figure 13.21**).

An important function of DNA repair enzymes in our skin cells is to repair genetic damage caused by the ultraviolet rays of sunlight. One example of this damage is when adjacent thymine bases on a DNA strand become covalently linked. Such *thymine dimers* cause the DNA to buckle (see Figure 13.21), interfering with DNA replication. The importance of repairing

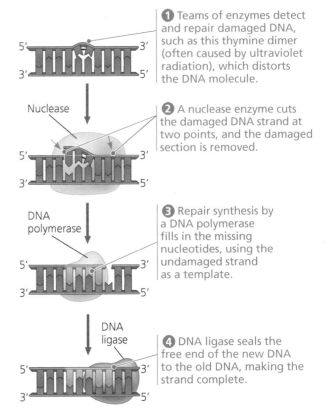

1 Teams of enzymes detect and repair damaged DNA, such as this thymine dimer (often caused by ultraviolet radiation), which distorts the DNA molecule.

2 A nuclease enzyme cuts the damaged DNA strand at two points, and the damaged section is removed.

3 Repair synthesis by a DNA polymerase fills in the missing nucleotides, using the undamaged strand as a template.

4 DNA ligase seals the free end of the new DNA to the old DNA, making the strand complete.

▲ **Figure 13.21 Nucleotide excision repair of DNA damage.**

this kind of damage is underscored by the disorder xeroderma pigmentosum (XP), which in most cases is caused by an inherited defect in a nucleotide excision repair enzyme. Individuals with XP are hypersensitive to sunlight; mutations in their skin cells caused by ultraviolet light are left uncorrected, often resulting in skin cancer. The effects are extreme: Without sun protection, children who have XP can develop skin cancer by age 10.

Evolutionary Significance of Altered DNA Nucleotides

EVOLUTION Faithful replication of the genome and repair of DNA damage are important for the functioning of the organism and for passing on a complete, accurate genome to the next generation. The error rate after proofreading and repair is extremely low, but rare mistakes do slip through. Once a mismatched nucleotide pair is replicated, the sequence change is permanent in the daughter molecule that has the incorrect nucleotide as well as in any subsequent copies. As you know, a permanent change in the DNA sequence is called a mutation.

Mutations can change the phenotype of an organism (as you'll learn in Concept 14.5). And if they occur in germ cells, which give rise to gametes, mutations can be passed on from generation to generation. The vast majority of such changes are harmful, but a very small percentage can be beneficial. In either case, mutations are the source of the variation on which natural selection operates during evolution and are ultimately responsible for the appearance of new species. (You'll learn more about this process in Unit Three.) The balance between complete fidelity of DNA replication and repair and a low mutation rate has, over long periods of time, allowed the evolution of the rich diversity of species we see on Earth today.

Replicating the Ends of DNA Molecules

For linear DNA, such as the DNA of eukaryotic chromosomes, the usual replication machinery cannot complete the 5' ends of daughter DNA strands. (This is a consequence of the fact that a DNA polymerase can add nucleotides only to the 3' ends of a pre-existing polynucleotide.) As a result, repeated rounds of replication produce shorter and shorter DNA molecules with uneven ends.

What protects the genes near the ends of eukaryotic chromosomes from being eroded away during successive replications? Eukaryotic chromosomal DNA molecules have special nucleotide sequences called **telomeres** at their ends (Figure 13.22). Telomeres do not contain genes; instead, the DNA typically consists of multiple repetitions of one short nucleotide sequence. In each human telomere, for example, the sequence TTAGGG is repeated 100 to 1,000 times. Telomeric DNA acts as a buffer zone that protects the organism's genes.

Telomeres do not prevent the erosion of genes near ends of chromosomes; they merely postpone it. As you would expect, telomeres tend to be shorter in cultured cells that have divided many times and in dividing somatic cells of older individuals. Shortening of telomeres is proposed to play a role in the aging process of some tissues and even of the organism as a whole.

If the chromosomes of germ cells became shorter in every cell cycle, essential genes would eventually be missing from the gametes they produce. However, this does not occur: An enzyme called *telomerase* catalyzes the lengthening of telomeres in eukaryotic germ cells, thus restoring their original length and compensating for the shortening that occurs during DNA replication. Telomerase is not active in most human somatic

cells, but shows inappropriate activity in some cancer cells that may remove limits to a cell's normal life span. Thus, telomerase is under study as a target for cancer therapies.

CONCEPT CHECK 13.2

1. What role does base pairing play in the replication of DNA?
2. Make a table listing the functions of seven proteins involved in DNA replication in *E. coli*.
3. **MAKE CONNECTIONS** What is the relationship between DNA replication and the S phase of the cell cycle? See Figure 9.6.

For suggested answers, see Appendix A.

CONCEPT 13.3

A chromosome consists of a DNA molecule packed together with proteins

Now that you have learned about the structure and replication of DNA, let's take a step back and examine how DNA is packaged into chromosomes, the structures that carry genetic information. The main component of the genome in most bacteria is one double-stranded, circular DNA molecule that is associated with a small amount of protein. Although we refer to this structure as a bacterial chromosome, it is very different from a eukaryotic chromosome, which consists of one linear DNA molecule associated with a large amount of protein. In *E. coli*, the chromosomal DNA consists of about 4.6 million nucleotide pairs, representing about 4,400 genes. This is 100 times more DNA than is found in a typical virus, but only about one-thousandth as much DNA as in a human somatic cell. Still, that is a lot of DNA to be packaged in such a small container.

Stretched out, the DNA of an *E. coli* cell would measure about a millimeter in length, 500 times longer than the cell. Within a bacterium, however, certain proteins cause the chromosome to coil and "supercoil," densely packing it so that it fills only part of the cell. Unlike the nucleus of a eukaryotic cell, this dense region of DNA in a bacterium, called the **nucleoid**, is not surrounded by membrane (see Figure 4.4).

Each eukaryotic chromosome contains a single linear DNA double helix that, in humans, averages about 1.5×10^8 nucleotide pairs. This is an enormous amount of DNA relative to a chromosome's condensed length. If completely stretched out, such a DNA molecule would be about 4 cm long, thousands of times the diameter of a cell nucleus—and that's not even considering the DNA of the other 45 human chromosomes!

In the cell, eukaryotic DNA is precisely combined with a large amount of protein. Together, this complex of DNA and protein, called **chromatin**, fits into the nucleus through an elaborate, multilevel system of packing.

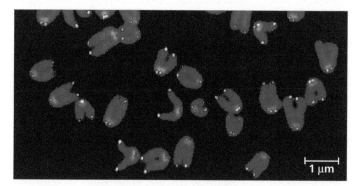

▲ **Figure 13.22 Telomeres.** Eukaryotes have repetitive, noncoding sequences called telomeres at the ends of their DNA. Telomeres are stained orange in these mouse chromosomes (LM).

Chromatin undergoes striking changes in its degree of packing during the course of the cell cycle (see Figure 9.7). In interphase cells stained for light microscopy, the chromatin usually appears as a diffuse mass within the nucleus, suggesting that the chromatin is highly extended. As a cell prepares for mitosis, its chromatin coils and folds up (condenses), eventually forming a characteristic number of short, thick metaphase chromosomes that are distinguishable from each other with the light microscope. Our current view of the successive levels of DNA packing in a chromosome is outlined in **Figure 13.23**.

Though interphase chromatin is generally much less condensed than the chromatin of mitotic chromosomes, it shows several of the same levels of higher-order packing. Some of the chromatin comprising a chromosome seems to be present as a 10-nm fiber, but much is compacted into a 30-nm fiber, which in some regions is further folded into looped domains. Even during interphase, the centromeres of chromosomes, as well as other chromosomal regions in some cells, exist in a highly condensed state similar to that seen in a metaphase chromosome. This type of interphase chromatin, visible as irregular clumps with a light

▼ Figure 13.23   Exploring Chromatin Packing in a Eukaryotic Chromosome

This illustration, accompanied by transmission electron micrographs, depicts a current model for the progressive levels of DNA coiling and folding. The illustration zooms out from a single molecule of DNA to a metaphase chromosome, which is large enough to be seen with a light microscope.

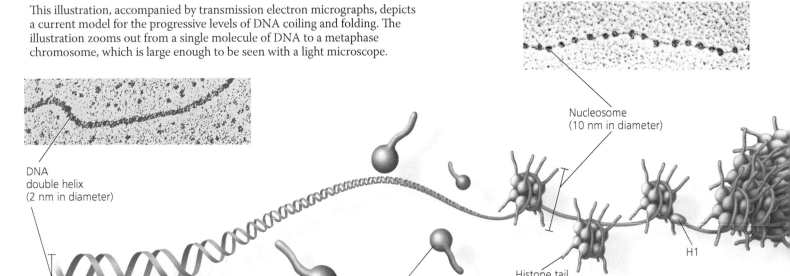

Nucleosome (10 nm in diameter)

DNA double helix (2 nm in diameter)

Histones

Histone tail

H1

DNA, the double helix

Shown above is a ribbon model of DNA, with each ribbon representing one of the polynucleotide strands. Recall that the phosphate groups along the backbone contribute a negative charge along the outside of each strand. The TEM shows a molecule of naked (protein-free) DNA; the double helix alone is 2 nm across.

Histones

Proteins called **histones** are responsible for the first level of DNA packing in chromatin. Although each histone is small—containing only about 100 amino acids—the total mass of histone in chromatin roughly equals the mass of DNA. More than a fifth of a histone's amino acids are positively charged (lysine or arginine) and therefore bind tightly to the negatively charged DNA.

Four types of histones are most common in chromatin: H2A, H2B, H3, and H4. The histones are very similar among eukaryotes; for example, all but two of the amino acids in cow H4 are identical to those in pea H4. The apparent conservation of histone genes during evolution probably reflects the important role of histones in organizing DNA within cells.

These four types of histones are critical to the next level of DNA packing. (A fifth type of histone, called H1, is involved in a further stage of packing.)

Nucleosomes, or "beads on a string" (10-nm fiber)

In electron micrographs, unfolded chromatin is 10 nm in diameter (the *10-nm fiber*). Such chromatin resembles beads on a string (see the TEM). Each "bead" is a **nucleosome**, the basic unit of DNA packing; the "string" between beads is called *linker* DNA.

A nucleosome consists of DNA wound twice around a protein core of eight histones, two each of the main histone types (H2A, H2B, H3, and H4). The amino end (N-terminus) of each histone (the *histone tail*) extends outward from the nucleosome.

In the cell cycle, the histones leave the DNA only briefly during DNA replication. Generally, they do the same during transcription, another process that requires access to the DNA by the cell's molecular machinery. Nucleosomes, and in particular their histone tails, are involved in the regulation of gene expression.

microscope, is called **heterochromatin**, to distinguish it from the less compacted, more dispersed **euchromatin** ("true chromatin"). Because of its compaction, heterochromatic DNA is largely inaccessible to the machinery in the cell responsible for transcribing the genetic information coded in the DNA, a crucial early step in gene expression. In contrast, the looser packing of euchromatin makes its DNA accessible to this machinery, so the genes present in euchromatin can be transcribed.

The chromosome is a dynamic structure that is condensed, loosened, modified, and remodeled as necessary for various cell processes, including mitosis, meiosis, and gene activity. Certain chemical modifications of histones affect the state of chromatin condensation and also have multiple effects on gene activity (as you'll see in Concept 15.2).

CONCEPT CHECK 13.3

1. Describe the structure of a nucleosome, the basic unit of DNA packing in eukaryotic cells.
2. What two properties, one structural and one functional, distinguish heterochromatin from euchromatin?

For suggested answers, see Appendix A.

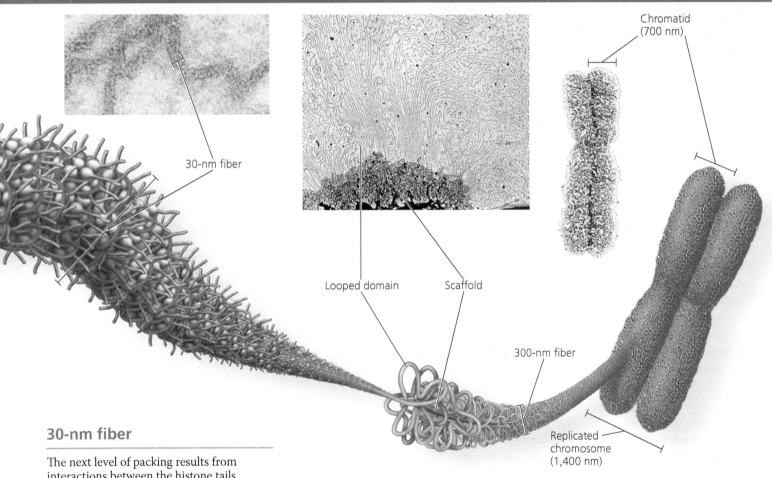

Chromatid (700 nm)

30-nm fiber

Looped domain

Scaffold

300-nm fiber

Replicated chromosome (1,400 nm)

30-nm fiber

The next level of packing results from interactions between the histone tails of one nucleosome and the linker DNA and nucleosomes on either side. The fifth histone, H1, is involved at this level. These interactions cause the extended 10-nm fiber to coil or fold, forming a chromatin fiber roughly 30 nm in thickness, the *30-nm fiber*. Although the 30-nm fiber is quite prevalent in the interphase nucleus, the packing arrangement of nucleosomes in this form of chromatin is still a matter of some debate.

Looped domains (300-nm fiber)

The 30-nm fiber, in turn, forms loops called *looped* domains attached to a chromosome scaffold composed of proteins, thus making up a *300-nm fiber*. The scaffold is rich in one type of topoisomerase, and H1 molecules also appear to be present.

Metaphase chromosome

In a mitotic chromosome, the looped domains themselves coil and fold in a manner not yet fully understood, further compacting all the chromatin to produce the characteristic metaphase chromosome (also shown in the micrograph above). The width of one chromatid is 700 nm. Particular genes always end up located at the same places in metaphase chromosomes, indicating that the packing steps are highly specific and precise.

Understanding DNA structure and replication makes genetic engineering possible

The discovery of the structure of DNA marked a milestone in biology and changed the course of biological research. Most notable was the realization that the two strands of a DNA molecule are complementary to each other. This fundamental structural property of DNA is the basis for **nucleic acid hybridization**, the base pairing of one strand of a nucleic acid to a complementary sequence on another strand. Nucleic acid hybridization forms the foundation of virtually every technique used in **genetic engineering**, the direct manipulation of genes for practical purposes. Genetic engineering has launched a revolution in fields as varied as agriculture, criminal law, and medical and basic biological research. In this section, we'll describe several of the most important techniques and their uses.

DNA Cloning: Making Multiple Copies of a Gene or Other DNA Segment

A molecular biologist studying a particular gene faces a challenge. Naturally occurring DNA molecules are very long, and a single molecule usually carries many genes. Moreover, in many eukaryotic genomes, genes occupy only a small proportion of the chromosomal DNA, the rest being noncoding nucleotide sequences. A single human gene, for example, might constitute only 1/100,000 of a chromosomal DNA molecule. As a further complication, the distinctions between a gene and the surrounding DNA are subtle, consisting only of differences in nucleotide sequence. To work directly with specific genes, scientists have developed methods for preparing well-defined segments of DNA in multiple identical copies, a process called *DNA cloning*.

Most methods for cloning pieces of DNA in the laboratory share certain general features. One common approach uses bacteria, most often *E. coli*. Recall from Figure 13.15 that the *E. coli* chromosome is a large circular molecule of DNA. In addition, *E. coli* and many other bacteria have **plasmids**, small circular DNA molecules that are replicated separately. A plasmid has only a small number of genes; these genes may be useful when the bacterium is in a particular environment but may not be required for survival or reproduction under most conditions.

To clone pieces of DNA using bacteria, researchers first obtain a plasmid (originally isolated from a bacterial cell and genetically engineered for efficient cloning) and insert DNA from another source ("foreign" DNA) into it **(Figure 13.24)**. The resulting plasmid is now a **recombinant DNA molecule**, a molecule containing DNA from two different sources, very often different species. The plasmid is then returned to a bacterial cell, producing a *recombinant bacterium*. This single cell

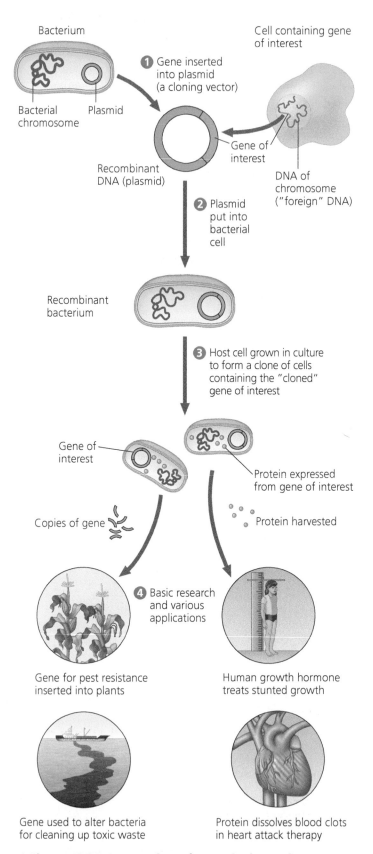

▲ **Figure 13.24 An overview of gene cloning and some uses of cloned genes.** In this simplified diagram of gene cloning, we start with a plasmid (originally isolated from a bacterial cell) and a gene of interest from another organism. Only one plasmid and one copy of the gene of interest are shown at the top of the figure, but the starting materials would include many of each.

reproduces through repeated cell divisions to form a clone of cells, a population of genetically identical cells. Because the dividing bacteria replicate the recombinant plasmid and pass it on to their descendants, the foreign DNA and any genes it carries are cloned at the same time. The production of multiple copies of a single gene is a type of DNA cloning called **gene cloning**. In our example in Figure 13.24, the plasmid acts as a **cloning vector**, a DNA molecule that can carry foreign DNA into a cell and be replicated there. The foreign DNA segment could be a gene from a eukaryotic cell; we will describe in more detail how it was obtained later in this section.

Gene cloning is useful for two basic purposes: to make many copies of, or *amplify*, a particular gene and to produce a protein product from it. Researchers can isolate copies of a cloned gene from bacteria for use in basic research or to endow another organism with a new metabolic trait, such as pest resistance. For example, a resistance gene present in one crop species might be cloned and transferred into plants of another species. (Such organisms are called Genetically Modified Organisms, or GMOs; see Concept 30.3.) Alternatively, a protein with medical uses, such as human growth hormone, can be harvested in large quantities from cultures of bacteria carrying a cloned gene for the protein. Since a single gene is usually a very small part of the total DNA in a cell, the ability to amplify such rare DNA fragments is crucial for any application involving a single gene.

Using Restriction Enzymes to Make a Recombinant DNA Plasmid

Gene cloning and genetic engineering generally rely on the use of enzymes that cut DNA molecules at a limited number of specific locations. These enzymes, called restriction endonucleases, or **restriction enzymes**, were discovered in the late 1960s by biologists doing basic research on bacteria. Restriction enzymes protect the bacterial cell by cutting up foreign DNA from other organisms or phages.

Hundreds of different restriction enzymes have been identified and isolated. Each restriction enzyme is very specific, recognizing a particular short DNA sequence, or **restriction site**, and cutting both DNA strands at precise points within this restriction site. The DNA of a bacterial cell is protected from the cell's own restriction enzymes by the addition of methyl groups (—CH₃) to adenines or cytosines within the sequences recognized by the enzymes.

Figure 13.25 shows how restriction enzymes are used to clone a foreign DNA fragment into a bacterial plasmid. At the top is a plasmid (like the one in Figure 13.24) that has a single restriction site recognized by a particular restriction enzyme from *E. coli*. (Various such plasmids are available from commercial suppliers.) As shown in this example, most restriction sites are symmetrical. That is, the sequence of nucleotides is the same on both strands when read in the 5′ → 3′ direction. The most commonly used restriction enzymes recognize sequences containing four to eight nucleotide pairs. Because any sequence this short

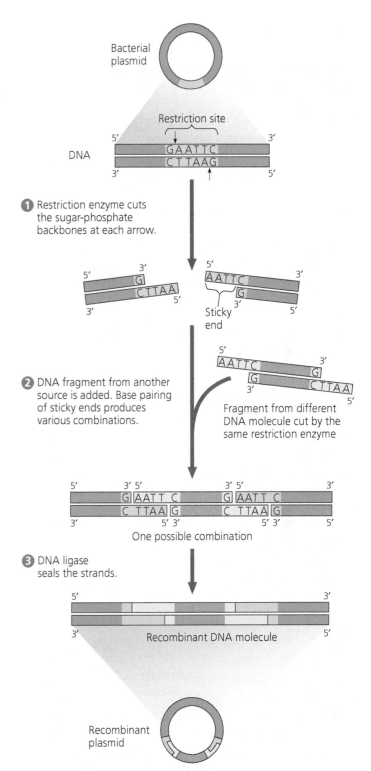

▲ **Figure 13.25 Using a restriction enzyme and DNA ligase to make a recombinant DNA plasmid.** The restriction enzyme in this example (called *Eco*RI) recognizes a single six-base-pair restriction site present in the plasmid. It makes staggered cuts in the sugar-phosphate backbones, producing fragments with "sticky ends." Foreign DNA fragments with complementary sticky ends can base-pair with the plasmid ends; the ligated product is a recombinant plasmid. (If the two plasmid sticky ends base-pair, the original non-recombinant plasmid would re-form.)

DRAW IT *The restriction enzyme Hind III recognizes the sequence 5′-AAGCTT-3′, cutting between the two A's. Draw the double-stranded sequence before and after the enzyme cuts.*

usually occurs (by chance) many times in a long DNA molecule, a restriction enzyme will make many cuts in such a DNA molecule, yielding a set of **restriction fragments**. All copies of a given DNA molecule always yield the same set of restriction fragments when exposed to the same restriction enzyme.

The most useful restriction enzymes cleave the sugar-phosphate backbones in the two DNA strands in a staggered manner, as indicated in Figure 13.25. The resulting double-stranded restriction fragments have at least one single-stranded end, called a **sticky end**. These short extensions can form hydrogen-bonded base pairs (hybridize) with complementary sticky ends on any other DNA molecules cut with the same enzyme, such as the inserted DNA in Figure 13.25. The associations formed in this way are only temporary but can be made permanent by DNA ligase, which catalyzes the formation of covalent bonds that close up the sugar-phosphate backbones of DNA strands (see Figure 13.18). You can see at the bottom of Figure 13.25 that the ligase-catalyzed joining of DNA from the plasmid and the foreign DNA produces a stable recombinant DNA molecule, in this example a recombinant plasmid.

To check the recombinant plasmids after they have been copied many times in host cells, researchers might cut the products again using the same restriction enzyme, expecting two DNA fragments, one the size of the plasmid and one the size of the inserted DNA. To separate and visualize the fragments, they would next carry out a technique called **gel electrophoresis**, which uses a gel made of a polymer as a sieve to separate a mixture of nucleic acid fragments by length **(Figure 13.26)**. Gel electrophoresis is used in conjunction with many different techniques in molecular biology.

Amplifying DNA: The Polymerase Chain Reaction (PCR) and Its Use in Cloning

Today, most researchers have some information about the sequence of the foreign gene or DNA fragment they want to clone. Using this information, they can start with the entire collection of genomic DNA from the particular species of interest and obtain many copies of the desired gene by using a technique called the **polymerase chain reaction**, or **PCR**. **Figure 13.27** illustrates the steps in PCR. Within a few hours, this technique can make billions of copies of a specific target DNA segment in a sample, even if that segment makes up less than 0.001% of the total DNA in the sample.

In the PCR procedure, a three-step cycle brings about a chain reaction that produces an exponentially growing population of identical DNA molecules. During each cycle, the reaction mixture is heated to denature (separate) the DNA strands and then cooled to allow annealing (hybridization) of short, single-stranded DNA primers complementary to sequences on opposite strands at each end of the target segment; finally, a DNA polymerase extends the primers in the $5' \rightarrow 3'$ direction. If a standard DNA polymerase were used, the protein would be denatured along with the DNA during the first heating step and would have to be replaced after each cycle.

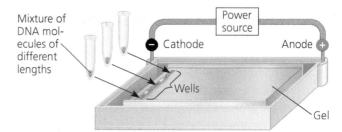

(a) Each sample, a mixture of different DNA molecules, is placed in a separate well near one end of a thin slab of agarose gel. The gel is set into a small plastic support and immersed in an aqueous, buffered solution in a tray with electrodes at each end. The current is then turned on, causing the negatively charged DNA molecules to move toward the positive electrode.

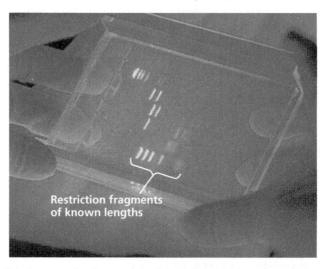

(b) Shorter molecules are slowed down less than longer ones, so they move faster through the gel. After the current is turned off, a DNA-binding dye is added that fluoresces pink in UV light. Each pink band corresponds to many thousands of DNA molecules of the same length. The horizontal ladder of bands at the bottom of the gel is a set of restriction fragments of known lengths for comparison with samples of unknown length.

▲ **Figure 13.26 Gel electrophoresis.** A gel made of a polymer acts as a molecular sieve to separate nucleic acids or proteins differing in size, electrical charge, or other physical properties as they move in an electric field. In the example shown here, DNA molecules are separated by length in a gel made of a polysaccharide called agarose.

The key to automating PCR was the discovery of an unusually heat-stable DNA polymerase called *Taq* polymerase, named after the bacterial species from which it was first isolated. This bacterial species, *Thermus aquaticus*, lives in hot springs, and the stability of its DNA polymerase at high temperatures is an evolutionary adaptation that enables the enzyme to function at temperatures up to 95°C. Today, researchers also use a DNA polymerase from the archaean species *Pyrococcus furiosus*. This enzyme, called *Pfu* polymerase, is more accurate, more stable, and costlier than *Taq* polymerase.

PCR is speedy and very specific. Only minuscule amounts of DNA need be present in the starting material, and this DNA can be partially degraded, as long as a few molecules contain the complete target segment. The key to this high specificity is the primers, the sequences of which are chosen so they

The Polymerase Chain Reaction (PCR)

Application With PCR, any specific segment—the so-called target sequence—in a DNA sample can be copied many times (amplified) within a test tube.

Technique PCR requires double-stranded DNA containing the target sequence, a heat-resistant DNA polymerase, all four nucleotides, and two 15- to 20-nucleotide DNA strands that serve as primers. One primer is complementary to one end of the target sequence on one strand; the second primer is complementary to the other end of the sequence on the other strand.

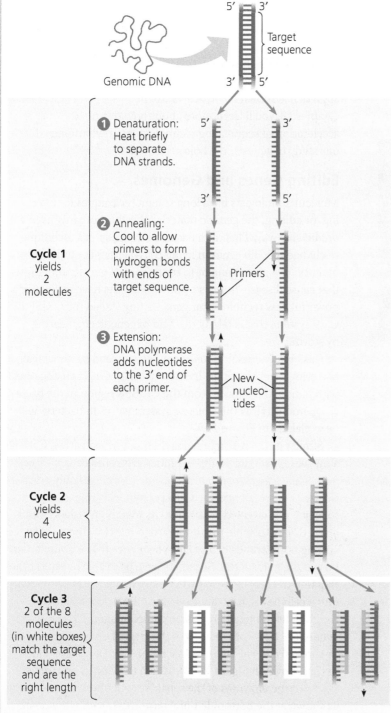

Results After three cycles, two molecules match the target sequence exactly. After 30 more cycles, over 1 billion (10^9) molecules match the target sequence.

hybridize *only* with complementary sequences at opposite ends of the target segment. (For high specificity, the primers must be at least 15 or so nucleotides long.) With each successive cycle, the number of target segment molecules of the correct length doubles, so the number of molecules equals $2n$, where n is the number of cycles. After 30 or so cycles, about a billion copies of the target sequence are present!

Despite its speed and specificity, PCR amplification alone cannot substitute for gene cloning in cells to make large amounts of a gene. This is because occasional errors during PCR replication limit the number of good copies and the length of DNA fragments that can be copied. Instead, PCR is used to provide the specific DNA fragment for cloning. PCR primers are synthesized to include a restriction site at each end of the DNA fragment that matches the site in the cloning vector, and the fragment and vector are cut and ligated together (**Figure 13.28**). The resulting plasmids are sequenced so that those with error-free inserts can be selected.

Devised in 1985, PCR has had a major impact on biological research and genetic engineering. PCR has been used to amplify DNA from a wide variety of sources: a 40,000-year-old frozen woolly mammoth; fingerprints or tiny amounts of blood, tissue, or semen found at crime scenes; single embryonic cells for rapid prenatal diagnosis of genetic disorders; and cells infected with viruses that are difficult to detect, such as HIV (in the latter case, viral genes are amplified).

DNA Sequencing

Once a gene is cloned, researchers can exploit the principle of complementary base pairing to determine the gene's complete nucleotide sequence, a process called **DNA sequencing**. In the last 15 years, "next-generation" sequencing techniques have been developed that are rapid and inexpensive. In machines that carry out next-generation

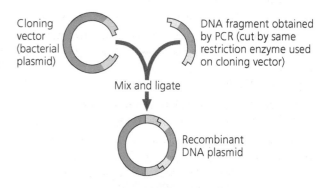

▲ **Figure 13.28 Use of a restriction enzyme and PCR in gene cloning.** In a closer look at the process shown at the top of Figure 13.24, PCR is used to produce the DNA fragment or gene of interest that will be ligated into a cloning vector, in this case a bacterial plasmid. Both the plasmid and the DNA fragments are cut with the same restriction enzyme, combined so the sticky ends can hybridize, and ligated together. The resulting plasmids will then be introduced into bacterial cells.

sequencing **(Figure 13.29a)**, a single template strand is immobilized, and DNA polymerase and other reagents are added that allow so-called *sequencing by synthesis* of the complementary strand, one nucleotide at a time. A specialized chemical technique enables electronic monitors to identify which of the four nucleotides is being added, allowing determination of the sequence **(Figure 13.29b)**.

Next-generation sequencing is rapidly being complemented or even replaced by "third-generation" sequencing techniques, with each new technique being faster and less expensive than the previous one. In some of these new methods, the DNA is neither cut into fragments nor amplified. Instead, a single, very long DNA molecule is sequenced on its own. Several groups have been working on moving a single strand of a DNA molecule through a very small pore (a *nanopore*) in a membrane. This is one of the many approaches to further increase the

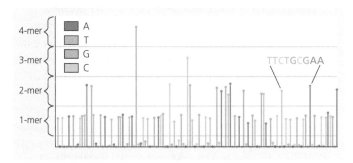

(a) Next-generation sequencing machines

(b) A "flow-gram" from a next-generation sequencing machine

▲ **Figure 13.29 Next-generation sequencing. (a)** Next-generation sequencing machines use "sequencing by synthesis" to sequence many 300-nucleotide fragments in parallel. In this way, one machine can sequence about 2 billion nucleotides in 24 hours. **(b)** The results for one fragment are displayed as a "flow-gram," where the nucleotides are identified by color, one by one. The sequences of the entire set of fragments are analyzed using computer software, which "stitches" them together into a whole sequence—often, an entire genome.

INTERPRET THE DATA *If the template strand has two or more identical nucleotides in a row, the complementary nucleotides on the synthesized strand will be added, one after the other, in the same step. How are two or more of the same nucleotide in a row displayed in the flow-gram? (See example sequence on the right.) Write out the sequence of the first 25 nucleotides in the flow-gram, starting from the left as the 5′ end. (Ignore the very short lines.)*

▶ **Figure 13.30 An example of a third-generation sequencing technique.** In this approach, a single strand of an uncut DNA molecule would be passed, nucleotide by nucleotide, through a nanopore in a membrane. Here, the pore is a protein channel embedded in a lipid membrane. The nucleotides are identified by slight differences in the amount of time they interrupt an electrical current across the opening.

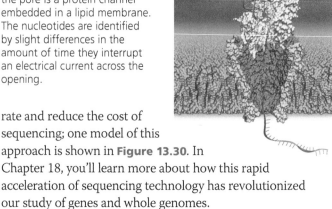

rate and reduce the cost of sequencing; one model of this approach is shown in **Figure 13.30**. In Chapter 18, you'll learn more about how this rapid acceleration of sequencing technology has revolutionized our study of genes and whole genomes.

Editing Genes and Genomes

Molecular biologists have long sought techniques for altering, or editing, the genetic material of cells or organisms in a predictable way. Their aim has been to use such a technique to change specific genes in living cells—either to study the function of a given gene or to try to correct genetic mutations that cause disease. In recent years, biologists have developed a powerful new technique for gene editing, called the CRISPR-Cas9 system, that is taking the field of genetic engineering by storm.

Cas9 is a bacterial protein that helps defend bacteria against bacteriophage infections. In bacterial cells, Cas9 acts together with "guide RNA" made from the CRISPR region of the bacterial genome. (How this defense system works in bacteria will be explained in Figure 17.6.)

Similar to the restriction enzymes described earlier, Cas9 is a nuclease that cuts double-stranded DNA molecules. However, while a given restriction enzyme recognizes only one particular DNA sequence, the Cas9 protein will cut any sequence to which it is directed. Cas9 takes its marching orders from a guide RNA molecule that it binds and uses as a homing device, cutting both strands of any DNA sequence that is complementary to the guide RNA. Scientists have been able to exploit the function of Cas9 by introducing a Cas9–guide RNA complex into a cell they wish to alter **(Figure 13.31)**. The guide RNA in the complex is engineered to be complementary to the "target" gene. Cas9 cuts both strands of the target DNA, and the resulting broken ends of DNA trigger a DNA repair system (similar to that shown in Figure 13.21). When there is no undamaged DNA for the enzymes of the repair system to use as a template, as shown at the bottom left of Figure 13.31, part a, the repair enzymes introduce or remove random nucleotides while rejoining the ends. Generally, this alters the DNA sequence so that the gene no longer works properly. This technique is a

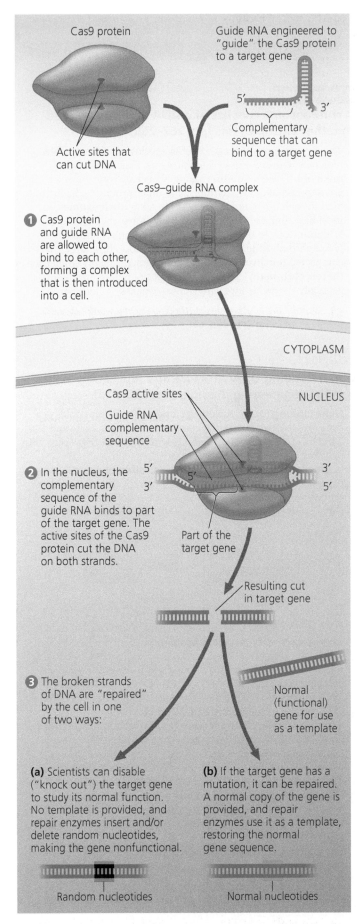

1 Cas9 protein and guide RNA are allowed to bind to each other, forming a complex that is then introduced into a cell.

Cas9 protein

Guide RNA engineered to "guide" the Cas9 protein to a target gene

5′ 3′

Complementary sequence that can bind to a target gene

Active sites that can cut DNA

Cas9–guide RNA complex

CYTOPLASM

NUCLEUS

Cas9 active sites

Guide RNA complementary sequence

2 In the nucleus, the complementary sequence of the guide RNA binds to part of the target gene. The active sites of the Cas9 protein cut the DNA on both strands.

5′ 5′ 3′
3′ 5′

Part of the target gene

Resulting cut in target gene

3 The broken strands of DNA are "repaired" by the cell in one of two ways:

Normal (functional) gene for use as a template

(a) Scientists can disable ("knock out") the target gene to study its normal function. No template is provided, and repair enzymes insert and/or delete random nucleotides, making the gene nonfunctional.

(b) If the target gene has a mutation, it can be repaired. A normal copy of the gene is provided, and repair enzymes use it as a template, restoring the normal gene sequence.

Random nucleotides

Normal nucleotides

▲ **Figure 13.31 Gene editing using the CRISPR-Cas9 system.**

highly successful way for researchers to "knock out" (disable) a given gene to study what that gene does in an organism.

But what about using this system to help treat genetic diseases? Researchers have modified the technique so that the CRISPR-Cas9 system can be used to repair a gene that has a mutation. They introduce a segment from the normal (functional) gene along with the CRISPR-Cas9 system. After Cas9 cuts the target DNA, repair enzymes can use the normal DNA as a template to repair the target DNA at the break point. In this way, the CRISPR-Cas9 system edits the defective gene so that it is corrected (see the bottom right of Figure 13.31, part b).

In 2014, a group of researchers reported success in correcting a genetic defect in mice using CRISPR technology. The lab mice had been genetically engineered to have a mutation in a gene encoding a liver enzyme that metabolizes the amino acid tyrosine, mimicking a fatal genetic disorder in humans called tyrosinemia. A guide RNA molecule complementary to the mutated region of the gene was introduced into the mouse along with the Cas9 protein and a segment of DNA from the same region of the normal gene for use as a template. Subsequent analysis indicated that the faulty gene had been corrected in enough of the liver cells that the amount of functional enzyme made was sufficient to alleviate the disease symptoms. There are still many hurdles to overcome before this approach can be tried in humans, but the CRISPR technology is sparking widespread excitement among researchers and physicians alike.

In this section, you have learned how understanding the elegant structure of DNA has led to powerful techniques for genetic engineering. Earlier in the chapter, you also saw how DNA molecules are arranged in chromosomes and how DNA replication provides the copies of genes that parents pass to offspring. However, it is not enough that genes be copied and transmitted; the information they carry must be used by the cell. In other words, genes must also be "expressed." In the next few chapters, we'll examine how the cell expresses the genetic information encoded in DNA. We'll also return to the subject of genetic engineering by exploring a few techniques for analyzing gene expression.

CONCEPT CHECK 13.4

1. **MAKE CONNECTIONS** The restriction site for an enzyme called *Pvu*I is the following sequence:

   5′-C G A T C G-3′
   3′-G C T A G C-5′

   Staggered cuts are made between the T and C on each strand. What type of bonds are being cleaved? (See Concept 3.6.)

2. **DRAW IT** One strand of a DNA molecule has the following sequence: 5′-CCTTGACGATCGTTACCG-3′. Draw the other strand. Will *Pvu*I (see question 1) cut this molecule? If so, draw the products.

3. Describe the role of complementary base pairing during cloning, PCR, DNA sequencing, and gene editing using the CRISPR-Cas9 system.

For suggested answers, see Appendix A.

13 Chapter Review

Go to **MasteringBiology**® for Assignments, the eText, and the Study Area with Animations, Activities, Vocab Self-Quiz, and Practice Tests.

SUMMARY OF KEY CONCEPTS

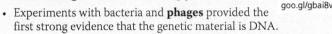

VOCAB SELF-QUIZ

goo.gl/gbai8v

CONCEPT 13.1

DNA is the genetic material (pp. 254–259)

- Experiments with bacteria and **phages** provided the first strong evidence that the genetic material is DNA.
- Watson and Crick deduced that DNA is a **double helix** and built a structural model. Two **antiparallel** sugar-phosphate chains wind around the outside of the molecule; the nitrogenous bases project into the interior, where they hydrogen-bond in specific pairs: A with T, G with C.

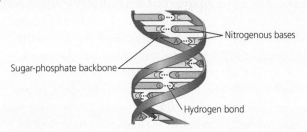

Nitrogenous bases

Sugar-phosphate backbone

Hydrogen bond

? *What does it mean when we say that the two DNA strands in the double helix are antiparallel? What would an end of the double helix look like if the strands were parallel?*

CONCEPT 13.2

Many proteins work together in DNA replication and repair (pp. 259–267)

- The Meselson-Stahl experiment showed that **DNA replication** is **semiconservative**: The parental molecule unwinds, and each strand then serves as a template for the synthesis of a new strand according to base-pairing rules.
- DNA replication at one **replication fork** is summarized here:

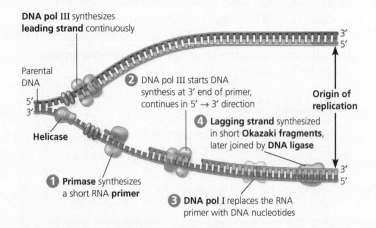

DNA pol III synthesizes **leading strand** continuously

Parental DNA

Helicase

❷ DNA pol III starts DNA synthesis at 3' end of primer, continues in 5' → 3' direction

❹ **Lagging strand** synthesized in short Okazaki fragments, later joined by **DNA ligase**

Origin of replication

❶ **Primase** synthesizes a short RNA **primer**

❸ **DNA pol I** replaces the RNA primer with DNA nucleotides

- **DNA polymerases** proofread new DNA, replacing incorrect nucleotides. In **mismatch repair**, enzymes correct errors that persist. **Nucleotide excision repair** is a general process by which **nucleases** cut out and replace damaged stretches of DNA.

? *Compare DNA replication on the leading and lagging strands, including both similarities and differences.*

CONCEPT 13.3

A chromosome consists of a DNA molecule packed together with proteins (pp. 267–269)

- The chromosome of most bacterial species is a circular DNA molecule with some associated proteins, making up the **nucleoid**. The **chromatin** making up a eukaryotic chromosome is composed of DNA, **histones**, and other proteins. The histones bind to each other and to the DNA to form **nucleosomes**, the most basic units of DNA packing. Additional coiling and folding lead ultimately to the highly condensed chromatin of the metaphase chromosome. In interphase cells, most chromatin is less compacted (**euchromatin**), but some remains highly condensed (**heterochromatin**). Euchromatin, but not heterochromatin, is generally accessible for transcription of genes.

? *Describe the levels of chromatin packing you would expect to see in an interphase nucleus.*

CONCEPT 13.4

Understanding DNA structure and replication makes genetic engineering possible (pp. 270–275)

- **Gene cloning** (or DNA cloning) produces multiple copies of a gene (or DNA segment) that can be used to manipulate and analyze DNA and to produce useful new products or organisms with beneficial traits.
- In **genetic engineering**, bacterial **restriction enzymes** are used to cut DNA molecules within short, specific nucleotide sequences (**restriction sites**), yielding a set of double-stranded **restriction fragments** with single-stranded **sticky ends**.

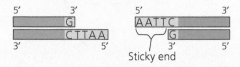

Sticky end

- DNA fragments of different lengths can be separated and their lengths assessed by **gel electrophoresis**.
- The sticky ends on restriction fragments from one DNA source—such as a bacterial **plasmid** or other **cloning vector**—can base-pair with complementary sticky ends on fragments from other DNA molecules; sealing the base-paired fragments with DNA ligase produces **recombinant DNA molecules**.
- The **polymerase chain reaction (PCR)** can amplify (produce many copies of) a specific target segment of DNA for use as a DNA fragment for cloning. PCR uses primers that bracket the desired segment and requires a heat-resistant DNA polymerase.
- The rapid development of fast, inexpensive techniques for **DNA sequencing** is based on *sequencing by synthesis*: DNA polymerase is used to replicate a stretch of DNA from a single-stranded template, and the order in which nucleotides are added reveals the sequence.
- The CRISPR-Cas9 system allows researchers to edit genes in a specific, desired way. This may ultimately be used for treatment of genetic diseases.

? *Describe how the process of gene cloning results in a cell clone containing a recombinant plasmid.*

TEST YOUR UNDERSTANDING

PRACTICE TEST

goo.gl/CRZjvS

Level 1: Knowledge/Comprehension

1. In his work with pneumonia-causing bacteria and mice, Griffith found that
   (A) the protein coat from pathogenic cells was able to transform nonpathogenic cells.
   (B) heat-killed pathogenic cells caused pneumonia.
   (C) some substance from pathogenic cells was transferred to nonpathogenic cells, making them pathogenic.
   (D) the polysaccharide coat of bacteria caused pneumonia.

2. What is the basis for the difference in how the leading and lagging strands of DNA molecules are synthesized?
   (A) DNA polymerase can join new nucleotides only to the 3' end of a preexisting strand.
   (B) Helicases and single-strand binding proteins work at the 5' end.
   (C) The origins of replication occur only at the 5' end.
   (D) DNA ligase works only in the $3' \rightarrow 5'$ direction.

3. In analyzing the number of different bases in a DNA sample, which result would be consistent with the base-pairing rules?
   (A) A = G   (C) A + T = G + C
   (B) A + G = C + T   (D) A = C

4. The elongation of the leading strand during DNA synthesis
   (A) progresses away from the replication fork.
   (B) occurs in the $3' \rightarrow 5'$ direction.
   (C) produces Okazaki fragments.
   (D) depends on the action of DNA polymerase.

5. In a nucleosome, the DNA is wrapped around
   (A) polymerase molecules.   (C) histones.
   (B) ribosomes.   (D) a thymine dimer.

6. Which of the following sequences in double-stranded DNA is most likely to be recognized as a cutting site for a restriction enzyme?
   (A) AAGG   (B) GGCC   (C) ACCA   (D) AAAA
       TTCC   CCGG   TGGT   TTTT

Level 2: Application/Analysis

7. *E. coli* cells grown on ^{15}N medium are transferred to ^{14}N medium and allowed to grow for two more generations (two rounds of DNA replication). DNA extracted from these cells is centrifuged. What density distribution of DNA would you expect in this experiment?
   (A) one high-density and one low-density band
   (B) one intermediate-density band
   (C) one high-density and one intermediate-density band
   (D) one low-density and one intermediate-density band

8. A student isolates, purifies, and combines in a test tube a variety of molecules needed for DNA replication. After adding some DNA to the mixture, replication occurs, but each DNA molecule consists of a normal strand paired with numerous segments of DNA a few hundred nucleotides long. What has the student probably left out of the mixture?
   (A) DNA polymerase   (C) Okazaki fragments
   (B) DNA ligase   (D) primase

9. The spontaneous loss of amino groups from adenine in DNA results in hypoxanthine, an uncommon base, opposite thymine. What combination of proteins could repair such damage?
   (A) nuclease, DNA polymerase, DNA ligase
   (B) topoisomerase, primase, DNA polymerase
   (C) topoisomerase, helicase, single-strand binding protein
   (D) DNA ligase, replication fork proteins, adenylyl cyclase

10. **MAKE CONNECTIONS** Although the proteins that cause the *E. coli* chromosome to coil are not histones, identify a property you would expect them to share with histones, given their ability to bind to DNA (see Figure 3.18).

Level 3: Synthesis/Evaluation

11. **SCIENTIFIC INQUIRY**

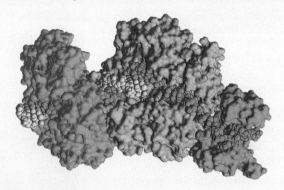

DRAW IT Model building can be an important part of the scientific process. The illustration shown here is a computer-generated model of a DNA replication complex. The parental and newly synthesized DNA strands are color-coded differently, as are each of the following three proteins: DNA pol III, the sliding clamp, and single-strand binding protein. (a) Using what you've learned in this chapter to clarify this model, label each DNA strand and each protein. (b) Draw an arrow to indicate the overall direction of DNA replication.

12. **FOCUS ON EVOLUTION**
    Some bacteria may be able to respond to environmental stress by increasing the rate at which mutations occur during cell division. How might this be accomplished? Might there be an evolutionary advantage of this ability? Explain.

13. **FOCUS ON ORGANIZATION**
    The continuity of life is based on heritable information in the form of DNA, and structure and function are correlated at all levels of biological organization. In a short essay (100–150 words), describe how the structure of DNA is correlated with its role as the molecular basis of inheritance.

14. **SYNTHESIZE YOUR KNOWLEDGE**
    This image shows DNA interacting with a computer-generated model of a TAL protein, one of a family of proteins found only in a species of the bacterium *Xanthomonas*. The bacterium uses proteins like this one to find particular gene sequences in cells of the organisms it infects, such as tomatoes, rice, and citrus fruits. Researchers are excited about working with this family of proteins. Their goal is to generate modified versions that can home in on specific gene sequences. Such proteins could then be used in an approach called gene therapy to "fix" mutated genes in individuals with genetic diseases. Given what you know about DNA structure and considering the image shown here, discuss what the TAL protein's structure suggests about how it functions.

For selected answers, see Appendix A.

14 Gene Expression: From Gene to Protein

KEY CONCEPTS

14.1 Genes specify proteins via transcription and translation

14.2 Transcription is the DNA-directed synthesis of RNA: *a closer look*

14.3 Eukaryotic cells modify RNA after transcription

14.4 Translation is the RNA-directed synthesis of a polypeptide: *a closer look*

14.5 Mutations of one or a few nucleotides can affect protein structure and function

▲ **Figure 14.1** How does a single faulty gene result in the dramatic appearance of an albino donkey?

The Flow of Genetic Information

The island of Asinara lies off the coast of Sardinia, an Italian island. The name Asinara probably originated from the Latin word *sinuaria*, which means "sinus-shaped." A second meaning of Asinara is "donkey-inhabited," which is particularly appropriate because Asinara is home to a wild population of albino donkeys (**Figure 14.1**). The donkeys were brought to Asinara in the early 1800s and abandoned there in 1885 when the 500 residents were forced to leave the island so it could be used as a penal colony. What is responsible for the phenotype of the albino donkey, strikingly different from its pigmented relative?

Inherited traits are determined by genes, and the trait of albinism is caused by a recessive allele of a pigmentation gene (see Concept 11.4). The information content of genes is in the form of specific sequences of nucleotides along strands of DNA, the genetic material. But how does this information determine an organism's traits? Put another way, what does a gene actually say? And how is its message translated by cells into a specific trait, such as brown hair, type A blood, or, in the case of an albino donkey, a total lack of pigment? The albino donkey has a faulty version of a key protein, an enzyme required for pigment synthesis, and this protein is faulty because the gene that codes for it contains incorrect information.

This example illustrates the main point of this chapter: The DNA inherited by an organism leads to specific traits by dictating the synthesis of proteins and of RNA molecules involved in protein synthesis. In other words, proteins are the link between genotype and phenotype. **Gene expression** is the process by which DNA directs the synthesis of proteins (or, in some cases, just RNAs). The expression of genes that code for proteins includes two stages: transcription and translation. This chapter describes the flow of information from gene to protein and explains how genetic mutations affect organisms through their proteins. Understanding the processes of gene expression, which are similar in all three domains of life, will allow us to revisit the concept of the gene in more detail at the end of the chapter.

Genes specify proteins via transcription and translation

Before going into the details of how genes direct protein synthesis, let's step back and examine how the fundamental relationship between genes and proteins was discovered.

Evidence from the Study of Metabolic Defects

In 1902, British physician Archibald Garrod was the first to suggest that genes dictate phenotypes through enzymes, proteins that catalyze specific chemical reactions in the cell. He postulated that the symptoms of an inherited disease reflect an inability to make a particular enzyme. For example, people with a disease called alkaptonuria have black urine because it contains a chemical called alkapton. Garrod reasoned that these people cannot make an enzyme that breaks down alkapton, so the chemical is expelled in their urine.

Several decades later, research supported Garrod's hypothesis that a gene dictates the production of a specific enzyme. Biochemists learned that cells synthesize and degrade most organic molecules via metabolic pathways, in which each chemical reaction in a sequence is catalyzed by a specific enzyme (see Concept 6.1). Such metabolic pathways lead, for instance, to the synthesis of the pigments that give the brown donkey in Figure 14.1 its fur color or fruit flies (*Drosophila*) their eye color (see Figure 12.3). In the 1930s, the American geneticist George Beadle and his French colleague Boris Ephrussi speculated that in *Drosophila* each mutation affecting eye color blocks pigment synthesis at a specific step by preventing production of the enzyme that catalyzes that step. But neither the chemical reactions nor the enzymes that catalyze them were known.

Nutritional Mutants: Scientific Inquiry

A breakthrough in demonstrating the relationship between genes and enzymes came a few years later at Stanford University, where Beadle and Edward Tatum began experimenting with the bread mold *Neurospora crassa*. Unlike the diploid organisms studied by Mendel (peas) and T. H. Morgan (fruit flies), *Neurospora* is a haploid species. In order to observe a change in a mutant's phenotype, Beadle and Tatum needed to disable just one allele (rather than two) of a protein-coding gene required for a specific metabolic activity. By cleverly electing to work with *Neurospora*, they could cause a mutation in one allele in a cell and directly deduce the function of the wild-type gene.

Another advantage was that *Neurospora* has modest food requirements. For this species, the *minimal medium*, the culture containing minimal nutrients for growth of wild-type cells, is a simple solution of inorganic salts, glucose, and the vitamin biotin. On a gel-like substance called agar, saturated with minimal medium, single wild-type cells can synthesize all the nutrients they need for growth, dividing repeatedly and forming visible colonies of genetically identical cells.

Beadle and Tatum designed an experiment in which they generated different "nutritional mutants" of *Neurospora* cells, each of which was unable to synthesize a particular essential nutrient. Such cells could not grow on minimal medium but could grow on *complete medium*, which contains all nutrients needed for growth, including any that a mutant cell can't synthesize. For *Neurospora*, the complete medium consists of the minimal medium supplemented with all 20 amino acids and a few other nutrients. Beadle and Tatum hypothesized that in each nutritional mutant, the gene for the enzyme that synthesizes a particular nutrient had been disabled. **Figure 14.2** summarizes their experimental approach, in which they tested each type of mutant to determine which nutrient it was unable to synthesize.

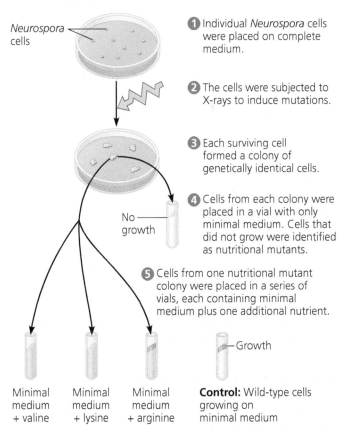

Neurospora cells

1 Individual *Neurospora* cells were placed on complete medium.

2 The cells were subjected to X-rays to induce mutations.

3 Each surviving cell formed a colony of genetically identical cells.

4 Cells from each colony were placed in a vial with only minimal medium. Cells that did not grow were identified as nutritional mutants.

No growth

5 Cells from one nutritional mutant colony were placed in a series of vials, each containing minimal medium plus one additional nutrient.

Growth

| Minimal medium + valine | Minimal medium + lysine | Minimal medium + arginine | **Control:** Wild-type cells growing on minimal medium |

6 The vials were observed for growth. In this example, the mutant cells grew only on minimal medium + arginine, indicating that this mutant was missing the enzyme for the synthesis of arginine.

▲ **Figure 14.2 The experimental approach of Beadle and Tatum.** To obtain nutritional mutants, Beadle and Tatum exposed *Neurospora* cells to X-rays to induce mutations. They then screened mutants with new nutritional requirements, such as arginine, as shown here.

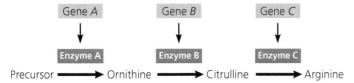

▲ **Figure 14.3 The one gene–one protein hypothesis.** Based on results from work in their lab on nutritional mutants, Beadle and Tatum proposed that the function of a specific gene is to dictate production of a specific enzyme that catalyzes a particular reaction. The model shown here for the arginine-synthesizing pathway illustrates their hypothesis.

Beadle and Tatum amassed a valuable collection of mutant strains of *Neurospora*, catalogued not only by their defects in a particular metabolic pathway but also at different steps in that pathway. For example, a series of experiments on mutants requiring the amino acid arginine revealed that they could be grouped into distinct classes, each corresponding to a particular blocked step in the biochemical pathway for arginine synthesis. Presumably, the enzyme that normally catalyzes that step was unable to do so as a result of a mutation in its encoding gene **(Figure 14.3)**.

Beadle and Tatum concluded that, taken together, the collected results provided strong support for their so-called *one gene–one enzyme hypothesis*: that the function of a gene is to dictate the production of a specific enzyme. Further support for this hypothesis came from experiments that identified the specific enzymes lacking in the mutants. Beadle and Tatum shared a Nobel Prize in 1958 for "their discovery that genes act by regulating definite chemical events," in the words of the Nobel committee. Their experimental approach of disabling genes and observing the results plays a central role in genetic research today.

Today, we know of countless examples in which a mutation in a gene causes a faulty enzyme that in turn leads to an identifiable condition. The albino donkey in Figure 14.1 lacks a key enzyme called tyrosinase in the metabolic pathway that produces melanin, a dark pigment. The absence of melanin causes white fur and other effects throughout the donkey's body. Its nose, ears, and hooves, as well as its eyes, are pink because no melanin is present to mask the reddish color of the blood vessels that run through those structures.

The Products of Gene Expression: A Developing Story

As researchers learned more about proteins, they made revisions to the one gene–one enzyme hypothesis. First of all, not all proteins are enzymes. Keratin, the structural protein of animal hair, and the hormone insulin are two examples of nonenzyme proteins. Because proteins that are not enzymes are nevertheless gene products, molecular biologists began to think in terms of one gene–one protein. However, many proteins are constructed from two or more different polypeptide

chains, and each polypeptide is specified by its own gene. For example, hemoglobin, the oxygen-transporting protein of vertebrate red blood cells, contains two kinds of polypeptides, and thus two genes code for this protein (Figure 3.22). Beadle and Tatum's idea was therefore restated as the *one gene–one polypeptide hypothesis*. Even this description is not entirely accurate, though. First, in many cases, a eukaryotic gene can code for a set of closely related polypeptides via a process called alternative splicing, which you will learn about later in this chapter. Second, quite a few genes code for RNA molecules that have important functions in cells even though they are never translated into protein. For now, we will focus on genes that do code for polypeptides. (Note that it is common to refer to these gene products as proteins—a practice you'll encounter in this text—rather than more precisely as polypeptides.)

Basic Principles of Transcription and Translation

Genes provide the instructions for making specific proteins. But a gene does not build a protein directly. The bridge between DNA and protein synthesis is the nucleic acid RNA. RNA is chemically similar to DNA except that it contains ribose instead of deoxyribose as its sugar and has the nitrogenous base uracil rather than thymine (see Concept 3.6). Thus, each nucleotide along a DNA strand has A, G, C, or T as its base, and each nucleotide along an RNA strand has A, G, C, or U as its base. An RNA molecule usually consists of a single strand.

It is customary to describe the flow of information from gene to protein in linguistic terms. Just as specific sequences of letters communicate information in a language like English, both nucleic acids and proteins are polymers with specific sequences of monomers that convey information. In DNA or RNA, the monomers are the four types of nucleotides, which differ in their nitrogenous bases. Genes are typically hundreds or thousands of nucleotides long, each gene having a specific sequence of nucleotides. Each polypeptide of a protein also has monomers arranged in a particular linear order (the protein's primary structure; see Figure 3.22), but its monomers are amino acids. Thus, nucleic acids and proteins contain information written in two different chemical languages. Getting from DNA to protein requires two major stages: transcription and translation.

Transcription is the synthesis of RNA using information in the DNA. The two nucleic acids are written in different forms of the same language, and the information is simply transcribed, or "rewritten," from DNA to RNA. Just as a DNA strand provides a template for making a new complementary strand during DNA replication, it also can serve as a template for assembling a complementary sequence of RNA nucleotides. For a protein-coding gene, the resulting RNA molecule is a faithful transcript of the gene's protein-building instructions.

This type of RNA molecule is called **messenger RNA (mRNA)** because it carries a genetic message from the DNA to the protein-synthesizing machinery of the cell. (Transcription is the general term for the synthesis of *any* kind of RNA on a DNA template. Later, you'll learn about some other types of RNA produced by transcription.)

Translation is the synthesis of a polypeptide using the information in the mRNA. During this stage, there is a change in language: The cell must translate the nucleotide sequence of an mRNA molecule into the amino acid sequence of a polypeptide. The sites of translation are **ribosomes**, molecular complexes that facilitate the orderly linking of amino acids into polypeptide chains.

Transcription and translation occur in all organisms. Because most studies of transcription and translation have used bacteria and eukaryotic cells, they are our main focus in this chapter. While our understanding of transcription and translation in archaea lags behind, we do know that archaeal cells share some features of gene expression with bacteria and others with eukaryotes.

The basic mechanics of transcription and translation are similar for bacteria and eukaryotes, but there is an important difference in the flow of genetic information within the cells. Bacteria do not have nuclei. Therefore, nuclear membranes do not separate bacterial DNA and mRNA from ribosomes and the other protein-synthesizing equipment **(Figure 14.4a)**. This lack of compartmentalization allows translation of an mRNA to begin while its transcription is still in progress, as you'll see later. By contrast, eukaryotic cells have nuclei. The presence of a nuclear envelope separates transcription from translation in space and time **(Figure 14.4b)**. Transcription occurs in the nucleus, but the mRNA must be transported to the cytoplasm for translation. Before eukaryotic RNA transcripts from protein-coding genes can leave the nucleus, they are modified in various ways to produce the final, functional mRNA. The transcription of a protein-coding eukaryotic gene results in *pre-mRNA*, and further processing yields the finished mRNA. The initial RNA transcript from any gene, including those specifying RNA that is not translated into protein, is more generally called a **primary transcript**.

To summarize: Genes program protein synthesis via genetic messages in the form of messenger RNA. Put another way, cells are governed by a molecular chain of command with a directional flow of genetic information, shown here by arrows:

This concept was dubbed the *central dogma* by Francis Crick in 1956. How has the concept held up over time? In the 1970s, scientists were surprised to discover that some enzymes

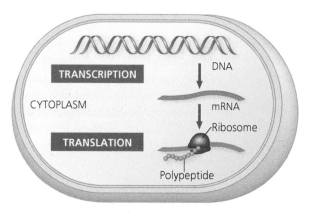

(a) Bacterial cell. In a bacterial cell, which lacks a nucleus, mRNA produced by transcription is immediately translated without additional processing.

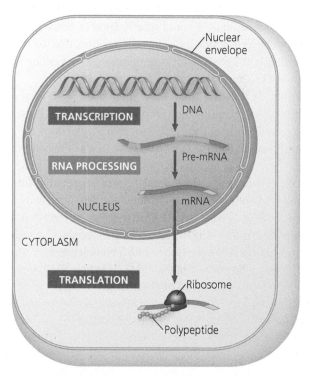

(b) Eukaryotic cell. The nucleus provides a separate compartment for transcription. The original RNA transcript, called pre-mRNA, is processed in various ways before leaving the nucleus as mRNA.

▲ **Figure 14.4 Overview: the roles of transcription and translation in the flow of genetic information.** In a cell, inherited information flows from DNA to RNA to protein. The two main stages of information flow are transcription and translation. A miniature version of part (a) or (b) accompanies several figures later in the chapter as an orientation diagram to help you see where a particular figure fits into the overall scheme of gene expression.

exist that use RNA molecules as templates for DNA synthesis (a process you'll read about in Chapter 17). However, these exceptions do not invalidate the idea that, in general, genetic information flows from DNA to RNA to protein. Now let's discuss how the instructions for assembling amino acids into a specific order are encoded in nucleic acids.

The Genetic Code

When biologists began to suspect that the instructions for protein synthesis were encoded in DNA, they recognized a problem: There are only four nucleotide bases to specify 20 amino acids. Thus, the genetic code cannot be a language like Chinese, where each written symbol corresponds to a word. How many nucleotides, then, correspond to an amino acid?

Codons: Triplets of Nucleotides

If each kind of nucleotide base were translated into an amino acid, only four amino acids could be specified, one per nucleotide base. Would a language of two-letter code words suffice? The two-nucleotide sequence AG, for example, could specify one amino acid, and GT could specify another. Since there are four possible nucleotide bases in each position, this would give us 16 (that is, 4^2) possible arrangements—still not enough to code for all 20 amino acids.

Triplets of nucleotide bases are the smallest units of uniform length that can code for all the amino acids. If each arrangement of three consecutive nucleotide bases specifies an amino acid, there can be 64 (that is, 4^3) possible code words—more than enough to specify all the amino acids. Experiments have verified that the flow of information from gene to protein is based on a **triplet code**: The genetic instructions for a polypeptide chain are written in the DNA as a series of nonoverlapping, three-nucleotide words. The series of words in a gene is transcribed into a complementary series of nonoverlapping, three-nucleotide words in mRNA, which is then translated into a chain of amino acids **(Figure 14.5)**.

During transcription, the gene determines the sequence of nucleotide bases along the length of the RNA molecule that is being synthesized. For each gene, only one of the two DNA strands is transcribed. This strand is called the **template strand** because it provides the pattern, or template, for the sequence of nucleotides in an RNA transcript. For any given gene, the same strand is used as the template every time the gene is transcribed. However, on the same DNA molecule farther along the chromosome, the opposite strand may be the one that functions as the template for another gene.

An mRNA molecule is complementary rather than identical to its DNA template because RNA nucleotides are assembled on the template according to base-pairing rules (see Figure 14.5). The pairs are similar to those that form during DNA replication, except that U (the RNA substitute for T) pairs with A and the mRNA nucleotides contain ribose instead of deoxyribose. Like a new strand of DNA, the RNA molecule is synthesized in an antiparallel direction to the template strand of DNA. (To review what is meant by "antiparallel" and the 5′ and 3′ ends of a nucleic acid chain, see Figure 13.8.) In the example in Figure 14.5, the nucleotide

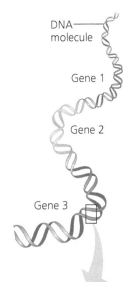

▶ **Figure 14.5 The triplet code.** For each gene, one DNA strand functions as a template for transcription of RNAs, such as mRNA. The base-pairing rules for DNA synthesis also guide transcription, except that uracil (U) takes the place of thymine (T) in RNA. During translation, the mRNA is read as a sequence of nucleotide triplets, called codons. Each codon specifies an amino acid to be added to the growing polypeptide chain. The mRNA is read in the 5′ → 3′ direction.

? *Compare the sequence of the mRNA to that of the nontemplate DNA strand, in both cases reading from 5′ → 3′.*

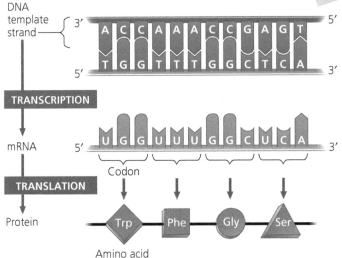

triplet ACC along the DNA template strand (written as 3′-ACC-5′) provides a template for 5′-UGG-3′ in the mRNA molecule. The mRNA nucleotide triplets are called **codons**, and they are customarily written in the 5′ → 3′ direction. In our example, UGG is the codon for the amino acid tryptophan (abbreviated Trp). The term *codon* is also used for the DNA nucleotide triplets along the *nontemplate* strand. These codons are complementary to the template strand and thus identical in sequence to the mRNA, except that they have T wherever there is a U in the mRNA. (For this reason, the nontemplate DNA strand is often called the *coding strand*.)

During translation, the sequence of codons along an mRNA molecule is decoded, or translated, into a sequence of amino acids making up a polypeptide chain. The codons are read by the translation machinery in the 5′ → 3′ direction along the mRNA. Each codon specifies which one of the 20 amino acids will be incorporated at the corresponding position along a polypeptide. Because codons are nucleotide triplets, the number of nucleotides making up a genetic message must be three times the number of amino acids in the protein product. For example, it takes 300 nucleotides along an mRNA strand to code for the amino acids in a polypeptide that is 100 amino acids long.

Cracking the Code

Molecular biologists cracked the genetic code of life in the early 1960s when a series of elegant experiments disclosed the amino acid translations of each of the RNA codons. The first codon was deciphered in 1961 by Marshall Nirenberg, of the National Institutes of Health, along with his colleagues. Nirenberg synthesized an artificial mRNA by linking identical RNA nucleotides containing uracil as their base. No matter where this message started or stopped, it could contain only one codon in repetition: UUU. Nirenberg added this "poly-U" codon to a test-tube mixture that contained all 20 amino acids, ribosomes, and the other components required for protein synthesis. His artificial system translated the poly-U into a polypeptide containing many units of the amino acid phenylalanine (Phe), strung together as a polyphenylalanine chain. Thus, Nirenberg determined that the mRNA codon UUU specifies the amino acid phenylalanine. Soon, the amino acids specified by the codons AAA, GGG, and CCC were determined in the same way.

Although more elaborate techniques were required to decode mixed triplets such as AUA and CGA, all 64 codons were deciphered by the mid-1960s. As **Figure 14.6** shows, 61 of the 64 triplets code for amino acids. The three codons that do not designate amino acids are "stop" signals, or termination codons, marking the end of translation. Notice that the codon AUG has a dual function: It codes for the amino acid methionine (Met) and also functions as a "start" signal, or initiation codon. Genetic messages usually begin with the mRNA codon AUG, which signals the protein-synthesizing machinery to begin translating the mRNA at that location. (Because AUG also stands for methionine, polypeptide chains begin with methionine when they are synthesized. However, an enzyme may subsequently remove this starter amino acid from the chain.)

Notice in Figure 14.6 that there is redundancy in the genetic code, but no ambiguity. For example, although codons GAA and GAG both specify glutamic acid (redundancy), neither of them ever specifies any other amino acid (no ambiguity). The redundancy in the code is not altogether random. In many cases, codons that are synonyms for a particular amino acid differ only in the third nucleotide base of the triplet. We'll consider the significance of this redundancy later in the chapter.

Our ability to extract the intended message from a written language depends on reading the symbols in the correct groupings—that is, in the correct **reading frame**. Consider this statement: "The red dog ate the bug." Group the letters incorrectly by starting at the wrong point, and the result will

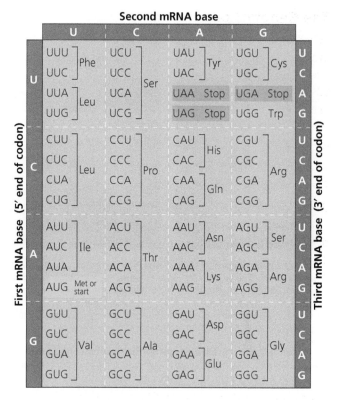

▲ **Figure 14.6 The codon table for mRNA.** The three nucleotide bases of an mRNA codon are designated here as the first, second, and third bases, reading in the 5′ → 3′ direction along the mRNA. (Practice using this table by finding the codons in Figure 14.5.) The codon AUG not only stands for the amino acid methionine (Met) but also functions as a "start" signal for ribosomes to begin translating the mRNA at that point. Three of the 64 codons function as "stop" signals, marking where ribosomes end translation. See Figure 3.18 for a list of the full names of all the amino acids.

probably be gibberish: for example, "her edd oga tet heb ug." The reading frame is also important in the molecular language of cells. The short stretch of polypeptide shown in Figure 14.5, for instance, will be made correctly only if the mRNA nucleotides are read from left to right (5′ → 3′) in the groups of three shown in the figure: UGG UUU GGC UCA. Although a genetic message is written with no spaces between the codons, the cell's protein-synthesizing machinery reads the message as a series of nonoverlapping three-letter words. The message is *not* read as a series of overlapping words—UGGUUU, and so on—which would convey a very different message.

Evolution of the Genetic Code

EVOLUTION The genetic code is nearly universal, shared by organisms from the simplest bacteria to the most complex plants and animals. The mRNA codon CCG, for instance, is translated as the amino acid proline in all organisms whose genetic code has been examined. In laboratory experiments, genes can be transcribed and translated after being transplanted from one species to another, sometimes with quite

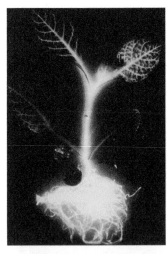

(a) Tobacco plant expressing a firefly gene. The yellow glow is produced by a chemical reaction catalyzed by the protein product of the firefly gene.

(b) Pig expressing a jellyfish gene. Researchers injected the gene for a fluorescent protein into fertilized pig eggs. One of the eggs developed into this fluorescent pig.

▲ **Figure 14.7 Expression of genes from different species.** Because diverse forms of life share a common genetic code, one species can be programmed to produce proteins characteristic of a second species by introducing DNA from the second species into the first.

striking results, as shown in **Figure 14.7**. Bacteria can be programmed by the insertion of human genes to synthesize certain human proteins for medical use, such as insulin. Such applications have produced many exciting developments in the area of genetic engineering (see Concept 13.4).

Despite a small number of exceptions in which a few codons differ from the standard ones, the evolutionary significance of the code's *near* universality is clear. A language shared by all living things must have been operating very early in the history of life—early enough to be present in the common ancestor of all present-day organisms. A shared genetic vocabulary is a reminder of the kinship that bonds all life on Earth.

CONCEPT CHECK 14.1

1. **MAKE CONNECTIONS** In a research article about alkaptonuria published in 1902, Garrod suggested that humans inherit two "characters" (alleles) for a particular enzyme and that both parents must contribute a faulty version for the offspring to have the disorder. Today, would this disorder be called dominant or recessive? (See Concept 11.4.)
2. What polypeptide product would you expect from a poly-G mRNA that is 30 nucleotides long?
3. **DRAW IT** The template strand of a gene contains the sequence 3'-TTCAGTCGT-5'. Suppose that the nontemplate sequence could be transcribed instead of the template sequence. Draw the nontemplate sequence in 3' to 5' order. Then draw the mRNA sequence and translate it using Figure 14.6. (Be sure to pay attention to the 5' and 3' ends, remembering that the mRNA is antiparallel to the DNA strand.) Predict how well the protein synthesized from the nontemplate strand would function, if at all.

For suggested answers, see Appendix A.

Transcription is the DNA-directed synthesis of RNA: *a closer look*

Now that we have considered the linguistic logic and evolutionary significance of the genetic code, we are ready to reexamine transcription, the first stage of gene expression, in more detail.

Molecular Components of Transcription

Messenger RNA, the carrier of information from DNA to the cell's protein-synthesizing machinery, is transcribed from the template strand of a gene. An enzyme called an **RNA polymerase** pries the two strands of DNA apart and joins together RNA nucleotides complementary to the DNA template strand, thus elongating the RNA polynucleotide **(Figure 14.8)**. Like the DNA polymerases that function in DNA replication, RNA polymerases can assemble a polynucleotide only in its 5' → 3' direction. Unlike DNA polymerases, however, RNA polymerases are able to start a chain from scratch; they don't need a primer.

Specific sequences of nucleotides along the DNA mark where transcription of a gene begins and ends. The DNA sequence where RNA polymerase attaches and initiates transcription is known as the **promoter**; in bacteria, the sequence that signals the end of transcription is called the **terminator**. (The termination mechanism is different in eukaryotes; we'll describe it later.) Molecular biologists refer to the direction of transcription as "downstream" and the other direction as "upstream." These terms are also used to describe the positions of nucleotide sequences within the DNA or RNA. Thus, the promoter sequence in DNA is said to be upstream from the terminator. The stretch of DNA downstream from the promoter that is transcribed into an RNA molecule is called a **transcription unit**.

Bacteria have a single type of RNA polymerase that synthesizes not only mRNA but also other types of RNA that function in protein synthesis, such as ribosomal RNA. In contrast, eukaryotes have at least three types of RNA polymerase in their nuclei; the one used for pre-mRNA synthesis is called RNA polymerase II. In the discussion that follows, we start with the features of mRNA synthesis common to both bacteria and eukaryotes and then describe some key differences.

Synthesis of an RNA Transcript

The three stages of transcription, as shown in Figure 14.8 and described next, are initiation, elongation, and termination of the RNA chain. Study Figure 14.8 to familiarize yourself with the stages and the terms used to describe them.

RNA Polymerase Binding and Initiation of Transcription

The promoter of a gene includes within it the transcription **start point** (the nucleotide where RNA synthesis actually begins) and typically extends several dozen or more nucleotide pairs upstream from the start point. RNA polymerase binds in a precise location and orientation on the promoter, thereby determining where transcription starts and which of the two strands of the DNA helix is used as the template.

Certain sections of a promoter are especially important for binding RNA polymerase. In bacteria, part of the RNA polymerase itself specifically recognizes and binds to the promoter.

In eukaryotes, a collection of proteins called **transcription factors** mediate the binding of RNA polymerase and the initiation of transcription. Only after transcription factors are attached to the promoter does RNA polymerase II bind to it. The whole complex of transcription factors and RNA polymerase II bound to the promoter is called a **transcription initiation complex**. **Figure 14.9** shows the role of transcription factors

Promoter Transcription unit

5′
3′
DNA
Start point
RNA polymerase

1 **Initiation.** After RNA polymerase binds to the promoter, the DNA strands unwind, and the polymerase initiates RNA synthesis at the start point on the template strand.

Nontemplate strand of DNA

5′
3′
3′
5′
Template strand of DNA

Unwound DNA
RNA transcript

2 **Elongation.** The polymerase moves downstream, unwinding the DNA and elongating the RNA transcript 5′ → 3′. In the wake of transcription, the DNA strands re-form a double helix.

Rewound DNA

5′
3′
3′
5′
3′
5′
RNA transcript

3 **Termination.** Eventually, the RNA transcript is released, and the polymerase detaches from the DNA.

5′
3′
3′
5′

5′ Completed RNA transcript 3′

Direction of transcription ("downstream")

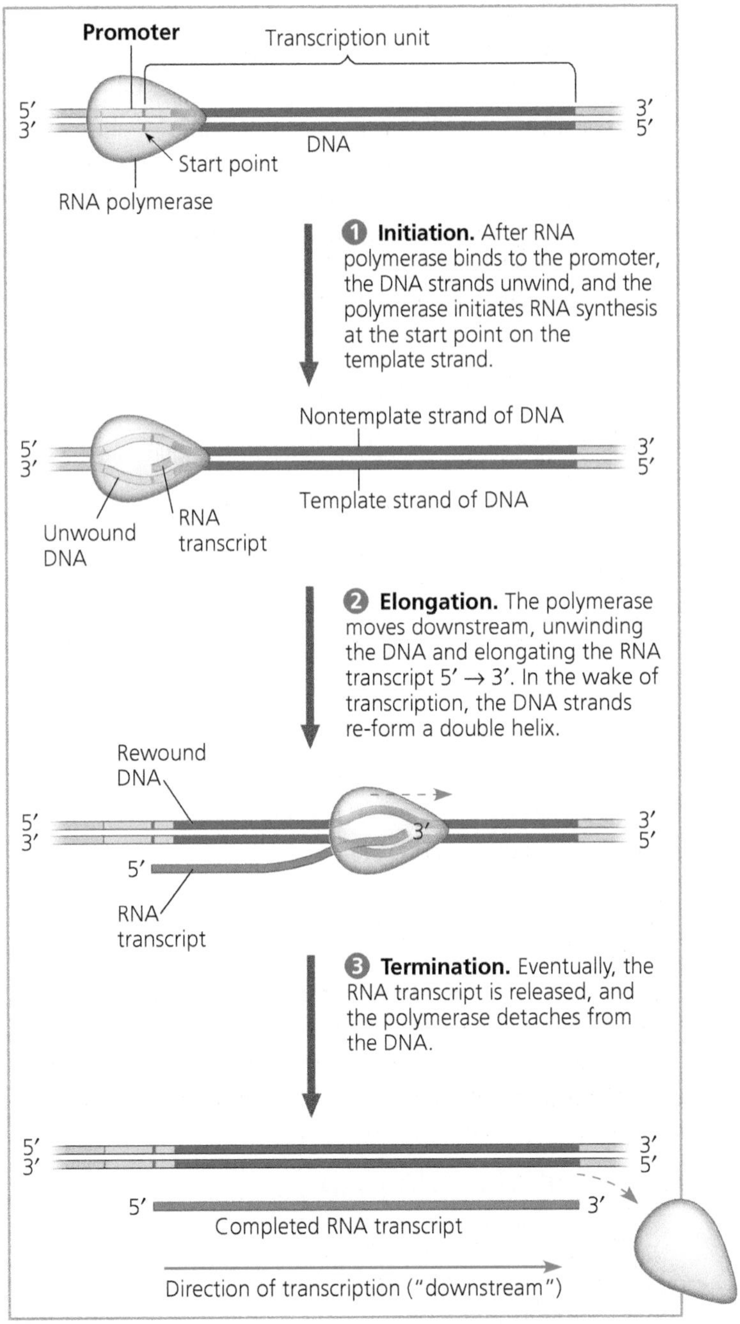

▲ **Figure 14.8 The stages of transcription: initiation, elongation, and termination.** This general depiction of transcription applies to both bacteria and eukaryotes, but the details of termination differ, as described in the text. Also, in a bacterium, the RNA transcript is immediately usable as mRNA; in a eukaryote, the RNA transcript must first undergo processing.

MAKE CONNECTIONS *Compare the use of a template strand during transcription and replication. See Figure 13.19.*

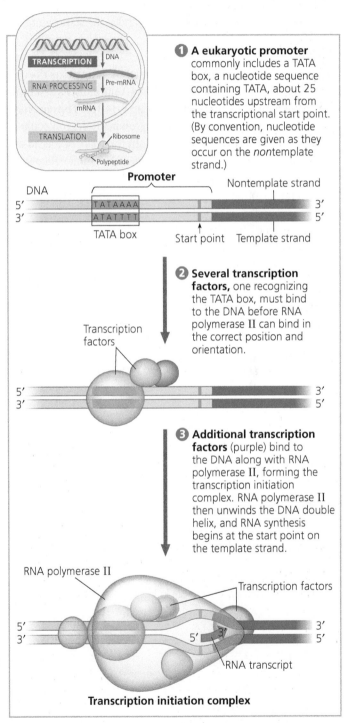

1 **A eukaryotic promoter** commonly includes a TATA box, a nucleotide sequence containing TATA, about 25 nucleotides upstream from the transcriptional start point. (By convention, nucleotide sequences are given as they occur on the *non*template strand.)

2 **Several transcription factors,** one recognizing the TATA box, must bind to the DNA before RNA polymerase II can bind in the correct position and orientation.

3 **Additional transcription factors** (purple) bind to the DNA along with RNA polymerase II, forming the transcription initiation complex. RNA polymerase II then unwinds the DNA double helix, and RNA synthesis begins at the start point on the template strand.

Transcription initiation complex

▲ **Figure 14.9 The initiation of transcription at a eukaryotic promoter.** In eukaryotic cells, proteins called transcription factors mediate the initiation of transcription by RNA polymerase II.

❓ *Explain how the interaction of RNA polymerase with the promoter would differ if the figure showed transcription initiation for bacteria.*

and a crucial promoter DNA sequence called the **TATA box** in forming the initiation complex at a eukaryotic promoter.

The interaction between eukaryotic RNA polymerase II and transcription factors is an example of the importance of protein-protein interactions in controlling eukaryotic transcription. Once the appropriate transcription factors are firmly attached to the promoter DNA and the polymerase is bound in the correct orientation, the enzyme unwinds the two DNA strands and begins transcribing the template strand at the start point.

Elongation of the RNA Strand

As RNA polymerase moves along the DNA, it untwists the double helix, exposing about 10–20 DNA nucleotides at a time for pairing with RNA nucleotides **(Figure 14.10)**. The enzyme adds nucleotides to the 3′ end of the growing RNA molecule as it continues along the double helix. In the wake of this advancing wave of RNA synthesis, the new RNA molecule peels away from its DNA template, and the DNA double helix reforms. Transcription progresses at a rate of about 40 nucleotides per second in eukaryotes.

A single gene can be transcribed simultaneously by several molecules of RNA polymerase following each other like trucks in a convoy. A growing strand of RNA trails off from each polymerase, with the length of each new strand reflecting how far along the template the enzyme has traveled from the start point (see the mRNA molecules in Figure 14.23). The congregation of many polymerase molecules simultaneously transcribing a single gene increases the amount of mRNA transcribed from it, which helps the cell make the encoded protein in large amounts.

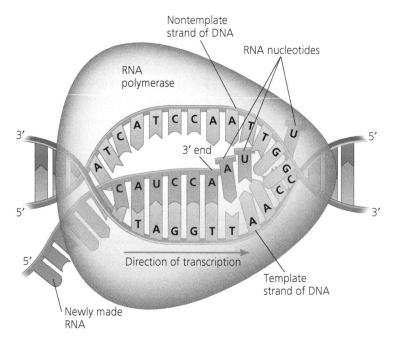

▲ **Figure 14.10 Transcription elongation.** RNA polymerase moves along the DNA template strand, joining complementary RNA nucleotides to the 3′ end of the growing RNA transcript. Behind the polymerase, the new RNA peels away from the template strand, which re-forms a double helix with the nontemplate strand.

Termination of Transcription

The mechanism of termination differs between bacteria and eukaryotes. In bacteria, transcription proceeds through a terminator sequence in the DNA. The transcribed terminator (an RNA sequence) functions as the termination signal, causing the polymerase to detach from the DNA and release the transcript, which requires no further modification before translation. In eukaryotes, RNA polymerase II transcribes a sequence on the DNA called the polyadenylation signal sequence, which specifies a polyadenylation signal (AAUAAA) in the pre-mRNA. This is called a "signal" because when this stretch of six RNA nucleotides appears, it is immediately bound by certain proteins in the nucleus. Then, at a point about 10–35 nucleotides downstream from the AAUAAA signal, these proteins cut the RNA transcript free from the polymerase, releasing the pre-mRNA. The pre-mRNA then undergoes processing, the topic of the next section.

CONCEPT CHECK 14.2

1. What is a promoter? Is it located at the upstream or downstream end of a transcription unit?
2. What enables RNA polymerase to start transcribing a gene at the right place on the DNA in a bacterial cell? In a eukaryotic cell?
3. **WHAT IF?** Suppose X-rays caused a sequence change in the TATA box of a particular gene's promoter. How would that affect transcription of the gene? (See Figure 14.9.)

For suggested answers, see Appendix A.

CONCEPT 14.3

Eukaryotic cells modify RNA after transcription

Enzymes in the eukaryotic nucleus modify pre-mRNA in specific ways before the genetic message is dispatched to the cytoplasm. During this **RNA processing**, both ends of the primary transcript are altered. Also, in most cases, certain interior sections of the RNA molecule are cut out and the remaining parts spliced together. These modifications produce an mRNA molecule ready for translation.

Alteration of mRNA Ends

Each end of a pre-mRNA molecule is modified in a particular way **(Figure 14.11)**. The 5′ end, which is synthesized first, receives a **5′ cap**, a modified form of a guanine (G) nucleotide added onto the 5′ end after transcription of the first 20–40 nucleotides. The 3′ end of the pre-mRNA molecule is also modified before the mRNA exits the nucleus. Recall that the pre-mRNA is released soon after the polyadenylation signal, AAUAAA, is transcribed. At the 3′ end, an enzyme then adds 50–250 more adenine (A) nucleotides, forming a **poly-A tail**. The 5′ cap and poly-A tail share several important functions. First, they seem to facilitate the export of the mature

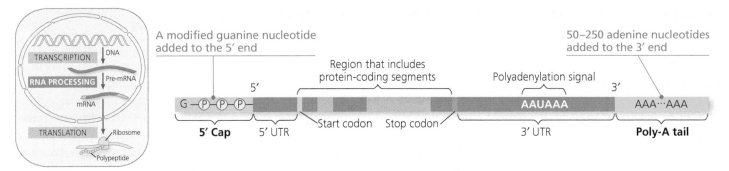

▲ **Figure 14.11 RNA processing: Addition of the 5′ cap and poly-A tail.** Enzymes modify the two ends of a eukaryotic pre-mRNA molecule. The modified ends may promote the export of mRNA from the nucleus, and they help protect the mRNA from degradation. When the mRNA reaches the cytoplasm, the modified ends, in conjunction with certain cytoplasmic proteins, facilitate ribosome attachment. The 5′ cap and poly-A tail are not translated into protein, nor are the regions called the 5′ untranslated region (5′ UTR) and 3′ untranslated region (3′ UTR). The pink segments will be described shortly.

mRNA from the nucleus. Second, they help protect the mRNA from degradation by hydrolytic enzymes. And third, they help ribosomes attach to the 5′ end of the mRNA once the mRNA reaches the cytoplasm. Figure 14.11 shows a diagram of a eukaryotic mRNA molecule with cap and tail. The figure also shows the untranslated regions (UTRs) at the 5′ and 3′ ends of the mRNA (referred to as the 5′ UTR and 3′ UTR). The UTRs are parts of the mRNA that will not be translated into protein, but they have other functions, such as ribosome binding.

Split Genes and RNA Splicing

A remarkable stage of RNA processing in the eukaryotic nucleus is the removal of large portions of the RNA molecule and reconnection of the remaining portions. This cut-and-paste job, called **RNA splicing**, is similar to editing a video. The average length of a transcription unit along a human DNA molecule is about 27,000 nucleotide pairs, so the primary RNA transcript is also that long. However, the average-sized protein of 400 amino acids requires only 1,200 nucleotides in RNA to code for it. (Remember, each amino acid is encoded by a *triplet* of nucleotides.) This is because most eukaryotic genes and their RNA transcripts

have long noncoding stretches of nucleotides, regions that are not translated. Even more surprising is that most of these noncoding sequences are interspersed between coding segments of the gene and thus between coding segments of the pre-mRNA. In other words, the sequence of DNA nucleotides that codes for a eukaryotic polypeptide is usually not continuous; it is split into segments. The noncoding segments of nucleic acid that lie between coding regions are called *in*tervening sequences, or **introns**. The other regions are called **exons**, because they are eventually *ex*pressed, usually by being translated into amino acid sequences. (Exceptions include the UTRs of the exons at the ends of the RNA, which make up part of the mRNA but are not translated into protein. Because of these exceptions, you may prefer to think of exons as sequences of RNA that *exit* the nucleus.) The terms *intron* and *exon* are used for both RNA sequences and the DNA sequences that specify them.

In making a primary transcript from a gene, RNA polymerase II transcribes both introns and exons from the DNA, but the mRNA molecule that enters the cytoplasm is an abridged version **(Figure 14.12)**. The introns are cut out from the molecule and the exons joined together, forming an mRNA

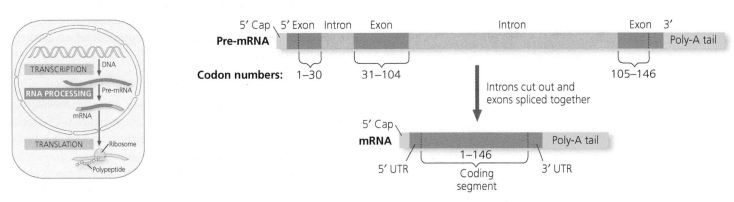

▲ **Figure 14.12 RNA processing: RNA splicing.** The RNA molecule shown here codes for β-globin, one of the polypeptides of hemoglobin. The numbers under the RNA refer to codons; β-globin is 146 amino acids long. The β-globin gene and its pre-mRNA transcript have three exons, corresponding to sequences that will leave the nucleus as mRNA. (The 5′ UTR and 3′ UTR are parts of exons because they are included in the mRNA; however, they do not code for protein.) During RNA processing, the introns are cut out and the exons spliced together. In many genes, the introns are much larger than the exons.

? *On the mRNA, indicate the sites of the start and stop codons.*

molecule with a continuous coding sequence. This is the process of RNA splicing.

One important consequence of the presence of introns in genes is that a single gene can encode more than one kind of polypeptide. Many genes are known to give rise to two or more different polypeptides, depending on which segments are treated as exons during RNA processing; this is called **alternative RNA splicing** (see Figure 15.12). Because of alternative splicing, the number of different protein products an organism produces can be much greater than its number of genes.

How is pre-mRNA splicing carried out? The removal of introns is accomplished by a large complex made of proteins and small RNAs called a **spliceosome**. This complex binds to several short nucleotide sequences along the intron, including key sequences at each end **(Figure 14.13)**. The intron is then released (and rapidly degraded), and the spliceosome joins together the two exons that flanked the intron. It turns out that the small RNAs in the spliceosome not only participate in the assembly of the spliceosome and recognition of the splice site but also catalyze the splicing process.

Ribozymes

The idea of a catalytic role for the RNAs in the spliceosome arose from the discovery of **ribozymes**, RNA molecules that function as enzymes. In some organisms, RNA splicing can occur without proteins or even additional RNA molecules: The intron RNA functions as a ribozyme and catalyzes its own excision! For example, in the ciliate protist *Tetrahymena*, self-splicing occurs in the production of ribosomal RNA (rRNA), a component of the organism's ribosomes. The pre-rRNA actually removes its own introns. The discovery of ribozymes rendered obsolete the idea that all biological catalysts are proteins.

Three properties of RNA enable some RNA molecules to function as enzymes. First, because RNA is single-stranded, a region of an RNA molecule may base-pair, in an antiparallel arrangement, with a complementary region elsewhere in the same molecule; this gives the molecule a particular three-dimensional structure. A specific structure is essential to the catalytic function of ribozymes, just as it is for enzymatic proteins. Second, like certain amino acids in an enzymatic protein, some of the bases in RNA contain functional groups that can participate in catalysis. Third, the ability of RNA to hydrogen-bond with other nucleic acid molecules (either RNA or DNA) adds specificity to its catalytic activity. For example, complementary base pairing between the RNA of the spliceosome and the RNA of a primary RNA transcript precisely locates the region where the ribozyme catalyzes splicing. Later in this chapter, you'll see how these properties of RNA also allow it to perform important noncatalytic roles in the cell, such as recognition of the three-nucleotide codons on mRNA.

CONCEPT CHECK 14.3

1. Given that there are about 20,000 human genes, how can human cells make 75,000–100,000 different proteins?
2. How is RNA splicing similar to how you would watch a TV show recorded earlier using a DVR? In what ways is it different? What would introns correspond to in this analogy?
3. **WHAT IF?** What would be the effect of treating cells with an agent that removed the cap from mRNAs?

For suggested answers, see Appendix A.

CONCEPT 14.4

Translation is the RNA-directed synthesis of a polypeptide: *a closer look*

We will now examine in greater detail how genetic information flows from mRNA to protein—the process of translation. As we did for transcription, we'll concentrate on the basic steps of translation that occur in both bacteria and eukaryotes, while pointing out key differences.

Molecular Components of Translation

In the process of translation, a cell "reads" a genetic message and builds a polypeptide accordingly. The message is a series of codons along an mRNA molecule, and the translator is called a **transfer RNA (tRNA)**. The function of a tRNA is to transfer amino acids from the cytoplasmic pool of amino acids to a growing polypeptide in a ribosome. A cell keeps its cytoplasm stocked with all 20 amino acids, either by synthesizing them from other compounds or by taking them up from the surrounding solution. The ribosome, a structure made of proteins and RNAs, adds each amino acid brought to it by a tRNA to the growing end of a polypeptide chain **(Figure 14.14)**.

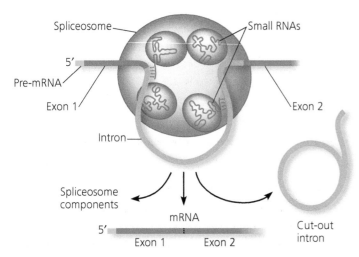

▲ **Figure 14.13 A spliceosome splicing a pre-mRNA.** The diagram shows a portion of a pre-mRNA transcript, with an intron (pink) flanked by two exons (red). Small RNAs within the spliceosome base-pair with nucleotides at specific sites along the intron. Next, small spliceosome RNAs also catalyze cutting of the pre-mRNA and the splicing together of the exons, releasing the intron for rapid degradation. (These RNAs are *ribozymes*, discussed in the next section.)

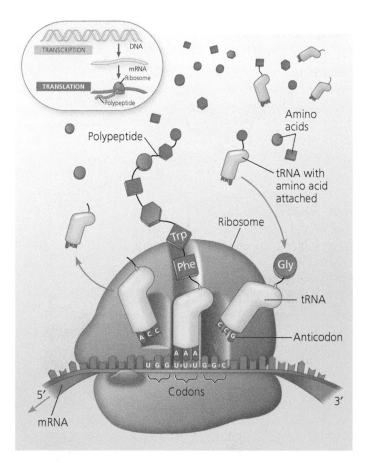

Polypeptide

Amino acids

tRNA with amino acid attached

Ribosome

Trp

Phe

Gly

tRNA

Anticodon

A C C

A A A

C C G

U G G U U U G G C

Codons

5′

mRNA

3′

▲ **Figure 14.14 Translation: the basic concept.** As a molecule of mRNA is moved through a ribosome, codons are translated into amino acids, one by one. The translators, or interpreters, are tRNA molecules, each type with a specific nucleotide triplet called an anticodon at one end and a corresponding amino acid at the other end. A tRNA adds its amino acid cargo to a growing polypeptide chain after the anticodon hydrogen-bonds to the complementary codon on the mRNA. The figures that follow show some of the details of translation in a bacterial cell.

ANIMATION Visit the Study Area in **MasteringBiology** for the BioFlix® 3-D Animation on Protein Synthesis.

Translation is simple in principle but complex in its biochemistry and mechanics. In dissecting translation, we'll focus on the slightly less complicated version of the process that occurs in bacteria. We'll first look at the major players in this cellular process.

The Structure and Function of Transfer RNA

The key to translating a genetic message into a specific amino acid sequence is the fact that each tRNA enables translation of a given mRNA codon into a certain amino acid. This is possible because a tRNA bears a specific amino acid at one end of its three-dimensional structure, while at the other end is a nucleotide triplet that can base-pair with the complementary codon on mRNA.

A tRNA molecule consists of a single RNA strand that is only about 80 nucleotides long (compared to hundreds of

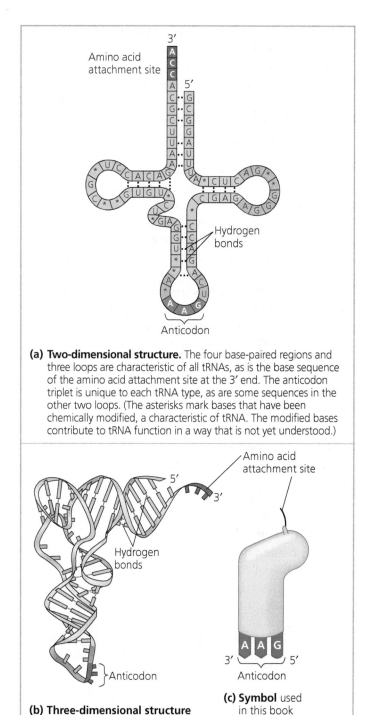

Amino acid attachment site

3′

5′

Hydrogen bonds

Anticodon

(a) Two-dimensional structure. The four base-paired regions and three loops are characteristic of all tRNAs, as is the base sequence of the amino acid attachment site at the 3′ end. The anticodon triplet is unique to each tRNA type, as are some sequences in the other two loops. (The asterisks mark bases that have been chemically modified, a characteristic of tRNA. The modified bases contribute to tRNA function in a way that is not yet understood.)

Amino acid attachment site

5′

3′

Hydrogen bonds

Anticodon

A A G

3′

5′

Anticodon

(c) Symbol used in this book

(b) Three-dimensional structure

▲ **Figure 14.15 The structure of transfer RNA (tRNA).**

nucleotides for most mRNA molecules). Because of the presence of complementary stretches of nucleotide bases that can hydrogen-bond to each other, this single strand can fold back on itself and form a molecule with a three-dimensional structure. Flattened into one plane to clarify this base pairing, a tRNA molecule looks like a cloverleaf **(Figure 14.15a)**. The tRNA actually twists and folds into a compact three-dimensional structure that is roughly L-shaped, with the 5′ and 3′ ends of the linear tRNA both located near one end of the structure **(Figure 14.15b)**. The protruding 3′ end acts as the attachment site for an amino acid. The loop extending from the other end of the L includes the **anticodon**, the particular nucleotide triplet that base-pairs to a specific mRNA codon. Thus, the structure of a tRNA molecule fits its function.

Anticodons are conventionally written $3' \rightarrow 5'$ to align properly with codons written $5' \rightarrow 3'$ (see Figure 14.14). (For base pairing, RNA strands must be antiparallel, like DNA.) As an example of how tRNAs work, consider the mRNA codon 5'-GGC-3', which is translated as the amino acid glycine. The tRNA that base-pairs with this codon by hydrogen bonding has 3'-CCG-5' as its anticodon and carries glycine at its other end (see the incoming tRNA approaching the ribosome in Figure 14.14). As an mRNA molecule is moved through a ribosome, glycine will be added to the polypeptide chain whenever the codon 5'-GGC-3' is presented for translation. Codon by codon, the genetic message is translated as tRNAs position each amino acid, in the order prescribed, and the ribosome adds that amino acid onto the growing polypeptide chain. The tRNA molecule is a translator in the sense that, in the context of the ribosome, it can read a nucleic acid word (the mRNA codon) and interpret it as a protein word (the amino acid).

Like mRNA and other types of cellular RNA, transfer RNA molecules are transcribed from DNA templates. In a eukaryotic cell, tRNA, like mRNA, is made in the nucleus and then travels from the nucleus to the cytoplasm, where translation occurs. In both bacterial and eukaryotic cells, each tRNA molecule is used repeatedly, picking up its designated amino acid in the cytosol, depositing this cargo onto a polypeptide chain at the ribosome, and then leaving the ribosome, ready to pick up another of the same amino acid.

The accurate translation of a genetic message requires two instances of molecular recognition. First, a tRNA that binds to an mRNA codon specifying a particular amino acid must carry that amino acid, and no other, to the ribosome. The correct matching up of tRNA and amino acid is carried out by a family of related enzymes called **aminoacyl-tRNA synthetases (Figure 14.16)**. The active site of each type of aminoacyl-tRNA synthetase fits only a specific combination of amino acid and tRNA. (Regions of both the amino acid attachment end and the anticodon end of the tRNA are instrumental in ensuring the specific fit.) There are 20 different synthetases, one that joins each amino acid to the right tRNA; each synthetase is able to bind to all the different tRNAs that code for its particular amino acid. The synthetase catalyzes the covalent attachment of the amino acid to its tRNA in a process driven by the hydrolysis of ATP. The resulting aminoacyl tRNA, also called a charged tRNA, is released from the enzyme and is then available to deliver its amino acid to a growing polypeptide chain on a ribosome.

The second instance of molecular recognition is the pairing of the tRNA anticodon with the appropriate mRNA codon. If one tRNA variety existed for each mRNA codon specifying an amino acid, there would be 61 tRNAs (see Figure 14.6). In fact, there are only about 45, signifying that some tRNAs must be able to bind to more than one codon. Such versatility

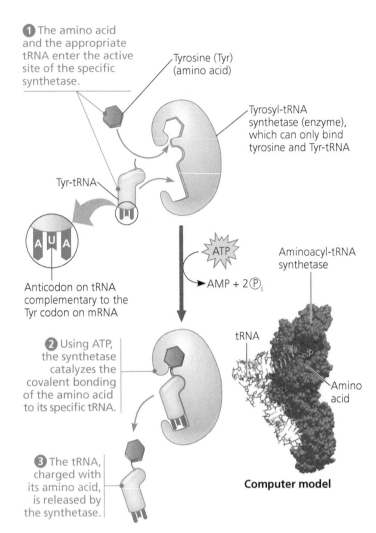

❶ The amino acid and the appropriate tRNA enter the active site of the specific synthetase.

Tyrosine (Tyr) (amino acid)

Tyrosyl-tRNA synthetase (enzyme), which can only bind tyrosine and Tyr-tRNA

Tyr-tRNA

Anticodon on tRNA complementary to the Tyr codon on mRNA

ATP

AMP + 2 (P)$_i$

Aminoacyl-tRNA synthetase

❷ Using ATP, the synthetase catalyzes the covalent bonding of the amino acid to its specific tRNA.

tRNA

Amino acid

❸ The tRNA, charged with its amino acid, is released by the synthetase.

Computer model

▲ **Figure 14.16 Aminoacyl-tRNA synthetases provide specificity in joining amino acids to their tRNAs.** Linkage of a tRNA to its amino acid is an endergonic process that occurs at the expense of ATP (which loses two phosphate groups, becoming AMP).

is possible because the rules for base pairing between the third nucleotide base of a codon and the corresponding base of a tRNA anticodon are relaxed compared to those at other codon positions. For example, the nucleotide base U at the 5' end of a tRNA anticodon can pair with A or G in the third position (at the 3' end) of an mRNA codon. The flexible base pairing at this codon position is called **wobble**. Wobble explains why synonymous codons for an amino acid most often differ in their third nucleotide base but not in the other bases. One such case is that a tRNA with the anticodon 3'-UCU-5' can base-pair with either the mRNA codon 5'-AGA-3' or 5'-AGG-3', both of which code for arginine (see Figure 14.6).

Ribosomes

Ribosomes facilitate the specific coupling of tRNA anticodons with mRNA codons during protein synthesis. A ribosome consists of a large subunit and a small subunit, each made up of proteins and one or more **ribosomal RNAs (rRNAs) (Figure 14.17)**. In eukaryotes, the subunits are made in the nucleolus. Ribosomal RNA genes are transcribed, and the RNA

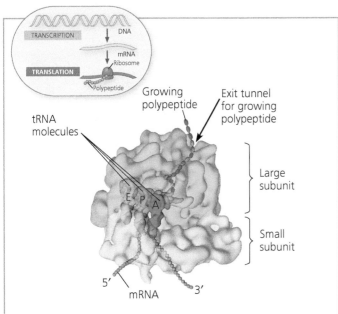

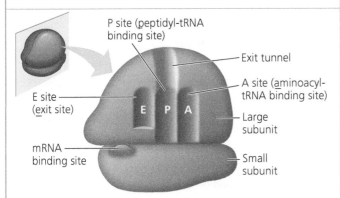

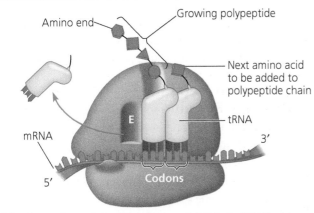

(a) **Computer model of functioning ribosome.** This is a model of a bacterial ribosome, showing its overall shape. The eukaryotic ribosome is roughly similar. A ribosomal subunit is a complex of ribosomal RNA molecules and proteins.

(b) **Schematic model showing binding sites.** A ribosome has an mRNA binding site and three tRNA binding sites, known as the A, P, and E sites. This schematic ribosome will appear in later diagrams.

(c) **Schematic model with mRNA and tRNA.** A tRNA fits into a binding site when its anticodon base-pairs with an mRNA codon. The P site holds the tRNA attached to the growing polypeptide. The A site holds the tRNA carrying the next amino acid to be added to the polypeptide chain. Discharged tRNAs leave from the E site. The polypeptide grows at its carboxyl end.

▲ **Figure 14.17 The anatomy of a functioning ribosome.**

is processed and assembled with proteins imported from the cytoplasm. Completed ribosomal subunits are then exported via nuclear pores to the cytoplasm. In both bacteria and eukaryotes, a large and a small subunit join to form a functional ribosome only when attached to an mRNA molecule. About one-third of the mass of a ribosome is made up of proteins; the rest consists of rRNAs, either three molecules (in bacteria) or four (in eukaryotes). Because most cells contain thousands of ribosomes, rRNA is the most abundant type of cellular RNA.

Although the ribosomes of bacteria and eukaryotes are very similar in structure and function, eukaryotic ribosomes are slightly larger, as well as differing somewhat from bacterial ribosomes in their molecular composition. The differences are medically significant. Certain antibiotic drugs can inactivate bacterial ribosomes without affecting eukaryotic ribosomes to make proteins. These drugs, including tetracycline and streptomycin, are used to combat bacterial infections.

The structure of a ribosome reflects its function of bringing mRNA together with tRNAs carrying amino acids. In addition to a binding site for mRNA, each ribosome has three binding sites for tRNA, as described in Figure 14.17. The **P site** (peptidyl-tRNA binding site) holds the tRNA carrying the growing polypeptide chain, while the **A site** (aminoacyl-tRNA binding site) holds the tRNA carrying the next amino acid to be added to the chain. Discharged tRNAs leave the ribosome from the **E site** (exit site). The ribosome holds the tRNA and mRNA in close proximity and positions the new amino acid so that it can be added to the carboxyl end of the growing polypeptide. It then catalyzes the formation of the peptide bond. As the polypeptide becomes longer, it passes through an *exit tunnel* in the ribosome's large subunit. When the polypeptide is complete, it is released through the exit tunnel.

The widely accepted model is that rRNA, not the proteins, is primarily responsible for both the structure and the function of the ribosome. The proteins, which are largely on the exterior, support the shape changes of the rRNA molecules as they carry out catalysis during translation. Ribosomal RNA is the main constituent of the A and P sites and of the interface between the two ribosomal subunits; it also acts as the catalyst of peptide bond formation. Thus, a ribosome could actually be considered one colossal ribozyme!

Building a Polypeptide

We can divide translation, the synthesis of a polypeptide chain, into three stages: initiation, elongation, and termination. All three stages require protein "factors" that aid in the translation process. For certain aspects of chain initiation and elongation, energy is also required. It is provided by the hydrolysis of guanosine triphosphate (GTP).

Ribosome Association and Initiation of Translation

The initiation stage of translation brings together mRNA, a tRNA bearing the first amino acid of the polypeptide, and the two subunits of a ribosome. First, a small ribosomal subunit binds to both mRNA and a specific initiator tRNA, which carries the amino acid methionine. In bacteria, the small subunit can bind these two in either order; it binds the mRNA at a specific RNA sequence, just upstream of the start codon, AUG. In eukaryotes, the small subunit, with the initiator tRNA already bound, binds to the 5′ cap of the mRNA and then moves, or *scans*, downstream along the mRNA until it reaches the AUG start codon, where the initiator tRNA hydrogen-bonds, as shown in step 1 of **Figure 14.18**. In either case, the start codon signals the start of translation; this is important because it establishes the codon reading frame for the mRNA. In the **Scientific Skills Exercise**, you can work with DNA sequences encoding the ribosomal binding sites on the mRNAs of a group of *Escherichia coli* (*E. coli*) genes.

The union of mRNA, initiator tRNA, and a small ribosomal subunit is followed by the attachment of a large ribosomal subunit, completing the *translation initiation complex*. Proteins called *initiation factors* are required to bring all these components together. The cell also expends energy obtained by hydrolysis of a GTP molecule to form the initiation complex. At the completion of the initiation process, the initiator tRNA sits in the P site of the ribosome, and the vacant A site is ready for the next aminoacyl tRNA. Note that a polypeptide is always synthesized in one direction, from the initial methionine at the amino end, also called the N-terminus, toward the final amino acid at the carboxyl end, also called the C-terminus (see Figure 3.19).

Elongation of the Polypeptide Chain

In the elongation stage of translation, amino acids are added one by one to the previous amino acid at the C-terminus of the growing chain. Each addition involves the participation of several proteins called *elongation factors* and occurs in a three-step cycle described in **Figure 14.19**. Energy expenditure occurs in the first and third steps. Codon recognition requires hydrolysis of one molecule of GTP, which increases the accuracy and efficiency of this step. One more GTP is hydrolyzed to provide energy for the translocation step.

The mRNA is moved through the ribosome in one direction only, 5′ end first; this is equivalent to the ribosome moving 5′ → 3′ on the mRNA. The important point is that the ribosome and the mRNA move relative to each other, unidirectionally, codon by codon. The elongation cycle takes less than a tenth of a second in bacteria and is repeated as each amino acid is added to the chain until the polypeptide is completed. The empty tRNAs that are released from the E site return to the cytoplasm, where they will be reloaded with the proper amino acid (see Figure 14.16).

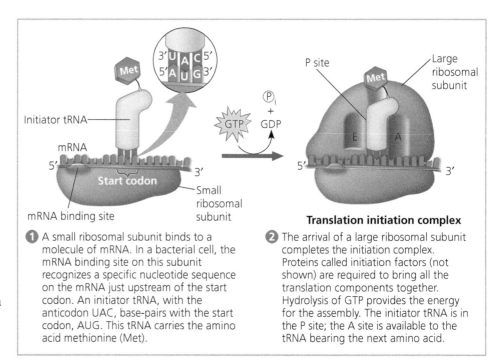

1 A small ribosomal subunit binds to a molecule of mRNA. In a bacterial cell, the mRNA binding site on this subunit recognizes a specific nucleotide sequence on the mRNA just upstream of the start codon. An initiator tRNA, with the anticodon UAC, base-pairs with the start codon, AUG. This tRNA carries the amino acid methionine (Met).

2 The arrival of a large ribosomal subunit completes the initiation complex. Proteins called initiation factors (not shown) are required to bring all the translation components together. Hydrolysis of GTP provides the energy for the assembly. The initiator tRNA is in the P site; the A site is available to the tRNA bearing the next amino acid.

▲ **Figure 14.18** **The initiation of translation.**

Termination of Translation

The final stage of translation is termination **(Figure 14.20)**. Elongation continues until a stop codon in the mRNA reaches the A site. The nucleotide base triplets UAG, UAA, and UGA (all written 5′ → 3′) do not code for amino acids but instead act as signals to stop translation. A *release factor*, a protein shaped like an aminoacyl tRNA, binds directly to the stop codon in the A site. The release factor causes the addition of a water molecule instead of an amino acid to the polypeptide chain. (Water molecules are abundant in the aqueous cellular environment.) This reaction breaks (hydrolyzes) the bond between the completed polypeptide and the tRNA in the P site, releasing the polypeptide through the exit tunnel of the ribosome's large subunit. The remainder of the translation assembly then comes apart in a multistep process, aided by other protein factors. Breakdown of the translation assembly requires the hydrolysis of two more GTP molecules.

Completing and Targeting the Functional Protein

The process of translation is often not sufficient to make a functional protein. In this section, you'll learn about modifications that polypeptide chains undergo after the translation process as well as some of the mechanisms used to target completed proteins to specific sites in the cell.

Protein Folding and Post-Translational Modifications

During its synthesis, a polypeptide chain begins to coil and fold spontaneously as a consequence of its amino acid sequence (primary structure), forming a protein with a specific shape: a three-dimensional molecule with secondary and tertiary

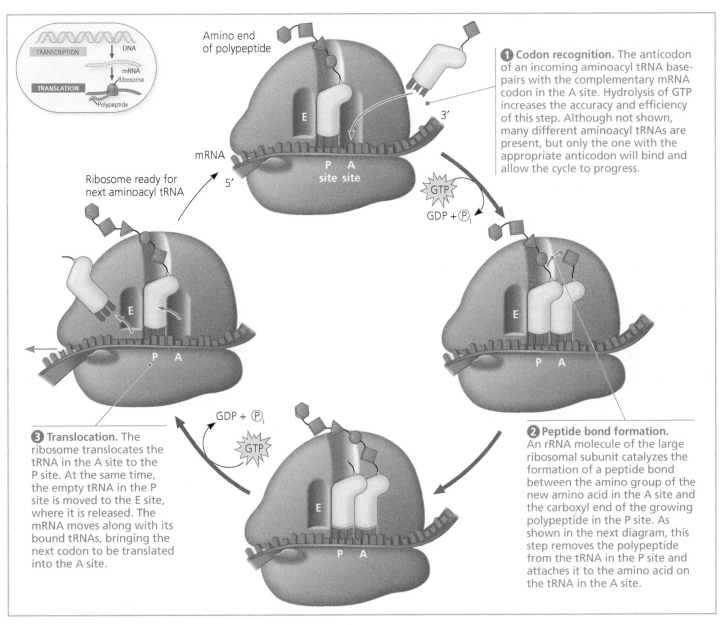

Amino end of polypeptide

Ribosome ready for next aminoacyl tRNA

mRNA

5'

P A site site

E

1 Codon recognition. The anticodon of an incoming aminoacyl tRNA base-pairs with the complementary mRNA codon in the A site. Hydrolysis of GTP increases the accuracy and efficiency of this step. Although not shown, many different aminoacyl tRNAs are present, but only the one with the appropriate anticodon will bind and allow the cycle to progress.

GTP

GDP + P_i

TRANSCRIPTION
DNA
mRNA
Ribosome
TRANSLATION
Polypeptide

E
P A

3'

2 Peptide bond formation. An rRNA molecule of the large ribosomal subunit catalyzes the formation of a peptide bond between the amino group of the new amino acid in the A site and the carboxyl end of the growing polypeptide in the P site. As shown in the next diagram, this step removes the polypeptide from the tRNA in the P site and attaches it to the amino acid on the tRNA in the A site.

3 Translocation. The ribosome translocates the tRNA in the A site to the P site. At the same time, the empty tRNA in the P site is moved to the E site, where it is released. The mRNA moves along with its bound tRNAs, bringing the next codon to be translated into the A site.

GDP + P_i

GTP

E
P A

▲ **Figure 14.19 The elongation cycle of translation.** The hydrolysis of GTP plays an important role in the elongation process. Not shown are the proteins called elongation factors.

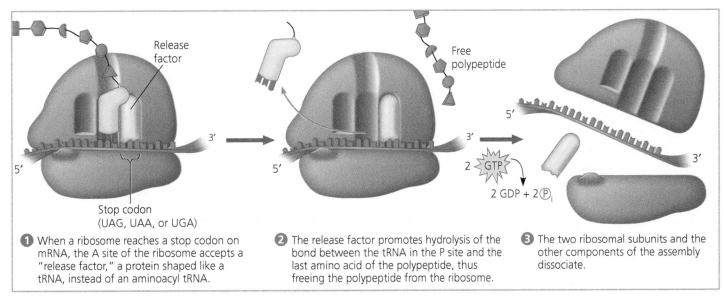

Release factor

Stop codon (UAG, UAA, or UGA)

5'

3'

Free polypeptide

5'

3'

2 GTP

2 GDP + 2 P_i

5'

3'

1 When a ribosome reaches a stop codon on mRNA, the A site of the ribosome accepts a "release factor," a protein shaped like a tRNA, instead of an aminoacyl tRNA.

2 The release factor promotes hydrolysis of the bond between the tRNA in the P site and the last amino acid of the polypeptide, thus freeing the polypeptide from the ribosome.

3 The two ribosomal subunits and the other components of the assembly dissociate.

▲ **Figure 14.20 The termination of translation.** Like elongation, termination requires GTP hydrolysis as well as additional protein factors, which are not shown here.

Ribosome binding site on mRNA

Interpreting a Sequence Logo

How Can a Sequence Logo Be Used to Identify Ribosome Binding Sites? When initiating translation, ribosomes bind to an mRNA at a ribosome binding site upstream of the 5'-AUG-3' start codon. Because mRNAs from different genes all bind to a ribosome, the genes encoding these mRNAs are likely to have a similar base sequence where the ribosomes bind. Therefore, candidate ribosome binding sites on mRNA can be identified by comparing DNA sequences (and thus the mRNA sequences) of multiple genes in a species, searching the region upstream of the start codon for shared ("conserved") stretches of bases. In this exercise you will analyze DNA sequences from multiple such genes, represented by a visual graphic called a sequence logo.

How the Experiment Was Done The DNA sequences of 149 genes from the *E. coli* genome were aligned and analyzed using computer software. The aim was to identify similar base sequences—at the appropriate location in each gene—as potential ribosome binding sites. Rather than presenting the data as a series of 149 sequences aligned in a column (a sequence alignment), the researchers used a sequence logo.

Data from the Experiment To show how sequence logos are made, the potential ribosome binding regions from 10 of the *E. coli* genes are shown in a sequence alignment, followed by the sequence logo derived from the aligned sequences. Note that the DNA shown is the nontemplate (coding) strand, which is how DNA sequences are typically presented.

thrA	G G T A A C G A G G T A A C A A C C A T G C G A G T G
lacA	C A T A A C G G A G T G A T C G C A T T G A A C A T G
lacY	C G C G T A A G G A A A T C C A T T A T G T A C T A T
lacZ	T T C A C A C A G G A A A C A G C T A T G A C C A T G
lacI	C A A T T C A G G G T G G T G A A T G T G A A A C C A
recA	G G C A T G A C A G G A G T A A A A A T G G C T A T C
galR	A C C C A C T A A G G T A T T T T C A T G G C G A C C
metJ	A A G A G G A T T A A G T A T C T C A T G G C T G A A
lexA	A T A C A C C C A G G G G G C G G A A T G A A A G C G
trpR	T A A C A A T G G C G A C A T A T T A T G G C C C A A

5'———————————————————————3'
−18 −17 −16 −15 −14 −13 −12 −11 −10 −9 −8 −7 −6 −5 −4 −3 −2 −1 0 1 2 3 4 5 6 7 8

▲ Sequence alignment

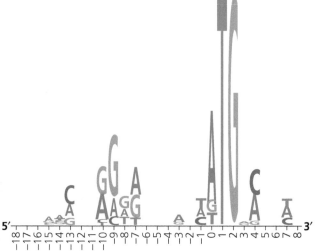

▲ Sequence logo

Further Reading T. D. Schneider and R. M. Stephens, Sequence logos: A new way to display consensus sequences, *Nucleic Acids Research* 18:6097–6100 (1990).

INTERPRET THE DATA

1. In the sequence logo (bottom, left), the horizontal axis shows the primary sequence of the DNA by nucleotide position. Letters for each base are stacked on top of each other according to their relative frequency at that position among the aligned sequences, with the most common base as the largest letter at the top of the stack. The height of each letter represents the relative frequency of that base *at that position*. (a) In the sequence alignment, count the number of each base at position −9 and order them from most to least frequent. Compare this to the size and placement of each base at −9 in the logo. (b) Do the same for positions 0 and 1.

2. The height of a stack of letters in a logo indicates the predictive power of that stack (determined statistically). If the stack is tall, we can be more confident in predicting what base will be in that position if a new sequence is added to the logo. For example, at position 2, all 10 sequences have a G; the probability of finding a G there in a new sequence is very high, as is the stack. For short stacks, the bases all have about the same frequency, and so it's hard to predict a base at those positions. (a) Which two positions have the most predictable bases? What bases do you predict would be at those positions in a newly sequenced gene? (b) Which 12 positions have the least predictable bases? How do you know? How does this reflect the relative frequencies of the bases shown in the 10 sequences? Use the two left-most positions of the 12 as examples in your answer.

3. In the actual experiment, the researchers used 149 sequences to build their sequence logo, which is shown below. There is a stack at each position, even if short, because the sequence logo includes more data. (a) Which three positions in this sequence logo have the most predictable bases? Name the most frequent base at each. (b) Which positions have the least predictable bases? How can you tell?

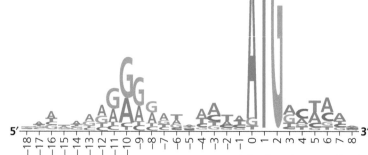

5'———————————————————————3'
−18 −17 −16 −15 −14 −13 −12 −11 −10 −9 −8 −7 −6 −5 −4 −3 −2 −1 0 1 2 3 4 5 6 7 8

All data from Thomas D. Schneider.

4. A consensus sequence identifies the base occurring most often at each position in the set of sequences. (a) Write out the consensus sequence of this (the nontemplate) strand. In any position where the base can't be determined, put a dash. (b) Which provides more information—the consensus sequence or the sequence logo? What is lost in the less informative method?

5. (a) Based on the logo, what five adjacent base positions in the 5' UTR region are most likely to be involved in ribosome binding? Explain. (b) What is represented by the bases in positions 0–2?

(MB) A version of this Scientific Skills Exercise can be assigned in MasteringBiology.

structure (see Figure 3.22). Thus, a gene determines primary structure, and primary structure in turn determines shape.

Additional steps—*post-translational modifications*—may be required before the protein can begin doing its particular job in the cell. Certain amino acids may be chemically modified by the attachment of sugars, lipids, phosphate groups, or other additions. Enzymes may remove one or more amino acids from the leading (amino) end of the polypeptide chain. In some cases, a polypeptide chain may be enzymatically cleaved into two or more pieces. For example, the protein insulin is first synthesized as a single polypeptide chain but becomes active only after an enzyme cuts out a central part of the chain, leaving a protein made up of two shorter polypeptide chains connected by disulfide bridges. In other cases, two or more polypeptides that are synthesized separately may come together, becoming the subunits of a protein that has quaternary structure. A familiar example is hemoglobin (see Figure 3.22).

Targeting Polypeptides to Specific Locations

In electron micrographs of eukaryotic cells active in protein synthesis, two populations of ribosomes are evident: free and bound (see Figure 4.9). Free ribosomes are suspended in the cytosol and mostly synthesize proteins that stay in the cytosol and function there. In contrast, bound ribosomes are attached to the cytosolic side of the endoplasmic reticulum (ER) or to the nuclear envelope. Bound ribosomes make proteins of the endomembrane system (the nuclear envelope, ER, Golgi apparatus, lysosomes, vacuoles, and plasma membrane) as well as proteins secreted from the cell, such as insulin. It is important to note that the ribosomes themselves are identical and can alternate between being free ribosomes one time they are used and being bound ribosomes the next time.

What determines whether a ribosome is free in the cytosol or bound to rough ER? Polypeptide synthesis always begins in the cytosol as a free ribosome starts to translate an mRNA molecule. There the process continues to completion—*unless* the growing polypeptide itself cues the ribosome to attach to the ER. The polypeptides of proteins destined for the endomembrane system or for secretion are marked by a **signal peptide**, which targets the protein to the ER **(Figure 14.21)**. The signal peptide, a sequence of about 20 amino acids at or near the leading end (N-terminus) of the polypeptide, is recognized as it emerges from the ribosome by a protein-RNA complex called a **signal-recognition particle (SRP)**. This particle functions as an escort that brings the ribosome to a receptor protein built into the ER membrane. The receptor is part of a multiprotein translocation complex. Polypeptide synthesis continues there, and the growing polypeptide snakes across the membrane into the ER lumen via a protein pore. The signal peptide is usually removed by an enzyme. The rest of the completed polypeptide, if it is to be secreted from the cell, is released into solution within the ER lumen (as in Figure 14.21). Alternatively, if the polypeptide is to be a membrane protein, it remains partially embedded in the ER membrane. In either

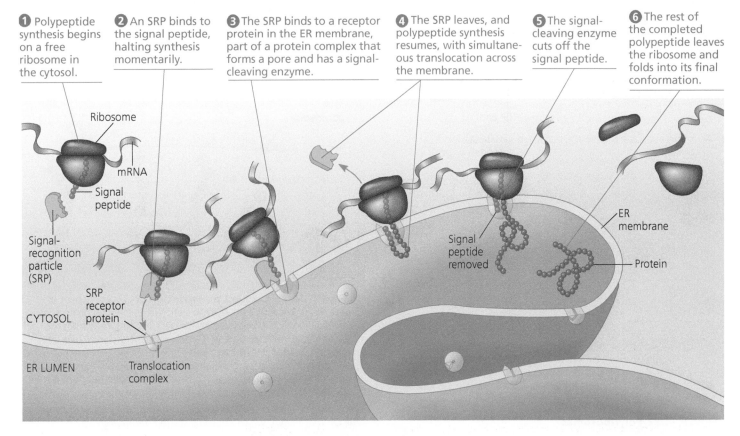

1 Polypeptide synthesis begins on a free ribosome in the cytosol.

2 An SRP binds to the signal peptide, halting synthesis momentarily.

3 The SRP binds to a receptor protein in the ER membrane, part of a protein complex that forms a pore and has a signal-cleaving enzyme.

4 The SRP leaves, and polypeptide synthesis resumes, with simultaneous translocation across the membrane.

5 The signal-cleaving enzyme cuts off the signal peptide.

6 The rest of the completed polypeptide leaves the ribosome and folds into its final conformation.

Ribosome

mRNA

Signal peptide

Signal-recognition particle (SRP)

SRP receptor protein

CYTOSOL

Translocation complex

ER LUMEN

Signal peptide removed

ER membrane

Protein

▲ Figure 14.21 **The signal mechanism for targeting proteins to the ER.**

case, it travels in a transport vesicle to the plasma membrane (see Figure 5.8).

Other kinds of signal peptides are used to target polypeptides to mitochondria, chloroplasts, the interior of the nucleus, and other organelles that are not part of the endomembrane system. The critical difference in these cases is that translation is completed in the cytosol before the polypeptide is imported into the organelle. Translocation mechanisms also vary, but in all cases studied to date, the "postal zip codes" that address proteins for secretion or to cellular locations are signal peptides of some sort. Bacteria also employ signal peptides to target proteins to the plasma membrane for secretion.

Making Multiple Polypeptides in Bacteria and Eukaryotes

In previous sections, you have learned how a single polypeptide is synthesized using the information encoded in an mRNA molecule. When a polypeptide is required in a cell, though, the need is for many copies, not just one.

In both bacteria and eukaryotes, multiple ribosomes translate an mRNA at the same time (**Figure 14.22**); that is, a single mRNA is used to make many copies of a polypeptide simultaneously. Once a ribosome is far enough past the start codon, a second ribosome can attach to the mRNA, eventually resulting in a number of ribosomes trailing along the mRNA. Such strings of ribosomes, called polyribosomes (or polysomes), can be seen with an electron microscope (see Figure 14.22); they can be either free or bound. They enable a cell to make many copies of a polypeptide very quickly.

Another way both bacteria and eukaryotes augment the number of copies of a polypeptide is by transcribing multiple mRNAs from the same gene, as we mentioned earlier. However, the coordination of the two processes—transcription and translation—differs in the two groups. The most important differences between bacteria and eukaryotes arise from the bacterial cell's lack of compartmental organization. Like a one-room workshop, a bacterial cell ensures a streamlined operation by coupling the two processes. In the absence of a nucleus, it can simultaneously transcribe and translate the same gene (**Figure 14.23**), and the newly made protein can quickly diffuse to its site of function.

In contrast, the eukaryotic cell's nuclear envelope segregates transcription from translation and provides a compartment for extensive RNA processing. This processing stage includes additional steps whose regulation can help coordinate the eukaryotic cell's elaborate activities (see Concept 15.2). **Figure 14.24** summarizes the path from gene to polypeptide in a eukaryotic cell.

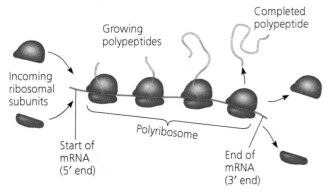

(a) An mRNA molecule is generally translated simultaneously by several ribosomes in clusters called polyribosomes.

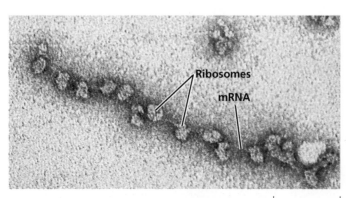

(b) This micrograph shows a large polyribosome in a bacterial cell. Growing polypeptides are not visible here (TEM).

0.1 μm

▲ **Figure 14.22 Polyribosomes.**

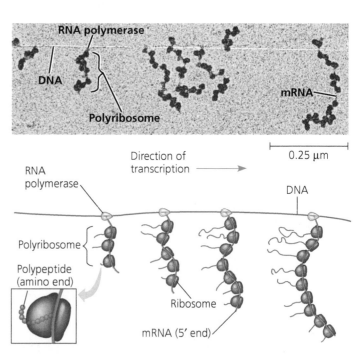

▲ **Figure 14.23 Coupled transcription and translation in bacteria.** In bacterial cells, the translation of mRNA can begin as soon as the leading (5′) end of the mRNA molecule peels away from the DNA template. The micrograph (TEM) shows a stretch of *E. coli* DNA being transcribed by RNA polymerase molecules. Attached to each RNA polymerase molecule is a growing strand of mRNA, which is already being translated by ribosomes. The newly synthesized polypeptides are not visible in the micrograph but are shown in the diagram.

? *Which one of the mRNA molecules started being transcribed first? On that mRNA, which ribosome started translating first?*

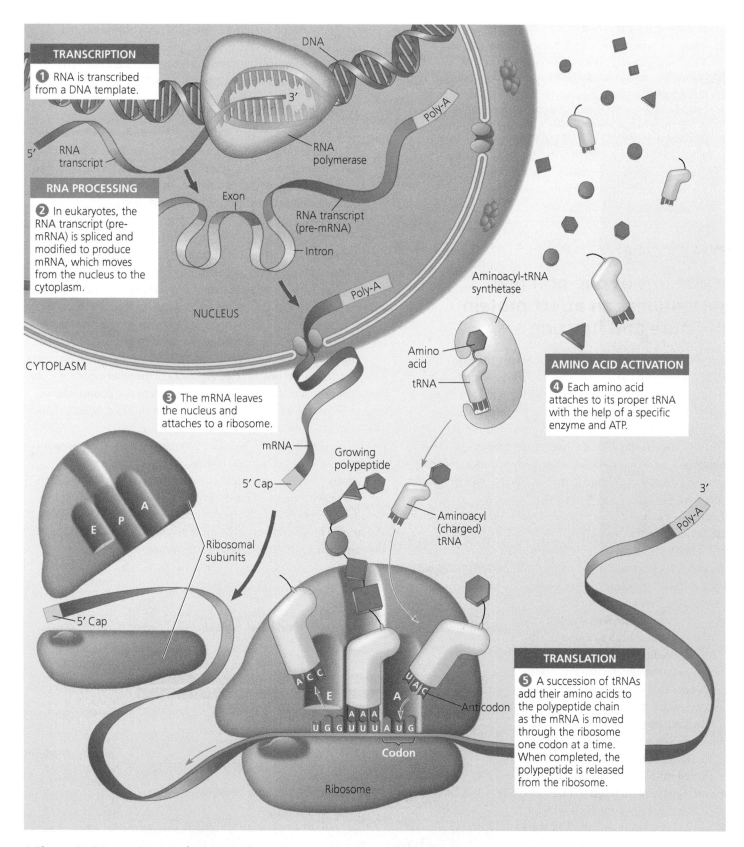

TRANSCRIPTION

1 RNA is transcribed from a DNA template.

DNA

RNA polymerase

Poly-A

RNA transcript

5′

RNA transcript (pre-mRNA)

RNA PROCESSING

2 In eukaryotes, the RNA transcript (pre-mRNA) is spliced and modified to produce mRNA, which moves from the nucleus to the cytoplasm.

Exon

Intron

Poly-A

NUCLEUS

CYTOPLASM

3 The mRNA leaves the nucleus and attaches to a ribosome.

Aminoacyl-tRNA synthetase

Amino acid

tRNA

AMINO ACID ACTIVATION

4 Each amino acid attaches to its proper tRNA with the help of a specific enzyme and ATP.

mRNA

Growing polypeptide

5′ Cap

Aminoacyl (charged) tRNA

E P A

Ribosomal subunits

5′ Cap

3′

Poly-A

TRANSLATION

5 A succession of tRNAs add their amino acids to the polypeptide chain as the mRNA is moved through the ribosome one codon at a time. When completed, the polypeptide is released from the ribosome.

A C C

E

U A C

A

Anticodon

A A A

U G G U U U A U G

Codon

Ribosome

▲ **Figure 14.24 A summary of transcription and translation in a eukaryotic cell.** This diagram shows the path from one gene to one polypeptide. Keep in mind that each gene in the DNA can be transcribed repeatedly into many identical RNA molecules and that each mRNA can be translated repeatedly to yield many identical polypeptide molecules. (Also, remember that the final products of some genes are not polypeptides but RNA molecules that don't get translated, including tRNA and rRNA.) In general, the steps of transcription and translation are similar in bacterial, archaeal, and eukaryotic cells. The major difference is the occurrence of RNA processing in the eukaryotic nucleus. Other significant differences are found in the initiation stages of both transcription and translation and in the termination of transcription.

CONCEPT 14.5

Mutations of one or a few nucleotides can affect protein structure and function

Now that you have explored the process of gene expression, you are ready to understand the effects of changes to the genetic information of a cell (or virus). These changes, called **mutations**, are responsible for the huge diversity of genes found among organisms because mutations are the ultimate source of new genes. Earlier, we considered chromosomal rearrangements that affect long segments of DNA (see Figure 12.14); these are considered large-scale mutations. Here we'll examine small-scale mutations of one or a few nucleotide pairs, including **point mutations**, changes in a single nucleotide pair of a gene.

If a point mutation occurs in a gamete or in a cell that gives rise to gametes, it may be transmitted to offspring and to a succession of future generations. If the mutation has an adverse effect on the phenotype of a person, the mutant condition is referred to as a genetic disorder or hereditary disease. For example, we can trace the genetic basis of sickle-cell disease to the mutation of a single nucleotide pair in the gene that encodes the β-globin polypeptide of hemoglobin. The change of a single nucleotide in the DNA's template strand leads to an altered mRNA and the production of an abnormal protein (**Figure 14.25**; also see Figure 3.23). In individuals who are homozygous for the mutant allele, the sickling of red blood cells caused by the altered hemoglobin produces the multiple symptoms associated with sickle-cell disease (see Concept 11.4 and Figure 21.15). Another disorder caused by a point mutation is a heart condition called familial

cardiomyopathy, which is responsible for some incidents of sudden death in young athletes. Point mutations in several genes encoding muscle proteins have been identified, any of which can lead to this disorder.

Types of Small-Scale Mutations

Let's now consider how small-scale mutations affect proteins. Small-scale mutations within a gene can be divided into two general categories: (1) single nucleotide-pair substitutions and (2) nucleotide-pair insertions or deletions. Insertions and deletions can involve one or more nucleotide pairs.

Substitutions

A **nucleotide-pair substitution** is the replacement of one nucleotide and its partner with another pair of nucleotides (**Figure 14.26a**). Some substitutions have no effect on the encoded protein, owing to the redundancy of the genetic code. For example, if 3′-CCG-5′ on the template strand mutated to 3′-CCA-5′, the mRNA codon that used to be GGC would become GGU, but a glycine would still be inserted at the proper location in the protein (see Figure 14.6). In other words, a change in a nucleotide pair may transform one codon into another that is translated into the same amino acid. Such a change is an example of a **silent mutation**, which has no observable effect on the phenotype. (Silent mutations can occur outside genes as well.) Substitutions that change one amino acid to another one are called **missense mutations**. Such a mutation may have little effect on the protein: The new amino acid may have properties similar to those of the amino acid it replaces, or it may be in a region of the protein where the exact sequence of amino acids is not essential to the protein's function.

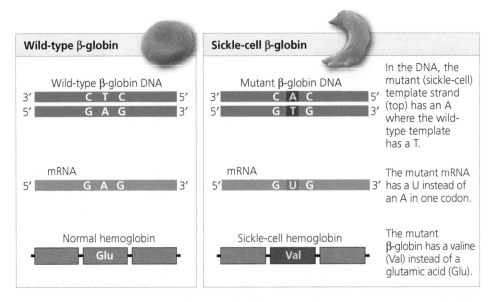

▲ **Figure 14.25 The molecular basis of sickle-cell disease: a point mutation.** The allele that causes sickle-cell disease differs from the wild-type (normal) allele by a single DNA nucleotide pair. The micrographs are SEMs of a normal red blood cell (on the left) and a sickled red blood cell (right) from individuals homozygous for wild-type and mutant alleles, respectively.

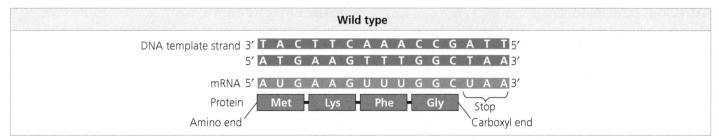

Wild type

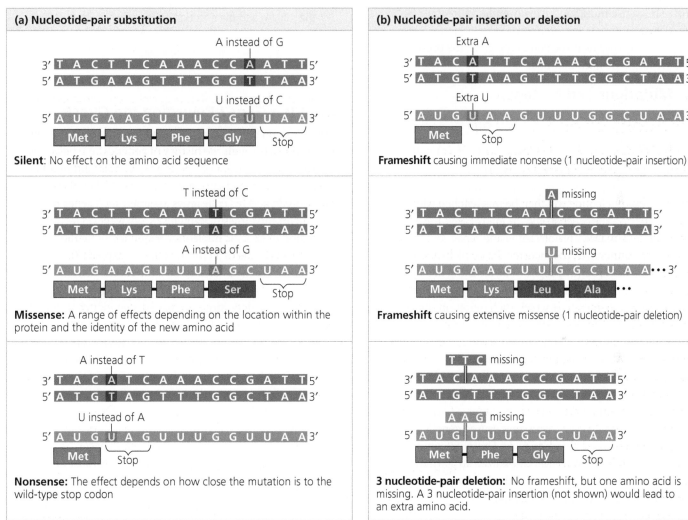

(a) Nucleotide-pair substitution

Silent: No effect on the amino acid sequence

Missense: A range of effects depending on the location within the protein and the identity of the new amino acid

Nonsense: The effect depends on how close the mutation is to the wild-type stop codon

(b) Nucleotide-pair insertion or deletion

Frameshift causing immediate nonsense (1 nucleotide-pair insertion)

Frameshift causing extensive missense (1 nucleotide-pair deletion)

3 nucleotide-pair deletion: No frameshift, but one amino acid is missing. A 3 nucleotide-pair insertion (not shown) would lead to an extra amino acid.

▲ **Figure 14.26 Types of small-scale mutations that affect mRNA sequence.** All but one of the types shown here also affect the amino acid sequence of the encoded polypeptide.

However, the nucleotide-pair substitutions of greatest interest are those that cause a major change in a protein. The alteration of a single amino acid in a crucial area of a protein—such as in the part of the β-globin subunit of hemoglobin shown in Figure 14.25 or in the active site of an enzyme—can significantly alter protein activity. Occasionally, such a mutation leads to an improved protein or one with novel capabilities, but much more often such mutations are neutral or detrimental, leading to a useless or less active protein that impairs cellular function.

Substitution mutations are usually missense mutations; that is, the altered codon still codes for an amino acid and thus

makes sense, although not necessarily the *right* sense. But a point mutation can also change a codon for an amino acid into a stop codon. This is called a **nonsense mutation**, and it causes translation to be terminated prematurely; the resulting polypeptide will be shorter than the polypeptide encoded by the normal gene. Nearly all nonsense mutations lead to nonfunctional proteins.

Insertions and Deletions

Insertions and **deletions** are additions or losses of nucleotide pairs in a gene **(Figure 14.26b)**. These mutations have a disastrous effect on the resulting protein more often than substitutions do. Insertion or deletion of nucleotides may alter the reading frame of the genetic message, the triplet grouping of nucleotides on the mRNA that is read during translation. Such a mutation, called a **frameshift mutation**, occurs whenever the number of nucleotides inserted or deleted is not a multiple of three. All nucleotides downstream of the deletion or insertion will be improperly grouped into codons; the result will be extensive missense mutations, usually ending sooner or later in a nonsense mutation and premature termination. Unless the frameshift is very near the end of the gene, the protein is almost certain to be nonfunctional.

New Mutations and Mutagens

Mutations can arise in a number of ways. Errors during DNA replication or recombination can lead to nucleotide-pair substitutions, insertions, or deletions, as well as to mutations affecting longer stretches of DNA. If an incorrect nucleotide is added to a growing chain during replication, for example, the base on that nucleotide will then be mismatched with the nucleotide base on the other strand. In many cases, the error will be corrected by DNA proofreading and repair systems (see Concept 13.2). Otherwise, the incorrect base will be used as a template in the next round of replication, resulting in a mutation. Such mutations are called *spontaneous mutations*. It is difficult to calculate the rate at which such mutations occur. Rough estimates have been made of the rate of mutation during DNA replication for both *E. coli* and eukaryotes, and the numbers are similar: About one nucleotide in every 10^{10} is altered, and the change is passed on to the next generation of cells.

A number of physical and chemical agents, called **mutagens**, interact with DNA in ways that cause mutations. In the 1920s, Hermann Muller discovered that X-rays caused genetic changes in fruit flies, and he used X-rays to make *Drosophila* mutants for his genetic studies. But he also recognized an alarming implication of his discovery: X-rays and other forms of high-energy radiation pose hazards to the genetic material of people as well as laboratory organisms. Mutagenic radiation, a physical mutagen, includes ultraviolet (UV) light, which can cause disruptive thymine dimers in DNA (see Figure 13.21).

Chemical mutagens fall into several categories. Nucleotide analogs are chemicals that are similar to normal DNA nucleotides but that pair incorrectly during DNA replication. Some other chemical mutagens interfere with correct DNA replication by inserting themselves into the DNA and distorting the double helix. Still other mutagens cause chemical changes in bases that change their pairing properties.

Researchers have developed a variety of methods to test the mutagenic activity of chemicals. A major application of these tests is the preliminary screening of chemicals to identify those that may cause cancer. This approach makes sense because most carcinogens (cancer-causing chemicals) are mutagenic, and conversely, most mutagens are carcinogenic.

CONCEPT CHECK 14.5

1. What happens when one nucleotide pair is lost from the middle of the coding sequence of a gene?
2. **MAKE CONNECTIONS** Individuals heterozygous for the sickle-cell allele show effects of the allele under some circumstances (see Concept 11.4). Explain in terms of gene expression.
3. **WHAT IF?** **DRAW IT** The template strand of a gene includes this sequence: 3′-TACTTGTCCGATATC-5′. It is mutated to 3′-TACTTGTCCAATATC-5′. For both versions, draw the DNA, the mRNA, and the encoded amino acid sequence. What is the effect on the amino acid sequence?

For suggested answers, see Appendix A.

What Is a Gene? *Revisiting the Question*

Our definition of a gene has evolved over the past few chapters, as it has through the history of genetics. We began with the Mendelian concept of a gene as a discrete unit of inheritance that affects a phenotypic character (Chapter 11). We saw that Morgan and his colleagues assigned such genes to specific loci on chromosomes (Chapter 12). We went on to view a gene as a region of specific nucleotide sequence along the length of the DNA molecule of a chromosome (Chapter 13). Finally, in this chapter, we have considered a functional definition of a gene as a DNA sequence that codes for a specific polypeptide chain. All these definitions are useful, depending on the context in which genes are being studied.

We now realize that saying a gene codes for a polypeptide is overly simplistic. Most eukaryotic genes contain noncoding segments (such as introns), so large portions of these genes have no corresponding segments in polypeptides. Molecular biologists also often include promoters and certain other regulatory regions of DNA within the boundaries of a gene. These DNA sequences are not transcribed, but they can be considered part of the functional gene because they must be present for transcription to occur. Our definition of a gene must also be broad enough to include the DNA that is transcribed into rRNA, tRNA, and other RNAs that are not translated. These genes have no polypeptide products but play crucial roles in the cell. Thus, we arrive at the following definition: *A gene is a region of DNA that can be expressed to produce a final functional product that is either a polypeptide or an RNA molecule.*

When considering phenotypes, however, it is useful to focus on genes that code for polypeptides. In this chapter, you have learned how a typical gene is expressed—by transcription into RNA and then translation into a polypeptide that forms a protein of specific structure and function. Proteins, in turn, bring about an organism's observable phenotype.

A given type of cell expresses only a subset of its genes. This is an essential feature in multicellular organisms: Gene expression is precisely regulated. We'll explore gene regulation in the next chapter, beginning with the simpler case of bacteria and continuing with eukaryotes.

Go to **MasteringBiology®** for Assignments, the eText, and the Study Area with Animations, Activities, Vocab Self-Quiz, and Practice Tests.

SUMMARY OF KEY CONCEPTS

VOCAB SELF-QUIZ

goo.gl/gbai8v

CONCEPT 14.1

Genes specify proteins via transcription and translation (pp. 279–284)

- Beadle and Tatum's studies of mutant strains of *Neurospora* led to the one gene–one polypeptide hypothesis. During **gene expression**, the information encoded in genes is used to make specific polypeptide chains (enzymes and other proteins) or RNA molecules.
- **Transcription** is the synthesis of RNA complementary to a **template strand** of DNA. **Translation** is the synthesis of a polypeptide whose amino acid sequence is specified by the nucleotide sequence in **mRNA**.
- Genetic information is encoded as a sequence of nonoverlapping nucleotide triplets, or **codons**. A codon in messenger RNA (mRNA) either is translated into an amino acid (61 of the 64 codons) or serves as a stop signal (3 codons). Codons must be read in the correct **reading frame**.

? *Describe the process of gene expression, by which a gene affects the phenotype of an organism.*

CONCEPT 14.2

Transcription is the DNA-directed synthesis of RNA: *a closer look* (pp. 284–286)

- RNA synthesis is catalyzed by **RNA polymerase**, which links together RNA nucleotides complementary to a DNA template strand. This process follows the same base-pairing rules as DNA replication, except that in RNA, uracil substitutes for thymine.

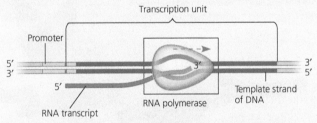

- The three stages of transcription are initiation, elongation, and termination. A **promoter**, often including a **TATA box** in eukaryotes, establishes where RNA synthesis is initiated. **Transcription factors** help eukaryotic RNA polymerase recognize promoter sequences, forming a **transcription initiation complex**. Termination differs in bacteria and eukaryotes.

? *What are the similarities and differences in the initiation of gene transcription in bacteria and eukaryotes?*

CONCEPT 14.3

Eukaryotic cells modify RNA after transcription (pp. 286–288)

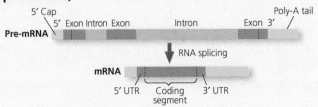

- Eukaryotic pre-mRNAs undergo **RNA processing**, which includes RNA splicing, the addition of a modified nucleotide **5′ cap** to the 5′ end, and the addition of a **poly-A tail** to the 3′ end. The processed mRNA includes an untranslated region (5′ UTR or 3′ UTR) at each end of the coding segment.
- Most eukaryotic genes are split into segments: They have **introns** interspersed among the **exons** (regions included in the mRNA). In **RNA splicing**, introns are removed and exons joined. RNA splicing is typically carried out by **spliceosomes**, but in some cases, RNA alone catalyzes its own splicing. The catalytic ability of some RNA molecules, called **ribozymes**, derives from the properties of RNA. The presence of introns allows for **alternative RNA splicing**.

? *What function do the 5′ cap and the poly-A tail serve on a eukaryotic mRNA?*

CONCEPT 14.4

Translation is the RNA-directed synthesis of a polypeptide: *a closer look* (pp. 288–298)

- A cell translates an mRNA message into protein using **transfer RNAs (tRNAs)**. After being bound to a specific amino acid by an **aminoacyl-tRNA synthetase**, a tRNA lines up via its **anticodon** at the complementary codon on mRNA. A ribosome, made up of **ribosomal RNAs (rRNAs)** and proteins, facilitates this coupling with binding sites for mRNA and tRNA.
- Ribosomes coordinate the three stages of translation: initiation, elongation, and termination. The formation of peptide bonds between amino acids is catalyzed by ribosomal RNAs as tRNAs move through the **A** and **P sites** and exit through the **E site**.
- After translation, modifications to proteins can affect their shape. Free ribosomes in the cytosol initiate synthesis of all proteins, but proteins with a **signal peptide** are synthesized on the ER.
- A gene can be transcribed by multiple RNA polymerases simultaneously. Also, a single mRNA molecule can be translated simultaneously by a number of ribosomes, forming a polyribosome. In bacteria, these processes are coupled, but in eukaryotes they are separated in time and space by the nuclear membrane.

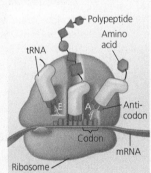

? *What function do tRNAs serve in the process of translation?*

CONCEPT 14.5

Mutations of one or a few nucleotides can affect protein structure and function (pp. 298–300)

- Small-scale **mutations** include **point mutations**, changes in one DNA nucleotide pair, which may lead to production of nonfunctional proteins. **Nucleotide-pair substitutions** can cause **missense** or **nonsense mutations**. Nucleotide-pair **insertions** or **deletions** may produce **frameshift mutations**.
- Spontaneous mutations can occur during DNA replication, recombination, or repair. Chemical and physical **mutagens** cause DNA damage that can alter genes.

TEST YOUR UNDERSTANDING

PRACTICE TEST

goo.gl/CRZjvS

Level 1: Knowledge/Comprehension

1. In eukaryotic cells, transcription cannot begin until
   (A) the two DNA strands have completely separated and exposed the promoter.
   (B) several transcription factors have bound to the promoter.
   (C) the 5′ caps are removed from the mRNA.
   (D) the DNA introns are removed from the template.

2. Which of the following is *not* true of a codon?
   (A) It may code for the same amino acid as another codon.
   (B) It never codes for more than one amino acid.
   (C) It extends from one end of a tRNA molecule.
   (D) It is the basic unit of the genetic code.

3. The anticodon of a particular tRNA molecule is
   (A) complementary to the corresponding mRNA codon.
   (B) complementary to the corresponding triplet in rRNA.
   (C) the part of tRNA that bonds with a specific amino acid.
   (D) catalytic, making the tRNA a ribozyme.

4. Which of the following is *not* true of RNA processing?
   (A) Exons are cut out before mRNA leaves the nucleus.
   (B) Nucleotides may be added at both ends of the RNA.
   (C) Ribozymes may function in RNA splicing.
   (D) RNA splicing can be catalyzed by spliceosomes.

5. Which component is *not* directly involved in translation?
   (A) GTP   (C) tRNA
   (B) DNA   (D) ribosomes

Level 2: Application/Analysis

6. Using Figure 14.6, identify a 5′ → 3′ sequence of nucleotides in the DNA template strand for an mRNA coding for the polypeptide sequence Phe-Pro-Lys.
   (A) 5′-UUUCCCAAA-3′
   (B) 5′-GAACCCCTT-3′
   (C) 5′-CTTCGGGAA-3′
   (D) 5′-AAACCCUUU-3′

7. Which of the following mutations would be *most* likely to have a harmful effect on an organism?
   (A) a deletion of three nucleotides near the middle of a gene
   (B) a single nucleotide deletion in the middle of an intron
   (C) a single nucleotide deletion near the end of the coding sequence
   (D) a single nucleotide insertion downstream of, and close to, the start of the coding sequence

8. Would the coupling of the processes shown in Figure 14.23 be found in a eukaryotic cell? Explain why or why not.

9. Fill in the following table:

Type of RNA	Functions
Messenger RNA (mRNA)	
Transfer RNA (tRNA)	
	Plays catalytic (ribozyme) roles and structural roles in ribosomes
Primary transcript	
Small RNAs in the spliceosome	

Level 3: Synthesis/Evaluation

10. **SCIENTIFIC INQUIRY**
    Knowing that the genetic code is almost universal, a scientist uses molecular biological methods to insert the human β-globin gene (shown in Figure 14.12) into bacterial cells, hoping the cells will express it and synthesize functional β-globin protein. Instead, the protein produced is nonfunctional and is found to contain many fewer amino acids than does β-globin made by a eukaryotic cell. Explain why.

11. **FOCUS ON EVOLUTION**
    Most amino acids are coded for by a set of similar codons (see Figure 14.6). What evolutionary explanation can you give for this pattern?

12. **FOCUS ON INFORMATION**
    Evolution accounts for the unity and diversity of life, and the continuity of life is based on heritable information in the form of DNA. In a short essay (100–150 words), discuss how the fidelity with which DNA is inherited is related to the processes of evolution. (Review the discussion of proofreading and DNA repair in Concept 13.2.)

13. **SYNTHESIZE YOUR KNOWLEDGE**

Some mutations result in proteins that function well at one temperature but are nonfunctional at a different (usually higher) temperature. Siamese cats have such a "temperature-sensitive" mutation in a gene encoding an enzyme that makes dark pigment in the fur. The mutation results in the breed's distinctive point markings and lighter body color (see the photo). Using this information and what you learned in the chapter, explain the pattern of the cat's fur pigmentation.

For selected answers, see Appendix A.

Unit 3 Evolution

19 Descent with Modification

Darwin proposed that the diversity of life and the match between organisms and their environments arose through **natural selection** over time, as species adapted to their environments.

20 Phylogeny

As organisms adapt to their environments over time, they become increasingly different from their ancestors. To reconstruct an organism's evolutionary history, or **phylogeny**, biologists use data ranging from fossils to molecules.

21 The Evolution of Populations

The evolutionary impact of natural selection appears in the genetic changes of a **population** of organisms over time.

22 The Origin of Species

Evolutionary changes in a population ultimately can result in **speciation**, a process in which one species gives rise to two or more species.

23 Broad Patterns of Evolution

As speciation occurs again and again, new groups of organisms arise while others disappear. These changes make up the **broad patterns of evolutionary change** documented in the fossil record.

Evolution

19 Descent with Modification
20 Phylogeny
21 The Evolution of Populations
22 The Origin of Species
23 Broad Patterns of Evolution

Genetics
Chemistry and Cells
Ecology
Animals
Plants
History of Life

19 Descent with Modification

KEY CONCEPTS

19.1 The Darwinian revolution challenged traditional views of a young Earth inhabited by unchanging species

19.2 Descent with modification by natural selection explains the adaptations of organisms and the unity and diversity of life

19.3 Evolution is supported by an overwhelming amount of scientific evidence

▲ **Figure 19.1** How is its resemblance to a fallen leaf helpful to this moth?

Endless Forms Most Beautiful

A hungry bird in the Peruvian rain forest would have to look very closely to spot a "dead-leaf moth" (*Oxytenis modestia*), which blends in well with its forest floor habitat **(Figure 19.1)**. This distinctive moth is a member of a diverse group, the more than 120,000 species of lepidopteran insects (moths and butterflies). All lepidopterans have a juvenile stage characterized by a well-developed head and many chewing mouthparts: the ravenous, efficient feeding machines we call caterpillars. As adults, all lepidopterans share other features, such as three pairs of legs and two pairs of wings covered with small scales. But the many lepidopterans also differ from one another, in both their caterpillar and adult forms. How did there come to be so many different moths and butterflies, and what causes their similarities and differences?

This moth and its many close relatives illustrate three key observations about life:

- the striking ways in which organisms are suited for life in their environments*

- the many shared characteristics (unity) of life
- the rich diversity of life

More than a century and a half ago, Charles Darwin was inspired to develop a scientific explanation for these three broad observations. When he published his hypothesis in his book *The Origin of Species*, Darwin ushered in a scientific revolution—the era of evolutionary biology.

For now, we will define **evolution** as *descent with modification*, a phrase Darwin used in proposing that Earth's many species are descendants of ancestral species that were different from the present-day species. Evolution can also be defined more narrowly as a change in the genetic composition of a population from generation to generation (as discussed further in Chapter 21).

Whether it is defined broadly or narrowly, we can view evolution in two related but different ways: as a pattern and as a process. The *pattern* of evolutionary change is revealed by data from many scientific disciplines, including biology, geology, physics, and chemistry. These data are facts—they are observations about the natural world. The *process* of evolution

---

*Here and throughout this book, the term *environment* refers to other organisms as well as to the physical aspects of an organism's surroundings.

consists of the mechanisms that produce the observed pattern of change. These mechanisms represent natural causes of the natural phenomena we observe. Indeed, the power of evolution as a unifying theory is its ability to explain and connect a vast array of observations about the living world.

As with all general theories in science, we continue to test our understanding of evolution by examining whether it can account for new observations and experimental results. In this and the following chapters, we'll examine how ongoing discoveries shape what we know about the pattern and process of evolution. To set the stage, we'll first retrace Darwin's quest to explain the adaptations, unity, and diversity of what he called life's "endless forms most beautiful."

CONCEPT 19.1

The Darwinian revolution challenged traditional views of a young Earth inhabited by unchanging species

What impelled Darwin to challenge the prevailing views about Earth and its life? Darwin developed his revolutionary proposal over time, influenced by the work of others and by his travels (Figure 19.2). As we'll see, his ideas also had deep historical roots.

Scala Naturae and Classification of Species

Long before Darwin was born, several Greek philosophers suggested that life might have changed gradually over time. But one philosopher who greatly influenced early Western science, Aristotle (384–322 BCE), viewed species as fixed (unchanging). Through his observations of nature, Aristotle recognized certain "affinities" among organisms. He concluded that life-forms could be arranged on a ladder, or scale, of increasing complexity, later called the *scala naturae* ("scale

of nature"). Each form of life, perfect and permanent, had its allotted rung on this ladder.

These ideas were generally consistent with the Old Testament account of creation, which holds that species were individually designed by God and therefore perfect. In the 1700s, many scientists interpreted the often remarkable match of organisms to their environment as evidence that the Creator had designed each species for a particular purpose.

One such scientist was Carolus Linnaeus (1707–1778), a Swedish physician and botanist who sought to classify life's diversity, in his words, "for the greater glory of God." Linnaeus developed the two-part, or *binomial*, format for naming species (such as *Homo sapiens* for humans) that is still used today. In contrast to the linear hierarchy of the *scala naturae*, Linnaeus adopted a nested classification system, grouping similar species into increasingly general categories. For example, similar species are grouped in the same genus, similar genera (plural of genus) are grouped in the same family, and so on (see Figure 20.3).

Linnaeus did not ascribe the resemblances among species to evolutionary kinship, but rather to the pattern of their creation. A century later, however, Darwin argued that classification should be based on evolutionary relationships. He also noted that scientists using the Linnaean system often grouped organisms in ways that reflected those relationships.

Ideas About Change over Time

Among other sources of information, Darwin drew from the work of scientists studying **fossils**, the remains or traces of organisms from the past. Many fossils are found in sedimentary rocks formed from the sand and mud that settle to the bottom of seas, lakes, and swamps (Figure 19.3). New layers

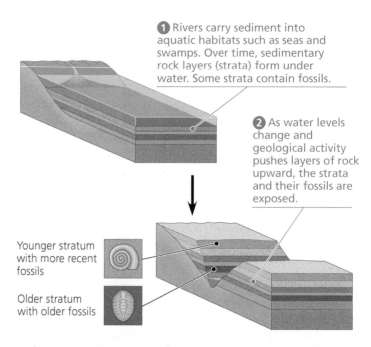

1 Rivers carry sediment into aquatic habitats such as seas and swamps. Over time, sedimentary rock layers (strata) form under water. Some strata contain fossils.

2 As water levels change and geological activity pushes layers of rock upward, the strata and their fossils are exposed.

Younger stratum with more recent fossils

Older stratum with older fossils

▲ Figure 19.3 **Formation of sedimentary strata with fossils.**

▲ Figure 19.2 **Unusual species inspired novel ideas.** Darwin observed this species of marine iguana and many other unique animals when he visited the Galápagos Islands in 1835.

of sediment cover older ones and compress them into layers of rock called **strata** (singular, *stratum*). The fossils in a particular stratum provide a glimpse of some of the organisms that populated Earth at the time that layer formed. Later, erosion may carve through upper (younger) strata, revealing deeper (older) strata that had been buried.

Paleontology, the study of fossils, was developed in large part by French scientist Georges Cuvier (1769–1832). In examining strata near Paris, Cuvier noted that the older the stratum, the more dissimilar its fossils were to current life-forms. He also observed that from one layer to the next, some new species appeared while others disappeared. He inferred that extinctions must have been a common occurrence, but he staunchly opposed the idea of evolution. Cuvier speculated that each boundary between strata represented a sudden catastrophic event, such as a flood, that had destroyed many of the species living in that area. Such regions, he reasoned, were later repopulated by different species immigrating from other areas.

In contrast to Cuvier's emphasis on sudden events, other scientists suggested that profound change could take place through the cumulative effect of slow but continuous processes. In 1795, Scottish geologist James Hutton (1726–1797) proposed that Earth's geologic features could be explained by gradual mechanisms, such as valleys being formed by rivers wearing through rocks. The leading geologist of Darwin's time, Charles Lyell (1797–1875), incorporated Hutton's thinking into his proposal that the same geologic processes are operating today as in the past, and at the same rate.

Hutton and Lyell's ideas strongly influenced Darwin's thinking. Darwin agreed that if geologic change results from slow, continuous actions rather than from sudden events, then Earth must be much older than the widely accepted age of a few thousand years. It would, for example, take a very long time for a river to carve a canyon by erosion. He later reasoned that perhaps similarly slow and subtle processes could produce substantial biological change. However, Darwin was not the first to apply the idea of gradual change to biological evolution.

Lamarck's Hypothesis of Evolution

Although some 18th-century naturalists suggested that life evolves as environments change, only one proposed a mechanism for *how* life changes over time: French biologist Jean-Baptiste de Lamarck (1744–1829). Alas, Lamarck is primarily remembered today *not* for his visionary recognition that evolutionary change explains patterns in fossils and the match of organisms to their environments, but for the incorrect mechanism he proposed.

Lamarck published his hypothesis in 1809, the year Darwin was born. By comparing living species with fossil forms, Lamarck had found what appeared to be several lines of

◀ **Figure 19.4 Acquired traits cannot be inherited.** This bonsai tree was "trained" to grow as a dwarf by pruning and shaping. However, seeds from this tree would produce offspring of normal size.

descent, each a chronological series of older to younger fossils leading to a living species. He explained his findings using two principles that were widely accepted at the time. The first was *use and disuse*, the idea that parts of the body that are used extensively become larger and stronger, while those that are not used deteriorate. Among many examples, he cited a giraffe stretching its neck to reach leaves on high branches. The second principle, *inheritance of acquired characteristics*, stated that an organism could pass these modifications to its offspring. Lamarck reasoned that the long, muscular neck of the living giraffe had evolved over many generations as giraffes stretched their necks ever higher.

Lamarck also thought that evolution happens because organisms have an innate drive to become more complex. Darwin rejected this idea, but he, too, thought that variation was introduced into the evolutionary process in part through inheritance of acquired characteristics. Today, however, our understanding of genetics refutes this mechanism: Experiments show that traits acquired by use during an individual's life are not inherited in the way proposed by Lamarck **(Figure 19.4)**.

Lamarck was vilified in his own time, especially by Cuvier, who denied that species ever evolve. In retrospect, however, Lamarck did recognize that the fact that organisms are well suited for life in their environments can be explained by gradual evolutionary change, and he did propose a testable explanation for how this change occurs.

CONCEPT CHECK 19.1

1. How did Hutton's and Lyell's ideas influence Darwin's thinking about evolution?
2. **MAKE CONNECTIONS** Scientific hypotheses must be testable (see Concept 1.3). Applying this criterion, are Cuvier's explanation of the fossil record and Lamarck's hypothesis of evolution scientific? Explain your answer in each case.

For suggested answers, see Appendix A.

CONCEPT 19.2

Descent with modification by natural selection explains the adaptations of organisms and the unity and diversity of life

As the 19th century dawned, it was generally thought that species had remained unchanged since their creation. A few clouds of doubt about the permanence of species were beginning to gather, but no one could have forecast the thundering storm just beyond the horizon. How did Charles Darwin become the lightning rod for a revolutionary view of life?

Darwin's Research

Charles Darwin (1809–1882) was born in Shrewsbury, England. He had a consuming interest in nature—reading nature books, fishing, hunting, and collecting insects. Darwin's father, a physician, could see no future for his son as a naturalist and sent him to medical school in Edinburgh. But Charles found medicine boring and surgery before the days of anesthesia horrifying. He quit medical school and enrolled at Cambridge University, intending to become a clergyman. (At that time many scholars of science belonged to the clergy.)

At Cambridge, Darwin became the protégé of John Henslow, a botany professor. Soon after Darwin graduated, Henslow recommended him to Captain Robert FitzRoy, who was preparing the survey ship HMS *Beagle* for a long voyage around the world. FitzRoy, who was himself an accomplished scientist, accepted Darwin because he was a skilled naturalist and because they were of similar age and social class.

The Voyage of the Beagle

Darwin embarked from England on the *Beagle* in December 1831. The primary mission of the voyage was to chart poorly known stretches of the South American coastline. Darwin, however, spent most of his time on shore, observing and collecting thousands of plants and animals. He described features of organisms that made them well suited to such diverse environments as Brazil's humid jungles, Argentina's broad grasslands, and the Andes' towering peaks.

Darwin observed that the plants and animals in temperate regions of South America more closely resembled species living in the South American tropics than species living in temperate regions of Europe. Furthermore, the fossils he found, though clearly different from living species, distinctly resembled the living organisms of South America.

Darwin also read Lyell's *Principles of Geology* during the voyage. He experienced geologic change firsthand when a violent earthquake shook the coast of Chile, and he observed afterward that rocks along the coast had been thrust upward by several meters. Finding fossils of ocean organisms high in the Andes, Darwin inferred that the rocks containing the fossils must have been raised there by many similar earthquakes. These observations reinforced what he had learned from Lyell: Physical evidence did not support the traditional view that Earth was only a few thousand years old.

Darwin's interest in the species (or fossils) found in an area was further stimulated by the *Beagle*'s stop at the Galápagos, a group of volcanic islands located near the equator about 900 km west of South America **(Figure 19.5)**. Darwin was fascinated by the unusual organisms there. The birds he collected included several kinds of mockingbirds. These mockingbirds, though similar to each other, seemed to be different species. Some were unique

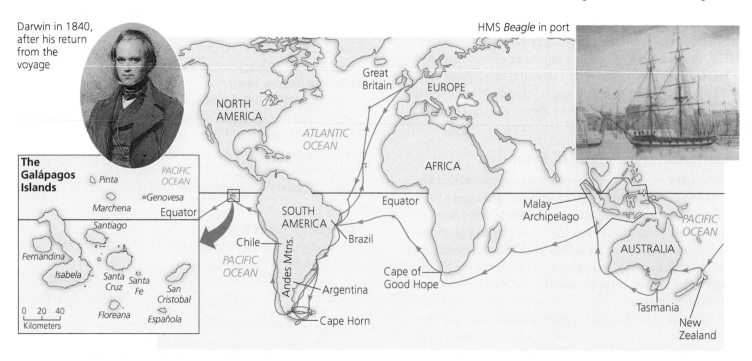

▲ **Figure 19.5 The voyage of HMS *Beagle* (December 1831–October 1836).**

to individual islands, while others lived on two or more adjacent islands. Furthermore, although the animals on the Galápagos resembled species living on the South American mainland, most of the Galápagos species were not known from anywhere else in the world. Darwin hypothesized that the Galápagos had been colonized by organisms that had strayed from South America and then diversified, giving rise to new species on the various islands.

Darwin's Focus on Adaptation

During the voyage of the *Beagle*, Darwin observed many examples of **adaptations**, inherited characteristics of organisms that enhance their survival and reproduction in specific environments. Later, as he reassessed his observations, he began to perceive adaptation to the environment and the origin of new species as closely related processes. Could a new species arise from an ancestral form by the gradual accumulation of adaptations to a different environment? From studies made years after Darwin's voyage, biologists have concluded that this is indeed what happened to a diverse group of finches found on the Galápagos Islands (see Figure 1.17). The finches' various beaks and behaviors are adapted to the specific foods available on their home islands **(Figure 19.6)**. Darwin realized that explaining such adaptations was essential to understanding evolution. His explanation of how adaptations arise centered on **natural selection**, a process in which individuals that have certain inherited traits tend to survive and reproduce at higher rates than do other individuals *because of* those traits.

By the early 1840s, Darwin had worked out the major features of his hypothesis. He set these ideas on paper in 1844, when he wrote a long essay on descent with modification and its underlying mechanism, natural selection. Yet he was still reluctant to publish his ideas, in part because he anticipated the uproar they would cause. During this time, Darwin continued to compile evidence in support of his hypothesis. By the mid-1850s, he had described his ideas to Lyell and a few others. Lyell, who was not yet convinced of evolution, nevertheless urged Darwin to publish on the subject before someone else came to the same conclusions and published first.

In June 1858, Lyell's prediction came true. Darwin received a manuscript from Alfred Russel Wallace (1823–1913), a British naturalist working in the South Pacific islands of the Malay Archipelago **(Figure 19.7)**. Wallace had developed a hypothesis of natural selection nearly identical to Darwin's. He asked Darwin to evaluate his paper and forward it to Lyell if it merited publication. Darwin complied, writing to Lyell: "Your words have come true with a vengeance. . . . I never saw

(a) **Cactus-eater.** The long, sharp beak of the common cactus finch (*Geospiza scandens*) helps it tear and eat cactus flowers and pulp.

(c) **Insect-eater.** The green warbler finch (*Certhidea olivacea*) uses its narrow, pointed beak to grasp insects.

(b) **Seed-eater.** The large ground finch (*Geospiza magnirostris*) has a large beak adapted for cracking seeds on the ground.

▲ **Figure 19.6 Three examples of beak variation in Galápagos finches.** The Galápagos Islands are home to more than a dozen species of closely related finches, some found only on a single island. A striking difference among them is their beaks, which are adapted for specific diets.

 *Review Figure 1.17. To which of the other two species shown above is the common cactus finch more closely related (that is, with which species does the common cactus finch share a more recent common ancestor)?*

▶ **Figure 19.7 Alfred Russel Wallace.** The inset is a painting Wallace made of a flying tree frog from the Malay Archipelago.

a more striking coincidence . . . so all my originality, whatever it may amount to, will be smashed." On July 1, 1858, Lyell and a colleague presented Wallace's paper, along with extracts from Darwin's unpublished 1844 essay, to the Linnean Society of London. Darwin quickly finished his book, titled *On the Origin of Species by Means of Natural Selection* (commonly referred to as *The Origin of Species*), and published it the next year. Although Wallace had submitted his ideas for publication first, he admired Darwin and thought that Darwin had developed and tested the idea of natural selection so extensively that he should be known as its main architect.

Within a decade, Darwin's book and its proponents had convinced most scientists that life's diversity is the product of evolution. Darwin succeeded where previous evolutionists had failed, mainly by presenting a plausible scientific mechanism with immaculate logic and an avalanche of supporting evidence.

Ideas from *The Origin of Species*

In his book, Darwin amassed evidence that descent with modification by natural selection explains three broad observations about nature—the unity of life, the diversity of life, and the striking ways in which organisms are suited for life in their environments.

Descent with Modification

In the first edition of *The Origin of Species*, Darwin never used the word *evolution* (although the final word of the book is "evolved"). Rather, he discussed *descent with modification*, a phrase that summarized his view of life. Organisms share many characteristics, leading Darwin to perceive unity in life. He attributed the unity of life to the descent of all organisms from an ancestor that lived in the remote past. He also thought that as the descendants of that ancestral organism lived in various habitats, they gradually accumulated diverse modifications, or adaptations, that fit them to specific ways of life. Darwin reasoned that over a long period of time, descent with modification eventually led to the rich diversity of life we see today.

Darwin viewed the history of life as a tree, with multiple branchings from a common trunk out to the tips of the youngest twigs **(Figure 19.8)**. In his diagram, the tips of the twigs that are labeled A through D represent several groups of organisms living in the present day, while the unlabeled branches represent groups that are extinct. Each fork of the tree represents the most recent common ancestor of all the lines of evolution that subsequently branch from that point. Darwin reasoned that such a branching process, along with past extinction events, could explain the large morphological gaps (differences in form) that sometimes exist between related groups of organisms.

As an example, consider the three living species of elephants: the Asian elephant (*Elephas maximus*) and two species of African elephants (*Loxodonta africana* and *L. cyclotis*). These closely related species are very similar because they shared the same line of descent until a relatively recent split from their common ancestor, as shown in the tree diagram in **Figure 19.9**.

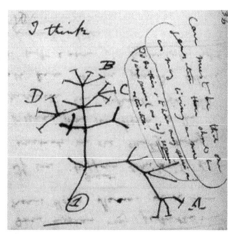

▶ **Figure 19.8** **"I think . . ."** In this 1837 sketch, Darwin envisioned the branching pattern of evolution. Branches that end in twigs labeled A–D represent particular groups of living organisms; all other branches represent extinct groups.

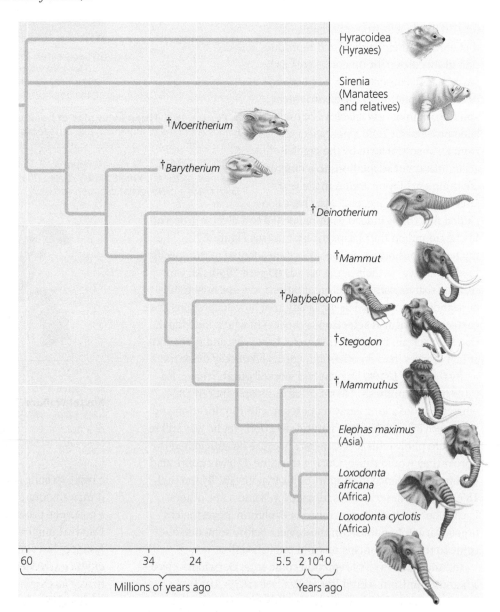

▲ **Figure 19.9** **Descent with modification.** This evolutionary tree of elephants and their relatives is based mainly on fossils—their anatomy, order of appearance in strata, and geographic distribution. Note that most branches of descent ended in extinction (denoted by the dagger symbol †). (Time line not to scale.)

? *Based on the tree shown here, approximately when did the most recent ancestor shared by* Mammuthus *(woolly mammoths), Asian elephants, and African elephants live?*

Note that seven lineages related to elephants have become extinct over the past 32 million years. As a result, there are no living species that fill the morphological gap between the elephants and their nearest relatives today, the hyraxes and manatees. Such extinctions are not uncommon. In fact, many evolutionary branches, even some major ones, are dead ends: Scientists estimate that over 99% of all species that have ever lived are now extinct. As in Figure 19.9, fossils of extinct species can document the divergence of present-day groups by "filling in" gaps between them.

Artificial Selection, Natural Selection, and Adaptation

Darwin proposed the mechanism of natural selection to explain the observable patterns of evolution. He crafted his argument carefully, hoping to persuade even the most skeptical readers. First he discussed familiar examples of selective breeding of domesticated plants and animals. Humans have modified other species over many generations by selecting and breeding individuals that possess desired traits, a process called **artificial selection** (**Figure 19.10**). As a result of artificial selection, crops, livestock animals, and pets often bear little resemblance to their wild ancestors.

Darwin then argued that a similar process occurs in nature. He based his argument on two observations, from which he drew two inferences.

Observation #1: Members of a population often vary in their inherited traits (**Figure 19.11**).

Observation #2: All species can produce more offspring than their environment can support (**Figure 19.12**), and many of these offspring fail to survive and reproduce.

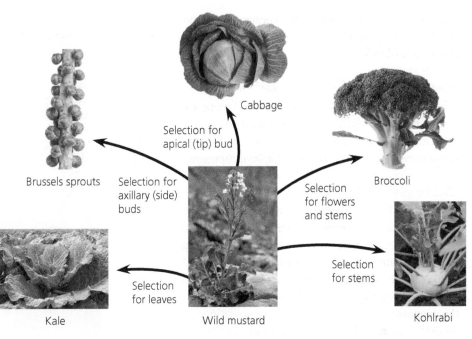

▲ **Figure 19.10 Artificial selection.** These different vegetables have all been selected from one species of wild mustard. By selecting variations in different parts of the plant, breeders have obtained these divergent results.

Inference #1: Individuals whose inherited traits give them a higher probability of surviving and reproducing in a given environment tend to leave more offspring than do other individuals.

Inference #2: This unequal ability of individuals to survive and reproduce will lead to the accumulation of favorable traits in the population over generations.

As these two inferences suggest, Darwin saw an important connection between natural selection and the capacity of organisms to "overreproduce." He began to make this connection after reading an essay by economist Thomas Malthus, who contended that much of human suffering—disease, famine, and war—resulted from the human population's potential to

▲ **Figure 19.11 Variation in a population.** Individuals in this population of Asian ladybird beetles vary in color and spot pattern. Natural selection may act on these variations only if (1) they are heritable and (2) they affect the beetles' ability to survive and reproduce.

◀ **Figure 19.12 Overproduction of offspring.** A single puffball fungus can produce billions of spores that give rise to offspring. If all of these offspring and their descendants survived to maturity, they would carpet the surrounding land.

increase faster than food supplies and other resources. Similarly, Darwin realized that the capacity to overreproduce was characteristic of all species. Of the many eggs laid, young born, and seeds spread, only a tiny fraction complete their development and leave offspring of their own. The rest are eaten, starved, diseased, unmated, or unable to tolerate physical conditions of the environment such as salinity or temperature.

An organism's heritable traits can influence not only its own performance, but also how well its offspring cope with environmental challenges. For example, an organism might have a trait that gives its offspring an advantage in escaping predators, obtaining food, or tolerating physical conditions. When such advantages increase the number of offspring that survive and reproduce, the traits that are favored will likely appear at a greater frequency in the next generation. Thus, over time, natural selection resulting from factors such as predators, lack of food, or adverse physical conditions can lead to an increase in the proportion of favorable traits in a population.

How rapidly do such changes occur? Darwin reasoned that if artificial selection can bring about dramatic change in a relatively short period of time, then natural selection should be capable of substantial modification of species over many hundreds of generations. Even if the advantages of some heritable traits over others are slight, the advantageous variations will gradually accumulate in the population, and less favorable variations will diminish. Over time, this process will increase the frequency of individuals with favorable adaptations, hence increasing the degree to which organisms are well suited for life in their environment.

Key Features of Natural Selection

Let's now recap the main ideas of natural selection:

- Natural selection is a process in which individuals that have certain heritable traits survive and reproduce at a higher rate than do other individuals because of those traits.
- Over time, natural selection can increase the frequency of adaptations that are favorable in a given environment **(Figure 19.13)**.
- If an environment changes, or if individuals move to a new environment, natural selection may result in adaptation to these new conditions, sometimes giving rise to new species.

One subtle but important point is that although natural selection occurs through interactions between individual organisms and their environment, *individuals do not evolve*. Rather, it is the population that evolves over time.

A second key point is that natural selection can amplify or diminish only those heritable traits that differ among the individuals in a population. Thus, even if a trait is heritable, if all the individuals in a population are genetically identical for that trait, evolution by natural selection cannot occur.

Third, remember that environmental factors vary from place to place and over time. A trait that is favorable in one place or time may be useless—or even detrimental—in other places or times. Natural selection is always operating, but

▲ **Figure 19.13 Camouflage as an example of evolutionary adaptation.** Related species of the insects called mantises have diverse shapes and colors that evolved in different environments, as seen in this Malaysian orchid mantis (top) and South African flower-eyed mantis (bottom).

? *Explain how these mantises demonstrate the three key observations about life introduced at the beginning of this chapter: how organisms are well suited for life in their environments, unity, and diversity.*

which traits are favored depends on the context in which a species lives and mates.

Next, we'll survey the wide range of observations that support a Darwinian view of evolution by natural selection.

CONCEPT CHECK 19.2

1. How does the concept of descent with modification explain both the unity and diversity of life?
2. **WHAT IF?** Predict whether a fossil of an extinct mammal that lived high in the Andes would more closely resemble present-day mammals that live in South American jungles or present-day mammals that live high in Asian mountains. Explain.
3. **MAKE CONNECTIONS** Review the relationship between genotype and phenotype (see Figure 11.6). Suppose that in a particular pea population, flowers with the white phenotype are favored by natural selection. Predict what would happen over time to the frequency of the p allele in the population, and explain your reasoning.

For suggested answers, see Appendix A.

Evolution is supported by an overwhelming amount of scientific evidence

In *The Origin of Species*, Darwin marshaled a broad range of evidence to support the concept of descent with modification. Still—as he readily acknowledged—there were instances in which key evidence was lacking. For example, Darwin referred to the origin of flowering plants as an "abominable mystery," and he lamented the lack of fossils showing how earlier groups of organisms gave rise to new groups.

In the last 150 years, new discoveries have filled many of the gaps that Darwin identified. The origin of flowering plants, for example, is much better understood (see Concept 26.4), and many fossils have been discovered that signify the origin of new groups of organisms (see Concept 23.1). In this section, we'll consider four types of data that document the pattern of evolution and illuminate how it occurs: direct observations, homology, the fossil record, and biogeography.

Direct Observations of Evolutionary Change

Biologists have documented evolutionary change in thousands of scientific studies. We'll examine many such studies throughout this unit, but let's look at two examples here.

Natural Selection in Response to Introduced Species

Animals that eat plants, called herbivores, often have adaptations that help them feed efficiently on their primary food sources. What happens when herbivores switch to a new food source with different characteristics?

An opportunity to study this question in nature is provided by soapberry bugs, which use their "beak," a hollow, needlelike mouthpart, to feed on seeds located within the fruits of various plants. In southern Florida, the soapberry bug (*Jadera haematoloma*) feeds on the seeds of a native plant, the balloon vine (*Cardiospermum corindum*). In central Florida, however, balloon vines have become rare. Instead, soapberry bugs in that region now feed on seeds of the goldenrain tree (*Koelreuteria elegans*), a species recently introduced from Asia.

Soapberry bugs feed most effectively when the length of their beak is similar to the depth at which seeds are found within the fruit. Goldenrain tree fruit consists of three flat lobes, and its seeds are much closer to the fruit surface than are the seeds of the plump, round fruit of the native balloon vine. These differences led researchers to predict that in populations that feed on goldenrain tree, natural selection would result in beaks that are *shorter* than those in populations that feed on balloon vine **(Figure 19.14)**. Indeed, beak lengths are shorter in the populations that feed on goldenrain tree.

Researchers have also studied beak length evolution in soapberry bug populations that feed on plants introduced to Louisiana, Oklahoma, and Australia. In each of these locations,

Can a change in a population's food source result in evolution by natural selection?

Field Study Soapberry bugs feed most effectively when the length of their "beak" closely matches the depth of the seeds within the fruit. Scott Carroll and his colleagues measured beak lengths in soapberry bug populations feeding on the native balloon vine. They also measured beak lengths in populations feeding on the introduced goldenrain tree. The researchers then compared the measurements with those of museum specimens collected in the two areas before the goldenrain tree was introduced.

Soapberry bug with beak inserted in balloon vine fruit

Results Beak lengths were shorter in populations feeding on the introduced species than in populations feeding on the native species, in which the seeds are buried more deeply. The average beak length in museum specimens from each population (indicated by red arrows) was similar to beak lengths in populations feeding on native species.

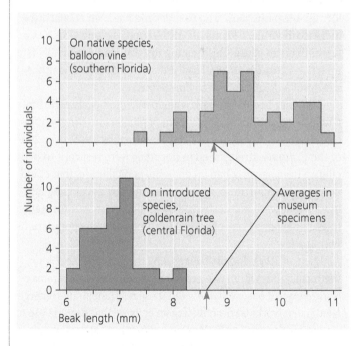

Conclusion Museum specimens and contemporary data suggest that a change in the size of the soapberry bug's food source can result in evolution by natural selection for matching beak size.

Data from S. P. Carroll and C. Boyd, Host race radiation in the soapberry bug: natural history with the history, *Evolution* 46:1052–1069 (1992).

WHAT IF? Data from additional studies showed that when soapberry bug eggs from a population fed on balloon vine fruits were reared on goldenrain tree fruits (or vice versa), the beak lengths of the adult insects matched those in the population from which the eggs were obtained. Interpret these results.

the fruit of the introduced plants is larger than the fruit of the native plant. Thus, in populations feeding on introduced species in these regions, researchers predicted that natural selection would result in the evolution of *longer* beaks. Again, data collected in field studies upheld this prediction.

The observed changes in beak lengths had important consequences. In Australia, for example, the increase in beak length nearly doubled the success with which soapberry bugs could eat the seeds of the introduced species. Furthermore, since historical data show that the goldenrain tree reached central Florida just 35 years before the scientific studies were initiated, the results demonstrate that natural selection can cause rapid evolution in a wild population.

The Evolution of Drug-Resistant Bacteria

An example of ongoing natural selection that dramatically affects humans is the evolution of drug-resistant pathogens (disease-causing organisms and viruses). This is a particular problem with bacteria and viruses because resistant strains of these pathogens can proliferate very quickly.

Consider the evolution of drug resistance in the bacterium *Staphylococcus aureus*. About one in three people harbor this species on their skin or in their nasal passages with no negative effects. However, certain genetic varieties (strains) of this species, known as methicillin-resistant *S. aureus* (MRSA), are formidable pathogens. The past decade has seen an alarming increase in virulent forms of MRSA such as clone USA300, a strain that can cause "flesh-eating disease" and potentially fatal infections **(Figure 19.15)**. How did clone USA300 and other strains of MRSA become so dangerous?

The story begins in 1943, when penicillin became the first widely used antibiotic. Since then, penicillin and other antibiotics have saved millions of lives. However, by 1945, over 20% of the *S. aureus* strains seen in hospitals were resistant to penicillin. These bacteria had an enzyme, penicillinase, that could destroy penicillin. Researchers responded by developing antibiotics that were not destroyed by penicillinase, but resistance to each new drug was observed in some *S. aureus* populations within a few years.

Then, in 1959, doctors began using the powerful antibiotic methicillin. But within two years, methicillin-resistant strains of *S. aureus* were observed. How did these resistant strains emerge? Methicillin works by deactivating an enzyme that bacteria use to synthesize their cell walls. However, different *S. aureus* populations exhibited variations in how strongly their members were affected by the drug. In particular, some individuals were able to synthesize their cell walls using a different enzyme that was not affected by methicillin. These individuals survived the methicillin treatments and reproduced at higher rates than did other individuals. Over time, these resistant individuals became increasingly common, leading to the spread of MRSA.

Initially, MRSA could be controlled by antibiotics that work differently from the way methicillin works. But this has become less effective because some MRSA strains are resistant to

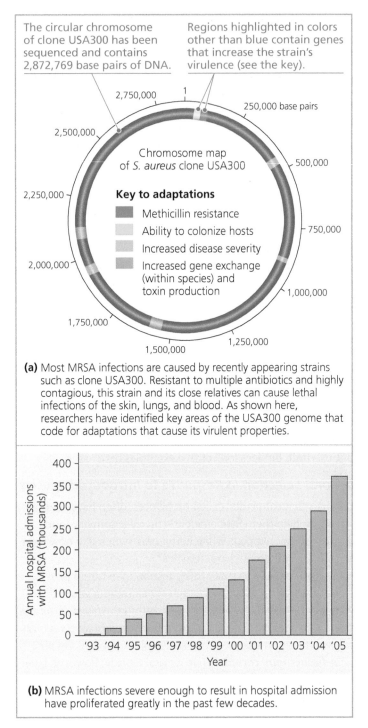

(a) Most MRSA infections are caused by recently appearing strains such as clone USA300. Resistant to multiple antibiotics and highly contagious, this strain and its close relatives can cause lethal infections of the skin, lungs, and blood. As shown here, researchers have identified key areas of the USA300 genome that code for adaptations that cause its virulent properties.

(b) MRSA infections severe enough to result in hospital admission have proliferated greatly in the past few decades.

▲ **Figure 19.15 The rise of methicillin-resistant *Staphylococcus aureus* (MRSA).**

multiple antibiotics—probably because bacteria can exchange genes with members of their own and other species (see Figure 24.17). Thus, the multidrug-resistant strains of today may have emerged over time as MRSA strains that were resistant to different antibiotics exchanged genes.

The *S. aureus* and soapberry bug examples highlight two key points about natural selection. First, natural selection is a process of editing, not a creative mechanism. A drug does not *create* resistant pathogens; it *selects for* resistant individuals that are already present in the population. Second, natural selection depends on time and place. It favors those characteristics in a genetically variable population that provide an advantage in the current, local environment. What is beneficial in one situation may be useless or even harmful in another. Beak lengths suitable for the size of the typical fruit eaten by members of a particular soapberry bug population are favored by natural selection. However, a beak length suitable for fruit of one size can be disadvantageous when the bug is feeding on fruit of another size.

Homology

A second type of evidence for evolution comes from analyzing similarities among different organisms. As we've discussed, evolution is a process of descent with modification: Characteristics present in an ancestral organism are altered (by natural selection) in its descendants over time as they face different environmental conditions. As a result, related species can have characteristics that have an underlying similarity yet function differently. Similarity resulting from common ancestry is known as **homology**. As we'll describe in this section, an understanding of homology can be used to make testable predictions and explain observations that are otherwise puzzling.

Anatomical and Molecular Homologies

The view of evolution as a remodeling process leads to the prediction that closely related species should share similar features—and they do. Of course, closely related species share the features used to determine their relationship, but they also share many other features. Some of these shared features make little sense except in the context of evolution. For example, the forelimbs of all mammals, including humans, cats, whales, and bats, show the same arrangement of bones from the shoulder to the tips of the digits, even though the appendages have very different functions: lifting, walking, swimming, and flying **(Figure 19.16)**. Such striking anatomical resemblances would be highly unlikely if these structures had arisen anew in each

species. Rather, the underlying skeletons of the arms, forelegs, flippers, and wings of different mammals are **homologous structures** that represent variations on a structural theme that was present in their common ancestor.

Comparing early stages of development in different animal species reveals additional anatomical homologies not visible in adult organisms. For example, at some point in their development, all vertebrate embryos have a tail located posterior to (behind) the anus, as well as structures called pharyngeal (throat) arches **(Figure 19.17)**. These homologous throat arches ultimately develop into structures with very different functions, such as gills in fishes and parts of the ears and throat in humans and other mammals.

Some of the most intriguing homologies concern "leftover" structures of marginal, if any, importance to the organism. These **vestigial structures** are remnants of features that served a function in the organism's ancestors. For instance, the skeletons of some snakes retain vestiges of the pelvis and leg bones of walking ancestors. Another example is provided by

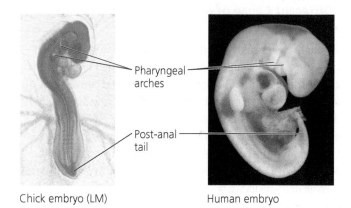

Chick embryo (LM)   Human embryo

▲ Figure 19.17 **Anatomical similarities in vertebrate embryos.** At some stage in their embryonic development, all vertebrates have a tail located posterior to the anus (referred to as a post-anal tail), as well as pharyngeal (throat) arches. Descent from a common ancestor can explain such similarities.

▶ Figure 19.16 **Mammalian forelimbs: homologous structures.** Even though they have become adapted for different functions, the forelimbs of all mammals are constructed from the same basic skeletal elements: one large bone (purple), attached to two smaller bones (orange and tan), attached to several small bones (gold), attached to several metacarpals (green), attached to approximately five digits, each of which is composed of multiple phalanges (blue).

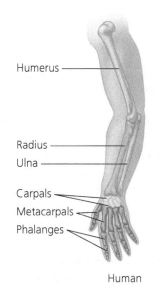

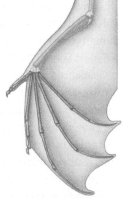
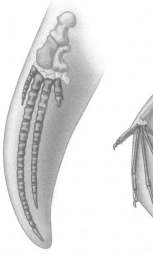

Humerus

Radius
Ulna

Carpals
Metacarpals
Phalanges

Human   Cat   Whale   Bat

eye remnants that are buried under scales in blind species of cave fishes. We would not expect to see these vestigial structures if snakes and blind cave fishes had origins separate from those of other vertebrate animals.

Biologists also observe similarities among organisms at the molecular level. All forms of life use essentially the same genetic code, suggesting that all species descended from common ancestors that used this code. But molecular homologies go beyond a shared code. For example, organisms as dissimilar as humans and bacteria share genes inherited from a very distant common ancestor. Some of these homologous genes have acquired new functions, while others, such as those coding for the ribosomal subunits used in protein synthesis (see Figure 14.17), have retained their original functions. It is also common for organisms to have genes that have lost their function, even though the homologous genes in related species may be fully functional. Like vestigial structures, it appears that such inactive "pseudogenes" may be present simply because a common ancestor had them.

A Different Cause of Resemblance: Convergent Evolution

Although organisms that are closely related share characteristics because of common descent, distantly related organisms can resemble one another for a different reason: **convergent evolution**, the independent evolution of similar features in different lineages. Consider marsupial mammals, many of which live in Australia. Marsupials are distinct from another group of mammals—the eutherians—few of which live in Australia. (Eutherians complete their embryonic development in the uterus, whereas marsupials are born as embryos and complete their development in an external pouch.) Some Australian marsupials have eutherian look-alikes with superficially similar adaptations.

For instance, as shown in **Figure 19.18**, the sugar glider, a forest-dwelling Australian marsupial, looks very similar to flying squirrels, gliding eutherians that live in North American forests. But the sugar glider has many other characteristics that make it a marsupial, much more closely related to kangaroos and other Australian marsupials than to flying squirrels or other eutherians. Once again, our understanding of evolution can explain these observations. Although they evolved independently from different ancestors, these two mammals have adapted to similar environments in similar ways. In such examples in which species share features because of convergent evolution, the resemblance is said to be **analogous**, not homologous. Analogous features share similar function, but not common ancestry, while homologous features share common ancestry, but not necessarily similar function.

▲ **Figure 19.18 Convergent evolution.** The ability to glide through the air evolved independently in these two distantly related mammals.

The Fossil Record

A third type of evidence for evolution comes from fossils. The fossil record documents the pattern of evolution, showing that past organisms differed from present-day organisms and that many species have become extinct. Fossils also show the evolutionary changes that have occurred in various groups of organisms. To give one of hundreds of possible examples, researchers found that the pelvic bone in fossil stickleback fish became greatly reduced in size over time in a number of different lakes. The consistent nature of this change suggests that the reduction in the size of the pelvic bone may have been driven by natural selection.

Fossils can also shed light on the origins of new groups of organisms. An example is the fossil record of cetaceans, the mammalian order that includes whales, dolphins, and porpoises. As shown in **Figure 19.19**, some of these fossils provided strong support for a hypothesis based on DNA sequence data: that cetaceans are closely related to even-toed ungulates, a group that includes deer, pigs, camels, and cows.

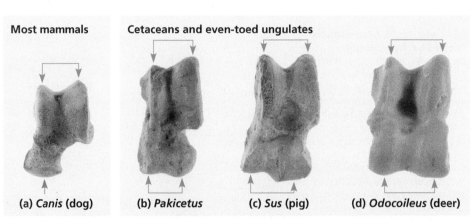

Most mammals **Cetaceans and even-toed ungulates**

(a) *Canis* (dog) (b) *Pakicetus* (c) *Sus* (pig) (d) *Odocoileus* (deer)

▲ **Figure 19.19 Ankle bones: one piece of the puzzle.** Comparing fossils and present-day examples of the astragalus (a type of ankle bone) indicates that cetaceans are closely related to even-toed ungulates. **(a)** In most mammals, the astragalus is shaped like that of a dog, with a double hump on one end (indicated by the red arrows) but not at the opposite end (blue arrow). **(b)** Fossils show that the early cetacean *Pakicetus* had an astragalus with double humps at both ends, a shape otherwise found only in **(c)** pigs, **(d)** deer, and all other even-toed ungulates.

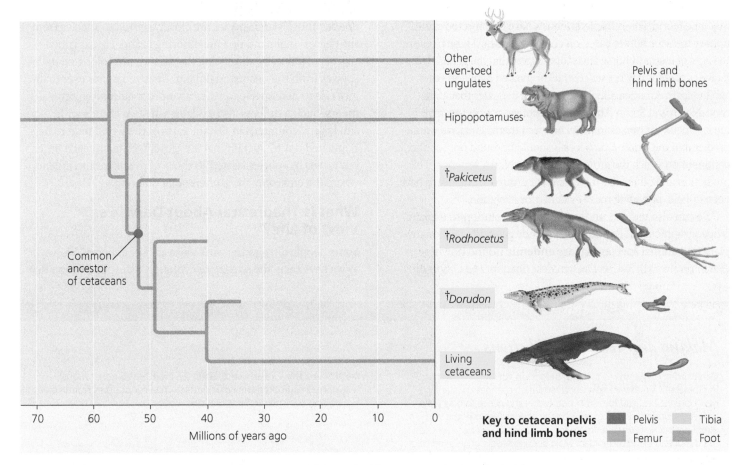

Key to cetacean pelvis
and hind limb bones

| Pelvis | Tibia |
| Femur | Foot |

▲ **Figure 19.20 The transition to life in the sea.** Multiple lines of evidence support the hypothesis that cetaceans (highlighted in yellow) evolved from terrestrial mammals. Fossils document the reduction over time in the pelvis and hind limb bones of extinct (†) cetacean ancestors, including *Pakicetus*, *Rodhocetus*, and *Dorudon*. DNA sequence data support the hypothesis that cetaceans are most closely related to hippopotamuses.

? *Which happened first during the evolution of cetaceans: changes in hind limb structure or the origin of tail flukes? Explain.*

What else can fossils tell us about cetacean origins? The earliest cetaceans lived 50–60 million years ago. The fossil record indicates that prior to that time, most mammals were terrestrial. Although scientists had long realized that whales and other cetaceans originated from land mammals, few fossils had been found that revealed how cetacean limb structure had changed over time, leading eventually to the loss of hind limbs and the development of flukes (the lobes on a whale's tail) and flippers. In the past few decades, however, a series of remarkable fossils have been discovered in Pakistan, Egypt, and North America. These fossils document steps in the transition from life on land to life in the sea, filling in some of the gaps between ancestral and living cetaceans **(Figure 19.20)**.

Collectively, the recent fossil discoveries document the origin of a new group of mammals, the cetaceans. These discoveries also show that cetaceans and their close living relatives (hippopotamuses, deer, and other even-toed ungulates) are much more different from each other than were *Pakicetus* and early even-toed ungulates, such as *Diacodexis* **(Figure 19.21)**. Similar patterns are seen in fossils documenting the origins of other new groups of organisms, including mammals (see Figure 23.5), flowering plants (see Concept 26.4), and

tetrapods (see Figure 27.23). In each of these cases, the fossil record shows that over time, descent with modification produced increasingly large differences among related groups of organisms, ultimately resulting in the diversity of life we see today.

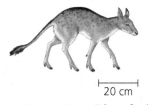

20 cm

▲ **Figure 19.21** *Diacodexis.*

Biogeography

A fourth type of evidence for evolution has to do with **biogeography**, the scientific study of the geographic distributions of species. The geographic distributions of organisms are influenced by many factors, including *continental drift*, the slow movement of Earth's continents over time. About 250 million years ago, these movements united all of Earth's landmasses into a single large continent called **Pangaea** (see Figure 23.9). Roughly 200 million years ago, Pangaea began to break apart; by 20 million years ago, the continents we know today were within a few hundred kilometers of their present locations.

We can use our understanding of evolution and continental drift to predict where fossils of different groups of organisms might be found. For example, scientists have constructed evolutionary trees for horses based on anatomical data. These trees and the ages of fossils of horse ancestors suggest that the genus that includes present-day horses (*Equus*) originated 5 million years ago in North America. Geologic evidence indicates that at that time, North and South America were not yet connected, making it difficult for horses to travel between them. Thus, we would predict that the oldest *Equus* fossils should be found only on the continent on which the group originated—North America. This prediction and others like it for different groups of organisms have been upheld, providing more evidence for evolution.

We can also use our understanding of evolution to explain biogeographic data. For example, islands generally have many plant and animal species that are **endemic** (found nowhere else in the world). Yet, as Darwin described in *The Origin of*

Species, most island species are closely related to species from the nearest mainland or a neighboring island. He explained this observation by suggesting that islands are colonized by species from the nearest mainland. These colonists eventually give rise to new species as they adapt to their new environments. Such a process also explains why two islands with similar environments in distant parts of the world tend to be populated not by species that are closely related to each other, but rather by species related to those of the nearest mainland, where the environment is often quite different.

What Is Theoretical About Darwin's View of Life?

Some people dismiss Darwin's ideas as "just a theory." However, as we have seen, the *pattern* of evolution—the observation that

---

Scientific Skills Exercise

Making and Testing Predictions

Can Predation Result in Natural Selection for Color Patterns in Guppies? What we know about evolution changes constantly as new observations lead to new hypotheses—and hence to new ways to test our understanding of evolutionary theory. Consider the wild guppies (*Poecilia reticulata*) that live in pools connected by streams on the Caribbean island of Trinidad. Male guppies have highly varied color patterns that are controlled by genes that are only expressed in adult males. Female guppies choose males with bright color patterns as mates more often than they choose males with drab coloring. But the bright colors that attract females also can make the males more conspicuous to predators. Researchers observed that in pools with few predator species, the benefits of bright colors appear to "win out," and males are more brightly colored than in pools where predation is more intense.

One guppy predator, the killifish, preys on juvenile guppies that have not yet displayed their adult coloration. Researchers predicted that if adult guppies with drab colors were transferred to a pool with only killifish, eventually the descendants of these guppies would be more brightly colored (because of the female preference for brightly colored males).

How the Experiment Was Done Researchers transplanted 200 guppies from pools containing pike-cichlid fish, intense predators of adult guppies, to pools containing killifish, less active predators that prey mainly on juvenile guppies. They tracked the number of bright-colored spots and the total area of those spots on male guppies in each generation.

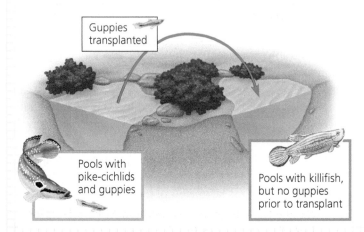

Data from the Experiment After 22 months (15 generations), researchers compared the color pattern data for guppies from the source and transplanted populations.

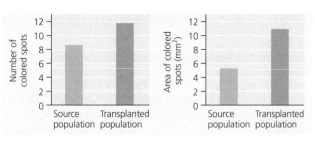

Data from J. A. Endler, Natural selection on color patterns in *Poecilia reticulata*, *Evolution* 34:76–91 (1980).

INTERPRET THE DATA

1. Identify the following elements of hypothesis-based science in this example: (a) question, (b) hypothesis, (c) prediction, (d) control group, and (e) experimental group. (For additional information about hypothesis-based science, see Chapter 1 and the Scientific Skills Review in Appendix F and the Study Area of MasteringBiology.)
2. Explain how the types of data the researchers chose to collect enabled them to test their prediction.
3. What conclusion do you draw from the data presented above?
4. Predict what would happen if, after 22 months, guppies from the transplanted population were returned to the source pool. Describe an experiment to test your prediction.

(MB) A related version of this Scientific Skills Exercise can be assigned in MasteringBiology.

life has evolved over time—has been documented directly and is supported by a great deal of evidence. In addition, Darwin's explanation of the *process* of evolution—that natural selection is the primary cause of the observed pattern of evolutionary change—makes sense of massive amounts of data. The effects of natural selection also can be observed and tested in nature.

What, then, is theoretical about evolution? Keep in mind that the scientific meaning of the term *theory* is very different from its meaning in everyday use. The colloquial use of the word *theory* comes close to what scientists mean by a hypothesis. In science, a theory is more comprehensive than a hypothesis. A theory, such as the theory of evolution by natural selection, accounts for many observations and explains and integrates a great variety of phenomena. Such a unifying theory does not become widely accepted unless its predictions stand up to thorough and continual testing by experiment and additional observation (see Concept 1.3). As the rest of this unit demonstrates, this has certainly been the case with the theory of evolution by natural selection.

The skepticism of scientists as they continue to test theories prevents these ideas from becoming dogma. For example, although Darwin thought that evolution was a very slow process, we now know that this isn't always true. New species can form in relatively short periods of time—a few thousand years or less. Furthermore, evolutionary biologists now recognize that natural selection is not the only mechanism responsible

for evolution. Indeed, the study of evolution today is livelier than ever as scientists use a wide range of experimental approaches and genetic analyses to test predictions based on natural selection and other evolutionary mechanisms. In the **Scientific Skills Exercise**, you'll work with data from an experiment on natural selection in wild guppies.

Although Darwin's theory attributes the diversity of life to natural processes, the diverse products of evolution nevertheless remain elegant and inspiring. As Darwin wrote in the final sentence of *The Origin of Species*, "There is grandeur in this view of life . . . [in which] endless forms most beautiful and most wonderful have been, and are being, evolved."

CONCEPT CHECK 19.3

1. Explain how the following statement is inaccurate: "Antibiotics have created drug resistance in MRSA."
2. How does evolution account for (a) the similar mammalian forelimbs with different functions shown in Figure 19.16 and (b) the similar forms of the two distantly related mammals shown in Figure 19.18?
3. **WHAT IF?** Fossils show that dinosaurs originated between 200 and 250 million years ago. Would you expect the geographic distribution of early dinosaur fossils to be broad (on many continents) or narrow (on one or a few continents only)? Explain.

For suggested answers, see Appendix A.

---

19 Chapter Review

Go to **MasteringBiology®** for Assignments, the eText, and the Study Area with Animations, Activities, Vocab Self-Quiz, and Practice Tests.

SUMMARY OF KEY CONCEPTS

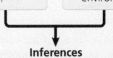

VOCAB SELF-QUIZ

goo.gl/gbai8v

CONCEPT 19.1

The Darwinian revolution challenged traditional views of a young Earth inhabited by unchanging species (pp. 380–381)

- Darwin proposed that life's diversity arose from ancestral species through natural selection, a departure from prevailing views.
- Cuvier studied **fossils** but denied that evolution occurs; he proposed that sudden catastrophic events in the past caused species to disappear from an area. Hutton and Lyell thought that geologic change could result from gradual, continuous mechanisms. Lamarck hypothesized that species evolve, but the underlying mechanisms he proposed are not supported by evidence.

? *Why was the age of Earth important for Darwin's ideas about evolution?*

CONCEPT 19.2

Descent with modification by natural selection explains the adaptations of organisms and the unity and diversity of life (pp. 382–386)

- Darwin's voyage on the *Beagle* gave rise to his idea that species originate from ancestral forms through the accumulation of

adaptations. He refined his theory for many years and finally published it in 1859 after learning that Wallace had come to the same idea.
- In *The Origin of Species*, Darwin proposed that over long periods of time, descent with modification produced the rich diversity of life through the mechanism of **natural selection**.

Observations

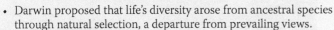

| Individuals in a population vary in their heritable characteristics. | Organisms produce more offspring than the environment can support. |

Inferences

Individuals that are well suited to their environment tend to leave more offspring than other individuals.

and

Over time, favorable traits accumulate in the population.

? *Describe how overreproduction and heritable variation relate to evolution by natural selection.*

Evolution is supported by an overwhelming amount of scientific evidence (pp. 387–393)

- Researchers have directly observed natural selection leading to adaptive evolution in many studies, including research on soapberry bug populations and on MRSA.
- Organisms share characteristics because of common descent (**homology**) or because natural selection affects independently evolving species in similar environments in similar ways (**convergent evolution**).
- Fossils show that past organisms differed from living organisms, that many species have become extinct, and that species have evolved over long periods of time; fossils also document the origin of major new groups of organisms.
- Evolutionary theory can explain some biogeographic patterns.

? *Summarize the different lines of evidence supporting the hypothesis that cetaceans descended from land mammals and are closely related to even-toed ungulates.*

TEST YOUR UNDERSTANDING

PRACTICE TEST

Level 1: Knowledge/Comprehension

goo.gl/CRZjvS

1. Which of the following is *not* an observation or inference on which natural selection is based?
   (A) There is heritable variation among individuals.
   (B) Poorly adapted individuals never produce offspring.
   (C) Species produce more offspring than the environment can support.
   (D) Only a fraction of an individual's offspring may survive.

2. Which of the following observations helped Darwin shape his concept of descent with modification?
   (A) Species diversity declines farther from the equator.
   (B) Fewer species live on islands than on the nearest continents.
   (C) Birds live on islands located farther from the mainland than the birds' maximum nonstop flight distance.
   (D) South American temperate plants are more similar to the tropical plants of South America than to the temperate plants of Europe.

Level 2: Application/Analysis

3. Within six months of effectively using methicillin to treat *S. aureus* infections in a community, all new *S. aureus* infections were caused by MRSA. How can this best be explained?
   (A) A patient must have become infected with MRSA from another community.
   (B) In response to the drug, *S. aureus* began making drug-resistant versions of the protein targeted by the drug.
   (C) Some drug-resistant bacteria were present at the start of treatment, and natural selection increased their frequency.
   (D) *S. aureus* evolved to resist vaccines.

4. The upper forelimbs of humans and bats have fairly similar skeletal structures, whereas the corresponding bones in whales have very different shapes and proportions. However, genetic data suggest that all three kinds of organisms diverged from a common ancestor at about the same time. Which of the following is the most likely explanation for these data?
   (A) Forelimb evolution was adaptive in people and bats, but not in whales.
   (B) Natural selection in an aquatic environment resulted in significant changes to whale forelimb anatomy.
   (C) Genes mutate faster in whales than in humans or bats.
   (D) Whales are not properly classified as mammals.

5. DNA sequences in many human genes are very similar to the sequences of corresponding genes in chimpanzees. The most likely explanation for this result is that
   (A) humans and chimpanzees share a relatively recent common ancestor.
   (B) humans evolved from chimpanzees.
   (C) chimpanzees evolved from humans.
   (D) convergent evolution led to the DNA similarities.

Level 3: Synthesis/Evaluation

6. **SCIENTIFIC INQUIRY**
   DRAW IT Mosquitoes resistant to the pesticide DDT first appeared in India in 1959, but now are found throughout the world. (a) Graph the data in the table below. (b) Examining the graph, hypothesize why the percentage of mosquitoes resistant to DDT rose rapidly. (c) Suggest an explanation for the global spread of DDT resistance.

Month	0	8	12
Mosquitoes Resistant* to DDT	4%	45%	77%

Data from C. F. Curtis et al., Selection for and against insecticide resistance and possible methods of inhibiting the evolution of resistance in mosquitoes, *Ecological Entomology* 3:273–287 (1978).

*Mosquitoes were considered resistant if they were not killed within 1 hour of receiving a dose of 4% DDT.

7. **FOCUS ON EVOLUTION**
   Explain why anatomical and molecular features often fit a similar nested pattern. In addition, describe a process that can cause this not to be the case.

8. **FOCUS ON INTERACTIONS**
   Write a short essay (about 100–150 words) evaluating whether changes to an organism's physical environment are likely to result in evolutionary change. Use an example to support your reasoning.

9. **SYNTHESIZE YOUR KNOWLEDGE**

This honeypot ant (genus *Myrmecocystus*) can store liquid food inside its expandable abdomen. Consider other ants you are familiar with, and explain how a honeypot ant exemplifies three key features of life: adaptation, unity, and diversity.

For selected answers, see Appendix A.

20 Phylogeny

KEY CONCEPTS

20.1 Phylogenies show evolutionary relationships

20.2 Phylogenies are inferred from morphological and molecular data

20.3 Shared characters are used to construct phylogenetic trees

20.4 Molecular clocks help track evolutionary time

20.5 New information continues to revise our understanding of evolutionary history

▲ **Figure 20.1** What kind of organism is this?

Investigating the Evolutionary History of Life

Look closely at the organism in **Figure 20.1**. Although it resembles a snake, this animal is actually a legless lizard known as the eastern glass lizard (*Ophisaurus ventralis*). Why isn't this glass lizard considered a snake? More generally, how do biologists distinguish and categorize the millions of species on Earth?

An understanding of evolutionary relationships suggests one way to address these questions: We can decide in which category to place a species by comparing its traits with those of potential close relatives. For example, the eastern glass lizard does not have a highly mobile jaw, a large number of vertebrae, or a short tail located behind the anus, three traits shared by all snakes. These and other characteristics suggest that despite a superficial resemblance, the glass lizard is not a snake.

Snakes and lizards are part of the continuum of life extending from the earliest organisms to the great variety of species alive today. To help make sense of that diversity, biologists trace **phylogeny**, the evolutionary history of a species or group of species. A phylogeny of lizards and snakes, for example, indicates that both the eastern glass lizard and snakes evolved

from lizards with legs—but they evolved from different lineages of legged lizards **(Figure 20.2)**. Thus, it appears that their legless conditions evolved independently.

In fact, a broader survey of the lizards reveals that a snakelike body form has evolved in many different groups of lizards. Most lizards with such a body form are burrowers or live in grasslands. The repeated evolution of a snakelike body form in a consistent set of environments suggests that this change has

▼ **Figure 20.2 Convergent evolution of limbless bodies.** A phylogeny based on DNA sequence data reveals that a legless body form evolved independently from legged ancestors in the lineages leading to the eastern glass lizard and to snakes.

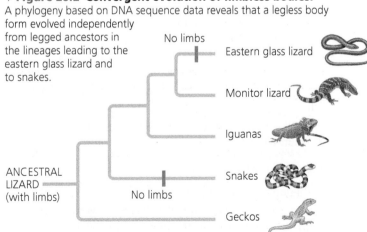

No limbs — Eastern glass lizard

Monitor lizard

Iguanas

ANCESTRAL LIZARD (with limbs)

No limbs — Snakes

Geckos

been driven by natural selection: The legs of these organisms became reduced in size, or even disappeared, over generations as the species adapted to their environments.

In this chapter, we'll examine how biologists reconstruct and interpret phylogenies using **systematics**, a discipline focused on classifying organisms and determining their evolutionary relationships.

CONCEPT 20.1

Phylogenies show evolutionary relationships

Organisms share many characteristics because of common ancestry (see Concept 19.3). As a result, we can learn a great deal about a species if we know its evolutionary history. For example, an organism is likely to share many of its genes, metabolic pathways, and structural proteins with its close relatives. We'll consider practical applications of such information later in this section, but first we'll examine how organisms are named and classified, the scientific discipline of **taxonomy**. We'll also look at how we can interpret and use diagrams that represent evolutionary history.

Binomial Nomenclature

Common names for organisms—such as monkey, finch, and lilac—convey meaning in casual usage, but they can also cause confusion. Each of these names, for example, refers to more than one species. Moreover, some common names do not accurately reflect the kind of organism they signify. Consider these three "fishes": jellyfish (a cnidarian), crayfish (a small lobsterlike crustacean), and silverfish (an insect). And of course, a given organism has different names in different languages.

To avoid ambiguity when communicating about their research, biologists refer to organisms by Latin scientific names. The two-part format of the scientific name, commonly called a **binomial**, was instituted in the 18th century by Carolus Linnaeus (see Concept 19.1). The first part of a binomial is the name of the **genus** (plural, *genera*) to which the species belongs. The second part, called the specific epithet, is unique for each species within the genus. An example of a binomial is *Panthera pardus*, the scientific name for the large cat commonly called the leopard. Notice that the first letter of the genus is capitalized and the entire binomial is italicized. (Newly created scientific names are also "latinized": You can name an insect you discover after a friend, but you must add a Latin ending.) Many of the more than 11,000 binomials assigned by Linnaeus are still used today, including the optimistic name he gave our own species—*Homo sapiens*, meaning "wise man."

Hierarchical Classification

In addition to naming species, Linnaeus also grouped them into a hierarchy of increasingly inclusive categories. The first grouping is built into the binomial: Species that appear to be closely related are grouped into the same genus. For example, the leopard (*Panthera pardus*) belongs to a genus that also includes the African lion (*Panthera leo*), the tiger (*Panthera tigris*), and the jaguar (*Panthera onca*). Beyond genera, taxonomists employ progressively more comprehensive categories of classification. The taxonomic system named after Linnaeus, the Linnaean system, places related genera into the same **family**, families into **orders**, orders into **classes**, classes into **phyla** (singular, *phylum*), phyla into **kingdoms**, and, more recently, kingdoms into **domains (Figure 20.3)**. The resulting biological classification of a particular organism is somewhat like a postal address identifying a person in a particular apartment, in a building with many apartments, on a street with many apartment buildings, in a city with many streets, and so on.

The named taxonomic unit at any level of the hierarchy is called a **taxon** (plural, *taxa*). In the leopard example, *Panthera* is a taxon at the genus level, and Mammalia is a taxon at the

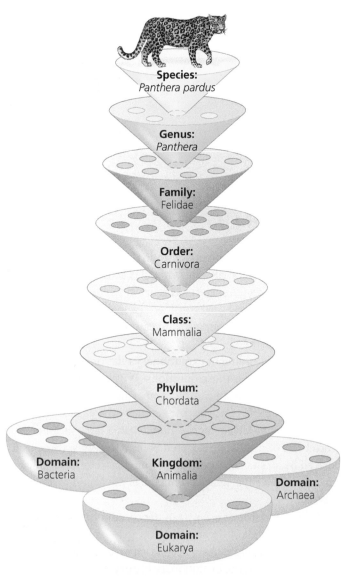

Species: *Panthera pardus*

Genus: *Panthera*

Family: Felidae

Order: Carnivora

Class: Mammalia

Phylum: Chordata

Domain: Bacteria

Kingdom: Animalia

Domain: Archaea

Domain: Eukarya

▲ **Figure 20.3 Linnaean classification.** At each level, or "rank," species are placed in groups within more inclusive groups.

class level that includes all the many orders of mammals. Note that in the Linnaean system, taxa broader than the genus are not italicized, though they are capitalized.

Classifying species is a way to structure our human view of the world. We lump together various species of trees to which we give the common name of pines and distinguish them from other trees that we call firs. Taxonomists have decided that pines and firs are different enough to be placed in separate genera, yet similar enough to be grouped into the same family, Pinaceae. As with pines and firs, higher levels of classification are usually defined by particular characters chosen by taxonomists. However, characters that are useful for classifying one group of organisms may not be appropriate for other organisms. For this reason, the larger categories often are not comparable between lineages; that is, an order of snails does not exhibit the same degree of morphological or genetic diversity as an order of mammals. Furthermore, as we'll see, the placement of species into orders, classes, and so on does not necessarily reflect evolutionary history.

Linking Classification and Phylogeny

The evolutionary history of a group of organisms can be represented in a branching diagram called a **phylogenetic tree**. As in **Figure 20.4**, the branching pattern often matches how

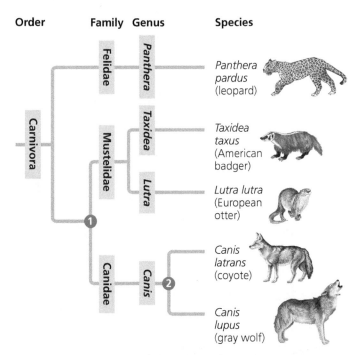

▲ **Figure 20.4 The connection between classification and phylogeny.** Hierarchical classification can reflect the branching patterns of phylogenetic trees. This tree traces possible evolutionary relationships between some of the taxa within order Carnivora, itself a branch of class Mammalia. The branch point ❶ represents the most recent common ancestor of all members of the weasel (Mustelidae) and dog (Canidae) families. The branch point ❷ represents the most recent common ancestor of coyotes and gray wolves.

? *What does this phylogenetic tree indicate about the evolutionary relationships between the leopard, badger, and wolf?*

taxonomists have classified groups of organisms nested within more inclusive groups. Sometimes, however, taxonomists have placed a species within a genus (or other group) to which it is *not* most closely related. One reason for such a mistake might be that over the course of evolution, a species has lost a key feature shared by its close relatives. If DNA or other new evidence indicates that an organism has been misclassified, the organism may be reclassified to accurately reflect its evolutionary history. Another issue is that while the Linnaean system may distinguish groups, such as amphibians, mammals, reptiles, and other classes of vertebrates, it tells us nothing about these groups' evolutionary relationships to one another. Such difficulties in aligning Linnaean classification with phylogeny have led many systematists to propose that classification be based entirely on evolutionary relationships.

Regardless of how groups are named, a phylogenetic tree represents a hypothesis about evolutionary relationships. These relationships often are depicted as a series of dichotomies, or two-way **branch points**. Each branch point represents the divergence of two evolutionary lineages from a common ancestor. In **Figure 20.5**, for example, branch point ❸ represents the common ancestor of taxa A, B, and C. The position of branch point ❹ to the right of ❸ indicates that taxa B and C diverged after their shared lineage split from the lineage leading to taxon A. Note also that tree branches can be rotated around a branch point without changing their evolutionary relationships.

In Figure 20.5, taxa B and C are **sister taxa**, groups of organisms that share an immediate common ancestor (branch point ❹) and hence are each other's closest relatives. In addition, this tree, like most of the phylogenetic trees in this book, is **rooted**, which means that a branch point within the tree (often drawn farthest to the left) represents the most recent

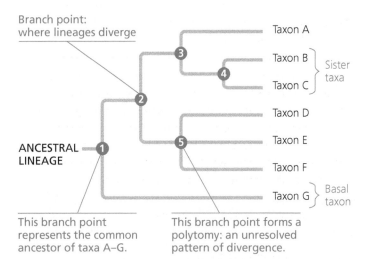

▲ **Figure 20.5 How to read a phylogenetic tree.**

DRAW IT *Redraw this tree, rotating the branches around branch points ❷ and ❹. Does your new version tell a different story about the evolutionary relationships between the taxa? Explain.*

common ancestor of all taxa in the tree. The term **basal taxon** refers to a lineage that diverges from all other lineages in its group early in the history of the group. Hence, like taxon G in Figure 20.5, a basal taxon lies on a branch that originates near the common ancestor of the group. Finally, on the lineage leading to taxa D–F, ❺ represents a **polytomy**, a branch point from which more than two descendant groups emerge. A polytomy signifies that evolutionary relationships among the taxa are not yet clear.

What We Can and Cannot Learn from Phylogenetic Trees

Let's summarize three key points about phylogenetic trees. First, they are intended to show patterns of descent, not phenotypic similarity. Although closely related organisms often resemble one another due to their common ancestry, they may not if their lineages have evolved at different rates or faced very different environmental conditions. For example, even though crocodiles are more closely related to birds than to lizards (see Figure 20.16), they look more like lizards because morphology has changed dramatically in the bird lineage.

Second, the sequence of branching in a tree does not necessarily indicate the actual (absolute) ages of the particular species. For example, the tree in Figure 20.4 does not indicate that the wolf evolved more recently than the European otter; rather, the tree shows only that the most recent common ancestor of the wolf and otter (branch point ❶) lived before the most recent common ancestor of the wolf and coyote (❷). To indicate when wolves and otters evolved, the tree would need to include additional divergences in each evolutionary lineage, as well as the dates when those splits occurred. Generally, unless given specific information about what the branch lengths in a phylogenetic tree mean—for example, that they are proportional to time—we should interpret the diagram solely in terms of patterns of descent. No assumptions should be made about when particular species evolved or how much change occurred in each lineage.

Third, we should not assume that a taxon on a phylogenetic tree evolved from the taxon next to it. Figure 20.4 does not indicate that wolves evolved from coyotes or vice versa. We can infer only that the lineage leading to wolves and the lineage leading to coyotes both evolved from the common ancestor ❷. That ancestor, which is now extinct, was neither a wolf nor a coyote. However, its descendants include the two *extant* (living) species shown here, wolves and coyotes.

Applying Phylogenies

Understanding phylogeny can have practical applications. Consider maize (corn), which originated in the Americas and is now an important food crop worldwide. From a phylogeny of maize based on DNA data, researchers have been able to identify two species of wild grasses that may be maize's closest living relatives. These two close relatives may be useful

as "reservoirs" of beneficial alleles that can be transferred to cultivated maize by cross-breeding or genetic engineering (see Concept 13.4).

A different use of phylogenetic trees is to infer species identities by analyzing the relatedness of DNA sequences from different organisms. Researchers have used this approach to investigate whether "whale meat" had been harvested illegally from whale species protected under international law rather than from species that can be harvested legally, such as Minke whales caught in the Southern Hemisphere (**Figure 20.6**).

How do researchers construct trees like those we've considered here? In the next section, we'll begin to answer that question by examining the data that are used to infer phylogenies.

▼ Figure 20.6 Inquiry

What is the species identity of food being sold as whale meat?

Experiment C. S. Baker and S. R. Palumbi purchased 13 samples of "whale meat" from Japanese fish markets. They sequenced part of the mitochondrial DNA (mtDNA) from each sample and compared their results with the comparable mtDNA sequence from known whale species. To infer the species identity of each sample, the team constructed a *gene tree*, a phylogenetic tree that shows patterns of relatedness among DNA sequences rather than among taxa.

Results The analysis yielded the following gene tree:

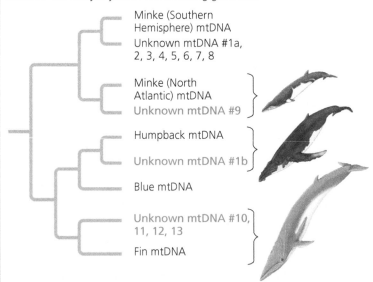

Minke (Southern Hemisphere) mtDNA
Unknown mtDNA #1a, 2, 3, 4, 5, 6, 7, 8

Minke (North Atlantic) mtDNA
Unknown mtDNA #9

Humpback mtDNA
Unknown mtDNA #1b

Blue mtDNA

Unknown mtDNA #10, 11, 12, 13

Fin mtDNA

Conclusion The mtDNA sequences of six of the unknown samples (in red) were most similar to mtDNA sequences of whales that are not legal to harvest, indicating that the unknown samples were from illegally harvested whales.

Data from C. S. Baker and S. R. Palumbi, Which whales are hunted? A molecular genetic approach to monitoring whaling, *Science* 265:1538–1539 (1994).

WHAT IF? What different results would have indicated that *none* of the whale meat had been harvested illegally?

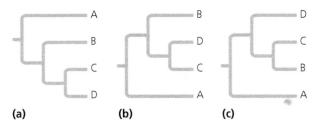
CONCEPT 20.2

Phylogenies are inferred from morphological and molecular data

To infer phylogeny, systematists must gather as much information as possible about the morphology, genes, and biochemistry of the relevant organisms. It is important to focus on features that result from common ancestry, because only such features reflect evolutionary relationships.

Morphological and Molecular Homologies

Recall that phenotypic and genetic similarities due to shared ancestry are called *homologies*. For example, the similarity in the number and arrangement of bones in the forelimbs of mammals is due to their descent from a common ancestor with the same bone structure; this is an example of a morphological homology (see Figure 19.16). In the same way, genes or other DNA sequences are homologous if they are descended from sequences carried by a common ancestor.

In general, organisms that share very similar morphologies or similar DNA sequences are likely to be more closely related than organisms with vastly different structures or sequences. In some cases, however, the morphological divergence between related species can be great and their genetic divergence small (or vice versa). Consider the Hawaiian silversword plants: Some of these species are tall, twiggy trees, while others are dense, ground-hugging shrubs (see Figure 23.16). But despite these striking phenotypic differences, the silverswords' genes are very similar. Based on these small molecular divergences, scientists estimate that the silversword group began to diverge 5 million years ago, which is also about the time when the oldest of the current Hawaiian islands formed. We'll discuss how scientists use molecular data to estimate such divergence times later in this chapter.

Sorting Homology from Analogy

A potential source of confusion in constructing a phylogeny is similarity between organisms that is due to convergent evolution—called **analogy**—rather than to shared ancestry (homology). Convergent evolution occurs when similar environmental pressures and natural selection produce similar (analogous) adaptations in organisms from different evolutionary lineages. For example, the two mole-like animals shown in **Figure 20.7** are similar in their external appearance. However, their internal anatomy, physiology, and reproductive systems are very dissimilar. Indeed, genetic and fossil evidence indicates that the common ancestor of these animals lived 140 million years ago. This common ancestor and most of its descendants were not mole-like, but analogous characteristics evolved independently in these two lineages as they became adapted to similar lifestyles.

Australian marsupial mole

North American eutherian mole

▲ **Figure 20.7 Convergent evolution in burrowers.** A long body, large front paws, small eyes, and a pad of thick skin that protects the nose all evolved independently in these species.

Distinguishing between homology and analogy is critical in reconstructing phylogenies. To see why, consider bats and birds, both of which have adaptations that enable flight. This superficial resemblance might imply that bats are more closely related to birds than they are to cats, which cannot fly. But a closer examination reveals that a bat's wing is more similar to the forelimbs of cats and other mammals than to a bird's wing. Bats and birds descended from a common tetrapod ancestor that lived about 320 million years ago. This common ancestor could not fly. Thus, although the underlying skeletal systems of bats and birds are homologous, their *wings* are not. Flight is enabled in different ways—stretched membranes in the bat wing versus feathers in the bird wing. Fossil evidence also documents that bat wings and bird wings arose independently from the forelimbs of different tetrapod ancestors. Thus, with respect to flight, a bat's wing is *analogous*, not homologous, to a bird's wing. Analogous structures that arose independently are also called **homoplasies** (from the Greek, meaning "to mold in the same way").

Besides corroborative similarities and fossil evidence, another clue to distinguishing between homology and analogy is the complexity of the characters being compared. The more elements that are similar in two complex structures, the more likely it is that the structures evolved from a common ancestor. For instance, the skulls of an adult human and an adult chimpanzee both consist of many bones fused together. The compositions of the skulls match almost perfectly, bone for bone. It is highly improbable that such complex structures, matching in so many details, have separate origins. More likely, the genes involved in the development of both skulls were inherited from a common ancestor. The same argument applies to comparisons at the gene level. Genes are sequences of thousands of nucleotides, each of which represents an inherited character in the form of one of the four DNA bases: A (adenine), G (guanine), C (cytosine), or T (thymine). If genes in two organisms share many portions of their nucleotide sequences, it is likely that the genes are homologous.

Evaluating Molecular Homologies

Comparing DNA molecules often poses challenges for researchers. The first step after sequencing the DNA is to align comparable sequences from the species being studied. If the species are very closely related, the sequences probably differ at only one or a few sites. In contrast, comparable nucleic acid sequences in distantly related species usually have different bases at many sites and may have different lengths. This is because insertions and deletions accumulate over long periods of time.

Suppose, for example, that certain noncoding DNA sequences near a particular gene are very similar in two species, except that the first base of the sequence has been deleted in one of the species. The effect is that the remaining sequence shifts back one notch. A comparison of the two sequences that does not take this deletion into account would overlook what in fact is a very good match. As described in **Figure 20.8**,

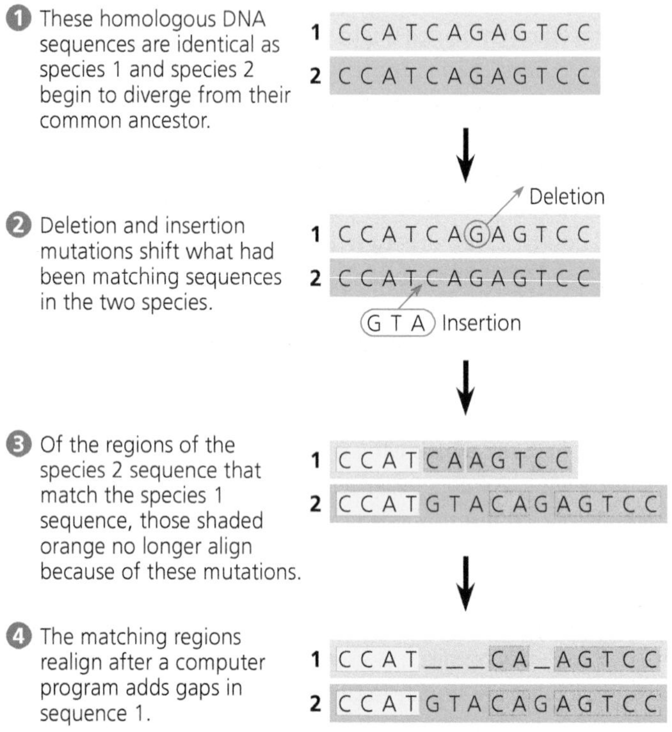

ACGGATAGTCCACTAGGCACTA
TCACCGACAGGTCTTTGACTAG

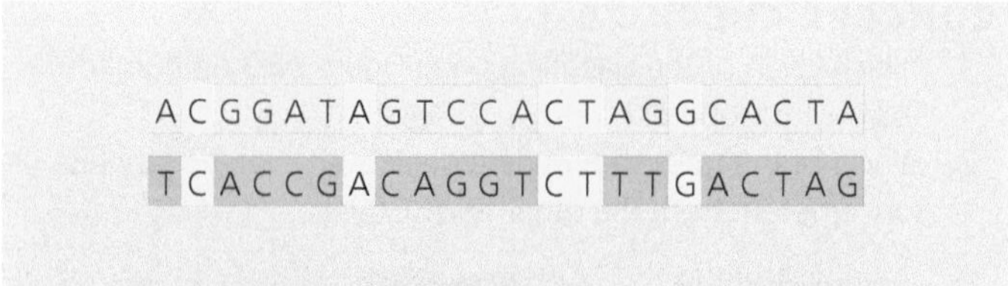

▲ **Figure 20.9 A molecular homoplasy.** These two DNA sequences from organisms that are not closely related coincidentally share 23% of their bases. Statistical tools have been developed to determine whether DNA sequences that share more than 25% of their bases do so because they are homologous.

? *Why might you expect organisms that are not closely related to nevertheless share roughly 25% of their bases?*

computer programs can help researchers identify such matches by testing possible alignments for comparable DNA segments of differing lengths.

Such molecular comparisons reveal that many base substitutions and other differences have accumulated in the comparable genes of an Australian mole and a North American mole. The many differences indicate that their lineages have diverged greatly since their common ancestor; thus, we say that the living species are not closely related. In contrast, the high degree of gene sequence similarity among the silversword plants indicates that they are all very closely related, in spite of their considerable morphological differences.

Just as with morphological characters, it is necessary to distinguish homology from analogy in evaluating molecular similarities for evolutionary studies. Two sequences that resemble each other at many points along their length most likely are homologous (see Figure 20.8). But in organisms that do not appear to be closely related, the bases that their otherwise very different sequences happen to share may simply be coincidental matches, called molecular homoplasies **(Figure 20.9)**. Scientists have developed statistical tools that can help distinguish "distant" homologies from such coincidental matches in extremely divergent sequences.

① These homologous DNA sequences are identical as species 1 and species 2 begin to diverge from their common ancestor.

1 C C A T C A G A G T C C
2 C C A T C A G A G T C C

② Deletion and insertion mutations shift what had been matching sequences in the two species.

Deletion
1 C C A T C A (G) A G T C C
2 C C A T C A G A G T C C
(G T A) Insertion

③ Of the regions of the species 2 sequence that match the species 1 sequence, those shaded orange no longer align because of these mutations.

1 C C A T C A A G T C C
2 C C A T G T A C A G A G T C C

④ The matching regions realign after a computer program adds gaps in sequence 1.

1 C C A T _ _ _ C A _ A G T C C
2 C C A T G T A C A G A G T C C

▲ **Figure 20.8 Aligning segments of DNA.** Systematists search for similar sequences along DNA segments from two species (only one DNA strand is shown for each species). In this example, 11 of the original 12 bases have not changed since the species diverged. Hence, those portions still align once the length is adjusted.

CONCEPT CHECK 20.2

1. Decide whether each of the following pairs of structures more likely represents analogy or homology, and explain your reasoning: (a) a porcupine's quills and a cactus's spines; (b) a cat's paw and a human's hand; (c) an owl's wing and a hornet's wing.

2. **WHAT IF?** Suppose that two species, A and B, have similar appearances but very divergent gene sequences, while species B and C have very different appearances but similar gene sequences. Which pair of species is more likely to be closely related: A and B, or B and C? Explain.

For suggested answers, see Appendix A.

Shared characters are used to construct phylogenetic trees

As we've discussed, a key step in reconstructing phylogenies is to distinguish homologous features from analogous ones (since only homology reflects evolutionary history). We must also choose a method of inferring phylogeny from these homologous characters. A widely used set of methods is known as cladistics.

Cladistics

In the approach to systematics called **cladistics**, common ancestry is the primary criterion used to classify organisms. Using this methodology, biologists attempt to place species into groups called **clades**, each of which includes an ancestral species and all of its descendants **(Figure 20.10a)**. Clades, like taxonomic categories of the Linnaean system, are nested within larger clades. In Figure 20.4, for example, the cat group (Felidae) represents a clade within a larger clade (Carnivora) that also includes the dog group (Canidae).

However, a taxon is equivalent to a clade only if it is **monophyletic** (from the Greek, meaning "single tribe"), signifying that it consists of an ancestral species and all of its descendants (see Figure 20.10a). Contrast this with a **paraphyletic** ("beside the tribe") group, which consists of an ancestral species and some, but not all, of its descendants **(Figure 20.10b)**, or a **polyphyletic** ("many tribes") group, which includes distantly related species but does not include their most recent common ancestor **(Figure 20.10c)**.

Note that in a paraphyletic group, the most recent common ancestor of all members of the group *is* part of the group, whereas in a polyphyletic group the most recent common ancestor *is not* part of the group. For example, a group consisting

of even-toed ungulates (hippopotamuses, deer, and their relatives) and their common ancestor is paraphyletic because it does not include cetaceans (whales, dolphins, and porpoises), which descended from that ancestor **(Figure 20.11)**.

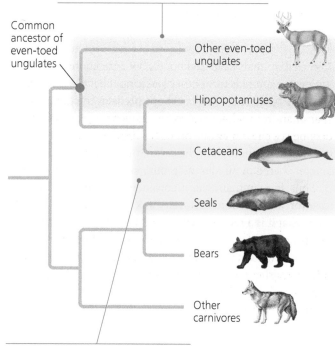

▲ **Figure 20.11 Paraphyletic vs. polyphyletic groups.**

? *Circle the branch point that represents the most recent common ancestor of cetaceans and seals. Explain why that ancestor would not be part of a cetacean-seal group defined by their similar body forms.*

▼ **Figure 20.10 Monophyletic, paraphyletic, and polyphyletic groups.**

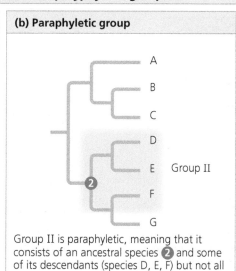

(a) Monophyletic group (clade)

Group I, consisting of three species (A, B, C) and their common ancestor **1**, is a monophyletic group (clade), meaning that it consists of an ancestral species and *all* of its descendants.

(b) Paraphyletic group

Group II is paraphyletic, meaning that it consists of an ancestral species **2** and some of its descendants (species D, E, F) but not all of them (does not include species G).

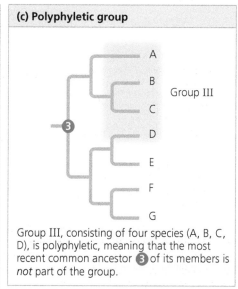

(c) Polyphyletic group

Group III, consisting of four species (A, B, C, D), is polyphyletic, meaning that the most recent common ancestor **3** of its members is *not* part of the group.

In contrast, a group consisting of seals and cetaceans (based on their similar body forms) would be polyphyletic because it does not include the common ancestor of seals and cetaceans. Biologists avoid defining such polyphyletic groups; if new evidence indicates that an existing group is polyphyletic, organisms in that group are reclassified.

Shared Ancestral and Shared Derived Characters

As a result of descent with modification, organisms have characteristics they share with their ancestors, and they also have characteristics that differ from those of their ancestors. For example, all mammals have backbones, but a backbone does not distinguish mammals from other vertebrates because *all* vertebrates have backbones. The backbone predates the branching of mammals from other vertebrates. Thus, for mammals, the backbone is a **shared ancestral character**, a character that originated in an ancestor of the taxon. In contrast, hair is a character shared by all mammals but *not* found in their ancestors. Thus, in mammals, hair is considered a **shared derived character**, an evolutionary novelty unique to a clade.

Note that it is a relative matter whether a character is considered ancestral or derived. A backbone can also qualify as a shared derived character, but only at a deeper branch point that distinguishes all vertebrates from other animals.

Inferring Phylogenies Using Derived Characters

Shared derived characters are unique to particular clades. Because all features of organisms arose at some point in the history of life, it should be possible to determine the clade in which each shared derived character first appeared and to use that information to infer evolutionary relationships.

To see an example of this approach, consider the set of characters shown in **Figure 20.12a** for each of five vertebrates—a leopard, turtle, frog, bass, and lamprey (a jawless aquatic vertebrate). As a basis of comparison, we need to select an outgroup. An **outgroup** is a closely related species or group of species from a lineage that is known to have diverged before the lineage that includes the species we are studying (the **ingroup**). A suitable outgroup can be determined based on evidence from morphology, paleontology, embryonic development, and gene sequences. An appropriate outgroup for our example is the lancelet, a small animal that lives in mudflats and (like vertebrates) is a member of the more inclusive group called the chordates. Unlike the vertebrates, however, the lancelet does not have a backbone.

By comparing members of the ingroup with each other and with the outgroup, we can determine which characters were derived at the various branch points of vertebrate evolution. For example, *all* of the vertebrates in the ingroup have backbones: This character was present in the ancestral vertebrate, but not in the outgroup. Now note that hinged jaws are a character absent in lampreys but present in other members of the ingroup; this character helps us to identify an early branch point in the vertebrate clade. Proceeding in this way, we can translate the data in our table of characters into a phylogenetic tree that places all the ingroup taxa into a hierarchy based on their derived characters **(Figure 20.12b)**.

Phylogenetic Trees with Proportional Branch Lengths

In the phylogenetic trees we have presented so far, the lengths of the tree's branches do not indicate the degree of

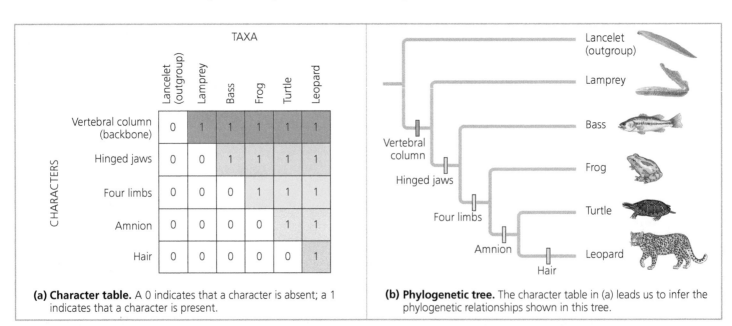

(a) Character table. A 0 indicates that a character is absent; a 1 indicates that a character is present.

(b) Phylogenetic tree. The character table in (a) leads us to infer the phylogenetic relationships shown in this tree.

▲ **Figure 20.12 Using derived characters to infer phylogeny.** The derived characters used here include the amnion, a membrane that encloses the embryo inside a fluid-filled sac (see Figure 27.28). Note that a different set of characters could lead us to infer a different phylogenetic tree.

DRAW IT *In (b), circle the most inclusive clade for which a hinged jaw is a shared ancestral character.*

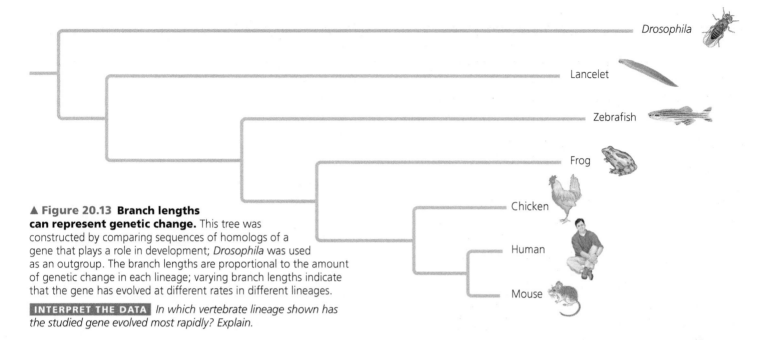

▲ **Figure 20.13 Branch lengths can represent genetic change.** This tree was constructed by comparing sequences of homologs of a gene that plays a role in development; *Drosophila* was used as an outgroup. The branch lengths are proportional to the amount of genetic change in each lineage; varying branch lengths indicate that the gene has evolved at different rates in different lineages.

INTERPRET THE DATA *In which vertebrate lineage shown has the studied gene evolved most rapidly? Explain.*

evolutionary change in each lineage. Furthermore, the chronology represented by the branching pattern of the tree is relative (earlier versus later) rather than absolute (how many millions of years ago). But in some tree diagrams, branch lengths are proportional to the amount of evolutionary change or to the length of time since particular events occurred.

In **Figure 20.13**, for example, the branch length of the phylogenetic tree reflects the number of changes that have taken place in a particular DNA sequence in that lineage. Note that the total length of the horizontal lines from the base of the tree to the mouse is less than that of the line leading to the outgroup species, the fruit fly *Drosophila*. This implies that in the time since the mouse and fly lineages diverged from their common ancestor, more genetic changes have occurred in the *Drosophila* lineage than in the mouse lineage.

Even though the branches of a phylogenetic tree may have different lengths, among organisms alive today, all the different lineages that descend from a common ancestor have survived for the same number of years. To take an extreme example, humans and bacteria had a common ancestor that lived over 3 billion years ago. Fossils and genetic evidence indicate that this ancestor was a single-celled prokaryote. Even though bacteria have apparently changed little in their morphology since that common ancestor, there have nonetheless been 3 billion years of evolution in the bacterial lineage, just as there have been 3 billion years of evolution in the lineage that ultimately gave rise to humans.

These equal spans of chronological time can be represented in a phylogenetic tree whose branch lengths are proportional to time (**Figure 20.14**). Such a tree draws on fossil data to place branch points in the context of geologic time. Additionally, it is possible to combine these two types of trees by labeling branch points with information about rates of genetic change or dates of divergence.

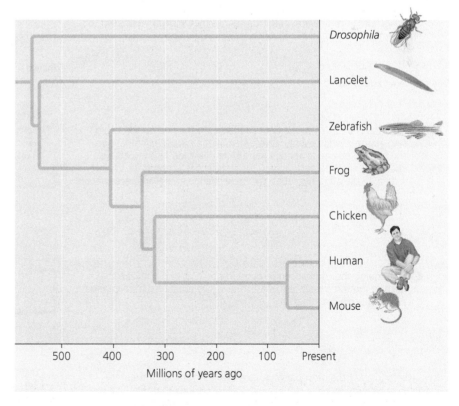

▲ **Figure 20.14 Branch lengths can indicate time.** This tree is based on the same molecular data as the tree in Figure 20.13, but here the branch points are mapped to dates based on fossil evidence. Thus, the branch lengths are proportional to time. Each lineage has the same total length from the base of the tree to the branch tip, indicating that all the lineages have diverged from the common ancestor for equal amounts of time.

Applying Parsimony to a Problem in Molecular Systematics

Application In considering possible phylogenies for a group of species, systematists compare molecular data for the species. An efficient way to begin is by identifying the most parsimonious hypothesis—the one that requires the fewest evolutionary events (molecular changes) to have occurred.

Technique Follow the numbered steps as we apply the principle of parsimony to a hypothetical phylogenetic problem involving three closely related bird species.

Species I   Species II   Species III

1 First, draw the three possible phylogenies for the species. (Although only 3 trees are possible when ordering 3 species, the number of possible trees increases rapidly with the number of species: There are 15 trees for 4 species and 34,459,425 trees for 10 species.)

Three phylogenetic hypotheses:

2 Tabulate the molecular data for the species. In this simplified example, the data represent a DNA sequence consisting of just four nucleotide bases. Data from several outgroup species (not shown) were used to infer the ancestral DNA sequence.

	Site 1	2	3	4
Species I	C	T	A	T
Species II	C	T	T	C
Species III	A	G	A	C
Ancestral sequence	A	G	T	T

3 Now focus on site 1 in the DNA sequence. In the tree on the left, a single base-change event, represented by the purple hatchmark on the branch leading to species I and II (and labeled 1/C, indicating a change at site 1 to nucleotide C), is sufficient to account for the site 1 data. In the other two trees, two base-change events are necessary.

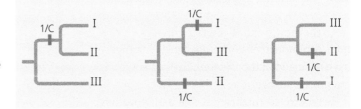

4 Continuing the comparison of bases at site 2, 3, and 4 reveals that each of the three trees requires a total of five additional base-change events (purple hatchmarks).

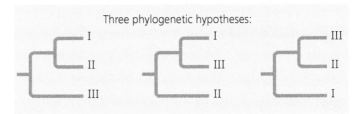

Results To identify the most parsimonious tree, we total all of the base-change events noted in steps 3 and 4. We conclude that the first tree is the most parsimonious of the three possible phylogenies. (In a real example, many more sites would be analyzed. Hence, the trees would often differ by more than one base-change event.)

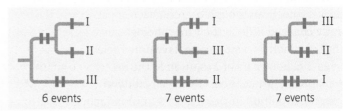
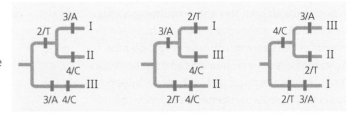

6 events   7 events   7 events

Maximum Parsimony

As the database of DNA sequences that enables us to study more species grows, the difficulty of building the phylogenetic tree that best describes their evolutionary history also grows. What if you are analyzing data for 50 species? There are 3×10^{76} different ways to arrange 50 species into a tree! And which tree in this huge forest reflects the true phylogeny? Systematists can never be sure of finding the most accurate tree in such a large data set, but they can narrow the possibilities by applying the principle of maximum parsimony.

According to the principle of **maximum parsimony**, we should first investigate the simplest explanation that is consistent with the facts. (The parsimony principle is also called "Occam's razor" after William of Occam, a 14th-century English philosopher who advocated this minimalist problem-solving approach of "shaving away" unnecessary complications.) In the case of trees based on morphology, the most parsimonious tree requires the fewest evolutionary events, as measured by the origin of shared derived morphological characters. For phylogenies based on DNA, the most parsimonious tree requires the fewest base changes.

Scientists have developed many computer programs to search for trees that are parsimonious. When a large amount of accurate data is available, the methods used in these programs usually yield similar trees. As an example of one method, **Figure 20.15** walks you through the process of identifying the most parsimonious molecular tree for a three-species problem. Computer programs use the principle of parsimony to estimate phylogenies in a similar way: They examine large numbers of possible trees and identify those that require the fewest evolutionary changes.

Phylogenetic Trees as Hypotheses

This is a good place to reiterate that any phylogenetic tree represents a hypothesis about how the organisms in the tree are related to one another. The best hypothesis is the one that best fits all the available data. A phylogenetic hypothesis may be modified when new evidence compels systematists to revise their trees. Indeed, while many older phylogenetic hypotheses have been supported by new morphological and molecular data, others have been changed or rejected.

Thinking of phylogenies as hypotheses also allows us to use them in a powerful way: We can make and test predictions based on the assumption that a particular phylogeny—our hypothesis—is correct. For example, in an approach known as *phylogenetic bracketing*, we can predict (by parsimony) that features shared by two groups of closely related organisms are present in their common ancestor and all of its descendants unless independent data indicate otherwise. (Note that "prediction" can refer to unknown past events as well as to evolutionary changes yet to occur.)

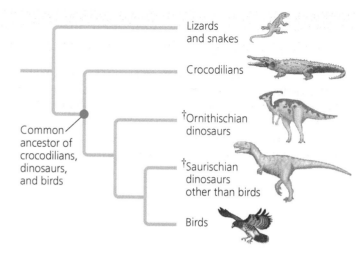

▲ **Figure 20.16 A phylogenetic tree of birds and their close relatives.** († indicates extinct lineages.)

? *What is the most basal taxon represented in this tree?*

This approach has been used to make novel predictions about dinosaurs. For example, there is evidence that birds descended from the theropods, a group of bipedal saurischian dinosaurs. As seen in **Figure 20.16**, the closest living relatives of birds are crocodiles. Birds and crocodiles share numerous features: They have four-chambered hearts, they "sing" to defend territories and attract mates (although a crocodile's "song" is more like a bellow), and they build nests **(Figure 20.17)**. Both birds and crocodiles also care for their eggs by *brooding*, a behavior in which a parent warms the eggs with its body. Birds brood by sitting on their eggs, whereas crocodiles cover their eggs with their neck. Reasoning that any feature shared by birds and crocodiles is likely to have been present in their common ancestor (denoted by the blue dot in Figure 20.16) and *all* of its descendants, biologists predicted that dinosaurs had four-chambered hearts, sang, built nests, and exhibited brooding.

▲ **Figure 20.17 A crocodile guards its nest.** After building its nest mound, this female African dwarf crocodile will care for the eggs until they hatch.

Internal organs, such as the heart, rarely fossilize, and it is, of course, difficult to test whether dinosaurs sang to defend territories and attract mates. However, fossilized dinosaur eggs and nests have provided evidence supporting the prediction of brooding in dinosaurs. First, a fossil embryo of an *Oviraptor* dinosaur was found, still inside its egg. This egg was identical to those found in another fossil, one that showed an *Oviraptor* crouching over a group of eggs in a posture similar to that seen in brooding birds today **(Figure 20.18)**. Researchers suggested that the *Oviraptor* dinosaur preserved in this second fossil died while incubating or protecting its eggs. The broader conclusion that emerged from this work—that dinosaurs built nests and exhibited brooding—has since been strengthened by additional fossil discoveries that show that other species of dinosaurs built nests and sat on their eggs. Finally, fossil discoveries of nests and brooding in dinosaurs support predictions based on the phylogenetic hypothesis shown in Figure 20.16. These fossils thus provide independent data which suggest that the hypothesis is correct.

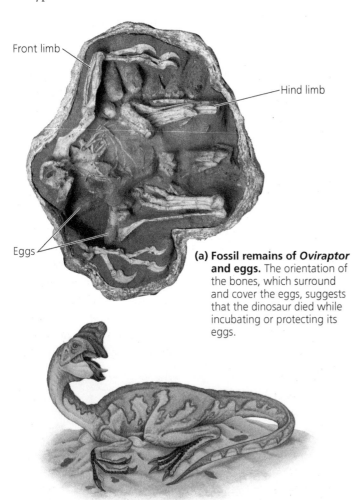

Front limb

Hind limb

Eggs

(a) **Fossil remains of *Oviraptor* and eggs.** The orientation of the bones, which surround and cover the eggs, suggests that the dinosaur died while incubating or protecting its eggs.

(b) **Artist's reconstruction of the dinosaur's posture based on the fossil findings.**

▲ **Figure 20.18 Fossil support for a phylogenetic prediction: Dinosaurs built nests and brooded their eggs.**

CONCEPT CHECK 20.3

1. To distinguish a particular clade of mammals within the larger clade that corresponds to class Mammalia, would hair be a useful character? Why or why not?
2. The most parsimonious tree of evolutionary relationships can be inaccurate. How can this occur?
3. **WHAT IF?** Draw a phylogenetic tree that includes the relationships from Figure 20.16 and those shown here. Traditionally, all the taxa shown besides birds and mammals were classified as reptiles. Would a cladistic approach support that classification? Explain.

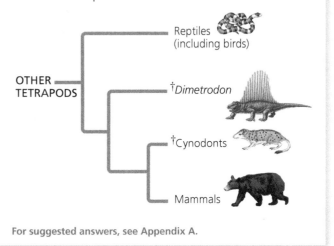

OTHER TETRAPODS

Reptiles (including birds)

†*Dimetrodon*

†Cynodonts

Mammals

For suggested answers, see Appendix A.

CONCEPT 20.4

Molecular clocks help track evolutionary time

One goal of evolutionary biology is to understand the relationships among all organisms, including those for which there is no fossil record. However, if we attempt to determine the timing of phylogenies that extend beyond the fossil record, we must rely on an important assumption about how change occurs at the molecular level.

Molecular Clocks

We stated earlier that researchers have estimated that the common ancestor of Hawaiian silversword plants lived about 5 million years ago. How did they make this estimate? They relied on the concept of a **molecular clock**, an approach for measuring the absolute time of evolutionary change based on the observation that some genes and other regions of genomes appear to evolve at constant rates. An assumption underlying the molecular clock is that the number of nucleotide substitutions in related genes is proportional to the time that has elapsed since the genes branched from their common ancestor (divergence time).

We can calibrate the molecular clock of a gene that has a reliable average rate of evolution by graphing the number of

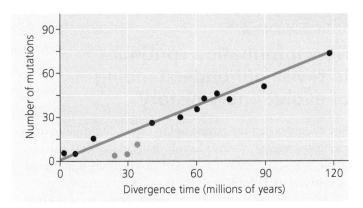

▲ **Figure 20.19 A molecular clock for mammals.** The number of accumulated mutations in seven proteins has increased over time in a consistent manner for most mammal species. The three green data points represent primate species, whose proteins appear to have evolved more slowly than those of other mammals. The divergence time for each data point was based on fossil evidence.

INTERPRET THE DATA *Use the graph to estimate the divergence time for a mammal with a total of 30 mutations in the seven proteins.*

genetic differences—for example, nucleotide, codon, or amino acid differences—against the dates of evolutionary branch points that are known from the fossil record **(Figure 20.19)**. The average rates of genetic change inferred from such graphs can then be used to estimate the dates of events that cannot be discerned from the fossil record, such as the origin of the silverswords discussed earlier.

Of course, no gene marks time with complete precision. In fact, some portions of the genome appear to have evolved in irregular bursts that are not at all clocklike. And even those genes that seem to act as reliable molecular clocks are accurate only in the statistical sense of showing a fairly smooth *average* rate of change. Over time, there may still be deviations from that average rate. Furthermore, the same gene may evolve at different rates in different groups of organisms. Finally, when comparing genes that are clocklike, the rate of the clock may vary greatly from one gene to another; some genes evolve a million times faster than others.

Differences in Clock Speed

What causes such differences in the speed at which clocklike genes evolve? The answer stems from the fact that some mutations are selectively neutral—neither beneficial nor detrimental. Of course, many new mutations are harmful and are removed quickly by selection. But if most of the rest are neutral and have little or no effect on survival and reproduction, then the rate of evolution of those neutral mutations should indeed be regular, like a clock. Differences in the clock rate for different genes are a function of how important a gene is. If the exact sequence of amino acids that a gene specifies is essential to survival, most of the mutational changes will be harmful and only a few will be neutral. As a result,

such genes change only slowly. But if the exact sequence of amino acids is less critical, fewer of the new mutations will be harmful and more will be neutral. Such genes change more quickly.

Potential Problems with Molecular Clocks

In fact, molecular clocks do not run as smoothly as would be expected if the underlying mutations were selectively neutral. Many irregularities are likely to be the result of natural selection in which certain DNA changes are favored over others. Indeed, evidence suggests that almost half the amino acid differences in proteins of two *Drosophila* species, *D. simulans* and *D. yakuba*, are not neutral but have resulted from natural selection. But because the direction of natural selection may change repeatedly over long periods of time (and hence may average out), some genes experiencing selection can nevertheless serve as approximate markers of elapsed time.

Another question arises when researchers attempt to extend molecular clocks beyond the time span documented by the fossil record. Although some fossils are more than 3 billion years old, these are very rare. An abundant fossil record extends back only about 550 million years, but molecular clocks have been used to date evolutionary divergences that occurred a billion or more years ago. These estimates assume that the clocks have been constant for all that time. Such estimates are highly uncertain.

In some cases, problems may be avoided by calibrating molecular clocks with data on the rates at which genes have evolved in different taxa. In other cases, problems may be avoided by using many genes rather just using one or a few genes. By using many genes, fluctuations in evolutionary rate due to natural selection or other factors that vary over time may average out. For example, one group of researchers constructed molecular clocks of vertebrate evolution from published sequence data for 658 nuclear genes. Despite the broad period of time covered (nearly 600 million years) and the fact that natural selection probably affected some of these genes, their estimates of divergence times agreed closely with fossil-based estimates. As this example suggests, if used with care, molecular clocks can aid our understanding of evolutionary relationships.

Applying a Molecular Clock: Dating the Origin of HIV

Researchers have used a molecular clock to date the origin of HIV infection in humans. Phylogenetic analysis shows that HIV, the virus that causes AIDS, is descended from viruses that infect chimpanzees and other primates. (Most of these viruses do not cause AIDS-like diseases in their native hosts.) When did HIV jump to humans? There is no simple answer, because the virus has spread to humans more than once. The multiple origins of HIV are reflected in the variety of strains

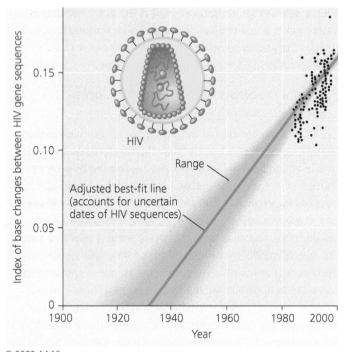

© 2000 AAAS

▲ **Figure 20.20 Dating the origin of HIV-1 M.** The black data points are based on DNA sequences of an HIV gene in patients' blood samples. (The dates when these individual HIV gene sequences arose are not certain because a person can harbor the virus for years before symptoms occur.) Projecting the gene's rate of change backward in time by this method suggests that the virus originated in the 1930s.

(genetic types) of the virus. HIV's genetic material is made of RNA, and like other RNA viruses, it evolves quickly.

The most widespread strain in humans is HIV-1 M. To pinpoint the earliest HIV-1 M infection, researchers compared samples of the virus from various times during the epidemic, including a sample from 1959. A comparison of gene sequences showed that the virus has evolved in a clock-like fashion **(Figure 20.20)**. Extrapolating backward in time using the molecular clock indicates that the HIV-1 M strain originated around 1930. A later study, which dated the origin of HIV using a more complex molecular clock approach than that covered in this book, estimated that the HIV-1 M strain originated about 1910.

CONCEPT CHECK 20.4

1. What is a molecular clock? What assumption underlies the use of a molecular clock?

2. **MAKE CONNECTIONS** Review Concept 14.5. Then explain how numerous base changes could occur in an organism's DNA yet have no effect on its survival and reproduction.

3. **WHAT IF?** Suppose a molecular clock dates the divergence of two taxa at 80 million years ago, but new fossil evidence shows that the taxa diverged at least 120 million years ago. Explain how this could happen.

For suggested answers, see Appendix A.

New information continues to revise our understanding of evolutionary history

The discovery that the glass lizard in Figure 20.1 evolved from a different lineage of legless lizards than did snakes is one example of how our understanding of life's diversity is informed by systematics. Indeed, in recent decades, systematists have gained insight into even the very deepest branches of the tree of life by analyzing DNA sequence data.

From Two Kingdoms to Three Domains

Taxonomists once classified all known species into two kingdoms: plants and animals. Classification schemes with more than two kingdoms gained broad acceptance in the late 1960s, when many biologists recognized five kingdoms: Monera (prokaryotes), Protista (a diverse kingdom consisting mostly of unicellular organisms), Plantae, Fungi, and Animalia. This system highlighted the two fundamentally different types of cells, prokaryotic and eukaryotic, and set the prokaryotes apart from all eukaryotes by placing them in their own kingdom, Monera.

However, phylogenies based on genetic data soon began to reveal a problem with this system: Some prokaryotes differ as much from each other as they do from eukaryotes. Such difficulties have led biologists to adopt a three-domain system **(Figure 20.21)**. The three domains—Bacteria, Archaea, and Eukarya—are a taxonomic level higher than the kingdom level. The validity of these domains is supported by many studies, including a recent study that analyzed nearly 100 completely sequenced genomes.

The domain Bacteria contains most of the currently known prokaryotes, while the domain Archaea consists of a diverse group of prokaryotic organisms that inhabit a wide variety of environments. The domain Eukarya consists of all the organisms that have cells containing true nuclei. This domain includes many groups of single-celled organisms as well as multicellular plants, fungi, and animals. Figure 20.21 represents one possible phylogenetic tree for the three domains and some of the many lineages they encompass.

The three-domain system highlights the fact that much of the history of life has been about single-celled organisms. The two prokaryotic domains consist entirely of single-celled organisms, and even in Eukarya, only the branches labeled in red type (plants, fungi, and animals) are dominated by multicellular organisms. Of the five kingdoms previously recognized by taxonomists, most biologists continue to recognize Plantae, Fungi, and Animalia, but not Monera and Protista. The kingdom Monera is obsolete because it would have members in two different domains. The kingdom Protista has also

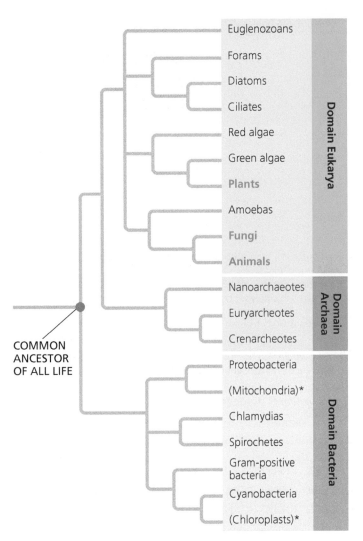

▲ **Figure 20.21 The three domains of life.** This phylogenetic tree is based on sequence data for rRNA and other genes. For simplicity, only some of the major branches in each domain are shown. Lineages within Eukarya that are dominated by multicellular organisms (plants, fungi, and animals) are in bold red type, while the two lineages denoted by an asterisk are based on DNA from cellular organelles. All other lineages consist solely or mainly of single-celled organisms.

MAKE CONNECTIONS *After reviewing endosymbiont theory (see Figure 4.16), explain the specific positions of the mitochondrion and chloroplast lineages on this tree.*

crumbled because it includes members that are more closely related to plants, fungi, or animals than to other protists (see Concept 25.3).

The Important Role of Horizontal Gene Transfer

In the phylogeny shown in Figure 20.21, the first major split in the history of life occurred when bacteria diverged from other organisms. If this tree is correct, eukaryotes and archaea are more closely related to each other than either is to bacteria.

This reconstruction of the tree of life is based in part on sequence comparisons of rRNA genes, which code for the RNA components of ribosomes. However, some other genes

reveal a different set of relationships. For example, researchers have found that many of the genes that influence metabolism in yeast (a unicellular eukaryote) are more similar to genes in the domain Bacteria than they are to genes in the domain Archaea—a finding that suggests that the eukaryotes may share a more recent common ancestor with bacteria than with archaea.

What causes trees based on data from different genes to yield such different results? Comparisons of complete genomes from the three domains show that there have been substantial movements of genes between organisms in the different domains. These took place through **horizontal gene transfer**, a process in which genes are transferred from one genome to another through mechanisms such as exchange of transposable elements and plasmids (see Concept 24.3), viral infection, and perhaps fusions of organisms (as when a host and its endosymbiont become a single organism). Because phylogenetic trees are based on the assumption that genes are passed vertically from one generation to the next, the occurrence of such horizontal transfer events helps to explain why trees built using different genes can give inconsistent results.

Recent research further highlights the importance of horizontal gene transfer. For example, a 2008 study showed that on average, 80% of the genes in 181 prokaryotic genomes had moved between species at some point during the course of evolution. Such findings have led some biologists to hypothesize that horizontal gene transfer was so common in the early history of life that this history should be represented as a tangled network of connected branches **(Figure 20.22)** rather than as a dichotomously branching tree like that in

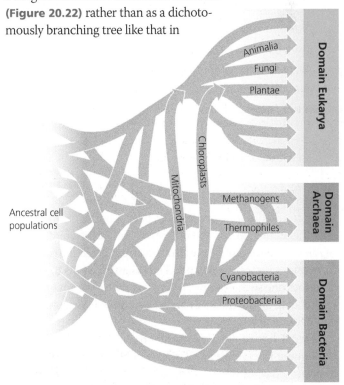

▲ **Figure 20.22 A tangled web of life.** Horizontal gene transfer may have been so common in the early history of life that the base of a "tree of life" might be more accurately portrayed as a tangled web.

Using Protein Sequence Data to Test an Evolutionary Hypothesis

Did Aphids Acquire Their Ability to Make Carotenoids Through Horizontal Gene Transfer? Carotenoids are colored molecules that have diverse functions in many organisms, such as photosynthesis in plants and light detection in animals. Plants and many microorganisms can synthesize carotenoids from scratch, but animals generally cannot (they must obtain carotenoids from their diet). One exception is the pea aphid *Acyrthosiphon pisum*, a small plant-dwelling insect whose genome includes a full set of genes for the enzymes needed to make carotenoids. Because other animals lack these genes, it is unlikely that aphids inherited them from a single-celled common ancestor shared with microorganisms and plants. So where did they come from? Evolutionary biologists hypothesize that an aphid ancestor acquired these genes by horizontal gene transfer from distantly related organisms.

How the Experiment Was Done Scientists obtained the DNA sequences for the carotenoid-biosynthesis genes from several species, including aphids, fungi, bacteria, and plants. A computer "translated" these sequences into amino acid sequences of the encoded polypeptides and aligned the amino acid sequences. This allowed the team to compare the corresponding polypeptides in the different organisms.

Data from the Experiment The sequences below show the first 60 amino acids of one polypeptide of the carotenoid-biosynthesis enzymes in the plant *Arabidopsis thaliana* (bottom) and the corresponding amino acids in five nonplant species, using the one-letter

abbreviations for the amino acids (see Figure 3.18). A hyphen (-) indicates a gap inserted in a sequence to optimize its alignment with the corresponding sequence in *Arabidopsis*.

1. In the rows of data for the organisms being compared with the aphid, highlight the amino acids that are identical to the corresponding amino acids in the aphid.
2. Which organism has the most amino acids in common with the aphid? Rank the partial polypeptides from the other four organisms in degree of similarity to that of the aphid.
3. Do these data support the hypothesis that aphids acquired the gene for this polypeptide by horizontal gene transfer? Why or why not? If horizontal gene transfer did occur, what type of organism is likely to have been the source?
4. What additional sequence data would support your hypothesis?
5. How would you account for the similarities between the aphid sequence and the sequences for the bacteria and plant?

(MB) A version of this Scientific Skills Exercise can be assigned in MasteringBiology.

Organism	Alignment of Amino Acid Sequences
Acyrthosiphon (aphid)	IKIIIIGSGV GGTAAAARLS KKGFQVEVYE KNSYNGGRCS IIR-HNGHRF DQGPSL--YL
Pantoea (bacterium)	KRTFVIGAGF GGLALAIRLQ AAGIATTVLE QHDKPGGRAY VWQ-DQGFTF DAGPTV--IT
Staphylococcus (bacterium)	MKIAVIGAGV TGLAAAARIA SQGHEVTIFE KNNNVGGRMN QLK-KDGFTF DMGPTI--VM
Ustilago (fungus)	KKVVIIGAGA GGTALAARLG RRGYSVTVLE KNSFGGGRCS LIH-HDGHRW DQGPSL--YL
Gibberella (fungus)	KSVIVIGAGV GGVSTAARLA KAGFKVTILE KNDFTGGRCS LIH-NDGHRF DQGPSL--LL
Arabidopsis (plant)	WDAVVIGGGH NGLTAAAYLA RGGLSVAVLE RRHVIGGAAV TEEIVPGFKF SRCSYLQGLL

Data from Nancy A. Moran, Yale University. See N. A. Moran and T. Jarvik, Lateral transfer of genes from fungi underlies carotenoid production in aphids, *Science* 328:624–627 (2010).

Figure 20.21. Moreover, horizontal gene transfer can also occur between eukaryotes. For example, over 200 cases of the horizontal transfer of transposons have been reported in eukaryotes, including humans and other primates, plants, birds, and reptiles. Nuclear genes have also been transferred horizontally from one eukaryote to another. The **Scientific Skills Exercise** describes one such example, giving you the opportunity to interpret data on the transfer of a pigment gene to an aphid from another species.

Overall, horizontal gene transfer has played a key role throughout the evolutionary history of life and it continues to occur today. Although scientists continue to debate whether early steps in the history of life are best represented as a tree or a tangled web, in recent decades there have been many exciting discoveries about evolutionary events that occurred over

time. We'll explore the mechanisms that underlie such events in the rest of this unit's chapters, beginning with factors that cause genetic change in populations.

CONCEPT CHECK 20.5

1. Why is the kingdom Monera no longer considered a valid taxon?
2. Explain why phylogenies based on different genes can yield different branching patterns for the tree of all life.
3. **WHAT IF?** Draw the three possible dichotomously branching trees showing evolutionary relationships for the domains Bacteria, Archaea, and Eukarya. Two of these trees have been supported by genetic data. Is it likely that the third tree might also receive such support? Explain your answer.

For suggested answers, see Appendix A.

Go to **MasteringBiology**® for Assignments, the eText, and the Study Area with Animations, Activities, Vocab Self-Quiz, and Practice Tests.

SUMMARY OF KEY CONCEPTS

VOCAB SELF-QUIZ

goo.gl/gbai8v

CONCEPT 20.1

Phylogenies show evolutionary relationships (pp. 396–399)

- Linnaeus's **binomial** classification system gives organisms two-part names: a **genus** plus a specific epithet.
- In the Linnaean system, species are grouped in increasingly broad taxa: Related genera are placed in the same **family**, families in **orders**, orders in **classes**, classes in **phyla**, phyla in **kingdoms**, and (more recently) kingdoms in **domains**.
- Systematists depict evolutionary relationships as branching **phylogenetic trees**. Many systematists propose that classification be based entirely on evolutionary relationships.

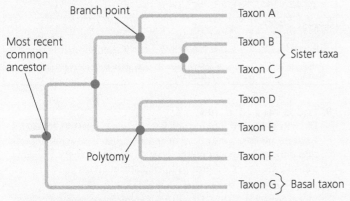

- Unless branch lengths are proportional to time or genetic change, a phylogenetic tree indicates only patterns of descent.
- Much information can be learned about a species from its evolutionary history; hence, phylogenies are useful in a wide range of applications.

> **?** *Humans and chimpanzees are sister species. Explain what that means.*

CONCEPT 20.2

Phylogenies are inferred from morphological and molecular data (pp. 399–400)

- Organisms with similar morphologies or DNA sequences are likely to be more closely related than organisms with very different structures and genetic sequences.
- To infer phylogeny, homology (similarity due to shared ancestry) must be distinguished from **analogy** (similarity due to convergent evolution).
- Computer programs are used to align comparable DNA sequences and to distinguish molecular homologies from coincidental matches between taxa that diverged long ago.

> **?** *Why is it necessary to distinguish homology from analogy to infer phylogeny?*

CONCEPT 20.3

Shared characters are used to construct phylogenetic trees (pp. 401–406)

- A **clade** is a **monophyletic** group that includes an ancestral species and all of its descendants.

- Clades can be distinguished by their **shared derived characters**.

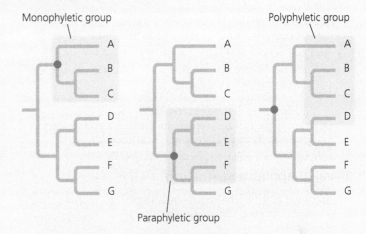

- Branch lengths can be proportional to amount of evolutionary change or time.
- Among phylogenies, the most parsimonious tree is the one that requires the fewest evolutionary changes.
- Well-supported phylogenetic hypotheses are consistent with a wide range of data.

> **?** *Explain the logic of using shared derived characters to infer phylogeny.*

CONCEPT 20.4

Molecular clocks help track evolutionary time (pp. 406–408)

- Some regions of DNA change at a rate consistent enough to serve as a **molecular clock**, in which the amount of genetic change is used to estimate the date of past evolutionary events. Other DNA regions change in a less predictable way.
- Molecular clock analyses suggest that the most common strain of HIV jumped from primates to humans in the early 1900s.

> **?** *Describe some assumptions and limitations of molecular clocks.*

CONCEPT 20.5

New information continues to revise our understanding of evolutionary history (pp. 408–410)

- Past classification systems have given way to the current view of the tree of life, which consists of three great domains: Bacteria, Archaea, and Eukarya.
- Phylogenies based in part on rRNA genes suggest that eukaryotes are most closely related to archaea, while data from some other genes suggest a closer relationship to bacteria.
- Genetic analyses indicate that extensive **horizontal gene transfer** has occurred throughout the evolutionary history of life.

> **?** *Why was the five-kingdom system abandoned for a three-domain system?*

TEST YOUR UNDERSTANDING

Level 1: Knowledge/Comprehension

PRACTICE TEST

goo.gl/CRZjvS

1. In a comparison of birds and mammals, the condition of having four limbs is
   (A) a shared ancestral character.
   (B) a shared derived character.
   (C) a character useful for distinguishing birds from mammals.
   (D) an example of analogy rather than homology.

2. To apply parsimony to constructing a phylogenetic tree,
   (A) choose the tree that assumes all evolutionary changes are equally probable.
   (B) choose the tree in which the branch points are based on as many shared derived characters as possible.
   (C) choose the tree that represents the fewest evolutionary changes, in either DNA sequences or morphology.
   (D) choose the tree with the fewest branch points.

Level 2: Application/Analysis

3. In Figure 20.4, which similarly inclusive taxon descended from the same common ancestor as Canidae?
   (A) Felidae
   (B) Mustelidae
   (C) Carnivora
   (D) *Lutra*

4. Three living species X, Y, and Z share a common ancestor T, as do extinct species U and V. A grouping that consists of species T, X, Y, and Z (but not U or V) makes up
   (A) a monophyletic taxon.
   (B) an ingroup, with species U as the outgroup.
   (C) a polyphyletic group.
   (D) a paraphyletic group.

5. Based on the tree below, which statement is *not* correct?

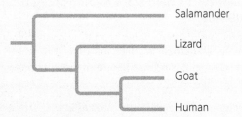

Salamander
Lizard
Goat
Human

   (A) The salamander lineage is a basal taxon.
   (B) Salamanders are a sister group to the group containing lizards, goats, and humans.
   (C) Salamanders are as closely related to goats as to humans.
   (D) Lizards are more closely related to salamanders than to humans.

6. If you were using cladistics to build a phylogenetic tree of cats, which of the following would be the best outgroup?
   (A) wolf
   (B) domestic cat
   (C) frog
   (D) leopard

7. The relative lengths of the frog and mouse branches in the phylogenetic tree in Figure 20.13 indicate that
   (A) frogs evolved before mice.
   (B) mice evolved before frogs.
   (C) the homolog has evolved more rapidly in mice.
   (D) the homolog has evolved more slowly in mice.

Level 3: Synthesis/Evaluation

8. **SCIENTIFIC INQUIRY**
   DRAW IT (a) Draw a phylogenetic tree based on characters 1–5 in the table below. Place hatch marks on the tree to indicate the origin(s) of characters 1–6. (b) Assume that tuna and dolphins are sister species, and redraw the phylogenetic tree accordingly. Use hatch marks to indicate the origin(s) of characters 1–6. (c) How many evolutionary changes are required in each tree? Which tree is most parsimonious?

Character	Lancelet (outgroup)	Lamprey	Tuna	Salamander	Turtle	Leopard	Dolphin
1. Backbone	0	1	1	1	1	1	1
2. Hinged jaw	0	0	1	1	1	1	1
3. Four limbs	0	0	0	1	1	1	1*
4. Amnion	0	0	0	0	1	1	1
5. Milk	0	0	0	0	0	1	1
6. Dorsal fin	0	0	1	0	0	0	1

*Although adult dolphins have only two obvious limbs (their flippers), as embryos they have two hind-limb buds, for a total of four limbs.

9. **FOCUS ON EVOLUTION**
   Darwin suggested looking at a species' close relatives to learn what its ancestors may have been like. Explain how his suggestion anticipates recent methods, such as phylogenetic bracketing and the use of outgroups in cladistic analysis.

10. **FOCUS ON INFORMATION**
    In a short essay (100–150 words), explain how genetic information—along with an understanding of the process of descent with modification—enables scientists to reconstruct phylogenies that extend hundreds of millions of years back in time.

11. **SYNTHESIZE YOUR KNOWLEDGE**

This West Indian manatee (*Trichechus manatus*) is an aquatic mammal. Like amphibians and reptiles, mammals are tetrapods (vertebrates with four limbs). Explain why manatees are considered tetrapods even though they lack hind limbs, and suggest traits that manatees likely share with leopards and other mammals (see Figure 20.12b). How might early members of the manatee lineage have differed from today's manatees?

For selected answers, see Appendix A.

21 The Evolution of Populations

KEY CONCEPTS

21.1 Genetic variation makes evolution possible

21.2 The Hardy-Weinberg equation can be used to test whether a population is evolving

21.3 Natural selection, genetic drift, and gene flow can alter allele frequencies in a population

21.4 Natural selection is the only mechanism that consistently causes adaptive evolution

▲ **Figure 21.1** Is this finch evolving?

The Smallest Unit of Evolution

One common misconception about evolution is that individual organisms evolve. It is true that natural selection acts on individuals: Each organism's traits affect its survival and reproductive success compared with that of other individuals. But the evolutionary impact of natural selection is only apparent in how a *population* of organisms changes over time.

Consider the medium ground finch (*Geospiza fortis*), a seed-eating bird that inhabits the Galápagos Islands **(Figure 21.1)**. In 1977, the *G. fortis* population on the island of Daphne Major was decimated by a long period of drought: Of some 1,200 birds, only 180 survived. Researchers Peter and Rosemary Grant observed that during the drought, small, soft seeds were in short supply. The finches mostly fed on large, hard seeds that were more plentiful. Birds with larger, deeper beaks were better able to crack and eat these larger seeds, and they survived at a higher rate than finches with smaller beaks. Since beak depth is an inherited trait in these birds, the offspring of surviving birds also tended to have deeper beaks. As a result, the average beak depth in the next generation of *G. fortis* was greater than it had been in the pre-drought

population **(Figure 21.2)**. The finch population had evolved by natural selection. However, the *individual* finches did not evolve. Each bird had a beak of a particular size, which did not grow larger during the drought. Rather, the proportion of large beaks in the population increased from generation to generation: The population evolved, not its individual members.

Focusing on evolutionary change in populations, we can define evolution on its smallest scale, called **microevolution**, as a change in allele frequencies in a population over generations. Let's apply this definition to the changes that occurred in

▶ **Figure 21.2 Evidence of selection by food source.** The data represent adult beak depth measurements of medium ground finches hatched in the generations before and after the 1977 drought. In a single generation, evolution by natural selection resulted in a larger average beak size in the population.

(MB) A related Experimental Inquiry Tutorial can be assigned in MasteringBiology.

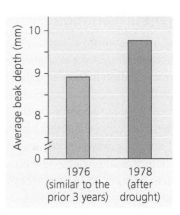

Average beak depth (mm)

1976 (similar to the prior 3 years)

1978 (after drought)

the *G. fortis* population on Daphne Major. As the proportion of individuals with large beaks increased from one generation to the next, so too did the frequency of alleles that encoded large beaks.

As the *G. fortis* example suggests, natural selection can cause allele frequencies to change over time. Moreover, as you will see in this chapter, natural selection is not the only cause of microevolution. In fact, there are three main mechanisms that can cause allele frequency change: natural selection, genetic drift (chance events that alter allele frequencies), and gene flow (the transfer of alleles between populations). Each of these mechanisms has distinctive effects on the genetic composition of populations. However, only natural selection consistently improves the degree to which organisms are well suited for life in their environment (adaptation). Before we examine natural selection and adaptation more closely, let's revisit a prerequisite for these processes in a population: genetic variation.

▲ **Figure 21.3 Phenotypic variation in horses.** In horses, coat color varies along a continuum and is influenced by multiple genes.

CONCEPT 21.1

Genetic variation makes evolution possible

In *The Origin of Species*, Darwin provided abundant evidence that life on Earth has evolved over time, and he proposed natural selection as the primary mechanism for that change. He observed that individuals differ in their inherited traits and that selection acts on such differences, leading to evolutionary change. Although Darwin realized that variation in heritable traits is a prerequisite for evolution, he did not know precisely how organisms pass heritable traits to their offspring.

Just a few years after Darwin published *The Origin of Species*, Gregor Mendel wrote a groundbreaking paper on inheritance in pea plants (see Concept 11.1). In that paper, Mendel proposed a model of inheritance in which organisms transmit discrete heritable units (now called genes) to their offspring. Although Darwin did not know about genes, Mendel's paper set the stage for understanding the genetic differences on which evolution is based. Here we'll examine such genetic differences and how they are produced.

Genetic Variation

Individuals within all species vary in their phenotypic traits. Among humans, for example, you can easily observe phenotypic variation in facial features, height, and voice. And though you cannot identify a person's blood group (A, B, AB, or O) from his or her appearance, this and many other molecular traits also vary extensively among individuals.

Such phenotypic variations often reflect **genetic variation**, differences among individuals in the composition of their genes or other DNA sequences. Some heritable phenotypic differences occur on an "either-or" basis, such as the flower colors of Mendel's pea plants: Each plant had flowers that were either purple or white (see Figure 11.3). Characters that vary in this way are typically determined by a single gene locus, with different alleles producing distinct phenotypes. In contrast, other phenotypic differences vary in gradations along a continuum. Such variation usually results from the influence of two or more genes on a single phenotypic character. In fact, many phenotypic characters are influenced by multiple genes, including coat color in horses **(Figure 21.3)**, seed number in maize (corn), and height in humans.

How much do genes and other DNA sequences vary from one individual to another? Genetic variation at the whole-gene level (*gene variability*) can be quantified as the average percentage of loci that are heterozygous. (Recall that a heterozygous individual has two different alleles for a given locus, whereas a homozygous individual has two identical alleles for that locus.) As an example, on average the fruit fly *Drosophila melanogaster* is heterozygous for about 1,920 of its 13,700 loci (14%) and homozygous for all the rest.

Considerable genetic variation can also be measured at the molecular level of DNA (*nucleotide variability*). But little of this variation results in phenotypic variation. Why? Many of the nucleotide variations occur within *introns*, noncoding segments of DNA lying between *exons*, the regions retained in mRNA after RNA processing (see Figure 14.12). And of the variations that occur within exons, most do not cause a change in the amino acid sequence of the protein encoded by the gene. For example, in the sequence comparison shown in **Figure 21.4**, there are 43 nucleotide sites with variable base pairs (where substitutions have occurred), as well as several sites where insertions or deletions have occurred. Although 18 variable sites occur within the four exons of the *Adh* gene, only one of these variations (at site 1,490) results in an amino acid change. Note, however, that this single variable site is enough to cause genetic variation at the level of the gene—and hence two different forms of the Adh enzyme are produced.

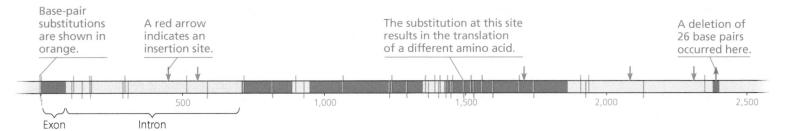

Base-pair substitutions are shown in orange.

A red arrow indicates an insertion site.

The substitution at this site results in the translation of a different amino acid.

A deletion of 26 base pairs occurred here.

1   500   1,000   1,500   2,000   2,500

Exon   Intron

▲ **Figure 21.4 Extensive genetic variation at the molecular level.** This diagram summarizes data from a study comparing the DNA sequence of the alcohol dehydrogenase (*Adh*) gene in several fruit flies (*Drosophila melanogaster*). The *Adh* gene has four exons (dark blue) separated by introns (light blue); the exons include the coding regions that are ultimately translated into the amino acids of the Adh enzyme. Only one substitution has a phenotypic effect, producing a different form of the Adh enzyme.

MAKE CONNECTIONS *Review Figures 14.6 and 14.12. Explain how a base-pair substitution that alters a coding region of the* Adh *locus could have no effect on amino acid sequence. Then explain how an insertion in an exon could have no effect on the protein produced.*

It is important to bear in mind that some phenotypic variation does not result from genetic differences among individuals (**Figure 21.5** shows a striking example in a caterpillar of the southwestern United States). Phenotype is the product of an inherited genotype and many environmental influences (see Concept 11.3). In a human example, bodybuilders alter their phenotypes dramatically but do not pass their huge muscles on to the next generation. In general, only the genetically determined part of phenotypic variation can have evolutionary consequences. As such, genetic variation provides the raw material for evolutionary change: Without genetic variation, evolution cannot occur.

Sources of Genetic Variation

The genetic variation on which evolution depends originates when mutation, gene duplication, or other processes produce new alleles and new genes. Genetic variants can be produced rapidly in organisms with short generation times. Sexual reproduction can also result in genetic variation as existing genes are arranged in new ways.

Formation of New Alleles

New alleles can arise by *mutation*, a change in the nucleotide sequence of an organism's DNA. A mutation is like a shot in the dark—we cannot predict accurately which segments of DNA will be altered or in what way. In multicellular organisms, only mutations in cell lines that produce gametes can be passed to offspring. In plants and fungi, this is not as limiting as it may sound, since many different cell lines can produce gametes. But in most animals, the majority of mutations occur in somatic cells and are not passed to offspring.

A change of as little as one base in a gene—a "point mutation"—can have a significant impact on phenotype, as in sickle-cell disease (see Figure 14.25). Organisms reflect many generations of past selection, and hence their phenotypes tend to be well-suited for life in their environments. As a result,

▲ **Figure 21.5 Nonheritable variation.** These caterpillars of the moth *Nemoria arizonaria* owe their different appearances to chemicals in their diets, not to differences in their genotypes. **(a)** Caterpillars raised on a diet of oak flowers resemble the flowers, whereas **(b)** their siblings raised on oak leaves resemble oak twigs.

most new mutations that alter a phenotype are at least slightly harmful. In some cases, natural selection quickly removes such harmful alleles. In diploid organisms, however, harmful alleles that are recessive can be hidden from selection. Indeed, a harmful recessive allele can persist for generations by propagation in heterozygous individuals (where its harmful effects are masked by the more favorable dominant allele). Such "heterozygote protection" maintains a huge pool of alleles that might not be favored under present conditions but that could be beneficial if the environment changes.

While many mutations are harmful, many others are not. Recall that much of the DNA in eukaryotic genomes does not encode proteins (see Figure 18.5). Point mutations in these noncoding regions generally result in **neutral variation**, differences in DNA sequence that do not confer a selective advantage or disadvantage. The redundancy in the genetic code is another source of neutral variation: Even a point mutation in a gene that encodes a protein will have no effect on the protein's function if the amino acid composition is not changed. And even where there is a change in the amino acid, it may not affect the protein's shape and function. Finally, as you will see later in this chapter, a mutant allele may on rare occasions actually make its bearer better suited to the environment, enhancing reproductive success.

Altering Gene Number or Position

Chromosomal changes that delete, disrupt, or rearrange many loci are usually harmful. However, when such large-scale changes leave genes intact, they may not affect the organisms' phenotypes. In rare cases, chromosomal rearrangements may even be beneficial. For example, the translocation of part of one chromosome to a different chromosome could link genes in a way that produces a positive effect.

A key potential source of variation is the duplication of genes due to errors in meiosis (such as unequal crossing over), slippage during DNA replication, or the activities of transposable elements (see Concept 18.4). Duplications of large chromosome segments, like other chromosomal aberrations, are often harmful, but the duplication of smaller pieces of DNA may not be. Gene duplications that do not have severe effects can persist over generations, allowing mutations to accumulate. The result is an expanded genome with new genes that may take on new functions.

Such increases in gene number appear to have played a major role in evolution. For example, the remote ancestors of mammals had a single gene for detecting odors that has since been duplicated many times. As a result, humans today have about 380 functional olfactory receptor genes, and mice have 1,200. This proliferation of olfactory genes has probably helped mammals over the course of evolution, enabling them to detect faint odors in their environment and to distinguish among many different smells.

Rapid Reproduction

Mutation rates tend to be low in plants and animals, averaging about one mutation in every 100,000 genes per generation, and they are often even lower in prokaryotes. But prokaryotes have many more generations per unit of time, so mutations can quickly generate genetic variation in their populations. The same is true of viruses. For instance, HIV has a generation time of about two days (that is, it takes two days for a newly formed virus to produce the next generation of viruses). HIV also has an RNA genome, which has a much higher mutation rate than a typical DNA genome because of the lack of RNA repair mechanisms in host cells. For this reason, single-drug treatments are unlikely to be effective against HIV: Mutant forms of the virus that are resistant to a particular drug would tend to proliferate in relatively short order. The most effective AIDS treatments to date have been drug "cocktails" that combine several medications. This approach has worked well because it is less likely that a set of mutations that together confer resistance to *all* the drugs will occur in a short time period.

Sexual Reproduction

In organisms that reproduce sexually, most of the genetic variation in a population results from the unique combination of alleles that each individual receives from its parents. Of course, at the nucleotide level, all the differences among these alleles have originated from past mutations. Sexual reproduction then shuffles existing alleles and deals them at random to produce individual genotypes.

Three mechanisms contribute to this shuffling: crossing over, independent assortment of chromosomes, and fertilization (see Concept 10.4). During meiosis, homologous chromosomes, one inherited from each parent, trade some of their alleles by crossing over. These homologous chromosomes and the alleles they carry are then distributed at random into gametes. Then, because myriad possible mating combinations exist in a population, fertilization brings together gametes that are likely to have different genetic backgrounds. The combined effects of these three mechanisms ensure that sexual reproduction rearranges existing alleles into fresh combinations each generation, providing much of the genetic variation that makes evolution possible.

CONCEPT CHECK 21.1

1. Explain why genetic variation within a population is a prerequisite for evolution.
2. Of all the mutations that occur in a population, why do only a small fraction become widespread?
3. **MAKE CONNECTIONS** If a population stopped reproducing sexually (but still reproduced asexually), how would its genetic variation be affected over time? Explain. (See Concept 10.4.)

For suggested answers, see Appendix A.

The Hardy-Weinberg equation can be used to test whether a population is evolving

Although the individuals in a population must differ genetically for evolution to occur, the presence of genetic variation does not guarantee that a population will evolve. For that to happen, one or more factors that cause evolution must be at work. In this section, we'll explore one way to test whether evolution is occurring in a population. First, let's clarify what we mean by a population.

Gene Pools and Allele Frequencies

A **population** is a group of individuals of the same species that live in the same area and interbreed, producing fertile offspring. Different populations of a species may be isolated geographically from one another, exchanging genetic material only rarely. Such isolation is common for species that live on widely separated islands or in different lakes. But not all populations are isolated (**Figure 21.6**). Still, members of a population typically breed with one another and thus on average are more closely related to each other than to members of other populations.

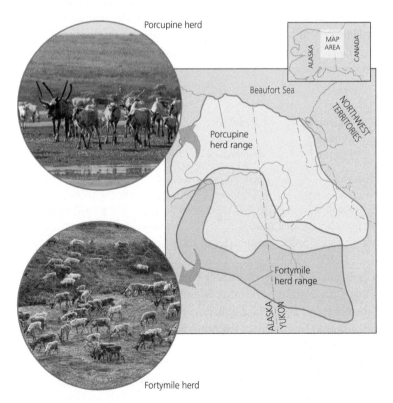

▲ **Figure 21.6 One species, two populations.** These two caribou populations in the Yukon are not totally isolated; they sometimes share the same area. Still, members of either population are most likely to breed within their own population.

We can characterize a population's genetic makeup by describing its **gene pool**, which consists of all copies of every type of allele at every locus in all members of the population. If only one allele exists for a particular locus in a population, that allele is said to be *fixed* in the gene pool, and all individuals are homozygous for that allele. But if there are two or more alleles for a particular locus in a population, individuals may be either homozygous or heterozygous.

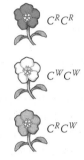

For example, imagine a population of 500 wildflower plants with two alleles, C^R and C^W, for a locus that codes for flower pigment. These alleles show incomplete dominance; thus, each genotype has a distinct phenotype. Plants homozygous for the C^R allele ($C^R C^R$) produce red pigment and have red flowers; plants homozygous for the C^W allele ($C^W C^W$) produce no red pigment and have white flowers; and heterozygotes ($C^R C^W$) produce some red pigment and have pink flowers.

Each allele has a frequency (proportion) in the population. For example, suppose our population has 320 plants with red flowers, 160 with pink flowers, and 20 with white flowers. Because these are diploid organisms, these 500 individuals have a total of 1,000 copies of the gene for flower color. The C^R allele accounts for 800 of these copies ($320 \times 2 = 640$ for $C^R C^R$ plants, plus $160 \times 1 = 160$ for $C^R C^W$ plants). Thus, the frequency of the C^R allele is $800/1,000 = 0.8$ (80%).

When studying a locus with two alleles, the convention is to use p to represent the frequency of one allele and q to represent the frequency of the other allele. Thus, p, the frequency of the C^R allele in the gene pool of this population, is 0.8 (80%). And because there are only two alleles for this gene, the frequency of the C^W allele, represented by q, must be $1 - p = 0.2$ (20%). For loci that have more than two alleles, the sum of all allele frequencies must still equal 1 (100%).

Next we'll see how allele and genotype frequencies can be used to test whether evolution is occurring in a population.

The Hardy-Weinberg Equation

One way to assess whether natural selection or other factors are causing evolution at a particular locus is to determine what the genetic makeup of a population would be if it were *not* evolving at that locus. We can then compare that scenario with the data we actually observed for the population. If there are no differences, we can conclude that the population is not evolving. If there are differences, this suggests that the population may be evolving—and then we can try to figure out why.

Hardy-Weinberg Equilibrium

In a population that is not evolving, allele and genotype frequencies will remain constant from generation to generation, provided that only Mendelian segregation and recombination of alleles are at work. Such a population is said to be in **Hardy-Weinberg equilibrium**, named for the British mathematician and German physician, respectively, who independently developed this idea in 1908.

To determine whether a population is in Hardy-Weinberg equilibrium, it is helpful to think about genetic crosses in a new way. Previously, we used Punnett squares to determine the genotypes of offspring in a genetic cross (see Figure 11.5). Here, instead of considering the possible allele combinations from one cross, we'll consider the combination of alleles in *all* of the crosses in a population.

Imagine that all the alleles for a given locus from all the individuals in a population are placed in a large bin **(Figure 21.7)**. We can think of this bin as holding the population's gene pool for that locus. "Reproduction" occurs by selecting alleles at random from the bin; somewhat similar events occur in nature when fish release sperm and eggs into the water or when pollen (containing plant sperm) is blown about by the wind. By viewing reproduction as a process of randomly selecting and combining alleles from the bin (the gene pool), we are in effect assuming that mating occurs at random—that is, that all male-female matings are equally likely.

Let's apply the bin analogy to the hypothetical wildflower population discussed earlier. In that population of 500 flowers,

the frequency of the allele for red flowers (C^R) is $p = 0.8$, and the frequency of the allele for white flowers (C^W) is $q = 0.2$. In other words, a bin holding all 1,000 copies of the flower-color gene in the population would contain 800 C^R alleles and 200 C^W alleles. Assuming that gametes are formed by selecting alleles at random from the bin, the probability that an egg or sperm contains a C^R or C^W allele is equal to the frequency of these alleles in the bin. Thus, as shown in Figure 21.7, each egg has an 80% chance of containing a C^R allele and a 20% chance of containing a C^W allele; the same is true for each sperm.

Using the rule of multiplication (see Figure 11.9), we can now calculate the frequencies of the three possible genotypes, assuming random unions of sperm and eggs. The probability that two C^R alleles will come together is $p \times p = p^2 = 0.8 \times 0.8 = 0.64$. Thus, about 64% of the plants in the next generation will have the genotype $C^R C^R$. The frequency of $C^W C^W$ individuals is expected to be about $q \times q = q^2 = 0.2 \times 0.2 = 0.04$, or 4%. $C^R C^W$ heterozygotes can arise in two different ways. If the sperm provides the C^R allele and the egg provides the C^W allele, the resulting heterozygotes will be $p \times q = 0.8 \times 0.2 = 0.16$, or 16% of the total. If the sperm provides the C^W allele and the egg the C^R allele, the heterozygous offspring will make up $q \times p = 0.2 \times 0.8 = 0.16$, or 16%. The frequency of heterozygotes is thus the sum of these possibilities: $pq + qp = 2pq = 0.16 + 0.16 = 0.32$, or 32%.

As shown in **Figure 21.8**, the genotype frequencies in the next generation must add up to 1 (100%). Thus, the equation for Hardy-Weinberg equilibrium states that at a locus with two alleles, the three genotypes will appear in the following proportions:

$$
\underset{\substack{\text{Expected} \\ \text{frequency} \\ \text{of genotype} \\ C^R C^R}}{p^2} + \underset{\substack{\text{Expected} \\ \text{frequency} \\ \text{of genotype} \\ C^R C^W}}{2pq} + \underset{\substack{\text{Expected} \\ \text{frequency} \\ \text{of genotype} \\ C^W C^W}}{q^2} = 1
$$

Note that for a locus with two alleles, only three genotypes are possible (in this case, $C^R C^R$, $C^R C^W$, and $C^W C^W$). As a result, the sum of the frequencies of the three genotypes must equal 1 (100%) in *any* population—regardless of whether the population is in Hardy-Weinberg equilibrium. The key point is that a population is in Hardy-Weinberg equilibrium only if the observed genotype frequency of one homozygote is p^2, the observed frequency of the other homozygote is q^2, and the observed frequency of heterozygotes is $2pq$. Finally, as suggested by Figure 21.8, if a population such as our wildflowers is in Hardy-Weinberg equilibrium and its members continue to mate randomly generation after generation, allele and genotype frequencies will remain constant. The system operates somewhat like a deck of cards: No matter how many times the deck is reshuffled to deal out new hands, the deck itself remains the same. Aces do not grow more numerous than jacks.

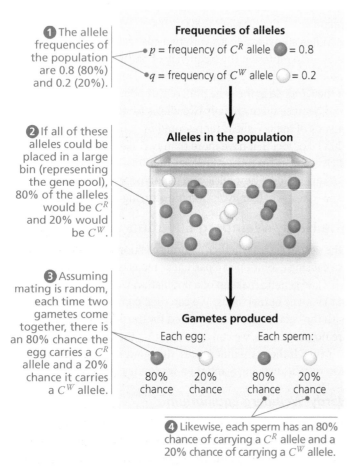

❶ The allele frequencies of the population are 0.8 (80%) and 0.2 (20%).

Frequencies of alleles

p = frequency of C^R allele ● = 0.8

q = frequency of C^W allele ○ = 0.2

❷ If all of these alleles could be placed in a large bin (representing the gene pool), 80% of the alleles would be C^R and 20% would be C^W.

Alleles in the population

❸ Assuming mating is random, each time two gametes come together, there is an 80% chance the egg carries a C^R allele and a 20% chance it carries a C^W allele.

Gametes produced

Each egg:

80% chance ● 20% chance ○

Each sperm:

80% chance ● 20% chance ○

❹ Likewise, each sperm has an 80% chance of carrying a C^R allele and a 20% chance of carrying a C^W allele.

▲ **Figure 21.7 Selecting alleles at random from a gene pool.**

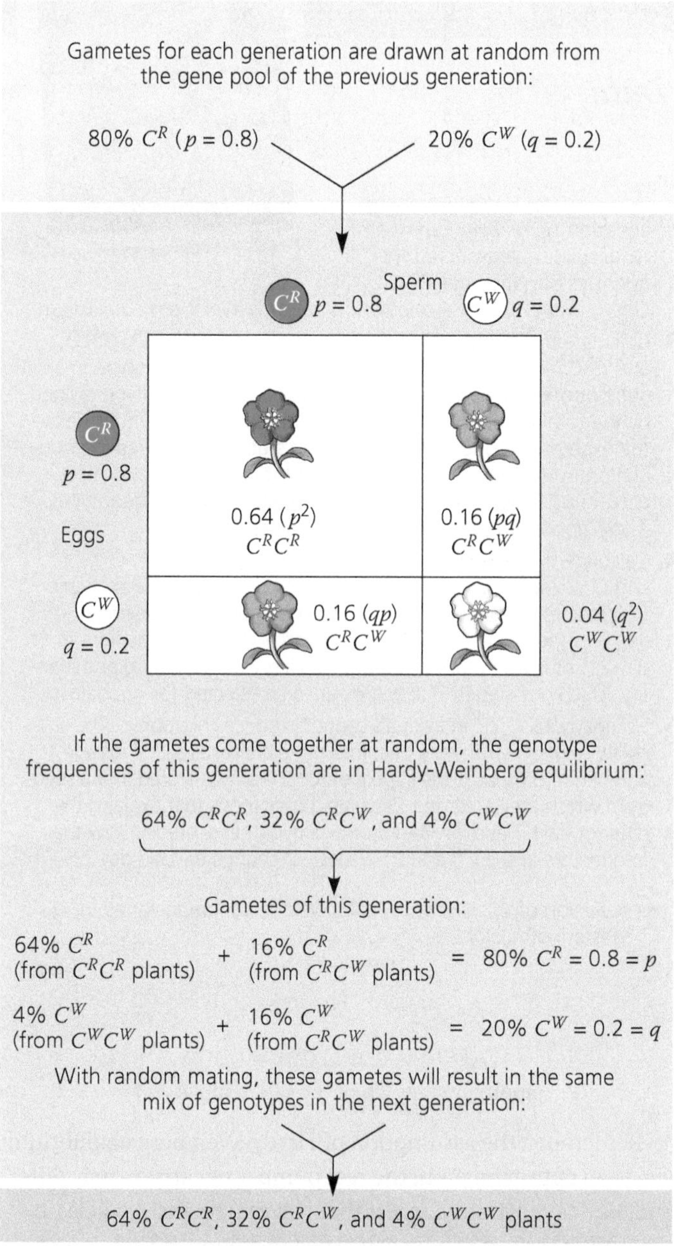

Gametes for each generation are drawn at random from the gene pool of the previous generation:

80% C^R ($p = 0.8$) 20% C^W ($q = 0.2$)

Sperm
C^R $p = 0.8$ C^W $q = 0.2$

C^R
$p = 0.8$

Eggs

C^W
$q = 0.2$

0.64 (p^2)
$C^R C^R$

0.16 (pq)
$C^R C^W$

0.16 (qp)
$C^R C^W$

0.04 (q^2)
$C^W C^W$

If the gametes come together at random, the genotype frequencies of this generation are in Hardy-Weinberg equilibrium:

64% $C^R C^R$, 32% $C^R C^W$, and 4% $C^W C^W$

Gametes of this generation:

64% C^R
(from $C^R C^R$ plants) + 16% C^R
(from $C^R C^W$ plants) = 80% $C^R = 0.8 = p$

4% C^W
(from $C^W C^W$ plants) + 16% C^W
(from $C^R C^W$ plants) = 20% $C^W = 0.2 = q$

With random mating, these gametes will result in the same mix of genotypes in the next generation:

64% $C^R C^R$, 32% $C^R C^W$, and 4% $C^W C^W$ plants

▲ **Figure 21.8 Hardy-Weinberg equilibrium.** In our wildflower population, the gene pool remains constant from one generation to the next. Mendelian processes alone do not alter frequencies of alleles or genotypes.

[?] *If the frequency of the C^R allele is 0.6, predict the frequencies of the $C^R C^R$, $C^R C^W$, and $C^W C^W$ genotypes.*

And the repeated shuffling of a population's gene pool over the generations cannot, in itself, change the frequency of one allele relative to another.

Conditions for Hardy-Weinberg Equilibrium

The Hardy-Weinberg equation describes a hypothetical population that is not evolving. But in real populations, the allele and genotype frequencies often *do* change over time. Such changes can occur when at least one of the following five conditions of Hardy-Weinberg equilibrium is not met.

1. **No mutations.** The gene pool is modified if mutations alter alleles or if entire genes are deleted or duplicated.
2. **Random mating.** If individuals tend to mate within a subset of the population, such as their near neighbors or close relatives (inbreeding), random mixing of gametes does not occur, and genotype frequencies change.
3. **No natural selection.** Allele frequencies can change when individuals with different genotypes differ in their survival or reproductive success.
4. **Extremely large population size.** The smaller the population, the more likely it is that allele frequencies will fluctuate by chance from one generation to the next (a process called genetic drift).
5. **No gene flow.** By moving alleles into or out of populations, gene flow can alter allele frequencies.

Departure from these conditions usually results in evolutionary change, which, as we've already described, is common in natural populations. But it is also common for natural populations to be in Hardy-Weinberg equilibrium for specific genes. One way this can occur is if selection alters allele frequencies at some loci but not others. In addition, some populations evolve so slowly that the changes in their allele and genotype frequencies are difficult to distinguish from those predicted for a non-evolving population.

Applying the Hardy-Weinberg Equation

The Hardy-Weinberg equation is often used as an initial test of whether evolution is occurring in a population (Concept Check 21.2, question 3 is an example). The equation also has medical applications, such as estimating the percentage of a population carrying the allele for an inherited disease. For example, consider phenylketonuria (PKU), a metabolic disorder that results from homozygosity for a recessive allele. This disorder occurs in about one out of every 10,000 babies born in the United States. Left untreated, PKU results in mental disability and other problems. (Newborns are now tested for PKU, and symptoms can be largely avoided with a diet very low in phenylalanine. For this reason, products that contain phenylalanine, such as diet colas, carry warning labels.)

To apply the Hardy-Weinberg equation, we must assume that no new PKU mutations are being introduced into the population (condition 1) and that people neither choose their mates on the basis of whether or not they carry this gene nor generally mate with close relatives (condition 2). We must also ignore any effects of differential survival and reproductive success among PKU genotypes (condition 3) and assume that there are no effects of genetic drift (condition 4) or of gene flow from

Using the Hardy-Weinberg Equation to Interpret Data and Make Predictions

Is Evolution Occurring in a Soybean Population? One way to test whether evolution is occurring in a population is to compare the observed genotype frequencies at a locus with those expected for a non-evolving population based on the Hardy-Weinberg equation. In this exercise, you'll test whether a soybean population is evolving at a locus with two alleles, C^G and C^Y, that affect chlorophyll production and hence leaf color.

How the Experiment Was Done Students planted soybean seeds and then counted the number of seedlings of each genotype at day 7 and again at day 21. Seedlings of each genotype could be distinguished visually because the C^G and C^Y alleles show incomplete dominance: $C^G C^G$ seedlings have green leaves, $C^G C^Y$ seedlings have green-yellow leaves, and $C^Y C^Y$ seedlings have yellow leaves.

Data from the Experiment

Time (days)	Green ($C^G C^G$)	Green-yellow ($C^G C^Y$)	Yellow ($C^Y C^Y$)	Total
	Number of Seedlings			
7	49	111	56	216
21	47	106	20	173

INTERPRET THE DATA

1. Use the observed genotype frequencies from the day 7 data to calculate the frequencies of the C^G allele (p) and the C^Y allele (q). (Remember that the frequency of an allele in a gene pool is the number of copies of that allele divided by the total number of copies of all alleles at that locus.)

2. Next, use the Hardy-Weinberg equation ($p^2 + 2pq + q^2 = 1$) to calculate the expected frequencies of genotypes $C^G C^G$, $C^G C^Y$, and $C^Y C^Y$ for a population in Hardy-Weinberg equilibrium.

3. Calculate the observed frequencies of genotypes $C^G C^G$, $C^G C^Y$, and $C^Y C^Y$ at day 7. (The observed frequency of a genotype in a gene pool is the number of individuals with that genotype divided by the total number of individuals.) Compare these frequencies to the expected frequencies calculated in step 2. Is the seedling population in Hardy-Weinberg equilibrium at day 7, or is evolution occurring? Explain your reasoning and identify which genotypes, if any, appear to be selected for or against.

4. Calculate the observed frequencies of genotypes $C^G C^G$, $C^G C^Y$, and $C^Y C^Y$ at day 21. Compare these frequencies to the expected frequencies calculated in step 2 and the observed frequencies at day 7. Is the seedling population in Hardy-Weinberg equilibrium at day 21, or is evolution occurring? Explain your reasoning and identify which genotypes, if any, appear to be selected for or against.

5. Homozygous $C^Y C^Y$ individuals cannot produce chlorophyll. The ability to photosynthesize becomes more critical as seedlings age and begin to exhaust the supply of food that was stored in the seed from which they emerged. Develop a hypothesis that explains the data for days 7 and 21. Based on this hypothesis, predict how the frequencies of the C^G and C^Y alleles will change beyond day 21.

(MB) A version of this Scientific Skills Exercise can be assigned in MasteringBiology.

---

other populations into the United States (condition 5). These assumptions are reasonable: The mutation rate for the PKU gene is low, inbreeding and other forms of nonrandom mating are not common in the United States, selection occurs only against the rare homozygotes (and then only if dietary restrictions are not followed), the U.S. population is very large, and populations outside the country have PKU allele frequencies similar to those seen in the United States.

If all these assumptions hold, then the frequency of individuals in the population born with PKU will correspond to q^2 in the Hardy-Weinberg equation (q^2 = frequency of homozygotes). Because the allele is recessive, we must estimate the number of heterozygotes rather than counting them directly as we did with the pink flowers. Since we know there is one PKU occurrence per 10,000 births ($q^2 = 0.0001$), the frequency (q) of the recessive allele for PKU is

$$q = \sqrt{0.0001} = 0.01$$

and the frequency of the dominant allele is

$$p = 1 - q = 1 - 0.01 = 0.99$$

The frequency of carriers, heterozygous people who do not have PKU but may pass the PKU allele to offspring, is

$$2pq = 2 \times 0.99 \times 0.01 = 0.0198$$
(approximately 2% of the U.S. population)

Remember, the assumption of Hardy-Weinberg equilibrium yields an approximation; the real number of carriers may differ. Still, our calculations suggest that harmful recessive alleles at this and other loci can be concealed in a population because they are carried by healthy heterozygotes. The **Scientific Skills Exercise** provides another opportunity for you to apply the Hardy-Weinberg equation to allele data.

CONCEPT CHECK 21.2

1. A population has 700 individuals, 85 of genotype AA, 320 of genotype Aa, and 295 of genotype aa. What are the frequencies of alleles A and a?

2. The frequency of allele a is 0.45 for a population in Hardy-Weinberg equilibrium. What are the expected frequencies of genotypes AA, Aa, and aa?

3. **WHAT IF?** A locus that affects susceptibility to a degenerative brain disease has two alleles, V and v. In a population, 16 people have genotype VV, 92 have genotype Vv, and 12 have genotype vv. Is this population evolving? Explain.

For suggested answers, see Appendix A.

CONCEPT 21.3

Natural selection, genetic drift, and gene flow can alter allele frequencies in a population

Note again the five conditions required for a population to be in Hardy-Weinberg equilibrium. A deviation from any of these conditions is a potential cause of evolution. New mutations (violation of condition 1) can alter allele frequencies, but because mutations are rare, the change from one generation to the next is likely to be very small. Nonrandom mating (violation of condition 2) can affect the frequencies of homozygous and heterozygous genotypes but by itself has no effect on allele frequencies in the gene pool. (Allele frequencies can change if individuals with certain inherited traits are more likely than other individuals to obtain mates. However, such a situation not only causes a deviation from random mating, but also violates condition 3, no natural selection.)

For the rest of this section, we will focus on the three mechanisms that alter allele frequencies directly and cause most evolutionary change: natural selection, genetic drift, and gene flow (violations of conditions 3–5).

Natural Selection

The concept of natural selection is based on differential success in survival and reproduction: Individuals in a population exhibit variations in their heritable traits, and those with traits that are better suited to their environment tend to produce more offspring than those with traits that are not as well suited.

In genetic terms, selection results in alleles being passed to the next generation in proportions that differ from those in the present generation. For example, the fruit fly *D. melanogaster* has an allele that confers resistance to several insecticides, including DDT. This allele has a frequency of 0% in laboratory strains of *D. melanogaster* established from flies collected in the wild in the early 1930s, prior to DDT use. However, in strains established from flies collected after 1960 (following 20 or more years of DDT use), the allele frequency is 37%. We can infer that this allele either arose by mutation between 1930 and 1960 or was present in 1930, but very rare. In any case, the rise in frequency of this allele most likely occurred because DDT is a powerful poison that is a strong selective force in exposed fly populations.

As the *D. melanogaster* example suggests, an allele that confers resistance to an insecticide will increase in frequency in a population exposed to that insecticide. Such changes are not coincidental. By consistently favoring some alleles over others, natural selection can cause *adaptive evolution* (a process in which traits that enhance survival or reproduction tend to increase in frequency over time). We'll explore this process in more detail later in this chapter.

Genetic Drift

If you flip a coin 1,000 times, a result of 700 heads and 300 tails might make you suspicious about that coin. But if you flip a coin only 10 times, an outcome of 7 heads and 3 tails would not be surprising. The smaller the number of coin flips, the more likely it is that chance alone will cause a deviation from the predicted result. (In this case, the prediction is an equal number of heads and tails.) Chance events can also cause allele frequencies to fluctuate unpredictably from one generation to the next, especially in small populations—a process called **genetic drift**.

Figure 21.9 models how genetic drift might affect a small population of our wildflowers. In this example, drift leads to the

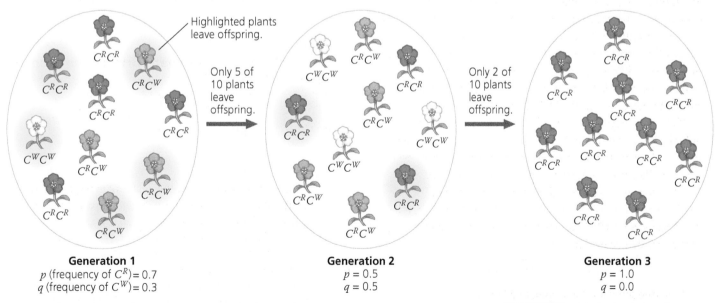

Generation 1
p (frequency of C^R) = 0.7
q (frequency of C^W) = 0.3

Generation 2
p = 0.5
q = 0.5

Generation 3
p = 1.0
q = 0.0

▲ **Figure 21.9 Genetic drift.** This small wildflower population has a stable size of ten plants. Suppose that by chance only five plants of generation 1 (those highlighted in yellow) produce fertile offspring. (This could occur, for example, if only those plants happened to grow in a location that provided enough nutrients to support the production of offspring.) Again by chance, only two plants of generation 2 leave fertile offspring. As a result, by chance the frequency of the C^W allele first increases in generation 2 and then falls to zero in generation 3.

 ANIMATION
Visit the Study Area in **MasteringBiology** for the BioFix® 3-D Animation on Mechanisms of Evolution.

loss of an allele from the gene pool, but it is a matter of chance that the C^W allele is lost and not the C^R allele. Such unpredictable changes in allele frequencies can be caused by chance events associated with survival and reproduction. Perhaps a large animal such as a moose stepped on the three $C^W C^W$ individuals in generation 2, killing them and increasing the chance that only the C^R allele would be passed to the next generation. Allele frequencies can also be affected by chance events that occur during fertilization. For example, suppose two individuals of genotype $C^R C^W$ had a small number of offspring. By chance alone, every egg and sperm pair that generated offspring could happen to have carried the C^R allele and not the C^W allele.

Certain circumstances can result in genetic drift having a significant impact on a population. Two examples are the founder effect and the bottleneck effect.

The Founder Effect

When a few individuals become isolated from a larger population, this smaller group may establish a new population whose gene pool differs from the source population; this is called the **founder effect**. The founder effect might occur, for example, when a few members of a population are blown by a storm to a new island. Genetic drift, in which chance events alter allele frequencies, can occur in such a case because the storm indiscriminately transports some individuals (and their alleles), but not others, from the source population.

The founder effect probably accounts for the relatively high frequency of certain inherited disorders among isolated human populations. For example, in 1814, 15 British colonists founded a settlement on Tristan da Cunha, a group of small islands in the Atlantic Ocean midway between Africa and South America. Apparently, one of the colonists carried a recessive allele for retinitis pigmentosa, a progressive form of blindness that afflicts homozygous individuals. Of the founding colonists' 240 descendants on the island in the late 1960s, 4 had retinitis pigmentosa. The frequency of the allele that causes this disease is ten times higher on Tristan da Cunha than in the populations from which the founders came.

The Bottleneck Effect

A sudden change in the environment, such as a fire or flood, may drastically reduce the size of a population. A severe drop in population size can cause the **bottleneck effect**, so named because the population has passed through a "bottleneck" that reduces its size **(Figure 21.10)**. By chance alone, certain alleles may be overrepresented among the survivors, others may be underrepresented, and some may be absent altogether. Ongoing genetic drift is likely to have substantial effects on the gene pool until the population becomes large enough that chance events have less impact. But even if a population that has passed through a bottleneck ultimately recovers in size, it may have low levels of genetic variation for a long period of time—a legacy of the genetic drift that occurred when the population was small.

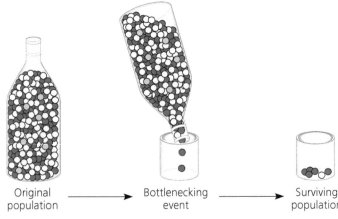

(a) Shaking just a few marbles through the narrow neck of a bottle is analogous to a drastic reduction in the size of a population. By chance, blue marbles are overrepresented in the surviving population, and gold marbles are absent.

(b) Similarly, bottlenecking a wild population tends to reduce genetic variation, as in the Florida panther (*Puma concolor coryi*), a subspecies in danger of extinction.

▲ **Figure 21.10 The bottleneck effect.**

One reason it is important to understand the bottleneck effect is that human actions sometimes create severe bottlenecks for other species, as the following example shows.

Case Study: *Impact of Genetic Drift on the Greater Prairie Chicken*

Millions of greater prairie chickens (*Tympanuchus cupido*) once lived on the prairies of Illinois. As these prairies were converted to farmland and other uses during the 19th and 20th centuries, the number of greater prairie chickens plummeted **(Figure 21.11a)**. By 1993, fewer than 50 birds remained. These few surviving birds had low levels of genetic variation, and less than 50% of their eggs hatched, compared with much higher hatching rates of the larger populations in Kansas and Nebraska **(Figure 21.11b)**.

These data suggest that genetic drift during the bottleneck may have led to a loss of genetic variation and an increase in the frequency of harmful alleles. To investigate this hypothesis, researchers extracted DNA from 15 museum specimens of Illinois greater prairie chickens. Of the 15 birds, 10 had been collected in the 1930s, when there were 25,000 greater prairie chickens in Illinois, and 5 had been collected in the 1960s,

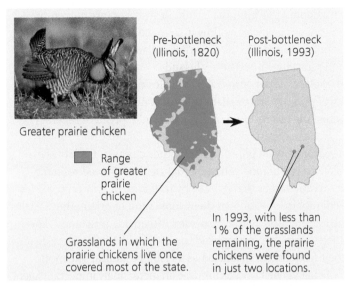

Greater prairie chicken

Pre-bottleneck (Illinois, 1820) Post-bottleneck (Illinois, 1993)

■ Range of greater prairie chicken

Grasslands in which the prairie chickens live once covered most of the state.

In 1993, with less than 1% of the grasslands remaining, the prairie chickens were found in just two locations.

(a) The Illinois population of greater prairie chickens dropped from millions of birds in the 1800s to fewer than 50 birds in 1993.

Location	Population size	Number of alleles per locus	Percentage of eggs hatched
Illinois			
1930–1960s	1,000–25,000	5.2	93
1993	<50	3.7	<50
Kansas, 1998 (no bottleneck)	750,000	5.8	99
Nebraska, 1998 (no bottleneck)	75,000–200,000	5.8	96

(b) As a consequence of the drastic reduction in the size of the Illinois population, genetic drift resulted in a drop in the number of alleles per locus (averaged across six loci studied) and a decrease in the percentage of eggs that hatched.

▲ **Figure 21.11 Genetic drift and loss of genetic variation.**

when there were 1,000 greater prairie chickens in Illinois. By studying the DNA of these specimens, the researchers were able to obtain a minimum, baseline estimate of how much genetic variation was present in the Illinois population *before* the population shrank to extremely low numbers. This baseline estimate is a key piece of information that is not usually available in cases of population bottlenecks.

The researchers surveyed six loci and found that the 1993 population had fewer alleles per locus than the pre-bottleneck Illinois or the current Kansas and Nebraska populations (see Figure 21.11b). Thus, as predicted, drift had reduced the genetic variation of the small 1993 population. Drift may also have increased the frequency of harmful alleles, leading to the low egg-hatching rate. To counteract these negative effects,

271 birds from neighboring states were added to the Illinois population over four years. This strategy succeeded: New alleles entered the population, and the egg-hatching rate improved to over 90%. Overall, studies on the Illinois greater prairie chicken illustrate the powerful effects of genetic drift in small populations and provide hope that in at least some populations, these effects can be reversed.

Effects of Genetic Drift: A Summary

The examples we've described highlight four key points:

1. **Genetic drift is significant in small populations.** Chance events can cause an allele to be disproportionately over- or underrepresented in the next generation. Although chance events occur in populations of all sizes, they tend to alter allele frequencies substantially only in small populations.
2. **Genetic drift can cause allele frequencies to change at random.** Because of genetic drift, an allele may increase in frequency one year and then decrease the next; the change from year to year is not predictable. Thus, unlike natural selection, which in a given environment consistently favors some alleles over others, genetic drift causes allele frequencies to change at random over time.
3. **Genetic drift can lead to a loss of genetic variation within populations.** By causing allele frequencies to fluctuate randomly over time, genetic drift can eliminate alleles from a population. Because evolution depends on genetic variation, such losses can influence how effectively a population can adapt to a change in the environment.
4. **Genetic drift can cause harmful alleles to become fixed.** Alleles that are neither harmful nor beneficial can be lost or become fixed by chance through genetic drift. In very small populations, genetic drift can also cause alleles that are slightly harmful to become fixed. When this occurs, the population's survival can be threatened (as in the case of the greater prairie chicken).

Gene Flow

Natural selection and genetic drift are not the only phenomena affecting allele frequencies. Allele frequencies can also change by **gene flow**, the transfer of alleles into or out of a population due to the movement of fertile individuals or their gametes. For example, suppose that near our original hypothetical wildflower population there is another population consisting primarily of white-flowered individuals ($C^W C^W$). Insects carrying pollen from these plants may fly to and pollinate plants in our original population. The introduced C^W alleles would modify our original population's allele frequencies in the next generation. Because alleles are transferred between populations, gene flow tends to reduce the genetic differences between populations. In fact, if it is extensive enough, gene flow can result in two populations combining into a single population with a common gene pool.

Alleles transferred by gene flow can also affect how well populations are adapted to local environmental conditions. Researchers studying the songbird *Parus major* (great tit) on the small Dutch island of Vlieland noted survival differences between two populations on the island. The survival rate of females born in the eastern population is twice that of females born in the central population, regardless of where the females eventually settle and raise offspring **(Figure 21.12)**. This finding suggests that females born in the eastern population are better adapted to life on the island than females born in the central population. But field studies also showed that the two populations are connected by high levels of gene flow (mating), which should reduce genetic differences between them. So how can the eastern population be better adapted to life on Vlieland than the central population?

The answer lies in the unequal amounts of gene flow from the mainland. In any given year, 43% of the first-time breeders in the central population are immigrants from the mainland, compared with only 13% in the eastern population. Birds with mainland genotypes survive and reproduce poorly on Vlieland, and in the eastern population, selection reduces the frequency of these genotypes. In the central population, however, gene flow from the mainland is so high that it overwhelms the effects of selection. As a result, females born in the central population have many immigrant genes, reducing the degree to which members of that population

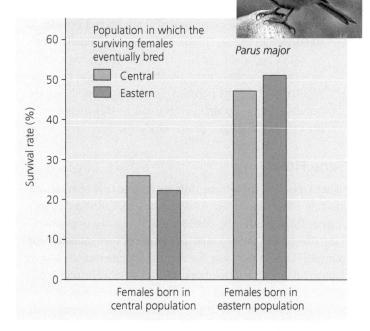

▲ **Figure 21.12 Gene flow and local adaptation.** In *Parus major* populations on Vlieland, the yearly survival rate of females born in the central population is lower than that of females born in the eastern population. Gene flow from the mainland is much higher to the central population than it is to the eastern population, and birds from the mainland are selected against in both populations. These data suggest that gene flow from the mainland has prevented the central population from adapting fully to its local conditions.

are adapted to life on the island. Researchers are currently investigating why gene flow is so much higher in the central population and why birds with mainland genotypes survive and reproduce poorly on Vlieland.

Gene flow can also transfer alleles that improve the ability of populations to adapt to local conditions. For example, gene flow has resulted in the worldwide spread of several insecticide-resistance alleles in the mosquito *Culex pipiens*, a vector of West Nile virus and other diseases. Each of these alleles has a unique genetic signature that allowed researchers to document that it arose by mutation in only one or a few geographic locations. In their population of origin, these alleles increased because they provided insecticide resistance. These alleles were then transferred to new populations, where again, their frequencies increased as a result of natural selection.

Finally, gene flow has become an increasingly important agent of evolutionary change in human populations. Humans today move much more freely about the world than in the past. As a result, mating is more common between members of populations that previously had very little contact, leading to an exchange of alleles and fewer genetic differences between those populations.

CONCEPT CHECK 21.3

1. In what sense is natural selection more "predictable" than genetic drift?

2. Distinguish genetic drift from gene flow in terms of (a) how they occur and (b) their implications for future genetic variation in a population.

3. **WHAT IF?** Suppose two plant populations exchange pollen and seeds. In one population, individuals of genotype *AA* are most common (9,000 *AA*, 900 *Aa*, 100 *aa*), while the opposite is true in the other population (100 *AA*, 900 *Aa*, 9,000 *aa*). If neither allele has a selective advantage, what will happen over time to the allele and genotype frequencies of these populations?

For suggested answers, see Appendix A.

CONCEPT 21.4

Natural selection is the only mechanism that consistently causes adaptive evolution

Evolution by natural selection is a blend of chance and "sorting": chance in the creation of new genetic variations (as in mutation) and sorting as natural selection favors some alleles over others. Because of this favoring process, the outcome of natural selection is *not* random. Instead, natural selection consistently increases the frequencies of alleles that provide reproductive advantage, thus leading to **adaptive evolution**.

Natural Selection: *A Closer Look*

In examining how natural selection brings about adaptive evolution, we'll begin with the concept of relative fitness and the different ways that an organism's phenotype is subject to natural selection.

Relative Fitness

The phrases "struggle for existence" and "survival of the fittest" are commonly used to describe natural selection, but these expressions are misleading if taken to mean direct competitive contests among individuals. There *are* animal species in which individuals, usually the males, lock horns or otherwise do combat to determine mating privilege. But reproductive success is generally more subtle and depends on many factors besides outright battle. For example, a barnacle that is more efficient at collecting food than its neighbors may have greater stores of energy and hence be able to produce a larger number of eggs. A moth may have more offspring than other moths in the same population because its body colors more effectively conceal it from predators, improving its chance of surviving long enough to produce more offspring. These examples illustrate how in a given environment, certain traits can lead to greater **relative fitness**: the contribution an individual makes to the gene pool of the next generation *relative to* the contributions of other individuals.

Although we often refer to the relative fitness of a genotype, remember that the entity that is subjected to natural selection is the whole organism, not the underlying genotype. Thus, selection acts more directly on the phenotype than on the genotype; it acts on the genotype indirectly, via how the genotype affects the phenotype.

Directional, Disruptive, and Stabilizing Selection

Natural selection can occur in three ways, depending on which phenotypes in a population are favored. These three modes of selection are called directional selection, disruptive selection, and stabilizing selection.

Directional selection occurs when conditions favor individuals exhibiting one extreme of a phenotypic range, thereby shifting a population's frequency curve for the phenotypic character in one direction or the other **(Figure 21.13a)**. Directional selection is common when a population's environment changes or when members of a population migrate to a new (and different) habitat. For instance, an increase in the relative abundance of large seeds over small seeds led to an increase in beak depth in a population of Galápagos finches (see Figure 21.2).

▼ **Figure 21.13 Modes of selection.** These cases describe three ways in which a hypothetical deer mouse population with heritable variation in fur coloration from light to dark might evolve. The graphs show how the frequencies of individuals with different fur colors change over time. The large white arrows symbolize selective pressures against certain phenotypes.

MAKE CONNECTIONS *Review Figure 19.14. Which mode of selection has occurred in soapberry bug populations that feed on the introduced goldenrain tree? Explain.*

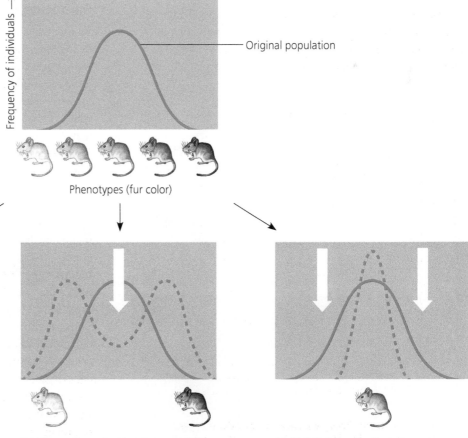

Original population

Phenotypes (fur color)

Frequency of individuals →

Original population   Evolved population

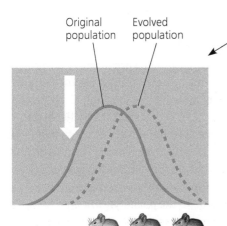

(a) Directional selection shifts the overall makeup of the population by favoring variants that are at one extreme of the distribution. In this case, lighter mice are selected against because they live among dark rocks, making it harder for them to hide from predators.

(b) Disruptive selection favors variants at both ends of the distribution. These mice have colonized a patchy habitat made up of light and dark rocks, with the result that mice of an intermediate color are selected against.

(c) Stabilizing selection removes extreme variants from the population and preserves intermediate types. If the environment consists of rocks of an intermediate color, both light and dark mice will be selected against.

Disruptive selection (Figure 21.13b) occurs when conditions favor individuals at both extremes of a phenotypic range over individuals with intermediate phenotypes. One example is a population of black-bellied seedcracker finches in Cameroon whose members display two distinctly different beak sizes. Small-billed birds feed mainly on soft seeds, whereas large-billed birds specialize in cracking hard seeds. It appears that birds with intermediate-sized bills are relatively inefficient at cracking both types of seeds and thus have lower relative fitness.

Stabilizing selection (Figure 21.13c) acts against both extreme phenotypes and favors intermediate variants. This mode of selection reduces variation and tends to maintain the status quo for a particular phenotypic character. For example, the birth weights of most human babies lie in the range of 3–4 kg (6.6–8.8 pounds); babies who are either much smaller or much larger suffer higher rates of mortality.

Regardless of the mode of selection, however, the basic mechanism remains the same. Selection favors individuals whose heritable phenotypic traits provide higher reproductive success than do the traits of other individuals.

The Key Role of Natural Selection in Adaptive Evolution

The adaptations of organisms include many striking examples. Certain octopuses, for example, have the ability to change color rapidly, enabling them to blend into different backgrounds. Another example is the remarkable jaws of snakes **(Figure 21.14)**, which allow them to swallow prey much larger

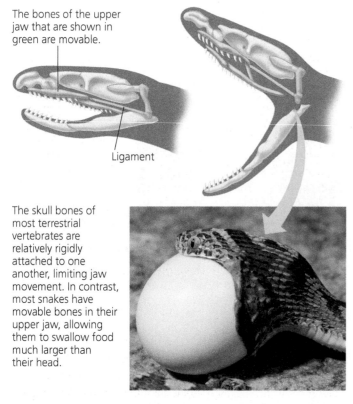

The bones of the upper jaw that are shown in green are movable.

Ligament

The skull bones of most terrestrial vertebrates are relatively rigidly attached to one another, limiting jaw movement. In contrast, most snakes have movable bones in their upper jaw, allowing them to swallow food much larger than their head.

▲ **Figure 21.14 Movable jaw bones in snakes.**

than their own head (a feat analogous to a person swallowing a whole watermelon). Other adaptations, such as a version of an enzyme that shows improved function in cold environments, may be less visually dramatic but just as important for survival and reproduction.

Such adaptations can arise gradually over time as natural selection increases the frequencies of alleles that enhance survival or reproduction. As the proportion of individuals that have favorable traits increases, the degree to which a species is well suited for life in its environment improves; that is, adaptive evolution occurs. However, the physical and biological components of an organism's environment may change over time. As a result, what constitutes a "good match" between an organism and its environment can be a moving target, making adaptive evolution a continuous, dynamic process.

And what about genetic drift and gene flow? Both can, in fact, increase the frequencies of alleles that enhance survival or reproduction, but neither does so consistently. Genetic drift can cause the frequency of a slightly beneficial allele to increase, but it also can cause the frequency of such an allele to decrease. Similarly, gene flow may introduce alleles that are advantageous or ones that are disadvantageous. Natural selection is the only evolutionary mechanism that consistently leads to adaptive evolution.

Balancing Selection

As we've seen, genetic variation is often found at loci affected by selection. What prevents natural selection from reducing the variation at those loci by culling all unfavorable alleles? As mentioned earlier, in diploid organisms, many unfavorable recessive alleles persist because they are hidden from selection when in heterozygous individuals. In addition, selection itself may preserve variation at some loci, thus maintaining two or more phenotypic forms in a population. Known as **balancing selection**, this type of selection includes heterozygote advantage and frequency-dependent selection.

Heterozygote Advantage

If individuals who are heterozygous at a particular locus have greater fitness than do both kinds of homozygotes, they exhibit **heterozygote advantage**. In such a case, natural selection tends to maintain two or more alleles at that locus. Note that heterozygote advantage is defined in terms of *genotype*, not phenotype. Thus, whether heterozygote advantage represents stabilizing or directional selection depends on the relationship between the genotype and the phenotype. For example, if the phenotype of a heterozygote is intermediate to the phenotypes of both homozygotes, heterozygote advantage is a form of stabilizing selection.

An example of heterozygote advantage occurs at the locus in humans that codes for the β polypeptide subunit of hemoglobin, the oxygen-carrying protein of red blood cells. In homozygous individuals, a recessive allele at that locus causes sickle-cell disease. The red blood cells of people with sickle-cell disease become distorted in shape, or *sickled*, under low-oxygen conditions (see Figure 3.23). These sickled cells can clump together and block the flow of blood, damaging organs such as the kidney, heart, and brain. Although some red blood cells become sickled in heterozygotes, not enough become sickled to cause sickle-cell disease.

Heterozygotes for the sickle-cell allele are protected against the most severe effects of malaria, a disease caused by a parasite that infects red blood cells (see Figure 25.26). One reason for this partial protection is that the body destroys sickled red blood cells rapidly, killing the parasites they harbor. Malaria is a major killer in some tropical regions. In such areas, selection favors heterozygotes over homozygous dominant individuals, who are more vulnerable to the effects of malaria, and also over homozygous recessive individuals, who develop sickle-cell disease. As we explore further in **Figure 21.15** on the next two pages, these selective pressures have enabled the frequency of the sickle-cell allele to exist at relatively high levels in areas where the malaria parasite is common.

Frequency-Dependent Selection

In **frequency-dependent selection**, the fitness of a phenotype depends on how common it is in the population. Consider the scale-eating fish (*Perissodus microlepis*) of Lake Tanganyika, in Africa. These fish attack other fish from behind, darting in to remove a few scales from the flank of their prey. Of interest here is a peculiar feature of the scale-eating fish: Some are "left-mouthed" and some are "right-mouthed." Simple Mendelian inheritance determines these phenotypes, with the right-mouthed allele being dominant to the left-mouthed allele.

Because their mouth twists to the left, left-mouthed fish always attack their prey's right flank **(Figure 21.16)**. (To see why, twist your lower jaw and lips to the left and imagine trying to take a bite from the left side of a fish, approaching it from behind.) Similarly, right-mouthed fish always attack from the left. Prey species guard against attack from whatever phenotype of scale-eating fish is most common in the lake. Thus, from year to year, selection favors whichever mouth phenotype is least common. As a result, the frequency of left- and right-mouthed fish oscillates over time, and balancing selection (due to frequency dependence) keeps the frequency of each phenotype close to 50%.

Sexual Selection

Charles Darwin was the first to explore the implications of **sexual selection**, a process in which individuals with certain inherited characteristics are more likely than other individuals of the same sex to obtain mates. Sexual selection can result in **sexual dimorphism**, a difference in secondary sexual characteristics between males and females of the same species **(Figure 21.17)**. These distinctions include differences in size, color, ornamentation, and behavior.

How does sexual selection operate? There are several ways. In *intrasexual selection*, meaning selection within the same sex, individuals of one sex compete directly for mates of the

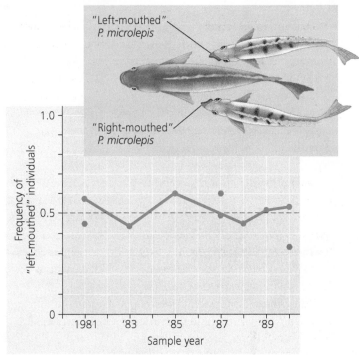

© 1993 AAAS

▲ **Figure 21.16 Frequency-dependent selection.** In a population of the scale-eating fish *Perissodus microlepis*, the frequency of left-mouthed individuals (red data points) rises and falls in a regular manner. The frequency of left-mouthed individuals among adults that reproduced was also recorded in three sample years (green data points).

INTERPRET THE DATA *For 1981, 1987, and 1990, compare the frequency of left-mouthed individuals among breeding adults to the frequency of left-mouthed individuals in the entire population. What do the data indicate about when natural selection favors left-mouthed individuals over right-mouthed individuals (or vice versa)? Explain.*

▲ **Figure 21.17 Sexual dimorphism and sexual selection.** Peacocks (left) and peahens (right) show extreme sexual dimorphism. Intrasexual selection between competing males is followed by intersexual selection when the females choose among the showiest males.

opposite sex. In many species, intrasexual selection occurs among males. For example, a single male may patrol a group of females and prevent other males from mating with them. The patrolling male may defend his status by defeating smaller, weaker, or less fierce males in combat. More often, this male is

▼ Figure 21.15

MAKE CONNECTIONS

The Sickle-Cell Allele

This child has sickle-cell disease, a genetic disorder that strikes individuals who have two copies of the sickle-cell allele. This allele causes an abnormality in the structure and function of hemoglobin, the oxygen-carrying protein in red blood cells. Although sickle-cell disease is lethal if not treated, in some regions the sickle-cell allele can reach frequencies as high as 15–20%. How can such a harmful allele be so common?

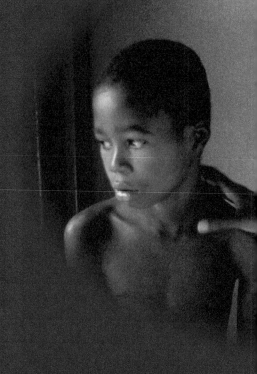

Events at the Molecular Level

- Due to a point mutation, the sickle-cell allele differs from the wild-type allele by a single nucleotide. (See Figure 14.25.)
- The resulting change in one amino acid leads to hydrophobic interactions between the sickle-cell hemoglobin proteins under low-oxygen conditions.
- As a result, the sickle-cell proteins bind to each other in chains that together form a fiber.

Consequences for Cells

- The abnormal hemoglobin fibers distort the red blood cell into a sickle shape under low-oxygen conditions, such as those found in small blood vessels returning to the heart.

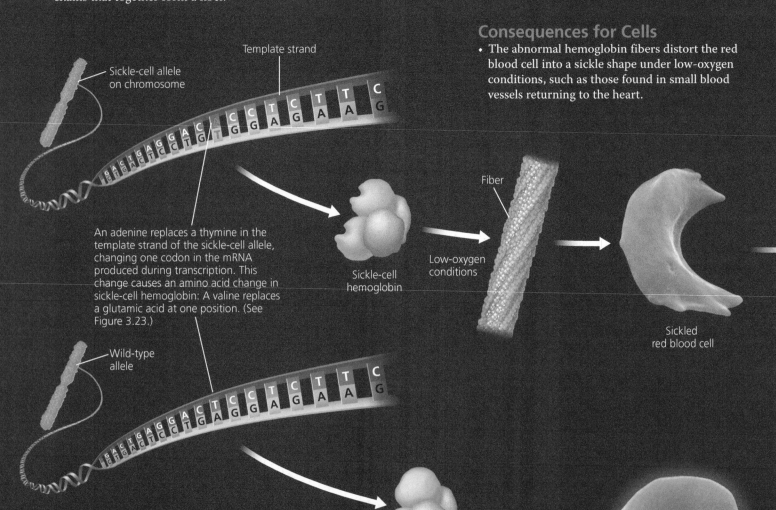

Template strand

Sickle-cell allele on chromosome

An adenine replaces a thymine in the template strand of the sickle-cell allele, changing one codon in the mRNA produced during transcription. This change causes an amino acid change in sickle-cell hemoglobin: A valine replaces a glutamic acid at one position. (See Figure 3.23.)

Wild-type allele

Fiber

Low-oxygen conditions

Sickle-cell hemoglobin

Sickled red blood cell

Normal hemoglobin (does not aggregate into fibers)

Normal red blood cell

Infected mosquitoes spread malaria when they bite people. (See Figure 25.26.)

Evolution in Populations

- Homozygotes with two sickle-cell alleles are strongly selected against because of mortality caused by sickle-cell disease. In contrast, heterozygotes experience few harmful effects from sickling yet are more likely to survive malaria than are homozygotes.
- In regions where malaria is common, the net effect of these opposing selective forces is heterozygote advantage. This has caused evolutionary change in populations—the products of which are the areas of relatively high frequencies of the sickle-cell allele shown in the map.

Effects on Individual Organisms

- The formation of sickled red blood cells causes homozygotes with two copies of the sickle-cell allele to have sickle-cell disease.
- Some sickling also occurs in heterozygotes, but not enough to cause the disease; they have sickle-cell trait.

The sickled blood cells of a homozygote block small blood vessels, causing great pain and damage to organs such as the heart, kidney, and brain.

Normal red blood cells are flexible and are able to flow freely through small blood vessels.

Key
Frequencies of the sickle-cell allele

	3.0–6.0%
	6.0–9.0%
	9.0–12.0%
	12.0–15.0%
	>15.0%

Distribution of malaria caused by *Plasmodium falciparum* (a parasitic unicellular eukaryote)

MAKE CONNECTIONS *In a region free of malaria, would individuals who are heterozygous for the sickle-cell allele be selected for or selected against? Explain.*

the psychological victor in ritualized displays that discourage would-be competitors but do not risk injury that would reduce his own fitness (see Figure 39.23). Intrasexual selection also occurs among females in a variety of species, including ring-tailed lemurs and broad-nosed pipefish.

In *intersexual selection*, also called *mate choice*, individuals of one sex (usually the females) are choosy in selecting their mates from the other sex. In many cases, the female's choice depends on the showiness of the male's appearance or behavior (see Figure 21.17). What intrigued Darwin about mate choice is that male showiness may not seem adaptive in any other way and may in fact pose some risk. For example, bright plumage may make male birds more visible to predators. But if such characteristics help a male gain a mate, and if this benefit outweighs the risk from predation, then both the bright plumage and the female preference for it will be reinforced because they enhance overall reproductive success.

How do female preferences for certain male characteristics evolve in the first place? One hypothesis is that females prefer male traits that are correlated with "good genes." If the trait preferred by females is indicative of a male's overall genetic quality, both the male trait and female preference for it should increase in frequency. **Figure 21.18** describes one experiment testing this hypothesis in gray tree frogs.

Other researchers have shown that in several bird species, the traits preferred by females are related to overall male health. Here, too, female preference appears to be based on traits that reflect "good genes," in this case alleles indicative of a robust immune system.

Why Natural Selection Cannot Fashion Perfect Organisms

Though natural selection leads to adaptation, nature abounds with examples of organisms that are less than ideally suited for their lifestyles. There are several reasons why.

1. **Selection can act only on existing variations.** Natural selection favors only the fittest phenotypes among those currently in the population, which may not be the ideal traits. New advantageous alleles do not arise on demand.
2. **Evolution is limited by historical constraints.** Each species has a legacy of descent with modification from ancestral forms. Evolution does not scrap the ancestral anatomy and build each new complex structure from scratch; rather, evolution co-opts existing structures and adapts them to new situations. We could imagine that if a terrestrial animal were to adapt to an environment in which flight would be advantageous, it might be best just to grow an extra pair of limbs that would serve as wings. However, evolution does not work this way; instead, it operates on the traits an organism already has. Thus, in birds and bats, an existing pair of limbs took on new functions for flight as these organisms evolved from nonflying ancestors.

▼ **Figure 21.18** Inquiry

Do females select mates based on traits indicative of "good genes"?

Experiment Female gray tree frogs (*Hyla versicolor*) prefer to mate with males that give long mating calls. Allison Welch and colleagues, at the University of Missouri, tested whether the genetic makeup of long-calling (LC) males is superior to that of short-calling (SC) males. The researchers fertilized half the eggs of each female with sperm from an LC male and fertilized the remaining eggs with sperm from an SC male. In two separate experiments (one in 1995, the other in 1996), the resulting half-sibling offspring were raised in a common environment and their survival and growth were monitored.

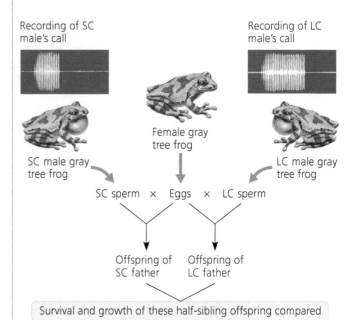

Results

Offspring Performance	1995	1996
Larval survival	LC better	NSD
Larval growth	NSD	LC better
Time to metamorphosis	LC better (shorter)	LC better (shorter)

NSD = no significant difference; LC better = offspring of LC males superior to offspring of SC males.

Conclusion Because offspring fathered by an LC male outperformed their half-siblings fathered by an SC male, the team concluded that the duration of a male's mating call is indicative of the male's overall genetic quality. This result supports the hypothesis that female mate choice can be based on a trait that indicates whether the male has "good genes."

Data from A. M. Welch et al., Call duration as an indicator of genetic quality in male gray tree frogs, *Science* 280:1928–1930 (1998).

Inquiry in Action Read and analyze the original paper in *Inquiry in Action: Interpreting Scientific Papers.*

WHAT IF? Why did the researchers split each female frog's eggs into two batches for fertilization by different males? Why didn't they mate each female with a single male frog?

3. **Adaptations are often compromises.** Each organism must do many different things. A seal spends part of its time on rocks; it could probably walk better if it had legs instead of flippers, but then it would not swim nearly as well. We humans owe much of our versatility and athleticism to our prehensile hands and flexible limbs, but these also make us prone to sprains, torn ligaments, and dislocations: Structural reinforcement has been compromised for agility. **Figure 21.19** depicts another example of evolutionary compromise.

4. **Chance, natural selection, and the environment interact.** Chance events can affect the subsequent evolutionary history of populations. For instance, when a storm blows insects or birds hundreds of kilometers over an ocean to an island, the wind does not necessarily transport those individuals that are best suited to the new environment. Thus, not all alleles present in the founding population's gene pool are better suited to the new environment than the alleles that are "left behind." In addition, the environment at a particular location may change unpredictably from year to year, again limiting the extent to which adaptive evolution results in organisms being well suited to current environmental conditions.

With these four constraints, evolution does not tend to craft perfect organisms. Natural selection operates on a "better than" basis. We can, in fact, see evidence for evolution in the many imperfections of the organisms it produces.

▲ **Figure 21.19 Evolutionary compromise.** The loud call that enables a Túngara frog to attract mates also attracts more dangerous characters in the neighborhood—in this case, a bat about to seize a meal.

CONCEPT CHECK 21.4

1. What is the relative fitness of a sterile mule? Explain.
2. Explain why natural selection is the only evolutionary mechanism that consistently leads to adaptive evolution.
3. **WHAT IF?** Consider a population in which heterozygotes at a certain locus have an extreme phenotype (such as being larger than homozygotes) that confers a selective advantage. Does such a situation represent directional, disruptive, or stabilizing selection? Explain your answer.

   For suggested answers, see Appendix A.

---

21   Chapter Review

Go to **MasteringBiology**® for Assignments, the eText, and the Study Area with Animations, Activities, Vocab Self-Quiz, and Practice Tests.

SUMMARY OF KEY CONCEPTS

VOCAB SELF-QUIZ

goo.gl/gbai8v

CONCEPT 21.1

Genetic variation makes evolution possible (pp. 414–416)

- **Genetic variation** refers to genetic differences among individuals within a population.
- The nucleotide differences that provide the basis of genetic variation originate when mutation and gene duplication produce new alleles and new genes.
- New genetic variants are produced rapidly in organisms with short generation times. In sexually reproducing organisms, most of the genetic differences among individuals result from crossing over, the independent assortment of chromosomes, and fertilization.

  ? *Typically, most of the nucleotide variability that occurs within a genetic locus does not affect the phenotype. Explain why.*

CONCEPT 21.2

The Hardy-Weinberg equation can be used to test whether a population is evolving (pp. 417–420)

- A **population**, a localized group of organisms belonging to one species, is united by its **gene pool**, the aggregate of all the alleles in the population.

- For a population in **Hardy-Weinberg equilibrium**, the allele and genotype frequencies will remain constant if the population is large, mating is random, mutation is negligible, there is no gene flow, and there is no natural selection. For such a population, if p and q represent the frequencies of the only two possible alleles at a particular locus, then p^2 is the frequency of one kind of homozygote, q^2 is the frequency of the other kind of homozygote, and $2pq$ is the frequency of the heterozygous genotype.

  ? *Is it circular reasoning to calculate* p *and* q *from observed genotype frequencies and then use those values of* p *and* q *to test whether the population is in Hardy-Weinberg equilibrium? Explain your answer. (Hint: Consider a specific case, such as a population with 195 individuals of genotype AA, 10 of genotype Aa, and 195 of genotype aa.)*

CONCEPT 21.3

Natural selection, genetic drift, and gene flow can alter allele frequencies in a population (pp. 421–424)

- In natural selection, individuals that have certain inherited traits tend to survive and reproduce at higher rates than other individuals *because of* those traits.
- In **genetic drift**, chance fluctuations in allele frequencies over generations tend to reduce genetic variation.

- **Gene flow**, the transfer of alleles between populations, tends to reduce genetic differences between populations over time.

> **?** *Would two small, geographically isolated populations in very different environments be likely to evolve in similar ways? Explain.*

CONCEPT 21.4

Natural selection is the only mechanism that consistently causes adaptive evolution (pp. 424–431)

- One organism has greater **relative fitness** than another if it leaves more fertile descendants. The modes of natural selection differ in their effect on phenotype (the white arrows in the summary diagram below represent selective pressure on a population).

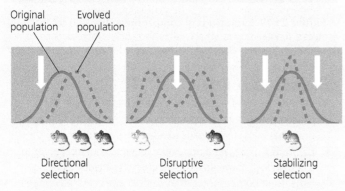

Original population / Evolved population

Directional selection | Disruptive selection | Stabilizing selection

- Unlike genetic drift and gene flow, natural selection consistently increases the frequencies of alleles that enhance survival and reproduction, thus improving the degree to which organisms are well suited for life in their environment.
- **Sexual selection** can result in secondary sex characteristics that can give individuals advantages in mating.
- **Balancing selection** occurs when natural selection maintains two or more forms in a population.
- There are constraints to evolution: Natural selection can act only on available variation; structures result from modified ancestral anatomy; adaptations are often compromises; and chance, natural selection, and the environment interact.

> **?** *How might secondary sex characteristics differ between males and females in a species in which females compete for mates?*

TEST YOUR UNDERSTANDING

Level 1: Knowledge/Comprehension

PRACTICE TEST goo.gl/CRZjvS

1. Natural selection changes allele frequencies because some _____ survive and reproduce better than others.
   (A) alleles
   (B) loci
   (C) species
   (D) individuals

2. No two people are genetically identical, except for identical twins. The main source of genetic variation among humans is
   (A) new mutations that occurred in the preceding generation.
   (B) genetic drift.
   (C) the reshuffling of alleles in sexual reproduction.
   (D) environmental effects.

3. Sparrows with average-sized wings survive severe storms better than those with longer or shorter wings, illustrating
   (A) the bottleneck effect.
   (B) disruptive selection.
   (C) frequency-dependent selection.
   (D) stabilizing selection.

Level 2: Application/Analysis

4. If the nucleotide variability of a locus equals 0%, what is the gene variability and number of alleles at that locus?
   (A) gene variability = 0%; number of alleles = 0
   (B) gene variability = 0%; number of alleles = 1
   (C) gene variability = 0%; number of alleles = 2
   (D) gene variability > 0%; number of alleles = 2

5. There are 25 individuals in population 1, all with genotype *AA*, and there are 40 individuals in population 2, all with genotype *aa*. Assume that these populations are located far from each other and that their environmental conditions are very similar. Based on the information given here, the observed genetic variation most likely resulted from
   (A) genetic drift.
   (B) gene flow.
   (C) nonrandom mating.
   (D) directional selection.

6. A fruit fly population has a gene with two alleles, *A1* and *A2*. Tests show that 70% of the gametes produced in the population contain the *A1* allele. If the population is in Hardy-Weinberg equilibrium, what proportion of the flies carry both *A1* and *A2*?
   (A) 0.7
   (B) 0.49
   (C) 0.42
   (D) 0.21

Level 3: Synthesis/Evaluation

7. **SCIENTIFIC INQUIRY**

   INTERPRET THE DATA Researchers studied genetic variation in the marine mussel *Mytilus edulis* around Long Island, New York. They measured the frequency of a particular allele (*lap⁹⁴*) for an enzyme involved in regulating the mussel's internal saltwater balance. The researchers presented their data as a series of pie charts linked to sampling sites within Long Island Sound, where the salinity is highly variable, and along the coast of the open ocean, where salinity is constant:

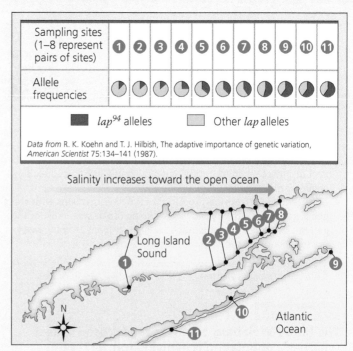

Data from R. K. Koehn and T. J. Hilbish, The adaptive importance of genetic variation, *American Scientist* 75:134–141 (1987).

(a) Create a data table for the 11 sampling sites by estimating the frequency of *lap⁹⁴* from the pie charts. (*Hint*: Think of each pie chart as a clock face to help you estimate the proportion of the shaded area.) (b) Graph the frequencies for sites 1–8 to show how the frequency of this allele changes with increasing salinity in Long Island Sound (from southwest to northeast). Evaluate how the data from sites 9–11 compare with the data from the sites within the Sound. (c) Construct a hypothesis that explains the patterns you observe in the data and that accounts for the following observations: (1) The lap^{94} allele helps mussels maintain osmotic balance in water with a high salt concentration but is costly to use in less salty water; and (2) mussels produce larvae that can disperse long distances before they settle on rocks and grow into adults.

8. **FOCUS ON EVOLUTION**
Using at least TWO examples, explain how the process of evolution is revealed by the imperfections of living organisms.

9. **FOCUS ON ORGANIZATION**
Heterozygotes at the sickle-cell locus produce both normal and abnormal (sickle-cell) hemoglobin (see Concept 11.4). When hemoglobin molecules are packed into a heterozygote's red blood cells, some cells receive relatively large quantities of abnormal hemoglobin, making these cells prone to sickling. In a short essay (approximately 100–150 words), explain how these molecular and cellular events lead to emergent properties at the individual and population levels of biological organization.

10. **SYNTHESIZE YOUR KNOWLEDGE**

This kettle lake formed 14,000 years ago when a glacier that covered the surrounding area melted. Initially devoid of animal life, over time the lake was colonized by invertebrates and other animals. Hypothesize how mutation, natural selection, genetic drift, and gene flow may have affected populations that colonized the lake.

For selected answers, see Appendix A.

22 The Origin of Species

KEY CONCEPTS

22.1 The biological species concept emphasizes reproductive isolation

22.2 Speciation can take place with or without geographic separation

22.3 Hybrid zones reveal factors that cause reproductive isolation

22.4 Speciation can occur rapidly or slowly and can result from changes in few or many genes

▲ **Figure 22.1** How did this flightless bird come to live on the isolated Galápagos Islands?

That "Mystery of Mysteries"

When Darwin came to the Galápagos Islands, he noted that these volcanic islands were teeming with plants and animals found nowhere else in the world **(Figure 22.1)**. Later he realized that these species had formed relatively recently. He wrote in his diary: "Both in space and time, we seem to be brought somewhat near to that great fact—that mystery of mysteries—the first appearance of new beings on this Earth."

The "mystery of mysteries" that captivated Darwin is **speciation**, the process by which one species splits into two or more species. Speciation fascinated Darwin (and many biologists since) because it has produced the tremendous diversity of life, repeatedly yielding new species that differ from existing ones. Speciation also helps to explain the many features that organisms share (the unity of life). When one species splits into two, the species that result share many characteristics because they are descended from this common ancestor. At the DNA sequence level, for example, such similarities indicate that the flightless cormorant (*Phalacrocorax harrisi*) in Figure 22.1 is closely related to flying cormorants found in the Americas. This suggests that the

flightless cormorant originated from an ancestral cormorant species that flew from the mainland to the Galápagos.

Speciation also forms a conceptual bridge between **microevolution**, changes over time in allele frequencies in a population, and **macroevolution**, the broad pattern of evolution above the species level. An example of macroevolutionary change is the origin of new groups of organisms, such as mammals or flowering plants, through a series of speciation events. We examined microevolutionary mechanisms in Chapter 21, and we'll turn to macroevolution in Chapter 23. In this chapter, we'll explore the "bridge" between microevolution and macroevolution—the mechanisms by which new species originate from existing ones. First, let's establish what we actually mean by a "species."

CONCEPT 22.1

The biological species concept emphasizes reproductive isolation

The word *species* is Latin for "kind" or "appearance." In daily life, we commonly distinguish between various "kinds" of organisms—dogs and cats, for instance—from differences in their appearance. But are organisms truly divided into the discrete units we call species, or is this classification an arbitrary attempt to impose order on the natural world? To answer this question, biologists compare not only the morphology (body form) of different groups of organisms but also less obvious differences in physiology, biochemistry, and DNA sequences. The results generally confirm that morphologically distinct species are indeed discrete groups, differing in many ways besides their body forms.

The Biological Species Concept

The primary definition of species used in this textbook is the **biological species concept**. According to this concept, a **species** is a group of populations whose members have the potential to interbreed in nature and produce viable, fertile offspring—but do not produce viable, fertile offspring with members of other such groups **(Figure 22.2)**. Thus, the members of a biological species are united by being reproductively compatible, at least potentially. All human beings, for example, belong to the same species. A businesswoman in Manhattan may be unlikely to meet a dairy farmer in Mongolia, but if the two should happen to meet and mate, they could have viable babies who develop into fertile adults. In contrast, humans and chimpanzees remain distinct biological species even where they live in the same region, because many factors keep them from interbreeding and producing fertile offspring.

What holds the gene pool of a species together, causing its members to resemble each other more than they resemble members of other species? To answer this question, recall the evolutionary mechanism of *gene flow*, the transfer of alleles between populations (see Concept 21.3). Typically, gene flow occurs between the different populations of a species. This ongoing exchange of alleles tends to hold the populations together genetically. But as we'll explore in this chapter, a reduction or lack of gene flow can play a key role in the formation of new species.

Reproductive Isolation

Because biological species are defined in terms of reproductive compatibility, the formation of a new species hinges on **reproductive isolation**—the existence of biological factors (barriers) that impede members of two species from interbreeding and producing viable, fertile offspring. Such barriers block gene flow between the species and limit the formation of **hybrids**, offspring that result from an interspecific mating. Although a single barrier may not prevent all gene flow, a combination of several barriers can effectively isolate a species' gene pool.

Clearly, a fly cannot mate with a frog or a fern, but the reproductive barriers between more closely related species are not so obvious. These barriers can be classified according to whether they contribute to reproductive isolation before or after fertilization. **Prezygotic barriers** ("before the zygote") block fertilization from occurring. Such barriers typically act in

(a) Similarity between different species. The eastern meadowlark (*Sturnella magna*, left) and the western meadowlark (*Sturnella neglecta*, right) have similar body shapes and colorations. Nevertheless, they are distinct biological species because their songs and other behaviors are different enough to prevent interbreeding should they meet in the wild.

(b) Diversity within a species. As diverse as we may be in appearance, all humans belong to a single biological species (*Homo sapiens*), defined by our capacity to interbreed successfully.

▲ **Figure 22.2 The biological species concept is based on the potential to interbreed, not on physical similarity.**

one of three ways: by impeding members of different species from attempting to mate, by preventing an attempted mating from being completed successfully, or by hindering fertilization if mating is completed successfully. If a sperm cell from one species overcomes prezygotic barriers and fertilizes an ovum from another species, a variety of **postzygotic barriers** ("after the zygote") may contribute to reproductive isolation after the hybrid zygote is formed. For example, developmental errors may reduce survival among hybrid embryos. Or problems after birth may cause hybrids to be infertile or decrease their chance of surviving long enough to reproduce. **Figure 22.3** describes prezygotic and postzygotic barriers in more detail.

▼ Figure 22.3 Exploring Reproductive Barriers

Prezygotic barriers impede mating or hinder fertilization if mating does occur

Habitat Isolation	Temporal Isolation	Behavioral Isolation	Mechanical Isolation

Individuals of different species

MATING ATTEMPT

Two species that occupy different habitats within the same area may encounter each other rarely, if at all, even though they are not isolated by obvious physical barriers, such as mountain ranges.

Species that breed during different times of the day, different seasons, or different years cannot mix their gametes.

Courtship rituals that attract mates and other behaviors unique to a species are effective reproductive barriers, even between closely related species. Such behavioral rituals enable *mate recognition*—a way to identify potential mates of the same species.

Mating is attempted, but morphological differences prevent its successful completion.

Example: These two fly species in the genus *Rhagoletis* occur in the same geographic areas, but the apple maggot fly (*Rhagoletis pomonella*) feeds and mates on hawthorns and apples **(a)** while its close relative, the blueberry maggot fly (*R. mendax*), mates and lays its eggs only on blueberries **(b)**.

Example: In North America, the geographic ranges of the western spotted skunk (*Spilogale gracilis*) **(c)** and the eastern spotted skunk (*Spilogale putorius*) **(d)** overlap, but *S. gracilis* mates in late summer and *S. putorius* mates in late winter.

Example: Blue-footed boobies, inhabitants of the Galápagos, mate only after a courtship display unique to their species. Part of the "script" calls for the male to high-step **(e)**, a behavior that calls the female's attention to his bright blue feet.

Example: The shells of two species of snails in the genus *Bradybaena* spiral in different directions: Moving inward to the center, one spirals in a counterclockwise direction (**f**, left), the other in a clockwise direction (**f**, right). As a result, the snails' genital openings (indicated by arrows) are not aligned, and mating cannot be completed.

(a)

(c)

(e)

(f)

(d)

(b)

Postzygotic barriers prevent a hybrid zygote from developing into a viable, fertile adult

| Gametic Isolation | Reduced Hybrid Viability | Reduced Hybrid Fertility | Hybrid Breakdown |

VIABLE, FERTILE OFFSPRING

Gametic Isolation

Sperm of one species may not be able to fertilize the eggs of another species. For instance, sperm may not be able to survive in the reproductive tract of females of the other species, or biochemical mechanisms may prevent the sperm from penetrating the membrane surrounding the other species' eggs.

Example: Gametic isolation separates certain closely related species of aquatic animals, such as sea urchins **(g)**. Sea urchins release their sperm and eggs into the surrounding water, where they fuse and form zygotes. It is difficult for gametes of different species, such as the red and purple urchins shown here, to fuse because proteins on the surfaces of the eggs and sperm bind very poorly to each other.

Reduced Hybrid Viability

The genes of different parent species may interact in ways that impair the hybrid's development or survival in its environment.

Example: Some salamander subspecies of the genus *Ensatina* live in the same regions and habitats, where they may occasionally hybridize. But most of the hybrids do not complete development, and those that do are frail **(h)**.

Reduced Hybrid Fertility

Even if hybrids are vigorous, they may be sterile. If the chromosomes of the two parent species differ in number or structure, meiosis in the hybrids may fail to produce normal gametes. Since the infertile hybrids cannot produce offspring when they mate with either parent species, genes cannot flow freely between the species.

Example: The hybrid offspring of a male donkey **(i)** and a female horse **(j)** is a mule **(k)**, which is robust but sterile. A "hinny" (not shown), the offspring of a female donkey and a male horse, is also sterile.

Hybrid Breakdown

Some first-generation hybrids are viable and fertile, but when they mate with one another or with either parent species, offspring of the next generation are feeble or sterile.

Example: Strains of cultivated rice have accumulated different mutant recessive alleles at two loci in the course of their divergence from a common ancestor. Hybrids between them are vigorous and fertile (l, left and right), but plants in the next generation that carry too many of these recessive alleles are small and sterile (l, center). Although these rice strains are not yet considered different species, they have begun to be separated by postzygotic barriers.

Limitations of the Biological Species Concept

One strength of the biological species concept is that it directs our attention to a way by which speciation can occur: by the evolution of reproductive isolation. However, the number of species to which this concept can be usefully applied is limited. There is, for example, no way to evaluate the reproductive isolation of fossils. The biological species concept also does not apply to organisms that reproduce asexually all or most of the time, such as prokaryotes. (Many prokaryotes do transfer genes among themselves, as we will discuss in Concept 24.3, but this is not part of their reproductive process.) Furthermore, in the biological species concept, species are designated by the *absence* of gene flow. But there are many pairs of species that are morphologically and ecologically distinct, and yet gene flow occurs between them. An example is the grizzly bear (*Ursus arctos*) and polar bear (*Ursus maritimus*), whose hybrid offspring have been dubbed "grolar bears" **(Figure 22.4)**. As we'll discuss, natural selection can cause such species to remain distinct even though some gene flow occurs between them. Because of the limitations to the biological species concept, alternative species concepts are useful in certain situations.

◀ Grizzly bear (*U. arctos*)

▼ Polar bear (*U. maritimus*)

▲ Hybrid "grolar bear"

▲ **Figure 22.4 Hybridization between two species of bears in the genus *Ursus*.**

Other Definitions of Species

While the biological species concept emphasizes the *separateness* of different species due to reproductive barriers, several other definitions emphasize the *unity within* a species. For example, the **morphological species concept** distinguishes a species by body shape and other structural features. The morphological species concept can be applied to asexual and sexual organisms, and it can be useful even without information on the extent of gene flow. In practice, scientists often distinguish species using morphological criteria. A disadvantage of this approach, however, is that it relies on subjective criteria; researchers may disagree on which structural features distinguish a species.

The **ecological species concept** defines a species in terms of its ecological niche, the sum of how members of the species interact with the nonliving and living parts of their environment. For example, two species of oak trees might differ in their size or in their ability to tolerate dry conditions, yet still occasionally interbreed. Because they occupy different ecological niches, these oaks would be considered separate species even though they are connected by some gene flow. Unlike the biological species concept, the ecological species concept can accommodate asexual as well as sexual species. It also emphasizes the role of disruptive natural selection as organisms adapt to different environments.

The **phylogenetic species concept** defines a species as the smallest group of individuals that share a common ancestor, forming one branch on the tree of life. Biologists trace the phylogenetic history of a species by comparing its characteristics, such as morphology or molecular sequences, with those of other organisms. Such analyses can distinguish groups of individuals that are sufficiently different to be considered separate species. Of course, the difficulty with this species concept is determining the degree of difference required to indicate separate species.

In addition to those discussed here, more than 20 other species definitions have been proposed. The usefulness of each definition depends on the situation and the research questions being asked. For our purposes of studying how species originate, the biological species concept, with its focus on reproductive barriers, is particularly helpful.

CONCEPT CHECK 22.1

1. (a) Which species concept(s) could you apply to both asexual and sexual species? (b) Which would be most useful for identifying species in the field? Explain.
2. **WHAT IF?** Suppose you are studying two bird species that live in a forest and are not known to interbreed. One species feeds and mates in the treetops and the other on the ground. But in captivity, the birds can interbreed and produce viable, fertile offspring. What type of reproductive barrier most likely keeps these species separate in nature? Explain.

For suggested answers, see Appendix A.

CONCEPT 22.2

Speciation can take place with or without geographic separation

Having discussed what constitutes a species, let's return to the process by which new species arise from existing species. We'll focus on the geographic setting in which gene flow is interrupted between populations of the existing species—in allopatric speciation the populations are geographically isolated, while in sympatric speciation they are not **(Figure 22.5)**.

Allopatric ("Other Country") Speciation

In **allopatric speciation** (from the Greek *allos*, other, and *patra*, homeland), gene flow is interrupted when a population is divided into geographically isolated subpopulations. For example, the water level in a lake may subside, resulting in two or more smaller lakes that are now home to separated populations (see Figure 22.5a). Or a river may change course and divide a population of animals that cannot cross it. Allopatric speciation can also occur without geologic remodeling, such as when individuals colonize a remote area and their descendants become geographically isolated from the parent population. The flightless cormorant shown in Figure 22.1 probably originated in this way from an ancestral flying species that reached the Galápagos Islands.

The Process of Allopatric Speciation

How formidable must a geographic barrier be to promote allopatric speciation? The answer depends on the ability of the organisms to move about. Birds, mountain lions, and coyotes can cross rivers and canyons—as can the windblown pollen of pine trees and the seeds of many flowering plants. In contrast, small rodents may find a wide river or deep canyon a formidable barrier.

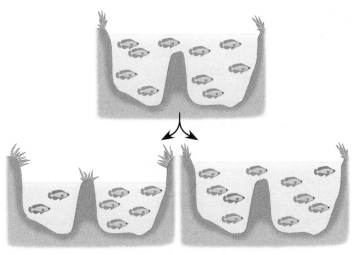

(a) Allopatric speciation. A population forms a new species while geographically isolated from its parent population.

(b) Sympatric speciation. A subset of a population forms a new species without geographic separation.

▲ **Figure 22.5 The geography of speciation.**

Once geographic isolation has occurred, the separated gene pools may diverge. Different mutations arise, and natural selection and genetic drift may alter allele frequencies in different ways in the separated populations. Reproductive isolation may then evolve as a by-product of these genetic changes.

Let's consider an example. On Andros Island, in the Bahamas, populations of the mosquitofish *Gambusia hubbsi* colonized a series of ponds that later became isolated from one another. Genetic analyses indicate that little or no gene flow currently occurs between the ponds. The environments of these ponds are very similar except that some contain predatory fishes, while others do not. In the ponds with predatory fishes, selection has favored the evolution of a mosquitofish body shape that enables rapid bursts of speed **(Figure 22.6)**. In ponds without predatory fishes, selection has favored a different body shape, one that improves the ability to swim for long periods of time. How have these different selective pressures affected the evolution of reproductive barriers? Researchers studied this question by bringing together mosquitofish from the two types of ponds. They found that female mosquitofish prefer to mate with males whose body shape is similar to their own. This preference establishes a behavioral barrier to reproduction between mosquitofish from ponds with predators and those from ponds without predators. Thus, as a by-product of selection for avoiding predators, reproductive barriers have formed in these allopatric populations.

In ponds with predatory fishes, the mosquitofish's head is streamlined and the tail is powerful, enabling rapid bursts of speed.

In ponds without predatory fishes, mosquitofish have a different body shape that favors long, steady swimming.

(a) Differences in body shape

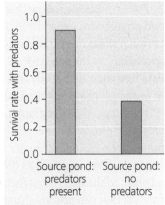

(b) Differences in escape acceleration and survival

▲ **Figure 22.6 Evolution in mosquitofish populations.** Different body shapes have evolved in mosquitofish populations from ponds with and without predators. These differences affect how quickly the fish can accelerate to escape and their survival rate when they are exposed to predators.

Evidence of Allopatric Speciation

Many studies provide evidence that speciation can occur in allopatric populations. For example, laboratory studies show that reproductive barriers can develop when populations are isolated experimentally and subjected to different environmental conditions **(Figure 22.7)**.

Field studies indicate that allopatric speciation also can occur in nature. Consider the 30 species of snapping shrimp in the genus *Alpheus* that live off the Isthmus of Panama, the land bridge that connects South and North America. Fifteen of these species live on the Atlantic side of the isthmus, while the other 15 live on the Pacific side. Before the isthmus formed, gene flow could occur between the Atlantic and Pacific populations of snapping shrimp. Did the species on different sides of the isthmus originate by allopatric speciation? Morphological and genetic data group these shrimp into 15 pairs of *sister species*, pairs whose member species are each other's closest relative (see Figure 20.5). In each of these 15 pairs, one of the sister species lives on the Atlantic side of the isthmus, while the other lives on the Pacific side **(Figure 22.8)**. This fact strongly suggests that in each case, the two species arose as a consequence of geographic separation. Furthermore, genetic analyses indicate that the *Alpheus* species originated from 9 to 3 million years ago, with the sister species that live in the deepest water diverging first. These divergence times are consistent with geologic evidence that the isthmus formed gradually, starting 10 million years ago and closing completely about 3 million years ago.

The importance of allopatric speciation is also suggested by the fact that regions that are isolated or highly subdivided by barriers typically have more species than do otherwise similar regions that lack such features. For example, many unique plants and animals are found on the geographically isolated Hawaiian Islands (we'll return to the origin of Hawaiian species in Concept 23.2). Similarly, unusually high numbers of butterfly species are found in regions of South America that are subdivided by many rivers.

Field studies also show that reproductive isolation between two populations generally increases as the geographic distance between them increases, a finding consistent with allopatric speciation. In the **Scientific Skills Exercise**, you will analyze data from one such study that examined reproductive isolation in geographically separated salamander populations.

Note that while geographic isolation prevents interbreeding between members of allopatric populations, physical separation is not a biological barrier to reproduction. Biological reproductive barriers such as those described in Figure 22.3 are intrinsic to the organisms themselves. Hence, it is biological barriers that can prevent interbreeding when members of different populations come into contact with one another.

Sympatric ("Same Country") Speciation

In **sympatric speciation** (from the Greek *syn*, together), speciation occurs in populations that live in the same geographic area (see Figure 22.5b). How can reproductive barriers form between sympatric populations while their members remain in contact

---

▼ Figure 22.7 Inquiry

Can divergence of allopatric populations lead to reproductive isolation?

Experiment A researcher divided a laboratory population of the fruit fly *Drosophila pseudoobscura*, raising some flies on a starch medium and others on a maltose medium. After one year (about 40 generations), natural selection resulted in divergent evolution: Populations raised on starch digested starch more efficiently, while those raised on maltose digested maltose more efficiently. The researcher then put flies from the same or different populations in mating cages and measured mating frequencies. All flies used in the mating preference tests were reared for one generation on a standard cornmeal medium.

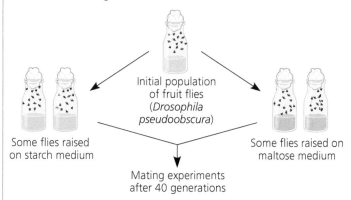

Initial population of fruit flies (*Drosophila pseudoobscura*)

Some flies raised on starch medium

Some flies raised on maltose medium

Mating experiments after 40 generations

Results Mating patterns among populations of flies raised on different media are shown below. When flies from "starch populations" were mixed with flies from "maltose populations," the flies tended to mate with like partners. But in the control group (shown on the right), flies from different populations adapted to starch were about as likely to mate with each other as with flies from their own population; similar results were obtained for control groups adapted to maltose.

		Female	
		Starch	Maltose
Male	Starch	22	9
	Maltose	8	20

Number of matings in experimental group

		Female	
		Starch population 1	Starch population 2
Male	Starch population 1	18	15
	Starch population 2	12	15

Number of matings in control group

Conclusion In the experimental group, the strong preference of "starch flies" and "maltose flies" to mate with like-adapted flies indicates that a reproductive barrier was forming between these fly populations. Although this barrier was not absolute (some mating between starch flies and maltose flies did occur), after 40 generations reproductive isolation appeared to be increasing. This barrier may have been caused by differences in courtship behavior that arose as an incidental by-product of differing selective pressures as these allopatric populations adapted to different sources of food.

Data from D. M. B. Dodd, Reproductive isolation as a consequence of adaptive divergence in *Drosophila pseudoobscura*, *Evolution* 43:1308–1311 (1989).

WHAT IF? Why were all flies used in the mating preference tests reared on a standard medium (rather than on starch or maltose)?

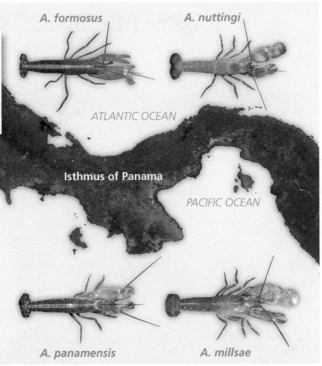

A. formosus

A. nuttingi

ATLANTIC OCEAN

Isthmus of Panama

PACIFIC OCEAN

A. panamensis

A. millsae

▶ **Figure 22.8**
Allopatric speciation in snapping shrimp (*Alpheus*). The shrimps pictured are just 2 of the 15 pairs of sister species that arose as populations were divided by the formation of the Isthmus of Panama. The color-coded type indicates the sister species.

with each other? Although such contact (and the ongoing gene flow that results) makes sympatric speciation less common than allopatric speciation, sympatric speciation can occur if gene flow is reduced by such factors as polyploidy, habitat differentiation, and sexual selection. (Note that these factors can also promote allopatric speciation.)

Polyploidy

A species may originate from an accident during cell division that results in extra sets of chromosomes, a condition called **polyploidy**. Polyploid speciation occasionally occurs in animals; for example, the gray tree frog *Hyla versicolor* (see Figure 21.18) is thought to have originated in this way. However, polyploidy is far more common in plants. Botanists estimate that more than 80% of the plant species alive today are descended from

Scientific Skills Exercise

Identifying Independent and Dependent Variables, Making a Scatter Plot, and Interpreting Data

Does Distance Between Salamander Populations Increase Their Reproductive Isolation? Allopatric speciation begins when populations become geographically isolated, preventing mating between individuals in different populations and thus stopping gene flow. It is logical that as distance between populations increases, so will their degree of reproductive isolation. To test this hypothesis, researchers studied populations of dusky salamanders (*Desmognathus ochrophaeus*) living on different mountains in the southern Appalachians.

How the Experiment Was Done The researchers tested the reproductive isolation of pairs of salamander populations by leaving one male and one female together and later checking the females for the presence of sperm. Four mating combinations were tested for each pair of populations (A and B)—two *within* the same population (female A with male A and female B with male B) and two *between* populations (female A with male B and female B with male A).

Data from the Experiment The researchers used an index of reproductive isolation that ranged from a value of 0 (no isolation) to a value of 2 (full isolation). The proportion of successful matings for each mating combination was measured, with 100% success = 1 and no success = 0. The reproductive isolation value for two populations is the sum of the proportion of successful matings of each type within populations (AA + BB) minus the sum of the proportion of successful matings of each type between populations (AB + BA). The

table provides distance and reproductive isolation data for 27 pairs of dusky salamander populations.

INTERPRET THE DATA

1. State the researchers' hypothesis, and identify the independent and dependent variables in this study. Explain why the researchers used four mating combinations for each pair of populations.

2. Calculate the value of the reproductive isolation index if (a) *all* of the matings within a population were successful, but *none* of the matings between populations were successful; (b) salamanders are equally successful in mating with members of their own population and members of another population.

3. Make a scatter plot to help you visualize any patterns that might indicate a relationship between the variables. Plot the independent variable on the *x*-axis and the dependent variable on the *y*-axis. (For additional information about graphs, see the Scientific Skills Review in Appendix F and the Study Area of MasteringBiology.)

4. Interpret your graph by (a) explaining in words any pattern indicating a possible relationship between the variables and (b) hypothesizing the possible cause of such a relationship.

(MB) A version of this Scientific Skills Exercise can be assigned in MasteringBiology.

Geographic Distance (km)	15	32	40	47	42	62	63	81	86	107	107	115	137	147
Reproductive Isolation Value	0.32	0.54	0.50	0.50	0.82	0.37	0.67	0.53	1.15	0.73	0.82	0.81	0.87	0.87
Distance (continued)	137	150	165	189	219	239	247	53	55	62	105	179	169	
Isolation (continued)	0.50	0.57	0.91	0.93	1.50	1.22	0.82	0.99	0.21	0.56	0.41	0.72	1.15	

Data from S. G. Tilley et al., Correspondence between sexual isolation and allozyme differentiation: A test in the salamander *Desmognathus ochrophaeus*, *Proceedings of the National Academy of Sciences USA* 87:2715–2719 (1990).

ancestors that formed by polyploid speciation.

Two distinct forms of polyploidy have been observed in plant (and a few animal) populations. An **autopolyploid** (from the Greek *autos*, self) is an individual that has more than two chromosome sets that are all derived from a single species. In plants, for example, a failure of cell division could double a cell's chromosome number from the original number ($2n$) to a tetraploid number ($4n$) **(Figure 22.9)**.

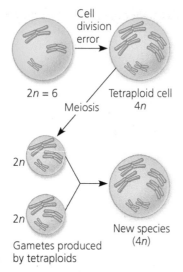

▲ **Figure 22.9 Sympatric speciation by autopolyploidy.**

A tetraploid can produce fertile tetraploid offspring by self-pollinating or by mating with other tetraploids. In addition, the tetraploids are reproductively isolated from $2n$ plants of the original population, because the triploid ($3n$) offspring of such unions have reduced fertility. Thus, in just one generation, autopolyploidy can generate reproductive isolation without any geographic separation.

A second form of polyploidy can occur when two different species interbreed and produce hybrid offspring. Most such hybrids are sterile because the set of chromosomes from one species cannot pair during meiosis with the set of chromosomes from the other species. However, an infertile hybrid may be able to propagate itself asexually (as many plants can do). In subsequent generations, various mechanisms can change a sterile hybrid into a fertile polyploid called an **allopolyploid** **(Figure 22.10)**. The allopolyploids are fertile when mating with each other but cannot interbreed with either parent species; thus, they represent a new biological species.

Although it can be challenging to study speciation in the field, scientists have documented at least five new plant species that have originated by polyploidy speciation since 1850. One of these examples involves the origin of a new species of goatsbeard plant (genus *Tragopogon*) in the Pacific Northwest. *Tragopogon* first arrived in the region when humans introduced three European species in the early 1900s: *T. pratensis*, *T. dubius*, and *T. porrifolius*. These three species are now common weeds in abandoned parking lots and other urban sites. In 1950, a new *Tragopogon* species was discovered near the Idaho-Washington border, a region where all three European species also were found. Genetic analyses revealed that this new species, *Tragopogon miscellus*, is a hybrid of two of the European species **(Figure 22.11)**. Although the *T. miscellus* population grows mainly by reproduction of its own members, additional episodes of hybridization between the parent species continue to add new members to the *T. miscellus* population. Later, scientists discovered

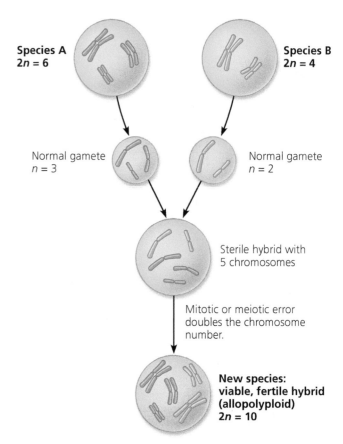

▲ **Figure 22.10 One mechanism for allopolyploid speciation in plants.** Most hybrids are sterile because their chromosomes are not homologous and cannot pair during meiosis. However, such a hybrid may be able to reproduce asexually. This diagram traces one mechanism that can produce fertile hybrids (allopolyploids) as new species. The new species has a diploid chromosome number equal to the sum of the diploid chromosome numbers of the two parent species.

another new *Tragopogon* species, *T. mirus*—this one a hybrid of *T. dubius* and *T. porrifolius* (see Figure 22.11). The *Tragopogon* story is just one of several well-studied examples in which scientists have observed speciation in progress.

Many important agricultural crops—such as oats, cotton, potatoes, tobacco, and wheat—are polyploids. The wheat used for bread, *Triticum aestivum*, is an allohexaploid (six sets of chromosomes, two sets from each of three different species). The first of the polyploidy events that eventually led to modern wheat probably occurred about 8,000 years ago in the Middle East as a spontaneous hybrid of an early cultivated wheat species and a wild grass. Today, plant geneticists generate new polyploids in the laboratory by using chemicals that induce meiotic and mitotic errors. By harnessing the evolutionary process, researchers can produce new hybrid species with desired qualities, such as a hybrid that combines the high yield of wheat with the hardiness of rye.

Habitat Differentiation

Sympatric speciation can also occur when a subpopulation exploits a habitat or resource not used by the parent population. Consider the North American apple maggot fly (*Rhagoletis pomonella*), a pest of apples. The fly's original habitat was the

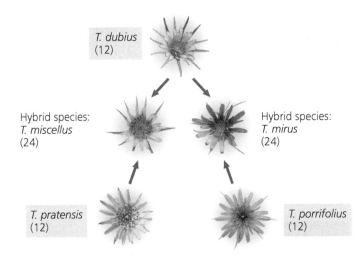

▲ Figure 22.11 Allopolyploid speciation in *Tragopogon*. The gray boxes indicate the three parent species. The diploid chromosome number of each species is shown in parentheses.

native hawthorn tree, but about 200 years ago, some populations colonized apple trees that had been introduced by European settlers. Apple maggot flies usually mate on or near their host plant. This results in a prezygotic barrier (habitat isolation) between populations that feed on apples and populations that feed on hawthorns (such as the fly shown in Figure 22.3a). Furthermore, because apples mature more quickly than hawthorn fruit, natural selection has favored apple-feeding flies with rapid development. These apple-feeding populations now show temporal isolation from the hawthorn-feeding *R. pomonella*, providing a second prezygotic restriction to gene flow between the two populations. Researchers have also identified alleles that benefit the flies that use one host plant but harm the flies that use the other host plant. Natural selection operating on these alleles has provided a postzygotic barrier to reproduction, further limiting gene flow. Altogether, although the two populations are still classified as subspecies rather than separate species, sympatric speciation appears to be well under way.

Sexual Selection

There is evidence that sympatric speciation can also be driven by sexual selection. Clues to how this can occur have been found in cichlid fish from one of Earth's hot spots of animal speciation, East Africa's Lake Victoria. This lake was once home to as many as 600 species of cichlids. Genetic data indicate that these species originated within the last 100,000 years from a small number of colonizing species that arrived from other lakes and rivers. How did so many species—more than double the number of freshwater fish species known in all of Europe—originate within a single lake?

One hypothesis is that subgroups of the original cichlid populations adapted to different food sources and the resulting genetic divergence contributed to speciation in Lake Victoria. But sexual selection, in which (typically) females select males based on their appearance (see Concept 21.4), may also have been a factor. Researchers have studied two closely related sympatric species of cichlids that differ mainly

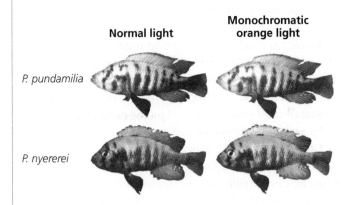
in the coloration of breeding males: Breeding *Pundamilia pundamilia* males have a blue-tinged back, whereas breeding *Pundamilia nyererei* males have a red-tinged back **(Figure 22.12)**. Their results suggest that mate choice based on male breeding coloration can act as a reproductive barrier that keeps the gene pools of these two species separate.

Allopatric and Sympatric Speciation: *A Review*

Now let's recap the processes by which new species form. In allopatric speciation, a new species forms in geographic isolation from its parent population. Geographic isolation severely restricts gene flow. Intrinsic barriers to reproduction with the parent population may then arise as a by-product of genetic changes that occur within the isolated population.

Many different processes can produce such genetic changes, including natural selection under different environmental conditions, genetic drift, and sexual selection. Once formed, reproductive barriers that arise in allopatric populations can prevent interbreeding with the parent population even if the populations come back into contact.

Sympatric speciation, in contrast, requires the emergence of a reproductive barrier that isolates a subset of a population from the remainder of the population in the same area. Though rarer than allopatric speciation, sympatric speciation can occur when gene flow to and from the isolated subpopulation is blocked. This can occur as a result of polyploidy, a condition in which an organism has extra sets of chromosomes. Sympatric speciation also can occur when a subset of a population becomes reproductively isolated because of natural selection that results from a switch to a habitat or food source not used by the parent population. Finally, sympatric speciation can result from sexual selection.

Having reviewed the geographic context in which species originate, we'll next explore in more detail what can happen when new or partially formed species come into contact.

CONCEPT CHECK 22.2

1. Contrast allopatric and sympatric speciation. Which type of speciation is more common, and why?
2. **WHAT IF?** Is allopatric speciation more likely to occur on an island close to a mainland or on a more isolated island of the same size? Explain your prediction.
3. **MAKE CONNECTIONS** Review the process of meiosis in Figure 10.8. Describe how an error during meiosis could lead to polyploidy.

For suggested answers, see Appendix A.

CONCEPT 22.3

Hybrid zones reveal factors that cause reproductive isolation

What happens if species with incomplete reproductive barriers come into contact with one another? One possible outcome is the formation of a **hybrid zone**, a region in which members of different species meet and mate, producing at least some offspring of mixed ancestry **(Figure 22.13)**. In this section, we'll

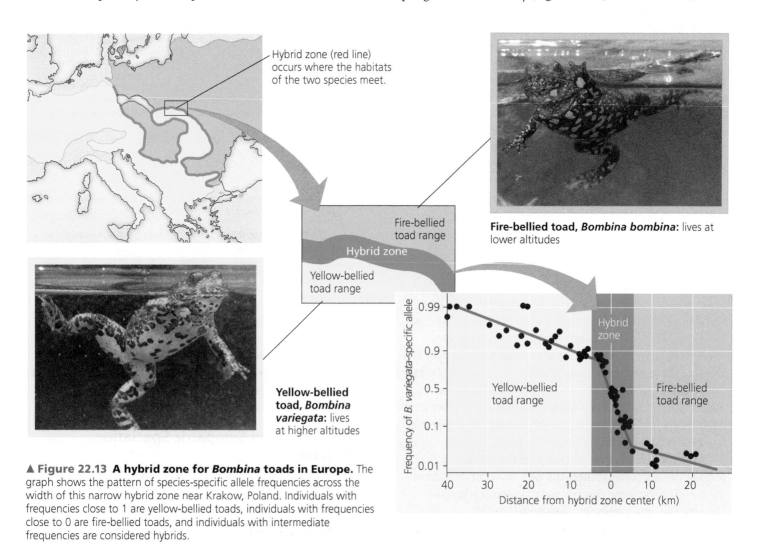

▲ **Figure 22.13 A hybrid zone for *Bombina* toads in Europe.** The graph shows the pattern of species-specific allele frequencies across the width of this narrow hybrid zone near Krakow, Poland. Individuals with frequencies close to 1 are yellow-bellied toads, individuals with frequencies close to 0 are fire-bellied toads, and individuals with intermediate frequencies are considered hybrids.

? *Does the graph indicate that gene flow is spreading fire-bellied toad alleles into the range of the yellow-bellied toad? Explain.*

explore hybrid zones and what they reveal about factors that cause the evolution of reproductive isolation.

Patterns Within Hybrid Zones

Some hybrid zones form as narrow bands, such as the one depicted in Figure 22.13 for the yellow-bellied toad (*Bombina variegata*) and its close relative, the fire-bellied toad (*B. bombina*). This hybrid zone, represented by the red line on the map, extends for 4,000 km but is less than 10 km wide in most places. The hybrid zone occurs where the higher-altitude habitat of the yellow-bellied toad meets the lowland habitat of the fire-bellied toad. Across a given "slice" of the zone, the frequency of alleles specific to yellow-bellied toads typically decreases from close to 100% at the edge where only yellow-bellied toads are found, to 50% in the central portion of the zone, to 0% at the edge where only fire-bellied toads are found.

What causes such a pattern of allele frequencies across a hybrid zone? We can infer that there is an obstacle to gene flow—otherwise, alleles from one parent species would also be common in the gene pool of the other parent species. Are geographic barriers reducing gene flow? Not in this case, since the toads can move throughout the hybrid zone. A more important factor is that hybrid toads have increased rates of embryonic mortality and a variety of morphological abnormalities, including ribs that are fused to the spine and malformed tadpole mouthparts. Because the hybrids have poor survival and reproduction, they produce few viable offspring with members of the parent species. As a result, hybrid individuals rarely serve as a stepping-stone from which alleles are passed from one species to the other. Outside the hybrid zone, additional obstacles to gene flow may be provided by natural selection in the different environments in which the parent species live.

Hybrid zones typically are located wherever the habitats of the interbreeding species meet. Those regions often resemble a group of isolated patches scattered across the landscape—more like the complex pattern of spots on a Dalmatian than the continuous band shown in Figure 22.13. But regardless of whether they have complex or simple spatial patterns, hybrid zones form when two species lacking complete barriers to reproduction come into contact. Once formed, how does a hybrid zone change over time?

Hybrid Zones over Time

Studying a hybrid zone is like observing a naturally occurring experiment on speciation. Will the hybrids become reproductively isolated from their parents and form a new species, as occurred by polyploidy in the goatsbeard plant of the Pacific Northwest? If not, there are three possible outcomes for the hybrid zone over time: reinforcement of barriers, fusion of species, or stability **(Figure 22.14)**. We'll discuss each of these outcomes in turn.

- **Reinforcement:** Hybrids often are less fit than members of their parent species. In such cases, natural selection should strengthen prezygotic barriers to reproduction, reducing the formation of unfit hybrids. Because this process involves *reinforcing* reproductive barriers, it is called reinforcement. If reinforcement is occurring, a logical prediction is that barriers to reproduction between species should be stronger

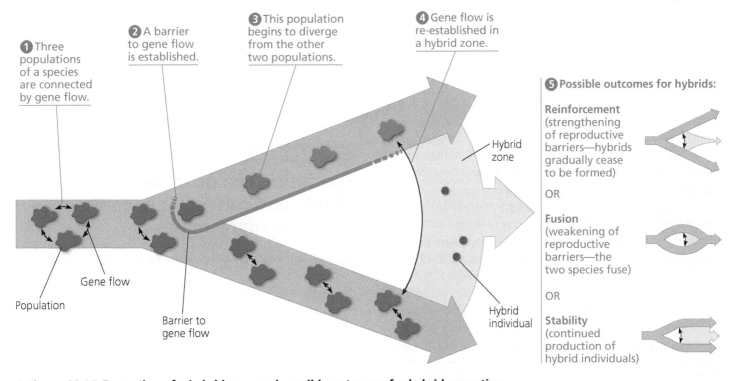

1 Three populations of a species are connected by gene flow.

2 A barrier to gene flow is established.

3 This population begins to diverge from the other two populations.

4 Gene flow is re-established in a hybrid zone.

5 Possible outcomes for hybrids:

Reinforcement (strengthening of reproductive barriers—hybrids gradually cease to be formed)

OR

Fusion (weakening of reproductive barriers—the two species fuse)

OR

Stability (continued production of hybrid individuals)

Hybrid zone

Hybrid individual

Gene flow

Population

Barrier to gene flow

▲ **Figure 22.14 Formation of a hybrid zone and possible outcomes for hybrids over time.** The thick colored arrows represent the passage of time.

WHAT IF? *Predict what might happen if gene flow were re-established at step 3 in this process.*

Pundamilia nyererei

Pundamilia pundamilia

Pundamilia "turbid water,"
hybrid offspring from a location
with turbid water

▲ **Figure 22.15 Fusion: The breakdown of reproductive barriers.** Increasingly cloudy water in Lake Victoria over the past several decades may have weakened reproductive barriers between *P. nyererei* and *P. pundamilia*. In areas of cloudy water, the two species have hybridized extensively, causing their gene pools to fuse.

for sympatric populations than for allopatric populations. Evidence in support of this prediction has been observed in birds, fishes, insects, plants, and other organisms.

- **Fusion:** Barriers to reproduction may be weak when two species meet in a hybrid zone. Indeed, so much gene flow may occur that reproductive barriers weaken further and the gene pools of the two species become increasingly alike. In effect, the speciation process reverses, eventually causing the two hybridizing species to fuse into a single species. For example, genetic and morphological evidence indicate that the recent loss of the large tree finch from the Galápagos island of Floreana resulted from extensive hybridization with another finch species on that island. Such a situation also may be occurring among Lake Victoria cichlids. Many pairs of ecologically similar cichlid species are reproductively isolated because the females of one species prefer to mate with males of one color, while females of the other species prefer to mate with males of a different color (see Figure 22.12). Murky waters caused by pollution may have reduced the ability of females to use color to distinguish males of their own species from males of closely related species. In some polluted waters, many hybrids have been produced, leading to fusion of the parent species' gene pools and a loss of species **(Figure 22.15).**

- **Stability:** Many hybrid zones are stable in the sense that hybrids continue to be produced. In some cases, this occurs

because the hybrids survive or reproduce better than members of either parent species, at least in certain habitats or years. But stable hybrid zones have also been observed in cases where the hybrids are selected *against*—an unexpected result. For example, hybrids continue to form in the *Bombina* hybrid zone even though they are strongly selected against. What could explain this finding? One possibility relates to the narrowness of the *Bombina* hybrid zone (see Figure 22.13). Evidence suggests that members of both parent species migrate into the zone from the parent populations located outside the zone, thus leading to the continued production of hybrids. If the hybrid zone were wider, this would be less likely to occur, since the center of the zone would receive little gene flow from distant parent populations located outside the hybrid zone.

Sometimes the outcomes in hybrid zones match our predictions (cichlid fishes), and sometimes they don't (*Bombina*). But whether our predictions are upheld or not, events in hybrid zones can shed light on how barriers to reproduction between closely related species change over time. In the next section, we'll examine how interactions between hybridizing species can also provide a glimpse into the speed and genetic control of speciation.

CONCEPT CHECK 22.3

1. What are hybrid zones, and why can they be viewed as "natural laboratories" in which to study speciation?

2. **WHAT IF?** Consider two species that diverged while geographically separated but resumed contact before reproductive isolation was complete. Predict what would happen over time if the two species mated indiscriminately and (a) hybrid offspring survived and reproduced more poorly than offspring from intraspecific matings or (b) hybrid offspring survived and reproduced as well as offspring from intraspecific matings.

For suggested answers, see Appendix A.

CONCEPT 22.4

Speciation can occur rapidly or slowly and can result from changes in few or many genes

Darwin faced many questions when he began to ponder that "mystery of mysteries"—speciation. He found answers to some of those questions when he realized that evolution by natural selection helps explain both the diversity of life and the adaptations of organisms. But biologists since Darwin have continued to ask fundamental questions about speciation. For example, how long does it take for new species to form? And how many genes change when one species splits into two? Answers to these questions are also emerging.

(a) In a punctuated model, new species change most as they branch from a parent species and then change little for the rest of their existence.

Time

(b) In a gradual model, species diverge from one another more slowly and steadily over time.

▲ **Figure 22.16 Two models for the tempo of speciation.**

The Time Course of Speciation

We can gather information about how long it takes new species to form from broad patterns in the fossil record and from studies that use morphological data (including fossils) or molecular data to assess the time interval between speciation events in particular groups of organisms.

Patterns in the Fossil Record

The fossil record includes many episodes in which new species appear suddenly in a geologic stratum, persist essentially unchanged through several strata, and then disappear. For example, there are dozens of species of marine invertebrates that make their debut in the fossil record with novel morphologies, but then change little for millions of years before becoming extinct. Paleontologists Niles Eldredge and Stephen Jay Gould coined the term **punctuated equilibria** to describe these periods of apparent stasis punctuated by sudden change **(Figure 22.16a)**. Other species do not show a punctuated pattern; instead, they appear to have changed more gradually over long periods of time **(Figure 22.16b)**.

What might punctuated and gradual patterns tell us about how long it takes new species to form? Suppose that a species survived for 5 million years, but most of the morphological changes that caused it to be designated a new species occurred during the first 50,000 years of its existence—just 1% of its total lifetime. Time periods this short (in geologic terms) often cannot be distinguished in fossil strata, in part because the rate of sediment accumulation may be too slow to separate layers this close in time. Thus, based on its fossils, the species would seem to have appeared suddenly and then lingered with little or no change before becoming extinct. Even though such a species may have originated more slowly than its fossils suggest (in this case taking up to 50,000 years), a punctuated pattern indicates that speciation occurred relatively rapidly. For species whose fossils changed much more gradually, we also cannot tell exactly when a new biological species formed, since information about reproductive isolation does not fossilize. However, it is likely that speciation in such groups occurred relatively slowly, perhaps taking millions of years.

Speciation Rates

The existence of fossils that display a punctuated pattern suggests that once the process of speciation begins, it can be completed relatively rapidly—a suggestion supported by a growing number of studies. For example, rapid speciation appears to have produced the wild sunflower *Helianthus anomalus*. Genetic evidence indicates that this species originated by the hybridization of two other sunflower species, *H. annuus* and *H. petiolaris*. The hybrid species *H. anomalus* is ecologically distinct and reproductively isolated from both parent species **(Figure 22.17)**.

▲ **Figure 22.17 A hybrid sunflower species and its dry sand dune habitat.** The wild sunflower *Helianthus anomalus* shown here originated via the hybridization of two other sunflowers, *H. annuus* and *H. petiolaris*, which live in nearby but moister environments.

Unlike the outcome of allopolyploid speciation, in which there is a change in chromosome number after hybridization, in these sunflowers the two parent species and the hybrid all have the same number of chromosomes ($2n = 34$). How, then, did speciation occur? To study this question, researchers performed an experiment designed to mimic events in nature: They crossed the two parent species and followed the fate of the hybrid offspring over several generations (Figure 22.18). Their results indicated that natural selection could produce extensive genetic changes in hybrid populations over short periods of time. These changes appear to have caused the hybrids to diverge reproductively from their parents and form a new species, *H. anomalus*.

The sunflower example, along with the apple maggot fly, Lake Victoria cichlid, and fruit fly examples discussed earlier, suggests that new species can arise rapidly *once divergence begins*. But what is the total length of time between speciation events? This interval consists of the time that elapses before populations of a newly formed species start to diverge from one another plus the time it takes for speciation to be complete once divergence begins. It turns out that the total time between speciation events varies considerably. In a survey of data from 84 groups of plants and animals, speciation intervals ranged from 4,000 years (in cichlids of Lake Nabugabo, Uganda) to 40 million years (in some beetles). Overall, the time between speciation events averaged 6.5 million years and was rarely less than 500,000 years.

These data suggest that on average, millions of years may pass before a newly formed plant or animal species will itself give rise to another new species. As we'll see in Concept 23.2, this finding has implications for how long it takes life on Earth to recover from mass extinction events. Moreover, the extreme variability in the time it takes new species to form indicates that organisms do not have an internal "speciation clock" that causes them to produce new species at regular intervals. Instead, speciation begins only after gene flow between populations is interrupted, perhaps by changing environmental conditions or by unpredictable events, such as a storm that transports a few individuals to a new area. Furthermore, once gene flow is interrupted, the populations must diverge genetically to such an extent that they become reproductively isolated—all before other events cause gene flow to resume, possibly reversing the speciation process (see Figure 22.14).

Studying the Genetics of Speciation

Studies of ongoing speciation (as in hybrid zones) can reveal traits that cause reproductive isolation. By identifying the genes that control those traits, scientists can explore a fundamental question of evolutionary biology: How many genes influence the formation of new species?

In some cases, the evolution of reproductive isolation results from the effects of a single gene. For example, in Japanese snails of the genus *Euhadra*, a change in a single gene results in a mechanical barrier to reproduction. This gene controls the direction in which the shells spiral. When their shells spiral in different directions, the snails' genitalia are

---

▼ **Figure 22.18** **Inquiry**

How does hybridization lead to speciation in sunflowers?

Experiment Researchers crossed the two parent sunflower species, *H. annuus* and *H. petiolaris*, to produce experimental hybrids in the laboratory (for each gamete, only two of the $n = 17$ chromosomes are shown).

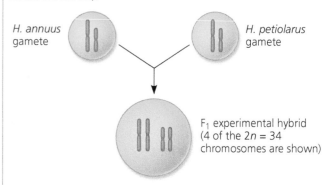

Note that in the first (F_1) generation, each chromosome of the experimental hybrids consisted entirely of DNA from one or the other parent species. The researchers then tested whether the F_1 and subsequent generations of experimental hybrids were fertile. They also used species-specific genetic markers to compare the chromosomes in the experimental hybrids with the chromosomes in the naturally occurring hybrid *H. anomalus*.

Results Although only 5% of the F_1 experimental hybrids were fertile, after just four more generations the hybrid fertility rose to more than 90%. The chromosomes of individuals from this fifth hybrid generation differed from those in the F_1 generation (see above) but were similar to those in *H. anomalus* individuals from natural populations:

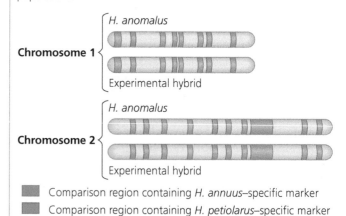

■ Comparison region containing *H. annuus*–specific marker
■ Comparison region containing *H. petiolarus*–specific marker

Conclusion Over time, the chromosomes in the population of experimental hybrids became similar to the chromosomes of *H. anomalus* individuals from natural populations. This suggests that the observed rise in the fertility of the experimental hybrids may have occurred as selection eliminated regions of DNA from the parent species that were not compatible with one another. Overall, it appeared that the initial steps of the speciation process occurred rapidly and could be mimicked in a laboratory experiment.

Data from L. H. Rieseberg et al., Role of gene interactions in hybrid speciation: Evidence from ancient and experimental hybrids, *Science* 272:741–745 (1996).

WHAT IF? The increased fertility of the experimental hybrids could have resulted from natural selection for thriving under laboratory conditions. Evaluate this alternative explanation for the result.

oriented in a manner that prevents mating (Figure 22.3f shows a similar example). Recent genetic analyses have uncovered other single genes that cause reproductive isolation in fruit flies or mice.

A major barrier to reproduction between two closely related species of monkey flower, *Mimulus cardinalis* and *M. lewisii*, also appears to be influenced by a relatively small number of genes. These two species are isolated by several prezygotic and postzygotic barriers. Of these, one prezygotic barrier, pollinator choice, accounts for most of the isolation: In a hybrid zone between *M. cardinalis* and *M. lewisii*, nearly 98% of pollinator visits were restricted to one species or the other.

The two monkey flower species are visited by different pollinators: Hummingbirds prefer the red-flowered *M. cardinalis*, and bumblebees prefer the pink-flowered *M. lewisii*.

(a) Typical *Mimulus lewisii*

(b) *M. lewisii* with an *M. cardinalis* flower-color allele

(c) Typical *Mimulus cardinalis*

(d) *M. cardinalis* with an *M. lewisii* flower-color allele

▲ **Figure 22.19 A locus that influences pollinator choice.** Pollinator preferences provide a strong barrier to reproduction between *Mimulus lewisii* and *M. cardinalis*. After transferring the *M. lewisii* allele for a flower-color locus into *M. cardinalis* and vice versa, researchers observed a shift in some pollinators' preferences.

WHAT IF? *If* M. cardinalis *individuals that had the* M. lewisii yup *allele were planted in an area that housed both monkey flower species, how might the production of hybrid offspring be affected?*

Pollinator choice is affected by at least two loci in the monkey flowers, one of which, the "yellow upper," or *yup*, locus, influences flower color (**Figure 22.19**). By crossing the two parent species to produce F_1 hybrids and then performing repeated backcrosses of these F_1 hybrids to each parent species, researchers succeeded in transferring the *M. cardinalis* allele at this locus into *M. lewisii*, and vice versa. In a field experiment, *M. lewisii* plants with the *M. cardinalis yup* allele received 68-fold more visits from hummingbirds than did wild-type *M. lewisii*. Similarly, *M. cardinalis* plants with the *M. lewisii yup* allele received 74-fold more visits from bumblebees than did wild-type *M. cardinalis*. Thus, a mutation at a single locus can influence pollinator preference and hence contribute to reproductive isolation in monkey flowers.

In other organisms, the speciation process is influenced by larger numbers of genes and gene interactions. For example, hybrid sterility between two subspecies of the fruit fly *Drosophila pseudoobscura* results from gene interactions among at least four loci, and postzygotic isolation in the sunflower hybrid zone discussed earlier is influenced by at least 26 chromosome segments (and an unknown number of genes). Overall, studies suggest that few or many genes can influence the evolution of reproductive isolation and hence the emergence of a new species.

From Speciation to Macroevolution

As you've seen, speciation may begin with differences as small as the color on a cichlid's back. However, as speciation occurs again and again, such differences can accumulate and become more pronounced, eventually leading to the formation of new groups of organisms that differ greatly from their ancestors (as in the origin of whales from terrestrial mammals; see Figure 19.20). Moreover, as one group of organisms increases in size by producing many new species, another group of organisms may shrink, losing species to extinction. The cumulative effects of many such speciation and extinction events have helped shape the sweeping evolutionary changes that are documented in the fossil record. In the next chapter, we turn to such large-scale evolutionary changes as we begin our study of macroevolution.

CONCEPT CHECK 22.4

1. Speciation can occur rapidly between diverging populations, yet the time between speciation events is often more than a million years. Explain this apparent contradiction.

2. Summarize evidence that the *yup* flower-color locus acts as a prezygotic barrier to reproduction in two species of monkey flowers. Do these results demonstrate that the *yup* locus alone controls barriers to reproduction between these species? Explain.

3. **MAKE CONNECTIONS** Compare Figure 10.11 with Figure 22.18. What cellular process could cause the hybrid chromosomes in Figure 22.18 to contain DNA from both parent species? Explain.

For suggested answers, see Appendix A.

Go to **MasteringBiology®** for Assignments, the eText, and the Study Area with Animations, Activities, Vocab Self-Quiz, and Practice Tests.

SUMMARY OF KEY CONCEPTS

VOCAB SELF-QUIZ

goo.gl/gbai8v

CONCEPT 22.1

The biological species concept emphasizes reproductive isolation (pp. 434–438)

- A biological **species** is a group of populations whose individuals may interbreed and produce viable, fertile offspring with each other but not with members of other species. The **biological species concept** emphasizes reproductive isolation through prezygotic and postzygotic barriers that separate gene pools.
- Although helpful in thinking about how speciation occurs, the biological species concept has limitations. For instance, it cannot be applied to organisms known only as fossils or to organisms that reproduce only asexually. Thus, scientists use other species concepts, such as the **morphological species concept**, in certain circumstances.

> **?** *Explain the role of gene flow in the biological species concept.*

CONCEPT 22.2

Speciation can take place with or without geographic separation (pp. 439–444)

- In **allopatric speciation**, gene flow is reduced when two populations of one species become geographically separated from each other. One or both populations may undergo evolutionary change during the period of separation, resulting in the establishment of prezygotic or postzygotic barriers to reproduction.
- In **sympatric speciation**, a new species originates while remaining in the same geographic area as the parent species. Plant species (and, more rarely, animal species) have evolved sympatrically through **polyploidy**. Sympatric speciation can also result from habitat shifts and sexual selection.

Original population

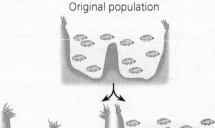

Allopatric speciation   Sympatric speciation

> **?** *Can factors that cause sympatric speciation also cause allopatric speciation? Explain.*

CONCEPT 22.3

Hybrid zones reveal factors that cause reproductive isolation (pp. 444–446)

- Many groups of organisms form **hybrid zones** in which members of different species meet and mate, producing at least some offspring of mixed ancestry.

- Many hybrid zones exhibit **stability** in that hybrid offspring continue to be produced over time. In others, **reinforcement** strengthens prezygotic barriers to reproduction, thus decreasing the formation of unfit hybrids. In still other hybrid zones, barriers to reproduction may weaken over time, resulting in the **fusion** of the species' gene pools (reversing the speciation process).

> **?** *What factors can support the long-term stability of a hybrid zone if the parent species live in different environments?*

CONCEPT 22.4

Speciation can occur rapidly or slowly and can result from changes in few or many genes (pp. 446–449)

- New species can form rapidly once divergence begins—but it can take millions of years for that to happen. The time interval between speciation events varies considerably, from a few thousand years to tens of millions of years.
- New developments in genetics have enabled researchers to identify specific genes involved in some cases of speciation. Results show that speciation can be driven by few or many genes.

> **?** *Is speciation something that happened only in the distant past, or are new species continuing to arise today? Explain.*

TEST YOUR UNDERSTANDING

PRACTICE TEST

goo.gl/CRZjvS

Level 1: Knowledge/Comprehension

1. The *largest* unit within which gene flow can readily occur is a
   - (A) population.
   - (B) species.
   - (C) genus.
   - (D) hybrid.

2. Males of different species of the fruit fly *Drosophila* that live in the same parts of the Hawaiian Islands have different elaborate courtship rituals. These rituals involve fighting other males and making stylized movements that attract females. What type of reproductive isolation does this represent?
   - (A) habitat isolation
   - (B) temporal isolation
   - (C) behavioral isolation
   - (D) gametic isolation

3. According to the punctuated equilibria model,
   - (A) natural selection is unimportant as a mechanism of evolution.
   - (B) given enough time, most existing species will branch gradually into new species.
   - (C) most evolution occurs in sympatric populations.
   - (D) most new species accumulate their unique features relatively rapidly as they come into existence, then change little for the rest of their duration as a species.

Level 2: Application/Analysis

4. Bird guides once listed the myrtle warbler and Audubon's warbler as distinct species. Recently, these birds were reclassified as eastern and western forms of a single species, the yellow-rumped warbler. Which of the following pieces of evidence, if true, would be cause for this reclassification?
   - (A) The two forms interbreed often in nature, and their offspring survive and reproduce well.
   - (B) The two forms live in similar habitats and have similar food requirements.
   - (C) The two forms have many genes in common.
   - (D) The two forms are very similar in appearance.

5. Which of the following factors would *not* contribute to allopatric speciation?
  (A) A population becomes geographically isolated from the parent population.
  (B) The separated population is small, and genetic drift occurs.
  (C) The isolated population is exposed to different selection pressures than the ancestral population.
  (D) Gene flow between the two populations is extensive.

6. Plant species A has a diploid number of 12. Plant species B has a diploid number of 16. A new species, C, arises as an allopolyploid from A and B. The diploid number for species C would probably be
  (A) 14.   (B) 16.   (C) 28.   (D) 56.

Level 3: Synthesis/Evaluation

7. SCIENTIFIC INQUIRY
DRAW IT In this chapter, you read that bread wheat (*Triticum aestivum*) is an allohexaploid, containing two sets of chromosomes from each of three different parent species. Genetic analysis suggests that the three species pictured following this question each contributed chromosome sets to *T. aestivum*. (The capital letters here represent sets of chromosomes rather than individual genes.) Evidence also indicates that the first polyploidy event was a spontaneous hybridization of the early cultivated wheat species *T. monococcum* and a wild *Triticum* grass species. Based on this information, draw a diagram of one possible chain of events that could have produced the allohexaploid *T. aestivum*.

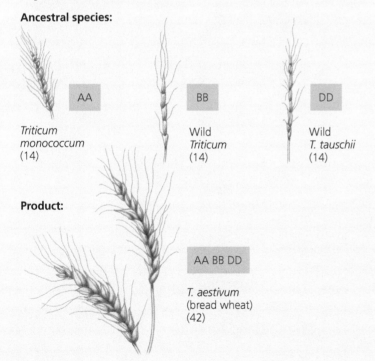

Ancestral species:

AA — *Triticum monococcum* (14)

BB — Wild *Triticum* (14)

DD — Wild *T. tauschii* (14)

Product:

AA BB DD — *T. aestivum* (bread wheat) (42)

8. SCIENCE, TECHNOLOGY, AND SOCIETY
In the United States, the rare red wolf (*Canis lupus*) has been known to hybridize with coyotes (*Canis latrans*), which are much more numerous. Although red wolves and coyotes differ in terms of morphology, DNA, and behavior, genetic evidence suggests that living red wolf individuals are actually hybrids. Red wolves are designated as an endangered species and hence receive legal protection under the Endangered Species Act. Some people think that their endangered status should be withdrawn because the remaining red wolves are hybrids, not members of a "pure" species. Do you agree? Why or why not?

9. FOCUS ON EVOLUTION
Explain the biological basis for assigning all human populations to a single species. Can you think of a scenario by which a second human species could originate in the future?

10. FOCUS ON INFORMATION
In sexually reproducing species, each individual begins life with DNA inherited from both parent organisms. In a short essay (100–150 words), apply this idea to what occurs when organisms of two species that have homologous chromosomes mate and produce (F_1) hybrid offspring. What percentage of the DNA in the F_1 hybrids' chromosomes comes from each parent species? As the hybrids mate and produce F_2 and later-generation hybrid offspring, describe how recombination and natural selection may affect whether the DNA in hybrid chromosomes is derived from one parent species or the other.

11. SYNTHESIZE YOUR KNOWLEDGE

Suppose that females of one population of strawberry poison dart frogs (*Dendrobates pumilio*) prefer to mate with males that have a bright red and black coloration. In a different population, the females prefer males with yellow skin. Propose a hypothesis to explain how such differences could have arisen in allopatric versus sympatric populations.

For selected answers, see Appendix A.

40 **Population Ecology and the Distribution of Organisms**

Ecologists study the interactions of organisms and the environment to understand the **distribution of species. Populations** of a species may be relatively stable in size or fluctuate greatly, driven by ecological and evolutionary factors.

41 **Species Interactions**

Populations of different species interact in ecological **communities** through processes such as competition, predation, and mutualism.

42 **Ecosystems and Energy**

Energy flow and chemical cycling occur in an **ecosystem**, the community of organisms living in an area and the physical factors with which they interact. Within an ecosystem, organisms transfer **energy** through trophic levels and are characterized by their main source of nutrition and energy.

43 **Global Ecology and Conservation Biology**

Human activities are changing climate patterns, trophic structures, energy flow, and disturbance patterns throughout the biosphere. Efforts to sustain ecosystem processes and to preserve biodiversity from habitat loss and other threats comprise the fields of **global ecology** and **conservation biology**.

Ecology

40
41
42
43

Population Ecology and the Distribution of Organisms

Species Interactions

Ecosystems and Energy

Global Ecology and Conservation Biology

Animals

Plants

History of Life

Evolution

Genetics

Chemistry and Cells

40 Population Ecology and the Distribution of Organisms

KEY CONCEPTS

40.1 Earth's climate influences the distribution of terrestrial biomes

40.2 Aquatic biomes are diverse and dynamic systems that cover most of Earth

40.3 Interactions between organisms and the environment limit the distribution of species

40.4 Biotic and abiotic factors affect population density, dispersion, and demographics

40.5 The exponential and logistic models describe the growth of populations

40.6 Population dynamics are influenced strongly by life history traits and population density

▲ **Figure 40.1** What limits the distribution of this tiny frog?

Discovering Ecology

Kneeling by a stream in Papua New Guinea in 2008, Cornell University undergraduate Michael Grundler heard a series of clicks. He first thought that the sounds must be coming from a nearby cricket. Turning to look, he saw instead a tiny frog inflating its vocal sac to call for a mate. Grundler would later learn that he had just discovered the first of two new frog species, *Paedophryne swiftorum* and *Paedophryne amauensis* **(Figure 40.1)**. The entire *Paedophryne* genus is known only from the Papuan Peninsula in eastern New Guinea. Adult frogs of both species are typically only 8 mm (0.3 inch) long and may be the smallest adult vertebrates on Earth.

What environmental factors limit the geographic distribution of *Paedophryne* frogs? How do variations in their food supply or interactions with other species, such as pathogens, affect the size of their population?

Questions like these are the subject of **ecology** (from the Greek *oikos*, home, and *logos*, study), the scientific study of the interactions between organisms and the environment. The interactions studied by ecologists can be organized into a hierarchy that ranges in scale from single organisms to the globe **(Figure 40.2)**.

Ecology is a rigorous experimental science that requires a breadth of biological knowledge. Ecologists observe nature, generate hypotheses, manipulate environmental variables, and observe outcomes. In this chapter, we'll first consider how Earth's climate and other factors determine the location of major life zones on land and in the oceans. We'll then examine how ecologists investigate what controls the distribution of species and the density and size of populations. The next three chapters focus on community, ecosystem, and global ecology, as we explore how ecologists apply biological knowledge to predict the global consequences of human activities and to conserve Earth's biodiversity.

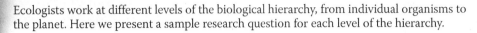

Ecologists work at different levels of the biological hierarchy, from individual organisms to the planet. Here we present a sample research question for each level of the hierarchy.

Organismal Ecology

Organismal ecology, which includes the subdisciplines of physiological, evolutionary, and behavioral ecology, is concerned with how an organism's structure, physiology, and behavior meet the challenges posed by its environment.

◀ How do flamingos select a mate?

Population Ecology

A **population** is a group of individuals of the same species living in an area. **Population ecology** analyzes factors that affect population size and how and why it changes through time.

◀ What environmental factors affect the reproductive rate of flamingos?

Community Ecology

A **community** is a group of populations of different species in an area. **Community ecology** examines how interactions between species, such as predation and competition, affect community structure and organization.

◀ What factors influence the diversity of species that interact at this African lake?

Ecosystem Ecology

An **ecosystem** is the community of organisms in an area and the physical factors with which those organisms interact. **Ecosystem ecology** emphasizes energy flow and chemical cycling between organisms and the environment.

◀ What factors control photosynthetic productivity in this aquatic ecosystem?

Landscape Ecology

A **landscape** (or seascape) is a mosaic of connected ecosystems. Research in **landscape ecology** focuses on the factors controlling exchanges of energy, materials, and organisms across multiple ecosystems.

◀ To what extent do nutrients from terrestrial ecosystems affect organisms in the lake?

Global Ecology

The **biosphere** is the global ecosystem—the sum of all the planet's ecosystems and landscapes. Global ecology examines how the regional exchange of energy and materials influences the functioning and distribution of organisms across the biosphere.

◀ How do global patterns of air circulation affect the distribution of organisms?

Latitudinal Variation in Sunlight Intensity

Earth's curved shape causes latitudinal variation in the intensity of sun light. Because sunlight strikes the tropics (those regions that lie between 23.5° north latitude and 23.5° south latitude) most directly, more heat and light per unit of surface area are delivered there. At higher latitudes, sunlight strikes Earth at an oblique angle, and thus the light energy is more diffuse on Earth's surface.

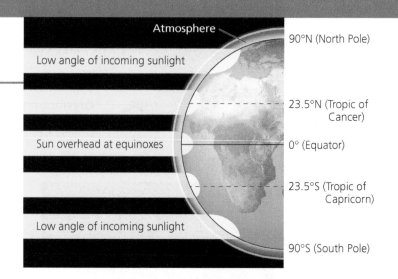

Atmosphere

Low angle of incoming sunlight

Sun overhead at equinoxes

Low angle of incoming sunlight

90°N (North Pole)

23.5°N (Tropic of Cancer)

0° (Equator)

23.5°S (Tropic of Capricorn)

90°S (South Pole)

Global Air Circulation and Precipitation Patterns

Intense solar radiation near the equator initiates a global pattern of air circulation and precipitation. High temperatures in the tropics evaporate water from Earth's surface and cause warm, wet air masses to rise (blue arrows) and flow toward the poles. As the rising air masses expand and cool, they release much of their water content, creating abundant precipitation in tropical regions. The high-altitude air masses, now dry, descend (tan arrows) toward Earth around 30° north and south, absorbing moisture from the land and creating an arid climate conducive to the development of the deserts that are common at those latitudes. Some of the descending air then flows toward the poles. At latitudes around 60° north and south, the air masses again rise and release abundant precipitation (though less than in the tropics). Some of the cold, dry rising air then flows to the poles, where it descends and flows back toward the equator, absorbing moisture and creating the comparatively rainless and bitterly cold climates of the polar regions.

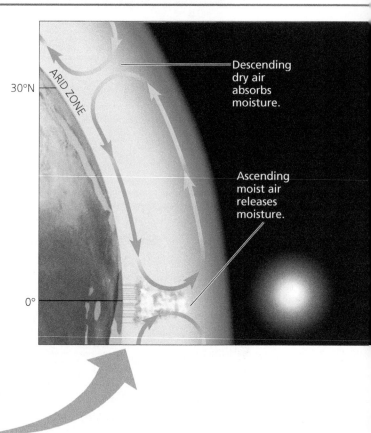

30°N

ARID ZONE

Descending dry air absorbs moisture.

Ascending moist air releases moisture.

0°

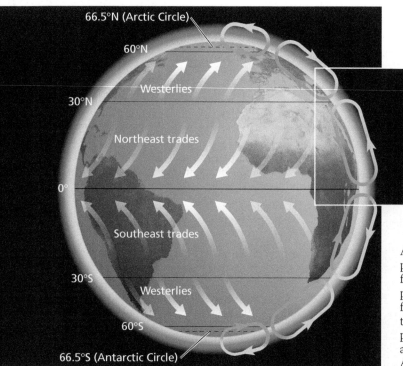

66.5°N (Arctic Circle)

60°N

Westerlies

30°N

Northeast trades

0°

Southeast trades

30°S

Westerlies

60°S

66.5°S (Antarctic Circle)

Air flowing close to Earth's surface creates predictable global wind patterns. As Earth rotates on its axis, land near the equator moves faster than that at the poles, deflecting the winds from the vertical paths shown above and creating the more easterly and westerly flows shown at left. Cooling trade winds blow from east to west in the tropics; prevailing westerlies blow from west to east in the temperate zones, defined as the regions between the Tropic of Cancer and the Arctic Circle and between the Tropic of Capricorn and the Antarctic Circle.

CONCEPT 40.1

Earth's climate influences the distribution of terrestrial biomes

The most significant influence on the distribution of organisms on land is **climate**, the long-term, prevailing weather conditions in a given area. Four physical factors—temperature, precipitation, sunlight, and wind—are particularly important components of climate. Such **abiotic**, or nonliving, factors are the chemical and physical attributes of the environment that influence the distribution and abundance of organisms. **Biotic**, or living, factors—the other organisms that are part of an individual's environment—also influence the distribution and abundance of life.

We begin by describing patterns in climate that can be observed at the global, regional, and landscape levels.

Global Climate Patterns

Global climate patterns are determined largely by the input of solar energy and Earth's movement in space. The sun warms the atmosphere, land, and water. This warming establishes the temperature variations, movements of air and water, and evaporation of water that cause dramatic latitudinal variations in climate. **Figure 40.3** summarizes Earth's climate patterns and how they are formed.

Regional Effects on Climate

Climate varies seasonally and can be modified by other factors, such as large bodies of water and mountain ranges.

Seasonality

In middle to high latitudes, Earth's tilted axis of rotation and its annual passage around the sun cause strong seasonal cycles in day length, solar radiation, and temperature **(Figure 40.4)**. The changing angle of the sun over the course of the year also affects local environments. For example, the belts of wet and dry air on either side of the equator move slightly northward and southward as the sun's angle changes; this produces marked wet and dry seasons around 20° north and 20° south latitude, where many tropical deciduous forests grow. In addition, seasonal changes in wind patterns alter ocean currents, sometimes causing the upwelling of cold water from deep ocean layers. This nutrient-rich water stimulates the growth of surface-dwelling phytoplankton and the organisms that feed on them. These upwelling zones make up only a small percentage of ocean area but are responsible for more than a quarter of fish caught globally.

Bodies of Water

Ocean currents influence climate along the coasts of continents by heating or cooling overlying air masses that pass across the land. Coastal regions are also generally wetter than inland areas at the same latitude. The cool, misty climate

▼ Figure 40.4 **Seasonal variation in sunlight intensity.** Because Earth is tilted on its axis relative to its plane of orbit around the sun, the intensity of solar radiation varies seasonally. This variation is smallest in the tropics and increases toward the poles.

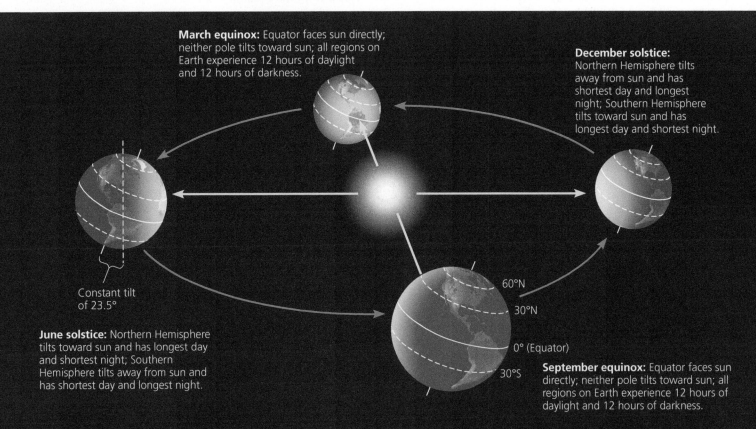

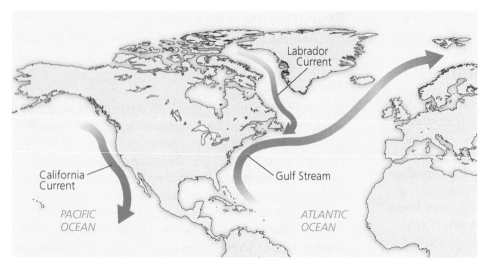

▲ **Figure 40.5 Circulation of surface water in the oceans around North America.** The California Current carries cold water southward along the western coast of North America. Along the eastern coast, the Labrador Current carries cold water southward, and the Gulf Stream moves warm water toward northern Europe.

produced by the cold California Current that flows southward along western North America supports a coniferous rain forest ecosystem along much of the continent's Pacific coast **(Figure 40.5)**. Conversely, the west coast of northern Europe has a mild climate because the Gulf Stream carries warm water from the equator to the North Atlantic. As a result, northwestern Europe is warmer during winter than southeastern Canada, which is farther south but is cooled by the Labrador Current flowing south from the coast of Greenland.

Because of the high specific heat of water (see Concept 2.5), oceans and large lakes tend to moderate the climate of nearby land. During a hot day, when land is warmer than the water, air over the land heats up and rises, drawing a cool breeze from the water across the land **(Figure 40.6)**. In contrast, because temperatures drop more quickly over land than over water at night, air over the now warmer water rises, drawing cooler air from the land back out over the water and replacing it with warmer air from offshore.

Mountains

Like large bodies of water, mountains influence air flow over land. When warm, moist air approaches a mountain, the air expands and cools as it rises, releasing moisture on the windward side of the peak (see Figure 40.6). On the leeward side, cooler, dry air descends, absorbing moisture and producing a "rain shadow." Such leeward rain shadows determine where many deserts are found, including the Mojave Desert of western North America and the Gobi Desert of Asia.

Mountains also affect the amount of sunlight reaching an area and thus the local temperature and rainfall. South-facing slopes in the Northern Hemisphere receive more sunlight than north-facing slopes and are therefore warmer and drier. These physical differences influence species distributions locally. In many mountains of western North America, spruce and other conifers grow on the cooler north-facing slopes, but shrubby, drought-resistant plants inhabit the south-facing slopes. In addition, every 1,000-m increase in elevation produces an average temperature drop of 6°C, equivalent to that produced by an 880-km increase in latitude. This is one reason that high-elevation communities near the equator, for example, can be similar to lower-elevation communities that are far from the equator.

Climate and Terrestrial Biomes

We turn now to the role of climate in determining the nature and location of Earth's **biomes**, major life zones characterized by vegetation type (in terrestrial biomes) or by the physical environment (in aquatic biomes, which we will survey in Concept 40.2).

▼ **Figure 40.6 How large bodies of water and mountains affect climate.** This figure illustrates what can happen on a hot summer day.

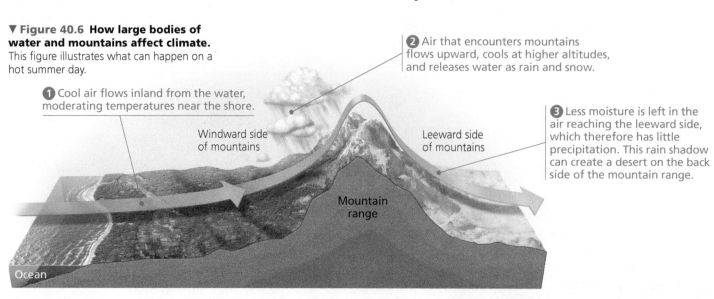

① Cool air flows inland from the water, moderating temperatures near the shore.

② Air that encounters mountains flows upward, cools at higher altitudes, and releases water as rain and snow.

③ Less moisture is left in the air reaching the leeward side, which therefore has little precipitation. This rain shadow can create a desert on the back side of the mountain range.

Windward side of mountains

Leeward side of mountains

Mountain range

Ocean

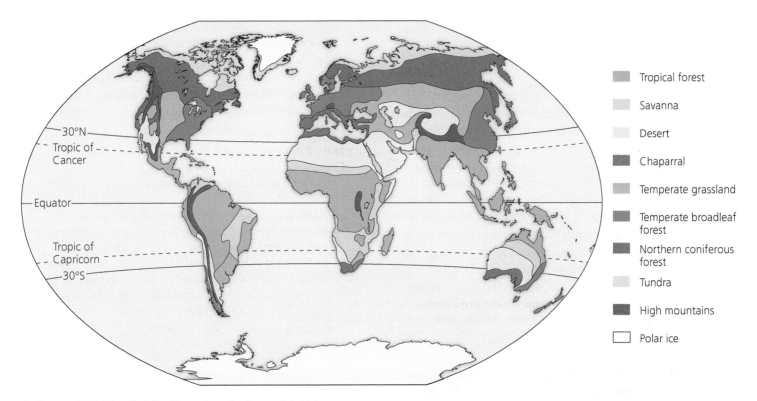

▲ Figure 40.7 **The distribution of major terrestrial biomes.**

Tropical forest

Savanna

Desert

Chaparral

Temperate grassland

Temperate broadleaf forest

Northern coniferous forest

Tundra

High mountains

Polar ice

Because of the latitudinal patterns of climate described in Figure 40.3, the locations of terrestrial biomes also show strong latitudinal patterns **(Figure 40.7)**. For example, the dry air that descends at 30° north and south often leads to the formation of deserts at those latitudes. We can highlight the importance of climate on the distribution of biomes is by constructing a **climograph**, a plot of the annual mean temperature and precipitation in a particular region **(Figure 40.8)**. Notice, for instance, that grasslands in North America are typically drier than forests and that deserts are drier still.

Factors other than mean temperature and precipitation also play a role in determining where biomes exist. For example, some areas in North America with a particular combination of temperature and precipitation support a temperate broadleaf forest, but other areas with similar values for these variables support a coniferous forest (see the overlap in Figure 40.8). One reason for this variation is that climographs are based on annual *averages*, but the *pattern* of climatic variation is often as important as the average climate. For example, some areas may receive regular precipitation throughout the year, whereas other areas may have distinct wet and dry seasons.

Natural and human-caused disturbances also alter the distribution of biomes. A **disturbance** is an event such as a storm, fire, or human activity that changes a community, removing organisms from it and altering resource availability. For instance, frequent fires can kill woody plants and keep a savanna from becoming the woodland that climate alone would support. Hurricanes and other storms create openings for new species in many tropical and temperate forests. Human-caused disturbances have altered much of Earth's surface, replacing natural communities with urban and agricultural ones.

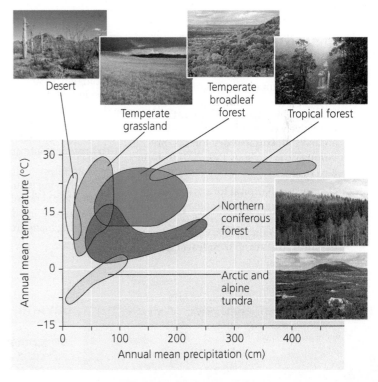

▲ Figure 40.8 **A climograph for some major types of biomes in North America.** The areas plotted here encompass the ranges of annual mean temperature and precipitation in the biomes.

INTERPRET THE DATA *Some arctic tundra ecosystems receive as little rainfall as deserts but have much denser vegetation. What climatic factor might explain this difference? Explain.*

General Features of Terrestrial Biomes

Most terrestrial biomes are named for major physical or climatic features and for their predominant vegetation. Temperate grasslands, for instance, are generally found in middle latitudes, where the climate is more moderate than in the tropics or polar regions, and are dominated by various grass species (see Figure 40.7). Each biome is also characterized by microorganisms, fungi, and animals adapted to that particular environment. Temperate grasslands are usually more likely than temperate forests to be populated by large grazing mammals and to have arbuscular mycorrhizal fungi (see Figure 29.14).

Vertical layering of vegetation is an important feature of terrestrial biomes. In many forests, the layers from top to bottom consist of the upper **canopy**, the low-tree layer, the shrub understory, the ground layer of herbaceous plants, the forest floor (litter layer), and the root layer. Nonforest biomes have similar, though usually less pronounced, layers. Layering of vegetation provides many different habitats for animals, which sometimes exist in well-defined feeding groups, from the insectivorous birds and bats that feed above canopies to the small mammals, worms, and arthropods that search for food in the litter and root layers below.

Figure 40.9 summarizes the major features of terrestrial biomes. Although Figure 40.7 shows distinct boundaries between the biomes, terrestrial biomes usually grade into neighboring biomes, sometimes over large areas. The area of intergradation, called an **ecotone**, may be wide or narrow.

CONCEPT CHECK 40.1

1. Explain how the sun's unequal heating of Earth's surface leads to the development of deserts around 30° north and south of the equator.
2. Using Figures 40.7 and 40.9, identify the natural biome in which you live and summarize its abiotic and biotic characteristics. Do these reflect your actual surroundings? Explain.
3. **WHAT IF?** If global warming increases average temperatures on Earth by 4°C in this century, predict which biome is most likely to replace tundra in some locations as a result (see Figures 40.7 and 40.8). Explain your answer.

For suggested answers, see Appendix A.

▼ **Figure 40.9** | **Exploring Terrestrial Biomes**

Tropical Forest

Distribution Equatorial and subequatorial regions

Climate Temperature is usually high, averaging 25–29°C with little seasonal variation. In **tropical rain forests**, rainfall is relatively constant, about 200–400 cm annually. In **tropical dry forests**, precipitation averages about 150–200 cm annually, with a six-to seven-month dry season.

Organisms Tropical forests are vertically layered, and plants compete strongly for light. Broadleaf evergreen trees are dominant in rain forests, whereas many dry forest trees drop their leaves during the dry season. Tropical forests are home to millions of animal species, including an estimated 5–30 million still undescribed species of insects, spiders, and other arthropods. Animal diversity is higher than in any other terrestrial biome. The animals are adapted to the vertically layered environment and are often inconspicuous.

Human Impact Humans long ago established thriving communities in tropical forests. Rapid population growth leading to agriculture and development is now destroying many tropical forests.

A tropical rain forest in Costa Rica

Savanna

Distribution Equatorial and subequatorial regions

Climate Rainfall averages 30–50 cm per year in **savannas** and is seasonal, with a dry season that can last up to nine months. Temperature averages 24–29°C but varies seasonally more than in tropical forests.

Organisms Scattered trees often are thorny and have small leaves, an apparent adaptation to the relatively dry conditions. Fires are common in the dry season, and the dominant plant species are fire-adapted and tolerant of seasonal drought.

Grasses and small nonwoody plants called forbs make up most of the ground cover. Large plant-eating mammals, such as wildebeests and zebras, and predators, including lions and hyenas, are common inhabitants. However, the dominant herbivores are insects, especially termites.

Human Impact The earliest humans may have lived in savannas. Overly frequent fires set by humans reduce tree regeneration by killing the seedlings and saplings. Cattle ranching and overhunting have led to declines in large-mammal populations.

A savanna in Kenya

Organ Pipe Cactus National Monument, Arizona

Desert

Distribution **Deserts** occur in bands near 30° north and south latitude or at other latitudes in the interior of continents (for instance, the Gobi Desert of north-central Asia).

Climate Precipitation is low and highly variable, generally less than 30 cm per year. Temperature varies seasonally and daily. It may exceed 50°C in hot deserts and fall below −30°C in cold deserts.

Organisms Desert landscapes are dominated by low, widely scattered vegetation. Common plants include succulents such as cacti or euphorbs, deeply rooted shrubs, and herbs that grow during the infrequent moist periods. Desert plant adaptations include tolerance to heat and desiccation, water storage, reduced leaf surface area, and physical defenses such as spines and toxins in leaves. Many desert plants carry out C4 or CAM photosynthesis. Common desert animals include scorpions, ants, beetles, snakes, lizards, migratory and resident birds, and seed-eating rodents. Many species in hot deserts are active at night, when the air is cooler. Water conservation is a common adaptation, and some animals can obtain all their water by breaking down carbohydrates in seeds.

Human Impact Long-distance transport of water and deep groundwater wells have allowed humans to maintain substantial populations in deserts. Urbanization and conversion to irrigated agriculture have reduced the natural biodiversity of some deserts.

Chaparral

Distribution Midlatitude coastal regions on several continents

Climate Annual precipitation is typically 30–50 cm and is highly seasonal, with rainy winters and dry summers. Fall, winter, and spring are cool, with average temperatures of 10–12°C. Average summer temperature can reach 30°C.

Organisms **Chaparral** is dominated by shrubs and small trees adapted to frequent fires. Some fire-adapted shrubs produce seeds that will germinate only after a hot fire; food reserves stored in their roots enable them to resprout quickly and use nutrients released by the fire. Adaptations to drought include tough, evergreen leaves, which reduce water loss. Animals include browsers, such as deer and goats, that feed on twigs and buds of woody vegetation; there are also many species of insects, amphibians, small mammals, and birds.

Human Impact Chaparral areas have been heavily settled and reduced through conversion to agriculture and urbanization. Humans contribute to the fires that sweep across the chaparral.

An area of chaparral in California

Temperate Grassland

Distribution Typically at midlatitudes, often in the interior of continents

Climate Annual precipitation in **temperate grasslands** generally averages 30 to 100 cm and can be highly seasonal, with relatively dry winters and wet summers. Average temperatures frequently are below −10°C in winter and reach 30°C in summer.

Organisms Dominant plants are grasses and forbs, which vary in height from a few centimeters to 2 m in tallgrass prairie. Many grassland plants have adaptations that help them survive periodic, protracted droughts and fire. Grazing by large mammals such as bison and wild horses helps prevent establishment of woody shrubs and trees. Burrowing mammals, such as prairie dogs in North America, are also common.

Human Impact Because of their deep, fertile soils, temperate grasslands in North America and Eurasia have frequently been converted to farmland. In some drier grasslands, cattle and other grazers have turned parts of the biome into desert.

A grassland in Mongolia

Northern Coniferous Forest

Distribution In a broad band across northern North America and Eurasia to the edge of the arctic tundra, the **northern coniferous forest**, or *taiga*, is the largest terrestrial biome.

Climate Annual precipitation generally ranges from 30 to 70 cm. Winters are cold. Some areas of coniferous forest in Siberia typically range in temperature from −50°C in winter to over 20°C in summer.

Organisms Cone-bearing trees (conifers), such as pine, spruce, fir, and hemlock, are common, and some species depend on fire to regenerate. The conical shape of many conifers prevents snow from accumulating and breaking their branches, and their needlelike or scalelike leaves reduce water loss. Plant diversity in the shrub and herb layers is lower than in temperate broadleaf forests. Many migratory birds nest in northern coniferous forests. Mammals include moose, brown bears, and Siberian tigers. Periodic outbreaks of insects can kill vast tracts of trees.

Human Impact Although they have not been heavily settled by human populations, northern coniferous forests are being logged at a fast rate, and old-growth stands may soon disappear.

A coniferous forest in Norway

Temperate Broadleaf Forest

Distribution Midlatitudes in the Northern Hemisphere, with smaller areas in Chile, South Africa, Australia, and New Zealand

Climate Precipitation averages about 70 to 200 cm annually. Significant amounts fall during all seasons, with winter snow in some forests. Winter temperatures average around 0°C. Summers are humid, with maximum temperatures near 35°C.

Organisms The dominant plants of **temperate broadleaf forests** in the Northern Hemisphere are deciduous trees, which drop their leaves before winter, when low temperatures would reduce photosynthesis. In Australia, evergreen eucalyptus trees are common. In the Northern Hemisphere, many mammals hibernate in winter, while many bird species migrate to areas with warmer climates.

Human Impact Temperate broadleaf forests have been heavily settled globally. Logging and land clearing for agriculture and urban development have destroyed virtually all the original deciduous forests in North America, but these forests are returning over much of their former range.

A temperate broadleaf forest in New Jersey

Tundra

Distribution **Tundra** covers expansive areas of the Arctic, amounting to 20% of Earth's land surface. High winds and low temperatures produce alpine tundra on very high mountaintops at all latitudes, including the tropics.

Climate Precipitation averages 20 to 60 cm annually in arctic tundra but may exceed 100 cm in alpine tundra. Winters are cold, with average temperatures in some areas below −30°C. Summer temperatures generally average less than 10°C.

Organisms The vegetation of tundra is mostly herbaceous, typically a mixture of mosses, grasses, and forbs, with some dwarf shrubs, trees, and lichens. A permanently frozen soil layer called permafrost restricts the growth of plant roots. Large grazing musk oxen are resident, while caribou and reindeer are migratory. Predators include bears, wolves, foxes, and snowy owls. Many bird species migrate to the tundra for summer nesting.

Human Impact Tundra is sparsely settled but has become the focus of significant mineral and oil extraction in recent years.

Dovrefjell -Sunndalsfjella National Park, Norway

Aquatic biomes are diverse and dynamic systems that cover most of Earth

Unlike terrestrial biomes, aquatic biomes are characterized primarily by their physical and chemical environment. For example, marine biomes generally have salt concentrations that average 3%, whereas freshwater biomes such as lakes and streams typically have a salt concentration of less than 0.1%.

Another important feature of many aquatic biomes is that they are divided into vertical and horizontal zones, as illustrated for a lake in **Figure 40.10**. Light is absorbed by water and by photosynthetic organisms, so its intensity decreases rapidly with depth. The upper **photic zone** is where there is sufficient light for photosynthesis, and the lower **aphotic zone** is where little light penetrates. These two zones together make up the **pelagic zone**. At the bottom of these zones, deep or shallow, is the **benthic zone**, which consists of organic and inorganic sediments and is occupied by communities of organisms called the **benthos**. In a lake, aquatic biomes can be divided horizontally into the **littoral zone**, waters close to shore that are shallow enough for rooted plants, and the **limnetic zone**, waters farther from shore that are too deep to support plants with roots.

Thermal energy from sunlight warms surface waters, but the deeper waters remain cold. In the ocean and in most lakes, a narrow layer of abrupt temperature change called a **thermocline** separates the more uniformly warm upper layer from more uniformly cold deeper waters.

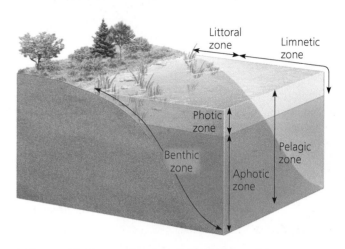

▲ **Figure 40.10 Zonation in a lake.** A lake environment is generally classified on the basis of three physical criteria: light penetration (photic and aphotic zones), distance from shore and water depth (littoral and limnetic zones), and whether the environment is open water (pelagic zone) or bottom (benthic zone).

Aquatic biomes show far less latitudinal variation than terrestrial biomes, with all types found across the globe **(Figure 40.11)**. The oceans make up the largest marine biome, covering about 75% of Earth's surface. Because of their vast size, they greatly impact the biosphere. Water evaporated from the oceans provides most of the planet's rainfall. Marine algae and photosynthetic bacteria supply much of the world's oxygen and consume large amounts of atmospheric carbon dioxide. Ocean temperatures have a major effect on global climate and wind patterns (see Figure 40.3), and along with large lakes, oceans tend to moderate the climate of nearby land.

▼ **Figure 40.11** | **Exploring Aquatic Biomes**

Wetlands and Estuaries

Physical and Chemical Environment
Wetlands are inundated by water at least sometimes and support plants adapted to water-saturated soil. In an **estuary**, the transition zone between a river and the sea, seawater flows up and down the estuary channel during the changing tides. Nutrients from upstream make wetlands and estuaries among the most productive habitats on Earth. Because of high organic production by plants and decomposition by microorganisms, the water and soils are often low in dissolved oxygen. Both habitats filter dissolved nutrients and chemical pollutants.

Geologic Features Wetlands develop in diverse habitats, including shallow basins, the flooded banks of rivers and streams, and lake coasts. Along seacoasts, sediments from rivers and tidal waters create channels, islands, and mudflats in estuaries.

Organisms Water-saturated soils favor the growth of plants, such as cattails and sedges in wetlands and saltmarsh grasses in estuaries, that can grow in water or in soil that is anaerobic at times. In freshwater wetlands, herbivores may include crustaceans, aquatic insect larvae, and muskrats, and carnivores may include dragonflies, frogs, alligators, and herons. Estuaries support an abundance of oysters, crabs, and fish species that humans eat. Many marine invertebrates and fishes use estuaries as breeding grounds.

A basin wetland in the United Kingdom

Human Impact Draining and filling have destroyed up to 90% of wetlands in Europe. Filling, dredging, and upstream pollution have disrupted estuaries worldwide.

Lakes

An oligotrophic lake in Alberta, Canada

Physical and Chemical Environment
Standing bodies of water range from ponds a few square meters in area to lakes covering thousands of square kilometers. Light decreases with depth, creating photic and aphotic zones. Temperate lakes may have a seasonal thermocline; tropical lowland lakes have a thermocline year-round. **Oligotrophic lakes** are nutrient-poor and generally oxygen-rich; **eutrophic lakes** are nutrient-rich and often depleted of oxygen in the deepest zone in summer and if covered with ice in winter. High rates of decomposition in deeper layers of eutrophic lakes cause periodic oxygen depletion.

Geologic Features Oligotrophic lakes may become more eutrophic over time as runoff adds sediments and nutrients. They tend to have less surface area relative to their depth than eutrophic lakes.

Organisms Rooted and floating aquatic plants live in the littoral zone, the shallow, well-lit waters close to shore. The limnetic zone, where water is too deep to support rooted aquatic plants, is inhabited by a variety of phytoplankton, including cyanobacteria, and small drifting heterotrophs, or zooplankton, that graze on the phytoplankton. The benthic zone is inhabited by assorted invertebrates whose species composition depends partly on oxygen levels. Fishes live in all zones with sufficient oxygen.

Human Impact Runoff from fertilized land and dumping of wastes lead to nutrient enrichment, which can produce algal blooms, oxygen depletion, and fish kills.

Streams and Rivers

Physical and Chemical Environment
Headwater streams are generally cold, clear, turbulent, and swift. Downstream in larger rivers, the water is generally warmer and more turbid because of suspended sediment. The salt and nutrient content of streams and rivers increases from the headwaters to the mouth, but oxygen content typically decreases.

Geologic Features Headwater stream channels are often narrow, have a rocky bottom, and alternate between shallow sections and deeper pools. Rivers are generally wide and meandering. River bottoms are often silty from sediments deposited through time.

Organisms Headwater streams that flow through grasslands or deserts may be rich in phytoplankton or rooted aquatic plants. Diverse fishes and invertebrates inhabit unpolluted rivers and streams. In streams flowing through forests, organic matter from terrestrial vegetation is the primary source of food for aquatic consumers.

Human Impact Municipal, agricultural, and industrial pollution degrade water quality and can kill aquatic organisms. Dams impair the natural flow of streams and rivers and threaten migratory species such as salmon.

A headwater stream in Washington

Intertidal Zones

A rocky intertidal zone on the Oregon coast

Physical and Chemical Environment
An **intertidal zone** is periodically submerged and exposed by the tides, twice daily on most marine shores. Upper strata experience longer exposures to air and greater variations in temperature and salinity, conditions that limit the distributions of many organisms to particular strata. Oxygen and nutrient levels are generally high and are renewed with each turn of the tides.

Geologic Features The rocky or sandy substrates of intertidal zones select for particular behavior and anatomy among intertidal organisms. The configuration of bays or coastlines influences the magnitude of tides and the exposure of intertidal zones to waves.

Organisms Diverse and plentiful marine algae grow on rocks in intertidal zones. Sandy intertidal zones exposed to waves generally lack attached plants or algae, while those in protected bays or lagoons often support rich beds of seagrass and algae. Some animals have structural adaptations that enable them to attach to rocks. Many animals in sandy or muddy intertidal zones, such as worms, clams, and predatory crustaceans, bury themselves and feed as the tides bring food. Other common animals are sponges, sea anemones, and small fishes.

Human Impact Oil pollution has disrupted many intertidal areas. Rock walls and barriers built to reduce erosion from waves and storm surges disrupt some areas.

Coral Reefs

photic zone of tropical oceans, primarily near islands and along the edge of some continents. They are sensitive to temperatures below about 18–20°C and above 30°C. Deep-sea coral reefs are found at a depth of 200–1,500 m. Corals require high oxygen levels and can be harmed or killed by high inputs of fresh water and nutrients.

Geologic Features Corals require a solid substrate for attachment. A typical coral reef begins as a fringing reef on a young, high island, forms an offshore barrier reef later, and becomes a coral atoll as the older island submerges.

Organisms Unicellular algae live within the tissues of the corals in a mutualism that provides the corals with organic molecules.

Diverse multicellular red and green algae also contribute substantial amounts of photosynthesis. Corals are the predominant animals on coral reefs, but fish and invertebrate diversity is also exceptionally high. Animal diversity on coral reefs rivals that of tropical forests.

Human Impact Collecting of coral skeletons and overfishing have reduced populations of corals and reef fishes. Global warming and pollution may be contributing to large-scale coral death. Development of coastal mangroves for aquaculture has also reduced spawning grounds for many species of reef fishes.

A coral reef in the Red Sea

Physical and Chemical Environment
Coral reefs are formed largely from the calcium carbonate skeletons of corals. Shallow reef-building corals live in the clear

Oceanic Pelagic Zone

Physical and Chemical Environment
The **oceanic pelagic zone** is a vast realm of open blue water, whose surface is constantly mixed by wind-driven currents. Because of higher water clarity, the photic zone extends to greater depths than in coastal marine waters. Oxygen content is generally high. Nutrient levels are generally lower than in coastal waters. Mixing of surface and deeper waters in fall and spring renews nutrients in the photic zones of temperate and high-latitude ocean areas.

Geologic Features This biome covers approximately 70% of Earth's surface. It has an

average depth of nearly 4,000 m and a maximum depth of more than 10,000 m.

Organisms The dominant photosynthetic organisms are bacteria and other phytoplankton, which drift with the currents and account for half of global productivity. Zooplankton, including protists, worms, krill, jellies, and small larvae of invertebrates and fishes, eat the phytoplankton. Free-swimming animals include large squids, fishes, sea turtles, and marine mammals.

Human Impact Overfishing has depleted fish stocks in all oceans, which have also been affected by climate warming and pollution.

Open ocean near Iceland

Marine Benthic Zone

while pressure increases. Organisms in the very deep benthic, or abyssal, zone are adapted to continuous cold (about 3°C) and high water pressure. Oxygen concentrations are generally sufficient to support diverse animal life.

Geologic Features Soft sediments cover most of the benthic zone, but there are areas of rocky substrate on reefs, submarine mountains, and new oceanic crust.

Organisms Photosynthetic organisms, mainly seaweeds and filamentous algae, live in shallow benthic areas with sufficient light. In the dark, hot environments near **deep sea hydrothermal vents**, the food producers are chemoautotrophic prokaryotes. Coastal benthic communities include

numerous invertebrates and fishes. Below the photic zone, most consumers depend entirely on organic matter raining down from above. Among the animals of the deep-sea hydrothermal vent communities are giant tube worms (pictured at left), some more than 1 m long. They are nourished by chemoautotrophic prokaryotes that live as symbionts within their bodies. Many other invertebrates, including arthropods and echinoderms, are also abundant around the hydrothermal vents.

Human Impact Overfishing has decimated important benthic fish populations, such as the cod of the Grand Banks off Newfoundland. Dumping of organic wastes has created oxygen-deprived benthic areas.

A deep-sea hydrothermal vent community

Physical and Chemical Environment
The **marine benthic zone** consists of the seafloor. Except for shallow, near-coastal areas, the marine benthic zone is dark. Water temperature declines with depth,

Freshwater biomes are closely linked to the soils and biotic components of the surrounding terrestrial biome. Freshwater biomes are also influenced by the patterns and speed of water flow and the climate to which the biome is exposed.

In both freshwater and marine environments, communities are distributed according to water depth, degree of light penetration, distance from shore, and whether they are found in open water or near the bottom. Plankton and many fish species occur in the relatively shallow photic zone (see Figure 40.10). Most of the deep ocean is virtually devoid of light (the aphotic zone) and harbors relatively little life.

CONCEPT CHECK 40.2

The first two questions refer to Figure 40.11.

1. Why are phytoplankton, and not benthic algae or rooted aquatic plants, the dominant photosynthetic organisms of the oceanic pelagic zone?

2. **MAKE CONNECTIONS** Many organisms living in estuaries experience both freshwater and saltwater conditions each day with the rising and falling of tides. Explain how these changing conditions challenge the survival of these organisms (see Concept 32.3).

3. **WHAT IF?** Water leaving a reservoir behind a dam is often taken from deep layers of the reservoir. Would you expect fish found in a river below a dam in summer to be species that prefer colder or warmer water than fish found in an undammed river? Explain.

For suggested answers, see Appendix A.

CONCEPT 40.3

Interactions between organisms and the environment limit the distribution of species

So far in this chapter, we've examined Earth's climate and the characteristics of terrestrial and aquatic biomes. We've also introduced the range of biological levels at which ecologists work (see Figure 40.2). In this section, we'll examine how ecologists determine what factors control the distribution of species, such as the *Paedophryne* frog shown in Figure 40.1.

Species distributions are a consequence of both ecological factors and evolutionary history. Consider kangaroos, which are found in Australia and nowhere else in the world. Fossil evidence indicates that kangaroos and their close relatives originated in Australia, roughly 5 million years ago. By that time, Australia had moved (by continental drift; see Concept 23.2) close to its present location and it was not connected to other landmasses. Thus, kangaroos occur only in Australia in part because of an accident of history: The kangaroo lineage originated there at a point in time when the continent was geographically isolated.

But ecological factors are also important. To date, kangaroos have not dispersed (on their own) to other continents; hence, they are restricted to the continent on which they originated. And within Australia, kangaroos are found in some habitats but not in others. The red kangaroo, for example, occurs in the arid grasslands of central Australia, but not in the tall, open forests of eastern Australia. Such observations can lead us to ask whether food availability, predators, temperature, or other factors cause red kangaroos to be found in some regions but not others.

As our discussion of kangaroos suggests, ecologists ask not only *where* species occur, but also *why* species occur where they do: What factors determine their distribution? Ecologists generally need to consider multiple factors and alternative hypotheses when attempting to explain the distribution of a species. We'll focus here on the ecological factors highlighted by the questions in the flowchart in **Figure 40.12**.

Dispersal and Distribution

One factor that contributes greatly to the global distribution of organisms is **dispersal**, the movement of individuals or gametes away from their area of origin or from centers of high population density. For example, while land-bound kangaroos have not reached North America under their own power, other organisms that disperse more readily, such as some birds, have. The dispersal of organisms is critical to understanding the

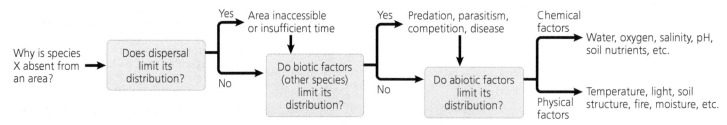

▲ **Figure 40.12 Flowchart of factors limiting geographic distribution.** An ecologist studying factors limiting a species' distribution might consider questions like these. As suggested by the arrows leading from the "yes" responses, the ecologist would answer all of these questions because more than one of these factors can limit a species' distribution.

? *How might the importance of various abiotic factors differ for aquatic and terrestrial ecosystems?*

role of geographic isolation in evolution (see Concept 22.2) as well as the broad patterns of species distribution that we see around the world today.

To determine if dispersal is a key factor limiting the distribution of a species, ecologists may observe the results of intentional or accidental transplants of the species to areas where it was previously absent. For a transplant to be successful, some of the organisms must not only survive in the new area but also reproduce there sustainably. If a transplant is successful, then we can conclude that the *potential* range of the species is larger than its *actual* range; in other words, the species *could* live in certain areas where it currently does not.

Species introduced to new geographic locations can disrupt the communities and ecosystems to which they have been introduced (see Concept 43.1). Consequently, ecologists rarely move species to new geographic regions. Instead, they document the outcome when a species has been transplanted for other purposes, as when a predator is introduced to control a pest species, or when a species has been moved to a new region accidentally.

Biotic Factors

Our next question is whether biotic factors—other species—limit the distribution of a species. Often, the ability of a species to survive and reproduce is reduced by its interactions with other species, such as predators (organisms that kill their prey) or herbivores (organisms that eat plants or algae). **Figure 40.13** describes a specific case in which an herbivore, a sea urchin, has the potential to limit the distribution of a food species, a seaweed.

In addition to predation and herbivory, the presence or absence of pollinators, food resources, parasites, pathogens, and competing organisms can act as a biotic limitation on species distribution. As you will see in Chapter 41, such biotic limitations are common in nature.

Abiotic Factors

The last question in the flowchart in Figure 40.12 considers whether abiotic factors—such as temperature, water, oxygen, salinity, sunlight, or soil—might be limiting a species' distribution. If the physical conditions at a site do not allow a species to survive and reproduce, then the species will not be found there.

▼ **Figure 40.13** **Inquiry**

Does feeding by sea urchins limit seaweed distribution?

Experiment W. J. Fletcher, of the University of Sydney, Australia, reasoned that if sea urchins are a limiting biotic factor in a particular ecosystem, then more seaweeds should invade an area from which sea urchins have been removed. To isolate the effect of sea urchins from that of a seaweed-eating mollusc, the limpet, he removed only urchins, only limpets, or both from study areas adjacent to a control site.

Results Fletcher observed a large difference in seaweed growth between areas with and without sea urchins.

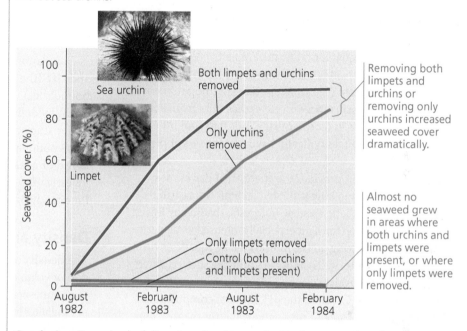

Conclusion Removing both limpets and urchins resulted in the greatest increase in seaweed cover, indicating that both species have some influence on seaweed distribution. But since removing only urchins greatly increased seaweed growth whereas removing only limpets had little effect, Fletcher concluded that sea urchins have a much greater effect than limpets in limiting seaweed distribution.

Data from W. J. Fletcher, Interactions among subtidal Australian sea urchins, gastropods, and algae: Effects of experimental removals, *Ecological Monographs* 57:89–109 (1987).

INTERPRET THE DATA Removing only limpets had little effect on seaweed growth compared to the control. Given this result, suggest a reason why removing both urchins and limpets resulted in greater seaweed growth than removing only urchins.

- **Temperature** Environmental temperature is an important factor in the distribution of organisms because of its effect on biological processes. Cells may rupture if the water they contain freezes (at temperatures below 0°C), and the proteins of most organisms denature at temperatures above 45°C. Most organisms function best within a specific range of environmental temperature.

- **Water and Oxygen** The dramatic variation in water availability among habitats is another important factor in species distribution. Species living at the seashore or in tidal wetlands can desiccate (dry out) as the tide recedes. Terrestrial organisms face a nearly constant threat of desiccation, and the distribution of terrestrial species reflects their ability to obtain and retain water. Many amphibians, such as the

Paedophryne frog in Figure 40.1, are particularly vulnerable to drying because they use their moist, delicate skin for gas exchange.

Water affects oxygen availability in aquatic environments and in flooded soils. Oxygen diffuses slowly in water. As a result, its concentration can be low in certain aquatic systems and soils, limiting cellular respiration and other physiological processes. Oxygen concentrations can be particularly low in both deep ocean and deep lake waters and sediments where organic matter is abundant.

- **Salinity** The salt concentration of water in the environment affects the water balance of organisms through osmosis. Most aquatic organisms are restricted to either freshwater or saltwater habitats by their limited ability to osmoregulate (see Concept 32.4). Although most terrestrial organisms can excrete excess salts from specialized glands or in feces or urine, salt flats and other high-salinity habitats typically have few species of plants or animals.
- **Sunlight** Sunlight provides the energy that drives most ecosystems, and too little sunlight can limit the distribution of photosynthetic species. In forests, shading by leaves makes competition for light especially intense, particularly for seedlings growing on the forest floor. In aquatic environments, most photosynthesis occurs near the surface, where sunlight is more available.
- **Rocks and Soil** On land, the pH, mineral composition, and physical structure of rocks and soil limit the distribution of plants and therefore of the animals that feed on them. The pH of soil can limit the distribution of organisms directly, through extreme acidic or basic conditions, or indirectly, by affecting the solubility of nutrients and toxins.

In a river, the composition of rocks and soil that make up the substrate (riverbed) can affect water chemistry, which in turn influences the resident organisms. In freshwater and marine environments, the structure of the substrate determines the organisms that can attach to it or burrow into it.

So far in this chapter, you have seen how the distributions of biomes and organisms depend on abiotic and biotic factors. In the rest of the chapter, we'll focus on how abiotic and biotic factors influence the ecology of populations.

CONCEPT CHECK 40.3

1. Give examples of human actions that could expand a species' distribution by changing its (a) dispersal or (b) biotic interactions.
2. **WHAT IF?** You suspect that deer are restricting the distribution of a tree species by preferentially eating the seedlings of the tree. How might you test this hypothesis?

For suggested answers, see Appendix A.

Biotic and abiotic factors affect population density, dispersion, and demographics

Population ecology explores how biotic and abiotic factors influence the density, distribution, and size of populations. A population is a group of individuals of a single species living in the same general area. Members of a population rely on the same resources, are influenced by similar environmental factors, and are likely to interact and breed with one another.

Populations are often described by their boundaries and size (the number of individuals living within those boundaries). Ecologists usually begin investigating a population by defining boundaries appropriate to the organism under study and to the questions being asked. A population's boundaries may be natural ones, as in the case of an island or a lake, or they may be arbitrarily defined by an investigator—for example, a specific county in Minnesota for a study of oak trees.

Density and Dispersion

The **density** of a population is the number of individuals per unit area or volume: the number of oak trees per square kilometer in the Minnesota county or the number of *Escherichia coli* bacteria per milliliter in a test tube. **Dispersion** is the pattern of spacing among individuals within the boundaries of the population.

Density: A Dynamic Perspective

In some cases, population size and density can be determined by counting all individuals within the boundaries of the population. We could count all the sea stars in a tide pool, for instance. Large mammals that live in herds, such as elephants, can sometimes be counted accurately from airplanes. In most cases, however, it is impractical or impossible to count all individuals in a population. Instead, ecologists use various sampling techniques to estimate densities and total population sizes. They might count the number of oak trees in several randomly located 100 × 100 m plots, calculate the average density in the plots, and then extend the estimate to the population size in the entire area. Such estimates are most accurate when there are many sample plots and when the habitat is fairly homogeneous. In other cases, instead of counting single organisms, ecologists estimate density from an indicator of population size, such as the number of nests, burrows, tracks, or fecal droppings.

Density is not a static property but changes as individuals are added to or removed from a population (**Figure 40.14**). Additions occur through birth (which we define here to include all forms of reproduction) and **immigration**, the influx of new individuals from other areas. The factors that remove

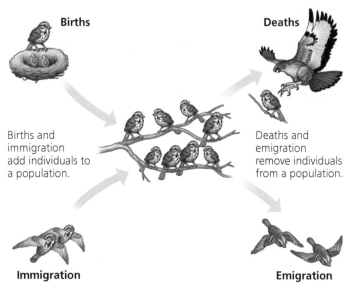

▲ Figure 40.14 **Population dynamics.**

(a) Clumped. Sea stars group together where food is abundant.

(b) Uniform. Nesting king penguins exhibit uniform spacing, maintained by aggressive interactions between neighbors.

(c) Random. Dandelions grow from windblown seeds that land at random and later germinate.

▲ Figure 40.15 **Patterns of dispersion within a population's geographic range.**

individuals from a population are death (mortality) and **emigration**, the movement of individuals out of a population and into other locations.

While birth and death rates influence the density of all populations, immigration and emigration also alter the density of many populations. Long-term studies of Belding's ground squirrels (*Spermophilus beldingi*) in the vicinity of Tioga Pass, in the Sierra Nevada of California, showed that some of the squirrels moved nearly 2 km from where they were born. This long-distance movement made them immigrants to other populations. In fact, immigrants made up 1–8% of the males and 0.7–6% of the females in the study population. Such immigration is a meaningful biological exchange between populations over time.

Patterns of Dispersion

Within a population's geographic range, local densities may differ substantially, creating contrasting patterns of dispersion. Differences in local density are among the most important characteristics for a population ecologist to study, since they provide insight into the environmental associations and social interactions of individuals in the population.

The most common pattern of dispersion is *clumped*, in which individuals are aggregated in patches. Plants and fungi are often clumped where soil conditions and other environmental factors favor germination and growth. Mushrooms, for instance, may be clumped within and on top of a rotting log. Insects and salamanders may be clumped under the same log because of the higher humidity there. Clumping of animals may also be associated with mating behavior. Sea stars group together in tide pools, where food is readily available and where they can breed successfully **(Figure 40.15a)**. Forming groups may also increase the effectiveness of predation or defense; for example, a wolf pack is more likely than a single wolf

to subdue a moose, and a flock of birds is more likely than a single bird to warn of a potential attack.

A *uniform*, or evenly spaced, pattern of dispersion may result from direct interactions between individuals in the population. Some plants secrete chemicals that inhibit the germination and growth of nearby individuals that could compete for resources. Animals often exhibit uniform dispersion as a result of antagonistic social interactions, such as **territoriality**—the defense of a bounded physical space against encroachment by other individuals **(Figure 40.15b)**.

In *random* dispersion (unpredictable spacing), the position of each individual in a population is independent of other individuals. This pattern occurs in the absence of strong attractions or repulsions among individuals or where key physical or chemical factors are relatively constant across the study area. Plants established by windblown seeds, such as dandelions, may be randomly distributed in a fairly uniform habitat **(Figure 40.15c)**.

Demographics

The factors that influence population density and dispersion patterns—ecological needs of a species, environmental conditions, and interactions among individuals within the population—also influence other characteristics of populations. **Demography** is the study of the vital statistics of populations and how they change over time. Of particular interest to demographers are birth rates and death rates. A useful way to summarize some of the vital statistics of a population is to make a life table.

Life Tables

A **life table** provides a summary of the age-specific survival and reproductive rates of individuals in a population. When it is possible to do so, the best way to construct a life table is to follow the fate of a **cohort**, a group of individuals of the same age, from birth until all of the individuals are dead. To build such a life table, we need to determine the number of individuals that die in each age-group and to calculate the proportion of the cohort surviving from one age class to the next. We also need to keep track of the number of offspring produced by females in each age-group.

Demographers who study sexually reproducing species often ignore the males and concentrate on the females in a population because only females produce offspring. When this is done, a population is viewed in terms of females giving rise to new females. **Table 40.1** illustrates this approach for female Belding's ground squirrels from a population located in the Sierra Nevada mountains of California. Next, we'll take a closer look at some of the data in a life table, beginning with a discussion of survivorship curves.

Survivorship Curves

The survival rate data in a life table can be represented graphically as a **survivorship curve**, a plot of the proportion or numbers in a cohort still alive at each age. Often, a survivorship curve begins with a cohort of a convenient size—say, 1,000 individuals. Though diverse, survivorship curves can be classified into three general types **(Figure 40.16)**.

A Type I curve is flat at the start, reflecting low death rates during early and middle life, and then drops steeply as death rates increase among older age-groups. Many large mammals, including humans, that produce few offspring but provide them with good care exhibit this kind of curve. In contrast, a Type III curve drops sharply at the start, reflecting very high

Table 40.1 Life Table for Female Belding's Ground Squirrels (Tioga Pass, in the Sierra Nevada of California)

Age (years)	Number Alive at Start of Year	Proportion Alive at Start of Year[†]	Death Rate[‡]	Average Number of Female Offspring
0–1	653	1.000	0.614	0.00
1–2	252	0.386	0.496	1.07
2–3	127	0.197	0.472	1.87
3–4	67	0.106	0.478	2.21
4–5	35	0.054	0.457	2.59
5–6	19	0.029	0.526	2.08
6–7	9	0.014	0.444	1.70
7–8	5	0.008	0.200	1.93
8–9	4	0.006	0.750	1.93
9–10	1	0.002	1.00	1.58

Data from P. W. Sherman and M. L. Morton, Demography of Belding's ground squirrel, *Ecology* 65:1617–1628 (1984).

[†]Indicates the proportion of the original cohort of 653 individuals that are still alive at the start of a time interval.

[‡]The death rate is the proportion of individuals alive at the start of a time interval that die during that time interval.

death rates for the young, but flattens out as death rates decline for those few individuals that survive the early period of die-off. This type of curve is usually associated with organisms that produce very large numbers of offspring but provide little or no care, such as long-lived plants, many fishes, and most marine invertebrates. An oyster, for example, may release millions of eggs, but most larvae hatched from fertilized eggs die from predation or other causes. Those few offspring that survive long enough to attach to a suitable substrate and begin growing a hard shell tend to survive for a relatively long time.

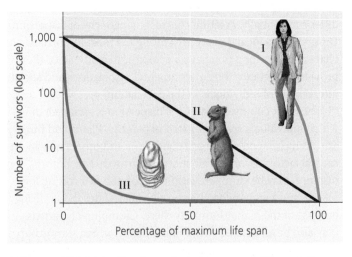

▲ **Figure 40.16 Idealized survivorship curves: Types I, II, and III.** The *y*-axis is logarithmic and the *x*-axis is on a relative scale so that species with widely varying life spans can be presented together on the same graph.

Type II curves are intermediate, with a constant death rate over the organism's life span. This kind of survivorship occurs in some rodents (including Belding's ground squirrel), invertebrates, lizards, and annual plants.

Many species fall somewhere between these basic types of survivorship or show more complex patterns. In birds, mortality is often high among the youngest individuals (as in a Type III curve) but fairly constant among adults (as in a Type II curve). Some invertebrates, such as crabs, may show a "stair-stepped" curve, with brief periods of increased mortality during molts, followed by periods of lower mortality when their protective exoskeleton is hard.

In populations not experiencing immigration or emigration, survivorship is one of the two key factors determining changes in population size. The other key factor determining population trends is reproductive rate.

Reproductive Rates

As mentioned above, demographers often ignore the males and concentrate on the females in a population because only females produce offspring. Therefore, demographers view populations in terms of females giving rise to new females. The simplest way to describe the reproductive pattern of a population is to ask how reproductive output varies with the ages of females.

Reproductive output for sexual organisms such as birds and mammals is typically measured as the average number of female offspring for each female in a given age-group. For Belding's ground squirrels, which begin to reproduce at age 1 year, reproductive output rises to a peak at 4–5 years of age and then gradually falls off in older females (see Table 40.1).

Age-specific reproductive rates vary considerably by species. Squirrels, for example, have a litter of two to six young once a year for less than a decade, whereas oak trees drop thousands of acorns each year for tens or hundreds of years. Mussels and other invertebrates may release millions of eggs and sperm in a spawning cycle. However, a high reproductive rate will not lead to rapid population growth unless conditions are near ideal for the growth and survival of offspring, as you'll learn in the next section.

CONCEPT CHECK 40.4

1. **DRAW IT** Each female of a particular fish species produces millions of eggs per year. Draw and label the most likely survivorship curve for this species, and explain your choice.
2. Imagine that you are constructing a life table for a different population of Belding's ground squirrels (see Table 40.1). If 485 individuals are alive at the start of year 0–1 and 218 are still alive at the start of year 1–2, what is the proportion alive at the start of each of these years (see column 3 in Table 40.1)?
3. **MAKE CONNECTIONS** A male stickleback fish attacks other males that invade its nesting territory (see Figure 39.16). Predict the likely pattern of dispersion for male sticklebacks, and explain your reasoning.

For suggested answers, see Appendix A.

CONCEPT 40.5

The exponential and logistic models describe the growth of populations

Populations of all species have the potential to expand greatly when resources are abundant. To appreciate the potential for population increase, consider a bacterium that can reproduce by fission every 20 minutes under ideal laboratory conditions. There would be two bacteria after 20 minutes, four after 40 minutes, and eight after 60 minutes. If reproduction continued at this rate for a day and a half without mortality, there would be enough bacteria to form a layer 30 cm deep over the entire globe! But unlimited growth does not occur for long in nature, where individuals typically have access to fewer resources as a population grows. Ecologists study population growth in idealized conditions and in the more realistic conditions where different factors limit growth. We'll examine both scenarios in this section.

Changes in Population Size

Imagine a population consisting of a few individuals living in an ideal, unlimited environment. Under these conditions, there are no external limits on the abilities of individuals to harvest energy, grow, and reproduce. The population will increase in size with every birth and with the immigration of individuals from other populations, and it will decrease in size with every death and with the emigration of individuals out of the population. We can thus define a change in population size during a fixed time interval with the following verbal equation:

$$\begin{array}{c} \text{Change in} \\ \text{population} \\ \text{size} \end{array} = \text{Births} + \begin{array}{c} \text{Immigrants} \\ \text{entering} \\ \text{population} \end{array} - \text{Deaths} - \begin{array}{c} \text{Emigrants} \\ \text{leaving} \\ \text{population} \end{array}$$

For now, we will simplify our discussion by ignoring the effects of immigration and emigration.

We can use mathematical notation to express this simplified relationship more concisely. If N represents population size and t represents time, then ΔN is the change in population size and Δt is the time interval (appropriate to the life span or generation time of the species) over which we are evaluating population growth. (The Greek letter delta, Δ, indicates change, such as change in time.) Using B for the number of births in the population during the time interval and D for the number of deaths, we can rewrite the verbal equation:

$$\frac{\Delta N}{\Delta t} = B - D$$

Typically, population ecologists are most interested in changes in population size—the number of individuals that are added to or subtracted from a population during a given time interval, symbolized by R. Here, R represents the *difference* between the number of births (B) and the number of deaths (D)

that occur in the time interval. Thus, $R = B - D$, and we can simplify our equation by writing:

$$\frac{\Delta N}{\Delta t} = R$$

Next, we can convert our model to one in which changes in population size are expressed on a per individual (per capita) basis. The *per capita* change in population size ($r_{\Delta t}$) represents the contribution that an average member of the population makes to the number of individuals added to the population during the time interval Δt. If, for example, a population of 1,000 individuals increases by 16 individuals per year, then on a per capita basis, the annual change in population size is 16/1,000, or 0.016. If we know the annual per capita change in population size, we can use the formula $R = r_{\Delta t}N$ to calculate how many individuals will be added to a population each year. For example, if $r_{\Delta t} = 0.016$ and the population size is 500,

$$R = r_{\Delta t}N = 0.016 \times 500 = 8 \text{ per year}$$

Since the number of individuals added to the population (R) can be expressed on a per capita basis as $R = r_{\Delta t}N$, we can revise our population growth equation to take this into account:

$$\frac{\Delta N}{\Delta t} = r_{\Delta t}N$$

Remember that our equation is for a specific time interval (often one year). However, many ecologists prefer to use differential calculus to express population growth as a rate of change *at each instant in time*:

$$\frac{dN}{dt} = rN$$

In this case, r represents the per capita change in population size that occurs at each instant in time (whereas $r_{\Delta t}$ represented the per capita change that occurred during the time interval Δt). If you have not yet studied calculus, don't be intimidated by the last equation; it is similar to the previous one, except that the time intervals Δt are very short and are expressed in the equation as dt.

Exponential Growth

Earlier we described a population whose members all have access to abundant food and are free to reproduce at their physiological capacity. In some cases, a population that experiences such ideal conditions increases in size by a constant proportion at each instant in time. When this occurs, the pattern of growth that results is called **exponential population growth**. The equation for exponential growth is the one presented at the end of the previous section, namely:

$$\frac{dN}{dt} = rN$$

In this equation, dN/dt represents the rate at which the population is increasing in size at each moment in time, akin to how a glance at the speedometer of a car reveals the speed at that instant in time. As seen in the equation, dN/dt equals the current population size, N, multiplied by a constant, r. Ecologists

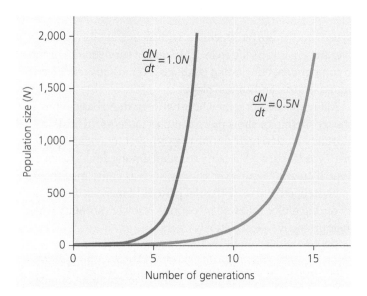

▲ **Figure 40.17 Population growth predicted by the exponential model.** This graph compares growth in a population with $r = 1.0$ (blue curve) to growth in a population with $r = 0.5$ (red curve).

? *How many generations does it take each of these populations to reach a size of 1,500 individuals?*

refer to r as the **intrinsic rate of increase**, the per capita rate at which an exponentially growing population increases in size at each instant in time.

On a per capita basis, the size of a population that is growing exponentially increases at a constant rate, resulting eventually in a J-shaped growth curve when population size is plotted over time **(Figure 40.17)**. Although the per capita rate of population growth is constant (and equals r), more new individuals are added per unit of time when the population is large than when it is small; thus, the curves in Figure 40.17 get progressively steeper over time. This occurs because population growth depends on N as well as r, and hence more individuals are added to larger populations than to small ones growing at the same per capita rate. It is also clear from Figure 40.17 that a population with a higher intrinsic rate of increase ($dN/dt = 1.0N$) will grow faster than one with a lower intrinsic rate of increase ($dN/dt = 0.5N$).

Exponential growth can occur in populations that are introduced into a new environment or whose numbers were drastically reduced by a catastrophic event and are rebounding. For example, the population of elephants in Kruger National Park, South Africa, grew exponentially for approximately 60 years after they were first protected from hunting **(Figure 40.18)**. The increasingly large number of elephants eventually caused enough damage to vegetation that a collapse in their food supply was likely. To protect other species and the park ecosystem before that happened, park managers began limiting the elephant population by using birth control and exporting elephants to other countries.

Carrying Capacity

The exponential growth model assumes that resources remain abundant, which is rarely the case in the real world. Instead, as the size of a population increases, each individual has access to fewer resources. Ultimately, there is a limit to the number

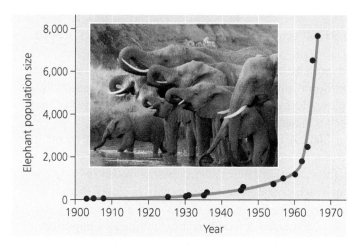

▲ **Figure 40.18 Exponential growth in the African elephant population of Kruger National Park, South Africa.**

Table 40.2 Logistic Growth of a Hypothetical Population ($K = 1,500$)

Population Size (N)	Intrinsic Rate of Increase (r)	$\dfrac{K - N}{K}$	Per Capita Rate of Increase $r\dfrac{(K - N)}{K}$	Population Growth Rate* $rN\dfrac{(K - N)}{K}$
25	1.0	0.983	0.983	+25
100	1.0	0.933	0.933	+93
250	1.0	0.833	0.833	+208
500	1.0	0.667	0.667	+333
750	1.0	0.500	0.500	+375
1,000	1.0	0.333	0.333	+333
1,500	1.0	0.000	0.000	0

*Rounded to the nearest whole number.

of individuals that can occupy a habitat. Ecologists define the **carrying capacity**, symbolized by K, as the maximum population size that a particular environment can sustain. Carrying capacity varies over space and time with the abundance of limiting resources. Energy, shelter, refuge from predators, nutrient availability, water, and suitable nesting sites can all be limiting factors. For example, the carrying capacity for bats may be high in a habitat with abundant flying insects and roosting sites, but lower where there is abundant food but fewer suitable shelters.

Crowding and resource limitation can have a profound effect on population growth rate. If individuals cannot obtain sufficient resources to reproduce, then the per capita birth rate will decline. Similarly, if starvation or disease increases with density, the per capita death rate may increase. Falling per capita birth rates or rising per capita death rates will cause the per capita rate of population growth to drop—a very different situation from the constant per capita growth rate (r) seen in a population that is growing exponentially.

The Logistic Growth Model

In the **logistic population growth** model, the per capita rate of population growth approaches zero as the population size nears the carrying capacity (K). To construct the logistic model, we start with the exponential population growth model and add an expression that reduces the per capita rate of population growth as N increases. If the carrying capacity is K, then $K - N$ is the number of additional individuals the environment can support, and $(K - N)/K$ is the fraction of K that is still available for population growth. By multiplying the exponential rate of population growth rN by $(K - N)/K$, we modify the change in population size as N increases:

$$\frac{dN}{dt} = rN\frac{(K - N)}{K}$$

When N is small compared to K, the term $(K - N)/K$ is close to 1. When this occurs, the per capita rate of increase, $r(K - N)/K$, will be close to (but slightly less than) r, the intrinsic rate of increase seen in exponential population growth. But when N is large and resources are limiting, then $(K - N)/K$ is close to 0,

and the per capita rate of increase is small. When N equals K, the population stops growing. **Table 40.2** shows calculations of population growth rate for a hypothetical population growing according to the logistic model, with $r = 1.0$ per individual per year. Notice that the overall population growth rate is highest, +375 individuals per year, when the population size is 750, or half the carrying capacity. At a population size of 750, the per capita rate of increase remains relatively high (one-half the value of r), but there are more reproducing individuals (N) in the population than at lower population sizes.

As shown in **Figure 40.19**, the logistic model of population growth produces a sigmoid (S-shaped) growth curve when N is plotted over time (the red line). New individuals are added to

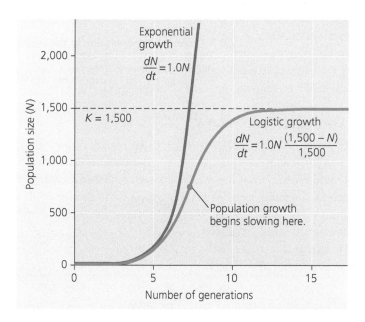

▲ **Figure 40.19 Population growth predicted by the logistic model.** The rate of population growth decreases as population size (N) approaches the carrying capacity (K) of the environment. The red line shows logistic growth in a population where $r = 1.0$ and $K = 1,500$ individuals. For comparison, the blue line illustrates a population continuing to grow exponentially with the same r.

the population most rapidly at intermediate population sizes, when there is not only a breeding population of substantial size, but also lots of available space and other resources in the environment. The number of individuals added to the population decreases dramatically as N approaches K. As a result, the population growth rate (dN/dt) also decreases as N approaches K.

Note that we haven't said anything yet about *why* the population growth rate decreases as N approaches K. For a population's growth rate to decrease, the birth rate must decrease, the death rate must increase, or both. Later in the chapter, we'll consider some of the factors affecting these rates, including the presence of disease, predation, and limited amounts of food and other resources.

The Logistic Model and Real Populations

The growth of laboratory populations of some small animals, such as beetles and crustaceans, and of some microorganisms, such as bacteria, *Paramecium*, and yeasts, fits an S-shaped curve fairly well under conditions of limited resources **(Figure 40.20a)**. These populations are grown in a constant environment lacking predators and competing species that may reduce growth of the populations, conditions that rarely occur in nature.

Some of the assumptions built into the logistic model clearly do not apply to all populations. The logistic model assumes that populations adjust instantaneously to growth and approach carrying capacity smoothly. In reality, there is often a delay before the negative effects of an increasing population are realized. If food becomes limiting for a population, for instance, reproduction will decline eventually, but females may use their energy reserves to continue reproducing for a short time. This may cause the population to overshoot its carrying capacity temporarily, as shown for the water fleas in **Figure 40.20b**. In the **Scientific Skills Exercise**, you can

▶ **Figure 40.20 How well do these populations fit the logistic growth model?** In each graph, the black dots plot the measured growth of the population, and the red curve is the growth predicted by the logistic model.

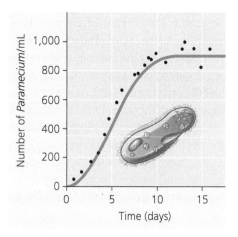

(a) A *Paramecium* population in the lab. Growth in a small culture closely approximates logistic growth if the researcher maintains a constant environment.

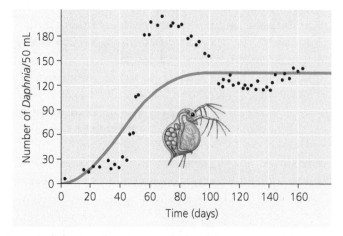

(b) A *Daphnia* (water flea) population in the lab. Growth in a small culture does not correspond well to the logistic model. This population overshoots the carrying capacity of its artificial environment before reaching an approximately stable size.

model what can happen to such a population when N becomes *greater* than K. Other populations fluctuate greatly, making it difficult even to define carrying capacity. We'll examine some possible reasons for such fluctuations later in the chapter.

CONCEPT CHECK 40.5

1. Explain why a constant rate of increase (r) for a population produces a growth curve that is J-shaped.
2. Explain why a population that fits the logistic growth model increases more rapidly at intermediate size than at relatively small and large sizes.
3. **MAKE CONNECTIONS** Many viruses are pathogens of animals and plants (see Concept 17.3). How might the presence of pathogens alter the carrying capacity of a population? Explain.

For suggested answers, see Appendix A.

CONCEPT 40.6

Population dynamics are influenced strongly by life history traits and population density

EVOLUTION Natural selection favors traits that improve an organism's chances of survival and reproductive success. In every species, there are trade-offs between survival and reproductive traits such as frequency of reproduction, number of offspring (number of seeds produced by plants; litter or clutch size for animals), and investment in parental care. The traits that affect an organism's schedule of reproduction and survival make up its **life history**. A life history entails three main variables: when reproduction begins (the age at first reproduction or age at maturity), how often the organism reproduces, and how many offspring are produced per reproductive episode.

"Trade-offs" and Life Histories

No organism could produce unlimited numbers of offspring *and* provision them well. There is a trade-off between reproduction and survival. For instance, researchers in Scotland found that female red deer that reproduced in a given summer were more likely to die the next winter than were females that did not reproduce.

Selective pressures also influence trade-offs between the number and size of offspring. Plants and animals whose young are more likely to die often produce many small offspring. Plants that colonize disturbed environments, for example, usually produce many small seeds, only a few of which may reach a suitable habitat. Small size may also increase the chance of seedling establishment by enabling the seeds to be carried longer distances to a broader range of habitats **(Figure 40.21a)**. Animals that suffer high predation rates, such as quail, sardines, and mice, also tend to produce many offspring.

In other organisms, extra investment on the part of the parent greatly increases the offspring's chance of survival. Walnut

(a) Dandelions grow quickly and release a large number of tiny fruits, each containing a single seed. Producing numerous seeds increases the chance that at least some will grow into plants that eventually produce seeds themselves.

(b) Some plants, such as the Brazil nut tree (right), produce a moderate number of large seeds in pods (above). Each seed's large endosperm provides nutrients for the embryo, an adaptation that helps a relatively large fraction of offspring survive.

▲ **Figure 40.21 Variation in the number and size of seeds in plants.**

and Brazil nut trees produce large seeds packed with nutrients that help the seedlings become established **(Figure 40.21b)**. Primates generally bear only one or two offspring at a time; parental care and an extended period of learning in the first several years of life are very important to offspring fitness. Such provisioning and extra care can be especially important in habitats with high population densities.

Ecologists have attempted to connect differences in favored traits at different population densities with the logistic growth model discussed in Concept 40.5. Selection for traits that are sensitive to population density and are favored at high densities is known as *K*-**selection**, or density-dependent selection. In contrast, selection for traits that maximize reproductive success in uncrowded environments (low densities) is called *r*-**selection**, or density-independent selection. These names follow from the variables of the logistic equation. *K*-selection is said to operate in populations living at a density near the limit imposed by their resources (the carrying capacity, *K*), where competition among individuals is stronger. Mature trees growing in an old-growth forest are an example of *K*-selected organisms.

In contrast, *r*-selection is said to maximize *r*, the intrinsic rate of increase, and occurs in environments in which population densities are well below carrying capacity or individuals face little competition. Such conditions are often found in disturbed habitats that are being recolonized. Weeds growing in an abandoned agricultural field are an example of *r*-selected organisms.

Population Change and Population Density

Similar to the case of *r*-selection, a birth rate or death rate that does *not* change with population density is said to be **density independent**. In a classic study of population regulation, Andrew Watkinson and John Harper, of the University of Wales, found that the mortality of dune fescue grass (*Vulpia fasciculata*) is mainly due to physical factors that kill similar proportions of a local population, regardless of its density. For example, drought stress that arises when the roots of the grass are uncovered by shifting sands is a density-independent factor. In contrast, a death rate that increases with population density or a birth rate that falls with rising density is said to be **density dependent**, a situation similar to *K*-selection. Watkinson and Harper found that reproduction by dune fescue declines as population density increases, in part because water or nutrients become more scarce. Thus, the key factors regulating birth rate in this population are density dependent, while death rate is largely regulated by density-independent factors. **Figure 40.22** shows how the combination of density-dependent reproduction and density-independent mortality can stop population growth, leading to an equilibrium population density in species such as dune fescue.

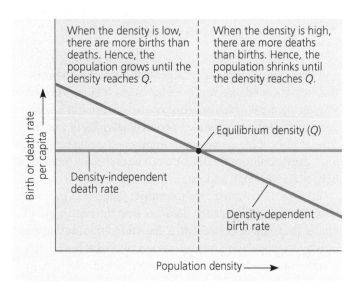

When the density is low, there are more births than deaths. Hence, the population grows until the density reaches *Q*.

When the density is high, there are more deaths than births. Hence, the population shrinks until the density reaches *Q*.

Equilibrium density (*Q*)

Density-independent death rate

Density-dependent birth rate

Birth or death rate per capita

Population density

▲ **Figure 40.22 Determining equilibrium for population density.** This simple model considers only birth and death rates. (Immigration and emigration rates are assumed to be either zero or equal.) In this example, the birth rate changes with population density, while the death rate is constant. At the equilibrium density (*Q*), the birth and death rates are equal.

DRAW IT *Redraw this figure for the case where the birth and death rates are both density dependent, as occurs for many species.*

Mechanisms of Density-Dependent Population Regulation

Without some type of negative feedback between population density and the rates of birth and death, a population would never stop growing. But no population can increase in size indefinitely. Ultimately, at large population sizes, negative feedback is provided by density-dependent regulation, which halts population growth through mechanisms that reduce birth rates or increase death rates. Several mechanisms of density-dependent population regulation are described in **Figure 40.23**.

These various examples of population regulation by negative feedback show how increased densities cause population growth rates to decline by affecting reproduction, growth, and survival. But although negative feedback helps explain why populations stop growing, it does not address why some populations fluctuate dramatically while others remain relatively stable. That is the topic we address next.

Population Dynamics

All populations show some fluctuation in size. Such population fluctuations from year to year or place to place, called **population dynamics**, are influenced by many factors and in turn affect other species. For example, fluctuations in fish populations influence seasonal harvests of commercially important species. The study of population dynamics focuses on the complex interactions between biotic and abiotic factors that cause variation in population sizes.

Stability and Fluctuation

Populations of large mammals were once thought to remain relatively stable, but long-term studies have challenged that idea. For instance, the moose population on Isle Royale in Lake Superior has fluctuated substantially since around 1900. At that time, moose from the Ontario mainland (25 km away) colonized the island, perhaps by walking across the lake when it was frozen. Wolves, which rely on moose for most of their food, reached the island around 1950 by walking across the frozen lake. The lake has not frozen over in recent years, and both populations appear to have been isolated from immigration and emigration since then. Despite this isolation, the

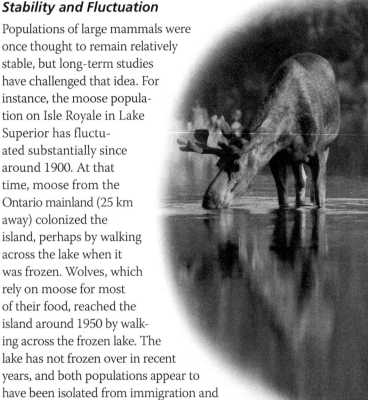

As population density increases, many density-dependent mechanisms slow or stop population growth by decreasing birth rates or increasing death rates.

Competition for Resources

Increasing population density intensifies competition for nutrients and other resources, reducing reproductive rates. Farmers minimize the effect of resource competition on the growth of grains such as wheat (*Triticum aestivum*) and other crops by applying fertilizers to reduce nutrient limitations on crop yield.

Predation

Predation can be an important cause of density-dependent mortality if a predator captures more food as the population density of the prey increases. As a prey population builds up, predators may also feed preferentially on that species. Population increases in the collared lemming (*Dicrostonyx groenlandicus*) lead to density-dependent predation by several predators, including the snowy owl (*Bubo scandiacus*).

Disease

If the transmission rate of a disease increases as a population becomes more crowded, then the disease's impact is density dependent. In humans, the respiratory diseases influenza (flu) and tuberculosis are spread through the air when an infected person sneezes or coughs. Both diseases strike a greater percentage of people in densely populated cities than in rural areas.

Toxic Wastes

Yeasts, such as the brewer's yeast *Saccharomyces cerevisiae*, are used to convert carbohydrates to ethanol in winemaking. The ethanol that accumulates in the wine is toxic to yeasts and contributes to density-dependent regulation of yeast population size. The alcohol content of wine is usually less than 13% because that is the maximum concentration of ethanol that most wine-producing yeast cells can tolerate.

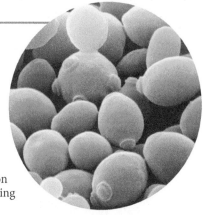

5 μm

Territoriality

Territoriality can limit population density when space becomes the resource for which individuals compete. Cheetahs (*Acinonyx jubatus*) use a chemical marker in urine to warn other cheetahs of their territorial boundaries. The presence of surplus, or nonbreeding, individuals is a good indication that territoriality is restricting population growth.

Intrinsic Factors

Intrinsic physiological factors (those operating within an individual organism) sometimes regulate population size. Reproductive rates of white-footed mice (*Peromyscus leucopus*) in a field enclosure can drop even when food and shelter are abundant. This drop in reproduction at high population density is associated with aggressive interactions and hormonal changes within individual mice that delay sexual maturation and depress the immune system.

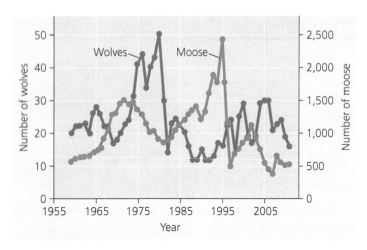

▲ **Figure 40.24 Fluctuations in moose and wolf populations on Isle Royale, 1959–2011.**

ANIMATION Visit the Study Area in **MasteringBiology** for the BioFlix® 3-D Animation on Population Ecology.

moose population experienced two major increases and collapses during the last 50 years **(Figure 40.24)**.

What factors cause the size of the moose population to change so dramatically? Harsh weather, particularly cold winters with heavy snowfall, can weaken moose and reduce food availability, decreasing the population size. When moose numbers are low and the weather is mild, food is readily available and the population grows quickly. Conversely, when moose numbers are high, factors such as predation and an increase in the density of ticks and other parasites cause the population to shrink. The effects of some of these factors can be seen in Figure 40.24. The first collapse coincided with a peak in the numbers of wolves from 1975 to 1980. The second major collapse, around 1995, coincided with harsh winter weather, which increased the energy needs of the animals and made it harder for the moose to find food under the deep snow.

Immigration, Emigration, and Metapopulations

So far, our discussion of population dynamics has focused mainly on the contributions of births and deaths. However, immigration and emigration also influence populations. When a population becomes crowded and resource competition increases, emigration often increases.

Immigration and emigration are particularly important when a number of local populations are linked, forming a **metapopulation**. Local populations in a metapopulation can be thought of as occupying discrete patches of suitable habitat in a sea of otherwise unsuitable habitat. Such patches vary in size, quality, and isolation from other patches, factors that influence how many individuals move among the populations. If one population becomes extinct, the patch it occupied may be recolonized by immigrants from another population.

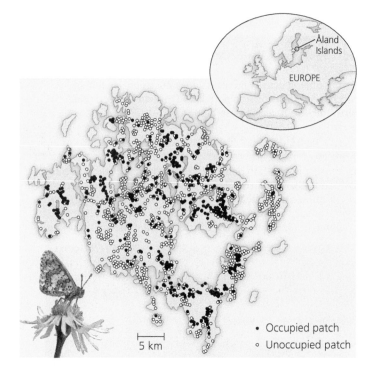

▲ **Figure 40.25 The Glanville fritillary: a metapopulation.** On the Åland Islands, local populations of this butterfly (filled circles) are found in only a fraction of the suitable habitat patches (open circles) at any given time. Individuals can move between local populations and colonize unoccupied patches.

The Glanville fritillary (*Melitaea cinxia*) illustrates the movement of individuals between populations. This butterfly is found in about 500 meadows across the Åland Islands of Finland, but its potential habitat in the islands is much larger, approximately 4,000 suitable patches. New populations of the butterfly regularly appear and existing populations become extinct, constantly shifting the locations of the 500 colonized patches **(Figure 40.25)**. The species persists in a balance of extinctions and recolonizations.

The metapopulation concept underscores the significance of immigration and emigration for the Glanville fritillary and many other species. It also helps ecologists understand population dynamics and gene flow in patchy habitats, providing a framework for the conservation of species living in a network of habitat fragments and reserves.

CONCEPT CHECK 40.6

1. In the fish called the peacock wrasse (*Symphodus tinca*), females disperse some of their eggs widely and lay other eggs in a nest. Only the latter receive parental care. Explain the trade-offs in reproduction that this behavior illustrates.

2. **WHAT IF?** Mice that experience stress such as a food shortage will sometimes abandon their young. Explain how this behavior might have evolved in the context of reproductive trade-offs and life history.

3. **MAKE CONNECTIONS** Negative feedback is a process that regulates biological systems (see Concept 32.2). Explain how the density-dependent birth rate of dune fescue grass exemplifies negative feedback.

For suggested answers, see Appendix A.

Go to MasteringBiology® for Assignments, the eText, and the Study Area with Animations, Activities, Vocab Self-Quiz, and Practice Tests.

SUMMARY OF KEY CONCEPTS

VOCAB SELF-QUIZ

goo.gl/gbai8v

CONCEPT 40.1

Earth's climate influences the distribution of terrestrial biomes (pp. 843–848)

- Global **climate** patterns are largely determined by the input of solar energy and Earth's revolution around the sun.
- The changing angle of the sun over the year, bodies of water, and mountains exert seasonal, regional, and local effects on climate.
- **Climographs** show that temperature and precipitation are correlated with **biomes**. Other factors also affect biome location.
- Terrestrial biomes are often named for major physical or climatic factors and for their predominant vegetation. Vertical layering is an important feature of terrestrial biomes.

? *Suppose global air circulation suddenly reversed, with most air ascending at 30° north and south latitude and descending at the equator. At what latitude would you most likely find deserts?*

CONCEPT 40.2

Aquatic biomes are diverse and dynamic systems that cover most of Earth (pp. 849–852)

- Aquatic biomes are characterized primarily by their physical environment rather than by climate and are often layered with regard to light penetration, temperature, and community structure.
- In the ocean and in most lakes, an abrupt temperature change called a **thermocline** separates a more uniformly warm upper layer from more uniformly cold deeper waters.

? *In which aquatic biomes might you find an aphotic zone?*

CONCEPT 40.3

Interactions between organisms and the environment limit the distribution of species (pp. 852–854)

- Ecologists want to know not only *where* species occur but also *why* those species occur where they do.
- The distribution of species may be limited by **dispersal**, **biotic** (living) factors, and **abiotic** (chemical and physical) factors, such as temperature extremes, salinity, and water availability.

? *If you were an ecologist studying the chemical and physical limits to the distributions of species, how might you rearrange the flowchart in Figure 40.12?*

CONCEPT 40.4

Biotic and abiotic factors affect population density, dispersion, and demographics (pp. 854–857)

- Population **density**—the number of individuals per unit area or volume—reflects the interplay of births, deaths, immigration, and emigration. Environmental and social factors influence the **dispersion** of individuals.
- Populations increase from births and **immigration** and decrease from deaths and **emigration**. **Life tables** and **survivorship curves** summarize specific trends in **demography**.

? *Gray whales (Eschrichtius robustus) gather each winter near Baja California to give birth. How might such behavior make it easier for ecologists to estimate birth and death rates for the species?*

CONCEPT 40.5

The exponential and logistic models describe the growth of populations (pp. 857–861)

- If immigration and emigration are ignored, a population's growth rate (the per capita rate of increase) equals its birth rate minus its death rate.
- The **exponential population growth** equation $dN/dt = rN$ represents a population's growth when resources are relatively abundant, where r is the (per capita) **intrinsic rate of increase** and N is the number of individuals in the population.

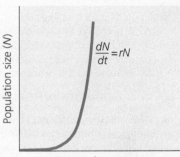

$$\frac{dN}{dt} = rN$$

Number of generations

- Exponential growth cannot be sustained for long in any population. A more realistic population model limits growth by incorporating **carrying capacity** (K), the maximum population size the environment can support. According to the **logistic population growth** equation $dN/dt = rN(K - N)/K$, growth levels off as population size approaches the carrying capacity.

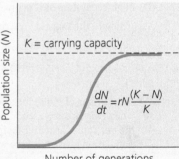

K = carrying capacity

$$\frac{dN}{dt} = rN\frac{(K - N)}{K}$$

Number of generations

- The logistic model fits few real populations perfectly, but it is useful for estimating possible growth.

? *As an ecologist who manages a wildlife preserve, you want to increase the preserve's carrying capacity for a particular endangered species. How might you go about accomplishing this?*

CONCEPT 40.6

Population dynamics are influenced strongly by life history traits and population density (pp. 861–864)

- **Life history** traits are evolutionary outcomes reflected in the development, physiology, and behavior of organisms.
- **Density-dependent** changes in birth and death rates curb population increase through negative feedback and can eventually stabilize a population near its carrying capacity. Density-dependent limiting factors include intraspecific competition for limited food or space, increased predation, disease, intrinsic physiological factors, and buildup of toxic substances.
- All populations exhibit some size fluctuations, and many undergo substantial changes in size that are influenced by complex interactions between biotic and abiotic factors. A **metapopulation** is a group of populations linked by immigration and emigration.

? *Name one biotic and one abiotic factor that could contribute to yearly fluctuations in the size of the human population in a given region.*

TEST YOUR UNDERSTANDING

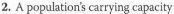

PRACTICE TEST

Level 1: Knowledge/Comprehension

1. Which of the following biomes is correctly paired with the description of its climate?
   (A) savanna—low temperature, precipitation uniform during the year
   (B) tundra—long summers, mild winters
   (C) temperate broadleaf forest—relatively short growing season, mild winters
   (D) tropical forests—nearly constant day length and temperature

2. A population's carrying capacity
   (A) may change as environmental conditions change.
   (B) can be accurately calculated using the logistic model.
   (C) generally remains constant over time.
   (D) increases as the per capita growth rate decreases.

Level 2: Application/Analysis

3. When climbing a mountain, we can observe transitions in biological communities that are analogous to the changes
   (A) in different depths in the ocean.
   (B) in biomes at different latitudes.
   (C) in a community through different seasons.
   (D) in an ecosystem as it evolves over time.

4. According to the logistic growth equation

   $$\frac{dN}{dt} = rN\frac{(K - N)}{K}$$

   (A) the number of individuals added per unit time is greatest when N is close to zero.
   (B) the per capita growth rate increases as N approaches K.
   (C) population growth is zero when N equals K.
   (D) the population grows exponentially when K is small.

Level 3: Synthesis/Evaluation

5. **WHAT IF?** If the direction of Earth's rotation reversed, the most predictable effect would be
   (A) the elimination of ocean currents.
   (B) a big change in the length of the year.
   (C) winds blowing from west to east along the equator.
   (D) a loss of seasonal variation at high latitudes.

6. **INTERPRET THE DATA** After examining Figure 40.13, you decide to study feeding relationships among sea otters, sea urchins, and kelp. You know that sea otters prey on sea urchins and that urchins eat kelp. At four coastal sites, you measure kelp abundance. Then you spend one day at each site and mark whether otters are present or absent every 5 minutes during the day. Graph kelp abundance (on the *y*-axis) versus otter density (on the *x*-axis), using the data below. Then formulate a hypothesis to explain the pattern you observed.

Site	Otter Density (# sightings per day)	Kelp Abundance (% cover)
1	98	75
2	18	15
3	85	60
4	36	25

7. **SCIENTIFIC INQUIRY**
   Jens Clausen and colleagues, at the Carnegie Institution of Washington, studied how the size of yarrow plants (*Achillea lanulosa*) growing on the slopes of the Sierra Nevada varied with elevation. They found that plants from low elevations were generally taller than plants from high elevations, as shown below:

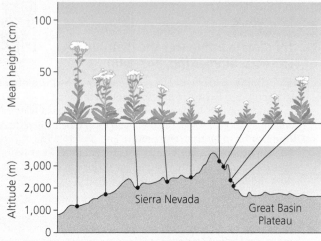

Data from J. Clausen et al., Experimental studies on the nature of species. III. Environmental responses of climatic races of *Achillea*, Carnegie Institution of Washington Publication No. 581 (1948).

Clausen and colleagues proposed two hypotheses to explain this variation within a species: (1) There are genetic differences between populations of plants found at different elevations. (2) The species has developmental flexibility and can assume tall or short growth forms, depending on local abiotic factors. If you had seeds from yarrow plants found at low and high elevations, describe the experiments you would perform to test these hypotheses.

8. **FOCUS ON EVOLUTION**
   Discuss how the distribution of a species can be affected both by its evolutionary history and by ecological factors.

9. **FOCUS ON INTERACTIONS**
   In a short essay (100–150 words), identify the factor or factors in Figure 40.23 that you think may ultimately be most important for density-dependent population regulation in humans, and explain your reasoning.

10. **SYNTHESIZE YOUR KNOWLEDGE**

Locusts (a type of grasshopper) undergo cyclic population outbreaks. Of the mechanisms of density-dependent regulation shown in Figure 40.23, choose the two that you think most apply to locust swarms, and explain why.

For selected answers, see Appendix A.

KEY CONCEPTS

41.1 Interactions within a community may help, harm, or have no effect on the species involved

41.2 Diversity and trophic structure characterize biological communities

41.3 Disturbance influences species diversity and composition

41.4 Biogeographic factors affect community diversity

41.5 Pathogens alter community structure locally and globally

▲ **Figure 41.1** Which species benefits from this interaction?

Communities in Motion

Deep in the Lembeh Strait of Indonesia, a carrier crab scuttles across the ocean floor using its modified rear legs to hold a large sea urchin on its back **(Figure 41.1)**. When a predatory fish arrives, the crab quickly settles into the sediments and puts its living shield to use. The fish darts in and tries to bite the crab. In response, the crab tilts the spiny sea urchin toward whichever side the fish attacks. The fish eventually gives up and swims away. Carrier crabs use many organisms to protect themselves, including jellies (see the small photo).

The crab in Figure 41.1 clearly benefits from having the sea urchin on its back. But how does the sea urchin fare in this relationship? Its association with the crab might harm it, help it, or have no effect on its survival and reproduction. For example, the sea urchin may be harmed if the crab sets it down in an unsuitable habitat or in a place where it is vulnerable to predators. On the other hand, the crab may also protect the sea urchin from predators while carrying it. Additional observations or experiments would be needed before ecologists could answer this question.

In Chapter 40, you learned how individuals within a population can affect other individuals of the same species. This chapter will examine ecological interactions between populations of different species. A group of populations of different species living close enough to interact is called a biological **community**. Ecologists define the boundaries of a particular community to fit their research questions: They might study the community of decomposers and other organisms living on a rotting log, the benthic community in Lake Superior, or the community of trees and shrubs in Sequoia National Park in California.

We begin this chapter by exploring the kinds of interactions that occur between species in a community, such as the crab and sea urchin in Figure 41.1. We'll then consider several of the factors that are most significant in structuring a community—in determining how many species there are, which particular species are present, and the relative abundance of these species. Finally, we'll apply some of the principles of community ecology to the study of human disease.

Interactions within a community may help, harm, or have no effect on the species involved

Some key relationships in the life of an organism are its interactions with individuals of other species in the community. These **interspecific interactions** include competition, predation, herbivory, parasitism, mutualism, and commensalism. In this section, we'll define and describe each of these interactions, grouping them according to whether they have positive (+) or negative (−) effects on the survival and reproduction of the two species engaged in the interaction.

For example, predation is a +/− interaction, with a positive effect on the survival and reproduction of the predator population and a negative effect on that of the prey population. Mutualism is a +/+ interaction because the survival and reproduction of both species are increased in the presence of the other. A 0 indicates that a population is not affected by the interaction in any known way. We'll consider three broad categories of ecological interactions: competition (−/−), exploitation (+/−), and positive interactions (+/+ or +/0).

Competition

Interspecific competition is a −/− interaction that occurs when individuals of different species compete for a resource that limits the survival and reproduction of each species. Weeds growing in a garden compete with garden plants for nutrients and water. Lynx and foxes in the northern forests of Alaska and Canada compete for prey such as snowshoe hares. In contrast, some resources, such as oxygen, are rarely in short supply, at least on land; most terrestrial species use this resource, but they do not usually compete for it.

Competitive Exclusion

What happens in a community when two species compete for limited resources? In 1934, Russian ecologist G. F. Gause studied this question using laboratory experiments with two closely related protist species, *Paramecium aurelia* and *Paramecium caudatum*. He cultured the species under stable conditions, adding a constant amount of food each day. When Gause grew the two species separately, each population increased rapidly in number and then leveled off at the apparent carrying capacity of the culture (see Figure 40.20a for an illustration of the logistic growth of a *Paramecium* population). But when Gause grew the two species together, *P. caudatum* became extinct. Gause inferred that *P. aurelia* had a competitive edge in obtaining food. More generally, he concluded that two species competing for the same limiting resources cannot coexist permanently in the same place. In the absence of disturbance, one species will use the resources more efficiently and reproduce more rapidly than the other. Even a slight reproductive

advantage will eventually lead to local elimination of the inferior competitor, an outcome called **competitive exclusion**.

Ecological Niches and Natural Selection

EVOLUTION The specific set of biotic and abiotic resources that an organism uses in its environment is called its **ecological niche**. American ecologist Eugene Odum used the following analogy to explain the niche concept: If an organism's habitat is its "address," the niche is the organism's "profession." The niche of a tropical tree lizard, for instance, includes the temperature range it tolerates, the size of branches on which it perches, the time of day when it is active, and the sizes and kinds of insects it eats. Such factors define the lizard's niche, or ecological role—how it fits into an ecosystem.

We can use the niche concept to restate the principle of competitive exclusion: Two species cannot coexist permanently in a community if their niches are identical. However, ecologically similar species *can* coexist in a community if one or more significant differences in their niches arise through time. Evolution by natural selection can result in one of the species using a different set of resources or similar resources at different times of the day or year. The differentiation of niches that enables similar species to coexist in a community is called **resource partitioning (Figure 41.2)**.

As a result of competition, a species' *fundamental niche*, which is the niche potentially occupied by that species, is often

A. *distichus* perches on fence posts and other sunny surfaces.

A. *insolitus* usually perches on shady branches.

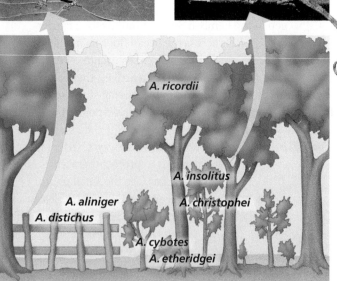

▲ **Figure 41.2 Resource partitioning among Dominican Republic lizards.** Seven species of *Anolis* lizards live in close proximity, and all feed on insects and other small arthropods. However, competition for food is reduced because each lizard species has a different preferred perch, thus occupying a distinct niche.

different from its *realized niche*, the portion of its fundamental niche that it actually occupies. Ecologists can identify the fundamental niche of a species by testing the range of conditions in which it grows and reproduces in the absence of competitors. They can also test whether a potential competitor limits a species' realized niche by removing the competitor and seeing if the first species expands into the newly available space. The classic experiment depicted in **Figure 41.3** clearly showed that competition between two barnacle species kept one species from occupying part of its fundamental niche.

Can a species' niche be influenced by interspecific competition?

Experiment Ecologist Joseph Connell studied two barnacle species—*Chthamalus stellatus* and *Balanus balanoides*—that have a stratified distribution on rocks along the coast of Scotland. *Chthamalus* is usually found higher on the rocks than *Balanus*. To determine whether the distribution of *Chthamalus* is the result of interspecific competition with *Balanus*, Connell removed *Balanus* from the rocks at several sites.

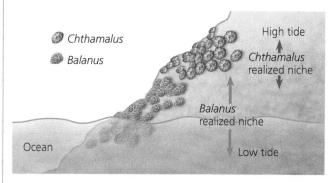

Results *Chthamalus* spread into the region formerly occupied by *Balanus*.

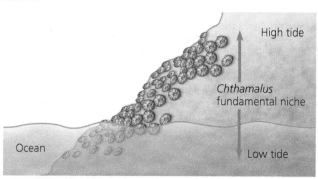

Conclusion Interspecific competition makes the realized niche of *Chthamalus* much smaller than its fundamental niche.

Data from J. H. Connell, The influence of interspecific competition and other factors on the distribution of the barnacle *Chthamalus stellatus*, *Ecology* 42:710–723 (1961).

(MB) See the related Experimental Inquiry Tutorial in MasteringBiology.

WHAT IF? Other observations showed that *Balanus* cannot survive high on the rocks because it dries out during low tides. How would *Balanus*'s realized niche compare with its fundamental niche?

Character Displacement

Closely related species whose populations are sometimes allopatric (geographically separate; see Concept 22.2) and sometimes sympatric (geographically overlapping) provide more evidence for the importance of competition in structuring communities. In some cases, the allopatric populations of such species are morphologically similar and use similar resources. By contrast, sympatric populations, which would potentially compete for resources, show differences in body structures and in the resources they use. This tendency for characteristics to diverge more in sympatric than in allopatric populations of two species is called **character displacement**. An example of character displacement in Galápagos finches is shown in **Figure 41.4**.

Exploitation

All nonphotosynthetic organisms must eat, and all organisms are at risk of being eaten. Thus, much of the drama in nature involves **exploitation**, a term for any type of +/− interaction in which one species benefits by feeding on the other species, which in turn is harmed by the interaction. Exploitative interactions include predation, herbivory, and parasitism.

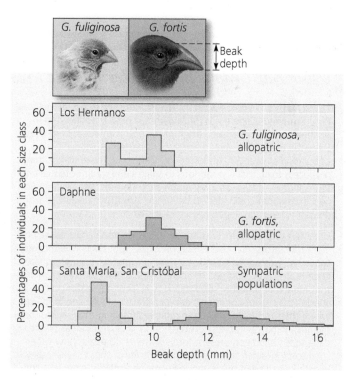

▲ **Figure 41.4 Character displacement: indirect evidence of past competition.** Allopatric populations of *Geospiza fuliginosa* and *Geospiza fortis* on Los Hermanos and Daphne Islands have similar beak morphologies (top two graphs) and presumably eat similarly sized seeds. However, where the two species are sympatric on Santa María and San Cristóbal, *G. fuliginosa* has a shallower, smaller beak and *G. fortis* a deeper, larger one (bottom graph), adaptations that favor eating different-sized seeds.

INTERPRET THE DATA *If the beak length of* G. fortis *is typically 12% longer than the beak depth, what is the predicted beak length of* G. fortis *individuals with the smallest beak depths observed on Santa María and San Cristóbal Islands?*

Predation

Predation refers to a +/− interaction between species in which one species, the predator, kills and eats the other, the prey. Though the term *predation* generally elicits such images as a lion attacking and eating an antelope, it applies to a wide range of interactions. A rotifer (a tiny aquatic animal that is smaller than many protists) that kills a unicellular alga by eating it can also be considered a predator. Because eating and avoiding being eaten are prerequisites to reproductive success, the adaptations of both predators and prey tend to be refined through natural selection. In the **Scientific Skills Exercise**, you can interpret data from an experiment investigating a specific predator-prey interaction.

Many important feeding adaptations of predators are obvious and familiar. Most predators have acute senses that enable them to find and identify potential prey. Rattlesnakes and other pit vipers, for example, find their prey with a pair of heat-sensing organs located between their eyes and nostrils (see Figure 38.17b). Many predators also have adaptations such as claws, fangs, or poison that help them catch and subdue their food. Predators that pursue their prey are generally fast

and agile, whereas those that lie in ambush are often disguised in their environments.

Just as predators possess adaptations for capturing prey, potential prey animals have adaptations that help them avoid being eaten. Some common behavioral defenses are hiding, fleeing, and forming herds or schools. Active self-defense is less common, though some large grazing mammals vigorously defend their young from predators such as lions.

Animals also display a variety of morphological and physiological defensive adaptations. **Cryptic coloration**, or camouflage, makes prey difficult to see (**Figure 41.5a**). Mechanical or chemical defenses protect species such as porcupines and skunks. Some animals, such as the European fire salamander, can synthesize toxins; others accumulate toxins passively from the plants they eat. Animals with effective chemical defenses often exhibit bright **aposematic coloration**, or warning coloration, such as that of poison dart frogs (**Figure 41.5b**). Such coloration seems to be adaptive because predators often avoid brightly colored prey.

Some prey species are protected by their resemblance to other species. For example, in **Batesian mimicry**, a palatable

Scientific Skills Exercise

Using Bar Graphs and Scatter Plots to Present and Interpret Data

Can a Native Predator Species Adapt Rapidly to an Introduced Prey Species? Cane toads (*Bufo marinus*) were introduced to Australia in 1935 in a failed attempt to control an insect pest. Since then, the toads have spread across northeastern Australia, with a population of over 200 million today. Cane toads have glands that produce a toxin that is poisonous to snakes and other potential predators. In this exercise, you will graph and interpret data from a two-part experiment conducted to determine whether native Australian predators have developed resistance to the cane toad toxin.

How the Experiment Was Done In part 1, researchers collected 12 black snakes (*Pseudechis porphyriacus*) from areas where cane toads had existed for 40–60 years and another 12 from areas free of cane toads. They recorded the percentage of snakes from each area that ate either a freshly killed native frog (*Limnodynastes peronii*, a species the snakes commonly eat) or a freshly killed cane toad from which the toxin gland had been removed (making the toad nonpoisonous). In part 2, researchers collected snakes from areas where cane toads had been present for 5–60 years. To assess how cane toad toxin affected the physiological activity of these snakes, they injected small amounts of the toxin into the snakes' stomachs and measured the snakes' swimming speed in a small pool.

Data from the Experiment, Part 1

Type of Prey Offered	Percentage of Snakes from Each Area That Ate the Native Frog vs. Cane Toad	
	Area with Cane Toads Present for 40–60 Years	Area with No Cane Toads
Native frog	100	100
Cane toad	0	50

Data from the Experiment, Part 2

Number of Years Cane Toads Were Present in the Area	5	10	10	20	50	60	60	60	60	60
Percent Reduction in Snake Swimming Speed	52	19	30	30	5	5	9	11	12	22

Data from B. L. Phillips and R. Shine, An invasive species induces rapid adaptive change in a native predator: cane toads and black snakes in Australia, *Proceedings of the Royal Society B* 273:1545–1550 (2006).

INTERPRET THE DATA

1. Make a bar graph of the data in part 1. (For additional information about graphs, see the Scientific Skills Review in Appendix F and in the Study Area in MasteringBiology.)

2. What do the data represented in the graph suggest about the effects of cane toads on the predatory behavior of black snakes in areas where the toads are and are not currently found?

3. Suppose a novel enzyme that deactivates the cane toad toxin evolved in a black snake population exposed to cane toads. If the researchers repeated part 1 of this study, predict how the results would change.

4. Identify the dependent and independent variables in part 2 and make a scatter plot. What conclusion would you draw about whether exposure to cane toads is having a selective effect on black snakes? Explain.

5. Explain why a bar graph is appropriate for presenting the data in part 1 and a scatter plot is appropriate for the data in part 2.

(MB) A version of this Scientific Skills Exercise can be assigned in MasteringBiology.

(a) Cryptic coloration

► Canyon tree frog

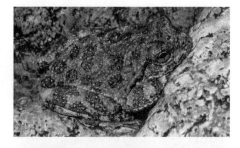

(b) Aposematic coloration

► Poison dart frog

(c) Batesian mimicry: A harmless species mimics a harmful one.

◄ Nonvenomous hawkmoth larva

▼ Venomous green parrot snake

▲ **Figure 41.5 Examples of defensive adaptations in animals.**

MAKE CONNECTIONS *Explain how natural selection could increase the resemblance of a harmless species to a distantly related harmful species. Along with selection, what else could account for a harmless species resembling a closely related harmful species? (See Concept 19.2.)*

or harmless species mimics an unpalatable or harmful species to which it is not closely related. The larva of the hawkmoth *Hemeroplanes ornatus* puffs up its head and thorax when disturbed, looking like the head of a small venomous snake **(Figure 41.5c)**. In this case, the mimicry even involves behavior; the larva weaves its head back and forth and hisses like a snake. In Batesian mimicry, the resemblance of a prey species to a distantly related unpalatable or harmful species is thought to have resulted from natural selection.

Many predators also use mimicry. The alligator snapping turtle has a tongue that resembles a wriggling worm, which is used to lure small fish. Any fish that tries to eat the "bait" is itself quickly consumed as the turtle's strong jaws snap closed.

▲ **Figure 41.6 A marine herbivore.** This West Indian manatee (*Trichechus manatus*) in Florida is grazing on *Hydrilla*, an introduced plant.

Herbivory

Ecologists use the term **herbivory** to refer to a $+/-$ interaction in which an organism—an herbivore—eats parts of a plant or alga, thereby harming it. While large mammalian herbivores such as cattle, sheep, and water buffalo may be most familiar, most herbivores are actually invertebrates, such as grasshoppers, caterpillars, and beetles. In the ocean, herbivores include sea urchins, some tropical fishes, and certain mammals, including the manatee **(Figure 41.6)**.

Like predators, herbivores have many specialized adaptations. Many herbivorous insects have chemical sensors on their feet that enable them to distinguish between plants based on their toxicity or their nutritional value. Some mammalian herbivores, such as goats, use their sense of smell to examine plants, rejecting some and eating others. They may also eat just a specific part of a plant, such as the flowers. Many herbivores also have specialized teeth or digestive systems adapted for processing vegetation (see Concept 33.4).

Unlike prey animals, plants cannot run away to avoid being eaten. Instead, a plant's arsenal against herbivores may feature chemical toxins or structures such as spines and thorns. Among the plant compounds that serve as chemical defenses are the poison strychnine, produced by the tropical vine *Strychnos toxifera*, and nicotine, from the tobacco plant. Compounds that are not toxic to humans but may be distasteful to many herbivores are responsible for the familiar flavors of cinnamon, cloves, and peppermint.

Parasitism

Parasitism is a $+/-$ exploitative interaction in which one organism, the **parasite**, derives its nourishment from another organism, its **host**, which is harmed in the process. Parasites that live within the body of their host, such as tapeworms, are called **endoparasites**; parasites that feed on the external surface of a host, such as ticks and lice, are called **ectoparasites**. Some ecologists have estimated that at least one-third of all species on Earth are parasites. In one particular type of parasitism, parasitoid insects—usually small wasps—lay eggs on or in living hosts, such as the braconid wasp parasitizing a tobacco hornworm (*Manduca sexta*) in the photo.

Many parasites have complex life cycles involving multiple hosts. The blood fluke, which currently infects approximately 200 million people around the world, requires two hosts at different times in its development: humans and freshwater snails. Some parasites change the behavior of their current host in ways that increase the likelihood that the parasite will reach its next host. For instance, crustaceans that are parasitized by acanthocephalan (spiny-headed) worms leave protective cover and move into the open, where they are more likely to be eaten by the birds that are the second host in the worm's life cycle.

Parasites can significantly affect the survival, reproduction, and density of their host population, either directly or indirectly. For example, ticks that feed as ectoparasites on moose can weaken their hosts by withdrawing blood and causing hair breakage and loss. In their weakened condition, the moose have a greater chance of dying from cold stress or predation by wolves (see Figure 40.24).

Positive Interactions

While nature abounds with dramatic and gory examples of exploitive interactions, ecological communities are also heavily influenced by **positive interactions**, a term that refers to a +/+ or +/0 interaction in which at least one species benefits and neither is harmed. Positive interactions include mutualism and commensalism. As we'll see, they can affect the diversity of species found in ecological communities.

Mutualism

Mutualism is an interspecific interaction that benefits both species (+/+). Mutualisms are common in nature, as illustrated by examples seen in previous chapters, including cellulose digestion by microorganisms in the digestive systems of termites and ruminant mammals, animals that pollinate flowers or disperse seeds, nutrient exchange between fungi and plant roots in mycorrhizae, and photosynthesis by unicellular algae in corals. In the acacia-ant example shown in **Figure 41.7**, each species depends on the other for their survival and reproduction. However, in other mutualisms—including some other acacia-ant interactions—both species can survive on their own.

Typically, both partners in a mutualism incur costs as well as benefits. In mycorrhizae, for example, the plant often

(a) Certain species of acacia trees in Central and South America have hollow thorns (not shown) that house stinging ants of the genus *Pseudomyrmex*. The ants feed on nectar produced by the tree and on protein-rich swellings (yellow in the photograph) at the tips of leaflets.

(b) The acacia benefits because the pugnacious ants, which attack anything that touches the tree, remove fungal spores, small herbivores, and debris. They also clip vegetation that grows close to the acacia.

▲ **Figure 41.7 Mutualism between acacia trees and ants.**

transfers carbohydrates to the fungus, while the fungus transfers limiting nutrients, such as phosphorus. Each partner benefits, but each partner also experiences a cost: It transfers materials that it could have used to support its own growth and metabolism. The key point is that for an interaction to be a mutualism, the benefits to each partner must exceed the costs.

Commensalism

An interaction between species that benefits one of the species but neither harms nor helps the other (+/0) is called **commensalism**. Like mutualism, commensal interactions are common in nature. For instance, many wildflowers that live on the forest floor depend entirely on the trees that tower above them—the trees provide the habitat in which they live. Yet the survival and reproduction of the trees are not affected by these wildflowers. Thus, these species are involved in a +/0 interaction in which the wildflowers benefit and the trees are not affected.

▲ **Figure 41.8 Commensalism between cattle egrets and an African buffalo.**

In another example of a commensal association, cattle egrets feed on insects flushed out of the grass by grazing bison, cattle, and other herbivores (**Figure 41.8**). Because the birds typically find more prey when they follow herbivores, they clearly benefit from the association. Much of the time, the herbivores are not affected by the birds. At times, however, they, too, may derive some benefit; the birds occasionally remove and eat ticks and other ectoparasites from the herbivores or may warn the herbivores of a predator's approach. This example illustrates another key point about ecological interactions: Their effects can change. In this case, an interaction whose effects are typically +/0 (commensalism) may at times become +/+ (mutualism).

Positive interactions can have large effects on ecological communities. For instance, the black rush *Juncus gerardii* makes the soil more hospitable for other plant species in some zones of New England salt marshes (**Figure 41.9a**). *Juncus* helps prevent salt buildup in the soil by shading the soil surface,

which reduces evaporation. *Juncus* also prevents the salt marsh soils from becoming oxygen depleted as it transports oxygen to its belowground tissues. In one study, when *Juncus* was removed from areas in the upper middle intertidal zone, those areas supported 50% fewer plant species (**Figure 41.9b**).

In fact, as is true for positive interactions, competition and exploitation (predation, herbivory, and parasitism) also can have large effects on ecological communities. You'll see examples of how this can occur throughout this chapter.

CONCEPT CHECK 41.1

1. Explain how interspecific competition, predation, and mutualism differ in their effects on the interacting populations of two species.
2. According to the principle of competitive exclusion, what outcome is expected when two species with identical niches compete for a resource? Why?
3. **MAKE CONNECTIONS** Figure 22.13 illustrates how a hybrid zone can change over time. Imagine that two finch species colonize a new island and are capable of hybridizing (mating and producing viable offspring). The island contains two plant species, one with large seeds and one with small seeds, growing in isolated habitats. If the two finch species specialize in eating different plant species, would reproductive barriers be reinforced, weakened, or unchanged in this hybrid zone? Explain.

For suggested answers, see Appendix A.

CONCEPT 41.2

Diversity and trophic structure characterize biological communities

Along with the specific interactions described in the previous section, communities are also characterized by more general attributes, including how diverse they are and the feeding relationships of their species. In this section, you'll see why such ecological attributes are important. You'll also learn how a few species sometimes exert strong control on a community's structure, particularly on the composition, relative abundance, and diversity of its species.

Species Diversity

The **species diversity** of a community—the variety of different kinds of organisms that make up the community—has two components. One is **species richness**, the number of different species in the community. The other is the **relative abundance** of the different species, the proportion each species represents of all individuals in the community.

Imagine two small forest communities, each with 100 individuals distributed among four tree species (A, B, C, and D) as follows:

Community 1: 25A, 25B, 25C, 25D

Community 2: 80A, 5B, 5C, 10D

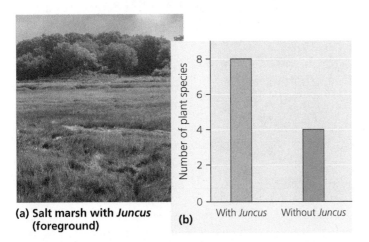

(a) Salt marsh with *Juncus* (foreground)

(b) With *Juncus* / Without *Juncus*

Number of plant species (y-axis: 0, 2, 4, 6, 8)

▲ **Figure 41.9 Facilitation by black rush (*Juncus gerardii*) in New England salt marshes.** Black rush increases the number of plant species that can live in the upper middle zone of the marsh.

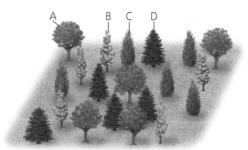

Community 1
A: 25% B: 25% C: 25% D: 25%

Community 2
A: 80% B: 5% C: 5% D: 10%

▲ **Figure 41.10 Which forest is more diverse?** Ecologists would say that community 1 has greater species diversity, a measure that includes both species richness and relative abundance.

The species richness is the same for both communities because they both contain four species of trees, but the relative abundance is very different **(Figure 41.10)**. You would easily notice the four types of trees in community 1, but without looking carefully, you might see only the abundant species A in the second forest. Most observers would intuitively describe community 1 as the more diverse of the two communities.

Ecologists use many tools to compare the diversity of communities across time and space. They often calculate indexes of diversity based on species richness and relative abundance. One widely used index is the **Shannon diversity index** (H):

$$H = -(p_A \ln p_A + p_B \ln p_B + p_C \ln p_C + \ldots)$$

where A, B, C . . . are the species in the community, p is the relative abundance of each species, and ln is the natural logarithm; the ln of each value of p can be determined using the "ln" key on a calculator. A higher value of H indicates a more diverse community. Let's use this equation to calculate the Shannon diversity index of the two communities in Figure 41.10. For community 1, $p = 0.25$ for each species, so

$$H = -4(0.25 \ln 0.25) = 1.39$$

For community 2,

$$H = -[0.8 \ln 0.8 + 2(0.05 \ln 0.05) + 0.1 \ln 0.1] = 0.71$$

These calculations confirm our intuitive description of community 1 as more diverse.

Determining the number and relative abundance of species in a community can be challenging. Because most species in a community are relatively rare, it may be hard to obtain a

sample size large enough to be representative. It can also be difficult to census highly mobile or less visible members of communities, such as microorganisms, insects, and nocturnal species. The small size of microorganisms makes them particularly difficult to sample, so ecologists now use molecular tools to help determine microbial diversity **(Figure 41.11)**.

▼ **Figure 41.11   Research Method**

Determining Microbial Diversity Using Molecular Tools

Application Ecologists are increasingly using molecular techniques to determine microbial diversity and richness in environmental samples. One such technique produces a DNA profile for microbial taxa based on sequence variations in the DNA that encodes the small subunit of ribosomal RNA. Noah Fierer and Rob Jackson, of Duke University, used this method to compare the diversity of soil bacteria in 98 habitats across North and South America to help identify environmental variables associated with high bacterial diversity.

Technique Researchers first extract and purify DNA from the microbial community in each sample. They use the polymerase chain reaction (PCR; see Figure 13.27) to amplify the ribosomal DNA and label it with a fluorescent dye. Restriction enzymes then cut the amplified, labeled DNA into fragments of different lengths, which are separated by gel electrophoresis. The number and abundance of these fragments characterize the DNA profile of the sample. Based on their analysis, Fierer and Jackson calculated the Shannon diversity index (H) of each sample. They then looked for a correlation between H and several environmental variables, including vegetation type, mean annual temperature and rainfall, and soil acidity.

Results The diversity of the sampled bacteria was related almost exclusively to soil pH, with the Shannon diversity index being highest in neutral soils and lowest in acidic soils. Amazonian rain forests, which have extremely high plant and animal diversity, had the most acidic soils and the lowest bacterial diversity of the samples tested.

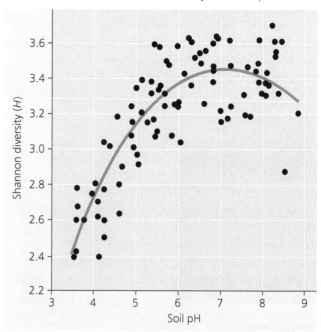

Data from N. Fierer and R. B. Jackson, The diversity and biogeography of soil bacterial communities, *Proceedings of the National Academy of Sciences USA* 103:626–631 (2006).

▲ **Figure 41.12 Study plots at the Cedar Creek Ecosystem Science Reserve, site of long-term experiments in which researchers have manipulated plant diversity.**

Diversity and Community Stability

In addition to measuring species diversity, ecologists manipulate diversity in experimental communities in nature and in the laboratory. They do this to examine the potential benefits of diversity, including increased productivity and stability of biological communities.

Researchers at the Cedar Creek Ecosystem Science Reserve, in Minnesota, have been manipulating plant diversity in experimental communities for more than two decades **(Figure 41.12)**. Higher-diversity communities generally are more productive and are better able to withstand and recover from environmental stresses, such as droughts. More diverse communities are also more stable year to year in their productivity. In one decade-long experiment, for instance, researchers at Cedar Creek created 168 plots, each containing 1, 2, 4, 8, or 16 perennial grassland species. The most diverse plots consistently produced more **biomass** (the total mass of all organisms in a habitat) than the single-species plots each year.

Higher-diversity communities are often more resistant to **invasive species**, which are organisms that become established outside their native range. Scientists working in Long Island Sound, off the coast of Connecticut, created communities with different levels of diversity consisting of sessile marine invertebrates, including tunicates (see Figure 27.15b). They then examined how vulnerable these experimental communities were to invasion by an exotic tunicate. They found that the exotic tunicate was four times more likely to survive in lower-diversity communities than in higher-diversity ones. The researchers concluded that relatively diverse communities captured more of the resources available in the system, leaving fewer resources for the invader and decreasing its survival.

Trophic Structure

Experiments like the ones just described often examine the importance of diversity within one trophic level. The structure and dynamics of a community also depend on the feeding

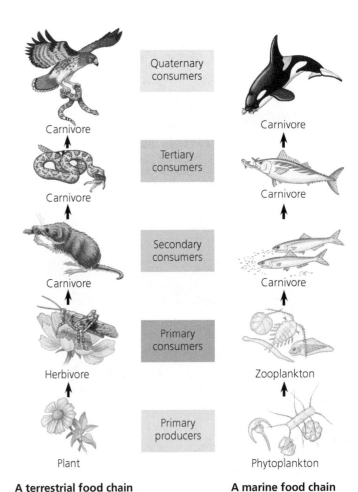

A terrestrial food chain   **A marine food chain**

▲ **Figure 41.13 Examples of terrestrial and marine food chains.** The arrows trace energy and nutrients that pass through the trophic levels of a community when organisms feed on one another. Decomposers, which feed on the remains of organisms from all trophic levels, are not shown here.

? *Suppose the abundance of carnivores that eat zooplankton increased greatly. How might that affect phytoplankton abundance?*

relationships between organisms—the **trophic structure** of the community. The transfer of food energy up the trophic levels from its source in plants and other autotrophs (primary producers) through herbivores (primary consumers) to carnivores (secondary, tertiary, and quaternary consumers) and eventually to decomposers is referred to as a **food chain** **(Figure 41.13)**.

In the 1920s, Oxford University biologist Charles Elton recognized that food chains are not isolated units but are linked together in **food webs**. Ecologists diagram the trophic relationships of a community using arrows that link species according to who eats whom. In an Antarctic pelagic community, for example, the primary producers are phytoplankton, which serve as food for the dominant grazing zooplankton, especially krill and copepods, both of which are crustaceans. These zooplankton species are in turn eaten by various carnivores, including other plankton, penguins, seals, fishes, and baleen whales. Squids, which are carnivores that feed on fish and zooplankton,

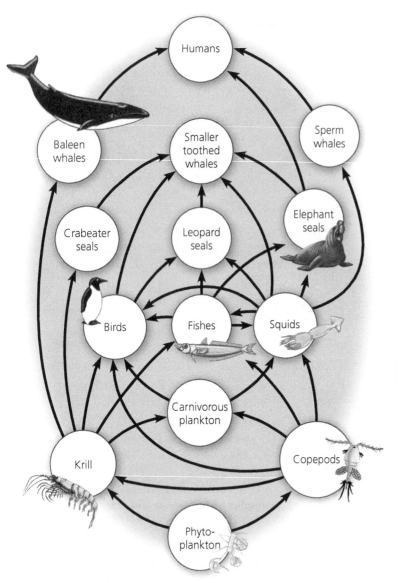

▲ **Figure 41.14 An Antarctic marine food web.** Arrows follow the transfer of food from the producers (phytoplankton) up through the trophic levels. For simplicity, this diagram omits decomposers.

? *In the food web shown here, indicate the number of organism types that each group eats. Which two groups are both predator and prey for each other?*

are another important link in these food webs, as they are in turn eaten by seals and toothed whales **(Figure 41.14)**.

Note that a given species may weave into the web at more than one trophic level. For example, in the food web shown in Figure 41.14, krill feed on phytoplankton as well as on other grazing zooplankton, such as copepods.

Species with a Large Impact

Certain species have an especially large impact on the structure of entire communities because they are highly abundant or play a pivotal role in community dynamics. The impact of these species occurs through trophic interactions and their influence on the physical environment.

Dominant species in a community are the species that are the most abundant or that collectively have the highest

biomass. There can be different explanations for why different species become dominant. One hypothesis suggests that dominant species are competitively superior in exploiting limited resources such as water or nutrients. Another hypothesis is that dominant species are most successful at avoiding predation or the impact of disease. The latter idea could explain the high biomass attained in some environments by invasive species. Such species may not face the natural predators or parasites that would otherwise hold their populations in check.

In contrast to dominant species, **keystone species** are not usually abundant in a community. They exert strong control on community structure not by numerical might but by their pivotal ecological roles, or niches. **Figure 41.15** highlights the importance of a keystone species, a sea star, in maintaining the diversity of an intertidal community.

Still other organisms exert their influence on a community not through trophic interactions but by changing their physical environment. Species that dramatically alter their environment are called **ecosystem engineers** or, to avoid implying

▼ **Figure 41.15** Inquiry

Is *Pisaster ochraceus* a keystone predator?

Experiment In rocky intertidal communities of western North America, the relatively uncommon sea star *Pisaster ochraceus* preys on mussels such as *Mytilus californianus*, a dominant species and strong competitor for space.

Robert Paine, of the University of Washington, removed *Pisaster* from an area in the intertidal zone and examined the effect on species richness.

Results In the absence of *Pisaster*, species richness declined as mussels monopolized the rock face and eliminated most other invertebrates and algae. In a control area where *Pisaster* was not removed, species richness changed very little.

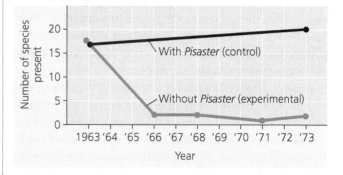

Conclusion *Pisaster* acts as a keystone species, exerting an influence on the community that is not reflected in its abundance.

Data from R. T. Paine, Food web complexity and species diversity, *American Naturalist* 100:65–75 (1966).

WHAT IF? Suppose that an invasive fungus killed most individuals of *Mytilus* at these sites. Predict how species richness would be affected if *Pisaster* were then removed.

▲ **Figure 41.16 Beavers as ecosystem engineers.** By felling trees, building dams, and creating ponds, beavers can transform large areas of forest into flooded wetlands.

conscious intent, "foundation species." A familiar ecosystem engineer is the beaver **(Figure 41.16)**. The effects of ecosystem engineers on other species can be positive or negative, depending on the needs of the other species.

Bottom-Up and Top-Down Controls

Simplified models based on relationships between adjacent trophic levels are useful for describing community organization. Let's consider the three possible relationships between plants (V for vegetation) and herbivores (H):

$$V \rightarrow H \qquad V \leftarrow H \qquad V \leftrightarrow H$$

The arrows indicate that a change in the biomass of one trophic level causes a change in the other trophic level. $V \rightarrow H$ means that an increase in vegetation will increase the numbers or biomass of herbivores, but not vice versa. In this situation, herbivores are limited by vegetation, but vegetation is not limited by herbivory. In contrast, $V \leftarrow H$ means that an increase in herbivore biomass will decrease the abundance of vegetation, but not vice versa. A double-headed arrow indicates that each trophic level is sensitive to changes in the biomass of the other.

Two models of community organization are common: the bottom-up model and the top-down model. The $V \rightarrow H$ linkage suggests a **bottom-up model**, which postulates a unidirectional influence from lower to higher trophic levels. In this case, the presence or absence of mineral nutrients (N) controls plant (V) numbers, which control herbivore (H) numbers, which in turn control predator (P) numbers. The simplified bottom-up model is thus $N \rightarrow V \rightarrow H \rightarrow P$. To change the community structure of a bottom-up community, you need to alter biomass at the lower trophic levels, allowing those changes to propagate up through the food web. If you add mineral nutrients to stimulate plant growth, then the higher trophic levels should also increase in biomass. If you change predator abundance, however, the effect should not extend down to the lower trophic levels.

In contrast, the **top-down model** postulates the opposite: Predation mainly controls community organization because predators limit herbivores, herbivores limit plants, and plants limit nutrient levels through nutrient uptake. The simplified top-down model, $N \leftarrow V \leftarrow H \leftarrow P$, is also called the *trophic cascade model*. In a lake community with four trophic levels, the model predicts that removing the top carnivores will increase the abundance of primary carnivores, in turn decreasing the number of herbivores, increasing phytoplankton abundance, and decreasing concentrations of mineral nutrients. The effects thus move down the trophic structure as alternating $+/-$ effects.

Ecologists have applied the top-down model to improve water quality in lakes with high abundances of algae. This approach, called **biomanipulation**, attempts to prevent algal blooms by altering the density of higher-level consumers. In lakes with three trophic levels, removing fish should improve water quality by increasing zooplankton density, thereby decreasing algal populations. In lakes with four trophic levels, adding top predators should have the same effect **(Figure 41.17)**.

Ecologists in Finland used biomanipulation to help purify Lake Vesijärvi, a large lake that was polluted with city sewage and industrial wastewater until 1976. After pollution controls reduced these inputs, the water quality of the lake began to improve. By 1986, however, massive blooms of cyanobacteria started to occur in the lake. These blooms coincided with an increase in the population of roach, a fish species that eats zooplankton, which otherwise keep the cyanobacteria and algae in check. To reverse these changes, ecologists removed nearly a million kilograms of fish from the lake between 1989 and 1993, reducing roach abundance by about 80%. At the same time, they added a fourth trophic level by stocking the lake with pike perch, a predatory fish that eats roach. The water became clear, and the last cyanobacterial bloom was in 1989. Ecologists continue to monitor the lake for evidence of cyanobacterial blooms and low oxygen availability, but the lake has remained clear, even though roach removal ended in 1993.

As these examples show, communities vary in their degree of bottom-up and top-down control. To manage agricultural landscapes, parks, reservoirs, and fisheries, we need to understand each particular community's dynamics.

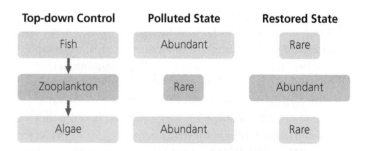

▲ **Figure 41.17 Results of biomanipulation in a lake with top-down control of community organization.** Decreasing the abundance of fish that ate zooplankton results in a decrease in the biomass of algae, improving water quality.

CONCEPT 41.3

Disturbance influences species diversity and composition

Decades ago, most ecologists favored the traditional view that biological communities are at equilibrium, a more or less stable balance, unless seriously disturbed by human activities. The "balance of nature" view focused on interspecific competition as a key factor determining community composition and maintaining stability in communities. *Stability* in this context refers to a community's tendency to reach and maintain a relatively constant composition of species.

One of the earliest proponents of this view, F. E. Clements, of the Carnegie Institution of Washington, argued in the early 1900s that the community of plants at a site had only one stable equilibrium, a *climax community* controlled solely by climate. According to Clements, biotic interactions caused the species in the community to function as an integrated unit—in effect, as a superorganism. His argument was based on the observation that certain species of plants are consistently found together, such as the oaks, maples, birches, and beeches in deciduous forests of the northeastern United States.

Other ecologists questioned whether most communities were at equilibrium or functioned as integrated units. A. G. Tansley, of Oxford University, challenged the concept of a climax community, arguing that differences in soils, topography, and other factors created many potential communities that were stable within a region. H. A. Gleason, of the University of Chicago, saw communities not as superorganisms but as chance assemblages of species found together because they happen to have similar abiotic requirements—for example, for temperature, rainfall, and soil type. Gleason and other ecologists also realized that disturbance keeps many communities from reaching a state of equilibrium in species diversity or

composition. A **disturbance** is an event—such as a storm, fire, flood, drought, or human activity—that changes a community by removing organisms from it or altering resource availability.

This emphasis on change has led to the formulation of the **nonequilibrium model**, which describes most communities as constantly changing after disturbance. Even relatively stable communities can be rapidly transformed into nonequilibrium communities. Let's examine some of the ways that disturbances influence community structure and composition.

Characterizing Disturbance

The types of disturbances and their frequency and severity vary among communities. Storms disturb almost all communities, even those in the oceans through the action of waves. Fire is a significant disturbance; in fact, chaparral and some grassland biomes require regular burning to maintain their structure and species composition. Many streams and ponds are disturbed by spring flooding and seasonal drying. A high level of disturbance is generally the result of frequent *and* intense disturbance, while low disturbance levels can result from either a low frequency or low intensity of disturbance.

The **intermediate disturbance hypothesis** states that moderate levels of disturbance foster greater species diversity than do high or low levels of disturbance. High levels of disturbance reduce diversity by creating environmental stresses that exceed the tolerances of many species or by disturbing the community so often that slow-growing or slow-colonizing species are excluded. At the other extreme, low levels of disturbance can reduce species diversity by allowing competitively dominant species to exclude less competitive ones. Meanwhile, intermediate levels of disturbance can foster greater species diversity by opening up habitats for occupation by less competitive species. Such intermediate disturbance levels rarely create conditions so severe that they exceed the environmental tolerances or recovery rates of potential community members.

The intermediate disturbance hypothesis is supported by many terrestrial and aquatic studies. In one study, ecologists in New Zealand compared the richness of invertebrates living in the beds of streams exposed to different frequencies and intensities of flooding (**Figure 41.18**). When floods occurred either very frequently or rarely, invertebrate richness was low. Frequent floods made it difficult for some species to become established in the streambed, while rare floods resulted in species being displaced by superior competitors. Invertebrate richness peaked in streams that had an intermediate frequency or intensity of flooding, as predicted by the hypothesis.

Although moderate levels of disturbance appear to maximize species diversity in some cases, small and large disturbances also can have important effects on community structure. Small-scale disturbances can create patches of different habitats across a landscape, which help maintain diversity in a community. Large-scale disturbances are also a natural part of many communities. Much of Yellowstone National

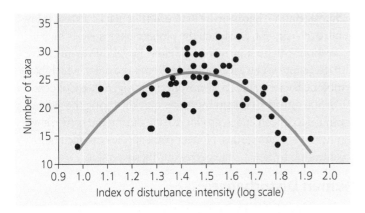

▲ Figure 41.18 Testing the intermediate disturbance hypothesis. Researchers identified the taxa (species or genera) of invertebrates at two locations in each of 27 New Zealand streams. They assessed the intensity of flooding at each location using an index of streambed disturbance. The number of invertebrate taxa peaked where the intensity of flooding was at intermediate levels.

Park, for example, is dominated by lodgepole pine, a tree species that requires the rejuvenating influence of periodic fires. Lodgepole pine cones remain closed until exposed to intense heat. When a forest fire burns the trees, the cones open and the seeds are released. The new generation of lodgepole pines can then thrive on nutrients released from the burned trees and in the sunlight that is no longer blocked by taller trees.

In the summer of 1988, extensive areas of Yellowstone burned during a severe drought. By 1989, burned areas in the park were largely covered with new vegetation, suggesting that the species in this community are adapted to rapid recovery after fire **(Figure 41.19)**. In fact, large-scale fires have periodically swept through the lodgepole pine forests of Yellowstone and other northern areas for thousands of years.

Studies of the Yellowstone forest community and many others indicate that they are nonequilibrium communities, changing continually because of natural disturbances and the internal processes of growth and reproduction. Mounting evidence suggests that nonequilibrium conditions are in fact the norm for most communities.

Ecological Succession

Changes in the composition and structure of terrestrial communities are most apparent after a severe disturbance, such as a volcanic eruption or a glacier, strips away all the existing vegetation. The disturbed area may be colonized by a variety of species, which are gradually replaced by other species, which are in turn replaced by still other species—a process called **ecological succession**. When this process begins in a virtually lifeless area where soil has not yet formed, such as on a new volcanic island or on the rubble (moraine) left by a retreating glacier, it is called **primary succession**. Another type of succession, **secondary succession**, occurs when an existing community has been cleared by a disturbance that leaves the soil intact, as in Yellowstone following the 1988 fires (see Figure 41.19).

(a) Soon after fire. While all trees in the foreground of this photograph were killed by the fire, unburned trees can be seen in other locations.

(b) One year after fire. The community has begun to recover. Herbaceous plants, different from those in the former forest, cover the ground.

▲ Figure 41.19 Recovery following a large-scale disturbance. The 1988 Yellowstone National Park fires burned large areas of forests dominated by lodgepole pines.

During primary succession, the only life-forms initially present are often prokaryotes and protists. Lichens and mosses, which grow from windblown spores, are commonly the first macroscopic photosynthesizers to colonize such areas. Soil develops gradually as rocks weather and organic matter accumulates from the decomposed remains of the early colonizers. Once soil is present, the lichens and mosses are usually overgrown by grasses, shrubs, and trees that sprout from seeds blown in from nearby areas or carried in by animals. Eventually, an area is colonized by plants that become the community's dominant form of vegetation. Producing such a community through primary succession may take hundreds or thousands of years.

Early-arriving species and later-arriving ones may be linked by one of three key processes. The early arrivals may *facilitate* the appearance of the later species by making the environment more favorable—for example, by increasing the fertility of the soil. Alternatively, the early species may *inhibit* establishment of the later species, so that successful colonization by later species occurs in spite of, rather than because of, the activities of the early species. Finally, the early species may be completely independent of the later species, which *tolerate* conditions created early in succession but are neither helped nor hindered by early species.

Ecologists have conducted some of the most extensive research on primary succession at Glacier Bay in southeastern Alaska, where glaciers have retreated more than 100 km since 1760 **(Figure 41.20)**. By studying the communities at different distances from the mouth of the bay, ecologists can examine different stages in succession. **❶** The exposed glacial moraine is colonized first by pioneering species that include liverworts, mosses, fireweed, scattered *Dryas* (a mat-forming shrub), and willows. **❷** After about three decades, *Dryas* dominates the plant community. **❸** A few decades later, the area is invaded by alder, which forms dense thickets up to 9 m tall. **❹** In the next two centuries, these alder stands are overgrown first by Sitka spruce and later by western hemlock and mountain hemlock. In areas of poor drainage, the forest floor of this spruce-hemlock forest is invaded by sphagnum moss, which holds water and acidifies the soil, eventually killing the trees. Thus, by about 300 years after glacial retreat, the vegetation consists of sphagnum bogs on the poorly drained flat areas and spruce-hemlock forest on the well-drained slopes.

Succession on glacial moraines is related to changes in soil nutrients and other environmental factors caused by transitions in the vegetation. Because the bare soil after glacial retreat is low in nitrogen content, almost all the pioneer plant species begin succession with poor growth and yellow leaves due to limited nitrogen supply. The exceptions are *Dryas* and alder, which have symbiotic bacteria that fix atmospheric nitrogen (see Concept 29.4). Soil nitrogen content increases quickly during the alder stage of succession and keeps increasing during the spruce stage. By altering soil properties, pioneer plant species can facilitate colonization by new plant species during succession.

Human Disturbance

Ecological succession is a response to disturbance of the environment, and the strongest disturbances are human activities. Agricultural development has disrupted what were once the vast grasslands of the North American prairie. Tropical rain forests are quickly disappearing as a result of clear-cutting for lumber, cattle grazing, and farmland. Centuries of overgrazing and agricultural disturbance have contributed to famine in parts of Africa by turning seasonal grasslands into vast barren areas.

Humans disturb marine ecosystems as well as terrestrial ones. The effects of ocean trawling, in which boats drag weighted nets across the seafloor, are similar to those of clear-cutting a forest or plowing a field **(Figure 41.21)**. The trawls scrape and scour corals and other life on the seafloor. In a typical year, ships trawl an area about the size of South America, 150 times larger than the area of forests that are clear-cut annually.

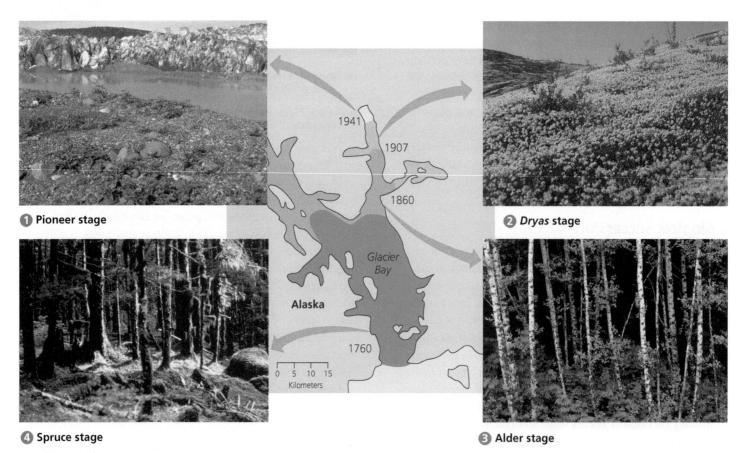

❶ Pioneer stage

❷ *Dryas* stage

❹ Spruce stage

❸ Alder stage

1941
1907
1860
Glacier Bay
Alaska
1760
0 5 10 15
Kilometers

▲ **Figure 41.20 Glacial retreat and primary succession at Glacier Bay, Alaska.** The different shades of blue on the map show retreat of the glacier since 1760, based on historical descriptions.

◀ Before trawling

After ▶ trawling

▲ **Figure 41.21 Disturbance of the ocean floor by trawling.** These photos show the seafloor off northwestern Australia before (top) and after (bottom) deep-sea trawlers have passed.

Because disturbance by human activities is often severe, it reduces species diversity in many communities. In Chapter 43, we'll take a closer look at how human-caused disturbance is affecting the diversity of life.

CONCEPT CHECK 41.3

1. Why do high and low levels of disturbance usually reduce species diversity? Why does an intermediate level of disturbance promote species diversity?

2. During succession, how might the early species facilitate the arrival of other species?

3. **WHAT IF?** Most prairies experience regular fires, typically every few years. If these disturbances were relatively modest, how would the species diversity of a prairie likely be affected if no burning occurred for 100 years? Explain your answer.

For suggested answers, see Appendix A.

CONCEPT 41.4

Biogeographic factors affect community diversity

So far, we have examined relatively small-scale or local factors that influence the diversity of communities, including the effects of species interactions, dominant species, and many types of disturbances. Ecologists also recognize that large-scale biogeographic factors contribute to the tremendous range of diversity observed in biological communities. The contributions of two biogeographic factors in particular—the latitude of a community and the area it occupies—have been investigated for more than a century.

Latitudinal Gradients

In the 1850s, both Charles Darwin and Alfred Wallace pointed out that plant and animal life was generally more abundant and diverse in the tropics than in other parts of the globe. Since that time, many researchers have confirmed this observation. One study found that a 6.6-hectare (1 ha = 10,000 m^2) plot in tropical Malaysia contained 711 tree species, while a 2-ha plot of deciduous forest in Michigan typically contained just 10 to 15 tree species. Many groups of animals show similar latitudinal gradients. For instance, there are more than 200 species of ants in Brazil, but only 7 in Alaska.

Two key factors that can affect latitudinal gradients of species richness are evolutionary history and climate. Over the course of evolution, species richness may increase in a community as more speciation events occur (see Concept 22.2). Tropical communities are generally older than temperate or polar communities, which have repeatedly "started over" after major disturbances such as glaciations. As a result, species diversity may be highest in the tropics simply because there has been more time for speciation to occur in tropical communities than in temperate or polar communities.

Climate is another key factor thought to affect latitudinal gradients of richness and diversity. In terrestrial communities, the two main climatic factors correlated with diversity are sunlight and precipitation, both of which occur at high levels in the tropics. These factors can be considered together by measuring a community's rate of **evapotranspiration**, the evaporation of water from soil and plants. Evapotranspiration, a function of solar radiation, temperature, and water availability, is much higher in hot areas with abundant rainfall than in areas with low temperatures or low precipitation. *Potential evapotranspiration*, a measure of potential water loss that assumes that water is readily available, is determined by the amount of solar radiation and temperature and is highest in regions where both are plentiful. The species richness of plants and animals correlates with both measures, as shown for vertebrates and potential evapotranspiration in **Figure 41.22**.

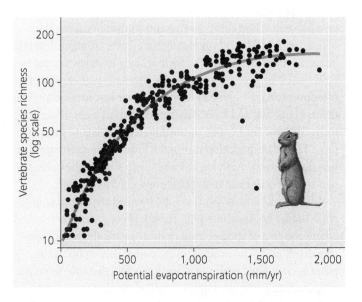

▲ **Figure 41.22 Energy, water, and species richness.** Vertebrate species richness in North America increases predictably with potential evapotranspiration, expressed as rainfall equivalents (mm/yr).

Area Effects

In 1807, naturalist and explorer Alexander von Humboldt described one of the first patterns of species richness to be recognized, the **species-area curve**: All other factors being equal, the larger the geographic area of a community, the more species it has, in part because larger areas offer a greater diversity of habitats and microhabitats. The basic concept of diversity increasing with increasing area applies in many situations, from surveys of ant diversity in New Guinea to studies of plant species richness on islands of different sizes.

Because of their isolation and limited size, islands provide excellent opportunities for studying the biogeographic factors that affect the species diversity of communities. By "islands," we mean not only oceanic islands, but also habitat islands on land, such as lakes, mountain peaks separated by lowlands, or habitat fragments—any patch surrounded by an environment not suitable for the "island" species. American ecologists Robert MacArthur and E. O. Wilson developed a general model of island biogeography, identifying the key determinants of species diversity on an island with a given set of physical characteristics.

Consider a newly formed oceanic island that receives colonizing species from a distant mainland. Two factors that determine the number of species on the island are the rate at which new species immigrate to the island and the rate at which species on the island become extinct. At any given time, an island's immigration and extinction rates are affected by the number of species already present. As the number of species on the island increases, the immigration rate of new species decreases, because any individual reaching the island is less likely to represent a species that is not already present. At the same time, as more species inhabit an island, extinction rates on the island increase because of the greater likelihood of competitive exclusion.

Two physical features of the island further affect immigration and extinction rates: its size and its distance from the mainland. Small islands generally have lower immigration rates because potential colonizers are less likely to reach a small island than a large one. Small islands also have higher extinction rates because they generally contain fewer resources, have less diverse habitats, and have smaller population sizes. Distance from the mainland is also important; a closer island generally has a higher immigration rate and a lower extinction rate than one farther away. Arriving colonists help sustain the presence of a species on a near island and prevent its extinction.

MacArthur and Wilson's model is called the *island equilibrium model* because an equilibrium will eventually be reached where the rate of species immigration equals the rate of species extinction. The number of species at this equilibrium point is correlated with the island's size and distance from the mainland. Like any ecological equilibrium, this species equilibrium is dynamic; immigration and extinction continue, and the exact species composition may change over time.

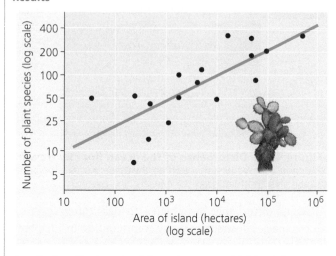

▼ **Figure 41.23** Inquiry

How does species richness relate to area?

Field Study Ecologists Robert MacArthur and E. O. Wilson studied the number of plant species on the Galápagos Islands in relation to the area of the different islands.

Results

Conclusion Plant species richness increases with island size, supporting the island equilibrium model.

Data from R. H. MacArthur and E. O. Wilson, The theory of island biogeography, Princeton University Press, Princeton, NJ (1967).

WHAT IF? Five islands in this study ranging in area from about 40 ha to 10,000 ha each contained about 50 plant species. What does such variation tell you about the simple assumptions of the island equilibrium model?

MacArthur and Wilson's studies of the diversity of plants and animals on island chains support the prediction that species richness increases with island size, in keeping with the island equilibrium model **(Figure 41.23)**. Species counts also fit the prediction that the number of species decreases with increasing remoteness of the island.

Over long periods, disturbances such as storms, adaptive evolutionary changes, and speciation generally alter the species composition and community structure on islands. Nonetheless, the island equilibrium model is widely applied in ecology. Conservation biologists in particular use it when designing habitat reserves or establishing a starting point for predicting the effects of habitat loss on species diversity.

CONCEPT CHECK 41.4

1. Describe two hypotheses that explain why species diversity is greater in tropical regions than in temperate and polar regions.
2. Describe how an island's size and distance from the mainland affect the island's species richness.
3. **WHAT IF?** Based on MacArthur and Wilson's island equilibrium model, how would you expect the richness of birds on islands to compare with the richness of snakes and lizards? Explain.

For suggested answers, see Appendix A.

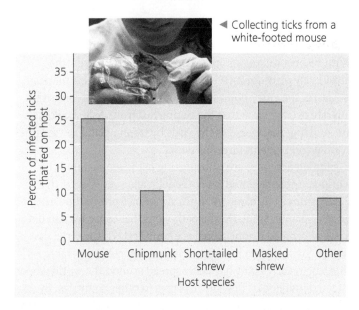

Collecting ticks from a white-footed mouse

▲ **Figure 41.24 Unexpected hosts of the Lyme disease pathogen.** A combination of ecological data and genetic analyses enabled scientists to show that more than half of ticks carrying the Lyme pathogen became infected by feeding on the short-tailed shrew (*Blarina brevicauda*) or the masked shrew (*Sorex cinereus*).

MAKE CONNECTIONS *Concept 21.1 describes genetic variation between populations. How might genetic variation between shrew populations in different locations affect the number of infected ticks?*

Pathogens alter community structure locally and globally

Now that we have examined several important factors that structure biological communities, we will finish the chapter by examining community interactions involving **pathogens**—disease-causing microorganisms and viruses. Scientists have only recently come to appreciate how universal the effects of pathogens are in structuring ecological communities.

Effects on Community Structure

Pathogens produce especially clear effects on community structure when they are introduced into new habitats. Coral reef communities, for example, are increasingly susceptible to the influence of newly discovered pathogens. White-band disease, caused by an unknown pathogen, has resulted in dramatic changes in the structure and composition of Caribbean reefs. The disease kills corals by causing their tissue to slough off in a band from the base to the tip of the branches. Because of the disease, staghorn coral (*Acropora cervicornis*) has virtually disappeared from the Caribbean since the 1980s. Populations of elkhorn coral (*Acropora palmata*) have also been decimated. Such corals provide key habitat for lobsters as well as snappers and other fish species. When the corals die, they are quickly overgrown by algae. Surgeonfish and other herbivores that feed on algae come to dominate the fish community. Eventually, the corals topple because of damage from storms and other disturbances. The complex, three-dimensional structure of the reef disappears, and diversity plummets.

Pathogens also influence community structure in terrestrial ecosystems. In the forests and savannas of California, trees of several species are dying from sudden oak death (SOD). This recently discovered disease is caused by the protist *Phytophthora ramorum* (see Concept 25.4). SOD was first described in California in 1995, when hikers noticed trees dying around San Francisco Bay. By 2014, it had spread more than 1,000 km, from the central California coast to southern Oregon, and it had killed more than a million oaks and other trees. The loss of the oaks has led to the decreased abundance of at least five bird species, including the acorn woodpecker and the oak titmouse, that rely on the oaks for food and habitat. Although there is currently no cure for SOD, scientists recently sequenced the genome of *P. ramorum* in hopes of finding a way to fight the pathogen.

Community Ecology and Zoonotic Diseases

Three-quarters of emerging human diseases and many of the most devastating diseases are caused by **zoonotic pathogens**—those that are transferred to humans from other animals, either through direct contact with an infected animal or by means of an intermediate species, called a **vector**. The

vectors that spread zoonotic diseases are often parasites, including ticks, lice, and mosquitoes.

Identifying the community of hosts and vectors for a pathogen can help prevent illnesses such as Lyme disease, which is spread by ticks. For years, scientists thought that the primary host for the Lyme pathogen was the white-footed mouse because mice are heavily parasitized by young ticks. When researchers vaccinated mice against Lyme disease and released them into the wild, however, the number of infected ticks hardly changed. Further investigation in New York revealed that two inconspicuous shrew species were the hosts of more than half the infected ticks collected in the field **(Figure 41.24)**. Identifying the dominant hosts for a pathogen provides information that may be used to control the hosts most responsible for spreading diseases.

Ecologists also use their knowledge of community interactions to track the spread of zoonotic diseases. One example, avian flu, is caused by highly contagious viruses transmitted through the saliva and feces of birds (see Concept 17.3). Most of these viruses affect wild birds mildly, but they often cause stronger symptoms in domesticated birds, the most common source of human infections. Since 2003, one particular viral strain, called H5N1, has killed hundreds of millions of poultry and more than 300 people.

Control programs that quarantine domestic birds or monitor their transport may be ineffective if avian flu spreads naturally through the movements of wild birds. From 2003 to 2006, the H5N1 strain spread rapidly from southeast Asia into Europe and Africa. By 2015, the virus had not appeared in Australia or South America, but one human case had occurred in North America; this took place in Canada when a person returning from China became ill with the virus and later died. With respect to the possible spread of H5N1 by birds, the most likely place for infected wild birds to enter the Americas is Alaska, the entry point for ducks, geese, and shorebirds that migrate every year across the Bering Sea from Asia. Ecologists are studying the spread of the virus by trapping and testing migrating and resident birds in Alaska.

Human activities are transporting pathogens around the world at unprecedented rates. Genetic analyses suggest that *P. ramorum* likely came to North America from Europe in nursery plants. Similarly, the pathogens that cause human diseases are spread by our global economy. H1N1, the virus that causes "swine flu" in humans, was first detected in Veracruz, Mexico, in early 2009. It quickly spread around the world when infected individuals flew on airplanes to other countries. By 2010, this flu outbreak had a confirmed death toll of more than 18,000 people. The actual number may have been significantly

higher since many people who died with flu-like symptoms were not tested for H1N1.

While our emphasis here has been on community ecology, pathogens are also greatly influenced by changes in the physical environment. To control pathogens and the diseases they cause, scientists need an ecosystem perspective—an intimate knowledge of how the pathogens interact with other species and with all aspects of their environment. Ecosystems are the subject of Chapter 42.

CONCEPT CHECK 41.5

1. What are pathogens?
2. **WHAT IF?** Rabies, a viral disease in mammals, is not currently found in the British Isles. If you were in charge of disease control there, what practical approaches might you employ to keep the rabies virus from reaching these islands?

For suggested answers, see Appendix A.

---

41 Chapter Review

Go to **MasteringBiology®** for Assignments, the eText, and the Study Area with Animations, Activities, Vocab Self-Quiz, and Practice Tests.

SUMMARY OF KEY CONCEPTS

VOCAB SELF-QUIZ

goo.gl/gbai8v

CONCEPT 41.1

Interactions within a community may help, harm, or have no effect on the species involved (pp. 868–873)

- As shown in the table, ecological interactions can be grouped into three broad categories: competition, exploitation, and positive interactions.

Interaction	Description
Competition (−/−)	Two or more species compete for a resource that is in short supply.
Exploitation (+/−)	One species benefits by feeding upon the other species, which is harmed. Exploitation includes:
Predation	One species, the predator, kills and eats the other, the prey.
Herbivory	An herbivore eats part of a plant or alga.
Parasitism	The **parasite** derives its nourishment from a second organism, its **host**, which is harmed.
Positive interactions (+/+ or +/0)	One species benefits, while the other species benefits or is not harmed. Positive interactions include:
Mutualism (+/+)	Both species benefit from the interaction.
Commensalism (+/0)	One species benefits, while the other is not affected.

- **Competitive exclusion** states that two species competing for the same resource cannot coexist permanently in the same place. **Resource partitioning** is the differentiation of **ecological niches** that enables species to coexist in a community.

? *For each interaction listed in the table above, give an example of a pair of species that exhibit the interaction.*

CONCEPT 41.2

Diversity and trophic structure characterize biological communities (pp. 873–878)

- **Species diversity** is affected by both the number of species in a community—its **species richness**—and their **relative abundance**. A community with similar abundances of species is more diverse than one in which one or two species are abundant and the remainder are rare.
- **Trophic structure** is a key factor in community dynamics. **Food chains** link the trophic levels from producers to top carnivores. Branching food chains and complex trophic interactions form **food webs**.
- **Dominant species** are the most abundant species in a community. **Keystone species** are usually less abundant species that exert a disproportionate influence on community structure. **Ecosystem engineers** influence community structure through their effects on the physical environment.
- The **bottom-up model** proposes a unidirectional influence from lower to higher trophic levels, in which nutrients and other abiotic factors primarily determine community structure. The **top-down model** proposes that control of each trophic level comes from the trophic level above, with the result that predators control herbivores, which in turn control primary producers.

? *Based on indexes such as Shannon diversity, is a community of higher species richness always more diverse than a community of lower species richness? Explain.*

CONCEPT 41.3

Disturbance influences species diversity and composition (pp. 878–881)

- Increasing evidence suggests that **disturbance** and lack of equilibrium, rather than stability and equilibrium, are the norm for most communities. According to the **intermediate disturbance hypothesis**, moderate levels of disturbance can foster higher species diversity than can low or high levels of disturbance.

- **Ecological succession** is the sequence of community and ecosystem changes after a disturbance. **Primary succession** occurs where no soil exists when succession begins; **secondary succession** begins in an area where soil remains after a disturbance.
- Humans are the most widespread agents of disturbance, and their effects on communities often reduce species diversity.

? *Is the disturbance pictured in Figure 41.21 more likely to initiate primary or secondary succession? Explain.*

CONCEPT 41.4

Biogeographic factors affect community diversity (pp. 881–882)

- Species richness generally declines along a latitudinal gradient from the tropics to the poles. Climate influences the diversity gradient through energy (heat and light) and water. The greater age of tropical environments also may contribute to their greater species richness.
- Species richness is directly related to a community's geographic size, a principle formalized in the **species-area curve**. The island equilibrium model maintains that species richness on an ecological island reaches an equilibrium where new immigrations are balanced by extinctions.

? *How have periods of glaciation influenced latitudinal patterns of diversity?*

CONCEPT 41.5

Pathogens alter community structure locally and globally (pp. 883–884)

- Recent work has highlighted the role that **pathogens** play in structuring terrestrial and marine communities.
- **Zoonotic pathogens** are transferred from other animals to humans. Community ecology provides the framework for identifying key species interactions associated with such pathogens and for helping us track and control their spread.

? *Suppose a pathogen attacks a keystone species. Explain how this could alter the structure of the community.*

TEST YOUR UNDERSTANDING

PRACTICE TEST

goo.gl/CRZjvS

Level 1: Knowledge/Comprehension

1. The feeding relationships among the species in a community determine the community's
   (A) secondary succession.
   (B) ecological niche.
   (C) species richness.
   (D) trophic structure.

2. Based on the intermediate disturbance hypothesis, a community's species diversity is increased by
   (A) frequent massive disturbance.
   (B) stable conditions with no disturbance.
   (C) moderate levels of disturbance.
   (D) human intervention to eliminate disturbance.

Level 2: Application/Analysis

3. Which of the following could qualify as a top-down control on a grassland community?
   (A) limitation of plant biomass by rainfall amount
   (B) influence of temperature on competition among plants
   (C) influence of soil nutrients on the abundance of grasses versus wildflowers
   (D) effect of grazing intensity by bison on plant species diversity

4. Community 1 contains 100 individuals distributed among four species: 5A, 5B, 85C, and 5D. Community 2 contains 100 individuals distributed among three species: 30A, 40B, and 30C. Calculate the Shannon diversity index (H) for each community. Identify which community is more diverse.

Level 3: Synthesis/Evaluation

5. **DRAW IT** In the Chesapeake Bay, the blue crab is an omnivore, eating eelgrass and other primary producers as well as clams. It is also a cannibal. In turn, the crabs are eaten by humans and by the endangered Kemp's Ridley sea turtle. Based on this information, draw a food web that includes the blue crab. Assuming that the top-down model holds for this system, describe what would happen to the abundance of eelgrass if humans stopped eating blue crabs.

6. **SCIENTIFIC INQUIRY**
   An ecologist studying plants in the desert performed the following experiment. She staked out two identical plots, containing sagebrush plants and small annual wildflowers. She found the same five wildflower species in roughly equal numbers on both plots. She then enclosed one of the plots with a fence to keep out kangaroo rats, the most common grain-eaters of the area. After two years, four of the wildflower species were no longer present in the fenced plot, but one species had increased drastically. The control plot had not changed in species diversity. Using the principles of community ecology, propose a hypothesis to explain her results. What additional evidence would support your hypothesis?

7. **FOCUS ON EVOLUTION**
   Explain why adaptations of particular organisms to interspecific competition may not necessarily represent instances of character displacement. What would a researcher have to demonstrate about two competing species to make a convincing case for character displacement?

8. **FOCUS ON INFORMATION**
   In Batesian mimicry, a palatable species gains protection by mimicking an unpalatable one. Imagine that individuals of a palatable, brightly colored fly species are blown to three remote islands. The first island has no predators of that species; the second has predators but no similarly colored, unpalatable species; and the third has both predators and a similarly colored, unpalatable species. In a short essay (100–150 words), predict what might happen to the coloration of the palatable species on each island over time if coloration is a genetically controlled trait. Explain your predictions.

9. **SYNTHESIZE YOUR KNOWLEDGE**

Describe two types of interspecific interactions that appear to be occurring between the three species shown in this photo. What morphological adaptation can be seen in the species that is at the highest trophic level in this scene?

For selected answers, see Appendix A.

42 Ecosystems and Energy

KEY CONCEPTS

42.1 Physical laws govern energy flow and chemical cycling in ecosystems

42.2 Energy and other limiting factors control primary production in ecosystems

42.3 Energy transfer between trophic levels is typically only 10% efficient

42.4 Biological and geochemical processes cycle nutrients and water in ecosystems

42.5 Restoration ecologists return degraded ecosystems to a more natural state

▲ **Figure 42.1** How can a fox transform a grassland into tundra?

Transformed to Tundra

The arctic fox (*Vulpes lagopus*) is a predator native to arctic regions of North America, Europe, and Asia **(Figure 42.1)**. Valued for its fur, it was introduced onto hundreds of islands between Alaska and Russia a century ago in an effort to establish populations that could be easily harvested. The introduction had a surprising effect—it transformed many habitats on the islands from grassland to tundra.

How did this remarkable change come about? The foxes fed on seabirds, decreasing their density almost 100-fold compared to that on fox-free islands. Fewer seabirds meant less bird guano, the primary source of nutrients for plants on the islands. The reduction in nutrient availability in turn favored slower-growing forbs and shrubs typical of tundra instead of grasses and sedges, which require more nutrients. To test this explanation, researchers added fertilizer to plots of tundra on one of the fox-infested islands in 2001. Three years later, the fertilized plots had turned back into grassland.

Each of these islands and the community of organisms on it make up an **ecosystem**, the sum of all the organisms living in a given area and the abiotic factors with which they interact. An ecosystem can encompass a large area, such as a lake, forest, or island, or a microcosm, such as a small desert spring or the space under a fallen log **(Figure 42.2)**. As with populations and communities, the boundaries of ecosystems are not always discrete. Many ecologists view the entire biosphere as a global ecosystem, a composite of all the local ecosystems on Earth.

Regardless of an ecosystem's size, two key ecosystem processes cannot be fully described by population or community phenomena: energy flow and chemical cycling. Energy enters most ecosystems as sunlight. It is converted to chemical energy by autotrophs, passed to heterotrophs in the organic compounds of food, and dissipated as heat. Chemical elements, such as carbon and nitrogen, are cycled among abiotic and biotic components of the ecosystem. Photosynthetic and chemosynthetic organisms take up these elements in inorganic form from the air, soil, and water and incorporate them into

▲ **Figure 42.2 A desert spring ecosystem.**

their biomass, some of which is consumed by animals. The elements are returned in inorganic form to the environment by the metabolism of plants and animals, and by bacteria and fungi that break down organic wastes and dead organisms.

Both energy and chemical elements are transformed in ecosystems through photosynthesis and feeding relationships. But unlike chemicals, energy cannot be recycled. An ecosystem must be powered by a continuous influx of energy from an external source—in most cases, the sun. As we'll see, energy flows through ecosystems, whereas chemicals cycle within them.

Resources critical to human survival and welfare—from the food we eat to the oxygen we breathe—are products of ecosystem processes. In this chapter, we'll explore the dynamics of energy flow and chemical cycling, emphasizing the results of ecosystem experiments. We'll also consider how human activities have affected energy flow and chemical cycling. Finally, we'll examine the science of restoration ecology, which focuses on returning degraded ecosystems to a more natural state.

CONCEPT 42.1

Physical laws govern energy flow and chemical cycling in ecosystems

Cells transform energy and matter, subject to the laws of thermodynamics (see Concept 6.1). Cell biologists study these transformations within organelles and cells and measure the amounts of energy and matter that cross the cell's boundaries. Ecosystem ecologists do the same thing, except in their case the "cell" is a complete ecosystem. By studying how populations change in size and by grouping the species in a community into trophic levels of feeding relationships (see Concept 41.2), ecologists can follow the transformations of energy in an ecosystem and map the movements of chemical elements.

Conservation of Energy

Because ecosystem ecologists study the interactions of organisms with the physical environment, many ecosystem

approaches are based on laws of physics and chemistry. The first law of thermodynamics states that energy cannot be created or destroyed but only transferred or transformed (see Concept 6.1). Plants and other photosynthetic organisms convert solar energy to chemical energy, but the total amount of energy does not change: The energy stored in organic molecules must equal the total solar energy intercepted by the plant minus the amounts reflected and dissipated as heat. Ecosystem ecologists measure transfers within and across ecosystems to understand how many organisms a habitat can support and the amount of food humans can harvest from a site.

One implication of the second law of thermodynamics, which states that every exchange of energy increases the entropy of the universe, is that energy conversions are inefficient. Some energy is always lost as heat. As a result, each unit of energy that enters an ecosystem eventually exits as heat. Thus, energy flows through ecosystems—it does not cycle within them for long periods of time. Because energy flowing through ecosystems is ultimately lost as heat, most ecosystems would vanish if the sun were not continuously providing energy to Earth.

Conservation of Mass

Matter, like energy, cannot be created or destroyed. This **law of conservation of mass** is as important for ecosystems as are the laws of thermodynamics. Because mass is conserved, we can determine how much of a chemical element cycles within an ecosystem or is gained or lost by that ecosystem over time.

Unlike energy, chemical elements are continually recycled within ecosystems. For example, a carbon atom in CO_2 is released from the soil by a decomposer, taken up by a blade of grass through photosynthesis, consumed by a grazing animal, and returned to the soil in the animal's waste. This process of chemical cycling is a key feature of how ecosystems work.

Although few elements are gained or lost from Earth, they can be gained by or lost from a particular ecosystem. In a forest, most mineral nutrients—the essential elements that plants obtain from soil—typically enter as dust or as solutes dissolved in rainwater or leached from rocks in the ground. Nitrogen is also supplied through the biological process of nitrogen fixation (see Figure 29.12). In terms of losses, some elements return to the atmosphere as gases, and others are carried out of the ecosystem by moving water or by wind. Like organisms, ecosystems are open systems, absorbing energy and mass and releasing heat and waste products.

In nature, most gains and losses to ecosystems are small compared to the amounts recycled within them. Still, the balance between inputs and outputs determines whether an ecosystem is a source or a sink for a given element. If a mineral nutrient's outputs exceed its inputs, it will eventually limit production in that system. Human activities often change the balance of inputs and outputs considerably, as we'll see later in this chapter and in Chapter 43.

Energy, Mass, and Trophic Levels

Ecologists group species into trophic levels based on their main source of nutrition and energy (see Concept 41.2). The trophic level that ultimately supports all others consists of autotrophs, also called the **primary producers** of the ecosystem. Most autotrophs are photosynthetic organisms that use light energy to synthesize sugars and other organic compounds, which they use as fuel for cellular respiration and as building material for growth. The most common autotrophs are plants, algae, and photosynthetic prokaryotes, although chemosynthetic prokaryotes are the primary producers in ecosystems such as deep-sea hydrothermal vents (see Figure 40.11) and places deep underground or beneath ice.

Organisms in trophic levels above the primary producers are heterotrophs, which depend directly or indirectly on the primary producers for their source of energy. Herbivores, which eat plants and other primary producers, are **primary consumers**. Carnivores that eat herbivores are **secondary consumers**, and carnivores that eat other carnivores are **tertiary consumers**.

Another group of heterotrophs is the **detritivores**, or **decomposers**, terms used synonymously in this text to refer to consumers that get their energy from detritus. **Detritus** is nonliving organic material, such as the remains of dead organisms, feces, fallen leaves, and wood. Although some animals (such as earthworms) feed on detritus, the most important detritivores are prokaryotes and fungi (**Figure 42.3**). These organisms secrete enzymes that digest organic material; they then absorb the breakdown products. Many detritivores are in turn eaten by secondary and tertiary consumers. In a forest, for instance, birds

▲ **Figure 42.3 Fungi decomposing a dead tree.**

eat earthworms that have been feeding on leaf litter and its associated prokaryotes and fungi. As a result, chemicals originally synthesized by plants pass from plants to leaf litter to detritivores to birds.

Detritivores also play a critical role in recycling chemical elements to primary producers. Detritivores convert organic matter from all trophic levels to inorganic compounds usable by primary producers. When the detritivores excrete waste products or die, those inorganic compounds are returned

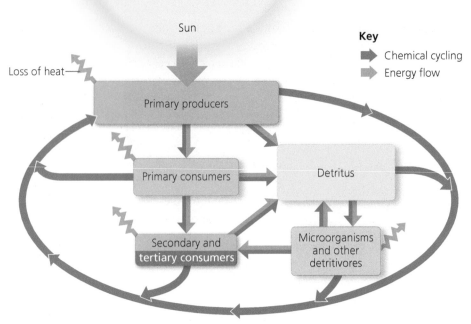

▲ **Figure 42.4 An overview of energy and nutrient dynamics in an ecosystem.** Energy enters, flows through, and exits an ecosystem, whereas chemical nutrients cycle within it. Energy (dark orange arrows) entering from the sun as radiation is transferred as chemical energy through the food web; each of these units of energy ultimately exits as heat radiated into space. Most transfers of nutrients (blue arrows) through the food web lead eventually to detritus; the nutrients then cycle back to the primary producers.

to the soil. Producers can then recycle these elements into organic compounds. If decomposition stopped, life as we know it would cease as detritus piled up and the supply of ingredients needed to synthesize organic matter was exhausted. **Figure 42.4** summarizes the trophic relationships in an ecosystem.

CONCEPT CHECK 42.1

1. Why is the transfer of energy in an ecosystem referred to as energy flow, not energy cycling?
2. **WHAT IF?** You are studying nitrogen cycling on the Serengeti Plain in Africa. During your experiment, a herd of migrating wildebeests grazes through your study plot. What would you need to know to measure their effect on nitrogen balance in the plot?
3. **MAKE CONNECTIONS** Use the second law of thermodynamics to explain why an ecosystem's energy supply must be continually replenished. (See Concept 6.1.)

For suggested answers, see Appendix A.

CONCEPT 42.2

Energy and other limiting factors control primary production in ecosystems

The theme of energy transfer underlies all biological interactions (see Concept 1.1). In most ecosystems, the amount of light energy converted to chemical energy—in the form of organic compounds—by autotrophs during a given time period is the ecosystem's **primary production**. These photosynthetic products are the starting point for most studies of ecosystem metabolism and energy flow. In ecosystems where the primary producers are chemoautotrophs, the initial energy input is chemical, and the initial products are the organic compounds synthesized by the microorganisms.

Ecosystem Energy Budgets

In most ecosystems, primary producers use light energy to synthesize energy-rich organic molecules, and consumers acquire their organic fuels secondhand (or even third- or fourth-hand) through food webs (see Figure 41.14). Therefore, the total amount of photosynthetic production sets the spending limit for the entire ecosystem's energy budget.

The Global Energy Budget

Each day, Earth's atmosphere is bombarded by a total of about 10^{22} joules of solar radiation (1 J = 0.239 cal). This is enough energy to supply the demands of the entire human population for 19 years at 2013 energy consumption levels. The intensity of the solar energy striking Earth varies with latitude, with the tropics receiving the greatest input (see Figure 40.3). About 50% of incoming solar radiation is absorbed, scattered, or reflected by clouds and dust in the atmosphere. The amount of solar radiation that ultimately reaches Earth's surface limits the possible photosynthetic output of ecosystems.

Only a small fraction of the sunlight that reaches Earth's surface is actually used in photosynthesis. Much of the radiation strikes materials that don't photosynthesize, such as ice and soil. Of the radiation that does reach photosynthetic organisms, only certain wavelengths are absorbed by photosynthetic pigments (see Figure 8.9); the rest is transmitted, reflected, or lost as heat. As a result, only about 1% of the visible light that strikes photosynthetic organisms is converted to chemical energy. Nevertheless, Earth's primary producers create about 150 billion metric tons (1.50×10^{14} kg) of organic material each year.

Gross and Net Production

Total primary production in an ecosystem is known as that ecosystem's **gross primary production (GPP)**—the amount of energy from light (or chemicals, in chemoautotrophic systems) converted to the chemical energy of organic molecules per unit time. Not all of this production is stored as organic material in the primary producers because they use some of the molecules as fuel in their own cellular respiration. **Net primary production (NPP)** is equal to gross primary production minus the energy used by the primary producers for their "autotrophic respiration" (R_a):

$$NPP = GPP - R_a$$

On average, NPP is about one-half of GPP. To ecologists, NPP is the key measurement because it represents the storage of

chemical energy that will be available to consumers in the ecosystem.

Net primary production can be expressed as energy per unit area per unit time [$J/(m^2 \cdot yr)$] or as biomass (mass of vegetation) added per unit area per unit time [$g/(m^2 \cdot yr)$]. (Note that biomass is usually expressed in terms of the dry mass of organic material.) An ecosystem's NPP should not be confused with the total biomass of photosynthetic autotrophs present, a measure called the *standing crop*. The net primary production is the amount of *new* biomass added in a given period of time. Although a forest has a large standing crop, its NPP may actually be less than that of some grasslands; grasslands do not accumulate as much biomass as forests because animals consume the plants rapidly and because grasses and herbs decompose more quickly than trees do.

Satellites provide a powerful tool for studying global patterns of primary production (**Figure 42.5**). Images produced from satellite data show that different ecosystems vary considerably in their NPP. Tropical rain forests are among the

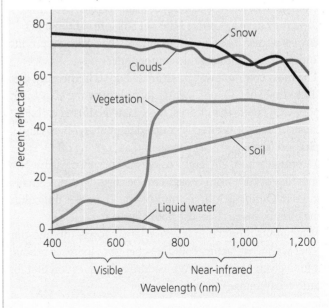

▼ **Figure 42.5** **Research Method**

Determining Primary Production with Satellites

Application Because chlorophyll captures visible light, photosynthetic organisms absorb more light at visible wavelengths (about 380–750 nm) than at near-infrared wavelengths (750–1,100 nm) (see Figure 8.6). Scientists use this difference in absorption to estimate the rate of photosynthesis in different regions of the globe using satellites.

Technique Most satellites determine what they "see" by comparing the ratios of wavelengths reflected back to them. Vegetation reflects much more near-infrared radiation than visible radiation, producing a reflectance pattern very different from that of snow, clouds, soil, and liquid water.

Results Scientists use the satellite data to help produce maps of primary production like the one in Figure 42.6.

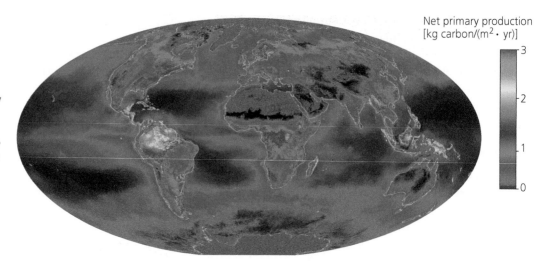

► **Figure 42.6 Global net primary production.** This map is based on satellite-collected data, such as amount of sunlight absorbed by vegetation. Note that tropical land areas have the highest rates of production (yellow and red on the map).

? *Does this map accurately reflect the importance of some highly productive habitats, such as wetlands, coral reefs, and coastal zones? Explain.*

Net primary production [kg carbon/($m^2 \cdot$ yr)]

most productive terrestrial ecosystems and contribute a large portion of the planet's NPP. Estuaries and coral reefs also have very high NPP, but their contribution to the global total is smaller because these ecosystems cover only about one-tenth the area covered by tropical rain forests. In contrast, while the open oceans are relatively unproductive **(Figure 42.6)**, their vast size means that together they contribute as much global NPP as terrestrial systems do.

Whereas NPP can be stated as the amount of new biomass added by producers in a given period of time, **net ecosystem production (NEP)** is a measure of the *total biomass accumulation* during that time. NEP is defined as gross primary production minus the total respiration of all organisms in the system (R_T)—not just primary producers, as for the calculation of NPP, but decomposers and other heterotrophs as well:

$$NEP = GPP - R_T$$

NEP is useful to ecologists because its value determines whether an ecosystem is gaining or losing carbon over time. A forest may have a positive NPP but still lose carbon if heterotrophs release it as CO_2 more quickly than primary producers incorporate it into organic compounds.

The most common way to estimate NEP is to measure the net flux (flow) of CO_2 or O_2 entering or leaving the ecosystem. If more CO_2 enters than leaves, the system is storing carbon. Because O_2 release is directly coupled to photosynthesis and respiration (see Figure 7.2), a system that is giving off O_2 is also storing carbon. On land, ecologists typically measure only the net flux of CO_2 from ecosystems because detecting small changes in O_2 flux in a large atmospheric O_2 pool is difficult. In the oceans, researchers use both approaches.

What limits production in ecosystems? To ask this question another way, what factors could we change to increase production for a given ecosystem? We'll address this question first for aquatic ecosystems.

Primary Production in Aquatic Ecosystems

In aquatic (marine and freshwater) ecosystems, both light and nutrients are important in controlling primary production.

Light Limitation

Because solar radiation drives photosynthesis, you would expect light to be a key variable in controlling primary production in oceans. Indeed, the depth of light penetration affects primary production throughout the photic zone of an ocean or lake (see Figure 40.10). About half of the solar radiation is absorbed in the first 15 m of water. Even in "clear" water, only 5–10% of the radiation may reach a depth of 75 m.

If light were the main variable limiting primary production in the ocean, you would expect production to increase along a gradient from the poles toward the equator, which receives the greatest intensity of light. However, you can see in Figure 42.6 that there is no such gradient. Another factor must strongly influence primary production in the ocean.

Nutrient Limitation

More than light, nutrients limit primary production in most oceans and lakes. A **limiting nutrient** is the element that must be added for production to increase. The nutrients that most often limit marine production are nitrogen and phosphorus. Concentrations of these nutrients are typically low in the photic zone because they are rapidly taken up by phytoplankton and because detritus tends to sink.

For example, as detailed in **Figure 42.7**, nutrient enrichment experiments found that nitrogen was limiting phytoplankton growth off the south shore of Long Island, New York. One practical application of this work is in preventing algal "blooms" caused by excess nitrogen runoff that fertilizes the phytoplankton. Prior to this research, phosphate contamination was thought to cause many such blooms in the ocean, but eliminating phosphates alone may not help unless nitrogen pollution is also controlled.

The macronutrients nitrogen and phosphorus are not the only nutrients that limit aquatic production. Several large areas of the ocean have low phytoplankton densities despite relatively high nitrogen concentrations. The Sargasso Sea, a subtropical region of the Atlantic Ocean, has some of the clearest water in the world because of its low phytoplankton

▼ Figure 42.7 Inquiry

Which nutrient limits phytoplankton production along the coast of Long Island?

Experiment Pollution from duck farms concentrated near Moriches Bay adds both nitrogen and phosphorus to the coastal water off Long Island, New York. To determine which nutrient limits phytoplankton growth in this area, John Ryther and William Dunstan, of the Woods Hole Oceanographic Institution, cultured the phytoplankton *Nannochloris atomus* with water collected from several sites, identified as A through G. They added either ammonium (NH_4^+) or phosphate (PO_4^{3-}) to some of the cultures.

Results The addition of ammonium caused heavy phytoplankton growth in the cultures, but the addition of phosphate did not.

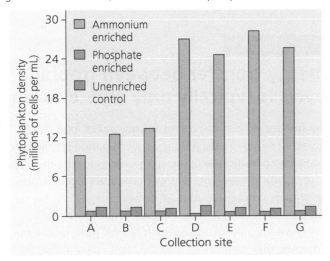

Conclusion The researchers concluded that nitrogen is the nutrient that limits phytoplankton growth in this ecosystem because adding phosphorus did not increase *Nannochloris* growth, whereas adding nitrogen increased phytoplankton density dramatically.

Data from J. H. Ryther and W. M. Dunstan, Nitrogen, phosphorus, and eutrophication in the coastal marine environment, *Science* 171:1008–1013 (1971).

WHAT IF? Predict how the results would change if water samples were drawn from areas where new duck farms had greatly increased the amount of pollution in the water. Explain.

Table 42.1 Nutrient Enrichment Experiment for Sargasso Sea Samples

Nutrients Added to Experimental Culture	Relative Uptake of ^{14}C by Cultures*
None (controls)	1.00
Nitrogen (N) + phosphorus (P) only	1.10
N + P + metals, excluding iron (Fe)	1.08
N + P + metals, including Fe	12.90
N + P + Fe	12.00

*^{14}C uptake by cultures measures primary production.

Data from D. W. Menzel and J. H. Ryther, Nutrients limiting the production of phytoplankton in the Sargasso Sea, with special reference to iron, *Deep Sea Research* 7:276–281 (1961).

INTERPRET THE DATA *The element molybdenum (Mo) is another micronutrient that can limit primary production in the oceans. If the researchers found the following results for additions of Mo, what would you conclude about its relative importance for growth?*

N + P + Mo	6.0
N + P + Fe + Mo	72.0

and in the coastal waters off Peru, California, and parts of western Africa.

Nutrient limitation is also common in freshwater lakes. During the 1970s, scientists showed that sewage and fertilizer runoff from farms and lawns adds considerable nutrients to lakes, promoting the growth of primary producers. When the primary producers die, detritivores decompose them, depleting the water of much or all of its oxygen. The ecological impacts of this process, known as **eutrophication** (from the Greek *eutrophos*, well nourished), include the loss of many fish species from the lakes (see Figure 40.11).

To control eutrophication, scientists need to know which nutrient is responsible. While nitrogen rarely limits primary production in lakes, whole-lake experiments showed that phosphorus availability limited cyanobacterial growth. This and other ecological research led to the use of phosphate-free detergents and other water quality reforms.

Primary Production in Terrestrial Ecosystems

At regional and global scales, temperature and moisture are the main factors controlling primary production in terrestrial ecosystems. Tropical rain forests, with their warm, wet conditions that promote plant growth, are the most productive terrestrial ecosystems (see Figure 42.6). In contrast, low-productivity systems are generally hot and dry, like many deserts, or cold and dry, like arctic tundra. Between these extremes lie the temperate forest and grassland ecosystems, with moderate climates and intermediate productivity.

The climate variables of moisture and temperature are very useful for predicting NPP in terrestrial ecosystems. Primary production is greater in wetter ecosystems, as shown for the

density. Nutrient enrichment experiments have revealed that the availability of the micronutrient iron limits primary production there **(Table 42.1)**. Windblown dust from land supplies most of the iron to the oceans but is relatively scarce in the Sargasso Sea and certain other regions compared to the oceans as a whole.

Areas of *upwelling*, where deep, nutrient-rich waters circulate to the ocean surface, have exceptionally high primary production. This fact supports the hypothesis that nutrient availability determines marine primary production. Because upwelling stimulates growth of the phytoplankton that form the base of marine food webs, upwelling areas typically host highly productive, diverse ecosystems and are prime fishing locations. The largest areas of upwelling occur in the Southern Ocean (also called the Antarctic Ocean), along the equator,

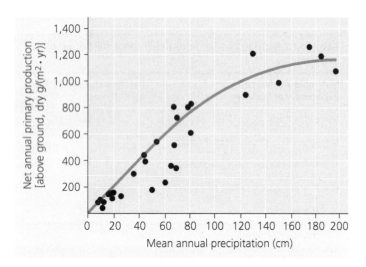

▲ **Figure 42.8 A global relationship between net primary production and mean annual precipitation for terrestrial ecosystems.**

plot of NPP and annual precipitation in **Figure 42.8**. Along with mean annual precipitation, a second useful predictor is *evapotranspiration*, the total amount of water transpired by plants and evaporated from a landscape. Evapotranspiration increases with the temperature and amount of solar energy available to drive evaporation and transpiration.

Nutrient Limitations and Adaptations That Reduce Them

EVOLUTION   Soil nutrients also limit primary production in terrestrial ecosystems. As in aquatic systems, nitrogen and phosphorus are the nutrients that most commonly limit terrestrial production. Globally, nitrogen limits plant growth most. Phosphorus limitations are common in older soils where phosphate molecules have been leached away by water, such as in many tropical ecosystems. Phosphorus availability is also often low in soils of deserts and other ecosystems with a basic pH, where some phosphorus precipitates and becomes unavailable to plants. Adding a nonlimiting nutrient, even one that is scarce, will not stimulate production. Conversely, adding more of the limiting nutrient will increase production until some other nutrient becomes limiting.

Various adaptations have evolved in plants that can increase their uptake of limiting nutrients. One important adaptation is the symbiosis between plant roots and nitrogen-fixing bacteria. Another is the mycorrhizal association between plant roots and fungi that supply phosphorus and other limiting elements to plants (see Concept 29.4). Plant roots also have hairs and other anatomical features that increase their surface area and, hence, the area of soil in contact with the roots (see Figure 28.4). Many plants release enzymes and other substances into the soil that increase the availability of limiting nutrients; such substances include phosphatases, which cleave a phosphate group from larger molecules, and certain molecules (called chelating agents) that make micronutrients such as iron more soluble in the soil.

Studies relating nutrients to terrestrial primary production have practical applications in agriculture. Farmers maximize

their crop yields by using fertilizers with the right balance of nutrients for the local soil and type of crop. This knowledge of limiting nutrients helps feed billions of people.

CONCEPT CHECK 42.2

1. Why is only a small portion of the solar energy that strikes Earth's atmosphere stored by primary producers?
2. How can ecologists experimentally determine the factor that limits primary production in an ecosystem?
3. MAKE CONNECTIONS   Explain how nitrogen and phosphorus, the nutrients that most often limit primary production, are necessary for the Calvin cycle to function in photosynthesis (see Concept 8.3).

For suggested answers, see Appendix A.

CONCEPT 42.3

Energy transfer between trophic levels is typically only 10% efficient

The amount of chemical energy in consumers' food that is converted to new biomass during a given period is called the **secondary production** of the ecosystem. Consider the transfer of organic matter from primary producers to herbivores, the primary consumers. In most ecosystems, herbivores eat only a small fraction of plant material produced; globally, they consume only about one-sixth of total plant production. Moreover, they cannot digest all the plant material that they *do* eat, as anyone who has walked through a field where cattle have been grazing will attest. Most of an ecosystem's production is eventually consumed by detritivores. Next, we'll look at how such processes affect the transfer of energy in ecosystems.

Production Efficiency

We'll begin by examining secondary production in one organism—a caterpillar. When a caterpillar feeds on a leaf, only about 33 J out of 200 J, or one-sixth of the potential energy in the leaf, is used for secondary production, or growth **(Figure 42.9)**. The caterpillar stores some of the remaining energy in organic compounds that will be used for cellular respiration and passes the rest in its feces. The energy in the feces remains in the ecosystem temporarily, but most of it is lost as heat after the feces are consumed by detritivores. The energy used for the caterpillar's respiration is also eventually lost from the ecosystem as heat. This is why energy is said to flow through, not cycle within, ecosystems. Only the chemical energy stored by herbivores as biomass, through growth or the production of offspring, is available as food to secondary consumers.

We can measure the efficiency of animals as energy transformers using the following equation:

$$\text{Production efficiency} = \frac{\text{Net secondary production} \times 100\%}{\text{Assimilation of primary production}}$$

Net secondary production is the energy stored in biomass represented by growth and reproduction. Assimilation consists

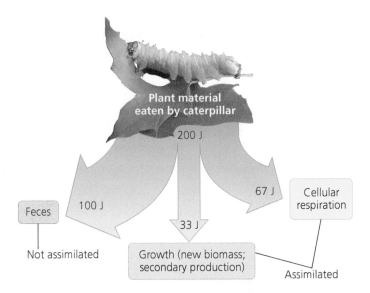

Plant material
eaten by caterpillar

200 J

Feces

100 J

Not assimilated

33 J

Growth (new biomass;
secondary production)

67 J

Cellular
respiration

Assimilated

▲ Figure 42.9 Energy partitioning within a link
of the food chain.

INTERPRET THE DATA *What percentage of the energy in the
caterpillar's food is actually used for secondary production (growth)?*

of the total amount of energy an organism has consumed and
used for growth, reproduction, and respiration. **Production
efficiency**, therefore, is the percentage of energy stored in assimilated food that is used for growth and reproduction, *not*
respiration. For the caterpillar in Figure 42.9, production efficiency is 33%; 67 J of the 100 J of assimilated energy is used
for respiration. (The 100 J of energy lost as undigested material
in feces does not count toward assimilation.) Birds and mammals typically have low production efficiencies, in the range
of 1–3%, because they use so much energy in maintaining a
constant, high body temperature. Fishes, which are mainly
ectothermic (see Concept 32.3), have production efficiencies
around 10%. Insects and microorganisms are even more efficient, with production efficiencies averaging 40% or more.

Trophic Efficiency and Ecological Pyramids

Let's scale up now from the production efficiencies of individual consumers to the flow of energy through trophic levels.

Trophic efficiency is the percentage of production transferred from one trophic level to the next. Trophic efficiencies must always be less than production efficiencies because
they take into account not only the energy contained in feces
and the energy lost through respiration, but also the energy
converted to new biomass in a lower trophic level but not
consumed by the next trophic level. Trophic efficiencies range
from roughly 5% to 20% in different ecosystems, but on average are only about 10%. In other words, 90% of the energy
available at one trophic level typically is *not* transferred to the
next. This loss is multiplied over the length of a food chain. If
10% of available energy is transferred from primary producers
to primary consumers, such as caterpillars, and 10% of that energy is transferred to secondary consumers (carnivores), then
only 1% of net primary production is available to secondary
consumers (10% of 10%). In the **Scientific Skills Exercise**, you

Scientific Skills Exercise

Interpreting Quantitative Data in a Table

How Efficient Is Energy Transfer in a Salt Marsh Ecosystem?
In a classic experiment, John Teal studied the flow of energy
through the producers, consumers, and detritivores in a salt
marsh. In this exercise, you will use the data from this study to
calculate some measures of energy transfer between trophic levels
in this ecosystem.

How the Study Was Done Teal measured the amount of solar
radiation entering a salt marsh in Georgia over a year. He also
measured the aboveground biomass of the dominant primary
producers, which were grasses, as well as the biomass of the
dominant consumers, including insects, spiders, and crabs, and
of the detritus that flowed out of the marsh to the surrounding
coastal waters. To determine the amount of energy in each unit
of biomass, he dried the biomass, burned it in a calorimeter, and
measured the amount of heat produced.

Data from the Study

Form of Energy	kcal/(m² · yr)
Solar radiation	600,000
Gross grass production	34,580
Net grass production	6,585
Gross insect production	305
Net insect production	81
Detritus leaving marsh	3,671

Data from J. M. Teal, Energy flow in the salt marsh ecosystem of Georgia,
Ecology 43:614–624 (1962).

INTERPRET THE DATA

1. What proportion of the solar energy that reaches the marsh is
   incorporated into gross primary production? Into net primary
   production? (A proportion is the same as a percentage divided
   by 100. Both measures are useful for comparing relative efficiencies across different ecosystems.)
2. How much energy is lost by primary producers as respiration in
   this ecosystem? How much is lost as respiration by the insect
   population?
3. If all of the detritus leaving the marsh is plant material, what
   proportion of all net primary production leaves the marsh as
   detritus each year?

MB A version of this Scientific Skills Exercise can be assigned
in MasteringBiology.

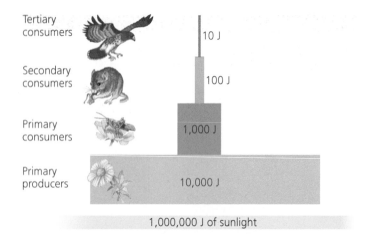

Tertiary consumers 10 J

Secondary consumers 100 J

Primary consumers 1,000 J

Primary producers 10,000 J

1,000,000 J of sunlight

▲ **Figure 42.10 An idealized pyramid of energy.** This example assumes a trophic efficiency of 10% for each link in the food chain. Notice that primary producers convert only about 1% of the energy available to them to net primary production.

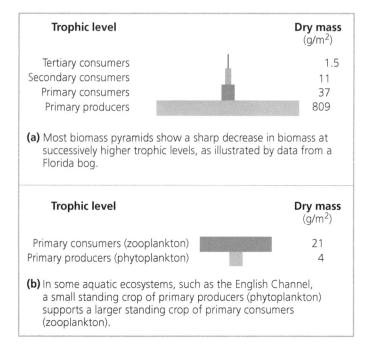

Trophic level	Dry mass (g/m²)
Tertiary consumers	1.5
Secondary consumers	11
Primary consumers	37
Primary producers	809

(a) Most biomass pyramids show a sharp decrease in biomass at successively higher trophic levels, as illustrated by data from a Florida bog.

Trophic level	Dry mass (g/m²)
Primary consumers (zooplankton)	21
Primary producers (phytoplankton)	4

(b) In some aquatic ecosystems, such as the English Channel, a small standing crop of primary producers (phytoplankton) supports a larger standing crop of primary consumers (zooplankton).

▲ **Figure 42.11 Pyramids of biomass.** Numbers denote the dry mass of all organisms at each trophic level.

can calculate trophic efficiency and other measures of energy flow in a salt marsh ecosystem.

The progressive loss of energy along a food chain limits the abundance of top-level carnivores that an ecosystem can support. Only about 0.1% of the chemical energy fixed by photosynthesis can flow all the way through a food web to a tertiary consumer, such as a snake or a shark. This explains why most food webs include only about four or five trophic levels (see Concept 41.2).

The loss of energy with each transfer in a food chain can be represented by an *energy pyramid*, in which the net productions of different trophic levels are arranged in tiers **(Figure 42.10)**. The width of each tier is proportional to the net production, expressed in joules, of each trophic level. The highest level, which represents top-level predators, contains relatively few individuals. The small population size typical of top predator species is one reason they tend to be vulnerable to extinction (and to the evolutionary consequences of small population size, discussed in Concept 21.3).

One important ecological consequence of low trophic efficiencies is represented in a *biomass pyramid*, in which each tier represents the standing crop (the total dry mass of all organisms) in one trophic level. Most biomass pyramids narrow sharply from primary producers at the base to top-level carnivores at the apex because energy transfers between trophic levels are so inefficient **(Figure 42.11a)**. Certain aquatic ecosystems, however, have inverted biomass pyramids: Primary consumers outweigh the producers **(Figure 42.11b)**.

Such inverted biomass pyramids occur because the producers—phytoplankton—grow, reproduce, and are consumed so quickly by the zooplankton that their total biomass remains at comparatively low levels. However, because the phytoplankton continually replace their biomass at such a rapid rate, they can support a biomass of zooplankton bigger than

their own biomass. Likewise, because phytoplankton reproduce so quickly and have much higher production than zooplankton, the pyramid of *energy* for this ecosystem is still bottom-heavy, like the one in Figure 42.10.

The dynamics of energy flow through ecosystems have important implications for human consumers. Eating meat is a relatively inefficient way of tapping photosynthetic production. The same pound of soybeans that a person could eat for protein produces only a fifth of a pound of beef or less when fed to a cow. Worldwide agriculture could, in fact, feed many more people and require less land if we all fed more efficiently—as primary consumers, eating plant material.

▲ Phytoplankton and zooplankton

CONCEPT CHECK 42.3

1. If an insect that eats plant seeds containing 100 J of energy uses 30 J of that energy for respiration and excretes 50 J in its feces, what is the insect's net secondary production? What is its production efficiency?

2. Tobacco leaves contain nicotine, a poisonous compound that is energetically expensive for the plant to make. What advantage might the plant gain by using some of its resources to produce nicotine?

3. **WHAT IF?** Detritivores are consumers that obtain their energy from detritus. How many joules of energy are potentially available to detritivores in the ecosystem represented in Figure 42.10?

For suggested answers, see Appendix A.

Biological and geochemical processes cycle nutrients and water in ecosystems

Although most ecosystems receive abundant solar energy, chemical elements are available only in limited amounts. Life therefore depends on the recycling of essential chemical elements. Much of an organism's chemical stock is replaced continuously as nutrients are assimilated and waste products are released. When the organism dies, the atoms in its body are returned to the atmosphere, water, or soil by decomposers. Decomposition replenishes the pools of inorganic nutrients that plants and other autotrophs use to build new organic matter.

Decomposition and Nutrient Cycling Rates

Decomposers are heterotrophs that get their energy from detritus. Their growth is controlled by the same factors that limit primary production in ecosystems, including temperature, moisture, and nutrient availability. Decomposers usually grow faster and decompose material more quickly in warmer ecosystems (Figure 42.12). In tropical rain forests, most organic material decomposes in a few months to a few years, whereas in temperate forests, decomposition takes four to six years, on average. The difference is largely the result of the higher temperatures and more abundant precipitation in tropical rain forests.

Because decomposition in a tropical rain forest is rapid, relatively little organic material accumulates as leaf litter on the forest floor; about 75% of the ecosystem's nutrients is present in the woody trunks of trees, and only about 10% is contained in the soil. Thus, the relatively low concentrations of some nutrients in the soil of tropical rain forests result from a short cycling time, not from a lack of these elements in the ecosystem. In temperate forests, where decomposition is much slower, the soil may contain as much as 50% of all the organic material in the ecosystem. The nutrients that are present in temperate forest detritus and soil may remain there for years before plants assimilate them.

Decomposition on land is also slower when conditions are either too dry for decomposers to thrive or too wet to supply them with enough oxygen. Ecosystems that are both cold and wet, such as peatlands, store large amounts of organic matter. Decomposers grow poorly there, and net primary production greatly exceeds the rate of decomposition.

In aquatic ecosystems, decomposition in anaerobic muds can take 50 years or longer. Bottom sediments are comparable to the detritus layer in terrestrial ecosystems, but algae and aquatic plants usually assimilate nutrients directly from the water. Thus, the sediments often constitute a nutrient sink, and aquatic ecosystems are very productive only when there is exchange between the bottom layers of water and surface waters (as occurs in the upwelling regions described earlier).

▼ Figure 42.12 Inquiry

How does temperature affect litter decomposition in an ecosystem?

Experiment Researchers with the Canadian Forest Service placed identical samples of organic material—litter—on the ground in 21 sites across Canada (marked by letters on the map below). Three years later, they returned to see how much of each sample had decomposed.

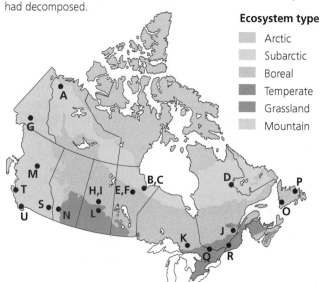

Results The mass of litter in the warmest ecosystem decreased four times faster than in the coldest ecosystem.

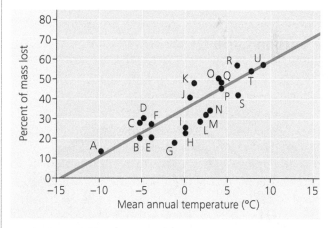

Conclusion Decomposition rate increases with temperature across much of Canada.

Data from T. R. Moore et al., Litter decomposition rates in Canadian forests, *Global Change Biology* 5:75–82 (1999).

WHAT IF? What other factors might have varied across these sites? How might this variation have affected the interpretation of the data?

Biogeochemical Cycles

Because nutrient cycles involve both biotic and abiotic components, they are called **biogeochemical cycles** (Figure 42.13). For convenience, we can recognize two general categories of biogeochemical cycles: global and local. Gaseous forms of carbon, oxygen, sulfur, and nitrogen occur in the atmosphere, and cycles of these elements are essentially

Examine each cycle closely, considering the major reservoirs of water, carbon, nitrogen, and phosphorus and the processes that drive each cycle. The widths of the arrows in the diagrams approximately reflect the relative contribution of each process to the movement of water or a nutrient in the biosphere.

The Water Cycle

Biological importance Water is essential to all organisms, and its availability influences the rates of ecosystem processes, particularly primary production and decomposition in terrestrial ecosystems.

Forms available to life All organisms are capable of exchanging water directly with their environment. Liquid water is the primary physical phase in which water is used, though some organisms can harvest water vapor. Freezing of soil water can limit water availability to terrestrial plants.

Reservoirs The oceans contain 97% of the water in the biosphere. Approximately 2% is bound in glaciers and polar ice caps, and the remaining 1% is in lakes, rivers, and groundwater, with a negligible amount in the atmosphere.

Key processes The main processes driving the water cycle are evaporation of liquid water by solar energy, condensation of water vapor into clouds, and precipitation. Transpiration by terrestrial plants also moves large volumes of water into the atmosphere. Surface and groundwater flow can return water to the oceans, completing the water cycle.

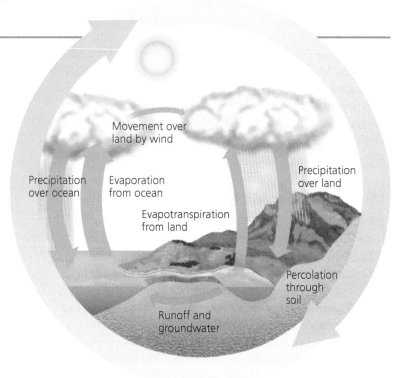

Movement over land by wind

Precipitation over ocean

Evaporation from ocean

Precipitation over land

Evapotranspiration from land

Percolation through soil

Runoff and groundwater

The Carbon Cycle

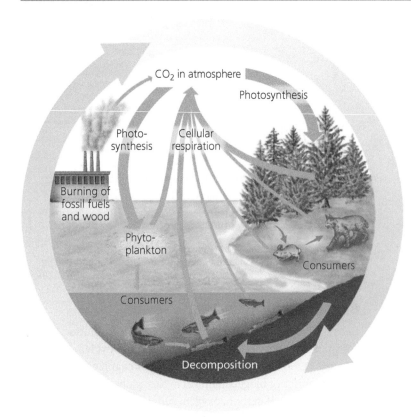

CO_2 in atmosphere

Photosynthesis

Photo-synthesis

Cellular respiration

Burning of fossil fuels and wood

Phyto-plankton

Consumers

Consumers

Decomposition

Biological importance Carbon forms the framework of the organic molecules essential to all organisms.

Forms available to life Photosynthetic organisms utilize CO_2 during photosynthesis and convert the carbon to organic forms that are used by consumers, including animals, fungi, and heterotrophic protists and prokaryotes.

Reservoirs The major reservoirs of carbon include fossil fuels, soils, the sediments of aquatic ecosystems, the oceans (dissolved carbon compounds), plant and animal biomass, and the atmosphere (CO_2). The largest reservoir is sedimentary rocks such as limestone; however, carbon remains in this pool for long periods of time. All organisms are capable of returning carbon directly to their environment in its original form (CO_2) through respiration.

Key processes Photosynthesis by plants and phytoplankton removes substantial amounts of atmospheric CO_2 each year. This quantity is approximately equaled by CO_2 added to the atmosphere through cellular respiration by producers and consumers. The burning of fossil fuels and wood is adding significant amounts of additional CO_2 to the atmosphere. Over geologic time, volcanoes are also a substantial source of CO_2.

ANIMATION Visit the Study Area in **MasteringBiology** for the BioFlix® 3-D Animation on The Carbon Cycle.

The Nitrogen Cycle

Biological importance Nitrogen is part of amino acids, proteins, and nucleic acids and is often a limiting plant nutrient.

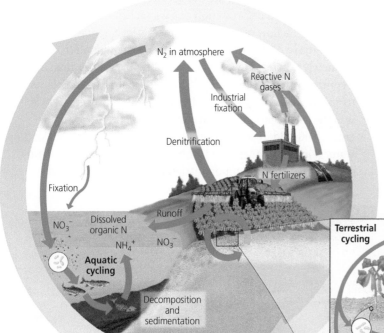

Forms available to life Plants can assimilate (use) two inorganic forms of nitrogen—ammonium (NH_4^+) and nitrate (NO_3^-)—and some organic forms, such as amino acids. Various bacteria can use all of these forms as well as nitrite (NO_2^-). Animals can use only organic forms of nitrogen.

Reservoirs The main reservoir of nitrogen is the atmosphere, which is 80% free nitrogen gas (N_2). The other reservoirs of inorganic and organic nitrogen compounds are soils and the sediments of lakes, rivers, and oceans; surface water and groundwater; and the biomass of living organisms.

Key processes The major pathway for nitrogen to enter an ecosystem is via *nitrogen fixation*, the conversion of N_2 to forms that can be used to synthesize organic nitrogen compounds. Certain bacteria, as well as lightning and volcanic activity, fix nitrogen naturally. Nitrogen inputs from human activities now outpace natural inputs on land. Two major contributors are industrially produced fertilizers and legume crops that fix nitrogen via bacteria in their root nodules. Other bacteria in soil convert nitrogen to different forms. Examples include nitrifying bacteria, which convert ammonium to nitrate, and denitrifying bacteria, which convert nitrate to nitrogen gas. Human activities also release large quantities of reactive nitrogen gases, such as nitrogen oxides, to the atmosphere.

The Phosphorus Cycle

Biological importance Organisms require phosphorus as a major constituent of nucleic acids, phospholipids, and ATP and other energy-storing molecules and as a mineral constituent of bones and teeth.

Forms available to life The most biologically important inorganic form of phosphorus is phosphate (PO_4^{3-}), which plants absorb and use in the synthesis of organic compounds.

Reservoirs The largest accumulations of phosphorus are in sedimentary rocks of marine origin. There are also large quantities of phosphorus in soil, in the oceans (in dissolved form), and in organisms. Because soil particles bind PO_4^{3-}, the recycling of phosphorus tends to be quite localized in ecosystems.

Key processes Weathering of rocks gradually adds PO_4^{3-} to soil; some leaches into groundwater and surface water and may eventually reach the sea. Phosphate taken up by producers and incorporated into biological molecules may be eaten by consumers. Phosphate is returned to soil or water by either decomposition of biomass or excretion by consumers. Because there are no significant phosphorus-containing gases, only relatively small amounts of phosphorus move through the atmosphere, usually in the forms of dust and sea spray.

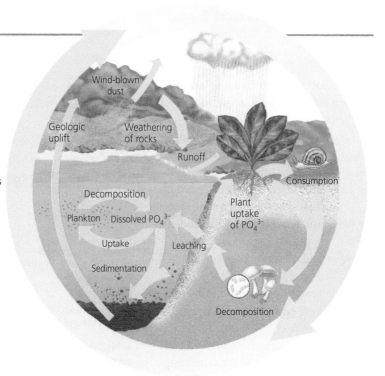

global. Other elements, including phosphorus, potassium, and calcium, are too heavy to occur as gases at Earth's surface. They cycle locally in terrestrial ecosystems and more broadly in aquatic ecosystems.

Figure 42.13 provides a detailed look at the cycling of water, carbon, nitrogen, and phosphorus. When you study each cycle, consider which steps are driven primarily by biological processes. For the carbon cycle, for instance, plants, animals, and other organisms control most of the key steps, including photosynthesis and decomposition. For the water cycle, however, purely physical processes control many key steps, such as evaporation from the oceans.

How have ecologists worked out the details of chemical cycling in various ecosystems? One common method is to follow the movement of naturally occurring, nonradioactive isotopes through the biotic and abiotic components of an ecosystem. Another method involves adding tiny amounts of radioactive isotopes of specific elements and tracing their progress. Scientists have also been able to make use of the radioactive carbon (^{14}C) released into the atmosphere during atom bomb testing in the 1950s and early 1960s. This "spike" of ^{14}C can reveal where and how quickly carbon flows into ecosystem components, including plants, soils, and ocean water.

Case Study: Nutrient Cycling in the Hubbard Brook Experimental Forest

Since 1963, ecologist Gene Likens and colleagues have been studying nutrient cycling at the Hubbard Brook Experimental Forest in the White Mountains of New Hampshire. Their research site is a deciduous forest that grows in six small valleys, each drained by a single creek. Impermeable bedrock underlies the soil of the forest.

The research team first determined the mineral budget for each of six valleys by measuring the input and outflow of several key nutrients. They collected rainfall at several sites to measure the amount of water and dissolved minerals added to the ecosystem. To monitor the loss of water and minerals, they constructed a small concrete dam with a V-shaped spillway across the creek at the bottom of each valley **(Figure 42.14a)**. They found that about 60% of the water added to the ecosystem as rainfall and snow exits through the stream, and the remaining 40% is lost by evapotranspiration.

Preliminary studies confirmed that internal cycling conserved most of the mineral nutrients in the system. For example, only about 0.3% more calcium (Ca^{2+}) leaves a valley via its creek than is added by rainwater, and this small net loss is probably replaced by chemical decomposition of the bedrock. During most years, the forest even registers small net gains of a few mineral nutrients, including nitrogen.

Experimental deforestation of a watershed dramatically increased the flow of water and minerals leaving the watershed **(Figure 42.14b)**. Over three years, water runoff from the newly deforested watershed was 30–40% greater than in a control watershed, apparently because there were no plants to absorb and transpire water from the soil. Most remarkable was the loss of nitrate, whose concentration in the creek increased 60-fold, reaching levels considered unsafe for drinking water **(Figure 42.14c)**. The Hubbard Brook deforestation study showed that the amount of nutrients leaving an intact forest

(a) Concrete dams and weirs built across streams at the bottom of watersheds enabled researchers to monitor the outflow of water and nutrients from the ecosystem.

(b) One watershed was clear-cut to study the effects of the loss of vegetation on drainage and nutrient cycling. All of the original plant material was left in place to decompose.

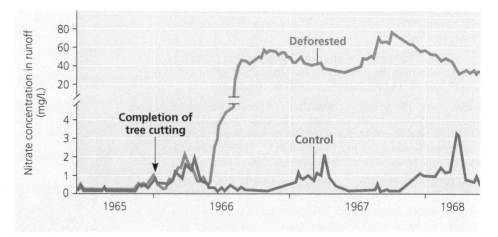

(c) The concentration of nitrate in runoff from the deforested watershed was 60 times greater than in a control (unlogged) watershed.

▲ **Figure 42.14 Nutrient cycling in the Hubbard Brook Experimental Forest: an example of long-term ecological research.**

(MB) A related Experimental Inquiry Tutorial can be assigned in MasteringBiology.

ecosystem is controlled mainly by the plants. Retaining nutrients in an ecosystem helps to maintain the productivity of the system, as well as to avoid algal "blooms" and other problems caused by excess nutrient runoff (see Figure 42.7).

CONCEPT 42.5

Restoration ecologists return degraded ecosystems to a more natural state

Ecosystems can recover naturally from most disturbances (including the experimental deforestation at Hubbard Brook) through the stages of ecological succession (see Concept 41.3). Sometimes that recovery takes centuries, though, particularly when humans have degraded the environment. Tropical areas that are cleared for farming may quickly become unproductive because of nutrient losses. Mining activities may last for several decades, and the lands are often abandoned in a degraded state. Ecosystems can also be damaged by salts that build up in soils from irrigation and by toxic chemicals or oil spills. Biologists increasingly are called on to help restore and repair damaged ecosystems.

Restoration ecologists seek to initiate or speed up the recovery of degraded ecosystems. One of the basic assumptions is that environmental damage is at least partly reversible. This optimistic view must be balanced by a second assumption—that ecosystems are not infinitely resilient. Restoration ecologists therefore work to identify and manipulate the processes that most limit recovery of ecosystems from disturbances. Where disturbance is so severe that restoring all of a habitat is impractical, ecologists try to reclaim as much of a habitat or ecological process as possible, within the limits of the time and money available to them.

In extreme cases, the physical structure of an ecosystem may need to be restored before biological restoration can occur. If a stream was straightened to channel water quickly through a suburb, ecologists may reconstruct a meandering channel to slow down the flow of water eroding the stream bank. To restore an open-pit mine, engineers may first grade the site with heavy equipment to reestablish a gentle slope, spreading topsoil when the slope is in place (**Figure 42.15**).

Once physical reconstruction of the ecosystem is complete—or when it is not needed—biological restoration is the next step. The long-term objective of restoration is to return an ecosystem as much as possible to its predisturbance state. **Figure 42.16** explores four ambitious and successful restoration projects.

There are many such projects throughout the world, and they often employ two key strategies: bioremediation and biological augmentation.

Bioremediation

Using organisms—usually prokaryotes, fungi, or plants—to detoxify polluted ecosystems is known as **bioremediation**. Some plants and lichens adapted to soils containing heavy metals can accumulate high concentrations of toxic metals such as lead and cadmium in their tissues. Restoration ecologists can introduce such species to sites polluted by mining and other human activities and then harvest these organisms to remove

(a) In 1991, before restoration

(b) In 2000, near the completion of restoration

▲ **Figure 42.15 A gravel and clay mine site in New Jersey before and after restoration.**

The examples highlighted on this page are just a few of the many restoration ecology projects taking place around the world.

Kissimmee River, Florida

In the 1960s, the Kissimmee River was converted from a meandering river to a 90-km canal to control flooding. This channelization diverted water from the floodplain, causing the wetlands to dry up, threatening many fish and wetland bird populations. Kissimmee River restoration has filled 12 km of drainage canal and reestablished 24 km of the original 167 km of natural river channel. Pictured here is a section of the Kissimmee canal that has been plugged (wide, light strip on the right side of the photo), diverting flow into remnant river channels (center of the photo). The project will also restore natural flow patterns, which will foster self-sustaining populations of wetland birds and fishes.

Succulent Karoo, South Africa

In the Succulent Karoo desert region of southern Africa, as in many arid regions, overgrazing by livestock has damaged vast areas. Private landowners and government agencies in South Africa are restoring large areas of this unique region, revegetating the land and employing more sustainable resource management. The photo shows a small sample of the exceptional plant diversity of the Succulent Karoo; its 5,000 plant species include the highest diversity of succulent plants in the world.

Maungatautari, New Zealand

Weasels, rats, pigs, and other introduced species pose a serious threat to New Zealand's native plants and animals, including kiwis, a group of flightless, ground-dwelling bird species. The goal of the Maungatautari restoration project is to exclude all exotic mammals from a 3,400-ha reserve located on a forested volcanic cone. A specialized fence around the reserve eliminates the need to continue setting traps and using poisons that can harm native wildlife. In 2006, a pair of critically endangered takahe (a species of flightless rail) were released into the reserve with the hope of reestablishing a breeding population of this colorful bird on New Zealand's North Island.

Coastal Japan

Seaweed and seagrass beds are important nursery grounds for a wide variety of fishes and shellfish. Once extensive but now reduced by development, these beds are being restored in the coastal areas of Japan. Techniques include constructing suitable seafloor habitat, transplanting seaweeds and seagrasses from natural beds using artificial substrates, and hand seeding (shown in this photograph).

the metals from the ecosystem. For instance, researchers in the United Kingdom have discovered a lichen species that grows on soil polluted with uranium dust left over from mining. The lichen concentrates uranium in a dark pigment, making it useful as a biological monitor and potentially as a remediator.

Ecologists already use the abilities of many prokaryotes to carry out bioremediation of soils and water. Scientists have sequenced the genomes of at least ten prokaryotic species specifically for their bioremediation potential. One of the species, the bacterium *Shewanella oneidensis*, appears particularly promising. It can metabolize a dozen or more elements under aerobic and anaerobic conditions. In doing so, it converts soluble forms of uranium, chromium, and nitrogen to insoluble forms that are less likely to leach into streams or groundwater. Researchers at Oak Ridge National Laboratory, in Tennessee, stimulated the growth of *Shewanella* and other uranium-reducing bacteria by adding ethanol to groundwater contaminated with uranium; the bacteria can use ethanol as an energy source. In just five months, the concentration of soluble uranium in the ecosystem dropped by 80% **(Figure 42.17)**.

Biological Augmentation

In contrast to bioremediation, which is a strategy for removing harmful substances from an ecosystem, **biological augmentation** uses organisms to *add* essential materials to a degraded ecosystem. To augment ecosystem processes, restoration ecologists need to determine which factors, such as chemical nutrients, have been lost from a system and are limiting its recovery.

Encouraging the growth of plants that thrive in nutrient-poor soils often speeds up succession and ecosystem recovery. In alpine ecosystems of the western United States, nitrogen-fixing plants such as lupines are often planted to raise nitrogen concentrations in soils disturbed by mining and other activities. Once these nitrogen-fixing plants become established, other native species are better able to obtain enough soil nitrogen to survive. In other systems where the soil has been severely disturbed or where topsoil is missing entirely, plant roots may lack the mycorrhizal symbionts that help them meet their nutritional needs (see Concept 26.2). Ecologists restoring a tallgrass prairie in Minnesota recognized this limitation and enhanced the recovery of native species by adding mycorrhizal symbionts to the soil they seeded.

Restoring the physical structure and plant community of an ecosystem does not always ensure that animal species will recolonize a site and persist there. Because animals provide critical ecosystem services, including pollination and seed dispersal, restoration ecologists sometimes help wildlife to reach and use restored ecosystems. They might release animals at a site or establish habitat corridors that connect a restored site to places where the animals are found. They may build perches for birds to use. These and other efforts can increase the biodiversity of restored ecosystems and help the community persist.

(a) Wastes containing uranium were dumped in these four unlined pits for more than 30 years, contaminating soils and groundwater.

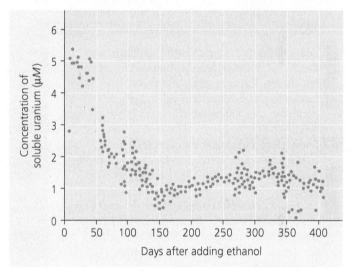

(b) After ethanol was added, microbial activity decreased the concentration of soluble uranium in groundwater near the pits.

▲ **Figure 42.17 Bioremediation of groundwater contaminated with uranium at Oak Ridge National Laboratory, Tennessee.**

CONCEPT CHECK 42.5

1. Identify the main goal of restoration ecology.
2. How do bioremediation and biological augmentation differ?
3. **WHAT IF?** In what way is the Kissimmee River project a more complete ecological restoration than the Maungatautari project (see Figure 42.16)?

For suggested answers, see Appendix A.

Ecosystems: *A Review*

Figure 42.18 illustrates energy transfer, nutrient cycling, and other key processes for an arctic tundra ecosystem. Note the conceptual similarities between this figure and Make Connections Figure 8.20 (The Working Cell). The scale of the two figures is different, but the physical laws and biological rules that govern life apply equally to both systems.

MAKE CONNECTIONS

The Working Ecosystem

This arctic tundra ecosystem teems with life in the short two-month growing season each summer. In ecosystems, organisms interact with each other and with the environment around them in diverse ways, including those illustrated here.

1 Caribou

2 Snow geese

Populations Are Dynamic (Chapter 40)

1 Populations change in size through births and deaths and through immigration and emigration. Caribou migrate across the tundra to give birth at their calving grounds each year. (See Figure 40.14.)

2 Snow geese and many other species migrate to the Arctic each spring for the abundant food found there in summer. (See Concept 39.3.)

3 Birth and death rates influence the density of all populations. Death in the tundra comes from many causes, including predation, competition for resources, and lack of food in winter. (See Figure 40.23.)

5 Herbivory

Arctic fox

3

4 Predation

Snow goose

Species Interact in Diverse Ways (Chapter 41)

4 In predation, an individual of one species kills and eats another. (See Concept 41.1.)

5 In herbivory, an individual of one species eats part of a plant or other primary producer, such as a caribou eating a lichen. (See Concept 41.1.)

6 In mutualism, two species interact in ways that benefit each other. In some mutualisms, the partners live in direct contact, forming a symbiosis; for example, a lichen is a symbiotic mutualism between a fungus and an alga or cyanobacterium. (See Concept 41.1 and Figure 26.29.)

7 In competition, individuals seek to acquire the same limiting resources. For example, snow geese and caribou both eat cottongrass. (See Concept 41.1.)

Nitrogen cycle

N_2

Denitrification

Organisms

N fixation

(12)

Carbon cycle

CO_2

Cellular respiration

Photosynthesis

Organisms Transfer Energy and Matter in Ecosystems (Chapter 42)

(8) Primary producers convert the energy in sunlight to chemical energy through photosynthesis. Their growth is often limited by abiotic factors such as low temperatures, scarce soil nutrients, and lack of light in winter. (See Figure 8.5, Figure 40.9, and Figure 42.4.)

(9) Food chains are typically short in the tundra because primary production is lower than in most other ecosystems. (See Figure 41.13.)

(10) When one organism eats another, the transfer of energy from one trophic level to the next is usually less than 10%. (See Figure 42.10.)

(11) Detritivores recycle chemical elements back to primary producers. (See Figures 42.3 and 42.4.)

(12) Chemical elements such as carbon and nitrogen move in cycles between the physical environment and organisms. (See Figure 42.14.)

Secondary consumers (wolves)

(9)

(10)

Primary consumers (caribou)

Chemical elements

Primary producers (plants and lichens)

(7) Competition

(8)

Detritivores (soil fungi and prokaryotes)

(11)

(6) Mutualism

Algal cell

Fungal hyphae

Lichen

MAKE CONNECTIONS *Human actions are causing climate change, thereby affecting Earth's ecosystems—few of which have been affected as greatly as those in the Arctic. Predict whether climate change will cause evolution in arctic tundra populations. Explain. (See Concepts 1.1, 19.2, and 27.7.)*

ANIMATION Visit the Study Area in **MasteringBiology** for the Bioflix® 3-D Animations on Population Ecology (Chapter 40) and The Carbon Cycle (Chapter 42).

42 Chapter Review

SUMMARY OF KEY CONCEPTS

VOCAB SELF-QUIZ

goo.gl/gbai8v

CONCEPT 42.1

Physical laws govern energy flow and chemical cycling in ecosystems (pp. 887–888)

- An **ecosystem** consists of all the organisms in a community and the abiotic factors with which they interact. Energy is conserved but degraded to heat during ecosystem processes. As a result, energy flows through ecosystems (rather than being recycled).
- Chemical elements enter and leave an ecosystem and cycle within it, subject to the **law of conservation of mass**. Inputs and outputs are generally small compared to recycled amounts, but their balance determines whether the ecosystem gains or loses an element over time.

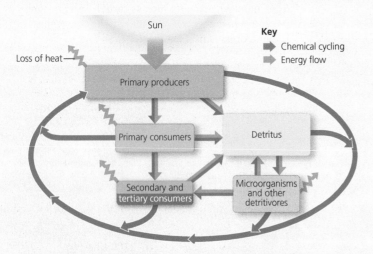

? *Considering the second law of thermodynamics, would you expect the typical biomass of primary producers in an ecosystem to be greater than or less than the biomass of secondary producers in the system? Explain your reasoning.*

CONCEPT 42.2

Energy and other limiting factors control primary production in ecosystems (pp. 888–892)

- **Primary production** sets the spending limit for the global energy budget. **Gross primary production** is the total energy assimilated by an ecosystem in a given period. **Net primary production**, the energy accumulated in autotroph biomass, equals gross primary production minus the energy used by the primary producers for respiration. **Net ecosystem production** is the total biomass accumulation of an ecosystem, defined as the difference between gross primary production and total ecosystem respiration.
- In aquatic ecosystems, light and nutrients limit primary production. In terrestrial ecosystems, climatic factors such as temperature and moisture affect primary production at large scales, but a soil nutrient is often the limiting factor locally.

? *If you know NPP, what additional variable do you need to know to estimate NEP? Why might measuring this variable be difficult, for instance, in a sample of ocean water?*

CONCEPT 42.3

Energy transfer between trophic levels is typically only 10% efficient (pp. 892–894)

- The amount of energy available to each trophic level is determined by the net primary production and the **production efficiency**, the efficiency with which food energy is converted to biomass at each link in the food chain.
- The percentage of energy transferred from one trophic level to the next, called **trophic efficiency**, is typically 10%. Pyramids of net production and biomass reflect low trophic efficiency.

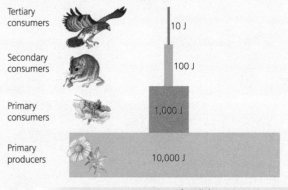

? *Why would runners have a lower production efficiency when running a long-distance race than when they are sedentary?*

CONCEPT 42.4

Biological and geochemical processes cycle nutrients and water in ecosystems (pp. 895–899)

- Water moves in a global cycle driven by solar energy. The carbon cycle primarily reflects the reciprocal processes of photosynthesis and cellular respiration. Nitrogen enters ecosystems through atmospheric deposition and nitrogen fixation by prokaryotes.
- The proportion of a nutrient in a particular form and its cycling in that form vary among ecosystems, largely because of differences in the rate of decomposition.
- Nutrient cycling is strongly regulated by vegetation. The Hubbard Brook case study showed that logging increases water runoff and can cause large losses of minerals.

? *If decomposers usually grow faster and decompose material more quickly in warmer ecosystems, why is decomposition in hot deserts so slow?*

CONCEPT 42.5

Restoration ecologists return degraded ecosystems to a more natural state (pp. 899–901)

- Restoration ecologists harness organisms to detoxify polluted ecosystems through the process of **bioremediation**.
- In **biological augmentation**, ecologists use organisms to add essential materials to ecosystems.

? *In preparing a site for surface mining and later restoration, why would engineers separate the topsoil from the deeper soil, rather than removing all soil at once and mixing it in a single pile?*

TEST YOUR UNDERSTANDING

PRACTICE TEST

goo.gl/CRZjvS

Level 1: Knowledge/Comprehension

1. Which of the following organisms is *incorrectly* paired with its trophic level?
   - (A) cyanobacterium—primary producer
   - (B) grasshopper—primary consumer
   - (C) zooplankton—primary producer
   - (D) fungus—detritivore

2. Which of these ecosystems has the *lowest* net primary production per square meter?
   - (A) a salt marsh
   - (B) an open ocean
   - (C) a coral reef
   - (D) a tropical rain forest

3. The discipline that applies ecological principles to returning degraded ecosystems to a more natural state is known as
   - (A) restoration ecology.
   - (B) thermodynamics.
   - (C) eutrophication.
   - (D) biogeochemistry.

Level 2: Application/Analysis

4. Nitrifying bacteria participate in the nitrogen cycle mainly by
   - (A) converting nitrogen gas to ammonia.
   - (B) releasing ammonium from organic compounds, thus returning it to the soil.
   - (C) converting ammonium to nitrate, which plants absorb.
   - (D) incorporating nitrogen into amino acids and organic compounds.

5. Which of the following has the greatest effect on the rate of chemical cycling in an ecosystem?
   - (A) the rate of decomposition in the ecosystem
   - (B) the production efficiency of the ecosystem's consumers
   - (C) the trophic efficiency of the ecosystem
   - (D) the location of the nutrient reservoirs in the ecosystem

6. The Hubbard Brook watershed deforestation experiment yielded all of the following results *except*:
   - (A) Most minerals were recycled within a forest ecosystem.
   - (B) Calcium levels remained high in the soil of deforested areas.
   - (C) Deforestation increased water runoff.
   - (D) The nitrate concentration in waters draining the deforested area became dangerously high.

7. Which of the following would be considered an example of bioremediation?
   - (A) adding nitrogen-fixing microorganisms to a degraded ecosystem to increase nitrogen availability
   - (B) using a bulldozer to regrade a strip mine
   - (C) reconfiguring the channel of a river
   - (D) adding seeds of a chromium-accumulating plant to soil contaminated by chromium

8. If you applied a fungicide to a cornfield, what would you expect to happen to the rate of decomposition and net ecosystem production (NEP)?
   - (A) Both decomposition rate and NEP would decrease.
   - (B) Neither would change.
   - (C) Decomposition rate would increase and NEP would decrease.
   - (D) Decomposition rate would decrease and NEP would increase.

Level 3: Synthesis/Evaluation

9. **INTERPRET THE DATA** Draw a simplified global water cycle showing ocean, land, atmosphere, and runoff from the land to the ocean. (a) Label your drawing with these annual water fluxes: ocean evaporation, 425 km^3; ocean evaporation that returns to the ocean as precipitation, 385 km^3; ocean evaporation that falls as precipitation on land, 40 km^3; evapotranspiration from plants and soil that falls as precipitation on land, 70 km^3; runoff to the oceans, 40 km^3. (b) What is the ratio of ocean evaporation that falls as precipitation on land compared with runoff from land to the oceans? (c) How would this ratio change during an ice age, and why?

10. **SCIENTIFIC INQUIRY**
    Using two neighboring ponds in a forest as your study site, design a controlled experiment to measure the effect of falling leaves on net primary production in a pond.

11. **FOCUS ON EVOLUTION**
    Some biologists have suggested that ecosystems are emergent, "living" systems capable of evolving. One manifestation of this idea is environmentalist James Lovelock's Gaia hypothesis, which views Earth itself as a living, homeostatic entity—a kind of superorganism. Are ecosystems capable of evolving? If so, would this be a form of Darwinian evolution? Why or why not? Explain.

12. **FOCUS ON ENERGY AND MATTER**
    Decomposition typically occurs quickly in moist tropical forests. However, waterlogging in the soil of some moist tropical forests results over time in a buildup of organic matter called peat. In a short essay (100–150 words), discuss the relationship of net primary production, net ecosystem production, and decomposition for such an ecosystem. Are NPP and NEP likely to be positive? What do you think would happen to NEP if a landowner drained the water from a tropical peatland, exposing the organic matter to air?

13. **SYNTHESIZE YOUR KNOWLEDGE**

This dung beetle (genus *Scarabaeus*) is burying a ball of dung it has collected from a large mammalian herbivore in Kenya. Explain why this process is important for the cycling of nutrients and for primary production.

For selected answers, see Appendix A.

APPENDIX A
Answers

NOTE: Answers to Scientific Skills Exercises, Interpret the Data questions, and short-answer essay questions are available only for instructors in the Instructor Resources area of MasteringBiology.

Chapter 1

Concept Check 1.1
1. Examples: A molecule consists of *atoms* bonded together. Each organelle has an orderly arrangement of *molecules*. Photosynthetic plant cells contain *organelles* called chloroplasts. A tissue consists of a group of similar *cells*. Organs such as the heart are constructed from several *tissues*. A complex multicellular organism, such as a plant, has several types of *organs*, such as leaves and roots. A population is a set of *organisms* of the same species. A community consists of *populations* of the various species inhabiting a specific area. An ecosystem consists of a biological *community* along with the nonliving factors important to life, such as air, soil, and water. The biosphere is made up of all of Earth's *ecosystems*.   **2.** (a) New properties emerge at successive levels of biological organization: Structure and function are correlated. (b) Life's processes involve the expression and transmission of genetic information. (c) Life requires the transfer and transformation of energy and matter.   **3.** Some possible answers: *Organization (emergent properties)*: The ability of a human heart to pump blood requires an intact heart; it is not a capability of any of the heart's tissues or cells working alone. *Organization (structure and function)*: The strong, sharp teeth of a wolf are well suited to grasping and dismembering its prey. *Information*: Human eye color is determined by the combination of genes inherited from the two parents. *Energy and matter*: A plant, such as a grass, absorbs energy from the sun and transforms it into molecules that act as stored fuel. Animals can eat parts of the plant and use the food for energy to carry out their activities. *Interactions*: A mouse eats food, such as nuts or grasses, and deposits some of the food material as wastes (feces and urine). Construction of a nest rearranges the physical environment and may hasten degradation of some of its components. The mouse may also act as food for a predator. *Evolution*: All plants have chloroplasts, indicating their descent from a common ancestor.

Concept Check 1.2
1. An address pinpoints a location by tracking from broader to narrower categories—a state, city, zip code, street, and building number. This is analogous to the groups-subordinate-to-groups structure of biological taxonomy.   **2.** The naturally occurring heritable variation in a population is "edited" by natural selection because individuals with heritable traits better suited to the environment survive and reproduce more successfully than others. Over time, better-suited individuals persist and their percentage in the population increases, while less well-suited individuals become less prevalent—a type of population editing.
3.

Ancestral eukaryotes
— Plants
— Fungi
— Animals

Concept Check 1.3
1. Inductive reasoning derives generalizations from specific cases; deductive reasoning predicts specific outcomes from general premises.   **2.** Mouse coat color matches the environment for both beach and inland populations.   **3.** Compared to a hypothesis, a scientific theory is usually more general and substantiated by a much greater amount of evidence. Natural selection is an explanatory idea that applies to all kinds of organisms and is supported by vast amounts of evidence.   **4.** Science aims to understand natural phenomena and how they work, while technology involves application of scientific discoveries for a particular purpose or to solve a specific problem.

Summary of Key Concepts Questions
1.1 Finger movements rely on the coordination of the many structural components of the hand (muscles, nerves, bones, etc.), each of which is composed of elements from lower levels of biological *organization* (cells, molecules). The development of the hand relies on the genetic *information* encoded in chromosomes found in cells throughout the body. To power the finger movements that result in a text message, muscle and nerve cells require chemical *energy* that they transform in powering muscle contraction or in propagating nerve impulses. Texting is in essence communication, an *interaction* that conveys information between organisms, in this case the same species. Finally, all of the anatomical and physiological features that allow the activity of texting are the outcome of a process of natural selection that resulted in the *evolution* of hands and of the mental facilities for use of language.   **1.2** Ancestors of the beach mouse may have exhibited variations in their coat color. Because of the prevalence of visual predators, the better camouflaged (lighter) mice may have survived longer and been able to produce more offspring. Over time, a higher and higher proportion of individuals in the population would have had the adaptation of lighter fur that acted to camouflage the mouse.   **1.3** Gathering and interpreting data are core activities in the scientific process, and they are affected by, and affect in turn, three other arenas of the

scientific process: exploration and discovery, community analysis and feedback, and societal benefits and outcomes.

Test Your Understanding
1. B   **2.** C   **3.** B   **4.** C   **5.** D
6. Your figure should show the following: (1) For the biosphere, Earth with an arrow coming out of a tropical ocean; (2) for the ecosystem, a distant view of a coral reef; (3) for the community, a collection of reef animals and algae, with corals, fishes, some seaweed, and any other organisms you can think of; (4) for the population, a group of fish of the same species; (5) for the organism, one fish from your population; (6) for the organ, the fish's stomach (see Chapter 33 for help); (7) for a tissue, a group of similar cells from the stomach; (8) for a cell, one cell from the tissue, showing its nucleus and a few other organelles; (9) for an organelle, the nucleus, where most of the cell's DNA is located; and (10) for a molecule, a DNA double helix. Your sketches can be very rough!

Chapter 2

Figure Questions
Figure 2.6 Atomic number = 12; 12 protons, 12 electrons; 3 electron shells; 2 valence electrons   **Figure 2.15** The plant is submerged in water (H_2O), in which the CO_2 is dissolved. The sun's energy is used to make sugar, which is found in the plant and can act as food for the plant itself, as well as for animals that eat the plant. The oxygen (O_2) is present in the bubbles.   **Figure 2.16** One possible answer is the following:

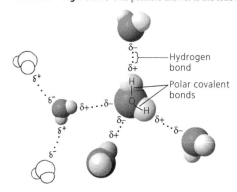

Hydrogen bond
Polar covalent bonds

Figure 2.20 Without hydrogen bonds, water would behave like other small molecules, and the solid phase (ice) would be denser than liquid water. The ice would sink to the bottom and would no longer insulate the body of water. All the water would eventually freeze because the average annual temperature at the South Pole is −50°C. The krill could not survive.   **Figure 2.21** Heating the solution would cause the water to evaporate faster than it is evaporating at room temperature. At a certain point, there wouldn't be enough water molecules to dissolve the salt ions. The salt would start coming out of solution and re-forming crystals. Eventually, all the water would evaporate, leaving behind a pile of salt like the original pile.   **Figure 2.24** By causing the loss of coral reefs, a decrease in the ocean's carbonate concentration would have a ripple effect on noncalcifying organisms. Some of these organisms depend on the reef structure for protection, while others feed on species associated with reefs.

Concept Check 2.1
1. Yes, because an organism requires trace elements, even though only in small amounts   **2.** A person with an iron deficiency will probably show fatigue and other effects of a low oxygen level in the blood. (The condition is called anemia and can also result from too few red blood cells or abnormal hemoglobin.)

Concept Check 2.2
1. $^{15}_{7}N$ **2.** 9 electrons; two electron shells; 1 electron is needed to fill the valence shell.   **3.** The elements in a row all have the same number of electron shells. In a column, all the elements have the same number of electrons in their valence shells.

Concept Check 2.3
1. Each carbon atom has only three covalent bonds instead of the required four.
2. The attraction between oppositely charged ions, forming ionic bonds   **3.** If you could synthesize molecules that mimic these shapes, you might be able to treat diseases or conditions caused by the inability of affected individuals to synthesize such molecules.

Concept Check 2.4
1. At equilibrium, the forward and reverse reactions occur at the same rate.
2. $C_6H_{12}O_6 + 6\ O_2 \rightarrow 6\ CO_2 + 6\ H_2O + Energy$. Glucose and oxygen react to form carbon dioxide and water, releasing energy. We breathe in oxygen because we need it for this reaction to occur, and we breathe out carbon dioxide because it is a product of this reaction. (This reaction is called cellular respiration, and you will learn more about it in Chapter 7.)

Concept Check 2.5

1. Hydrogen bonds hold neighboring water molecules together. This cohesion helps the chains of water molecules move upward against gravity in water-conducting cells as water evaporates from the leaves. Adhesion between water molecules and the walls of the water-conducting cells also helps counter gravity.   **2.** As water freezes, it expands because water molecules move farther apart in forming ice crystals. When there is water in a crevice of a boulder, expansion due to freezing may crack the boulder. **3.** 10^5, or 100,000   **4.** The covalent bonds of water molecules would not be polar, and water molecules would not form hydrogen bonds with each other. Water would therefore not have the unusual properties described in this chapter—such as cohesion, surface tension, high specific heat, high heat of vaporization, and versatility as a solvent.

Summary of Key Concepts Questions

2.1 Iodine (part of a thyroid hormone) and iron (part of hemoglobin in blood) are both trace elements, required in minute quantities. Calcium and phosphorus (components of bones and teeth) are needed by the body in much greater quantities.

2.2

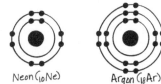

Neon ($_{10}$Ne) Argon ($_{18}$Ar)

Both neon and argon are unreactive because they have completed valence shells. They do not have unpaired electrons that could participate in chemical bonds.   **2.3** Electrons are shared equally between the two atoms in a nonpolar covalent bond. In a polar covalent bond, the electrons are drawn closer to the more electronegative atom. In the formation of ions, one or more electrons are completely transferred from one atom to a much more electronegative atom.   **2.4** The concentration of products would increase as the added reactants were converted to products. Eventually, an equilibrium would again be reached in which the forward and reverse reactions were proceeding at the same rate and the relative concentrations of reactants and products returned to where they were before the addition of more reactants.   **2.5** The polar covalent bonds of a water molecule allow it to form hydrogen bonds with other water molecules and other polar molecules as well. The sticking together of water molecules, called cohesion, and the sticking of water to other molecules, called adhesion, help water rise from the roots of plants to their leaves, among other biological benefits. Hydrogen bonding between water molecules is responsible for water's high specific heat (resistance to temperature change), which helps moderate temperature on Earth. Hydrogen bonding is also responsible for water's high heat of vaporization, which makes water useful for evaporative cooling. A lattice of stable hydrogen bonds in ice makes it less dense than liquid water, so that it floats, creating an insulating surface on bodies of water that allows organisms to live underneath. Finally, the polarity of water molecules resulting from their polar covalent bonds makes water an excellent solvent; polar and ionic atoms and molecules that are needed for life can exist in a dissolved state and participate in chemical reactions.

Test Your Understanding

1. B   **2.** D   **3.** D   **4.** D   **5.** B   **6.** C   **7.** D   **8.** D

9.

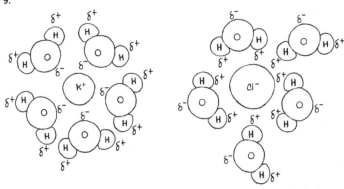

10. Both global warming and ocean acidification are caused by increasing levels of carbon dioxide in the atmosphere, the result of burning fossil fuels.

Chapter 3

Figure Questions

Figure 3.5

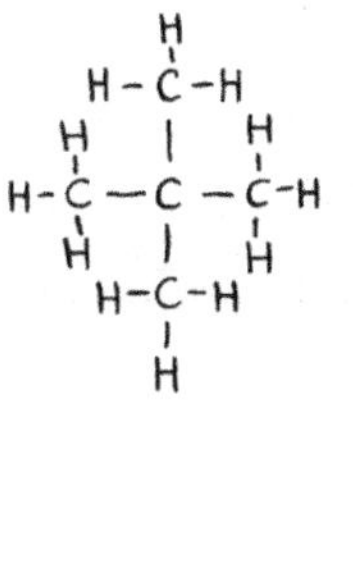

H–C–H structure

Figure 3.9

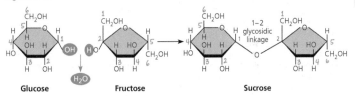

Linear form   Ring forming   Ring form

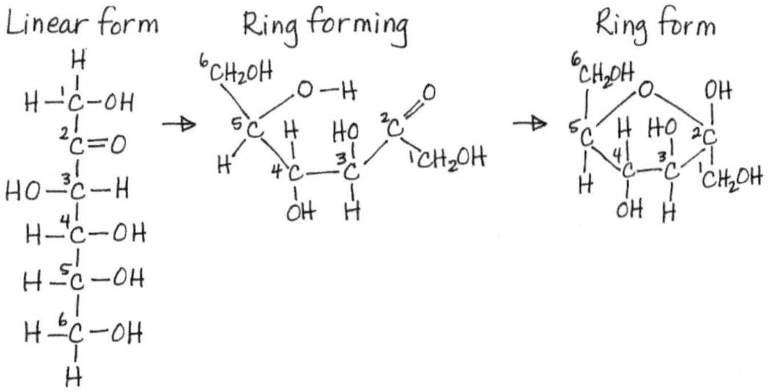

Note that the oxygen on carbon 5 lost its proton and that the oxygen on carbon 2, which used to be the carbonyl oxygen, gained a proton. Four carbons are in the fructose ring, and two are not. (The latter two carbons are attached to carbons 2 and 5, which are in the ring.) The fructose ring differs from the glucose ring, which has five carbons in the ring and one that is not. (Note that the orientation of this fructose molecule is flipped horizontally relative to that of the one in Figure 3.10.)

Figure 3.10

Glucose   Fructose   Sucrose

In sucrose, the linkage is called a 1–2 glycosidic linkage because the number 1 carbon in the left monosaccharide (glucose) is linked to the number 2 carbon in the right monosaccharide (fructose). (Note that the fructose molecule is oriented differently from the glucose molecules in Figures 3.9 and 3.10, and from the fructose shown in the answer for Figure 3.9, above. In Figure 3.10 and here, carbon 2 of fructose is close to carbon 1 of glucose.)

Figure 3.15

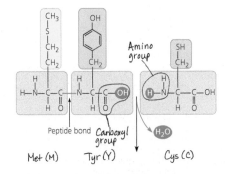

Figure 3.19

Met (M)   Tyr (Y)   Cys (C)

Figure 3.23 The R group of glutamic acid is acidic and hydrophilic, whereas that of valine is nonpolar and hydrophobic. Therefore, it is unlikely that valine can participate in the same intramolecular interactions that glutamic acid can. A change in these interactions would be expected to (and does) cause a disruption of molecular structure.   **Figure 3.30** Using a genomics approach allows us to use gene sequences to identify species and to learn about evolutionary relationships among any two species. This is because all species are related by their evolutionary history, and the evidence is in the DNA sequences. Proteomics—looking at proteins that are expressed—allows us to learn about how organisms or cells are functioning at a given time or in an association with another species.

Concept Check 3.1

1. Both consist largely of hydrocarbon chains, which provide fuel—gasoline for engines and fats for plant embryos and animals. Reactions of both types of molecule release energy.   **2.** The forms of C_4H_{10} in (b) are structural isomers, as are the butenes (forms of C_4H_8) in (c).   **3.** It has both an amino group (—NH_2), which makes it an amine, and a carboxyl group (—COOH), which makes it a carboxylic acid.   **4.** A chemical group that can act as a base (by picking up H^+) has been replaced with a group that can act as an acid, increasing the acidic properties of the molecule. The shape of the molecule would also change, likely changing the molecules with which it can interact.

The original cysteine molecule has an asymmetric carbon in the center. After replacement of the amino group with a carboxyl group, this carbon is no longer asymmetric.

Concept Check 3.2

1. Nine, with one water molecule required to hydrolyze each connected pair of monomers   **2.** The amino acids in the fish protein must be released in hydrolysis reactions and incorporated into other proteins in dehydration reactions.

Concept Check 3.3

1. $C_3H_6O_3$ **2.** $C_{12}H_{22}O_{11}$ **3.** The antibiotic treatment is likely to have killed the cellulose-digesting prokaryotes in the cow's stomach. The absence of these prokaryotes would hamper the cow's ability to obtain energy from food and could lead to weight loss and possibly death. Thus, prokaryotic species are reintroduced, in appropriate combinations, in the gut culture given to treated cows.

Concept Check 3.4

1. Both have a glycerol molecule attached to fatty acids. The glycerol of a fat has three fatty acids attached, whereas the glycerol of a phospholipid is attached to two fatty acids and one phosphate group.   **2.** Human sex hormones are steroids, a type of compound that is hydrophobic and thus classified as a lipid.   **3.** The oil droplet membrane could consist of a single layer of phospholipids rather than a bilayer, because an arrangement in which the hydrophobic tails of the membrane phospholipids were in contact with the hydrocarbon regions of the oil molecules would be more stable.

Concept Check 3.5

1. The function of a protein is a consequence of its specific shape, which is lost when a protein becomes denatured.   **2.** Secondary structure involves hydrogen bonds between atoms of the polypeptide backbone. Tertiary structure involves interactions between atoms of the side chains of the amino acid monomers.   **3.** These are all nonpolar, hydrophobic amino acids, so you would expect this region to be located in the interior of the folded polypeptide, where it would not contact the aqueous environment inside the cell.

Concept Check 3.6

1.

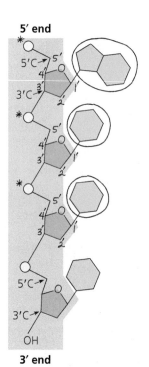

5′ end

3′ end

2.

$$5'-T\ A\ G\ G\ C\ C\ T-3'$$
$$3'-A\ T\ C\ C\ G\ G\ A-5'$$

Concept Check 3.7

1. The DNA of an organism encodes all of its proteins, and proteins are the molecules that carry out the work of cells, whether an organism is unicellular or multicellular. By knowing the DNA sequence of an organism, scientists would be able to catalog the protein sequences as well.   **2.** Ultimately, the DNA sequence carries the information necessary to make the proteins that determine the traits of a particular species. Because the traits of the two species are similar, you would expect the proteins to be similar as well, and therefore the gene sequences should also have a high degree of similarity.

Summary of Key Concepts Questions

3.1 The methyl group is nonpolar and not reactive. The other six groups are called functional groups because they can participate in chemical reactions. Except for the sulfhydryl group, these functional groups are hydrophilic; they increase the solubility of organic compounds in water.   **3.2** The polymers of large carbohydrates, proteins, and nucleic acids are built from three different types of monomers (monosaccharides, amino acids, and nucleotides, respectively).   **3.3** Both starch and cellulose are polymers of glucose, but the glucose monomers are in the α configuration in starch and the β configuration in cellulose. The glycosidic linkages thus have different geometries, giving the polymers different shapes and thus different properties. Starch is an energy-storage compound in plants; cellulose is a structural component of plant cell walls. Humans can hydrolyze starch to provide energy but cannot hydrolyze cellulose. Cellulose aids in the passage of food through the digestive tract.   **3.4** Lipids are not polymers because they do not exist as a chain of linked monomers. They are not considered macromolecules because they do not reach the giant size of many polysaccharides, proteins, and nucleic acids.   **3.5** A polypeptide, which may consist of hundreds of amino acids in a specific sequence (primary structure), has regions of coils and pleats (secondary structure), which are then folded into irregular contortions (tertiary structure) and may be noncovalently associated with other polypeptides (quaternary structure). The linear order of amino acids, with the varying properties of their side chains (R groups), determines what secondary and tertiary structures will form to produce a protein. The resulting unique three-dimensional shapes of proteins are key to their specific and diverse functions.   **3.6** The complementary base pairing of the two strands of DNA makes possible the precise replication of DNA every time a cell divides, ensuring that genetic information is faithfully transmitted. In some types of RNA, complementary base pairing enables RNA molecules to assume specific three-dimensional shapes that facilitate diverse functions.   **3.7** You would expect the human gene sequence to be most similar to that of the mouse (another mammal), and then to that of the fish (another vertebrate), and least similar to that of the fruit fly (an invertebrate).

Test Your Understanding

1. A   **2.** B   **3.** C   **4.** C   **5.** B   **6.** A   **7.** B   **8.** C   **9.** B

10.

	Monomers or Components	Polymer or larger molecule	Type of linkage
Carbohydrates	Monosaccharides	Polysaccharides	Glycosidic linkages
Fats	Fatty acids	Triacylglycerols	Ester linkages
Proteins	Amino acids	Polypeptides	Peptide bonds
Nucleic acids	Nucleotides	Polynucleotides	Phosphodiester linkages

11.

5′ 3′ OH

Original Strand   Complementary strand

Chapter 4

Figure Questions

Figure 4.5 A phospholipid is a lipid consisting of a glycerol molecule joined to two fatty acids and one phosphate group. Together, the glycerol and phosphate end of the phospholipid form the "head," which is hydrophilic, while the hydrocarbon chains on the fatty acids form hydrophobic "tails." The presence in a single molecule of both a hydrophilic and a hydrophobic region makes the molecule ideal as the main building block of a cell or organelle membrane, which is a phospholipid bilayer. In this bilayer, the hydrophobic regions can associate with each other on the inside of the membrane, while the hydrophilic region of each can be in contact with the aqueous solution on either side. **Figure 4.8** The DNA in a chromosome dictates synthesis of a messenger RNA (mRNA) molecule, which then moves out to the cytoplasm. There, the information is used for the production, on ribosomes, of proteins that carry out cellular functions. **Figure 4.9** Any of the bound ribosomes (attached to the endoplasmic reticulum) could be circled, because any could be making a protein that will be secreted. **Figure 4.22** Each centriole has 9 sets of 3 microtubules, so the entire centrosome (two centrioles) has 54 microtubules. Each microtubule consists of a helical array of tubulin dimers (as shown in Table 4.1).

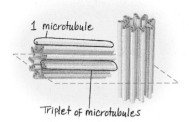

Figure 4.23 The two central microtubules terminate above the basal body, so they aren't present at the level of the cross section through the basal body, indicated by the lower red rectangle in **(a)**.

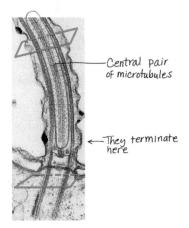

Concept Check 4.1

1. Stains used for light microscopy are colored molecules that bind to cell components, affecting the light passing through, while stains used for electron microscopy involve heavy metals that affect the beams of electrons. **2.** (a) Light microscope, (b) scanning electron microscope

Concept Check 4.2

1. See Figure 4.7. **2.** This cell would have the same volume as the cells in columns 2 and 3 but proportionally more surface area than that in column 2 and less than that in column 3. Thus, the surface-to-volume ratio should be greater than 1.2 but less than 6. To obtain the surface area, you would add the area of the six sides (the top, bottom, sides, and ends): 125 + 125 + 125 + 125 + 1 + 1 = 502. The surface-to-volume ratio equals 502 divided by a volume of 125, or 4.0.

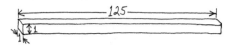

Concept Check 4.3

1. Ribosomes in the cytoplasm translate the genetic message, carried from the DNA in the nucleus by mRNA, into a polypeptide chain. **2.** Nucleoli consist of DNA and the ribosomal RNA (rRNA) made according to its instructions, as well as proteins imported from the cytoplasm. Together, the rRNA and proteins are assembled into large and small ribosomal subunits. (These are exported through nuclear pores to the cytoplasm, where they will participate in polypeptide synthesis.) **3.** Each chromosome consists of one long DNA molecule attached to numerous protein molecules, a combination called chromatin. As a cell begins division, each chromosome becomes "condensed" as its diffuse mass of chromatin coils up.

Concept Check 4.4

1. The primary distinction between rough and smooth ER is the presence of bound ribosomes on the rough ER. Both types of ER make phospholipids, but membrane proteins and secretory proteins are all produced by the ribosomes on the rough ER. The smooth ER also functions in detoxification, carbohydrate metabolism, and storage of calcium ions. **2.** Transport vesicles move membranes and the substances they enclose between other components of the endomembrane system. **3.** The mRNA is synthesized in the nucleus and then passes out through a nuclear pore to be translated on a bound ribosome, attached to the rough ER. The protein is synthesized into the lumen of the ER and perhaps modified there. A transport vesicle carries the protein to the Golgi apparatus. After further modification in the Golgi, another transport vesicle carries it back to the ER, where it will perform its cellular function.

Concept Check 4.5

1. Both organelles are involved in energy transformation, mitochondria in cellular respiration and chloroplasts in photosynthesis. They both have multiple membranes that separate their interiors into compartments. In both organelles, the innermost membranes—cristae, or infoldings of the inner membrane, in mitochondria, and the thylakoid membranes in chloroplasts—have large surface areas with embedded enzymes that carry out their main functions. **2.** Yes. Plant cells are able to make their own sugar by photosynthesis, but mitochondria in these eukaryotic cells are the organelles that are able to generate energy from sugars, a function required in all cells. **3.** Mitochondria and chloroplasts are not derived from the ER, nor are they connected physically or via transport vesicles to organelles of the endomembrane system. Mitochondria and chloroplasts are structurally quite different from vesicles derived from the ER, which are bounded by a single membrane.

Concept Check 4.6

1. Dynein arms, powered by ATP, move neighboring doublets of microtubules relative to each other. Because they are anchored within the organelle and with respect to one another, the doublets bend instead of sliding past each other. Synchronized bending of the nine microtubule doublets brings about bending of both cilia and flagella. **2.** Such individuals have defects in the microtubule-based movement of cilia and flagella. Thus, the sperm can't move because of malfunctioning or nonexistent flagella, and the airways are compromised because cilia that line the trachea malfunction or don't exist, and so mucus cannot be cleared from the lungs.

Concept Check 4.7

1. The most obvious difference is the presence of direct cytoplasmic connections between cells of plants (plasmodesmata) and animals (gap junctions). These connections result in the cytoplasm being continuous between adjacent cells. **2.** The cell would not be able to function properly and would probably soon die, as the cell wall or ECM must be permeable to allow the exchange of matter between the cell and its external environment. Molecules involved in energy production and use must be allowed entry, as well as those that provide information about the cell's environment. Other molecules, such as products synthesized by the cell for export and the byproducts of cellular respiration, must be allowed to exit. **3.** The parts of the protein that face aqueous regions would be expected to have polar or charged (hydrophilic) amino acids, while the parts that go through the membrane would be expected to have nonpolar (hydrophobic) amino acids. You would predict polar or charged amino acids at each end (tail), in the region of the cytoplasmic loop, and in the regions of the two extracellular loops. You would predict nonpolar amino acids in the four regions that go through the membrane between the tails and loops.

Summary of Key Concepts Questions

4.1 Both light and electron microscopy allow cells to be studied visually, thus helping us understand internal cellular structure and the arrangement of cell components. Cell fractionation techniques separate out different groups of cell components, which can then be analyzed biochemically to determine their function. Performing microscopy on the same cell fraction helps to correlate the biochemical function of the cell with the cell component responsible. **4.2** The separation of different functions in different organelles has several advantages. Reactants and enzymes can be concentrated in one area instead of spread throughout the cell. Reactions that require specific conditions, such as a lower pH, can be compartmentalized. And enzymes for specific reactions are often embedded in the membranes that enclose or partition an organelle. **4.3** The nucleus contains the genetic material of the cell in the form of DNA, which codes for messenger RNA, which in turn provides instructions for the synthesis of proteins (including the proteins that make up part of the ribosomes). DNA also codes for ribosomal RNA, which is combined with proteins in the nucleolus into the subunits of ribosomes. Within the cytoplasm, ribosomes join with mRNA to build polypeptides, using the genetic information in the mRNA. **4.4** Transport vesicles move proteins and membrane synthesized by the rough ER to the Golgi for further processing and then to the plasma membrane, lysosomes, or other locations in the cell, including back to the ER. **4.5** According to the endosymbiont theory, mitochondria originated from an oxygen-using prokaryotic cell that was engulfed by an ancestral eukaryotic cell. Over time, the host and endosymbiont evolved into a single unicellular organism. Chloroplasts originated when at least one of these eukaryotic cells containing mitochondria engulfed and then retained a photosynthetic prokaryote. **4.6** Inside the cell, motor proteins interact with components of the cytoskeleton to move cellular parts. Motor proteins may "walk" vesicles along microtubules. The movement of cytoplasm within a cell involves interactions of the motor protein myosin and microfilaments (actin filaments). Whole cells can be moved by the rapid bending of flagella or cilia, which is caused by the motor-protein-powered sliding of microtubules within these structures. Some cells move by amoeboid movement, which involves interactions of microfilaments with myosin. Interactions of motor proteins and microfilaments in muscle cells cause muscle contraction that can propel whole organisms (for example, by walking or swimming). **4.7** A plant cell wall is primarily composed of microfibrils of cellulose embedded in other polysaccharides and proteins. The ECM of animal cells is primarily composed of collagen and other protein fibers, such as fibronectin and other glycoproteins. These fibers are embedded in a network of carbohydrate-rich proteoglycans. A plant cell wall provides structural support for the cell and, collectively, for the plant body. In addition to giving support, the ECM of an animal cell allows for communication of environmental changes into the cell.

Test Your Understanding
1. B **2.** C **3.** B **4.** A **5.** A **6.** C **7.** C **8.** See Figure 4.7.

Chapter 5
Figure Questions
Figure 5.3

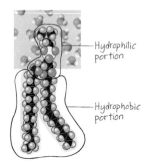

The hydrophilic portion is in contact with an aqueous environment (cytosol or extracellular fluid), and the hydrophobic portion is in contact with the hydrophobic portions of other phospholipids in the interior of the bilayer. **Figure 5.4** You couldn't rule out movement of proteins within membranes of the same species. You might propose that the membrane lipids and proteins from one species weren't able to mingle with those from the other species because of some incompatibility. **Figure 5.7** A transmembrane protein like the dimer in (f) might change its shape upon binding to a particular extracellular matrix (ECM) molecule. The new shape might enable the interior portion of the protein to bind to a second, cytoplasmic protein that would relay the message to the inside of the cell, as shown in (c).
Figure 5.8

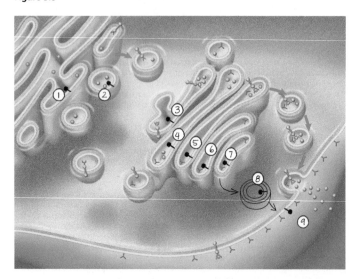

The protein would contact the extracellular fluid. **Figure 5.10** The orange dye would be evenly distributed throughout the solution on both sides of the membrane. The solution levels would not be affected because the orange dye can diffuse through the membrane and equalize its concentration. Thus, no additional osmosis would take place in either direction. **Figure 5.15** The diamond solutes are moving into the cell (down), and the round solutes are moving out of the cell (up); each is moving against its concentration gradient. **Figure 5.23** The aldosterone molecule is hydrophobic and can therefore pass directly through the lipid bilayer of the plasma membrane into the cell. (Hydrophilic molecules cannot do this.) **Figure 5.24** The active form of protein kinase 1

Concept Check 5.1
1. They are on the inner side of the transport vesicle membrane. **2.** The grasses living in the cooler region would be expected to have more unsaturated fatty acids in their membranes because those fatty acids remain fluid at lower temperatures. The grasses living immediately adjacent to the hot springs would be expected to have more saturated fatty acids, which would allow the fatty acids to "stack" more closely, making the membranes less fluid and therefore helping them to stay intact at higher temperatures. (Cholesterol could not moderate the effects of temperature on membrane fluidity in this case because it is not found within plant cell membranes.)

Concept Check 5.2
1. O_2 and CO_2 are both nonpolar molecules that can easily pass through the hydrophobic interior of a membrane. **2.** Water is a polar molecule, so it cannot pass very rapidly through the hydrophobic region in the middle of a phospholipid bilayer. **3.** The hydronium ion is charged, while glycerol is not. Charge is probably more significant than size as a basis for exclusion by the aquaporin channel.

Concept Check 5.3
1. CO_2 is a nonpolar molecule that can diffuse through the plasma membrane. As long as it diffuses away so that the concentration remains low outside the cell, it will continue to exit the cell in this way. (This is the opposite of the case for O_2, described in this section of the text.) **2.** The activity of *Paramecium caudatum*'s contractile vacuole will decrease. The vacuole pumps out excess water that accumulates in the cell; this accumulation occurs only in a hypotonic environment.

Concept Check 5.4
1. The pump uses ATP. To establish a voltage, ions have to be pumped against their gradients, which requires energy. **2.** Each ion is being transported against its electrochemical gradient. If either ion were transported down its electrochemical gradient, this process *would* be considered cotransport. **3.** The internal environment of a lysosome is acidic, so it has a higher concentration of H^+ than does the cytoplasm. Therefore, you might expect the membrane of the lysosome to have a proton pump such as that shown in Figure 5.16 to pump H^+ into the lysosome.

Concept Check 5.5
1. Exocytosis. When a transport vesicle fuses with the plasma membrane, the vesicle membrane becomes part of the plasma membrane.
2.

3. The glycoprotein would be synthesized in the ER lumen, move through the Golgi apparatus, and then travel in a vesicle to the plasma membrane, where it would undergo exocytosis and become part of the ECM.

Concept Check 5.6
1. Glycogen phosphorylase acts in the third stage, the response to epinephrine signaling. **2.** Protein phosphatases reverse the effects of the kinases, and unless the signaling molecule is at a high enough concentration that it is continuously rebinding the receptor, the kinase molecules will all be returned to their inactive states by phosphatases. **3.** At each step in a cascade of sequential activations, one molecule or ion may activate numerous molecules functioning in the next step.

Summary of Key Concepts Questions
5.1 Plasma membranes define the cell by separating the cellular components from the external environment. This allows conditions inside cells to be controlled by membrane proteins, which regulate entry and exit of molecules and even cell function (see Figure 5.7). The processes of life can be carried out inside the controlled environment of the cell, so membranes are crucial. In eukaryotes, membranes also function to subdivide the cytoplasm into different compartments where distinct processes can occur, even under differing conditions such as low or high pH. **5.2** Aquaporins are channel proteins that greatly increase the permeability of a membrane to water molecules, which are polar and therefore do not readily diffuse through the hydrophobic interior of the membrane. **5.3** There will be a net diffusion of water out of a cell into a hypertonic solution. The free water concentration is higher inside the cell than in the solution (where many water molecules are not free, but are clustered around the higher concentration of solute particles). **5.4** One of the solutes moved by the cotransporter is actively transported against its concentration gradient. The energy for this transport comes from the concentration gradient of the other solute, which was established by an electrogenic pump that used energy (usually provided by ATP) to transport the other solute across the membrane. **5.5** In receptor-mediated endocytosis, specific molecules bind to receptors on the plasma membrane in a region where a coated pit develops. The cell can acquire bulk quantities of those specific molecules when the coated pit forms a vesicle and carries the bound molecules into the cell. **5.6** A cell is able to respond to a hormone only if it has a receptor protein on the cell surface or inside the cell that can bind to the hormone. The response to a hormone depends on the specific signal transduction pathway within the cell, which will lead to the specific cellular response. The response can vary for different types of cells.

Test Your Understanding
1. B **2.** A **3.** C **4.** B **5.** C **6.** B

Chapter 6
Figure Questions
Figure 6.9 Glutamic acid (Glu) has a carboxyl group at the end of its R group. Glutamine (Gln) has exactly the same structure as glutamic acid, except that there is an amino group in place of the —OH on the R group. Thus, in this figure, Gln is drawn as a Glu with an attached NH_2.

Figure 6.12

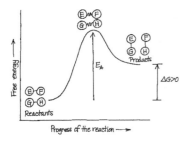

Figure 6.16

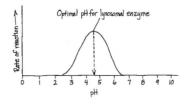

Concept Check 6.1

1. The second law is the trend toward randomization, or increasing entropy. When the concentrations of a substance on both sides of a membrane are equal, the distribution is more random than when they are unequal. Diffusion of a substance to a region where it is initially less concentrated increases entropy, making it an energetically favorable (spontaneous) process as described by the second law. (This explains the process seen in Figure 5.9.) **2.** The apple has potential energy in its position hanging on the tree, and the sugars and other nutrients it contains have chemical energy. The apple has kinetic energy as it falls from the tree to the ground. Finally, when the apple is digested and its molecules broken down, some of the chemical energy is used to do work, and the rest is lost as thermal energy.

Concept Check 6.2

1. Cellular respiration is a spontaneous and exergonic process. The energy released from glucose is used to do work in the cell or is lost as heat. **2.** Catabolism breaks down organic molecules, releasing their chemical energy and resulting in smaller products with more entropy, as when moving from the top to the bottom of part (c). Anabolism consumes energy to synthesize larger molecules from simpler ones, as when moving from the bottom to the top of part (c). **3.** The reaction is exergonic because it releases energy—in this case, in the form of light. (This is a nonbiological version of the bioluminescence seen in Figure 6.1.)

Concept Check 6.3

1. ATP usually transfers energy to endergonic processes by phosphorylating (adding phosphate groups to) other molecules. (Exergonic processes phosphorylate ADP to regenerate ATP.) **2.** A set of coupled reactions can transform the first combination into the second. Since this is an exergonic process overall, ΔG is negative and the first combination must have more free energy (see Figure 6.9). **3.** Active transport: The solute is being transported against its concentration gradient, which requires energy, provided by ATP hydrolysis.

Concept Check 6.4

1. A spontaneous reaction is a reaction that is exergonic. However, if it has a high activation energy that is rarely attained, the rate of the reaction may be low. **2.** Only the specific substrate(s) will fit properly into the active site of an enzyme, the part of the enzyme that carries out catalysis. **3.** In the presence of malonate, increase the concentration of the normal substrate (succinate) and see whether the rate of reaction increases. If it does, malonate is a competitive inhibitor.

Concept Check 6.5

1. The activator binds in such a way that it stabilizes the active form of an enzyme, whereas the inhibitor stabilizes the inactive form.

Summary of Key Concepts Questions

6.1 The process of "ordering" a cell's structure is accompanied by an increase in the entropy, or disorder, of the universe. For example, an animal cell takes in highly ordered organic molecules as the source of matter and energy used to build and maintain its structures. In the same process, however, the cell releases heat and the simple molecules of carbon dioxide and water to the surroundings. The increase in entropy of the latter process offsets the entropy decrease in the former. **6.2** Spontaneous reactions supply the energy to perform cellular work. **6.3** The free energy released from the hydrolysis of ATP may drive endergonic reactions through the transfer of a phosphate group to a reactant molecule, forming a more reactive phosphorylated intermediate. ATP hydrolysis also powers the mechanical and transport work of a cell, often by powering shape changes in the relevant motor proteins. Cellular respiration, the catabolic breakdown of glucose, provides the energy for the endergonic regeneration of ATP from ADP and $\mathcircledP_i$. **6.4** Activation energy barriers prevent the complex molecules of the cell, which are rich in free energy, from spontaneously breaking down to less ordered, more stable molecules. Enzymes permit a regulated metabolism by binding to specific substrates and forming enzyme-substrate complexes that selectively lower the E_A for the chemical reactions in a cell. **6.5** A cell tightly regulates its metabolic pathways in response to fluctuating needs for energy and materials. The binding of

activators or inhibitors to regulatory sites on allosteric enzymes stabilizes either the active or inactive form of the subunits. For example, the binding of ATP to a catabolic enzyme in a cell with excess ATP would inhibit that pathway. Such types of feedback inhibition preserve chemical resources within a cell. If ATP supplies are depleted, binding of ADP to the regulatory site of catabolic enzymes will activate that pathway, generating more ATP.

Test Your Understanding
1. B **2.** C **3.** B **4.** A **5.** C **6.** D **7.** C
8.

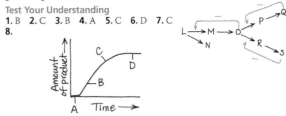

A. The substrate molecules are entering the cells, so no product is made yet.
B. There is sufficient substrate, so the reaction is proceeding at a maximum rate.
C. As the substrate is used up, the rate decreases (the slope is less steep).
D. The line is flat because no new substrate remains and thus no new product appears.

Chapter 7

Figure Questions
Figure 7.7 Because there is no external source of energy for the reaction, it must be exergonic, and the reactants must be at a higher energy level than the products.
Figure 7.9 The removal would probably stop glycolysis, or at least slow it down, since it would push the equilibrium for step 5 toward the bottom (toward DHAP). If less (or no) glyceraldehyde 3-phosphate were available, step 6 would slow down (or be unable to occur).
Figure 7.13

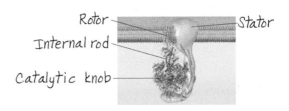

Figure 7.14 At first, some ATP could be made, since electron transport could proceed as far as complex III, and a small H^+ gradient could be built up. Soon, however, no more electrons could be passed to complex III because it could not be reoxidized by passing its electrons to complex IV. **Figure 7.15** First, there are 2 NADH from the oxidation of pyruvate plus 6 NADH from the citric acid cycle (CAC); 8 NADH × 2.5 ATP/NADH = 20 ATP. Second, there are 2 $FADH_2$ from the CAC; 2 $FADH_2$ × 1.5 ATP/$FADH_2$ = 3 ATP. Third, the 2 NADH from glycolysis enter the mitochondrion through one of two types of shuttle. They pass their electrons either to 2 FAD, which become $FADH_2$ and result in 3 ATP, or to 2 NAD^+, which become NADH and result in 5 ATP. Thus, 20 + 3 + 3 = 26 ATP or 20 + 3 + 5 = 28 ATP from all NADH and $FADH_2$.

Concept Check 7.1
1. Both processes include glycolysis, the citric acid cycle, and oxidative phosphorylation. In aerobic respiration, the final electron acceptor is molecular oxygen (O_2); in anaerobic respiration, the final electron acceptor is a different substance. **2.** Substrate-level phosphorylation, which occurs during glycolysis and the citric acid cycle, involves the direct transfer of a phosphate group from an organic substrate to ADP by an enzyme. The process of oxidative phosphorylation occurs during the third stage of cellular respiration, which is called oxidative phosphorylation. In this process, the synthesis of ATP from ADP and inorganic phosphate ($\mathircledP_i$) is powered by the redox reactions of the electron transport chain. **3.** $C_4H_6O_5$ would be oxidized, and NAD^+ would be reduced.

Concept Check 7.2
1. NAD^+ acts as the oxidizing agent in step 6, accepting electrons from glyceraldehyde 3-phosphate (G3P), which thus acts as the reducing agent.

Concept Check 7.3
1. NADH and $FADH_2$; they will donate electrons to the electron transport chain.
2. CO_2 is released from the pyruvate that is the end product of glycolysis, and CO_2 is also released during the citric acid cycle.

Concept Check 7.4
1. Oxidative phosphorylation would eventually stop entirely, resulting in no ATP production by this process. Without oxygen to "pull" electrons down the electron transport chain, H^+ would not be pumped into the mitochondrion's intermembrane space and chemiosmosis would not occur. **2.** Decreasing the pH means the addition of H^+. This would establish a proton gradient even without the function of the electron transport chain, and we would expect ATP synthase to function and synthesize ATP. (In fact, it was experiments like this that provided support for chemiosmosis as an energy-coupling mechanism.) **3.** One of the components of the electron transport chain, ubiquinone (Q), must be able to diffuse within the membrane. It could not do so if the membrane components were locked rigidly into place.

Concept Check 7.5

1. A derivative of pyruvate, such as acetaldehyde during alcohol fermentation, or pyruvate itself during lactic acid fermentation; oxygen during aerobic respiration
2. The cell would need to consume glucose at a rate about 16 times the consumption rate in the aerobic environment (2 ATP are generated by fermentation versus up to 32 ATP by cellular respiration).

Concept Check 7.6

1. The fat is much more reduced; it has many —CH_2— units, and in all these bonds the electrons are equally shared. The electrons present in a carbohydrate molecule are already somewhat oxidized (shared unequally in bonds), as quite a few of them are bound to oxygen. Electrons that are equally shared, as in fat, have a higher energy level than electrons that are unequally shared, as in carbohydrates. Thus, fats are much better fuels than carbohydrates.   **2.** When you consume more food than necessary for metabolic processes, your body synthesizes fat as a way of storing energy for later use.
3. When oxygen is present, the fatty acid chains containing most of the energy of a fat are oxidized and fed into the citric acid cycle and the electron transport chain. During intense exercise, however, oxygen is scarce in muscle cells, so ATP must be generated by glycolysis alone. A very small part of the fat molecule, the glycerol backbone, can be oxidized via glycolysis, but the amount of energy released by this portion is insignificant compared with that released by the fatty acid chains. (This is why moderate exercise, staying below 70% maximum heart rate, is better for burning fat—because enough oxygen remains available to the muscles.)

Summary of Key Concepts Questions

7.1 Most of the ATP produced in cellular respiration comes from oxidative phosphorylation, in which the energy released from redox reactions in an electron transport chain is used to produce ATP. In substrate-level phosphorylation, an enzyme directly transfers a phosphate group to ADP from an intermediate substrate. All ATP production in glycolysis occurs by substrate-level phosphorylation; this form of ATP production also occurs at one step in the citric acid cycle.   **7.2** The oxidation of the three-carbon sugar glyceraldehyde 3-phosphate yields energy. In this oxidation, electrons and H^+ are transferred to NAD^+, forming NADH, and a phosphate group is attached to the oxidized substrate. ATP is then formed by substrate-level phosphorylation when this phosphate group is transferred to ADP.   **7.3** The release of six molecules of CO_2 represents the complete oxidation of glucose. During the processing of two pyruvates to acetyl CoA, the fully oxidized carboxyl groups (—COO^-) are given off as 2 CO_2. The remaining four carbons are released as CO_2 in the citric acid cycle as citrate is oxidized back to oxaloacetate.   **7.4** The flow of H^+ through the ATP synthase complex causes the rotor and attached rod to rotate, exposing catalytic sites in the knob portion that produce ATP from ADP and Ⓟᵢ. ATP synthases are found in the inner mitochondrial membrane, the plasma membrane of prokaryotes, and membranes within chloroplasts.   **7.5** Anaerobic respiration yields more ATP. The 2 ATP produced by substrate-level phosphorylation in glycolysis represent the total energy yield of fermentation. NADH passes its "high-energy" electrons to pyruvate or a derivative of pyruvate, recycling NAD^+ and allowing glycolysis to continue. In anaerobic respiration, the NADH produced during glycolysis, as well as additional molecules of NADH produced as pyruvate is oxidized, are used to generate ATP molecules. An electron transport chain captures the energy of the electrons in NADH via a series of redox reactions; ultimately, the electrons are transferred to an electronegative molecule other than oxygen. Also, additional molecules of NADH are produced in anaerobic respiration as pyruvate is oxidized.   **7.6** The ATP produced by catabolic pathways is used to drive anabolic pathways. Also, many of the intermediates of glycolysis and the citric acid cycle are used in the biosynthesis of a cell's molecules.

Test Your Understanding

1. C   **2.** C   **3.** B   **4.** A   **5.** D   **6.** A   **7.** B
8.

H^+ would continue to be pumped across the membrane into the intermembrane space, increasing the difference between the matrix pH and the intermembrane space pH. H^+ would not be able to flow back through ATP synthase, since the enzyme is inhibited by the poison, so rather than maintaining a constant difference across the membrane, the difference would continue to increase. (Ultimately, the H^+ concentration in the intermembrane space would be so high that no more H^+ would be able to be pumped against the gradient, but this isn't shown in the graph.)

Chapter 8

Figure Questions

Figure 8.15 You would (a) decrease the pH outside the mitochondrion (thus increasing the H^+ concentration) and (b) increase the pH in the chloroplast stroma (thus decreasing the H^+ concentration). In both cases, this would generate an H^+ gradient across the membrane that would cause ATP synthase to synthesize ATP.

Figure 8.17

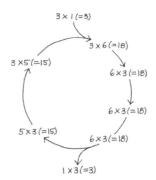

Three carbon atoms enter the cycle, one by one, as individual CO_2 molecules and leave the cycle in one three-carbon molecule (G3P) per three turns of the cycle.
Figure 8.19 Yes, plants can break down the sugar (in the form of glucose) by cellular respiration, producing ATPs for various cellular processes such as endergonic chemical reactions, transport of substances across membranes, and movement of molecules in the cell.   **Figure 8.20** The gene encoding hexokinase is part of the DNA of a chromosome in the nucleus. There, the gene is transcribed into mRNA, which is transported to the cytoplasm where it is translated on a free ribosome into a polypeptide. The polypeptide folds into a functional protein with secondary and tertiary structure. Once functional, it carries out the first reaction of glycolysis in the cytoplasm.

Concept Check 8.1

1. CO_2 enters the leaves via stomata, and water enters the plant via roots and is carried to the leaves through veins.   **2.** Using ^{18}O, a heavy isotope of oxygen, as a label, researchers were able to confirm van Niel's hypothesis that the oxygen produced during photosynthesis comes from water, not from carbon dioxide.   **3.** The light reactions could *not* keep producing NADPH and ATP without the $NADP^+$, ADP, and Ⓟᵢ that the Calvin cycle generates. The two cycles are interdependent.

Concept Check 8.2

1. Green, because green light is mostly transmitted and reflected—not absorbed—by photosynthetic pigments   **2.** Water (H_2O) is the initial electron donor; $NADP^+$ accepts electrons at the end of the electron transport chain, becoming reduced to NADPH.   **3.** The rate of ATP synthesis would slow and eventually stop. Because the added compound would not allow a proton gradient to build up across the membrane, ATP synthase could not catalyze ATP production.

Concept Check 8.3

1. The more energy and reducing power a molecule stores, the more energy and reducing power are required for formation of that molecule. Glucose is a valuable energy source because it is highly reduced, storing lots of potential energy in its electrons. To reduce CO_2 to glucose, a large amount of energy and reducing power are required in the form of large numbers of ATP and NADPH molecules, respectively.   **2.** The light reactions require ADP and $NADP^+$, which would not be formed in sufficient quantities from ATP and NADPH if the Calvin cycle stopped.   **3.** Photorespiration decreases photosynthetic output by adding oxygen, instead of carbon dioxide, to the Calvin cycle. As a result, no sugar is generated (no carbon is fixed), and O_2 is used rather than generated.

Summary of Key Concepts Questions

8.1 CO_2 and H_2O are the products of respiration; they are the reactants in photosynthesis. In respiration, glucose is oxidized to CO_2 and electrons are passed through an electron transfer chain from glucose to O_2, producing H_2O. In photosynthesis, H_2O is the source of electrons, which are energized by light, temporarily stored in NADPH, and used to reduce CO_2 to carbohydrate.   **8.2** The action spectrum of photosynthesis shows that some wavelengths of light that are not absorbed by chlorophyll *a* are still effective at promoting photosynthesis. The light-harvesting complexes of photosystems contain accessory pigments, such as chlorophyll *b* and carotenoids, which absorb different wavelengths and pass the energy to chlorophyll *a*, broadening the spectrum of light usable for photosynthesis.
8.3

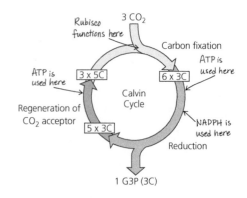

In the reduction phase of the Calvin cycle, ATP phosphorylates a three-carbon compound, and NADPH then reduces this compound to G3P. ATP is also used in the regeneration phase, when five molecules of G3P are converted to three molecules of the five-carbon compound RuBP. Rubisco catalyzes the first step of carbon fixation—the addition of CO_2 to RuBP.

Test Your Understanding
1. D **2.** B **3.** C **4.** A **5.** C **6.** B **7.** C **8.** 6; 18; 12
10.

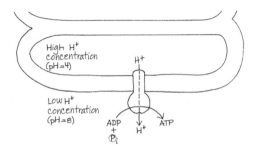

The ATP would end up outside the thylakoid. The thylakoids were able to make ATP in the dark because the researchers set up an artificial proton concentration gradient across the thylakoid membrane; thus, the light reactions were not necessary to establish the H^+ gradient required for ATP synthesis by ATP synthase.

Chapter 9

Figure Questions
Figure 9.4

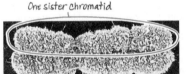

Circling the other chromatid instead would also be correct. **Figure 9.5** The chromosome has four chromatid arms. The single (duplicated) chromosome in step 2 becomes two (unduplicated) chromosomes in step 3. The duplicated chromosome in step 2 is considered one single chromosome. **Figure 9.7** 12; 2; 2; 1
Figure 9.8

Figure 9.9 The mark would have moved toward the nearer pole. The lengths of fluorescent microtubules between that pole and the mark would have decreased, while the lengths between the chromosomes and the mark would have remained the same.
Figure 9.14 In both cases, the G_1 nucleus would have remained in the time it normally would have entered the S phase. Chromosome condensation and spindle formation would not have occurred until the S and G_2 phases had been completed.
Figure 9.16 The cell would divide under conditions where it was inappropriate to do so. If the daughter cells and their descendants also ignored either of the checkpoints and divided, there would soon be an abnormal mass of cells. (This type of inappropriate cell division can contribute to the development of cancer.) **Figure 9.17** The cells in the vessel with PDGF would not be able to respond to the growth factor signal and thus would not divide. The culture would resemble that without the added PDGF.

Concept Check 9.1
1. 1; 1; 2 **2.** 39; 39; 78

Concept Check 9.2
1. 6 chromosomes; they are duplicated; 12 chromatids **2.** Following mitosis, cytokinesis results in two genetically identical daughter cells in both plant cells and animal cells. However, the mechanism of dividing the cytoplasm is different in animals and plants. In an animal cell, cytokinesis occurs by cleavage, which divides the parent cell in two with a contractile ring of actin filaments. In a plant cell, a cell plate forms in the middle of the cell and grows until its membrane fuses with the plasma membrane of the parent cell. A new cell wall grows inside the cell plate. **3.** From the end of S phase in interphase through the end of metaphase in mitosis **4.** During eukaryotic cell division, tubulin is involved in spindle formation and chromosome movement, while actin functions during cytokinesis. In bacterial binary fission, it's the opposite: Tubulin-like molecules are thought to act in daughter cell separation, and actin-like molecules are thought to move the daughter bacterial chromosomes to opposite ends of the cell.

Concept Check 9.3
1. The nucleus on the right was originally in the G_1 phase; therefore, it had not yet duplicated its chromosomes. The nucleus on the left was in the M phase, so it had already duplicated its chromosomes. **2.** Most body cells are in a nondividing state called G_0. **3.** Both types of tumors consist of abnormal cells, but their characteristics are different. A benign tumor stays at the original site and can usually be surgically removed; the cells have some genetic and cellular changes from normal, non-tumor cells. Cancer cells from a malignant tumor have more significant genetic and cellular changes, can spread from the original site by metastasis, and may impair the functions of one or more organs. **4.** The cells might divide even in the absence of PDGF. In addition, they would not stop when the surface of the culture vessel was covered; they would continue to divide, piling on top of one another.

Summary of Key Concepts Questions
9.1 The DNA of a eukaryotic cell is packaged into structures called *chromosomes*. Each chromosome is a long molecule of DNA, which carries hundreds to thousands of genes, with associated proteins that maintain chromosome structure and help control gene activity. This DNA-protein complex is called *chromatin*. The chromatin of each chromosome is long and thin when the cell is not dividing. Prior to cell division, each chromosome is duplicated, and the resulting sister *chromatids* are attached to each other by proteins at the centromeres and, for many species, all along their lengths (a phenomenon called sister chromatid cohesion). **9.2** Chromosomes exist as single DNA molecules in G_1 of interphase and in anaphase and telophase of mitosis. During S phase, DNA replication produces sister chromatids, which persist during G_2 of interphase and through prophase, prometaphase, and metaphase of mitosis.
9.3 Checkpoints allow cellular surveillance mechanisms to determine whether the cell is prepared to go to the next stage. Internal and external signals move a cell past these checkpoints. The G_1 checkpoint, called the "restriction point" in mammalian cells, determines whether a cell will complete the cell cycle and divide or switch into the G_0 phase. The signals to pass this checkpoint often are external—such as growth factors. Regulation of the cell cycle is carried out by a molecular system, including proteins called cyclins and other proteins that are kinases. The signal to pass the M phase checkpoint is not activated until all chromosomes are attached to kinetochore fibers and are aligned at the metaphase plate. Only then will sister chromatid separation occur.

Test Your Understanding
1. B **2.** A **3.** B **4.** A **5.** D
6.

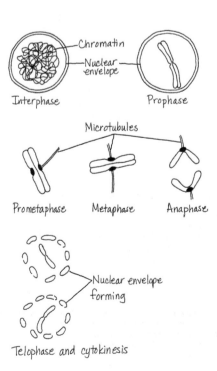

7. See Figure 9.7 for a description of major events.

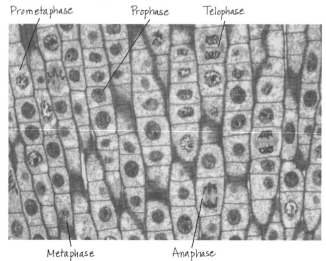

Prometaphase Prophase Telophase

Metaphase Anaphase

Only one cell is indicated for each stage, but other correct answers are also present in this micrograph.

Chapter 10

Figure Questions
Figure 10.4 Two sets of chromosomes are present. Three pairs of homologous chromosomes are present.
Figure 10.7

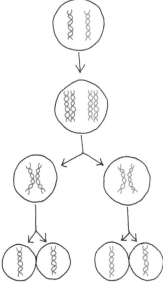

(A short strand of DNA is shown here for simplicity, but each chromosome or chromatid contains a very long coiled and folded DNA molecule.) **Figure 10.8** If a cell with six chromosomes undergoes two rounds of mitosis, each of the four resulting cells will have six chromosomes, while the four cells resulting from meiosis in Figure 10.8 each have three chromosomes. In mitosis, DNA replication (and thus chromosome duplication) precedes each prophase, ensuring that daughter cells have the same number of chromosomes as the parent cell. In meiosis, in contrast, DNA replication occurs only before prophase I (not before prophase II). Thus, in two rounds of mitosis, the chromosomes duplicate twice and divide twice, while in meiosis, the chromosomes duplicate once and divide twice. **Figure 10.10** Yes. Each of the six chromosomes (three per cell) shown in telophase I has one nonrecombinant chromatid and one recombinant chromatid. Therefore, eight possible sets of chromosomes can be generated for the cell on the left and eight for the cell on the right.

Concept Check 10.1
1. Parents pass genes to their offspring; by dictating the production of messenger RNAs (mRNAs), the genes program cells to make specific enzymes and other proteins, whose cumulative action produces an individual's inherited traits. **2.** Such organisms reproduce by mitosis, which generates offspring whose genomes are exact copies of the parent's genome (in the absence of mutations). **3.** She should clone it. Crossbreeding it with another plant would generate offspring that have additional variation, which she no longer desires now that she has obtained her ideal orchid.

Concept Check 10.2
1. Each of the six chromosomes is duplicated, so each contains two DNA double helices. Therefore, there are 12 DNA molecules in the cell. The haploid number, n, is 3. One set is always haploid. **2.** There are 23 pairs of chromosomes and two sets.
3. The haploid number (n) is 7; the diploid number ($2n$) is 14. **4.** This organism has the life cycle shown in Figure 10.6c. Therefore, it must be a fungus or a protist, perhaps an alga.

Concept Check 10.3
1. The chromosomes are similar in that each is composed of two sister chromatids, and the individual chromosomes are positioned similarly at the metaphase plate. The chromosomes differ in that in a mitotically dividing cell, sister chromatids of each chromosome are genetically identical, but in a meiotically dividing cell, sister chromatids are genetically distinct because of crossing over in meiosis I. Moreover, the chromosomes in metaphase of mitosis can be a diploid set or a haploid set, but the chromosomes in metaphase of meiosis II always consist of a haploid set. **2.** If crossing over did not occur, the two homologs would not be associated in any way; each sister chromatid would be either all maternal or all paternal, and would only be attached to its sister, not to a nonsister chromatid. This might result in incorrect arrangement of homologs during metaphase I and ultimately in formation of gametes with an abnormal number of chromosomes.

Concept Check 10.4
1. Mutations in a gene lead to the different versions (alleles) of that gene. **2.** If the segments of the maternal and paternal chromatids that undergo crossing over are genetically identical and thus have the same two alleles for every gene, then the recombinant chromosomes will be genetically equivalent to the parental chromosomes. Crossing over contributes to genetic variation only when it involves the rearrangement of different alleles.

Summary of Key Concepts Questions
10.1 Genes program specific traits, and offspring inherit their genes from each parent, accounting for similarities in their appearance to one or the other parent. Humans reproduce sexually, which ensures new combinations of genes (and thus traits) in the offspring. Consequently, the offspring are not clones of their parents (which would be the case if humans reproduced asexually). **10.2** Animals and plants both reproduce sexually, alternating meiosis with fertilization. Both have haploid gametes that unite to form a diploid zygote, which then goes on to divide mitotically, forming a diploid multicellular organism. In animals, haploid cells become gametes and don't undergo mitosis, while in plants, the haploid cells resulting from meiosis undergo mitosis to form a haploid multicellular organism, the gametophyte. This organism then goes on to generate haploid gametes. (In plants such as trees, the gametophyte is quite reduced in size and not obvious to the casual observer.) **10.3** At the end of meiosis I, the two members of a homologous pair end up in different cells, so they cannot pair up and undergo crossing over. **10.4** First, during independent assortment in metaphase I, each pair of homologous chromosomes lines up independent of every other pair at the metaphase plate, so a daughter cell of meiosis I randomly inherits either a maternal or paternal chromosome. Second, due to crossing over, each chromosome is not exclusively maternal or paternal, but includes regions at the ends of the chromatid from a nonsister chromatid (a chromatid of the other homolog). (The nonsister segment can also be in an internal region of the chromatid if a second crossover occurs beyond the first one before the end of the chromatid.) This provides much additional diversity in the form of new combinations of alleles. Third, random fertilization ensures even more variation, since any sperm of a large number containing many possible genetic combinations can fertilize any egg of a similarly large number of possible combinations.

Test Your Understanding
1. A **2.** B **3.** D **4.** C
5. (a)

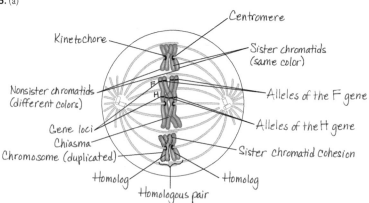

Centromere

Kinetochore

Sister chromatids (same color)

Nonsister chromatids (different colors)

Alleles of the F gene

Alleles of the H gene

Gene loci

Chiasma

Sister chromatid cohesion

Chromosome (duplicated)

Homolog Homolog

Homologous pair

(b) Metaphase I (c) A haploid set is made up of one long, one medium, and one short chromosome, no matter what combination of colors. For example, one red long, one blue medium, and one red short chromosome make up a haploid set. (In cases where crossovers have occurred, a haploid set of one color may include segments of chromatids of the other color.) All red and blue chromosomes together make up a diploid set.
6. This cell must be undergoing meiosis because homologous chromosomes are associated with each other at the metaphase plate; this does not occur in mitosis.

Chapter 11

Figure Questions

Figure 11.3 All offspring would have purple flowers. (The ratio would be 1 purple : 0 white.) The P generation plants are true-breeding, so mating two purple-flowered plants produces the same result as self-pollination: All the offspring have the same trait.

Figure 11.8

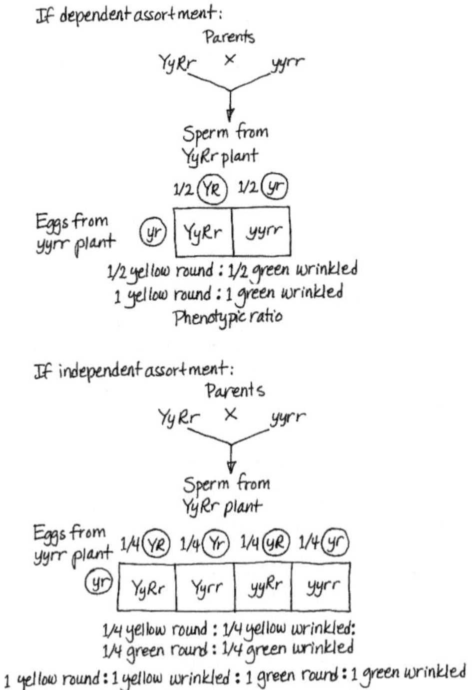

If dependent assortment:
Parents
YyRr × yyrr
Sperm from YyRr plant
1/2 YR 1/2 yr
Eggs from yyrr plant
yr
YyRr yyrr
1/2 yellow round : 1/2 green wrinkled
1 yellow round : 1 green wrinkled
Phenotypic ratio
If independent assortment:
Parents
YyRr × yyrr
Sperm from YyRr plant
Eggs from yyrr plant
1/4 YR 1/4 Yr 1/4 yR 1/4 yr
yr
YyRr Yyrr yyRr yyrr
1/4 yellow round : 1/4 yellow wrinkled:
1/4 green round : 1/4 green wrinkled
1 yellow round : 1 yellow wrinkled : 1 green round : 1 green wrinkled
Phenotypic ratio

Yes, this cross would also have allowed Mendel to make different predictions for the two hypotheses, thereby allowing him to distinguish the correct one. **Figure 11.10** Your classmate would probably point out that the F_1 generation hybrids show an intermediate phenotype between those of the homozygous parents, which supports the blending hypothesis. You could respond that crossing the F_1 hybrids results in the reappearance of the white phenotype, rather than identical pink offspring, which fails to support the idea of traits blending during inheritance, in which case the white trait would have been lost after the F_1 generation. **Figure 11.11** Both the I^A and I^B alleles are dominant to the *i* allele, which is recessive and results in no attached carbohydrate. The I^A and I^B alleles are codominant; both are expressed in the phenotype of I^AI^B heterozygotes, who have type AB blood. **Figure 11.15** In the Punnett square, two of the three individuals with normal coloration are carriers, so the probability is ⅔. (Note that you must take into account everything you know when you calculate probability: You know she is not *aa*, so there are only three possible genotypes to consider.)

Concept Check 11.1

1. According to the law of independent assortment, 25 plants (1/16 of the offspring) are predicted to be *aatt*, or recessive for both characters. The actual result is likely to differ slightly from this value.

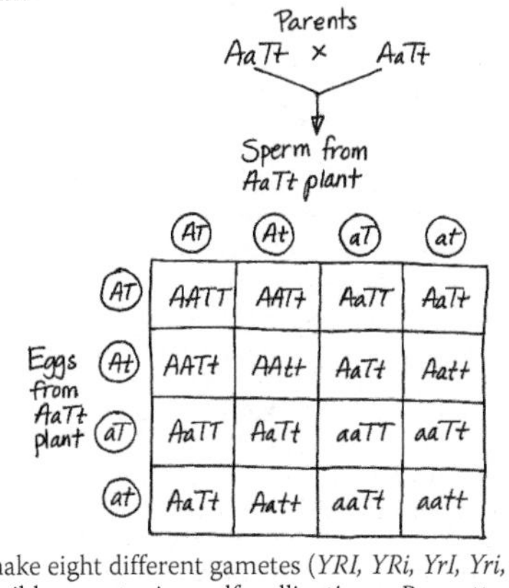

Parents
AaTt × AaTt
Sperm from AaTt plant
AT At aT at
Eggs from AaTt plant
AT AATT AATt AaTT AaTt
At AATt AAtt AaTt Aatt
aT AaTT AaTt aaTT aaTt
at AaTt Aatt aaTt aatt

2. The plant could make eight different gametes (*YRI, YRi, YrI, Yri, yRI, yRi, yrI,* and *yri*). To fit all the possible gametes in a self-pollination, a Punnett square would need 8 rows and 8 columns. It would have spaces for the 64 possible unions of gametes in the offspring. **3.** Self-pollination is sexual reproduction because meiosis is involved in forming gametes, which unite during fertilization. As a result, the offspring in self-pollination are genetically different from the parent.

Concept Check 11.2

1. ½ homozygous dominant (*AA*), 0 homozygous recessive (*aa*), and ½ heterozygous (*Aa*) **2.** ¼ *BBDD*; ¼ *BbDD*; ¼ *BBDd*; ¼ *BbDd* **3.** The genotypes that fulfill this condition are *ppyyIi, ppYyii, Ppyyii, ppYYii,* and *ppyyii*. Use the multiplication rule to find the probability of getting each genotype and then use the addition rule to find the overall probability of meeting the conditions of this problem:

ppyyIi	½ (probability of *pp*) × ¼ (*yy*) × ½ (*Ii*)	= 1/16
ppYyii	½ (*pp*) × ½ (*Yy*) × ½ (*ii*)	= 2/16
Ppyyii	½ (*Pp*) × ¼ (*yy*) × ½ (*ii*)	= 1/16
ppYYii	½ (*pp*) × ¼ (*YY*) × ½ (*ii*)	= 1/16
ppyyii	½ (*pp*) × ¼ (*yy*) × ½ (*ii*)	= 1/16
Fraction predicted to have at least two recessive traits		= 6/16 or 3/8

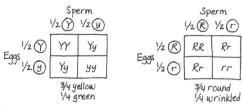

Concept Check 11.3

1. Incomplete dominance describes the relationship between two alleles of a single gene, whereas epistasis relates to the genetic relationship between two genes (and the respective alleles of each). **2.** Half of the children would be expected to have type A blood and half type B blood. **3.** The black and white alleles are incompletely dominant, with heterozygotes being gray in color. A cross between a gray rooster and a black hen should yield approximately equal numbers of gray and black offspring.

Concept Check 11.4

1. 1/9 (Since cystic fibrosis is caused by a recessive allele, Beth and Tom's siblings who have CF must be homozygous recessive. Therefore, each parent must be a carrier of the recessive allele. Since neither Beth nor Tom has CF, this means they each have a ⅔ chance of being a carrier. If they are both carriers, there is a ¼ chance that they will have a child with CF. ⅔ × ⅔ × ¼ = 1/9); 0 (Both Beth and Tom would have to be carriers to produce a child with the disease.) **2.** In the monohybrid cross involving flower color, the ratio is 3.15 purple : 1 white, while in the human family in the pedigree, the ratio in the third generation is 1 can taste PTC : 1 cannot taste PTC. The difference is due to the small sample size (two offspring) in the human family. If the second-generation couple in this pedigree were able to have 929 offspring as in the pea plant cross, the ratio would likely be closer to 3:1. (Note that none of the pea plant crosses in Table 11.1 yielded *exactly* a 3:1 ratio.)

Summary of Key Concepts Questions

11.1 Alternative versions of genes, called alleles, are passed from parent to offspring during sexual reproduction. In a cross between purple- and white-flowered homozygous parents, the F_1 offspring are all heterozygous, each inheriting a purple allele from one parent and a white allele from the other. Because the purple allele is dominant, it determines the phenotype of the F_1 offspring to be purple, and the expression of the recessive white allele is masked. Only in the F_2 generation is it possible for a white allele to exist in the homozygous state, which causes the white trait to be expressed.

11.2

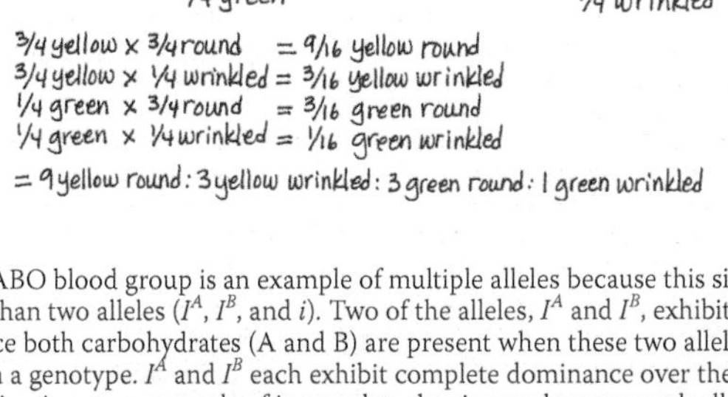

Sperm
1/2 Y 1/2 y
Eggs
1/2 Y YY Yy
1/2 y Yy yy
3/4 yellow
1/4 green
Sperm
1/2 R 1/2 r
Eggs
1/2 R RR Rr
1/2 r Rr rr
3/4 round
1/4 wrinkled
3/4 yellow × 3/4 round = 9/16 yellow round
3/4 yellow × 1/4 wrinkled = 3/16 yellow wrinkled
1/4 green × 3/4 round = 3/16 green round
1/4 green × 1/4 wrinkled = 1/16 green wrinkled
= 9 yellow round : 3 yellow wrinkled : 3 green round : 1 green wrinkled

11.3 The ABO blood group is an example of multiple alleles because this single gene has more than two alleles (I^A, I^B, and *i*). Two of the alleles, I^A and I^B, exhibit codominance, since both carbohydrates (A and B) are present when these two alleles exist together in a genotype. I^A and I^B each exhibit complete dominance over the *i* allele. This situation is not an example of incomplete dominance because each allele affects the phenotype in a distinguishable way, so the result is not intermediate between the two phenotypes. Because this situation involves a single gene, it is not an example of epistasis or polygenic inheritance. **11.4** The chance of the fourth child having cystic fibrosis is ¼, as it was for each of the other children, because each birth is an independent event. We already know that both parents are carriers, so whether their first three children are carriers or not has no bearing on the probability that their next child will have the disease. The parents' genotypes provide the only relevant information.

Test Your Understanding

1.

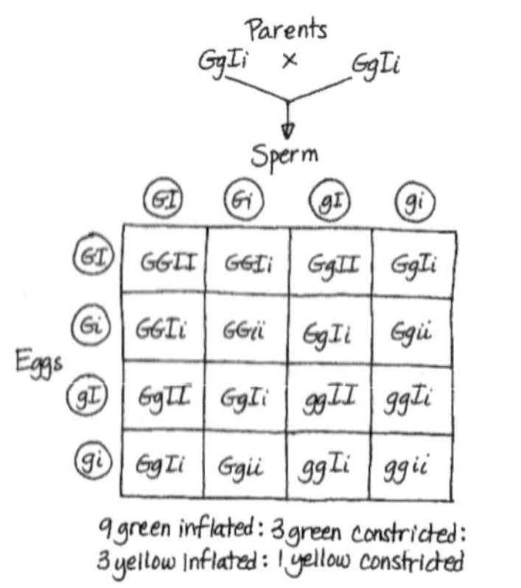
Parents
GgIi × GgIi
Sperm
GI Gi gI gi
Eggs
GI GGII GGIi GgII GgIi
Gi GGIi GGii GgIi Ggii
gI GgII GgIi ggII ggIi
gi GgIi Ggii ggIi ggii
9 green inflated : 3 green constricted :
3 yellow inflated : 1 yellow constricted

2. Man I^Ai; woman I^Bi; child ii. Genotypes for future children are predicted to be $\frac{1}{4}\, I^AI^B$, $\frac{1}{4}\, I^Ai$, $\frac{1}{4}\, I^Bi$, $\frac{1}{4}\, ii$. **3.** $\frac{1}{2}$ **4.** A cross of *Ii* × *ii* would yield offspring with a genotypic ratio of 1 *Ii* : 1 *ii* (2:2 is an equivalent answer) and a phenotypic ratio of 1 inflated : 1 constricted (2:2 is equivalent).

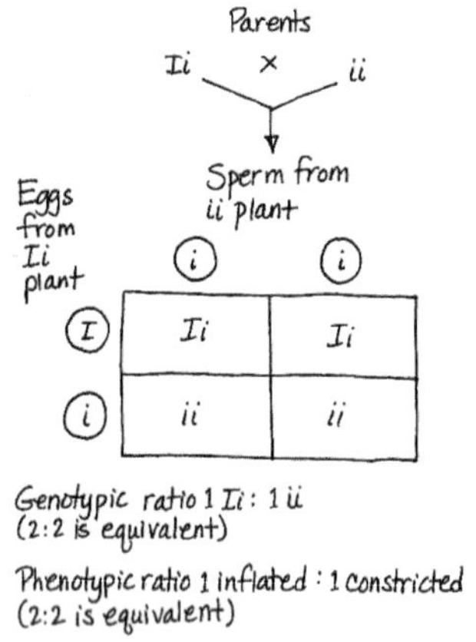
Parents
Ii × ii
Sperm from ii plant
Eggs from Ii plant
i i
I Ii Ii
i ii ii
Genotypic ratio 1 Ii : 1 ii
(2:2 is equivalent)
Phenotypic ratio 1 inflated : 1 constricted
(2:2 is equivalent)

5. (a) $\frac{1}{64}$; (b) $\frac{1}{64}$; (c) $\frac{1}{8}$; (d) $\frac{1}{32}$ **6.** (a) $\frac{3}{4} \times \frac{3}{4} \times \frac{3}{4} = \frac{27}{64}$; (b) $1 - \frac{27}{64} = \frac{37}{64}$; (c) $\frac{1}{4} \times \frac{1}{4} \times \frac{1}{4} = \frac{1}{64}$; (d) $1 - \frac{1}{64} = \frac{63}{64}$ **7.** (a) $\frac{1}{256}$; (b) $\frac{1}{16}$; (c) $\frac{1}{256}$; (d) $\frac{1}{64}$; (e) $\frac{1}{128}$ **8.** (a) 1; (b) $\frac{1}{32}$; (c) $\frac{1}{8}$; (d) $\frac{1}{2}$ **9.** $\frac{1}{9}$ **10.** Matings of the original mutant cat with true-breeding noncurl cats will produce both curl and noncurl F_1 offspring if the curl allele is dominant, but only noncurl offspring if the curl allele is recessive. You would obtain some true-breeding offspring homozygous for the curl allele from matings between the F_1 cats resulting from the original curl × noncurl crosses. If dominant, you wouldn't be able to tell true-breeding, homozygous offspring from heterozygotes without further crosses whether the curl trait is dominant or recessive. You know that cats are true-breeding when curl × curl matings produce only curl offspring for several generations. As it turns out, the allele that causes curled ears is dominant. **11.** 25%, or $\frac{1}{4}$, will be cross-eyed; all (100%) of the cross-eyed offspring will also be white. **12.** The dominant allele *I* is epistatic to the *P/p* locus, and thus the genotypic ratio for the F_1 generation will be 9 *I–P–* (colorless) : 3 *I–pp* (colorless) : 3 *iiP–* (purple) : 1 *iipp* (red). Overall, the phenotypic ratio is 12 colorless : 3 purple : 1 red. **13.** Recessive. All affected individuals (Arlene, Tom, Wilma, and Carla) are homozygous recessive *aa*. George is *Aa*, since some of his children with Arlene are affected. Sam, Ann, Daniel, and Alan are each *Aa*, since they are all unaffected children with one affected parent. Michael also is *Aa*, since he has an affected child (Carla) with his heterozygous wife Ann. Sandra, Tina, and Christopher can each have either the *AA* or *Aa* genotype. **14.** $\frac{1}{6}$

Chapter 12

Figure Questions

Figure 12.2 The ratio would be 1 yellow round : 1 green round : 1 yellow wrinkled : 1 green wrinkled. **Figure 12.4** About $\frac{3}{4}$ of the F_2 offspring would have red eyes and about $\frac{1}{4}$ would have white eyes. About half of the white-eyed flies would be female and half would be male; similarly, about half of the red-eyed flies would be female and half would be male. (Note that the homologs with the eye-color alleles would be the same shape in the Punnett square, and each offspring would inherit two alleles. The sex of the flies would be determined separately by inheritance of the sex chromosomes. Thus your Punnett square would have four possible combinations in sperm and four in eggs; it would have 16 squares altogether.) **Figure 12.7** All the males would be color-blind, and all the females would be carriers. (Another way to say this is that $\frac{1}{2}$ the offspring would be color-blind males, and $\frac{1}{2}$ the offspring would be carrier females.) **Figure 12.9** The two largest classes would still be the offspring with the phenotypes of the true-breeding P generation flies, but now they would be gray vestigial and black normal because those were the specific allele combinations in the P generation. **Figure 12.10** The two chromosomes on the left side of the sketch are like the two chromosomes inherited by the F_1 female, one from each P generation fly. They are passed by the F_1 female intact to the offspring and thus could be called "parental" chromosomes. The other two chromosomes result from crossing over during meiosis in the F_1 female. Because they have combinations of alleles not seen in either of the F_1 female's chromosomes, they can be called "recombinant" chromosomes. (Note that in this example, the alleles on the recombinant chromosomes, $b^+\ vg^+$ and *b vg*, are the allele combinations that were on the parental chromosomes in the cross shown in Figures 12.9 and 12.10. The basis for calling them parental chromosomes is that they have the combination of alleles that was present on the P generation chromosomes.)

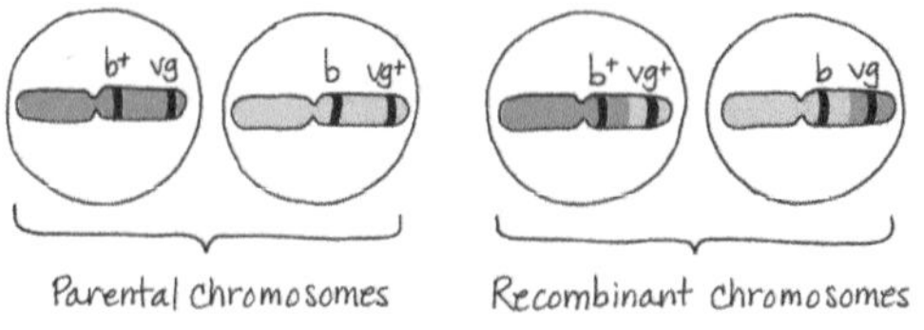
b+ vg
b vg+
b+ vg+
b vg
Parental Chromosomes
Recombinant Chromosomes

Concept Check 12.1

1. The law of segregation relates to the inheritance of alleles for a single character. The law of independent assortment of alleles relates to the inheritance of alleles for two characters. **2.** The physical basis for the law of segregation is the separation of homologs in anaphase I. The physical basis for the law of independent assortment is the alternative arrangements of all the different homologous chromosome pairs in metaphase I. **3.** To show the mutant phenotype, a male needs to possess only one mutant allele. If this gene had been on a pair of autosomes, the two alleles would both have had to be mutant for an individual to show the recessive mutant phenotype, a much less probable situation.

Concept Check 12.2

1. Because the gene for this eye-color character is located on the X chromosome, all female offspring will be red-eyed and heterozygous ($X^{w^+}X^w$); all male offspring will inherit a Y chromosome from the father and be white-eyed (X^wY). (Another way to say this is that $\frac{1}{2}$ the offspring will be red-eyed, heterozygous [carrier] females, and $\frac{1}{2}$ will be white-eyed males.) **2.** $\frac{1}{4}$ ($\frac{1}{2}$ chance that the child will inherit a Y chromosome from the father and be male × $\frac{1}{2}$ chance that he will inherit the X carrying the disease allele from his mother); if the child is a boy, there is a $\frac{1}{2}$ chance he will have the disease; a female would have zero chance (but $\frac{1}{2}$ chance of being a carrier). **3.** With a disorder caused by a dominant allele, there is no such thing as a "carrier," since those with the allele have the disorder. Because the allele is dominant, the females lose any "advantage" in having two X chromosomes, since one disorder-associated allele is sufficient to result in the disorder. All fathers who have the dominant allele will pass it along to *all* their daughters, who will also have the disorder. A mother who has the allele (and thus the disorder) will pass it to half of her sons and half of her daughters.

Concept Check 12.3

1. Crossing over during meiosis I in the heterozygous parent produces some gametes with recombinant genotypes for the two genes. Offspring with a recombinant phenotype arise from fertilization of the recombinant gametes by homozygous recessive gametes from the double-mutant parent. **2.** In each case, the alleles contributed by the female parent (in the egg) determine the phenotype of the offspring because the male in this cross contributes only recessive alleles. Thus, identifying the phenotype of the offspring tells you what alleles were in its mother's (the dihybrid female's) egg. **3.** No. The order could be *A-C-B* or *C-A-B*. To determine which possibility is correct, you need to know the recombination frequency between *B* and *C*.

Concept Check 12.4

1. In meiosis, a combined 14-21 chromosome will behave as one chromosome. If a gamete receives the combined 14-21 chromosome and a normal copy of chromosome 21, trisomy 21 will result when this gamete combines with a normal gamete during fertilization. **2.** No. The child can be either I^AI^Ai or I^Aii. A sperm of genotype I^AI^A could result from nondisjunction in the father during meiosis II, while an egg with the genotype *ii* could result from nondisjunction in the mother during either meiosis I or meiosis II. **3.** Activation of this gene could lead to the production of too much of this kinase. If the kinase is involved in a signaling pathway that triggers cell division, too much of it could trigger unrestricted cell division, which in turn could contribute to the development of a cancer (in this case, a cancer of one type of white blood cell). **4.** The inactivation of two X chromosomes in XXX women would leave them with one genetically active X, as in women with the normal number of chromosomes. Microscopy should reveal two Barr bodies in XXX women.

Summary of Key Concepts Questions

12.1 Because the sex chromosomes are different from each other and because they determine the sex of the offspring, Morgan could use the sex of the offspring as a phenotypic character to follow the parental chromosomes. (He could also have followed them under a microscope, as the X and Y chromosomes look different.) At the same time, he could record eye color to follow the eye-color alleles. **12.2** Males have only one X chromosome, along with a Y chromosome, while females have two X chromosomes. The Y chromosome has very few genes on it, while the X has about 1,000. When a recessive X-linked allele that causes a disorder is inherited by a male on the X from his mother, there isn't a second allele present on the Y (males are hemizygous), so the male has the disorder. Because females have two X chromosomes, they must inherit two recessive alleles in order to have the disorder, a rarer occurrence. **12.3** Crossing over results in new combinations of alleles. Crossing over is a random occurrence, and the more distance there is between two genes, the more chances there are for crossing over to occur, leading to a new allele combination. **12.4** In inversions and reciprocal translocations, the same genetic material is present in the same relative amount but just organized differently. In aneuploidy, duplications, deletions, and nonreciprocal translocations, the balance of genetic material is upset, as large segments are either missing or present in more than one copy. Apparently, this type of imbalance is very damaging to the organism. (Although it isn't lethal in the developing embryo, the reciprocal translocation that produces the Philadelphia chromosome can lead to a serious condition, cancer, by altering the expression of important genes.)

Test Your Understanding

1. 0; ½; ⅟₁₆ **2.** Recessive; if the disorder were dominant, it would affect at least one parent of a child born with the disorder. The disorder's inheritance is sex-linked because it is seen only in boys. For a girl to have the disorder, she would have to inherit recessive alleles from *both* parents. This would be very rare, since males with the recessive allele on their X chromosome die in their early teens. **3.** Between *T* and *A*, 12%; between *A* and *S*, 5% **4.** Between *T* and *S*, 18%; sequence of genes is *T–A–S*. **5.** ¼ for each daughter (½ chance that the child will be female × ½ chance of a homozygous recessive genotype); ½ for first son **6.** About one-third of the distance from the vestigial-wing locus to the brown-eye locus **7.** 6%; wild-type heterozygous for normal wings and red eyes × recessive homozygous for vestigial wings and purple eyes **8.** Fifty percent of the offspring will show phenotypes resulting from crossovers. These results would be the same as those from a cross where *A* and *B* were *not* on the same chromosome, and you would interpret the results to mean that the genes are unlinked. (Further crosses involving other genes on the same chromosome would reveal the genetic linkage and map distances.) **9.** 450 each of blue-oval and white-round (parentals) and 50 each of blue-round and white-oval (recombinants) **10.** (a) For each pair of genes, you had to generate an F₁ dihybrid fly; let's use the *A* and *B* genes as an example. You obtained homozygous parental flies, either the first with dominant alleles of the two genes (*AABB*) and the second with recessive alleles (*aabb*), or the first with dominant alleles of gene *A* and recessive alleles of gene *B* (*AAbb*) and the second with recessive alleles of gene *A* and dominant alleles of gene *B* (*aaBB*). Breeding either of these pairs of P generation flies gave you an F₁ dihybrid, which you then testcrossed with a doubly homozygous recessive fly (*aabb*). You classed the offspring as parental or recombinant, based on the genotypes of the P generation parents (either of the two pairs described above). You added up the number of recombinant types and then divided by the total number of offspring. This gave you the recombination percentage (in this case, 8%), which you can translate into map units (8 map units) to construct your map.
(b)

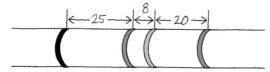

Chapter 13

Figure Questions

Figure 13.3 The living S cells found in the blood sample were able to reproduce to yield more S cells, indicating that the S trait is a permanent, heritable change, rather than just a one-time use of the dead S cells' capsules. **Figure 13.5** The radioactivity would have been found in the pellet when proteins were labeled (batch 1) because proteins would have had to enter the bacterial cells to program them with genetic instructions. It's hard for us to imagine now, but the DNA might have played a structural role that allowed some of the proteins to be injected while it remained outside the bacterial cell (thus no radioactivity in the pellet in batch 2). **Figure 13.13** The tube from the first replication would look the same, with a middle band of hybrid ¹⁵N - ¹⁴N DNA, but the second tube would not have the upper band of two light blue strands. Instead, it would have a bottom band of two dark blue strands, like the bottom band in the result predicted after one replication in the conservative model. **Figure 13.15** In the bubble at the top of the micrograph in (b), arrows should be drawn pointing left and right to indicate the two replication forks. **Figure 13.16** Looking at any of the DNA strands, we see that one end is called the 5′ end and the other the 3′ end. If we proceed from the 5′ end to the 3′ end on the left-most strand, for example, we list the components in this order: phosphate group → 5′ C of the sugar → 3′ C → phosphate → 5′ C → 3′ C. Going in the opposite direction on the same strand, the components proceed in the reverse order: 3′ C → 5′ C → phosphate. Thus, the two directions are distinguishable, which is what we mean when we say that the strands have directionality. (Review Figure 13.6 if necessary.)

Figure 13.19

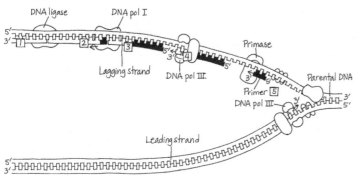

Figure 13.20

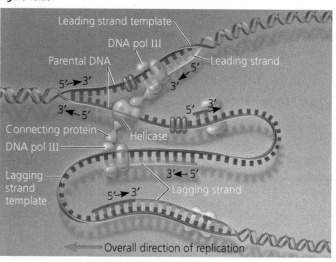

Figure 13.25

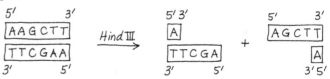

Concept Check 13.1

1. In order to tell which end is the 5′ end, you need to know which end has a phosphate group on the 5′ carbon (the 5′ end) or which end has an —OH group on the 3′ carbon (the 3′ end). **2.** Griffith expected that the mouse injected with the mixture of heat-killed S cells and living R cells would survive, since neither type of cell alone could kill the mouse.

Concept Check 13.2

1. Complementary base pairing ensures that the two daughter molecules are exact copies of the parental molecule. When the two strands of the parental molecule separate, each serves as a template on which nucleotides are arranged, by the base-pairing rules, into new complementary strands.
2.

Protein	Function
Helicase	Unwinds parental double helix at replication forks
Single-strand binding protein	Binds to and stabilizes single-stranded DNA until it can be used as a template
Topoisomerase	Relieves "overwinding" strain ahead of replication forks by breaking, swiveling, and rejoining DNA strands
Primase	Synthesizes an RNA primer at 5′ end of leading strand and at 5′ end of each Okazaki fragment of lagging strand
DNA pol III	Using parental DNA as a template, synthesizes new DNA strand by covalently adding nucleotides to 3′ end of a preexisting DNA strand or RNA primer
DNA pol I	Removes RNA nucleotides of previous fragment's primer from its 5′ end and replaces them with DNA nucleotides attached to 3′ end of next fragment
DNA ligase	Joins 3′ end of DNA that replaces primer to rest of leading strand and joins Okazaki fragments of lagging strand

3. In the cell cycle, DNA synthesis occurs during the S phase, between the G₁ and G₂ phases of interphase. DNA replication is therefore complete before the mitotic phase begins.

Concept Check 13.3

1. A nucleosome is made up of eight histone proteins, two each of four different types, around which DNA is wound. Linker DNA runs from one nucleosome to the next.
2. Euchromatin is chromatin that becomes less compacted during interphase and is accessible to the cellular machinery responsible for gene activity. Heterochromatin, on the other hand, remains quite condensed during interphase and contains genes that are largely inaccessible to this machinery.

Concept Check 13.4

1. The covalent sugar-phosphate bonds of the DNA strands   **2.** Yes, *Pvu*I will cut the molecule (at the position indicated by the dashed red line).

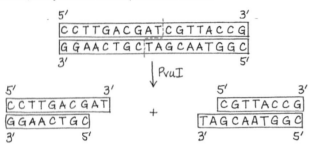

3. Cloning requires joining two pieces of DNA—a cloning vector, such as a bacterial plasmid, and a gene or DNA fragment from another source. Both pieces must be cut with the same restriction enzyme, creating sticky ends that will base-pair with complementary ends on other fragments. (The sugar-phosphate backbones will then be ligated together by ligase.) In PCR, the primers must base-pair with their target sequences in the DNA mixture, bracketing one specific region among many, and complementary base pairing is the basis for the building of the new strand during the extension step. In DNA sequencing, primers base-pair to the template, allowing DNA synthesis to start, and then nucleotides are added to the growing strand based on complementarity of base pairing. Using the CRISPR-Cas9 system to edit genes involves an RNA used as a guide that is complementary to the sequence to be edited. Complementary base pairing anchors the Cas9 protein to the target DNA sequence it will then cut.

Summary of Key Concepts Questions

13.1 Each strand in the double helix has polarity, the end with a phosphate group on the 5′ carbon of the sugar being called the 5′ end, and the end with an —OH group on the 3′ carbon of the sugar being called the 3′ end. The two strands run in opposite directions, one running 5′ → 3′ and the other running 3′ → 5′. Thus, each end of the molecule has both a 5′ and a 3′ end. This arrangement is called "antiparallel." If the strands were parallel, they would both run 5′ → 3′ in the same direction, so an end of the molecule would have either two 5′ ends or two 3′ ends.   **13.2** On both the leading and lagging strands, DNA polymerase adds onto the 3′ end of an RNA primer synthesized by primase, synthesizing DNA in the 5′ → 3′ direction. Because the parental strands are antiparallel, however, only on the leading strand does synthesis proceed continuously into the replication fork. The lagging strand is synthesized bit by bit in the direction away from the fork as a series of shorter Okazaki fragments, which are later joined together by DNA ligase. Each fragment is initiated by synthesis of an RNA primer by primase as soon as a given stretch of single-stranded template strand is opened up. Although both strands are synthesized at the same rate, synthesis of the lagging strand is delayed because initiation of each fragment begins only when sufficient template strand is available.   **13.3** Most of the chromatin in an interphase nucleus is fairly uncondensed. Much is present as the 30-nm fiber, with some in the form of the 10-nm fiber and some as looped domains of the 30-nm fiber. (These different levels of chromatin packing may reflect differences in gene expression occurring in these regions.) Also, a small percentage of the chromatin, such as that at the centromeres and telomeres, is highly condensed heterochromatin.   **13.4** A plasmid vector and a source of foreign DNA to be cloned are both cut with the same restriction enzyme, generating restriction fragments with sticky ends. These fragments are mixed together, ligated, and reintroduced into bacterial cells, which can then make many copies of the foreign DNA or its product.

Test Your Understanding

1. C   **2.** A   **3.** B   **4.** D   **5.** C   **6.** B   **7.** D   **8.** B   **9.** A   **10.** Like histones, the *E. coli* proteins would be expected to contain many basic (positively charged) amino acids, such as lysine and arginine, which can form weak bonds with the negatively charged phosphate groups on the sugar-phosphate backbone of the DNA molecule.

11.

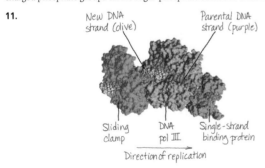

Chapter 14

Figure Questions

Figure 14.5 The mRNA sequence (5′-UGGUUUGGCUCA-3′) is the same as the nontemplate DNA strand sequence (5′-TGGTTTGGCTCA-3′), except there is a U in the mRNA wherever there is a T in the DNA.   **Figure 14.8** The processes are similar in that polymerases form polynucleotides complementary to an antiparallel DNA template strand. In replication, however, both strands act as templates, whereas in transcription, only one DNA strand acts as a template.   **Figure 14.9** The RNA polymerase would bind directly to the promoter, rather than being dependent on the previous binding of other factors.

Figure 14.12

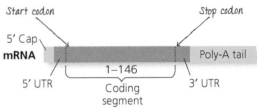

Figure 14.23 The mRNA farthest to the right (the longest one) started being transcribed first. The ribosome at the top, closest to the DNA, started translating first and thus has the longest polypeptide.

Concept Check 14.1

1. Recessive   **2.** A polypeptide made up of 10 Gly (glycine) amino acids
3.

> Nontemplate sequence in 3′ to 5′ order: 3′-ACGACTGAA-5′
> mRNA sequence: 5′-UGCUGACUU-3′
> Translated: Cys-STOP

If the nontemplate sequence could have been used as a template for transcribing the mRNA, the protein translated from the mRNA would have a completely different amino acid sequence and would most likely be nonfunctional. (It would also be shorter because of the UGA stop signal shown in the mRNA sequence above—and possibly others earlier in the mRNA sequence.)

Concept Check 14.2

1. A promoter is the region of DNA to which RNA polymerase binds to begin transcription. It is at the upstream end of the gene (transcription unit).   **2.** In a bacterial cell, part of the RNA polymerase recognizes the gene's promoter and binds to it. In a eukaryotic cell, transcription factors mediate the binding of RNA polymerase to the promoter. In both cases, sequences in the promoter bind precisely to the RNA polymerase, so the enzyme is in the right location and orientation.
3. The transcription factor that recognizes the TATA sequence would be unable to bind, so RNA polymerase could not bind and transcription of that gene probably would not occur.

Concept Check 14.3

1. Due to alternative splicing of exons, each gene can result in multiple different mRNAs and can thus direct synthesis of multiple different proteins.   **2.** In watching a show recorded with a DVR, you watch segments of the show itself (exons) and fast-forward through the commercials, which are like introns. However, unlike introns, commercials remain in the recording, while the introns are cut out of the RNA transcript during RNA processing.   **3.** Once the mRNA has exited the nucleus, the cap prevents it from being degraded by hydrolytic enzymes and facilitates its attachment to ribosomes. If the cap were removed from all mRNAs, the cell would no longer be able to synthesize any proteins and would probably die.

Concept Check 14.4

1. First, each aminoacyl-tRNA synthetase specifically recognizes a single amino acid and attaches it only to an appropriate tRNA. Second, a tRNA charged with its specific amino acid binds only to an mRNA codon for that amino acid.   **2.** The structure and function of the ribosome seem to depend more on the rRNAs than on the ribosomal proteins. Because it is single-stranded, an RNA molecule can hydrogen-bond with itself and with other RNA molecules. RNA molecules make up the interface between the two ribosomal subunits, so presumably RNA-RNA binding helps hold the ribosome together. The binding site for mRNA in the ribosome includes rRNA that can bind the mRNA. Also, complementary hydrogen bonding within an RNA molecule allows it to assume a particular three-dimensional shape and, along with the RNA's functional groups, presumably enables rRNA to catalyze peptide bond formation during translation.   **3.** A signal peptide on the leading end of the polypeptide being synthesized is recognized by a signal-recognition particle that brings the ribosome to the ER membrane. There the ribosome attaches and continues to synthesize the polypeptide, depositing it in the ER lumen.   **4.** Because of wobble, the tRNA could bind to either 5′-GCA-3′ or 5′-GCG-3′, both of which code for alanine (Ala). Alanine would be attached to the tRNA (see diagram, upper right).

Concept Check 14.5

1. In the mRNA, the reading frame downstream from the deletion is shifted, leading to a long string of incorrect amino acids in the polypeptide, and in most cases, a stop codon will arise, leading to premature termination. The polypeptide will most likely be nonfunctional. **2.** Heterozygous individuals, said to have sickle-cell trait, have a copy each of the wild-type allele and the sickle-cell allele. Both alleles will be expressed, so these individuals will have both normal and sickle-cell hemoglobin molecules. Apparently, having a mix of the two forms of β-globin has no effect under most conditions, but during prolonged periods of low blood oxygen (such as at higher altitudes), these individuals can show some signs of sickle-cell disease.

3.

Normal DNA sequence
(template strand is on top): 3′–TACTTGTCCGATATC–5′
                              5′–ATGAACAGGCTATAG–3′

mRNA sequence: 5′–AUGAACAGGCUAUAG–3′

Amino acid Sequence: Met-Asn-Arg-Leu-STOP

Mutated DNA sequence
(template strand is on top): 3′–TACTTGTCCAATATC–5′
                              5′–ATGAACAGGTTATAG–3′

mRNA sequence: 5′–AUGAACAGGUUAUAG–3′

Amino acid sequence: Met-Asn-Arg-Leu-STOP

No effect: The amino acid sequence is Met-Asn-Arg-Leu both before and after the mutation because the mRNA codons 5′-CUA-3′ and 5′-UUA-3′ both code for Leu. (The fifth codon is a stop codon.)

Summary of Key Concepts Questions

14.1 A gene contains genetic information in the form of a nucleotide sequence. The gene is first transcribed into an RNA molecule, and a messenger RNA molecule is ultimately translated into a polypeptide. The polypeptide makes up part or all of a protein, which performs a function in the cell and contributes to the phenotype of the organism. **14.2** Both bacterial and eukaryotic genes have promoters, regions where RNA polymerase ultimately binds and begins transcription. In bacteria, RNA polymerase binds directly to the promoter; in eukaryotes, transcription factors bind first to the promoter, and then RNA polymerase binds to the transcription factors and promoter together. **14.3** Both the 5′ cap and the 3′ poly-A tail help the mRNA exit from the nucleus and then, in the cytoplasm, help ensure mRNA stability and allow it to bind to ribosomes. **14.4** In the context of the ribosome, tRNAs function as translators between the nucleotide-based language of mRNA and the amino-acid-based language of polypeptides. A tRNA carries a specific amino acid, and the anticodon on the tRNA is complementary to the codon on the mRNA that codes for that amino acid. In the ribosome, the tRNA binds to the A site. Then the polypeptide being synthesized (currently on the tRNA in the P site) is joined to the new amino acid, which becomes the new (C-terminal) end of the polypeptide. Next, the tRNA in the A site moves to the P site. After the polypeptide is transferred to the new tRNA, thus adding the new amino acid, the now empty tRNA moves from the P site to the E site, where it exits the ribosome. **14.5** When a nucleotide base is altered chemically, its base-pairing characteristics may be changed. When that happens, an incorrect nucleotide is likely to be incorporated into the complementary strand during the next replication of the DNA, and successive rounds of replication will perpetuate the mutation. Once the gene is transcribed, the mutated codon may code for a different amino acid that inhibits or changes the function of a protein. If the chemical change in the base is detected and repaired by the DNA repair system before the next replication, no mutation will result.

Test Your Understanding

1. B **2.** C **3.** A **4.** A **5.** B **6.** C **7.** D **8.** No. Transcription and translation are separated in space and time in a eukaryotic cell, as a result of the eukaryotic cell's nuclear membrane.

9.

Type of RNA	Functions
Messenger RNA (mRNA)	Carries information specifying amino acid sequences of proteins from DNA to ribosomes
Transfer RNA (tRNA)	Serves as translator molecule in protein synthesis; translates mRNA codons into amino acids
Ribosomal RNA (rRNA)	Plays catalytic (ribozyme) roles and structural roles in ribosomes
Primary transcript	Is a precursor to mRNA, rRNA, or tRNA, before being processed; some intron RNA acts as a ribozyme, catalyzing its own splicing
Small RNAs in spliceosome	Play structural and catalytic roles in spliceosomes, the complexes of protein and RNA that splice pre-mRNA

results show that being reared from the egg stage on one plant species or the other did not result in the adult having a beak length appropriate for that host; instead, adult beak lengths were determined primarily by the population from which the eggs were obtained. Because an egg from a balloon vine population likely had long-beaked parents, while an egg from a goldenrain tree population likely had short-beaked parents, these results indicate that beak length is an inherited trait. **Figure 19.20** Hind limb structure changed first. *Rodhocetus* lacked flukes, but its pelvic bones and hind limbs had changed substantially from how those bones were shaped and arranged in *Pakicetus*. For example, in *Rodhocetus*, the pelvis and hind limbs appear to be oriented for paddling, whereas they were oriented for walking in *Pakicetus*.

Concept Check 19.1

1. Hutton and Lyell proposed that geologic events in the past were caused by the same processes operating today, at the same gradual rate. This principle suggested that Earth must be much older than a few thousand years, the age that was widely accepted in the early 19th century. Hutton's and Lyell's ideas also stimulated Darwin to reason that the slow accumulation of small changes could ultimately produce the profound changes documented in the fossil record. In this context, the age of Earth was important to Darwin, because unless Earth was very old, he could not envision how there would have been enough time for evolution to occur. **2.** By this criterion, Cuvier's explanation of the fossil record and Lamarck's hypothesis of evolution are both scientific. Cuvier thought that species did not evolve over time. He also suggested that sudden, catastrophic events caused extinctions in particular areas. These assertions can be tested against the fossil record. With respect to Lamarck, his principle of use and disuse can be used to make testable predictions for fossils of groups such as whale ancestors as they adapted to a new habitat. Lamarck's principle of use and disuse and his associated principle of the inheritance of acquired characteristics can also be tested directly in living organisms.

Concept Check 19.2

1. Organisms share characteristics (the unity of life) because they share common ancestors; the great diversity of life occurs because new species have repeatedly formed when descendant organisms gradually adapted to different environments, becoming different from their ancestors. **2.** The fossil mammal species (or its ancestors) would most likely have colonized the Andes from within South America, whereas ancestors of mammals currently found in Asian mountains would most likely have colonized those mountains from other parts of Asia. As a result, the Andes fossil species would share a more recent common ancestor with South American mammals than with mammals in Asia. Thus, for many of its traits, the fossil mammal species would probably more closely resemble mammals that live in South American jungles than mammals that live on Asian mountains. It is also possible, however, that the fossil mammal species could resemble the Asian mountain mammals because similar environments selected for similar adaptations (even though they were only distantly related to one another). **3.** As long as the white phenotype (encoded by the genotype *pp*) continues to be favored by natural selection, the frequency of the *p* allele will likely increase over time in the population. If the proportion of white individuals increases relative to purple individuals, the frequency of the recessive *p* allele will also increase relative to that of the *P* allele, which only appears in purple individuals (some of which also carry a *p* allele).

Concept Check 19.3

1. An environmental factor such as a drug does not *create* new traits, such as drug resistance, but rather *selects for* traits among those that are already present in the population. **2.** (a) Despite their different functions, the forelimbs of different mammals are structurally similar because they all represent modifications of a structure found in the common ancestor. (b) This is a case of convergent evolution. The similarities between the sugar glider and flying squirrel indicate that similar environments selected for similar adaptations despite different ancestry. **3.** At the time that dinosaurs originated, Earth's landmasses formed a single large continent, Pangaea. Because many dinosaurs were large and mobile, it is likely that early members of these groups lived on many different parts of Pangaea. When Pangaea broke apart, fossils of these organisms would have moved with the rocks in which they were deposited. As a result, we would predict that fossils of early dinosaurs would have a broad geographic distribution (this prediction has been upheld).

Summary of Key Concepts Questions

19.1 Darwin thought that descent with modification occurred as a gradual, steplike process. The age of Earth was important to him because if Earth were only a few thousand years old (as conventional wisdom suggested), there wouldn't have been sufficient time for major evolutionary change. **19.2** All species have the potential to overreproduce—that is, to produce more offspring than can be supported by the environment. This ensures that there will be what Darwin called a "struggle for existence" in which many of the offspring are eaten, starved, diseased, or unable to reproduce for a variety of other reasons. Members of a population exhibit a range of heritable variations, some of which make it likely that their bearers will leave more offspring than other individuals (for example, the bearer may escape predators more effectively or be more tolerant of the physical conditions of the environment). Over time, natural selection resulting from factors such as predators, lack of food, or the physical conditions of the environment can increase the proportion of individuals with favorable traits in a population (evolutionary adaptation). **19.3** The hypothesis that cetaceans originated from a terrestrial mammal and are closely related to even-toed ungulates is supported by several lines of evidence. For example, fossils document that early cetaceans had hind limbs, as expected for organisms that descended from a land mammal; these fossils also show that cetacean hind limbs became reduced over time. Other fossils show that early cetaceans had a type of ankle bone that is otherwise found only in even-toed ungulates, providing strong evidence that even-toed ungulates are the land mammals to which cetaceans are most closely related. DNA sequence data also indicate that even-toed ungulates are the land mammals to which cetaceans are most closely related.

Test Your Understanding

1. B **2.** D **3.** C **4.** B **5.** A

Chapter 19

Figure Questions

Figure 19.6 The common cactus finch is more closely related to the large ground finch; Figure 1.17 shows that they share a more recent common ancestor than the common cactus finch shares with the green warbler finch. **Figure 19.9** The common ancestor lived more than 5.5 million years ago. **Figure 19.13** The colors and body forms of these mantises allow them to blend into their surroundings, providing an example of how organisms are well suited for life in their environments. The mantises also share features with one another (and with all other mantises), such as six legs, grasping forelimbs, and large eyes. These shared features illustrate another key observation about life: the unity of life that results from descent from a common ancestor. Over time, as these mantises diverged from a common ancestor, they accumulated different adaptations that made them well suited for life in their different environments. Eventually, as enough differences accumulated between mantis populations, new species were formed, thus contributing to the great diversity of life. **Figure 19.14** These

6. (a)

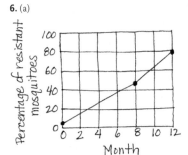

(b) The rapid rise in the percentage of mosquitoes resistant to DDT was most likely caused by natural selection in which mosquitoes resistant to DDT could survive and reproduce while other mosquitoes could not. (c) In India—where DDT resistance first appeared—natural selection would have caused the frequency of resistant mosquitoes to increase over time. If resistant mosquitoes then migrated from India (for example, transported by wind or in planes, trains, or ships) to other parts of the world, the frequency of DDT resistance would increase there as well. In addition, if resistance to DDT were to arise independently in mosquito populations outside of India, those populations would also experience an increase in the frequency of DDT resistance.

Chapter 20

Figure Questions
Figure 20.4 The branching pattern of the tree indicates that the badger and the wolf share a common ancestor that is more recent than the ancestor these two animals share with the leopard. **Figure 20.5** The new version (shown below) does not alter any of the evolutionary relationships shown in Figure 20.5. For example, B and C remain sister taxa, taxon A is still as closely related to taxon B as it is to taxon C, and so on.

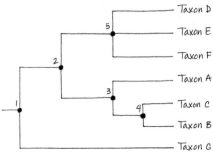

Figure 20.6 Unknown mtDNA sample #1b (a portion of sample #1) and unknown mtDNA samples #9–13 all would have to be located on the branch of the gene tree that currently leads to Minke (Southern Hemisphere) mtDNA and unknown mtDNA #1a and 2–8. **Figure 20.9** There are four possible bases (A, C, G, T) at each nucleotide position. If the base at each position depends on chance, not common descent, we would expect roughly one out of four (25%) of them to be the same. **Figure 20.11** You should have circled the branch point that is drawn farthest to the left (the common ancestor of all taxa shown). Both cetaceans and seals descended from terrestrial lineages of mammals, indicating that the cetacean-seal common ancestor had legs and lacked a streamlined body form. As a result, that ancestor would not be part of the cetacean-seal group. **Figure 20.12** You should have circled the frog, turtle, and leopard lineages, along with their most recent common ancestor. **Figure 20.16** The lizard and snake lineage is the most basal taxon shown (closest to the root of the tree). **Figure 20.21** This tree indicates that the sequences of rRNA and other genes in mitochondria are most closely related to those of proteobacteria, while the sequences of chloroplast genes are most closely related to those of cyanobacteria. These gene sequence relationships are what would be predicted from endosymbiont theory, which posits that both mitochondria and chloroplasts originated as engulfed prokaryotic cells.

Concept Check 20.1
1. We are classified the same from the domain level to the class level; both the leopard and human are mammals. Leopards belong to order Carnivora, whereas humans do not. **2.** The tree in (c) shows a different pattern of evolutionary relationships. In (c), C and B are sister taxa, whereas C and D are sister taxa in (a) and (b).
3.

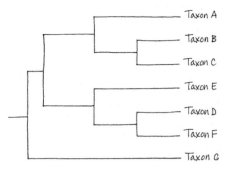

Concept Check 20.2
1. (a) Analogy, since porcupines and cacti are not closely related and since most other animals and plants do not have similar structures; (b) homology, since cats and humans are both mammals and have homologous forelimbs, of which the hand and paw are the lower part; (c) analogy, since owls and hornets are not closely related and since the structure of their wings is very different **2.** Species B and C are more likely to be closely related. Small genetic changes (as between species B and C) can produce divergent physical appearances, but if many genes have diverged greatly (as in species A and B), then the lineages have probably been separate for a long time.

Concept Check 20.3
1. No; hair is a shared ancestral character common to all mammals and thus is not helpful in distinguishing different mammalian subgroups. **2.** The principle of maximum parsimony states that the hypothesis about nature we investigate first should be the simplest explanation found to be consistent with the facts. Actual evolutionary relationships may differ from those inferred by parsimony owing to complicating factors such as convergent evolution. **3.** The traditional classification provides a poor match to evolutionary history, thus violating the basic principle of cladistics—that classification should be based on common descent. Both birds and mammals originated from groups traditionally designated as reptiles, making reptiles (as traditionally delineated) a paraphyletic group. These problems can be addressed by removing *Dimetrodon* and cynodonts from the reptiles and by regarding birds as a group of reptiles (specifically, as a group of dinosaurs).

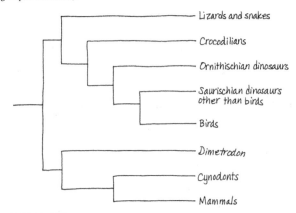

Concept Check 20.4
1. A molecular clock is a method of estimating the actual time of evolutionary events based on numbers of base changes in genes that are related by descent. It is based on the assumption that the regions of genomes being compared evolve at constant rates. **2.** There are many portions of the genome that do not code for genes; mutations that alter the sequence of bases in such regions could accumulate without affecting an organism's survival and reproduction. Even in coding regions of the genome, some mutations may not have a critical effect on genes or proteins. **3.** The gene (or genes) used for the molecular clock may have evolved more slowly in these two taxa than in the species used to calibrate the clock; as a result, the clock would underestimate the time at which the taxa diverged from each other.

Concept Check 20.5
1. The kingdom Monera included bacteria and archaea, but we now know that these organisms are in separate domains. Kingdoms are subsets of domains, so a single kingdom (like Monera) that includes taxa from different domains is not valid. **2.** Because of horizontal gene transfer, some genes in eukaryotes are more closely related to bacteria, while others are more closely related to archaea; thus, depending on which genes are used, phylogenetic trees constructed from DNA data can yield conflicting results.
3.

The fossil record indicates that prokaryotes originated long before eukaryotes. This suggests that the third tree, in which the eukaryotic lineage diverged first, is not accurate and hence is not likely to receive support from genetic data.

Summary of Key Concepts Questions
20.1 The fact that humans and chimpanzees are sister species indicates that we share a more recent common ancestor with chimpanzees than we do with any other living primate species. But that does not mean that humans evolved from chimpanzees, or vice versa; instead, it indicates that both humans and chimpanzees are descendants of that common ancestor. **20.2** Homologous characters result from shared ancestry. As organisms diverge over time, some of their homologous characters will also diverge. The homologous characters of organisms that diverged long ago typically differ more than do the homologous characters of organisms that diverged more recently. As a result, differences in homologous characters can be used to infer phylogeny. In contrast, analogous characters result from convergent evolution, not shared ancestry, and hence can give misleading estimates of phylogeny. **20.3** All features of organisms arose at some point in the history of life. In the group in which a new feature first arose, that feature is a shared derived character that is unique to that clade. The group in which each shared derived character first appeared can be determined, and the resulting nested

pattern can be used to infer evolutionary history.   **20.4** A key assumption of molecular clocks is that nucleotide substitutions occur at fixed rates, and hence the number of nucleotide differences between two DNA sequences is proportional to the time since the sequences diverged from each other. Some limitations of molecular clocks: No gene marks time with complete precision; natural selection can favor certain DNA changes over others; nucleotide substitution rates can change over long periods of time (causing molecular clock estimates of when events in the distant past occurred to be highly uncertain); and the same gene can evolve at different rates in different organisms.   **20.5** Genetic data indicated that many prokaryotes differed as much from each other as they did from eukaryotes. This indicated that organisms should be grouped into three "super-kingdoms," or domains (Archaea, Bacteria, Eukarya). These data also indicated that the previous kingdom Monera (which had contained all the prokaryotes) did not make biological sense and should be abandoned. Later genetic and morphological data also indicated that the former kingdom Protista (which had primarily contained single-celled organisms) should be abandoned because some protists are more closely related to plants, fungi, or animals than they are to other protists.

Test Your Understanding
1. A **2.** C **3.** B **4.** D **5.** D **6.** A **7.** D
8.

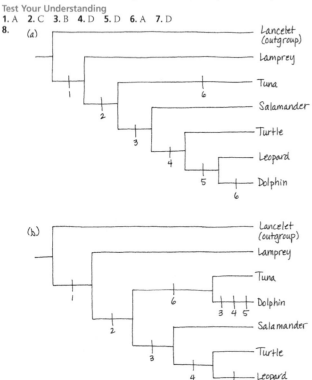

(c) The tree in (a) requires seven evolutionary changes, while the tree in (b) requires nine evolutionary changes. Thus, the tree in (a) is more parsimonious, since it requires fewer evolutionary changes.

Chapter 21

Figure Questions
Figure 21.4 The genetic code is redundant, meaning that more than one codon can specify the same amino acid. As a result, a substitution at a particular site in a coding region of the *Adh* gene might change the codon but not the translated amino acid, and thus not the resulting protein encoded by the gene. One way an insertion in an exon would not affect the gene produced is if it occurs in an untranslated region of the exon. This is the case for the insertion at location 1,703.   **Figure 21.8** The predicted frequencies are 36% $C^R C^R$, 48% $C^R C^W$, and 16% $C^W C^W$.   **Figure 21.13** Directional selection. Goldenrain tree has smaller fruit than does the native host, balloon vine. Thus, in soapberry bug populations feeding on goldenrain tree, bugs with shorter beaks had an advantage, resulting in directional selection for shorter beak length.
Figure 21.15 Under prolonged low-oxygen conditions, some of the red blood cells of a heterozygote may sickle, leading to harmful effects. This does not occur in individuals with two wild-type hemoglobin alleles, suggesting that there may be selection against heterozygotes in malaria-free regions (where there is no heterozygote advantage). However, since heterozygotes are healthy under most conditions, selection against them is unlikely to be strong.   **Figure 21.18** Crossing a single female's eggs with both an SC and an LC male's sperm allowed the researchers to directly compare the effects of the males' contribution to the next generation, since both batches of offspring had the same maternal contribution. This isolation of the male's impact enabled researchers to draw conclusions about differences in genetic "quality" between the SC and LC males.

Concept Check 21.1
1. Within a population, genetic differences among individuals provide the raw material on which natural selection and other mechanisms can act. Without such differences, allele frequencies could not change over time—and hence the population

could not evolve.   **2.** Many mutations occur in somatic cells, which do not produce gametes and so are lost when the organism dies. Of mutations that do occur in cell lines that produce gametes, many do not have a phenotypic effect on which natural selection can act. Others have a harmful effect and are thus unlikely to increase in frequency because they decrease the reproductive success of their bearers.   **3.** Its genetic variation (whether measured at the level of the gene or at the level of nucleotide sequences) would probably drop over time. During meiosis, crossing over and the independent assortment of chromosomes produce many new combinations of alleles. In addition, a population contains a vast number of possible mating combinations, and fertilization brings together the gametes of individuals with different genetic backgrounds. Thus, via crossing over, independent assortment of chromosomes, and fertilization, sexual reproduction reshuffles alleles into fresh combinations each generation. Without sexual reproduction, the rate of forming new combinations of alleles would be vastly reduced, causing the overall amount of genetic variation to drop.

Concept Check 21.2
1. Each individual has two alleles, so the total number of alleles is 1,400. To calculate the frequency of allele *A*, note that each of the 85 individuals of genotype *AA* has two *A* alleles, each of the 320 individuals of genotype *Aa* has one *A* allele, and each of the 295 individuals of genotype *aa* has zero *A* alleles. Thus, the frequency (*p*) of allele *A* is

$$p = \frac{(2 \times 85) + (1 \times 320) + (0 \times 295)}{1,400} = 0.35$$

There are only two alleles (*A* and *a*) in our population, so the frequency of allele *a* must be $q = 1 - p = 0.65$.   **2.** Because the frequency of allele *a* is 0.45, the frequency of allele *A* must be 0.55. Thus, the expected genotype frequencies are $p^2 = 0.3025$ for genotype *AA*, $2pq = 0.495$ for genotype *Aa*, and $q^2 = 0.2025$ for genotype *aa*.   **3.** There are 120 individuals in the population, so there are 240 alleles. Of these, there are 124 *V* alleles—32 from the 16 *VV* individuals and 92 from the 92 *Vv* individuals. Thus, the frequency of the *V* allele is $p = 124/240 = 0.52$; hence, the frequency of the *v* allele is $q = 0.48$. Based on the Hardy-Weinberg equation, if the population were not evolving, the frequency of genotype *VV* should be $p^2 = 0.52 \times 0.52 = 0.27$; the frequency of genotype *Vv* should be $2pq = 2 \times 0.52 \times 0.48 = 0.5$; and the frequency of genotype *vv* should be $q^2 = 0.48 \times 0.48 = 0.23$. In a population of 120 individuals, these expected genotype frequencies lead us to predict that there would be 32 *VV* individuals (0.27 × 120), 60 *Vv* individuals (0.5 × 120), and 28 *vv* individuals (0.23 × 120). The actual numbers for the population (16 *VV*, 92 *Vv*, 12 *vv*) deviate from these expectations (fewer homozygotes and more heterozygotes than expected). This indicates that the population is not in Hardy-Weinberg equilibrium and hence may be evolving at this locus.

Concept Check 21.3
1. Natural selection is more "predictable" in that it alters allele frequencies in a nonrandom way: It tends to increase the frequency of alleles that increase the organism's reproductive success in its environment and decrease the frequency of alleles that decrease the organism's reproductive success. Alleles subject to genetic drift increase or decrease in frequency by chance alone, whether or not they are advantageous.
2. Genetic drift results from chance events that cause allele frequencies to fluctuate at random from generation to generation; within a population, this process tends to decrease genetic variation over time. Gene flow is the transfer of alleles between populations, a process that can introduce new alleles to a population and hence may increase its genetic variation (albeit slightly, since rates of gene flow are often low).   **3.** Selection is not important at this locus; furthermore, the populations are not small, and hence the effects of genetic drift should not be pronounced. Gene flow is occurring via the movement of pollen and seeds. Thus, allele and genotype frequencies in these populations should become more similar over time as a result of gene flow.

Concept Check 21.4
1. Zero, because fitness includes reproductive contribution to the next generation, and a sterile mule cannot produce offspring.   **2.** Although both gene flow and genetic drift can increase the frequency of advantageous alleles in a population, they can also decrease the frequency of advantageous alleles or increase the frequency of harmful alleles. Only natural selection *consistently* results in an increase in the frequency of alleles that enhance survival or reproduction. Thus, natural selection is the only mechanism that consistently leads to adaptive evolution.   **3.** The three modes of natural selection (directional, stabilizing, and disruptive) are defined in terms of the selective advantage of different *phenotypes*, not different genotypes. Thus, the type of selection represented by heterozygote advantage depends on the phenotype of the heterozygotes. In this question, because heterozygous individuals have a more extreme phenotype than either homozygote, heterozygote advantage represents directional selection.

Summary of Key Concepts Questions
21.1 Much of the nucleotide variability at a genetic locus occurs within introns. Nucleotide variation at these sites typically does not affect the phenotype because introns do not code for the protein product of the gene. (Note: In certain circumstances, it is possible that a change in an intron could affect RNA splicing and ultimately have some phenotypic effect on the organism, but such mechanisms are not covered in this introductory text.) There are also many variable nucleotide sites within exons. However, most of the variable sites within exons reflect changes to the DNA sequence that do not change the sequence of amino acids encoded by the gene (and hence may not affect the phenotype).   **21.2** No, this is not an example of circular reasoning. Calculating *p* and *q* from observed genotype frequencies does not imply that those genotype frequencies must be in Hardy-Weinberg equilibrium. For example, consider a population that has 195 individuals of genotype *AA*, 10 of genotype *Aa*, and 195 of genotype *aa*. Calculating *p* and *q* from these values yields

$p = q = 0.5$. Using the Hardy-Weinberg equation, the predicted equilibrium frequencies are $p^2 = 0.25$ for genotype AA, $2pq = 0.5$ for genotype Aa, and $q^2 = 0.25$ for genotype aa. Since there are 400 individuals in the population, these predicted genotype frequencies indicate that there should be 100 AA individuals, 200 Aa individuals, and 100 aa individuals—numbers that differ greatly from the values that we used to calculate p and q. **21.3** It is unlikely that two such populations would evolve in similar ways. Since their environments are very different, the alleles favored by natural selection would probably differ between the two populations. Although genetic drift may have important effects in each of these small populations, drift causes unpredictable changes in allele frequencies, so it is unlikely that drift would cause the populations to evolve in similar ways. Both populations are geographically isolated, suggesting that little gene flow would occur between them (again making it less likely that they would evolve in similar ways). **21.4** Compared to males, it is likely that the females of such species would be larger, more colorful, endowed with more elaborate ornamentation (for example, a large morphological feature such as the peacock's tail), and more apt to engage in behaviors intended to attract mates or prevent other members of their sex from obtaining mates.

Test Your Understanding
1. D **2.** C **3.** D **4.** B **5.** A **6.** C

Chapter 22

Figure Questions
Figure 22.7 If this had not been done, the strong preference of "starch flies" and "maltose flies" to mate with like-adapted flies could have occurred simply because the flies could detect (for example, by sense of smell) what their potential mates had eaten as larvae—and they preferred to mate with flies that had a similar smell to their own.
Figure 22.12 In murky waters where females distinguish colors poorly, females of each species might mate often with males of the other species. Hence, since hybrids between these species are viable and fertile, the gene pools of the two species could become more similar over time. **Figure 22.13** The graph suggests there has been gene flow of some fire-bellied toad alleles into the range of the yellow-bellied toad. Otherwise, all individuals located to the left of the hybrid zone portion of the graph would have allele frequencies close to 1. **Figure 22.14** Because the populations had only just begun to diverge from one another at this point in the process, it is likely that any existing barriers to reproduction would weaken over time.
Figure 22.18 Over time, the chromosomes of the experimental hybrids came to resemble those of *H. anomalus*. This occurred even though conditions in the laboratory differed greatly from conditions in the field, where *H. anomalus* is found, suggesting that selection for laboratory conditions was not strong. Thus, it is unlikely that the observed rise in the fertility of the experimental hybrids was due to selection for life under laboratory conditions. **Figure 22.19** The presence of *M. cardinalis* plants that carry the *M. lewisii yup* allele would make it more likely that bumblebees would transfer pollen between the two monkey flower species. As a result, we would expect the number of hybrid offspring to increase.

Concept Check 22.1
1. (a) All except the biological species concept can be applied to both asexual and sexual species because they define species on the basis of characteristics other than the ability to reproduce. In contrast, the biological species concept can be applied only to sexual species. (b) The easiest species concept to apply in the field would be the morphological species concept because it is based only on the appearance of the organism. Additional information about its ecological habits, evolutionary history, and reproduction is not required. **2.** Because these birds live in fairly similar environments and can breed successfully in captivity, the reproductive barrier in nature is probably prezygotic; given the species' differences in habitat preference, this barrier could result from habitat isolation.

Concept Check 22.2
1. In allopatric speciation, a new species forms while in geographic isolation from its parent species; in sympatric speciation, a new species forms in the absence of geographic isolation. Geographic isolation greatly reduces gene flow between populations, whereas ongoing gene flow is more likely in sympatric populations. As a result, sympatric speciation is less common than allopatric speciation. **2.** Allopatric speciation would be less likely to occur on an island near a mainland than on a more isolated island of the same size. We expect this result because continued gene flow between mainland populations and those on a nearby island reduces the chance that enough genetic divergence will take place for allopatric speciation to occur. **3.** If all of the homologs failed to separate during anaphase I of meiosis, some gametes would end up with an extra set of chromosomes (and others would end up with no chromosomes). If a gamete with an extra set of chromosomes fused with a normal gamete, a triploid would result; if two gametes with an extra set of chromosomes fused with each other, a tetraploid would result.

Concept Check 22.3
1. Hybrid zones are regions in which members of different species meet and mate, producing some offspring of mixed ancestry. Such regions can be viewed as "natural laboratories" in which to study speciation because scientists can directly observe factors that cause (or fail to cause) reproductive isolation. **2.** (a) If hybrids consistently survived and reproduced poorly compared with the offspring of intraspecific matings, reinforcement could occur. If it did, natural selection would cause prezygotic barriers to reproduction to strengthen over time, decreasing the production of unfit hybrids and leading to a completion of the speciation process. (b) If hybrid offspring survived and reproduced as well as the offspring of intraspecific matings, indiscriminate mating between the parent species would lead to the production

of large numbers of hybrid offspring. As these hybrids mated with each other and with members of both parent species, the gene pools of the parent species could fuse over time, reversing the speciation process.

Concept Check 22.4
1. The time between speciation events includes (1) the length of time that it takes for populations of a newly formed species to begin diverging reproductively from one another and (2) the time it takes for speciation to be complete once this divergence begins. Although speciation can occur rapidly once populations have begun to diverge from one another, it may take millions of years for that divergence to begin. **2.** Investigators transferred alleles at the *yup* locus (which influences flower color) from each parent species to the other. *M. lewisii* plants with an *M. cardinalis* *yup* allele received many more visits from hummingbirds than usual; hummingbirds usually pollinate *M. cardinalis* but avoid *M. lewisii*. Similarly, *M. cardinalis* plants with an *M. lewisii yup* allele received many more visits from bumblebees than usual; bumblebees usually pollinate *M. lewisii* and avoid *M. cardinalis*. Thus, alleles at the *yup* locus can influence pollinator choice, which in these species provides the primary barrier to interspecific mating. Nevertheless, the experiment does not prove that the *yup* locus alone controls barriers to reproduction between *M. lewisii* and *M. cardinalis*; other genes might enhance the effect of the *yup* locus (by modifying flower color) or cause entirely different barriers to reproduction (for example, gametic isolation or a postzygotic barrier). **3.** Crossing over. If crossing over did not occur, each chromosome in an experimental hybrid would remain as in the F_1 generation: composed entirely of DNA from one parent species or the other.

Summary of Key Concepts Questions
22.1 According to the biological species concept, a species is a group of populations whose members interbreed and produce viable, fertile offspring; thus, gene flow occurs between populations of a species. In contrast, members of different species do not interbreed, and hence no gene flow occurs between their populations. Overall, then, in the biological species concept, species can be viewed as designated by the *absence* of gene flow—making gene flow of central importance to the biological species concept. **22.2** Sympatric speciation can be promoted by factors such as polyploidy, habitat shifts, and sexual selection, all of which can reduce gene flow between the subpopulations of a larger population. But such factors can also occur in allopatric populations and hence can also promote allopatric speciation. **22.3** If the hybrids are selected against, the hybrid zone could persist if individuals from the parent species regularly travel into the zone, where they mate to produce hybrid offspring. If hybrids are not selected against, there is no cost to the continued production of hybrids, and large numbers of hybrid offspring may be produced. However, natural selection for life in different environments may keep the gene pools of the two parent species distinct, thus preventing the loss (by fusion) of the parent species and once again causing the hybrid zone to be stable over time. **22.4** As the goatsbeard plant, Bahamas mosquitofish, and apple maggot fly illustrate, speciation continues to happen today. A new species can begin to form whenever gene flow is reduced between populations of the parent species. Such reductions in gene flow can occur in many ways: A new, geographically isolated population may be founded by a few colonists; some members of the parent species may begin to utilize a new habitat; and sexual selection may isolate formerly connected populations or subpopulations. These and many other such events are happening today.

Test Your Understanding
1. B **2.** C **3.** D **4.** A **5.** D **6.** C
7. Here is one possibility:

1.

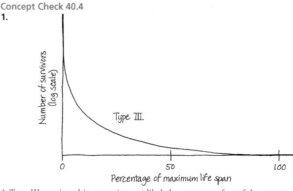

A Type III survivorship curve is most likely because very few of the young probably survive. **2.** The proportion alive at the start of year 0–1 is 485/485 = 1.0. The proportion alive at the start of year 1–2 is 218/485 = 0.449. **3.** Male sticklebacks would likely have a uniform pattern of dispersion, with antagonistic interactions maintaining a relatively constant spacing between them.

Concept Check 40.5
1. Though r is constant, N, the population size, is increasing. As r is applied to an increasingly large N, population growth (rN) accelerates, producing the J-shaped curve. **2.** When N (population size) is small, there are relatively few individuals producing offspring. When N is large, near the carrying capacity, the per capita growth rate is relatively small because it is limited by available resources. The steepest part of the logistic growth curve corresponds to a population with a number of reproducing individuals that is substantial but not yet near carrying capacity. **3.** If a population becomes too crowded, the likelihood of disease and mortality may increase because of the effects of pathogens. Thus, pathogens can reduce the long-term carrying capacity of a population.

Concept Check 40.6
1. By preferentially investing in the eggs it lays in the nest, the peacock wrasse increases the chance those eggs will survive. The eggs it disperses widely and does not provide care for are less likely to survive, at least some of the time, but require a lower investment by the adults. (In this sense, the adults avoid the risk of placing all their eggs in one basket.) **2.** If a parent's survival is compromised greatly by bearing young during times of stress, the animal's fitness may increase if it abandons its current young and survives to produce healthier young at a later time. **3.** In negative feedback, the output, or product, of a process slows that process. In populations that have a density-dependent birth rate, such as dune fescue grass, an accumulation of product (more individuals, resulting in a higher population density) slows the process (population growth) by decreasing the birth rate.

Summary of Key Concepts Questions
40.1 Because dry air would descend at the equator instead of at 30° north and south latitude (where deserts exist today), deserts would be more likely to exist along the equator (see Figure 40.3). **40.2** An aphotic zone is most likely to be found in the deep waters of a lake, the oceanic pelagic zone, or the marine benthic zone. **40.3** You might arrange a flowchart that begins with abiotic limitations—first determining the physical and chemical conditions under which a species could survive—and then moves through the other factors listed in the flowchart. **40.4** Ecologists can potentially estimate birth rates by counting the number of young whales born each year, and they can estimate death rates by seeing how the number of adults changes each year. **40.5** There are many things you can do to increase the carrying capacity of the species, including increasing its food supply, protecting it from predators, and providing more sites for nesting or reproduction. **40.6** An example of a biotic factor would be disease caused by a pathogen; natural disasters, such as earthquakes and floods, are examples of abiotic factors.

Test Your Understanding
1. D **2.** A **3.** B **4.** C **5.** C

Chapter 41

Figure Questions
Figure 41.3 Its realized and fundamental niches would be similar, unlike those of *Chthamalus*. **Figure 41.5** Individuals of a harmless species that resembled a distantly related harmful species might be attacked by predators less often than other individuals of the harmless species that did not resemble the harmful species. As a result, individuals of the harmless species that resembled a harmful species would tend to contribute more offspring to the next generation than would other individuals of the harmless species. Over time, as natural selection by predators continued to favor those individuals of the harmless species that most closely resembled the harmful species, the resemblance of the harmless species to the harmful species would increase. Selection is not the only process that could cause a harmless species to resemble a closely related harmful species. In this case, the two species also could resemble each other because they descended from a recent common ancestor and hence share many traits (including a resemblance to one another). **Figure 41.13** An increase in the abundance of carnivores that ate zooplankton might cause zooplankton abundance to drop, thereby causing phytoplankton abundance to increase. **Figure 41.14** The number of other organism types eaten is zero for phytoplankton; one for copepods, crabeater seals, baleen whales, and sperm whales; two for krill, carnivorous plankton, and elephant seals; three for squids, fishes, leopard seals, and humans; and five for birds and smaller toothed whales. The

Chapter 40

Figure Questions
Figure 40.12 Some factors, such as fire, are relevant only for terrestrial systems. At first glance, water availability is primarily a terrestrial factor, too. However, species living along the intertidal zone of oceans or along the edge of lakes also suffer desiccation (drying out). Salinity stress is important for species in some aquatic and terrestrial systems. Oxygen availability is an important factor primarily for species in some aquatic systems and in soils and sediments. **Figure 40.17** The population with $r = 1.0$ (blue curve) reaches 1,500 individuals in about 7.5 generations, whereas the population with $r = 0.5$ (red curve) reaches 1,500 individuals in about 14.5 generations.
Figure 40.22

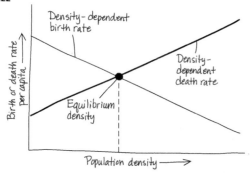

Concept Check 40.1
1. In the tropics, high temperatures evaporate water and cause warm, moist air to rise. The rising air cools and releases much of its water as rain over the tropics. The remaining dry air descends at approximately 30° north and south, causing deserts to occur in those regions. **2.** Answers will vary by location but should be based on the information and maps in Figures 40.7 and 40.9. How much your local area has been altered from its natural state will influence how much it reflects the expected characteristics of your biome, particularly the expected plants and animals. **3.** Northern coniferous forest is likely to replace tundra along the boundary between these biomes. To see why, note that northern coniferous forest is adjacent to tundra throughout North America, northern Europe, and Asia (see Figure 40.7) and that the temperature range for northern coniferous forest is just above that for tundra (see Figure 40.8).

Concept Check 40.2
1. In the oceanic pelagic zone, the ocean bottom lies below the photic zone, so there is too little light to support benthic algae or rooted plants. **2.** Aquatic organisms either gain or lose water by osmosis if the osmolarity of their environment differs from their internal osmolarity. Water gain can cause cells to swell, and water loss can cause them to shrink. To avoid excessive changes in cell volume, organisms that live in estuaries must be able to compensate for both water gain (under freshwater conditions) and water loss (under saltwater conditions). **3.** In a river below a dam, the fish are more likely to be species that prefer colder water. In summer, the deep layers of a reservoir are colder than the surface layers, so a river below a dam will be colder than an undammed river.

Concept Check 40.3
1. (a) Humans might transplant a species to a new area that it could not previously reach because of a geographic barrier. (b) Humans might eliminate a predator or herbivore species, such as sea urchins, from an area. **2.** One test would be to build a fence around a plot of land in an area that has trees of that species, excluding all deer from the plot. You could then compare the abundance of tree seedlings inside and outside the fenced plot over time.

two groups that both consume and are consumed by each other are fishes and squids. **Figure 41.15** The death of individuals of *Mytilus*, a dominant species, should open up space for other species and increase species richness even in the absence of *Pisaster*. **Figure 41.23** Other factors not included in the model must contribute to the number of species. **Figure 41.24** Shrew populations in different locations and habitats might show substantial genetic variation in their susceptibility to the Lyme pathogen. As a result, there might be fewer infected ticks where shrew populations were less susceptible to the Lyme pathogen and more infected ticks where shrews were more susceptible.

Concept Check 41.1

1. Interspecific competition has negative effects on both species $(-/-)$. In predation, the predator population benefits at the expense of the prey population; this is an example of exploitative interaction $(+/-)$. Mutualism is an interaction in which both species benefit $(+/+)$. **2.** One of the competing species will become locally extinct because of the greater reproductive success of the more efficient competitor. **3.** By specializing in eating seeds of different plant species, individuals of the two finch species may be less likely to come into contact in the separate habitats, reinforcing a barrier to hybridization.

Concept Check 41.2

1. Species richness (the number of species in the community) and relative abundance (the proportions of the community represented by the various species) both contribute to species diversity. Compared to a community with a very high proportion of one species, one with a more even proportion of species is considered more diverse. **2.** A food chain presents a set of one-way transfers of food energy up to successively higher trophic levels. A food web documents how food chains are linked together, with many species weaving into the web at more than one trophic level. **3.** According to the bottom-up model, adding extra predators would have little effect on lower trophic levels, particularly vegetation. If the top-down model applied, increased bobcat numbers would decrease raccoon numbers, increase snake numbers, decrease mouse numbers, and increase grass biomass. **4.** A decrease in krill abundance might increase the abundance of organisms that krill eat (phytoplankton and copepods), while decreasing the abundance of organisms that eat krill (baleen whales, crabeater seals, birds, fishes, and carnivorous plankton); baleen whales and crabeater seals might be particularly at risk because they only eat krill. However, many of these possible changes could lead to other changes as well, making the overall outcome hard to predict. For example, a decrease in krill abundance could cause an increase in copepod abundance—but an increase in copepod abundance could counteract some of the other effects of decreased krill abundance (since like krill, copepods eat phytoplankton and are eaten by carnivorous plankton and fishes).

Concept Check 41.3

1. High levels of disturbance are generally so disruptive that they eliminate many species from communities, leaving the community dominated by a few tolerant species. Low levels of disturbance permit competitively dominant species to exclude other species from the community. On the other hand, moderate levels of disturbance can facilitate coexistence of a greater number of species in a community by preventing competitively dominant species from becoming abundant enough to eliminate other species from the community. **2.** Early successional species can facilitate the arrival of other species in many ways, including increasing the fertility or water-holding capacity of soils or providing shelter to seedlings from wind and intense sunlight. **3.** The absence of fire for 100 years would represent a change to a low level of disturbance. According to the intermediate disturbance hypothesis, this change should cause diversity to decline as competitively dominant species gain sufficient time to exclude less competitive species.

Concept Check 41.4

1. Ecologists propose that the greater species richness of tropical regions is the result of their longer evolutionary history and the greater solar energy input and water availability in tropical regions. **2.** Immigration to islands declines with distance from the mainland and increases with island area. Extinction of species is lower on larger islands and on less isolated islands. Since the number of species on islands is largely determined by the difference between rates of immigration and extinction, the number of species will be highest on large islands near the mainland and lowest on small islands far from the mainland. **3.** Because of their greater mobility, birds disperse to islands more often than snakes and lizards, so birds should have greater richness.

Concept Check 41.5

1. Pathogens are microorganisms or viruses that cause disease. **2.** To keep the rabies virus out, you could ban imports of all mammals, including pets. Potentially, you could also attempt to vaccinate all dogs in the British Isles against the virus. A more practical approach might be to quarantine all pets brought into the country that are potential carriers of the disease, the approach the British government actually takes.

Summary of Key Concepts Questions

41.1 Note: Sample answers follow; other answers could also be correct. Competition: a fox and a bobcat competing for prey. Predation: an orca eating a sea otter. Herbivory: a bison grazing in a prairie. Parasitism: a parasitoid wasp that lays its eggs on a caterpillar. Mutualism: a fungus and an alga that make up a lichen. Commensalism: a beetle (that feeds upon wildflowers growing in a maple forest) and a maple tree. **41.2** Not necessarily if the more species-rich community is dominated by only one or a few species. **41.3** Similar to clear-cutting a forest or plowing a field, some species would be present initially. As a result, the disturbance would initiate secondary succession in spite of its severe appearance. **41.4** Glaciations are major disturbances that can completely destroy communities found in temperate and polar regions. As a result, tropical communities are older than temperate or polar communities. This can cause species diversity to be high in the tropics simply because there has been more time for speciation to occur. **41.5** A keystone species is one with a pivotal ecological role. Hence, a pathogen that reduces the abundance or otherwise harms a keystone species could greatly alter the structure of the community. For example, if a novel pathogen drove a keystone species to local extinction, drastic changes in species diversity could occur.

Test Your Understanding

1. D **2.** C **3.** D **4.** Community 1: $H = -(0.05 \ln 0.05 + 0.05 \ln 0.05 + 0.85 \ln 0.85 + 0.05 \ln 0.05) = 0.59$. Community 2: $H = -(0.30 \ln 0.30 + 0.40 \ln 0.40 + 0.30 \ln 0.30) = 1.1$. Community 2 is more diverse. **5.** Crab numbers should increase, reducing the abundance of eelgrass.

Chapter 42

Figure Questions

Figure 42.6 The map does not accurately reflect the productivity of wetlands, coral reefs, and coastal zones because these habitats cover areas that are too small to show up clearly on global maps. **Figure 42.7** New duck farms would add extra nitrogen and phosphorus to the water samples used in the experiment. We would expect that the extra phosphorus from these new duck farms would not alter the results (because in the original experiment, phosphorus levels were *already* so high that adding phosphorus did not increase phytoplankton growth). However, the new duck farms might increase nitrogen levels to the point where adding extra nitrogen in an experiment would not increase phytoplankton density. **Figure 42.12** Water availability is probably another factor that varied across the sites. Such factors not included in the experimental design could make the results more difficult to interpret. Multiple factors can be correlated to each other in nature, so ecologists must be careful that the factor they are studying is actually causing the observed response and is not just correlated with it. **Figure 42.18** Populations evolve as organisms interact with each other and with the physical and chemical conditions of their environment. As a result, any human action that alters the environment has the potential to cause evolutionary change. In particular, since climate change has greatly affected Arctic ecosystems, we would expect that climate change will cause evolution in Arctic tundra populations.

Concept Check 42.1

1. Energy passes through an ecosystem, entering as sunlight and leaving as heat. It is not recycled within the ecosystem. **2.** You would need to know how much biomass the wildebeests ate from your plot and how much nitrogen was contained in that biomass. You would also need to know how much nitrogen they deposited in urine or feces. **3.** The second law states that in any energy transfer or transformation, some of the energy is dissipated to the surroundings as heat. For the ecosystem to remain intact, this "escape" of energy from the ecosystem must be offset by the continuous influx of solar radiation.

Concept Check 42.2

1. Only a fraction of solar radiation strikes plants or algae, only a portion of that fraction is of wavelengths suitable for photosynthesis, and much energy is lost as a result of reflection or heating of plant tissue. **2.** By manipulating the level of the factors of interest, such as phosphorus availability or soil moisture, and measuring responses by primary producers. **3.** The enzyme rubisco, which catalyzes the first step in the Calvin cycle, is the most abundant protein on Earth. Like all proteins, rubisco contains nitrogen, and rubisco is so abundant that photosynthetic organisms require considerable nitrogen to make it. Phosphorus is also needed as a component of several metabolites in the Calvin cycle and as a component of both ATP and NADPH (see Figure 8.17).

Concept Check 42.3

1. 20 J; 40% **2.** Nicotine protects the plant from herbivores. **3.** Total net production is $10{,}000 + 1{,}000 + 100 + 10$ J $= 11{,}110$ J. This is the amount of energy theoretically available to detritivores.

Concept Check 42.4

1. For example, for the carbon cycle:

Cycling of a carbon atom

2. Removal of the trees stops nitrogen uptake from the soil, allowing nitrate to accumulate there. The nitrate is washed away by precipitation and enters the streams. **3.** Most of the nutrients in a tropical rain forest are contained in the trees, so removing the trees by logging rapidly depletes nutrients from the ecosystem. The nutrients that remain in the soil are quickly carried away into streams and groundwater by the abundant precipitation.

Concept Check 42.5

1. The main goal is to restore degraded ecosystems to a more natural state.
2. Bioremediation uses organisms, generally prokaryotes, fungi, or plants, to detoxify or remove pollutants from ecosystems. Biological augmentation uses organisms, such

as nitrogen-fixing plants, to add essential materials to degraded ecosystems.   **3.** The Kissimmee River project returns the flow of water to the original channel and restores natural flow, a self-sustaining outcome. Ecologists at the Maungatautari reserve will need to maintain the integrity of the fence indefinitely, an outcome that is not self-sustaining in the long term.

Summary of Key Concepts Questions

42.1 Because energy conversions are inefficient, with some energy inevitably lost as heat, you would expect that a given mass of primary producers would support a smaller biomass of secondary producers.   **42.2** For estimates of NEP, you need to measure the respiration of all organisms in an ecosystem, not just the respiration of primary producers. In a sample of ocean water, primary producers and other organisms are usually mixed together, making their respective respirations hard to separate.   **42.3** Runners use much more energy in respiration when they are running than when they are sedentary, reducing their production efficiency.   **42.4** Factors other than temperature, including a shortage of water and nutrients, slow decomposition in hot deserts.   **42.5** If the topsoil and deeper soil are kept separate, the engineers could return the deeper soil to the site first and then apply the more fertile topsoil to improve the success of revegetation and other restoration efforts.

Test Your Understanding

1. C   **2.** B   **3.** A   **4.** C   **5.** A   **6.** B   **7.** D   **8.** D

Periodic Table of the Elements

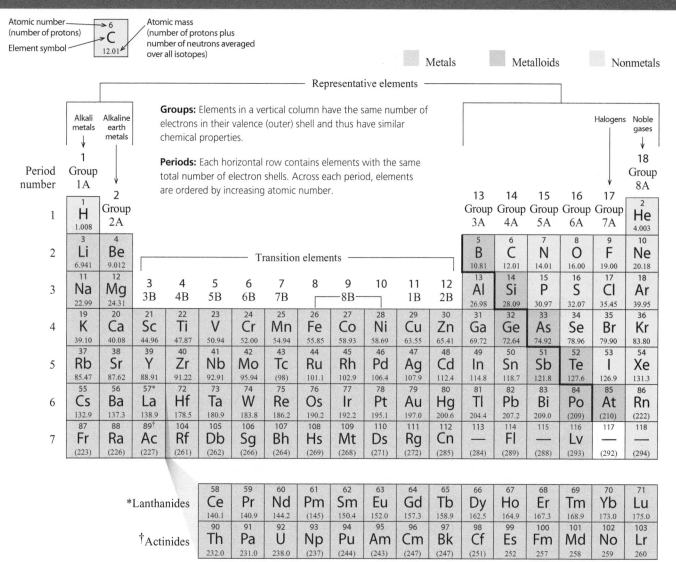

Atomic number (number of protons)
Element symbol
Atomic mass (number of protons plus number of neutrons averaged over all isotopes)

6
C
12.01

Metals   Metalloids   Nonmetals

Representative elements

Groups: Elements in a vertical column have the same number of electrons in their valence (outer) shell and thus have similar chemical properties.

Periods: Each horizontal row contains elements with the same total number of electron shells. Across each period, elements are ordered by increasing atomic number.

Alkali metals   Alkaline earth metals   Halogens   Noble gases

Transition elements

*Lanthanides

| 58 Ce 140.1 | 59 Pr 140.9 | 60 Nd 144.2 | 61 Pm (145) | 62 Sm 150.4 | 63 Eu 152.0 | 64 Gd 157.3 | 65 Tb 158.9 | 66 Dy 162.5 | 67 Ho 164.9 | 68 Er 167.3 | 69 Tm 168.9 | 70 Yb 173.0 | 71 Lu 175.0 |

†Actinides

| 90 Th 232.0 | 91 Pa 231.0 | 92 U 238.0 | 93 Np (237) | 94 Pu (244) | 95 Am (243) | 96 Cm (247) | 97 Bk (247) | 98 Cf (251) | 99 Es 252 | 100 Fm 257 | 101 Md 258 | 102 No 259 | 103 Lr 260 |

Name (Symbol)	Atomic Number	Name (Symbol)	Atomic Number	Name (Symbol)	Atomic Number	Name (Symbol)	Atomic Number	Name (Symbol)	Atomic Number
Actinium (Ac)	89	Copernicium (Cn)	112	Iodine (I)	53	Osmium (Os)	76	Silicon (Si)	14
Aluminum (Al)	13	Copper (Cu)	29	Iridium (Ir)	77	Oxygen (O)	8	Silver (Ag)	47
Americium (Am)	95	Curium (Cm)	96	Iron (Fe)	26	Palladium (Pd)	46	Sodium (Na)	11
Antimony (Sb)	51	Darmstadtium (Ds)	110	Krypton (Kr)	36	Phosphorus (P)	15	Strontium (Sr)	38
Argon (Ar)	18	Dubnium (Db)	105	Lanthanum (La)	57	Platinum (Pt)	78	Sulfur (S)	16
Arsenic (As)	33	Dysprosium (Dy)	66	Lawrencium (Lr)	103	Plutonium (Pu)	94	Tantalum (Ta)	73
Astatine (At)	85	Einsteinium (Es)	99	Lead (Pb)	82	Polonium (Po)	84	Technetium (Tc)	43
Barium (Ba)	56	Erbium (Er)	68	Lithium (Li)	3	Potassium (K)	19	Tellurium (Te)	52
Berkelium (Bk)	97	Europium (Eu)	63	Livermorium (Lv)	116	Praseodymium (Pr)	59	Terbium (Tb)	65
Beryllium (Be)	4	Fermium (Fm)	100	Lutetium (Lu)	71	Promethium (Pm)	61	Thallium (Tl)	81
Bismuth (Bi)	83	Flerovium (Fl)	114	Magnesium (Mg)	12	Protactinium (Pa)	91	Thorium (Th)	90
Bohrium (Bh)	107	Fluorine (F)	9	Manganese (Mn)	25	Radium (Ra)	88	Thulium (Tm)	69
Boron (B)	5	Francium (Fr)	87	Meitnerium (Mt)	109	Radon (Rn)	86	Tin (Sn)	50
Bromine (Br)	35	Gadolinium (Gd)	64	Mendelevium (Md)	101	Rhenium (Re)	75	Titanium (Ti)	22
Cadmium (Cd)	48	Gallium (Ga)	31	Mercury (Hg)	80	Rhodium (Rh)	45	Tungsten (W)	74
Calcium (Ca)	20	Germanium (Ge)	32	Molybdenum (Mo)	42	Roentgenium (Rg)	111	Uranium (U)	92
Californium (Cf)	98	Gold (Au)	79	Neodymium (Nd)	60	Rubidium (Rb)	37	Vanadium (V)	23
Carbon (C)	6	Hafnium (Hf)	72	Neon (Ne)	10	Ruthenium (Ru)	44	Xenon (Xe)	54
Cerium (Ce)	58	Hassium (Hs)	108	Neptunium (Np)	93	Rutherfordium (Rf)	104	Ytterbium (Yb)	70
Cesium (Cs)	55	Helium (He)	2	Nickel (Ni)	28	Samarium (Sm)	62	Yttrium (Y)	39
Chlorine (Cl)	17	Holmium (Ho)	67	Niobium (Nb)	41	Scandium (Sc)	21	Zinc (Zn)	30
Chromium (Cr)	24	Hydrogen (H)	1	Nitrogen (N)	7	Seaborgium (Sg)	106	Zirconium (Zr)	40
Cobalt (Co)	27	Indium (In)	49	Nobelium (No)	102	Selenium (Se)	34		

APPENDIX B PERIODIC TABLE

The Metric System

Metric Prefixes:
10^9 = giga (G)	10^{-2} = centi (c)	10^{-9} = nano (n)
10^6 = mega (M)	10^{-3} = milli (m)	10^{-12} = pico (p)
10^3 = kilo (k)	10^{-6} = micro (μ)	10^{-15} = femto (f)

Measurement	Unit and Abbreviation	Metric Equivalent	Metric-to-English Conversion Factor	English-to-Metric Conversion Factor
Length	1 kilometer (km)	= 1,000 (10^3) meters	1 km = 0.62 mile	1 mile = 1.61 km
	1 meter (m)	= 100 (10^2) centimeters = 1,000 millimeters	1 m = 1.09 yards 1 m = 3.28 feet 1 m = 39.37 inches	1 yard = 0.914 m 1 foot = 0.305 m
	1 centimeter (cm)	= 0.01 (10^{-2}) meter	1 cm = 0.394 inch	1 foot = 30.5 cm 1 inch = 2.54 cm
	1 millimeter (mm)	= 0.001 (10^{-3}) meter	1 mm = 0.039 inch	
	1 micrometer (μm) (formerly micron, μ)	= 10^{-6} meter (10^{-3} mm)		
	1 nanometer (nm) (formerly millimicron, mμ)	= 10^{-9} meter (10^{-3} μm)		
	1 angstrom (Å)	= 10^{-10} meter (10^{-4} μm)		
Area	1 hectare (ha)	= 10,000 square meters	1 ha = 2.47 acres	1 acre = 0.405 ha
	1 square meter (m^2)	= 10,000 square centimeters	1 m^2 = 1.196 square yards 1 m^2 = 10.764 square feet	1 square yard = 0.8361 m^2 1 square foot = 0.0929 m^2
	1 square centimeter (cm^2)	= 100 square millimeters	1 cm^2 = 0.155 square inch	1 square inch = 6.4516 cm^2
Mass	1 metric ton (t)	= 1,000 kilograms	1 t = 1.103 tons	1 ton = 0.907 t
	1 kilogram (kg)	= 1,000 grams	1 kg = 2.205 pounds	1 pound = 0.4536 kg
	1 gram (g)	= 1,000 milligrams	1 g = 0.0353 ounce 1 g = 15.432 grains	1 ounce = 28.35 g
	1 milligram (mg)	= 10^{-3} gram	1 mg = approx. 0.015 grain	
	1 microgram (μg)	= 10^{-6} gram		
Volume (solids)	1 cubic meter (m^3)	= 1,000,000 cubic centimeters	1 m^3 = 1.308 cubic yards 1 m^3 = 35.315 cubic feet	1 cubic yard = 0.7646 m^3 1 cubic foot = 0.0283 m^3
	1 cubic centimeter (cm^3 or cc)	= 10^{-6} cubic meter	1 cm^3 = 0.061 cubic inch	1 cubic inch = 16.387 cm^3
	1 cubic millimeter (mm^3)	= 10^{-9} cubic meter = 10^{-3} cubic centimeter		
Volume (liquids and gases)	1 kiloliter (kL or kl)	= 1,000 liters	1 kL = 264.17 gallons	
	1 liter (L or l)	= 1,000 milliliters	1 L = 0.264 gallon 1 L = 1.057 quarts	1 gallon = 3.785 L 1 quart = 0.946 L
	1 milliliter (mL or ml)	= 10^{-3} liter = 1 cubic centimeter	1 mL = 0.034 fluid ounce 1 mL = approx. ¼ teaspoon 1 mL = approx. 15–16 drops (gtt.)	1 quart = 946 mL 1 pint = 473 mL 1 fluid ounce = 29.57 mL 1 teaspoon = approx. 5 mL
	1 microliter (μL or μl)	= 10^{-6} liter (10^{-3} milliliter)		
Pressure	1 megapascal (MPa)	= 1,000 kilopascals	1 MPa = 10 bars	1 bar = 0.1 MPa
	1 kilopascal (kPa)	= 1,000 pascals	1 kPa = 0.01 bar	1 bar = 100 kPa
	1 pascal (Pa)	= 1 newton/m^2 (N/m^2)	1 Pa = 1.0×10^{-5} bar	1 bar = 1.0×10^5 Pa
Time	1 second (s or sec)	= $\frac{1}{60}$ minute		
	1 millisecond (ms or msec)	= 10^{-3} second		
Temperature	Degrees Celsius (°C) (0 K [Kelvin] = −273.15°C)		°F = $\frac{9}{5}$°C + 32	°C = $\frac{5}{9}$ (°F − 32)

A Comparison of the Light Microscope and the Electron Microscope

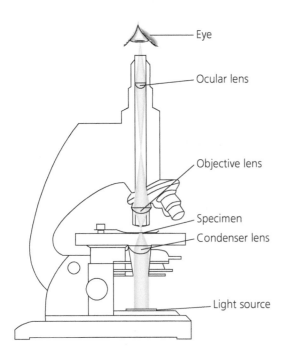

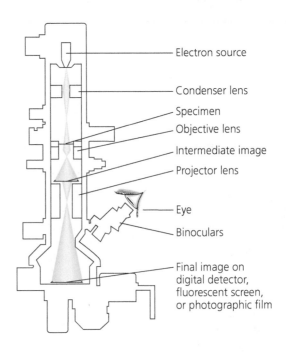

Light Microscope

In light microscopy, light is focused on a specimen by a glass condenser lens; the image is then magnified by an objective lens and an ocular lens for projection on the eye, digital camera, digital video camera, or photographic film.

Electron Microscope

In electron microscopy, a beam of electrons (top of the microscope) is used instead of light, and electromagnets are used instead of glass lenses. The electron beam is focused on the specimen by a condenser lens; the image is magnified by an objective lens and a projector lens for projection on a digital detector, fluorescent screen, or photographic film.

Classification of Life

This appendix presents a taxonomic classification for the major extant groups of organisms discussed in this text; not all phyla are included. The classification presented here is based on the three-domain system, which assigns the two major groups of prokaryotes, bacteria and archaea, to separate domains (with eukaryotes making up the third domain).

Various alternative classification schemes are discussed in Unit Four of the text. The taxonomic turmoil includes debates about the number and boundaries of kingdoms and about the alignment of the Linnaean classification hierarchy with the findings of modern cladistic analysis. In this review, asterisks (*) indicate currently recognized phyla thought by some systematists to be paraphyletic.

DOMAIN BACTERIA

- **Proteobacteria**
- **Chlamydia**
- **Spirochetes**
- **Cyanobacteria**
- **Gram-positive bacteria**

DOMAIN ARCHAEA

- **Korarchaeota**
- **Euryarchaeota**
- **Crenarchaeota**
- **Nanoarchaeota**

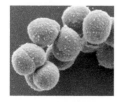

DOMAIN EUKARYA

In the phylogenetic hypothesis we present in Chapter 25, major clades of eukaryotes are grouped together in the four "supergroups" listed in green type. Formerly, all the eukaryotes generally called protists were assigned to a single kingdom, Protista. However, advances in systematics have made it clear that some protists are more closely related to plants, fungi, or animals than they are to other protists. As a result, the kingdom Protista has been abandoned.

Excavata
- Diplomonadida (diplomonads)
- Parabasala (parabasalids)
- Euglenozoa (euglenozoans)
    - Kinetoplastida (kinetoplastids)
    - Euglenophyta (euglenids)

SAR
- Stramenopila (stramenopiles)
    - Bacillariophyta (diatoms)
    - Phaeophyta (brown algae)
- Alveolata (alveolates)
    - Dinoflagellata (dinoflagellates)
    - Apicomplexa (apicomplexans)
    - Ciliophora (ciliates)

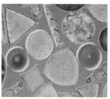

- Rhizaria
    - Foraminifera (forams)
    - Cercozoa (cercozoans)

Archaeplastida
- Rhodophyta (red algae)
- Chlorophyta (green algae: chlorophytes)
- Charophyta (green algae: charophytes)
- Plantae
    - Phylum Hepatophyta (liverworts) ⎱ Nonvascular
    - Phylum Bryophyta (mosses) ⎰ plants (bryophytes)
    - Phylum Anthocerophyta (hornworts)
    - Phylum Lycophyta (lycophytes) ⎱ Seedless vascular
    - Phylum Monilophyta (ferns, horsetails, ⎰ plants
       whisk ferns)
    - Phylum Ginkgophyta (ginkgo) ⎱
    - Phylum Cycadophyta (cycads) ⎰ Gymnosperms
    - Phylum Gnetophyta (gnetophytes) ⎱ Seed plants
    - Phylum Coniferophyta (conifers)
    - Phylum Anthophyta (flowering ⎰ Angiosperms
       plants)

Unikonta
- Amoebozoa (amoebozoans)
  - Tubulinea (tubulinids)
  - Dictyostelida (cellular slime molds)
- Nucleariida (nucleariids)
- Fungi
  - *Phylum Chytridiomycota (chytrids)
  - *Phylum Zygomycota (zygomycetes)
  - Phylum Glomeromycota (glomeromycetes)
  - Phylum Ascomycota (sac fungi)
  - Phylum Basidiomycota (club fungi)

- Choanoflagellata (choanoflagellates)
- Animalia
  - Phylum Porifera (sponges)
  - Phylum Ctenophora (comb jellies)
  - Phylum Cnidaria (cnidarians)
  - Lophotrochozoa (lophotrochozoans)
    - Phylum Platyhelminthes (flatworms)
    - Phylum Ectoprocta (ectoprocts)
    - Phylum Brachiopoda (brachiopods)
    - Phylum Rotifera (rotifers)
    - Phylum Mollusca (molluscs)
    - Phylum Annelida (segmented worms)

Ecdysozoa (ecdysozoans)
- Phylum Nematoda (roundworms)
- Phylum Arthropoda (This survey groups arthropods into a single phylum, but some zoologists now split the arthropods into multiple phyla.)
  - Chelicerata (horseshoe crabs, arachnids)
  - Myriapoda (millipedes, centipedes)
  - Pancrustacea (crustaceans, insects)

Deuterostomia (deuterostomes)
- Phylum Hemichordata (hemichordates)
- Phylum Echinodermata (echinoderms)
- Phylum Chordata (chordates)
  - Cephalochordata (lancelets)
  - Urochordata (tunicates)
  - Cyclostomata (cyclostomes)   ⎫
    - Myxini (hagfishes)   ⎪
    - Petromyzontida (lampreys)   ⎪
  - Gnathostomata (gnathostomes) ⎬ Vertebrates
    - Chondrichthyes (sharks, rays, chimaeras) ⎪
    - Actinopterygii (ray-finned fishes)   ⎪
    - Actinistia (coelacanths)   ⎪
    - Dipnoi (lungfishes)   ⎪
    - Amphibia (amphibians)   ⎪
    - Reptilia (tuataras, lizards, snakes, turtles, crocodilians, birds) ⎪
    - Mammalia (mammals)   ⎭

Graphs

Graphs provide a visual representation of numerical data. They may reveal patterns or trends in the data that are not easy to recognize in a table. A graph is a diagram that shows how one variable in a data set is related (or perhaps not related) to another variable. The **independent variable** is the factor that is manipulated or changed by the researchers. The **dependent variable** is the factor that the researchers are measuring in relationship to the independent variable. The independent variable is typically plotted on the x-axis and the dependent variable on the y-axis. Types of graphs that are frequently used in biology include scatter plots, line graphs, bar graphs, and histograms.

▶ A **scatter plot** is used when the data for all variables are numerical and continuous. Each piece of data is represented by a point. In a **line graph**, each data point is connected to the next point in the data set with a straight line, as in the graph to the right. (To practice making and interpreting scatter plots and line graphs, see the Scientific Skills Exercises in Chapters 2, 5, 6, 8, 10, 17, 22, 35, 38, 39, 41, and 43.)

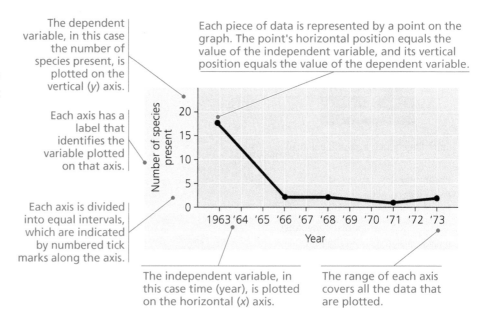

The dependent variable, in this case the number of species present, is plotted on the vertical (y) axis.

Each axis has a label that identifies the variable plotted on that axis.

Each axis is divided into equal intervals, which are indicated by numbered tick marks along the axis.

Each piece of data is represented by a point on the graph. The point's horizontal position equals the value of the independent variable, and its vertical position equals the value of the dependent variable.

The independent variable, in this case time (year), is plotted on the horizontal (x) axis.

The range of each axis covers all the data that are plotted.

▼ Two or more data sets can be plotted on the same line graph to show how two dependent variables are related to the same independent variable. (To practice making and interpreting line graphs with two or more data sets, see the Scientific Skills Exercises in Chapters 5, 35, 38, 39, and 43.)

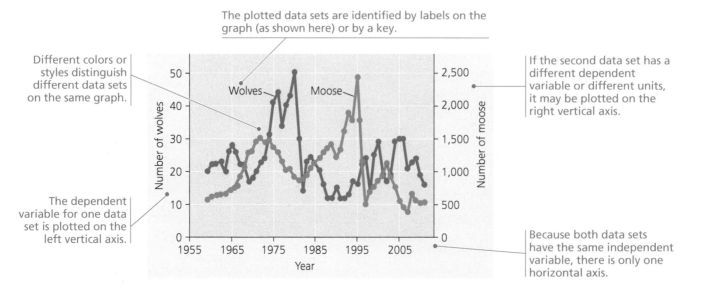

The plotted data sets are identified by labels on the graph (as shown here) or by a key.

Different colors or styles distinguish different data sets on the same graph.

The dependent variable for one data set is plotted on the left vertical axis.

If the second data set has a different dependent variable or different units, it may be plotted on the right vertical axis.

Because both data sets have the same independent variable, there is only one horizontal axis.

▼ In some scatter plot graphs, a straight or curved line is drawn through the entire data set to show the general trend in the data. A straight line that mathematically best fits the data is called a *regression line*. Alternatively, a mathematical function that best fits the data may describe a curved line, often termed a *best-fit curve*. (To practice making and interpreting regression lines, see the Scientific Skills Exercises in Chapters 2 and 8.)

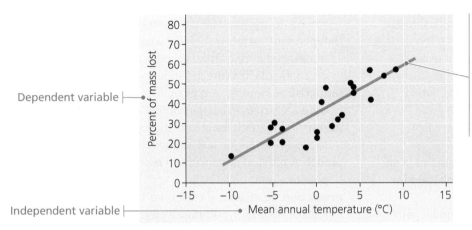

The regression line can be expressed as a mathematical equation. It allows you to predict the value of the dependent variable for any value of the independent variable within the range of the data set and, less commonly, beyond the range of the data.

Dependent variable

Independent variable

▼ A **bar graph** is a kind of graph in which the independent variable represents groups or non-numerical categories and the values of the dependent variable(s) are shown by bars. (To practice making and interpreting bar graphs, see the Scientific Skills Exercises in Chapters 1, 7, 15, 16, 19, 23, 24, 27, 28, 31, and 41.)

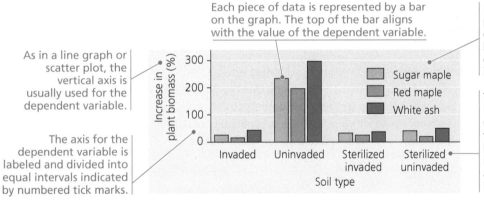

Each piece of data is represented by a bar on the graph. The top of the bar aligns with the value of the dependent variable.

If multiple data sets are plotted on the same bar graph, they are distinguished by bars of different colors or styles and identified by labels or a key.

As in a line graph or scatter plot, the vertical axis is usually used for the dependent variable.

The axis for the dependent variable is labeled and divided into equal intervals indicated by numbered tick marks.

The groups or categories of the independent variable are usually spaced equally along the horizontal axis. (In some bar graphs, the horizontal axis is used for the dependent variable and the vertical axis for the independent variable.)

▶ A variant of a bar graph called a **histogram** can be made for numeric data by first grouping, or "binning," the variable plotted on the x-axis into intervals of equal width. The "bins" may be integers or ranges of numbers. In the histogram at right, the intervals are 25 mg/dL wide. The height of each bar shows the percent (or, alternatively, the number) of experimental subjects whose characteristics can be described by one of the intervals plotted on the x-axis. (To practice making and interpreting histograms, see the Scientific Skills Exercises in Chapters 9, 11, and 34.)

The height of this bar shows the percent of individuals (about 4%) whose plasma LDL cholesterol levels are in the range indicated on the x-axis.

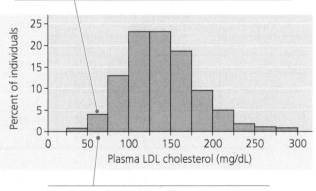

This interval runs from 50 to 74 mg/dL.

Glossary of Scientific Inquiry Terms

See Concept 1.3 for more discussion of the process of scientific inquiry.

control group In a controlled experiment, a set of subjects that lacks (or does not receive) the specific factor being tested. Ideally, the control group should be identical to the experimental group in other respects.

controlled experiment An experiment designed to compare an experimental group with a control group; ideally, the two groups differ only in the factor being tested.

data Recorded observations.

deductive reasoning A type of logic in which specific results are predicted from a general premise.

dependent variable A factor whose value is measured in an experiment to see whether it is influenced by changes in another factor (the independent variable).

experiment A scientific test. Often carried out under controlled conditions that involve manipulating one factor in a system in order to see the effects of changing that factor.

experimental group A set of subjects that has (or receives) the specific factor being tested in a controlled experiment. Ideally, the experimental group should be identical to the control group for all other factors.

hypothesis A testable explanation for a set of observations based on the available data and guided by inductive reasoning. A hypothesis is narrower in scope than a theory.

independent variable A factor whose value is manipulated or changed during an experiment to reveal possible effects on another factor (the dependent variable).

inductive reasoning A type of logic in which generalizations are based on a large number of specific observations.

inquiry The search for information and explanation, often focusing on specific questions.

model A physical or conceptual representation of a natural phenomenon.

prediction In deductive reasoning, a forecast that follows logically from a hypothesis. By testing predictions, experiments may allow certain hypotheses to be rejected.

theory An explanation that is broader in scope than a hypothesis, generates new hypotheses, and is supported by a large body of evidence.

variable A factor that varies during an experiment.

Chi-Square (χ^2) Distribution Table

To use the table, find the row that corresponds to the degrees of freedom in your data set. (The degrees of freedom is the number of categories of data minus 1.) Move along that row to the pair of values that your calculated χ^2 value lies between. Move up from those numbers to the probabilities at the top of the columns to find the probability range for your χ^2 value. A probability of 0.05 or less is generally considered significant. (To practice using the chi-square test, see the Scientific Skills Exercise in Chapter 12.)

Degrees of Freedom (df)	Probability										
	0.95	0.90	0.80	0.70	0.50	0.30	0.20	0.10	0.05	0.01	0.001
1	0.004	0.02	0.06	0.15	0.45	1.07	1.64	2.71	3.84	6.64	10.83
2	0.10	0.21	0.45	0.71	1.39	2.41	3.22	4.61	5.99	9.21	13.82
3	0.35	0.58	1.01	1.42	2.37	3.66	4.64	6.25	7.82	11.34	16.27
4	0.71	1.06	1.65	2.19	3.36	4.88	5.99	7.78	9.49	13.28	18.47
5	1.15	1.61	2.34	3.00	4.35	6.06	7.29	9.24	11.07	15.09	20.52
6	1.64	2.20	3.07	3.83	5.35	7.23	8.56	10.64	12.59	16.81	22.46
7	2.17	2.83	3.82	4.67	6.35	8.38	9.80	12.02	14.07	18.48	24.32
8	2.73	3.49	4.59	5.53	7.34	9.52	11.03	13.36	15.51	20.09	26.12
9	3.33	4.17	5.38	6.39	8.34	10.66	12.24	14.68	16.92	21.67	27.88
10	3.94	4.87	6.18	7.27	9.34	11.78	13.44	15.99	18.31	23.21	29.59

Credits

Photo Credits

Cover image, Title Page, Ready-to-Go Teaching Modules Klaus Honal/age fotostock.

Endpapers **Unit 1** Albert Tousson; **Unit 2** Andrey Prokhorov/Getty Images; **Unit 3** Sylvain Cordier/Science Source; **Unit 4** Lisa-Ann Gershwin; **Unit 5** Dennis Frates; **Unit 6** Oliver Wien/epa; European Pressphoto Agency/Alamy; **Unit 7** Juan Carlos Munoz/age fotostock.

Preface Gerard Lacz/FLPA.

Organization and New Content **Chapter 1** J.B. Miller/Florida Park Service; **Unit 1** Albert Tousson; **Unit 2** Andrey Prokhorov/Getty Images; **Unit 3** Sylvain Cordier/Science Source; **Unit 4** Lisa-Ann Gershwin; **Unit 5** Dennis Frates; **Unit 6** Oliver Wien/epa; European Pressphoto Agency/Alamy; **Unit 7** Juan Carlos Muñoz/age fotostock.

Detailed Contents **ants** Paul Quagliana/BNPS; **gecko** Martin Harvey/Photolibrary/Getty Images; **cell** Michael W. Davidson/Molecular Expressions; **geyser** Jack Dykinga/NaturePL.com; **kelp** Lawrence Naylor/Science Source; **dividing cells** Steve Gschmeissner/Science Source; **chromosome** Peter Menzel/Science Source; **protein** Barry Stoddard; **embryo** Stephen W. Paddock; **adenovirus** Linda M. Stannard, University of Cape Town/Science Source; **flower mantid** Lighthouse/UIG/age fotostock; **fossils** B. O'Kane/Alamy; ***Pandorina*** De Agostini Picture Library/Science Source; **mycelium** Hecker/blickwinkel/Alamy; **fern** John Martin/Alamy; **turtle** Juniors Bildarchiv/age fotostock; **flytrap** Chris Mattison/NaturePL.com; **bobcat** Thomas Kitchin & Victoria Hurst/All Canada Photos/age fotostock; **capillary** Ed Reschke/Getty Images; **spider** Stefan Hetz Supplied by WENN.com/Newscom; **locusts** Stringer/Reuters; **urchins** Scott Ling, Institute for Marine & Antarctic Studies, University of Tasmania.

Unit Openers **Unit 1: 2** Paul Quagliana/BNPS; **3** Mark J. Winter/Science Source; **4** Don W. Fawcett/Science Source; **5** Used by permission of B. L. de Groot. Related to work done for: Water Permeation Across Biological Membranes: Mechanism and Dynamics of Aquaporin-1 and GlpF. BL de Groot, H Grubmüller. *Science* 294:2353–2357 (2001); **6** Doug Perrine/Nature Picture Library; **7** Uryadnikov Sergey/Shutterstock; **8** Aflo/Nature Picture Library; **9** George von Dassow; **Unit 2: 10** Mango Productions/Corbis; **11** John Swithinbank/age fotostock; **12** Peter Menzel/Science Source; **13** Andrey Prokhorov/Getty Images; **14** Alessandro Bianchi/Reuters; **15** Andreas Werth; **16** Stephen W. Paddock; **17** Richard Bizley/Science Source; **18** Karen Huntt/Corbis; **Unit 3: 19** William Mullins/Alamy; **20** Pierson Hill; **21** Sylvain Cordier/Science Source; **22** Joel Sartore/Getty Images; **23** Juergen Ritterbach/Alamy; **Unit 4: 24** B Christopher/Alamy; **25** Biophoto Associates/Science Source; **26** Christopher Meder/Shutterstock; **27** Scott Linstead/Science Source; **Unit 5: 28** John Walker; **29** Dennis Frates/Alamy; **30** Ch'ien Lee; **31** Ernesto Gianoli, Departamento de Biología, Universidad de La Serena, Chile; **Unit 6: 32** Matthias Wittlinger; **33** Jeff Foott/Discovery Channel Images/Getty Images; **34** Jane Burton/BRUCE COLEMAN/Alamy; **35** SPL/Science Source; **36** Colin Marshall/FLPA; **37** Franco Banfi/Science Source; **38** Tamily Weissman; **39** Manamana/Shutterstock; **Unit 7: 40** Christopher Austin; **41** Jurgen Freund/Nature Picture Library; **42** Jordi Bas Casas/Photoshot; **43** Phung My Trung, vncreatures.net.

Chapter 1 **1.1** J.B. Miller/Florida Park Service; **1.2** Shawn P. Carey, Migration Productions; **1.UN1 hummingbird** Jim Zipp/Science Source; **1.3.1** Leonello Calvetti/Stocktrek Images/Getty Images; **1.3.2** Terry Donnelly/Alamy; **1.3.3, 1.3.4** Floris van Breugel/Nature Picture Library; **1.3.5** Greg Vaughn/Alamy; **1.3.6** Pat Burner, Pearson Education; **1.3.7** Jeremy Burgess/Science Source; **1.3.8** Texas A & M University; **1.3.9** Jeremy Burgess/Science Source; **1.4a** Steve Gschmeissner/Science Source; **1.4b** A. Barry Dowsett/Science Source; **1.5** Conly Rieder; **1.6** Gelpi/fotolia; **1.7a** Photodisc/Getty Images; **1.8a.1** Carol Yepes/Moment/Getty Images; **1.8a.2** Ralf Dahm/Max Planck Institute of Neurobiology; **1.10** WaterFrame/Alamy; **1.11** Rod Williams/Nature Picture Library; **1.12a** Oliver Meckes and Nicole Ottawa/Eye of Science/Science Source; **1.12b** Eye of Science/Science Source; **1.12c1** Kunst & Scheidulin/age fotostock; **1.12c2** daksel/fotolia; **1.12c3** Anup Shah/Nature Picture Library; **1.12c4** M. I. Walker/Science Source; **1.13** Dede Randrianarisata/Macalester College; **1.14a** From: *Origin of Species* by Charles Darwin, 1859. Murray edition; **1.14b** ARCHIV/Science Source; **1.15a** zhaoyan/Shutterstock; **1.15b** Sebastian Knight/Shutterstock; **1.15c** Volodymyr Goinyk/Shutterstock; **1.18 inset** Karl Ammann/Corbis; **1.18** Tim Ridley/Dorling Kindersley; **1.19 clockwise from top** Martin Shields/Alamy; Maureen Spuhler, Pearson Education; Rolf Hicker Photography/All Canada Photos/Alamy; xPacifica/The Image Bank/Getty Images; **1.20a** From: Darwin to DNA: The Genetic Basis of Color Adaptations. From *In the Light of Evolution: Essays from the Laboratory and Field*, by J. Losos, Roberts and Co. Photo by Sacha Vignieri; **1.20a inset** Courtesy of Hopi Hoekstra, Harvard University; **1.20b** Sacha Vignieri; **1.20b inset** Shawn P. Carey, Migration Productions; **1.21** From: The selective advantage of cryptic coloration in mice. S. N. Vignieri, J. Larson, and H. E. Hoekstra. 2010. *Evolution* 64:2153–2158. Fig. 1; **1 SSE** Imagebroker/FLPA; **Chapter Review eukaryotic cell** Steve Gschmeissner/Science Source; **prokaryotic cell** A. Barry Dowsett/Science Source; **turtle** WaterFrame/Alamy; **SYK** Chris Mattison/Alamy.

Chapter 2 **2.1** Paul Quagliana/BNPS; **2.2a** Chip Clark; **2.2bc** Stephen Frisch/Pearson Education; **2.4** National Library of Medicine; **2.11** Stephen Frisch/Pearson Education; **2.UN01 gecko** Martin Harvey/Photolibrary/Getty Images; **2.15** Nigel Cattlin/Science Source; **2.17** N.C. Brown Center for Ultrastructure Studies, SUNY, Syracuse, NY; **2.18** Alasdair Thomson/E+/Getty Images; **2.20** Jan van Franeker, Alfred-Wegener Institute fur Polar-und-Meeresforschung; **2.23a** Paulista/fotolia; **2.23b** Fotofermer/fotolia; **2.23c** SciePro/SPL/age fotostock; **2.23d** Beth Van Trees/Shutterstock; **2 SSE** From: Coral reefs under rapid climate change and ocean acidification. O. Hoegh-Guldberg et al. *Science*. 2007 Dec 14; 318(5857): 1737–42. Fig. 5a; **Chapter Review moth** Rolf Nussbaumer/Nature Picture Library; **SYK** Eric Guilloret/Biosphoto/Science Source.

Chapter 3 **3.1** Mark J. Winter/Science Source; **3.11 clockwise from top left** Dougal Waters/Getty Images; John N.A. Lott/Biological Photo Service; Paul Lazarow; Biophoto Associates/Science Source; John Durham/Science Source; **3.14a** Jim Forrest/Dorling Kindersley; **3.14b** David Murray/Dorling Kindersley; **3.17a** Andrey Stratilatov/Shutterstock; **3.17bc** Nina Zanetti/Pearson Education; **3.20ab** PDB ID 2LYZ, From: Real-space refinement of the structure of hen egg-white lysozyme. R. Diamond. *Journal of Molecular Biology* 82(3):371–91 (Jan 25, 1974); **3.20c** Clive Freeman, The Royal Institution/Science Source; **3.21** Peter Colman; **3.22 spider** Dieter Hopf/Imagebroker/age fotostock; **blood cells** SciePro/SPL/age fotostock; **3.23** Eye of Science/Science Source; **3.25 top** CC-BY-3.0 Photo: Dsrjsr; **3.25 bottom** Laguna Design/Science Source; **3.29** P. Morris/Garvan Institute of Medical Research; **3.30 DNA** Alfred Pasieka/Science Source; **hippo** Frontline Photography/Alamy; **whale** WaterFrame/Alamy; **elephants** Imagebroker/FLPA; **Neanderthal** Illustration by Viktor Deak; **doctor** Chassenet/BSIP SA/Alamy; **fungus** David Read, Department of Animal and Plant Sciences, University of Sheffield; **3 SSE.1** lanych/Shutterstock; **3 SSE.2** David Bagnall/Alamy; **3 SSE.3** Eric Isselée/Shutterstock; **Chapter Review butter** Jim Forrest/Dorling Kindersley; **oil** David Murray/Dorling Kindersley; **SYK** Africa Studio/Shutterstock.

Chapter 4 **4.1** Don W. Fawcett/Science Source; **4.UNCO paramecium** M.I. Walker/Science Source; **4.3.1–4.3.4** Elisabeth Pierson, Pearson Education; **4.3.5** Michael W. Davidson/Molecular Expressions; **4.3.6** Karl Garsha; **4.3.7a** J.L. Carson/Custom Medical Stock Photo; **4.3.7b** William Dentler/Biological Photo Service; **4.4** CNRI/Science Source; **4.5** Daniel S. Friend; **4.7 left to right** S. Cinti/Science Source; SPL/Science Source; A. Barry Dowsett/Science Source; Biophoto Associates/Science Source; SPL/Science Source; The University of Kansas Center for Bioinformatics; **4 SSE** Kelly Tatchell; **4.UN01 nucleus** Thomas Deerinck and Mark Ellisman, NCMIR; **4.8.1** Reproduced with permission from Freeze-Etch Histology, by L. Orci and A. Perrelet, Springer-Verlag, Heidelberg, 1975, Plate 25, page 53. Copyright © 1975 by Springer-Verlag GmbH & Co KG; **4.8.2** Don W. Fawcett/Science Source; **4.8.3** Ueli Aebi; **4.9.1** Don W. Fawcett/Science Source; **4.9.2** Harry Noller; **4.10** Don Fawcett; R. Bolender/Science Source; **4.11** Don W. Fawcett/Science Source; **4.12–4.13** Daniel S. Friend; **4.14** Eldon H. Newcomb; **4.17a** Daniel S. Friend; **4.17b** From: The shape of mitochondria and the number of mitochondrial nucleoids during the cell cycle of *Euglena gracilis*. Y. Hayashi and K. Ueda. *Journal of Cell Science*, 93:565–570, Copyright © 1989 by Company of Biologists; **4.18a** Jeremy Burgess/Science Source; **4.18b** Franz Golig, Philipps-University, Marburg, Germany; **4.19** Eldon H. Newcomb; **4.20** Albert Tousson; **4.21b** Bruce J. Schnapp; **Table 4.1 left to right** Mary Osborn; Frank Solomon; Mark Ladinsky; **4.23a** Omikron/Science Source; **4.23b** Dartmouth Electron Microscope Facility, Dartmouth College; **4.23c** Richard W. Linck; **4.24** From: Cross-linker system between neurofilaments, microtubules, and membranous organelles in frog axons revealed by the quick-freeze, deep-etching method. Hirokawa Nobutaka. *Journal of Cell Biology* 94(1): 129–142, 1982. Reproduced by permission of Rockefeller University Press; **4.25** G. F. Leedale/Science Source; **4.27.1** Reproduced with permission from *Freeze-Etch Histology*, by L. Orci and A. Perrelet, Springer-Verlag, Heidelberg, 1975. Plate 32. Page 68. Copyright © 1975 by Springer-Verlag GmbH & Co KG; **4.27.2** From: Fine structure of desmosomes, hemidesmosomes, and an adepidermal globular layer in developing newt epidermis. D. E. Kelly. *J Cell Biol*. 1966 Jan; 28(1):51–72. Fig. 7; **4.27.3** From: Low resistance junctions in crayfish. Structural changes with functional uncoupling. C. Peracchia and A. F. Dulhunty. *The Journal of Cell Biology*. 1976 Aug; 70(2 pt 1):419–39. Fig. 6. Reproduced by permission of Rockefeller University Press; **4.28** Eye of Science/Science Source; **Chapter Review vacuole, peroxisome** Eldon H. Newcomb; **SYK** Susumu Nishinaga/Science Source.

Chapter 5 **5.1** Used by permission of B. L. de Groot. Related to work done for: Water Permeation Across Biological Membranes: Mechanism and Dynamics of Aquaporin-1 and GlpF. B. L. de Groot and H. Grubmüller. *Science* 294:2353–2357 (2001); **5.12** Michael Abbey/Science Source; **5 SSE** Photo Fun/Shutterstock; **5.18 phagocytosis** Biophoto Associates/Science Source; **pinocytosis** Don W. Fawcett/Science Source; **endocytosis** From M. M. Perry and A. B. Gilbert, *Journal of Cell Science* 39: 257–272, Fig. 11 (1979). © 1979 The Company of Biologists Ltd; **Chapter Review cheetah** Federico Veronesi/Alamy; **SYK** Kristoffer Tripplaar/Alamy.

Chapter 6 **6.1** Doug Perrine/Nature Picture Library; **6.2** Stephen Simpson/Photolibrary/Getty Images; **6.3** Robert N. Johnson; **6.4a** Image Quest Marine; **6.4b** asharkyu/Shutterstock; **6.14** Thomas A. Steitz; **6 SSE** Fer Gregory/Shutterstock; **6.16** Jack Dykinga/Nature Picture Library; **6.20** Nicolae Simionescu; **Chapter Review SYK** PayPal/Flickr/Moment Select/Getty Images.

Chapter 7 **7.1** Sergey Uryadnikov/Shutterstock; **7.4** Dionisvera/fotolia; **7.13b** The image of the ATP synthase is reproduced with the kind permission of Professor Sir John Walker and Dr. Martin Montgomery of the Medical Research Council's Mitochondrial Biology Unit; **7 SSE** Kitchin and Hurst/All Canada Photos/age fotostock; **Chapter Review SYK** Stephen Rees/Shutterstock.

Chapter 8 **8.1** Aflo/Nature Picture Library; **8.2a** Jean-Paul Nacivet/age fotostock; **8.2b** Lawrence Naylor/Science Source; **8.2c** M. I. Walker/Science Source; **8.2d** Susan M. Barns; **8.2e** Heide Schulz; **8.3a** Andreas Holzenburg and Stanislav Vitha, Dept. of Biology and Microscopy & Imaging Center, Texas A&M University; **8.3b** Jeremy Burgess/Science Source; **8.11b** Christine L. Case; **8.18a** Doukdouk/Alamy; **8.18b** Keysurfing/Shutterstock; **8 SSE** Dennis Barnes/Agstockusa/age fotostock; **8.19** Andreas Holzenburg and Stanislav Vitha, Dept. of Biology and Microscopy & Imaging Center, Texas A&M University; **Chapter Review SYK** Gary Yim/Shutterstock.

Chapter 9 **9.1** George von Dassow; **9.2a** Biophoto Associates/Science Source; **9.2b** Biology Pics/Science Source; **9.2c** Biophoto/Science Source; **9.3** J. M. Murray, Univ. of Pennsylvania Medical School; **9.4, 9.5b** Biophoto/Science Source; **9.7** Conly L. Rieder; **9.8.1 top** J. Richard McIntosh; **9.8.2** From: The kinetochore fiber structure in the acentric spindles of the green alga *Oedogonium*. M. J. Schibler and J. D. Pickettheaps. *Protoplasma*, 1987; 137(1): 29–44. Fig. 17. Springer-Verlag GmbH & Co. KG; **9.10a** Don W. Fawcett/Science Source; **9.10b** Eldon H. Newcomb; **9.11** Elizabeth Pierson, Pearson Education; **9.17** Guenter Albrecht-Buehler, Northwestern University; **9.18** Lan Bo Chen; **9.19** Anne Weston/Wellcome Institute Library; **9 SSE** Mike Davidson; **Chapter Review mitosis** J.L. Carson/Custom Medical Stock Photo; **SYK** Steve Gschmeissner/Science Source.

Chapter 10 **10.1** Mango Productions/Comet/Corbis; **10.2a** Roland Birke/OKAPIA/Science Source; **10.2b** George Ostertag/SuperStock; **10.3a** Ermakoff/Science Source; **10.3c** CNRI/Science Source; **10 SSE** SciMAT/Science Source; **10.12** Mark Petronczki and Maria Siomos; **Chapter Review SYK** Randy Ploetz.

Chapter 11 **11.1** John Swithinbank/age fotostock; **11 SSE** Alberto Pomares/Getty Images; **11.14** Barbara Bowman, Pearson Education; **11.15** Rick Guidotti, Positive Exposure; **11.17** Michael Ciesielski Photography; **Chapter Review hairlines** Barbara Bowman, Pearson Education; **cat** Breeder/owner Patricia Speciale, photographer Norma JubinVille; **SYK** Rene Maltete/RAPHO/Gamma-Rapho via Getty Images.

Chapter 12 **12.1** Peter Menzel/Science Source; **12.3** From: Learning to Fly: Phenotypic Markers in *Drosophila*. A poster of common phenotypic markers used in *Drosophila* genetics. Jennifer Childress, Richard Behringer, and Georg Halder. 2005. *Genesis* 43(1). Cover illustration; **12.5** Andrew Syred/Science Source; **12.8** Jagodka/Shutterstock; **12 SSE** Oliver911119/Shutterstock; **12.15a** SPL/Science Source; **12.15b** denys_kuvaiev/fotolia; **Chapter Review SYK** James K. Adams, Biology, Dalton State College, Dalton, Georgia.

Chapter 13 **13.1** Andrey Prokhorov/Getty Images; **13.2** A. Barrington Brown/Science Source; **13.4** Oliver Meckes/Science Source; **13 SSE** Marevision/age fotostock; **13.7a** Library of Congress; **13.7b** From: *The Double Helix* by James D. Watson, Atheneum Press, N. Y., p. 215. © 1968. Courtesy CSHL Archive; **13.8c** Photodisc/Getty Images; **13.15a** Micrograph by Jerome Vinograd. From: *Molecular Biology of the Cell*. 4th edition. DNA Replication Mechanisms. Figure 5-6; **13.15b** From: Enrichment and visualization of small replication units from cultured mammalian cells. D. J. Burks et al. *J Cell Biol*. 1978 Jun; 77(3):762–73. Fig. 6A; **13.22** Peter Lansdorp; **13.23 left to right** Gopal Murti/Science Source; Victoria E. Foe; Barbara Hamkalo; U. Laemmli/Science Source; Biophoto/Science Source; **13.26b** Repligen Corporation; **13.29a** P. Morris/Garvan Institute of Medical Research; **13.30** Ian Derrington; **Chapter Review DNA model** Thomas A. Steitz, Yale University; **SYK** Barry Stoddard.

Chapter 14 **14.1** Alessandro Bianchi/Reuters; **14.7a** Keith V. Wood, University of California, San Diego; **14.7b** Reuters; **14.22b** Barbara Hamkalo; **14.23** Reproduced with permission from O. L. Miller, Jr., B. A. Hamkalo, and C. A. Thomas, Jr., *Science* 169 (1970):392. Copyright © 1970 American Association for the Advancement of Science. Fig. 3; **14.25** Eye of Science/Science Source; **Chapter Review SYK** Vasiliy Koval/Shutterstock.

Chapter 15 **15.1** Andreas Werth; **15 SSE** Amanda Rohde/Getty Images; **15.14** Ethan Bier; **15.17** George S. Watts and Bernard W. Futscher, University of Arizona Cancer Center; **Chapter Review SYK** Peter Herring/Image Quest Marine.

Chapter 16 **16.1** Stephen W. Paddock; **16.2** Mike Wu; **16 SSE mouse** Joseph Zellner/E+/Getty Images; **paws** Thomas Montavon; **16.5** Gopal Murti/Science Source; **16.6** From: Mesenchymal cells engulf and clear apoptotic footplate cells in macrophageless PU. 1 null mouse embryos. William Wood, et al. *Development* 127, 5245–5252 (2000). Fig. 2abc; **16.8** F. Rudolf Turner, Indiana University; **16.9** Wolfgang Driever, University of Freiburg, Freiburg, Germany; **16.10** Ruth Lehmann, The Whitehead Institution; **16.12** The Roslin Institute, The University of Edinburgh, Roslin, Scotland, UK; **16.13** Pat Sullivan/AP Images; **16.14a** Steve Gschmeissner/Science Source; **16.14b** SPL/Science Source; **16.14c** Steve Gschmeissner/Science Source; **16.21** David Paul Morris/Bloomberg via Getty Images; **Chapter Review SYK** i love images/Cultura/Getty Images.

Chapter 17 **17.1** Richard Bizley/Science Source; **17.2a** Omikron/Science Source; **17.2b** Linda M. Stannard, University of Cape Town/Science Source; **17.2c** Hazel Appleton/Science Source; **17.2d** Ami Images/Science Source; **17.8** C. Dauguet/Institute Pasteur/Science Source; **17.10** National Institute of Allergy and Infectious Diseases (NIAID) and CDC; **17.11a** NIBSC/Science Source; **17.11b** Seo Myung-gon/AP Images; **17 SSE** AP Images; **17.12** Nigel Cattlin/Alamy; **Chapter Review SYK** Nelson Hale/Shutterstock.

Chapter 18 **18.1** Karen Huntt/Corbis; **18.4** Affymetrix; **18.6a** AP Images; **18.6b** Virginia Walbot; **18.9a** Oscar L. Miller Jr., Dept. of Biology, University of Virginia; **18.16a** Nicholas Bergkessel, Jr./Science Source; **Chapter Review SYK** Patrick Landmann/Science Source.

Chapter 19 **19.1** William Mullins/Alamy; **19.2** Wayne Lynch/All Canada Photos/age fotostock; **19.4** Karen Moskowitz/Stone/Getty Images; **19.5 left to right** ARCHIV/Science Source; Owen Stanley, 1841/New York Public Library/Science Source; **19.6a** Michael Gunther/Science Source; **19.6b** David Hosking/Alamy; **19.6c** David Hosking/FLPA; **19.7 left to right** Alfred Russel Wallace Memorial Fund; The Natural History Museum, London/Alamy; **19.8** Darwin's Tree of Life sketch, MS. DAR.121:p36. Reproduced with permission of the Cambridge University Library; **19.10 clockwise from bottom left** Željko Radojko/fotolia; Pablo Paul/Alamy; Guy Shapira/Shutterstock; YinYang/E+/Getty Images; motorolka/Shutterstock; Gerhard Schulz-Naturphoto; **19.11** Laura Jesse, Extension Entomologist, Iowa State University; **19.12** Richard Packwood/Oxford Scientific/Getty Images; **19.13.1** Lighthouse/UIG/age fotostock; **19.13.2** Emil Von Maltitz/Oxford Scientific/Getty Images; **19.14** Scott P. Carroll; **19.17.1** Keith Wheeler/Science Source; **19.17.2** Omikron/Science Source; **19.18 left to right** ANT Photo Library/Science Source; Joe McDonald/Steve Bloom Images/Alamy; **19.19** Chris Linz, Thewissen Lab, Northeastern Ohio Universities College of Medicine (NEOUCOM); **Chapter Review SYK** John Cancalosi/Nature Picture Library.

Chapter 20 **20.1** Pierson Hill; **20.17** Martin Harvey/NHPA/Photoshot; **20.18a** Mick Ellison; **20.18b** Ed Heck; **20 SSE** Nigel Cattlin/Alamy; **Chapter Review SYK** David Fleetham/Nature Picture Library.

Chapter 21 **21.1** Sylvain Cordier/Science Source; **21.3** David Stoecklein/Lithium/age fotostock; **21.5a** From: A diet-induced developmental polymorphism in a caterpillar. E Greene. *Science*. 1989 Feb 3; 243(4891):643–6; **21.5b** Erick Greene/Univ. of Montana; **21.6.1** Gary Schultz/Photoshot; **21.6.2** Patrick Valkenburg, Alaska DFG/AP Images; **21 SSE** DLeonis/fotolia; **21.10b** Lynn M. Stone/Nature Picture Library; **21.11a** William Ervin/Science Source; **21.12** Jan Visser; **21.14** John Visser/Bruce Coleman/Photoshot; **21.15 blood cells** Eye of Science/Science Source; **boy** Caroline Penn/Alamy; **mosquito** Kletr/Shutterstock; **21.17** Dave Blackey/All Canada Photos/age fotostock; **21.19** Merlin D. Tuttle/Science Source; **Chapter Review SYK** Thomas & Pat Leeson/Science Source.

Chapter 22 **22.1** Joel Sartore/National Geographic/Getty Images; **22.2a left to right** Malcolm Schuyl/Alamy; Photolibrary/Getty Images; **22.2b top left to right** Robert Kneschke/Kalium/age fotostock; Justin Horrocks/E+/Getty Images; Ryan McVay/Getty Images; **bottom left to right** Dragon Images/Shutterstock; arek_malang/Shutterstock; jaki good photography/Moment Open/Getty Images; **22.3a** Phil Huntley Franck; **22.3b** Jerry A. Payne, USDA Agricultural Research Service, Bugwood.org; **22.3c** Hogle Zoo; **22.3d** USDA; **22.3e** Michael Dietrich/Imagebroker/Alamy; **22.3f** Reprinted by permission from *Nature*. Evolution: single-gene speciation by left-right reversal. R. Ueshima and T. Asami. *Nature*. 2003. October 16; 425(6959):679; Fig.1 Copyright © 2003 Macmillan Magazines Limited; **22.3g** William E. Ferguson; **22.3h** Charles W. Brown; **22.3i** EyeWire Collection/PhotoDisc/Getty Images; **22.3j** bagicat/fotolia; **22.3k** FreeReinDesigns/fotolia; **22.3l** Kazutoshi Okuno; **22.4 grizzly** CLFProductions/Shutterstock; **polar** Boris Karpinski/Alamy; **grolar** Troy Maben/Associated Press; **22.6** Brian Langerhans; **22.8 maps** NASA EOS Earth Observing System; **shrimp** Arthur Anker, Florida Museum of Natural History; **22 SSE** John Shaw/NHPA/Photoshot; **22.11** Pam and Doug Soltis; **22.12** Ole Seehausen; **22.13** Jeroen Speybroeck, Research Institute for Nature and Forest; **22.15** Ole Seehausen; **22.17** Jason Rick and Loren Rieseberg; **22.19** Reprinted by permission from *Nature*. Allele substitution at a flower colour locus produces a pollinator shift in monkeyflowers. H. D. Bradshaw and D. W. Schemske. *Nature*. 2003 November 12; 426(6963):176–8. Fig. 1. Copyright © 2003. Macmillan Magazines Limited; **Chapter Review SYK** Thomas Marent/Rolf Nussbaumer Photography/Alamy.

Chapter 23 **23.1** Juergen Ritterbach/Alamy; **23.2** B. O'Kane/Alamy; **23.3 left column down** Maureen Spuhler, Pearson Education; Roger Jones; S.M. Awramik/Biological Photo Service; Sinclair Stammers/Science Source; **right column down** Franz Xaver Schmidt; Ted Daeschler, Academy of Natural Sciences; Chip Clark; Lisa-Ann Gershwin; Andrew H. Knoll; **23 SSE** Biophoto Associates/Science Source; **23.16 top middle** Bruce G. Baldwin; **all other images** Gerald D. Carr; **23.17** Jean Kern; **23.18** Jack Milchanowski/age fotostock; **23.19** Juniors Bildarchiv/Alamy; **23.21 top** David Horsley; **all other images** From: Genetic and developmental basis of evolutionary pelvic reduction in threespine sticklebacks. M. D. Shapiro et al. *Nature*. Erratum. 2006 February 23; 439(7079):1014; Fig. 1; **23.UN01 squid eye** Andrey Nekrasov/Imagebroker/Getty Images; **Chapter Review SYK** Solent News/Splash News/Newscom.

Chapter 24 **24.1** B. Christopher/Alamy; **24.2** Science Pictures Ltd./Science Source; **24.3** Carlos Gutierrez/UPI/Newscom; **24.4b** F. M. Menger and Kurt Gabrielson; **24.4c** From: Experimental models of primitive cellular compartments: encapsulation, growth, and division. M. M. Hanczyc et al. *Science*. 2003 Oct 24; 302(5645):618–22. Fig. 2i; **24.5 top left** Ken Sugitani at Nagoya University, Japan; **top right** Francois Gohier/Science Source; **bottom** Andrew Knoll, Harvard University; **24.6a** Janice Haney Carr, CDC; **24.6b** Karl Lounatmaa/Science Source; **24.6c** Stem Jems/Science Source; **24.7** L. Brent Selinger, Pearson Education; **24.8** Immo Rantala/SPL/Science Source; **24.9** Kwangshin Kim/Science Source; **24.10** Julius Adler; **24.11a** From: Taxonomic Considerations of the Family Nitrobacteraceae Buchanan; Requests for Opinions. S. W. Watson. *IJSEM (International Journal of Systematic and Evolutionary Microbiology*, formerly (in 1971) *Intl. Journal of Systematic Bacteriology*), July 1971 vol. 21 no. 3, 254–270. Fig. 14; **24.11b** N. J. Lang; **24.12** Huntington Potter; **24.13** Susan M. Barns; **24.16** Charles C. Brinton, Jr; **24.19.1** L. Evans; **24.19.2** Yuichi Suwa; **24.19.3** National Library of Medicine; **24.19.4** Patricia Grilione; **24.19.5** A. Barry Dowsett/Science Source; **24.19.6** Moredon Animal Health/SPL/Science Source; **24.19.7** CNRI/SPL/Science Source; **24.19.8** Culture Collection CCALA; **24.19.9** Paul Alan Hoskisson; **24.19.10** David M. Phillips/Science Source; **24.20** Shaeri Mukherjee; **24.21** Verena Tunnicliffe/Newscom; **24.21 inset** Reinhard Rachel, Universitaet Regensburg; **24.22** Pascale Frey-Klett; **24.23** Biological Photo Service; **24.24 left to right** Scott Camazine/Science Source; David M. Phillips/Science Source; James Gathany, CDC; **24.25** From: RNA-directed gene editing specifically eradicates latent and prevents new HIV-1 infection. W. Hu et al. *Proc Natl Acad Sci U S A*. 2014 Aug 5; 111(31):11461–6. Fig. 3D; **24 SSE** igor.stevanovic/Shutterstock; **24.26a** Metabolix Media; **24.26b** Kathleen Spuhler; **24.27** Accent Alaska.com/Alamy; **Chapter Review SYK** Biophoto Associates/Science Source.

Chapter 25 **25.1** Biophoto Associates/Science Source; **25.2a** David Lamb; **25.2b** Andrew H. Knoll; **25.2cd** Nicholas J. Butterfield, University of Cambridge; **25.2e** Susannah Porter; **25.2f** Xunlai Yuan; **25.2g** South Australian Museum; **25 SSE** Marbury/Shutterstock; **25.5** Michael Abbey/Science Source; **25.6.1** De Agostini Picture Library/Getty Images; **25.6.2** Biophoto Associates/Science Source; **25.6.3** De Agostini Picture Library/Science Source; **25.6.4** Ed Reschke/Photolibrary/Getty Images; **25.9 Giardia** Joel Mancuso; **diatoms** M.I. Walker/NHPA/Photoshot; **Volvox inset** David J. Patterson; **Volvox** Frank Fox/Science Source; **Globigerina inset** National Oceanic and Atmospheric Administration (NOAA); **Globigerina** Howard Spero, University of California Davis; **amoeba** Michael Abbey/Science Source; **25.10** David M. Phillips/Science Source; **25.11** David Patterson; **25.12** Oliver Meckes/Eye of Science/Science Source; **25.13** Steve Gschmeissner/Science Source; **25.14** Colin Bates; **25.15** Guy Brugerolle, Universitad Clermont-Ferrand, France; **25.16** Virginia Institute of Marine Science; **25.17** M.I. Walker/Science Source; **25.18** Eva Nowack; **25.19 top** D.P. Wilson; Eric & David Hosking/Science Source; **middle** Biophoto Associates/Science Source; **bottom** David Murray/Dorling Kindersley; **25.20a** Laurie Campbell/NHPA/Photoshot; **25.20b** David L. Ballantine, Marine Sciences, University of Puerto Rico; **25.22** Robert Kay; **25.25** Kevin Carpenter and Patrick Keeling; **26.26** Masamichi Aikawa, Tokai University School of Medicine, Japan; **Chapter Review SYK** Donald L Ferry.

Chapter 26 **26.1** Christopher Meder/Shutterstock; **26.3** S. C. Mueller and R. M. Brown, Jr; **26.4 left** M. I. Walker/Science Source; **26.6 left** Linda Graham, University of Wisconsin–Madison; **right** Karen S. Renzaglia; **26.7 left** Johan De Meester/Arterra Picture Library/Alamy; **right** Mike Peres RBP SPAS/Custom Medical Stock; **26.8** Charles H. Wellman, Centre for Palynology, University of Sheffield, UK; **26.9** From: A vascular conducting strand in the early land plant *Cooksonia*. D. Edwards, K. L. Davies & L. Axe. *Nature* 357, 683–685 (25 June 1992). Figure 1A; **26.10** Hans Kerp, University of Münster, Germany; **26.12** From: Glomalean fungi from the Ordovician. Dirk Redecker, Robin Kodner, and Linda E. Graham. *Science* 15. September 2000; 289:1920–1921. Figure 1A; **26.13 top** Nata-Lia/Shutterstock; **bottom** Fred Rhoades, Mycena Consulting; **inset** George Barron; **26.14 flatworm** Amar and Isabelle Guillen/Alamy; **mycelium** Hecker/blickwinkel/Alamy; **chloroplasts** From: Cytochemical localization of catalase in leaf microbodies (peroxisomes). SE Frederick, EH Newcomb. *J Cell Biol*. 1969 Nov; 43(2):343–53. Figure 6; **villi** MedicalRF.com/age fotostock; **26.15** From: Four hundred-million-year-old vesicular arbuscular mycorrhizae. W. Remy et al. *Proc Natl Acad Sci U S A*. 1994 Dec 6; 91(25):11841–3. Figures 1 and 4; **26.16.1** John Taylor; **26.16.2** Ray Watson, Canadian Photography; **26.16.3** M. F. Brown/Biological Photo Service; **26.16.4** Lenz/blickwinkel/Alamy; **26.16.5** Phil Dotson/Science Source; **26 SSE** DOE Photo; **26.19ac** The Hidden Forest (hiddenforest.co.nz); **26.19b** Tony Wharton/FLPA; **26.20a** Helga & Kurt Rasbach; **26.20b** John Martin/Alamy; **26.22 top** Maureen Spuhler; **bottom** FloralImages/Alamy; **26.24a** Warren Price Photography/Shutterstock; **26.24b** Svetlana Tikhonova/Shutterstock; **26.24c** vincentlouis/fotolia; **26.26a** David L. Dilcher and Ge Sun; **26.28 Amborella** Stephen McCabe; **water lily** Howard Rice/Dorling Kindersley; **anise** Jack Scheper, Floridata.com; **magnolia** Andrew Butler/Dorling Kindersley; **palm** John Dransfield; **zucchini** Gerald Carr; **26.29a left** Ralph Lee Hopkins/Getty Images; **right** Geoff Simpson/Nature Picture Library; **26.29b** Eye of Science/Science Source; **26.30** John Watson © The Open University; **26.32a** Scott Camazine/Alamy; **26.32b** Peter Chadwick/Dorling Kindersley; **26.32c** Hecker-Sauer/age fotostock; **26.33** NASA images courtesy Landsat team; **Chapter Review sporangia** Mike Peres RBP SPAS/Custom Medical Stock; **SYK** © W. Barthlott, Lotus-Salvinia.de.

Chapter 27 **27.1** Scott Linstead/Science Source; **27.2a** Lisa-Ann Gershwin; **27.2b** From: The Late Precambrian fossil *Kimberella* is a mollusc-like bilaterian organism. M. Fedonkin and B. M. Waggoner. *Nature* 388, 868–871(28 August 1997). Fig. 1; **27.3 27.4a** Andrew J. Martinez/Science Source; **27.4b** mirpic/fotolia; **27.4c** Neil G. McDaniel/Science Source; **27.6 left** Chip Clark; **right** The Natural History Museum Trading Company Ltd; **27.7a** From: Taxonomic Considerations of the Family Nitrobacteraceae Buchanan. Requests for Opinions. S. W. Watson. *IJSEM (International Journal of Systematic and Evolutionary Microbiology*, formerly (in 1971) *Intl. Journal of Systematic Bacteriology*), July 1971 vol. 21 no. 3, 254–270. Fig. 14; **27.7b** Shuhai Xiao, Virginia Tech; **27.11 ectoproct** Hecker/Sauer/Blickwinkel/age fotostock; **rotifer** W. I. Walker/Science Source; **fireworm** Gustavo A. Rojas/age fotostock; **roundworm** London Scientific Films/Getty Images; **spider** Reinhard Hölzl/Imagebroker/age fotostock; **acorn worm** Heather Angel; **sea star** Andrey Nekrasov/Image Quest Marine; **27.13.1** Robert Marien/Spirit/Corbis; **27.13.2** Andrew J. Martinez/Science Source; **27.13.3** Thierry Duran/Shutterstock; **27.14** Dan Cooper; **27.15** From: Evolution of the entire arthropod *Hox* gene set predated the origin and radiation of the onychophoran/arthropod clade. J. K. Grenier et al. *Curr Biol*. 1997 Aug 1; 7(8):547–53. Fig. 3c; **27.16** From: New evidence on the anatomy and phylogeny of the earliest vertebrates. Hou Xian-guang, Richard J. Aldridge et al. *Proceedings of the Royal Society of London-B-Biological Sciences*, Sept. 22, 2002; 269 (1503). Fig. 1c; **27.18a** Heather Angel/Natural Visions/Alamy; **27.18b** Robert Brons/Biological Photo Service; **27.19 hagfish** Tom McHugh/Science Source; **mouth** A. Hartl/Blickwinkel/age fotostock; **lamprey** Marevision/age fotostock; **shark** Carlos Villoch/Image Quest Marine; **lionfish** Jez Tryner/Image Quest Marine;

and Steven Miller, Center for Marine Science, University of North Carolina-Wilmington, Key Largo, Florida; **43.21** NASA/Goddard Space Flight Center; **43.23** Erich Hartmann/Magnum Photos; **43 SSE** Hank Morgan/Science Source; **43.28 resin canal** Biophoto Associates/Science Source; **tunnels** Ladd Livingston, Idaho Department of Lands, Bugwood.org; **aerial** Dezene Huber, University of Northern British Columbia; **pika** Photo by Becka Barkley, courtesy of Chris Ray, University of Colorado-Boulder; **caribou** E.A. Janes/robertharding.com; **chickweed** Gilles Delacroix/Garden World Images/age fotostock; **urchins** Scott Ling, Institute for Marine & Antarctic Studies, University of Tasmania; **43.32a** Serge de Sazo/Science Source; **43.32b** Javier Trueba/MSF/Science Source; **43.32c** Gabriel Rojo/Nature Picture Library; **43.32d** Titus Lacoste/Getty Images; **Chapter Review SYK** Don Johnston/age fotostock.

Appendix A **4.ANS2** Omikron/Science Source; **9.ANS1** Biophoto/Science Source; **9.ANS2** From: The kinetochore fiber structure in the acentric spindles of the green alga *Oedogonium*. M. J. Schibler, J. D. Pickettheaps. Protoplasma, 1987; 137(1): 29–44. Fig. 17. Springer-Verlag GmbH & Co. KG; **9.ANS4** J. L. Carson/Custom Medical Stock Photo; **13.ANS5** Thomas A. Steitz, Yale University; **28.ANS1** From: Anatomy of the vessel network within and between tree rings of *Fraxinus lanuginosa* (Oleaceae). Peter B. Kitin, Tomoyuki Fujii, Hisashi Abe and Ryo Funada. *American Journal of Botany*. 2004; 91:779–788.

Appendix E **bacteria** Oliver Meckes/Nicole Ottawa/Eye of Science/Science Source; **archaea** Eye of Science/Science Source; **diatoms** M. I. Walker/NHPA/Photoshot; **water lily** Howard Rice/Dorling Kindersley; **fungi** Phil Dotson/Science Source; **orangutan** Anup Shah/Image State/Alamy.

Illustration and Text Credits

Chapter 1 **p.18 Quote** ("To explain all . . .") Sir Isaac Newton, as quoted in Richard S. Westfall, *The Life of Isaac Newton* (1994), 256; **1.21** Data from S. N. Vignieri, J. G. Larson, and H. E. Hoekstra, The selective advantage of crypsis in mice, *Evolution* 64:2153–2158 (2010); **1 SSE.2** Data from D. W. Kaufman, Adaptive coloration in *Peromyscus polionotus*: Experimental selection by owls, *Journal of Mammalogy* 55:271–283 (1974).

Chapter 2 **2.22a** Based on M. Gerstein and M. Levitt. Simulating water and the molecules of life, *Scientific American* Nov. 1998, pp. 100–105; **2 SSE.1** Data from C. Langdon et al., Effect of calcium carbonate saturation state on the calcification rate of an experimental coral reef, *Global Biogeochemical Cycles* 14:639–654 (2000).

Chapter 3 **3.5** © Pearson Education, Inc.; **3.15** Adapted from *Biology: The Science of Life*, 3rd ed., by R. Wallace, G. Sanders and R. Ferl, 1991. Copyright © 1991 by Pearson Education, Inc. Reprinted and electronically reproduced by permission of Pearson Education, Inc. Upper Saddle River, NJ. **3.17h** PDB ID 1CGD: J. Bella, B. Brodsky, and H. M. Berman. Hydration structure of a collagen peptide, *Structure* 3:893–906 (1995); **3.20** PDB ID 2LYZ: Based on R. Diamond. Real-space refinement of the structure of hen egg-white lysozyme. *Journal of Molecular Biology* 82(3): 371–91 (Jan 25, 1974); **3.22** (part 4): PDB ID 3GS0: S.K. Palaninathan, N.N. Mohamedmohaideen, E. Orlandini, G. Ortore, S. Nencetti, A. Lapucci, A. Rossello, J.S. Freundlich, J.C. Sacchettini. Novel transthyretin amyloid fibril formation inhibitors: Synthesis, biological evaluation, and X-ray structural analysis. *Public Library of Science ONE* 4(7): e6290. doi:10.1371/journal.pone.0006290 (2009); **3.22** (part 6): PDB ID 1CGD: J. Bella, B. Brodsky, and H.M. Berman. Hydration structure of a collagen peptide, *Structure* 3:893–906 (1995); **3.22** (part 7): PDB ID 2HHB: G. Fermi, M.F. Perutz, B. Shaanan, and R. Fourme. The crystal structure of human deoxyhaemoglobin at 1.74 Å resolution. *J. Mol. Biol.* 175:159–174 (1984); **3 SSE Table** Data from human: http://www.ncbi.nlm.nih.gov/protein/AAA21113.1; Data from rhesus monkey: http://www.ncbi.nlm.nih.gov/protein/122634; Data from gibbon: http://www.ncbi.nlm.nih.gov/protein/122616.

Chapter 4 **4.5b** Adapted from *The World of the Cell*, 3rd Edition, by W.M. Becker, J.B. Reece, and M.F. Poenie, 1996. Copyright © 1996 by Pearson Education, Inc. Reprinted and electronically reproduced by permission of Pearson Education, Inc. Upper Saddle River, NJ; **4.7** Adapted from illustrations by Tomo Narashima in *Human Anatomy and Physiology*, 5th ed., by E.N. Marieb, 2001. Copyright © 2001 by E.N. Marieb. Reprinted and electronically reproduced with permission by Pearson Education, Inc. Upper Saddle River, NJ; **4.8** Adapted from *Human Anatomy and Physiology*, 5th ed., by E.N. Marieb, 2001. Copyright © 2001 by E.N. Marieb. Reprinted and electronically reproduced with permission by Pearson Education, Inc. Upper Saddle River, NJ; **4.10** Adapted from illustrations by Tomo Narashima in *Human Anatomy and Physiology*, 5th ed., by E.N. Marieb, 2001. Copyright © 2001 by E.N. Marieb. Reprinted and electronically reproduced with permission by Pearson Education, Inc. Upper Saddle River, NJ; **4.11** Adapted from illustrations by Tomo Narashima in *Human Anatomy and Physiology*, 5th ed., by E.N. Marieb, 2001. Copyright © 2001 by E.N. Marieb. Reprinted and electronically reproduced with permission by Pearson Education, Inc. Upper Saddle River, NJ; **Table 4.1** Adapted from *The World of the Cell*, 4th ed., by W.M. Becker, L.J. Kleinsmith, and J. Hardin, 2000. Copyright © 2000 by Pearson Education, Inc. Reprinted and electronically reproduced by permission of Pearson Education, Inc. Upper Saddle River, NJ; **4.15** © Pearson Education, Inc.

Chapter 5 **5.4** Based on L. D. Frye and M. Edidin, The rapid intermixing of cell surface antigens after formation of mouse-human heterokaryons, *Journal of Cell Science* 7:319 (1970); **5.6** PDB ID 3HAO: N.H. Joh, A. Oberai, D. Yang, J.P. Whitelegge, and J.U. Bowie. Similar energetic contributions of packing in the core of membrane and water-soluble proteins. *J. Am. Chem. Soc.* 131:10846–10847 (2009); **5.21** Adapted from *The World of the Cell*, 3rd Edition, by W.M. Becker, J.B. Reece, and M.F. Poenie, 1996. Copyright © 1996 by Pearson Education, Inc. Reprinted and electronically reproduced by permission of Pearson Education, Inc. Upper Saddle River, NJ; **5.25** Adapted from *The World of the Cell*, 3rd Edition, by W.M. Becker, J.B. Reece, and M.F. Poenie, 1996. Copyright © 1996 by Pearson Education, Inc. Reprinted and electronically reproduced by permission of Pearson Education, Inc. Upper Saddle River, NJ; **5 SSE.1** Data from Figure 1 in T. Kondo and E. Beutler, Developmental changes in glucose transport of guinea pig erythrocytes, *Journal of Clinical Investigation* 65:1–4 (1980).

Chapter 6 **6 SSE.1** Data from S. R. Commerford et al., Diets enriched in sucrose or fat increase gluconeogenesis and G-6-Pase but not basal glucose production in rats, *American Journal of Physiology–Endocrinology and Metabolism* 283:E545–E555 (2002).

Chapter 7 **7.5** Adapted from *Molecular Biology of the Cell*, 4th ed., by B. Alberts, et al. Copyright © 2002 by Garland Science/Taylor & Francis Books, LLC. Reprinted with permission; **7.9a** Adapted from *Biochemistry*, 2nd ed., by C.K. Matthews and K.E. van Holde, 1996. Copyright © 1996 by Pearson Education, Inc. Reprinted and electronically reproduced by permission of Pearson Education, Inc. Upper Saddle River, NJ; **7.9b** Adapted from *Biochemistry*, 2nd ed., by C.K. Matthews and K.E. van Holde, 1996. Copyright © 1996 by Pearson Education, Inc. Reprinted and electronically reproduced by permission of Pearson Education, Inc. Upper Saddle River, NJ; **7 SSE.1** Data from M. E. Harper and M. D. Brand, The quantitative contributions of mitochondrial proton leak and ATP turnover reactions to the changed respiration rates of hepatocytes from rats of different thyroid status, *Journal of Biological Chemistry* 268:14850–14860 (1993).

Chapter 8 **8.9c** Data from T. W. Engelmann, *Bacterium photometricum*. Ein Beitrag zur vergleichenden Physiologie des Licht-und Farbensinnes, *Archiv. für Physiologie* 30:95–124 (1883); **8.12b** PDB ID 2AXT: B. Loll, J. Kern, W. Saenger, A. Zouni, and J. Biesiadka. Towards complete cofactor arrangement in the 3.0 Å resolution structure of photosystem II. *Nature* 438:1040–1044 (2005); **8.14** Adapted from *Energy, Plants, and Man*, by R. Walker and D.A. Walker. Copyright © 1992 by Richard Walker and David Alan Walker. Reprinted with permission of Richard Walker and Shirley Walker; **8 SSE.1** Data from D.T. Patterson and E.P. Flint, Potential effects of global atmospheric CO_2 enrichment on the growth and competitiveness of C_3 and C_4 weed and crop plants, *Weed Science* 28(1):71–75 (1980).

Chapter 9 **p.182 Quote** ("Where a cell . . .") Rudolf Virchow, 1855, quoted in *Biology*, Helena Curtis, second edition, Worth, p. 90; **9.9** Data from G. J. Gorbsky, P. J. Sammak, and G. G. Borisy, Chromosomes move poleward in anaphase along stationary microtubules that coordinately disassemble from their kinetochore ends, *Journal of Cell Biology* 104:9–18 (1987); **9.13** Adapted from *Molecular Biology of the Cell*, 4th ed., by B. Alberts, et al. Copyright © 2002 by Garland Science/Taylor & Francis Books, LLC. Reprinted with permission; **9.14** Data from R. T. Johnson and P. N. Rao, Mammalian cell fusion: Induction of premature chromosome condensation in interphase nuclei, *Nature* 226:717–722 (1970); **9 SSE.1** Data from K. K. Velpula et al., Regulation of glioblastoma progression by cord blood stem cells is mediated by downregulation of cyclin D1, *PLoS ONE* 6(3): e18017 (2011). doi:10.1371/journal.pone.0018017.

Chapter 10 **10 SSE.1** Data from G. Simchen, Commitment to meiosis: What determines the mode of division in budding yeast? *BioEssays* 31:169–177 (2009). doi:10.1002/bies.200800124.

Chapter 11 **11 SSE.1** Data from R.A. Sturm, A golden age of human pigmentation genetics, *Trends in Genetics* 22:464–468 (2006); **11.3** Data from G. Mendel, Experiments in plant hybridization, *Proceedings of the Natural History Society of Brünn* 4:3–47 (1866). **11.8** Data from G. Mendel, Experiments in plant hybridization, *Proceedings of the Natural History Society of Brünn* 4:3–47 (1866).

Chapter 12 **p.238 Quote** ("Two years' work . . .") Thomas Hunt Morgan quoted in R.G. Harrison, Embryology and its relations, *Science* 85 (1937): 369–74. p. 370; **12.4** Data from T. H. Morgan, Sex-limited inheritance in *Drosophila*, *Science* 32:120–122 (1910); **12.9** Data from T. H. Morgan and C. J. Lynch, The linkage of two factors in *Drosophila* that are not sex-linked, *Biological Bulletin* 23:174–182 (1912).

Chapter 13 **p.259 Quote** ("It has not . . .") J. D. Watson and F. H. C. Crick. A Structure for Deoxyribose Nucleic Acid. *Nature*, 2 April 1953, VOL 171:737 1953; **p.260 Quote** ("Now our model . . .") J. D. Watson and F. H. C. Crick, Genetical implications of the structure of deoxyribonucleic acid, *Nature* 171:964–967 (1953); **13.3** Data from F. Griffith, The significance of pneumococcal types, *Journal of Hygiene* 27:113–159 (1928); **13.5** Data from A. D. Hershey and M. Chase, Independent functions of viral protein and nucleic acid in growth of bacteriophage, *Journal of General Physiology* 36:39–56 (1952); **13 SSE.1** Data from several papers by Chargaff: for example, E. Chargaff et al., Composition of the desoxypentose nucleic acids of four genera of sea-urchin, *Journal of Biological Chemistry* 195:155–160 (1952); **13.13** Data from M. Meselson and F. W. Stahl, The replication of DNA in *Escherichia coli*, *Proceedings of the National Academy of Sciences USA* 44:671–682 (1958); **13.27** Adapted from *The World of the Cell*, 3rd Edition, by W.M. Becker, J.B. Reece, and M.F. Poenie, 1996. Copyright © 1996 by Pearson Education, Inc. Reprinted and electronically reproduced by permission of Pearson Education, Inc. Upper Saddle River, NJ.

Chapter 14 **14.12** Adapted from *The World of the Cell*, 3rd Edition, by W.M. Becker, J.B. Reece and M.F. Poenie, 1996. Copyright © 1996 by Pearson Education, Inc. Reprinted and electronically reproduced by permission of Pearson Education, Inc. Upper Saddle River, NJ; **14.17b-c** Adapted from *Biochemistry*, 2nd ed., by C.K. Matthews and K.E. van Holde, 1996. Copyright © 1996 by Pearson Education, Inc. Reprinted and electronically reproduced by permission of Pearson Education, Inc. Upper Saddle River, NJ; **14 SSE.1–3** Material provided courtesy of Dr. Thomas Schneider, National Cancer Institute, National Institutes of Health, 2012.

Chapter 15 **15.9** PDB ID 1MDY: P. C. Ma et al. Crystal structure of MyoD bHLH domain-DNA complex: perspectives on DNA recognition and implications for transcriptional activation, *Cell* 77:451–459 (1994); **15 SSE.2** Adapted from "Regulation of human microsomal prostaglandin E synthase-1 by IL-1β requires a distal enhancer element with a unique role for C/EBPβ" by J.N. Walters et al., *Biochemical Journal*, 443(2): 561–571 (4/15/12). Copyright © 2012 by The Biochemical Society. Reprinted with permission of Portland Press Ltd.

Chapter 16 **16 SSE.1** Data from T. Montavon et al., A regulatory archipelago controls *Hox* genes transcription in digits, *Cell* 147:1132–1145 (2011). doi:10.1016/j.cell.2011.10.023; **16.10** C. Nüsslein-Volhard et al., Determination of anteroposterior polarity in *Drosophila*, *Science* 238:1675–1681 (1987); W. Driever and C. Nüsslein-Volhard, A gradient of Bicoid protein in *Drosophila* embryos, *Cell* 54:83–93 (1988); T. Berleth et al., The role of localization of bicoid RNA in organizing the anterior pattern of the *Drosophila* embryo, *EMBO Journal* 7:1749–1756 (1988); **16.11** Data from J. B. Gurdon et al., The developmental capacity of nuclei transplanted from keratinized cells of adult frogs, *Journal of Embryology and Experimental Morphology* 34:93–112 (1975); **16.16** Data from K. Takahashi et al., Induction of pluripotent stem cells from adult human fibroblasts by defined factors, *Cell* 131:861–872 (2007); **16.20** Adapted from *The World of the Cell*, 3rd Edition, by W.M. Becker, J.B. Reece, and M.F. Poenie, 1996. Copyright © 1996 by Pearson Education, Inc. Reprinted and electronically reproduced by permission of Pearson Education, Inc. Upper Saddle River, NJ.

Chapter 17 **17 SSE.1** Data from J-R. Yang et al., New variants and age shift to high fatality groups contribute to severe successive waves in the 2009 influenza pandemic in Taiwan, *PLoS ONE* 6(11): e28288 (2011).

Chapter 18 **18.3** Simulated screen shots based on Mac OS X and from data found at NCBI, U.S. National Library of Medicine using Conserved Domain Database, Sequence Alignment Viewer, and Cn3D; **18.7** Adapted from *The World of the Cell*, 3rd Edition, by W.M. Becker, J.B. Reece, and M.F. Poenie, 1996. Copyright © 1996 by Pearson Education, Inc. Reprinted and electronically reproduced by permission of Pearson Education, Inc. Upper Saddle River, NJ; **18.8** Adapted from *The World of the Cell*, 3rd Edition, by W.M. Becker, J.B. Reece, and M.F. Poenie, 1996. Copyright © 1996 by Pearson Education, Inc. Reprinted and electronically reproduced by permission of Pearson Education, Inc. Upper Saddle River, NJ; **18.9b** PDB ID 2HHB: G. Fermi, M.F. Perutz, B. Shaanan, and R. Fourme. The crystal structure of human deoxyhaemoglobin at 1.74 Å resolution. *J. Mol. Biol.* 175:159–174 (1984); **18.Un01a (lysozyme)** Drawn from data in Protein Data Bank ID 1LZ1: "Refinement of Human Lysozyme at 1.5 Å Resolution Analysis of Non-bonded and Hydrogen-bond Interactions" by P. J. Artymiuk and C. C. Blake, from *Journal of Molecular Biology*, 1981, 152:737–762; **18.Un01b (alpha-lactalbumin)** Drawn from data in Protein Data Bank ID 1A4V: "Structural Evidence for the Presence of a Secondary Calcium Binding Site in Human Alpha-Lactalbumin" by N. Chandra et al., from *Biochemistry*, 1998,

37:4767–4772; **18 SSE1 and 2** Compiled using data from the National Center for Biotechnology Information (NCBI); **18.16b** Data from W. Shu et al., Altered ultrasonic vocalization in mice with a disruption in the *Foxp2* gene, *Proceedings of the National Academy of Sciences USA* 102:9643–9648 (2005); **18.17** Adapted from *The Homeobox: Something Very Precious That We Share with Flies, From Egg to Adult* by Peter Radetsky. Copyright © 1992 by William McGinnis. Image provided by William McGinnis; **18.18** Adapted from "*Hox* genes and the evolution of diverse body plans" by M. Akam, *Philosophical Transactions of the Royal Society B: Biological Sciences*, 349(1329):313–319 (9/29/95). Copyright © 1995 by the Royal Society. Reprinted with permission. Permission conveyed through Copyright Clearance Center, Inc.

Chapter 19 **p.383 Quote** ("Your words have . . .") Darwin, Charles (1887:116), Darwin, F., ed., The life and letters of Charles Darwin, including an autobiographical chapter, London: John Murray (*The Autobiography of Charles Darwin*). Retrieved on 2006-12-15; **19.9** Adapted from artwork by U. Kikutani, as appeared in "What can make a four-ton mammal a most sensitive beast?", *Natural History* 106(1), 36–45 (11/97). Copyright ©1997 by Utako Kikutani. Reprinted with permission of the artist; **19.14b** Data from S. P. Carroll and C. Boyd, Host race radiation in the soapberry bug: natural history with the history, *Evolution* 46:1052–1069 (1992); **19.15a** Courtesy of B.A. Diep for author Michael Cain; **19.15b** From www.hcup.ahrq.gov: A. Elixhauser & C. Steiner, Statistical Brief #35. Infections with methicillin-resistant *Staphylococcus aureus* (MRSA) in U.S. hospitals, 1993–2005, Fig. 1. Healthcare Cost and Utilization Project. Agency for Healthcare Research and Quality, Rockville, MD (2007); **p.393 Quote** ("There is grandeur . . .") Charles Darwin, *The Origin of Species*, 1859; **19 SSE.1** Data from J. A. Endler, Natural selection on color patterns in *Poecilia reticulata*, *Evolution* 34:76–91 (1980); **19 EOC Table** Data from C. F. Curtis et al., Selection for and against insecticide resistance and possible methods of inhibiting the evolution of resistance in mosquitoes, *Ecological Entomology* 3:273–287 (1978).

Chapter 20 **20.6** Data from C. S. Baker and S. R. Palumbi, Which whales are hunted? A molecular genetic approach to monitoring whaling, *Science* 265:1538–1539 (1994); **20.13** Adapted from "The Evolution of the Hedgehog Gene Family in Chordates; Insights from Amphioxus Hedgehog" by S.M. Shimeld, *Developmental Genes and Evolution* 209(1): 40–47 (1/1/99). Copyright © 1999 by Springer. Reprinted with kind permission from Springer Science+Business Media B.V.; **20.19** Based on *Molecular Markers, Natural History, and Evolution*, 2nd ed., by J.C. Advise. Sinauer Associates, 2004; **20.20** Adapted from "Timing the Ancestor of the HIV-1 Pandemic Strains" by B. Korber et al., *Science* 288(5472):1789–1796 (6/9/00). Copyright © 2000 by AAAS. Reprinted with permission from AAAS; **20.22** "Phylogenetic Classification and the Universal Tree" by W.F. Doolittle, *Science* 284(5423):2124–2128 (6/25/99). Copyright © 1999 by AAAS. Reprinted with permission from AAAS; **20 SSE.1** Data from Nancy A. Moran, Yale University. See N. A. Moran and T. Jarvik, Lateral transfer of genes from fungi underlies carotenoid production in aphids, *Science* 328:624–627 (2010).

Chapter 21 **21.4** Data from M. Kreitman, Nucleotide polymorphism at the alcohol dehydrogenase locus of *Drosophila melanogaster*, *Nature* 304:412–416 (1983); **21.11** *Discover Biology*, 2nd ed., by M.L. Cain and H. Damman, by R.A. Lue and C.K. Loon (eds.). W. W. Norton & Company, Inc., 2002; **21.12** Data from "Gene Flow Maintains a Large Genetic Difference in Clutch Size at a Small Spatial Scale" by E. Postma and A.J. van Noordwijk, *Nature* 433(7021): 65–68 (1/6/05); **21.14** Adapted from many sources including D.J. Futuyma, *Evolution*, Fig. 11.3, Sinauer Associates, Sunderland, MA (2005) and from R.L. Carroll, *Vertebrate Paleontology and Evolution*, W.H. Freeman & Co. (1988); **21.15** Adapted from A.C. Allison. Abnormal hemoglobin and erythrocyte enzyme-deficiency traits. In *Genetic Variation in Human Populations*, by G.A. Harrison (ed.), Oxford: Elsevier Science (1961), and from S. I. Hay et al., A world malaria map: *Plasmodium falciparum* endemicity in 2007, *PLoS Medicine* 6:291 (2009), fig. 3; **21.16** Adapted from "Frequency-Dependent Natural Selection in the Handedness of Scale-Eating Cichlid Fish" by M. Hori, *Science* 260(5105):216–219 (4/9/93). Copyright © 1993 by AAAS. Reprinted with permission from AAAS; **21.18** Data from A. M. Welch et al., Call duration as an indicator of genetic quality in male gray tree frogs, *Science* 280:1928–1930 (1998); **21 EOC02** Data from R. K. Koehn and T. J. Hilbish, The adaptive importance of genetic variation, *American Scientist* 75:134–141 (1987).

Chapter 22 **p.434 Quote** ("Both in space . . .") Charles Darwin, *The Voyage of the Beagle* (1839), chapter VIII: "Excursion to Colonia del Sacramiento, etc." (second edition, 1845), entry for 19 November 1833, pages 147–148; **22.6** R. Brian Langerhans, an original unpublished graph; **22.7** Data from D. M. B. Dodd, Reproductive isolation as a consequence of adaptive divergence in *Drosophila pseudoobscura*, *Evolution* 43:1308–1311 (1989); **22.12** Data from O. Seehausen and J. J. M. van Alphen, The effect of male coloration on female mate choice in closely related Lake Victoria cichlids (*Haplochromis nyererei* complex), *Behavioral Ecology and Sociobiology* 42:1–8 (1998); **22.13** Based on "Analysis of Hybrid Zones with *Bombina*" by J.M. Szymura, by R.G. Harrison (ed.), *Hybrid Zone and the Evolutionary Process*. Oxford University Press, 1993; **22 SSE.1** Data from S. G. Tilley, P. A. Verrell, and S. J. Arnold, Correspondence between sexual isolation and allozyme differentiation: A test in the salamander *Desmognathus ochrophaeus*, *Proceedings of the National Academy of Sciences USA*. 87:2715–2719 (1990); **22.18** Data from L. H. Rieseberg et al., Role of gene interactions in hybrid speciation: Evidence from ancient and experimental hybrids, *Science* 272:741–745 (1996).

Chapter 23 **23.4** Figure 6.1 adapted from *Geologic Time* by D.L. Eicher, 1976. Copyright © 1976 by Pearson Education, Inc. Reprinted and electronically reproduced by permission of Pearson Education, Inc. Upper Saddle River, NJ; **23.5c-f** Adapted from many sources including D.J. Futuyma, *Evolution*, fig. 4.10, Sunderland, MA: Sinauer Associates, Sunderland, MA (2005) and from R.L. Carroll, *Vertebrate Paleontology and Evolution*. W.H. Freeman & Co. (1988); **23.5g** Adapted from Z. Luo et al., A new mammalia form from the Early Jurassic and evolution of mammalian characteristics, *Science* 292:1535 (2001); **23.8** Adapted from http://geology.er.usgs.gov/eastern/plates.html; **23.10** Adapted from Figure 1 of "Amphibians as Indicators of Early Tertiary "Out-of-India" Dispersal of Vertebrates" by F. Bossuyt and M.C. Milinkovitch, *Science* 292(5514):93–95 (4/01). Copyright © 2001 by AAAS. Reprinted with permission from AAAS. Permission conveyed through Copyright Clearance Center, Inc.; **23.11** Graph created from D.M. Raup & J.J. Sepkoski, Jr., Mass extinctions in the marine fossil record, *Science* 215:1501–1503 (1982); J.J. Sepkoski, Jr., A kinetic model of Phanerozoic taxonomic diversity. III. Post-Paleozoic families and mass extinctions, *Paleobiology* 10:246–267 (1984); and D.J. Futuyma, The Evolution of Biodiversity, p. 143, fig. 7.3a and p. 145, fig. 7.6, Sinauer Associates, Sunderland, MA; **23.13** Based on data from "A Long-Term Association Between Global Temperature and Biodiversity, Origination and Extinction in the Fossil Record" by P.J. Mayhew, G.B. Jenkins and T.G. Benton, *Proceedings of the Royal Society B: Biological Sciences* 275(1630):47–53. The Royal Society, 2008; **23.14** Adapted from "Anatomical and ecological constraints on Phanerozoic animal diversity in the marine realm" by R.K. Bambach, A.H. Knoll and J.J. Sepkoski, Jr., *Proceedings of the National Academy of Sciences* 99(10):6854–6859 (5/14/02). Copyright © 2002 by National Academy of Sciences, U.S.A. Reprinted with permission; **23.15** Based on Hickman, Roberts, & Larson, *Zoology*, 10th ed., Wm. C. Brown, fig. 31.1 (1997); **23.20** Based on "Hox Protein Mutation and Macroevolution of the Insect Body Plan" by M. Ronshaugen, N. McGinnis and W. McGinnis, *Nature* 415(6874):914–917 (2/6/02); **23.21** Data from M. D. Shapiro et al., Genetic and developmental basis of evolutionary pelvic reduction in three-spine sticklebacks, *Nature* 428:717–723 (2004); **23.22** Based on M. Strickberger, *Evolution*, Jones & Bartlett, Boston, MA (1990); **23 SSE.1** Data from T. Hansen, Larval dispersal and species longevity in Lower Tertiary gastropods, *Science* 199:885–887 (1978).

Chapter 24 **24.3** Based on data from A.P. Johnson et al., The Miller volcanic spark discharge experiment, *Science* 322:404 (2008); **24.4a** Data from "Experimental Models of Primitive Cellular Compartments: Encapsulation, Growth, and Division" by M.M. Hanczyc, S.M. Fujikawa, and J.W. Szostak, *Science* 302(5645):618–622 (10/24/03). American Association for the Advancement of Science (AAAS), 2003; **24.14** Data from V. S. Cooper and R. E. Lenski, The population genetics of ecological specialization in evolving *Escherichia coli* populations, *Nature* 407: 736–739 (2000); **24.22a** Based on data from C. Calvaruso et al., Root-associated bacteria contribute to mineral weathering and to mineral nutrition in trees: A budgeting analysis, *Applied and Environmental Microbiology* 72:1258–1266 (2006); **24 SSE.1** Data from R. Mendes, et al. Deciphering the rhizosphere for disease-suppressive bacteria, *Science* 332:1097–1100 (2011); **24 EOC Table** Data from J. J. Burdon et al., Variation in the effectiveness of symbiotic associations between native rhizobia and temperate Australian *Acacia*: Within-species interactions, *Journal of Applied Ecology* 36:398–408 (1999).

Chapter 25 **25.4** Adaptation of Figure 2 from "The Number, Speed, and Impact of Plastid Endosymbioses in Eukaryotic Evolution" by Patrick J. Keeling, from *ANNUAL REVIEW OF PLANT BIOLOGY*, April 2013, Volume 64. Copyright © 2002 by Annual Reviews, Inc. Permission to reprint conveyed through Copyright Clearance Center, Inc.; **25.8** Based on H. Oda and M. Takeichi, Structural and functional diversity of cadherin at the adherens junction, *The Journal of Cell Biology* 193(7): 1137–1146 (2011); and M. Abedin and N. King, The premetazoan ancestry of cadherins, *Science* 319:946–948 (2011); **25.17** Adapted from an illustration by K. X. Probst in *Microbiology* by R.W. Bauman, 2004:350. Copyright © by Kenneth X. Probst. Reprinted with permission; **25.21** Data from A. Stechmann and T. Cavalier-Smith, Rooting the eukaryote tree by using a derived gene fusion, *Science* 297:89–91 (2002); **25.24** Data from D.G. Boyce et al., Global phytoplankton decline over the past century, *Nature* 466:591–596 (2010) and from personal communication; **25 SSE.1** Data from D. Yang, et al., Mitochondrial origins, *Proceedings of the National Academy of Sciences USA* 82:4443–4447 (1985).

Chapter 26 **26.27** Adapted from: "A revision of *Williamsoniella*" by T.M. Harris, *Philosophical Transactions of the Royal Society B: Biological Sciences* 231(583):313–328 (10/10/44). Copyright © 1944 by the Royal Society. Reprinted with permission, and Figure 11a from "Phylogenetic Analysis of Seed Plants and the Origin of Angiosperms" by P.R. Crane, *Annals of the Missouri Botanical Garden* 72:738 (1985). Copyright © 1985 by P.R. Crane. Reprinted with permission by Missouri Botanical Garden Press; **26.28a** Adapted from *Phylogeny and Evolution of Angiosperms*, by P. Soltis et al., Sinauer Associates, Inc., 2005; **26 SSE.1** Data from F. Martin et al., The genome of *Laccaria bicolor* provides insights into mycorrhizal symbiosis, *Nature* 452:88–93 (2008); **26.31** Data from A. E. Arnold et al., Fungal endophytes limit pathogen damage in a tropical tree, *Proceedings of the National Academy of Sciences USA* 100:15649–15654 (2003); **26 EOC Table** Data from R. S. Redman et al., *Science* 298:1581 (2002).

Chapter 27 **27.15** Data from J. K. Grenier et al., Evolution of the entire arthropod *Hox* gene set predated the origin and radiation of the onychophoran/arthropod clade, *Current Biology* 7:547–553 (1997); **27.26 Left** Adapted from "The Devonian tetrapod *Acanthostega gunnari Jarvik*: postcranial anatomy, basal tetrapod relationships and patterns of skeletal evolution" by M.I. Coates, *Transaction of the Royal Society of Edinburgh: Earth Sciences* 87: 363–421 (1996). Copyright © 1996 by M.I. Coates. Reprinted with permission of the Royal Society of Edinburgh; **27.26 Right** Adapted from "The Pectoral Fin of *Tiktaalik roseae* and the Origin of the Tetrapod Limb" by N.H. Shubin, E.B. Daeschler, and F.A. Jenkins, Jr., *Nature* 440(7085):764–771 (4/6/06); **27.33** Based on N.J. Butterfield, Animals and the invention of the Phanerozoic Earth system, *Trends in Ecology and Evolution* 26:81–87, fig. 1 (2011); **27.40** Adapted from "Correlates of recovery for Canadian Atlantic cod" by J.A. Hutchings and R.W. Rangeley, *Canadian Journal of Zoology* 89(5):386–400 (5/1/11). Copyright © 2011 by NRC Research Press. Reprinted with permission; **27.41** Adapted from "The Global Decline of Nonmarine Mollusks" by C. Lydeard, et al., *Bioscience* 54(4):321–330 (4/04). (Updated data are from International Union for Conservation of Nature, 2008.) **27 SSE.1** Data from R. Rochette, S. P. Doyle, and T. C. Edgell, Interaction between an invasive decapod and a native gastropod: Predator foraging tactics and prey architectural defenses, *Marine Ecology Progress Series* 330:179–188 (2007); **27 EOC Table** Data from D. Sol et al., Big-brained birds survive better in nature, *Proceedings of the Royal Society B* 274:763–769 (2007).

Chapter 28 **28 SSE.1** Data from D. L. Royer et al., Phenotypic plasticity of leaf shape along a temperature gradient in *Acer rubrum*, *PLoS ONE* 4(10): e7653 (2009).

Chapter 29 **29 SSE.1** Data from J.D. Murphy and D.L. Noland, Temperature effects on seed imbibition and leakage mediated by viscosity and membranes, *Plant Physiology* 69:428–431 (1982); **29.11b** Data from D.S. Lundberg et al., Defining the core *Arabidopsis thaliana* root microbiome, *Nature* 488:86–94 (2012).

Chapter 30 **30 SSE.1** Data from S. Sutherland and R. K. Vickery, Jr., Trade-offs between sexual and asexual reproduction in the genus *Mimulus*, *Oecologia* 76:330–335 (1988).

Chapter 31 **31.2** Data from C. R. Darwin, *The Power of Movement in Plants*, John Murray, London (1880). P. Boysen-Jensen, Concerning the performance of phototropic stimuli on the *Avena* coleoptile, *Berichte der Deutschen Botanischen Gesellschaft* (*Reports of the German Botanical Society*) 31:559–566 (1913); **31.3** Data from F. Went, A growth substance and growth, *Recueils des Travaux Botaniques Néerlandais* (*Collections of Dutch Botanical Works*) 25:1–116 (1928); **31.4** Data from L. Gälweiler et al., Regulation of polar auxin transport by AtPIN1 in *Arabidopsis* vascular tissue, *Science* 282:2226–2230 (1998); **31.12a** Based on M. Wilkins, *Plant Watching*, Facts on File Publ. (1988); **31.13** Data from H. Borthwick et al., A reversible photoreaction controlling seed germination, *Proceedings of the National Academy of Sciences, USA* 38:662–666 (1952); **31 SSE.1** Data from O. Falik et al., Rumor has it . . .: Relay communication of stress cues in plants, *PLoS ONE* 6(11): e23625 (2011).

Chapter 32 **32.18** Adapted from *Zoology*, by L.G. Mitchell, J.A. Mutchmor, and W.D. Dolphin, 1998. Copyright © 1998 by Pearson Education, Inc. Reprinted and electronically reproduced by permission of Pearson Education, Inc. Upper Saddle River, NJ; **32.21** Figure 25.3b adapted from *Human Anatomy and Physiology*, 8th ed., by E.N. Marieb and K.N. Hoehn, 2010. Copyright © 2010 by Pearson Education, Inc. Reprinted and electronically reproduced by permission of Pearson Education, Inc. Upper Saddle River, NJ; **32.22** Figure 25.3b adapted from *Human Anatomy and Physiology*, 8th ed., by E.N. Marieb and K.N. Hoehn, 2010. Copyright © 2010 by Pearson Education, Inc. Reprinted and electronically reproduced by permission of Pearson Education, Inc. Upper Saddle River, NJ; **32 SSE.1** Data from R.E. MacMillen et al., Water economy and energy metabolism of the sandy inland mouse, *Leggadina hermannsburgensis*, *Journal of Mammalogy* 53:529–539 (1972).

Chapter 33 **p.689 Quote** ("A vitamin is . . .") Albert Szent-Györgyi, Nobel Prize in Physiology or Medicine, 1937; **33.7** Adapted from *Human Anatomy and Physiology*, 8th ed., by E.N. Marieb and K.N. Hoehn, 2010. Copyright © 2010 by Pearson Education, Inc. Reprinted and electronically reproduced by permission of Pearson Education, Inc. Upper Saddle River, NJ; **33 SSE.1** Data from D. L. Coleman, Effects of parabiosis of obese mice with diabetes and normal mice, *Diabetologia* 9:294–298 (1973).

Chapter 34 **34.12** Adapted from *Human Anatomy and Physiology*, 8th ed., by E.N. Marieb and K.N. Hoehn, 2010. Copyright © 2010 by Pearson Education, Inc. Reprinted and electronically reproduced by permission of Pearson Education, Inc. Upper Saddle River, NJ; **34.21** Data from M. E. Avery and J. Mead, Surface properties in relation to atelectasis and hyaline membrane disease, *American Journal of Diseases of Children* 97:517–523 (1959); **34.24** Adapted from *Human Anatomy and Physiology*, 4th ed., by E.N. Marieb. Copyright © 1998 by Pearson Education, Inc. Reprinted and electronically reproduced by permission of Pearson Education, Inc., Upper Saddle River, NJ; **34.25** PDB ID 2HHB: G. Fermi, M.F. Perutz, B. Shaanan, and R. Fourme. The crystal structure of human deoxyhaemoglobin at 1.74 Å resolution. *J. Mol. Biol.* 175:159–174 (1984); **34 SSE.1** Data from J. C. Cohen et al., Sequence variations in PCSK9, low LDL, and protection against coronary heart disease, *New England Journal of Medicine* 354:1264–1272 (2006).

Chapter 35 **35.5** Adapted from *Microbiology: An Introduction*, 6th ed., by G. J. Tortora, B.R. Funke, and C.L. Case. Copyright © 1998 by Pearson Education, Inc. Reprinted and electronically reproduced by permission of Pearson Education, Inc. Upper Saddle River, NJ; **p.741 Quote** ("for the same . . .") Thucydides quoted in *The History of the Peloponnesian War*, by Thucydides, written 431 B.C.E., translated by Richard Crawley (Floating Press, © 2008); **35 SSE.1** Data from L. J. Morrison, et al., Probabilistic order in antigenic variation of *Trypanosoma brucei*, *International Journal for Parasitology* 35:961–972 (2005), and L. J. Morrison, et al., Antigenic variation in the African trypanosome: molecular mechanisms and phenotypic complexity, *Cellular Microbiology* 1: 1724–1734 (2009).

Chapter 36 **36 SSE.1** Data from A. Jost, Recherches sur la differenciation sexuelle de l'embryon de lapin (Studies on the sexual differentiation of the rabbit embryo), *Archives d'Anatomie Microscopique et de Morphologie Experimentale* 36:271–316 (1947).

Chapter 37 **37.12** Based on *Cellular Physiology of Nerve and Muscle*, 4th ed., by G. Matthews. Wiley-Blackwell, 2002; **37 SSE.1** Data from "Opiate Receptor: Demonstration in Nervous Tissue" by C.B. Pert and S.H. Snyder, *Science* 179(4077):1011–1014 (3/9/73). American Association for the Advancement of Science (AAAS), 1973.

Chapter 38 **38.8** Based on L.M. Mukhametov. Sleep in marine mammals. In *Sleep Mechanisms*, by A.A. Borbély and J.L. Valatx (eds.), pp. 227–238, Springer-Verlag, Munich (1984); **38.14** Based on E.D. Jarvis et al., Avian brains and a new understanding of vertebrate brain evolution, *Nature Reviews Neuroscience* 6:151–159, fig. 1c (2005); **38.19** Figure 15.23 adapted from *Human Anatomy and Physiology*, 8th ed., by E.N. Marieb and K.N. Hoehn, 2010. Copyright © 2010 by Pearson Education, Inc. Reprinted and electronically reproduced by permission of Pearson Education, Inc. Upper Saddle River, NJ; **38.23** Adapted from *Human Anatomy and Physiology*, 8th ed., by E.N. Marieb, 2001. Copyright © 2001 by E.N. Marieb. Reprinted and electronically reproduced with permission by Pearson Education, Inc. Upper Saddle River, NJ; **38.26a** Adapted from *Human Anatomy and Physiology*, 8th ed., by E.N. Marieb and K.N. Hoehn, 2010. Copyright © 2010 by Pearson Education, Inc. Reprinted and electronically reproduced by permission of Pearson Education, Inc. Upper Saddle River, NJ; **38.26c,d** Adapted from *Human Anatomy and Physiology*, 8th ed., by E.N. Marieb and K.N. Hoehn, 2010. Copyright © 2010 by Pearson Education, Inc. Reprinted and electronically reproduced by permission of Pearson Education, Inc. Upper Saddle River, NJ; **38 SSE.1** Data from M. R. Ralph et al., Transplanted suprachiasmatic nucleus determines circadian period, *Science* 247:975–978 (1990).

Chapter 39 **39.2** Adapted from *Human Anatomy and Physiology*, 4th ed., by E.N. Marieb. Copyright © 1998 by Pearson Education, Inc. Reprinted and electronically reproduced by permission of Pearson Education, Inc., Upper Saddle River, NJ; **39.6** Adapted from *Human Anatomy and Physiology*, 4th ed., by E.N. Marieb. Copyright © 1998 by Pearson Education, Inc. Reprinted and electronically reproduced by permission of Pearson Education, Inc., Upper Saddle River, NJ; **39.11** Grasshopper based on Hickman et al., *Integrated Principles of Zoology*, 9th ed., p. 518, fig. 22.6, McGraw-Hill Higher Education, NY (1993); **39.17** Figure 1 in "*Drosophila*: Genetics Meets Behavior" by Marla B. Sokolowski, *Nature Reviews: Genetics*, November 2001, Volume 2(11); **39.20a,b** Data from N. Tinbergen, *The Study of Instinct*, Clarendon Press, Oxford (1951); **39.22** Adapted from "Evolution of foraging behavior in *Drosophila* by density-dependent selection" by M.B. Sokolowski, H.S. Pereira, and K. Hughes, *Proceedings of the National Academy of Sciences* 94(14):7375 (7/8/97). Copyright © 1997 by National Academy of Sciences, U.S.A. Reprinted with permission; **39 SSE.1** Data from K. Schmidt-Nielsen, Locomotion: Energy cost of swimming, flying, and running, *Science* 177:222–228 (1972).

Chapter 40 **40.7** Based on H. Walter & S. Walter-Breckle, *Walter's Vegetation of the Earth*, p. 36, fig. 16, Springer-Verlag, Munich (2003); **40.13** Data from W.J. Fletcher, Interactions among subtidal Australian sea urchins, gastropods and algae: Effects of experimental removals, *Ecological Monographs* 57:89–109 (1987); **40.22** Based on J.T. Enright, Climate and population regulation: The biogeographer's dilemma, *Oecologia* 24:295–310 (1976); **40.24** Data courtesy of Rolf O. Peterson, Michigan Technological University; **Table 40.1** Data from P. W. Sherman and M. L. Morton, Demography of Belding's ground squirrel, *Ecology* 65:1617–1628 (1984); **40.EOC07** Data from J. Clausen et al., Experimental studies on the nature of species. III. Environmental responses of climatic races of *Achillea*, Carnegie Institution of Washington Publication No. 581 (1948).

Chapter 41 **41.2** Adapted from "The Anoles of La Palma: Aspects of Their Ecological Relationships" by A.S. Rand and E.E. Williams, *Breviora* 327:1–19. Copyright © 1969 by Museum of Comparative Zoology, Harvard University. Reprinted with permission; **41.3** Based on J. H. Connell, The influence of interspecific competition and other factors on the distribution of the barnacle *Chthamalus stellatus*, *Ecology* 42:710–723 (1961); **41.4** Data adapted from David Lambert Lack, *Darwin's Finches*, p. 57, Figure 9, and p. 82, Figure 17. Cambridge: Cambridge University Press, 1947; **41 SSE.1** Data from B. L. Phillips and R. Shine, An invasive species induces rapid adaptive change in a native predator: cane toads and black snakes in Australia, *Proceedings of the Royal Society B* 273:1545–1550 (2006); **41.9b** Data from S.D. Hacker and M.D. Bertness, Experimental evidence for factors maintaining plant species diversity in a New England salt marsh, *Ecology* 80:2064–2073(1999); **41.11** Data from Figure 1A in "The diversity and biogeography of soil bacterial communities" by N. Fierer and R.B. Jackson, *Proceedings of the National Academy of Sciences* 103(3):626–631 (1/17/06); **41.14** Based on E.A. Knox, Antarctic marine ecosystems. In *Antarctic Ecology* by M. W. Holdgate (ed.), 69–96, Academic Press, London (1970); **41.15b** Data from R.T. Paine, Food web complexity and species diversity, *American Naturalist* 100:65–75 (1966); **41.18** Data from Figure 2a in "The intermediate disturbance hypothesis, refugia, and biodiversity in streams" by C.R. Townsend, M.R. Scarsbrook, and S. Doledec, *Limnology and Oceanography* 42:938–949 (1997); **41.20** Based on R.L. Crocker & J. Major, Soil development in relation to vegetation and surface age at Glacier Bay, Alaska, *Journal of Ecology* 43:427–448 (1955); **41.22** Data from "Energy and Large-Scale Patterns of Animal- and Plant-Species Richness" by D.J. Currie, *American Naturalist* 137(1): 27–49 (1/91); **41.23** Data from R. H. MacArthur and E. O. Wilson, *The Theory of Island Biogeography*, Princeton University Press, Princeton, NJ (1967); **41.24** Data for mouse, chipmunk, short-tailed shrew, and squirrel (part of "other") from D. Brisson and D.E. Dykhuizen, ospC diversity in *Borrelia burgdorferi*: different hosts are different niches, *Genetics* 168: 713–722 (2004); data for mouse, chipmunk, short-tailed shrew, and "other" from K. LoGiudice et al., The ecology of infectious disease: Effects of host diversity and community composition on Lyme disease risk, *PNAS* 100(2):567–571 (2003); data for masked shrew from D. Brisson, D.E. Dykhuizen, and R.S. Ostfeld, Conspicuous impacts of inconspicuous hosts on the Lyme disease epidemic, *Proceedings of the Royal Society B* 275:227–235 (2008).

Chapter 42 **42.4** Based on D.L. DeAngelis, *Dynamics of Nutrient Cycling and Food Webs*, Chapman & Hall, New York (1992); **42.7** Data from J. H. Ryther and W. M. Dunstan, Nitrogen, phosphorus, and eutrophication in the coastal marine environment, *Science* 171:1008–1013 (1971); **42.8** Data from Fig. 4.1, p. 82, in *Communities and Ecosystems*, 1e by R.H. Whittaker, Macmillan, New York (1970); **42.12a** Figure based on "The Canadian Intersite Decomposition Experiment: Project and Site Establishment Report" (Information Report BC-X-378) by J. A. Trofymow and the CIDET Working Group. Natural Resources Canada, Canadian Forest Service, Pacific Forestry Centre, 1998; **42.12b** Data from "Litter Decomposition Rates in Canadian Forests" by T. R. Moore, et al., from *Global Change Biology*, Volume 5(1): 75–82; **42.13a** Based on *The Economy of Nature*, 5th ed., by R.E. Ricklefs. Copyright © 2001 by W.H. Freeman and Company. Reprinted with permission; **42.17** Data from "Pilot-Scale in Situ Bioremediation of Uranium in a Highly Contaminated Aquifer. 2. Reduction of U(VI) and Geochemical Control of U(VI) Bioavailability" by Wei-Min Wu et al., *Environmental Science Technology* 40(12):3986–3995 (5/13/06); **42.Table01** Based on data from D.W. Menzel & J.H. Ryther, Nutrients limiting the production of phytoplankton in the Sargasso Sea, with special reference to iron, *Deep Sea Research* 7:276–281 (1961); **42 SSE.1** Data from J. M. Teal, Energy flow in the salt marsh ecosystem of Georgia, *Ecology* 43:614–624 (1962).

Chapter 43 **p.908 Quote** ("We must consider . . .") G. H. Brundtland quoted in Editorial in *Science*, Vol. 277, July (1997); **43.10** Data from Gene Likens; **43.11** Adapted from Figure 19.1 in *Ecology: The Experimental Analysis of Distribution and Abundance*, 5th Edition, by C.J. Krebs, 2001. Copyright © 2001 by C.J. Krebs. Reprinted and electronically reproduced by permission of Pearson Education, Inc. Upper Saddle River, NJ; **43.12** Data from R. L. Westemeier et al., Tracking the long-term decline and recovery of an isolated population, *Science* 282:1695–1698 (1998); **43.18** Based on Ocean Biogeographic Information System; http://www.iobis.org/node/591; Conservation International Foundation, 2011. Reprinted with permission; **43.25** Based on CO$_2$ data from www.esrl.noaa.gov/gmd/ccgg/trends. Temperature data from www.giss.nasa.gov/gistemps/graphs/Fig.A.lrg.gif; **43.27** Adapted from "How Fast Can Trees Migrate?" by L. Roberts, *Science* 243(4892):735–737 (2/10/89). Copyright © 1989 by AAAS. Reprinted with permission from AAAS. Permission conveyed through Copyright Clearance Center, Inc.; **43.28a (pikas)** Data from J. A. E. Stewart et al., Revisiting the past to foretell the future: summer temperature and habitat area predict pika extirpations in California, *Journal of Biogeography* 42:880–890 (2015). doi:10.1111/jbi.12466; **43.28b (caribou)** Data from Post, *Ecology of climate change—the importance of biotic interactions*, Princeton University Press, Princeton, NJ (2013); **43.28c (sea urchins)** Based on S. D. Ling et al., Reproductive potential of a marine ecosystem engineer at the edge of a newly expanded range, *Global Change Biology* 14:907–915 (2008). doi:10.1111/j.1365-2486.2008.01543.x; **43.29** Based on data from U.S. Census Bureau International Database; **43.30** Based on data from U.S. Census Bureau International Database; **43.31** Ewing B., D. Moore, S. Goldfinger, A. Oursler, A. Reed, and M. Wackernagel. 2010. *The Ecological Footprint Atlas* 2010. Oakland: Global Footprint Network, p. 33 (www.footprintnetwork.org); **43 SSE.1** Data from National Oceanic & Atmospheric Administration, Earth System Research Laboratory, Global Monitoring Division.

Appendix A **3.Ans01** © Pearson Education, Inc.; **3.Ans04** Adapted from *Biology: The Science of Life*, 3rd ed., by R. Wallace, G. Sanders, and R. Ferl, 1991. Copyright © 1991 by Pearson Education, Inc. Reprinted and electronically reproduced by permission of Pearson Education, Inc. Upper Saddle River, NJ; **11.Ans01** Data from G. Mendel, Experiments in plant hybridization, *Proceedings of the Natural History Society of Brünn* 4:3–47 (1866); **14.Ans01** Adapted from *The World of the Cell*, 3rd Edition, by W.M. Becker, J.B. Reece, and M.F. Poenie, 1996. Copyright © 1996 by Pearson Education, Inc. Reprinted and electronically reproduced by permission of Pearson Education, Inc. Upper Saddle River, NJ; **37.Ans02** Based on *Cellular Physiology of Nerve and Muscle*, 4th ed., by G. Matthews. Wiley-Blackwell, 2002; **40.Ans01** Based on J. T. Enright, Climate and population regulation: The biogeographer's dilemma, *Oecologia* 24:295–310 (1976).

Test Bank **T34.02** © Pearson Education, Inc.; **T37.03** Data from http://www.sciencemag.org/content/342/6157/441; **T37.04** Data from http://www.sciencemag.org/content/342/6157/441; **T37.05** Data from http://www.sciencemag.org/content/342/6157/441.

Glossary

Pronunciation Key

Pronounce

ā	as in	ace
a/ah		ash
ch		chose
ĕ		meet
e/eh		bet
g		game
ī		ice
i		hit
ks		box
kw		quick
ng		song
ō		robe
o		ox
oy		boy
s		say
sh		shell
th		thin
ū		boot
u/uh		up
z		zoo

′ = primary accent
′ = secondary accent

5′ cap A modified form of guanine nucleotide added onto the end of a pre-mRNA molecule.

A site One of a ribosome's three binding sites for tRNA during translation. The A site holds the tRNA carrying the next amino acid to be added to the polypeptide chain. (A stands for aminoacyl tRNA.)

ABC hypothesis A model of flower formation identifying three classes of organ identity genes that direct formation of the four types of floral organs.

abiotic (ā′-bī-ot′-ik) Nonliving; referring to the physical and chemical properties of an environment.

abscisic acid (ABA) (ab-sis′-ik) A plant hormone that slows growth, often antagonizing the actions of growth hormones. Two of its many effects are to promote seed dormancy and facilitate drought tolerance.

absorption The third stage of food processing in animals: the uptake of small nutrient molecules by an organism's body.

absorption spectrum The range of a pigment's ability to absorb various wavelengths of light; also a graph of such a range.

accessory fruit A fruit, or assemblage of fruits, in which the fleshy parts are derived largely or entirely from tissues other than the ovary.

acetyl CoA Acetyl coenzyme A; the entry compound for the citric acid cycle in cellular respiration, formed from a two-carbon fragment of pyruvate attached to a coenzyme.

acetylcholine (as′-uh-til-kō′-lēn) One of the most common neurotransmitters; functions by binding to receptors and altering the permeability of the postsynaptic membrane to specific ions, either depolarizing or hyperpolarizing the membrane.

acid A substance that increases the hydrogen ion concentration of a solution.

acrosome (ak′-ruh-sōm) A vesicle in the tip of a sperm containing hydrolytic enzymes and other proteins that help the sperm reach the egg.

actin (ak′-tin) A globular protein that links into chains, two of which twist helically about each other, forming microfilaments (actin filaments) in muscle and other kinds of cells.

action potential An electrical signal that propagates (travels) along the membrane of a neuron or other excitable cell as a nongraded (all-or-none) depolarization.

action spectrum A graph that profiles the relative effectiveness of different wavelengths of radiation in driving a particular process.

activation energy The amount of energy that reactants must absorb before a chemical reaction will start; also called free energy of activation.

activator A protein that binds to DNA and stimulates gene transcription. In prokaryotes, activators bind in or near the promoter; in eukaryotes, activators generally bind to control elements in enhancers.

active site The specific region of an enzyme that binds the substrate and that forms the pocket in which catalysis occurs.

active transport The movement of a substance across a cell membrane against its concentration or electrochemical gradient, mediated by specific transport proteins and requiring an expenditure of energy.

adaptation Inherited characteristic of an organism that enhances its survival and reproduction in a specific environment.

adaptive evolution A process in which traits that enhance survival or reproduction tend to increase in frequency in a population over time.

adaptive immunity A vertebrate-specific defense that is mediated by B lymphocytes (B cells) and T lymphocytes (T cells) and that exhibits specificity, memory, and self-nonself recognition; also called acquired immunity.

adaptive radiation Period of evolutionary change in which groups of organisms form many new species whose adaptations allow them to fill different ecological roles in their communities.

addition rule A rule of probability stating that the probability of any one of two or more mutually exclusive events occurring can be determined by adding their individual probabilities.

adenosine triphosphate *See* ATP (adenosine triphosphate).

adhesion The clinging of one substance to another, such as water to plant cell walls, by means of hydrogen bonds.

aerobic respiration A catabolic pathway for organic molecules, using oxygen (O_2) as the final electron acceptor in an electron transport chain and ultimately producing ATP. This is the most efficient catabolic pathway and is carried out in most eukaryotic cells and many prokaryotic organisms.

aggregate fruit A fruit derived from a single flower that has more than one carpel.

AIDS (acquired immunodeficiency syndrome) The symptoms and signs present during the late stages of HIV infection, defined by a specified reduction in the number of T cells and the appearance of characteristic secondary infections.

alcohol fermentation Glycolysis followed by the reduction of pyruvate to ethyl alcohol, regenerating NAD^+ and releasing carbon dioxide.

alga (plural, **algae**) A general term for any species of photosynthetic protist, including both unicellular and multicellular forms. Algal species are included in three eukaryote supergroups (Excavata, SAR, and Archaeplastida).

alimentary canal (al′-uh-men′-tuh-rē) A complete digestive tract, consisting of a tube running between a mouth and an anus.

allele (uh-lē′-ul) Any of the alternative versions of a gene that may produce distinguishable phenotypic effects.

allergen An antigen that triggers an exaggerated immune response.

allopatric speciation (al′-uh-pat′-rik) The formation of new species in populations that are geographically isolated from one another.

allopolyploid (al′-ō-pol′-ē-ployd) A fertile individual that has more than two chromosome sets as a result of two different species interbreeding and combining their chromosomes.

allosteric regulation The binding of a regulatory molecule to a protein at one site that affects the function of the protein at a different site.

alpha (α) helix (al′-fuh hē′-liks) A coiled region constituting one form of the secondary structure of proteins, arising from a specific pattern of hydrogen bonding between atoms of the polypeptide backbone (not the side chains).

alternation of generations A life cycle in which there is both a multicellular diploid form, the sporophyte, and a multicellular haploid form, the gametophyte; characteristic of plants and some algae.

alternative RNA splicing A type of eukaryotic gene regulation at the RNA-processing level in which different mRNA molecules are produced from the same primary transcript, depending on which RNA segments are treated as exons and which as introns.

altruism (al′-trū-iz-um) Selflessness; behavior that reduces an individual's fitness while increasing the fitness of another individual.

alveolates (al-vē′-uh-lets) One of the three major subgroups for which the SAR eukaryotic supergroup is named. This clade arose by secondary endosymbiosis, and its members have membrane-enclosed sacs (alveoli) located just under the plasma membrane.

alveolus (al-vē′-uh-lus) (plural, **alveoli**) One of the dead-end air sacs where gas exchange occurs in a mammalian lung.

amino acid (uh-mēn′-ō) An organic molecule possessing both a carboxyl and an amino group. Amino acids serve as the monomers of polypeptides.

amino group A chemical group consisting of a nitrogen atom bonded to two hydrogen atoms; can act as a base in solution, accepting a hydrogen ion and acquiring a charge of 1+.

aminoacyl-tRNA synthetase An enzyme that joins each amino acid to the appropriate tRNA.

ammonia A small, toxic molecule (NH_3) produced by nitrogen fixation or as a metabolic waste product of protein and nucleic acid metabolism.

amniote (am′-nē-ōt) Member of a clade of tetrapods named for a key derived character, the amniotic egg, which contains specialized membranes, including the fluid-filled amnion, that protect the embryo. Amniotes include mammals as well as birds and other reptiles.

amniotic egg An egg that contains specialized membranes that function in protection, nourishment, and gas exchange. The amniotic egg was a major evolutionary innovation, allowing embryos to develop on land in a fluid-filled sac, thus reducing the dependence of tetrapods on water for reproduction.

amoeba (uh-mē′-buh) A member of one of several groups of unicellular eukaryotes that have pseudopodia.

amoebocyte (uh-mē′-buh-sīt′) An amoeba-like cell that moves by pseudopodia and is found in most animals. Depending on the species, it may digest and distribute food, dispose of wastes, form skeletal fibers, fight infections, or change into other cell types.

amoebozoan (uh-mē′-buh-zō′-an) A protist in a clade that includes many species with lobe- or tube-shaped pseudopodia.

amphibian Member of the tetrapod class Amphibia, including salamanders, frogs, and caecilians.

amphipathic (am′-fē-path′-ik) Having both a hydrophilic region and a hydrophobic region.

amplification The strengthening of stimulus energy during transduction.

amylase (am′-uh-lās′) An enzyme that hydrolyzes starch (a glucose polymer from plants) and glycogen (a glucose polymer from animals) into smaller polysaccharides and the disaccharide maltose.

anabolic pathway (an′-uh-bol′-ik) A metabolic pathway that consumes energy to synthesize a complex molecule from simpler molecules.

anaerobic respiration (an-er-ō′-bik) A catabolic pathway in which inorganic molecules other than oxygen accept electrons at the "downhill" end of electron transport chains.

analogous Having characteristics that are similar because of convergent evolution, not homology.

analogy (an-al′-uh-jē) Similarity between two species that is due to convergent evolution rather than to descent from a common ancestor with the same trait.

anaphase The fourth stage of mitosis, in which the chromatids of each chromosome have separated and the daughter chromosomes are moving to the poles of the cell.

anatomy The structure of an organism.

anchorage dependence The requirement that a cell must be attached to a substratum in order to initiate cell division.

aneuploidy (an′-yū-ploy′-dē) A chromosomal aberration in which one or more chromosomes are present in extra copies or are deficient in number.

angiosperm (an′-jē-ō-sperm) A flowering plant, which forms seeds inside a protective chamber called an ovary.

anion (an′-ī-on) A negatively charged ion.

anterior Pertaining to the front, or head, of a bilaterally symmetric animal.

anterior pituitary A portion of the pituitary that develops from non-neural tissue; consists of endocrine cells that synthesize and secrete several tropic and nontropic hormones.

anther In an angiosperm, the terminal pollen sac of a stamen, where pollen grains containing sperm-producing male gametophytes form.

antibody A protein secreted by plasma cells (differentiated B cells) that binds to a particular antigen; also called immunoglobulin. All antibodies have the same Y-shaped structure and in their monomer form consist of two identical heavy chains and two identical light chains.

anticodon (an′-tī-kō′-don) A nucleotide triplet at one end of a tRNA molecule that base-pairs with a particular complementary codon on an mRNA molecule.

antidiuretic hormone (ADH) (an′-tī-dī-yū-ret′-ik) A peptide hormone, also known as vasopressin, that promotes water retention by the kidneys. Produced in the hypothalamus and released from the posterior pituitary, ADH also functions in the brain.

antigen (an′-ti-jen) A substance that elicits an immune response by binding to receptors of B cells, antibodies, or T cells.

antigen presentation The process by which an MHC molecule binds to a fragment of an intracellular protein antigen and carries it to the cell surface, where it is displayed and can be recognized by a T cell.

antigen receptor The general term for a surface protein, located on B cells and T cells, that binds to antigens, initiating adaptive immune responses. The antigen receptors on B cells are called B cell receptors, and the antigen receptors on T cells are called T cell receptors.

antigen-presenting cell A cell that upon ingesting pathogens or internalizing pathogen proteins generates peptide fragments that are bound by class II MHC molecules and subsequently displayed on the cell surface to T cells. Macrophages, dendritic cells, and B cells are the primary antigen-presenting cells.

antiparallel Referring to the arrangement of the sugar-phosphate backbones in a DNA double helix (they run in opposite 5′ → 3′ directions).

aphotic zone (ā′-fō′-tik) The part of an ocean or lake beneath the photic zone, where light does not penetrate sufficiently for photosynthesis to occur.

apical bud (ā′-pik-ul) A bud at the tip of a plant stem; also called a terminal bud.

apical dominance (ā′-pik-ul) Tendency for growth to be concentrated at the tip of a plant shoot, because the apical bud partially inhibits axillary bud growth.

apical meristem (ā′-pik-ul mār′-uh-stem) Embryonic plant tissue in the tips of roots and buds of shoots. The dividing cells of an apical meristem enable the plant to grow in length.

apicomplexan (ap′-ē-kom-pleks′-un) A group of alveolate protists, this clade includes many species that parasitize animals. Some apicomplexans cause human disease.

apomixis (ap′-uh-mik′-sis) The ability of some plant species to reproduce asexually through seeds without fertilization by a male gamete.

apoplast (ap′-ō-plast) Everything external to the plasma membrane of a plant cell, including cell walls, intercellular spaces, and the space within dead structures such as xylem vessels and tracheids.

apoptosis (ā-puh-tō′-sus) A type of programmed cell death that is brought about by activation of enzymes that break down many chemical components in the cell.

aposematic coloration (ap′-ō-si-mat′-ik) The bright warning coloration of many animals with effective physical or chemical defenses.

appendix A small, finger-like extension of the vertebrate cecum; contains a mass of white blood cells that contribute to immunity.

aquaporin A channel protein in the plasma membrane of a plant, animal, or microorganism cell that specifically facilitates osmosis, the diffusion of free water across the membrane.

aqueous solution (ā′-kwē-us) A solution in which water is the solvent.

arbuscular mycorrhizae (ar-bus′-kyū-lur mī′-kō-rī′-zē) Associations of a fungus with a plant root system in which the fungus causes the invagination of the host (plant) cells' plasma membranes.

arbuscular mycorrhizal fungus A symbiotic fungus whose hyphae grow through the cell wall of plant roots and extend into the root cell (enclosed in tubes formed by invagination of the root cell plasma membrane).

Archaea (ar′-kē-uh) One of two prokaryotic domains, the other being Bacteria.

Archaeplastida (ar′-kē-plas′-tid-uh) One of four supergroups of eukaryotes proposed in a current hypothesis of the evolutionary history of eukaryotes. This monophyletic group, which includes red algae, green algae, and plants, descended from an ancient protistan ancestor that engulfed a cyanobacterium. *See also* Excavata, SAR, and Unikonta.

artery A vessel that carries blood away from the heart to organs throughout the body.

arthropod A segmented, molting bilaterian animal with a hard exoskeleton and jointed appendages. Familiar examples include insects, spiders, millipedes, and crabs.

artificial selection The selective breeding of domesticated plants and animals to encourage the occurrence of desirable traits.

asexual reproduction The generation of offspring from a single parent that occurs without the fusion of gametes (by budding, division of a single cell, or division of the entire organism into two or more parts). In most cases, the offspring are genetically identical to the parent.

associative learning The acquired ability to associate one environmental feature (such as a color) with another (such as danger).

aster A radial array of short microtubules that extends from each centrosome toward the plasma membrane in an animal cell undergoing mitosis.

atherosclerosis A cardiovascular disease in which fatty deposits called plaques develop in the inner walls of the arteries, obstructing the arteries and causing them to harden.

atom The smallest unit of matter that retains the properties of an element.

atomic mass The total mass of an atom, numerically equivalent to the mass in grams of 1 mole of the atom. (For an element with more than one isotope, the atomic mass is the average mass of the naturally occurring isotopes, weighted by their abundance.)

atomic nucleus An atom's dense central core, containing protons and neutrons.

atomic number The number of protons in the nucleus of an atom, unique for each element and designated by a subscript.

ATP (adenosine triphosphate) (a-den′-ō-sēn trī-fos′-fāt) An adenine-containing nucleoside triphosphate that releases free energy when its phosphate bonds are hydrolyzed. This energy is used to drive endergonic reactions in cells.

ATP synthase A complex of several membrane proteins that functions in chemiosmosis with adjacent electron transport chains, using the energy of a hydrogen ion (proton) concentration gradient to make ATP. ATP synthases are found in the inner mitochondrial membranes of eukaryotic cells and in the plasma membranes of prokaryotes.

atrioventricular (AV) node A region of specialized heart muscle tissue between the left and right atria where electrical impulses are delayed for about 0.1 second before spreading to both ventricles and causing them to contract.

atrioventricular (AV) valve A heart valve located between each atrium and ventricle that prevents a backflow of blood when the ventricle contracts.

atrium (ā′-trē-um) (plural, **atria**) A chamber of the vertebrate heart that receives blood from the veins and transfers blood to a ventricle.

autoimmune disease An immunological disorder in which the immune system turns against self.

autonomic nervous system (ot′-ō-nom′-ik) An efferent branch of the vertebrate peripheral nervous system that regulates the internal environment; consists of the sympathetic, parasympathetic, and enteric divisions.

autopolyploid (ot′-ō-pol′-ē-ployd) An individual that has more than two chromosome sets that are all derived from a single species.

autosome (ot′-ō-sōm) A chromosome that is not directly involved in determining sex; not a sex chromosome.

autotroph (ot′-ō-trōf) An organism that obtains organic food molecules without eating other organisms or substances derived from other organisms. Autotrophs use energy from the sun or from oxidation of inorganic substances to make organic molecules from inorganic ones.

auxin (ôk′-sin) A term that primarily refers to indoleacetic acid (IAA), a natural plant hormone that has a variety of effects, including cell elongation, root formation, secondary growth, and fruit growth.

axillary bud (ak′-sil-ār-ē) A structure that has the potential to form a lateral shoot, or branch. The bud appears in the angle formed between a leaf and a stem.

axon (ak′-son) A typically long extension, or process, of a neuron that carries nerve impulses away from the cell body toward target cells.

B cells The lymphocytes that complete their development in the bone marrow and become effector cells for the humoral immune response.

Bacteria One of two prokaryotic domains, the other being Archaea.

bacteriophage (bak-tēr′-ē-ō-fāj) A virus that infects bacteria; also called a phage.

bacteroid A form of the bacterium *Rhizobium* contained within the vesicles formed by the root cells of a root nodule.

balancing selection Natural selection that maintains two or more phenotypic forms in a population.

bar graph A graph in which the independent variable represents groups or nonnumerical categories. Each piece of data is represented by a bar, whose height (or length) represents the value of the independent variable for the group or category indicated.

bark All tissues external to the vascular cambium, consisting mainly of the secondary phloem and layers of periderm.

Barr body A dense object lying along the inside of the nuclear envelope in cells of female mammals, representing a highly condensed, inactivated X chromosome.

basal body (bā′-sul) A eukaryotic cell structure consisting of a "9 + 0" arrangement of microtubule triplets. The basal body may organize the microtubule assembly of a cilium or flagellum and is structurally very similar to a centriole.

basal taxon In a specified group of organisms, a taxon whose evolutionary lineage diverged early in the history of the group.

base A substance that reduces the hydrogen ion concentration of a solution.

Batesian mimicry (bāt′-zē-un mim′-uh-krē) A type of mimicry in which a harmless species resembles an unpalatable or harmful species to which it is not closely related.

behavior Individually, an action carried out by muscles or glands under control of the nervous system in response to a stimulus; collectively, the sum of an animal's responses to external and internal stimuli.

behavioral ecology The study of the evolution of and ecological basis for animal behavior.

benign tumor A mass of abnormal cells with specific genetic and cellular changes such that the cells are not capable of surviving at a new site and generally remain at the site of the tumor's origin.

benthic zone The bottom surface of an aquatic environment.

benthos (ben′-thōz) The communities of organisms living in the benthic zone of an aquatic biome.

beta (β) pleated sheet One form of the secondary structure of proteins in which the polypeptide chain folds back and forth. Two regions of the chain lie parallel to each other and are held together by hydrogen bonds between atoms of the polypeptide backbone (not the side chains).

beta oxidation A metabolic sequence that breaks fatty acids down to two-carbon fragments that enter the citric acid cycle as acetyl CoA.

bicoid A maternal effect gene that codes for a protein responsible for specifying the anterior end in *Drosophila melanogaster*.

bilateral symmetry Body symmetry in which a central longitudinal plane divides the body into two equal but opposite halves.

bilaterian (bī′-luh-ter′-ē-uhn) Member of a clade of animals with bilateral symmetry and three germ layers.

bile A mixture of substances that is produced in the liver and stored in the gallbladder; enables formation of fat droplets in water as an aid in the digestion and absorption of fats.

binary fission A method of asexual reproduction in single-celled organisms in which the cell grows to roughly double its size and then divides into two cells. In prokaryotes, binary fission does not involve mitosis, but in single-celled eukaryotes that undergo binary fission, mitosis is part of the process.

binomial A common term for the two-part, latinized format for naming a species, consisting of the genus and specific epithet; also called a binomen.

biodiversity hot spot A relatively small area with numerous endemic species and a large number of endangered and threatened species.

bioenergetics (1) The overall flow and transformation of energy in an organism. (2) The study of how energy flows through organisms.

biofilm A surface-coating colony of one or more species of prokaryotes that engage in metabolic cooperation.

biofuel A fuel produced from biomass.

biogeochemical cycle Any of the various chemical cycles that involve both biotic and abiotic components of ecosystems.

biogeography The scientific study of the past and present geographic distributions of species.

bioinformatics The use of computers, software, and mathematical models to process and integrate biological information from large data sets.

biological augmentation An approach to restoration ecology that uses organisms to add essential materials to a degraded ecosystem.

biological clock An internal timekeeper that controls an organism's biological rhythms. The biological clock marks time with or without environmental cues but often requires signals from the environment to remain tuned to an appropriate period. *See also* circadian rhythm.

biological magnification A process in which retained substances become more concentrated at each higher trophic level in a food chain.

biological species concept Definition of a species as a group of populations whose members have the potential to interbreed in nature and produce viable, fertile offspring, but do not produce viable, fertile offspring with members of other such groups.

biology The scientific study of life.

biomanipulation An approach that applies the top-down model of community organization to alter ecosystem characteristics. For example, ecologists can prevent algal blooms and eutrophication by altering the density of higher-level consumers in lakes instead of by using chemical treatments.

biomass The total mass of organic matter comprising a group of organisms in a particular habitat.

biome (bī'-ōm) Any of the world's major ecosystem types, often classified according to the predominant vegetation for terrestrial biomes and the physical environment for aquatic biomes and characterized by adaptations of organisms to that particular environment.

bioremediation The use of organisms to detoxify and restore polluted and degraded ecosystems.

biosphere The entire portion of Earth inhabited by life; the sum of all the planet's ecosystems.

biotic (bī-ot'-ik) Pertaining to the living factors—the organisms—in an environment.

blade (1) A leaflike structure of a seaweed that provides most of the surface area for photosynthesis. (2) The flattened portion of a typical leaf.

blastocoel (blas'-tuh-sēl) The fluid-filled cavity that forms in the center of a blastula.

blastula (blas'-tyū-luh) A hollow ball of cells that marks the end of the cleavage stage during early embryonic development in animals.

blood A connective tissue with a fluid matrix called plasma in which red blood cells, white blood cells, and cell fragments called platelets are suspended.

blue-light photoreceptor A type of light receptor in plants that initiates a variety of responses, including phototropism and slowing of hypocotyl elongation.

body cavity A fluid- or air-filled space located between the digestive tract and the outer body wall; also called a coelom.

body plan In multicellular eukaryotes, a set of morphological and developmental traits that are integrated into a functional whole—the living organism.

Bohr shift A lowering of the affinity of hemoglobin for oxygen, caused by a drop in pH. It facilitates the release of oxygen from hemoglobin in the vicinity of active tissues.

bolus A lubricated ball of chewed food.

bottleneck effect Genetic drift that occurs when the size of a population is reduced, as by a natural disaster or human actions. Typically, the surviving population is no longer genetically representative of the original population.

bottom-up model A model of community organization in which mineral nutrients influence community organization by controlling plant or phytoplankton numbers, which in turn control herbivore numbers, which in turn control predator numbers.

Bowman's capsule (bō'-munz) A cup-shaped receptacle in the vertebrate kidney that is the initial, expanded segment of the nephron where filtrate enters from the blood.

brain Organ of the central nervous system where information is processed and integrated.

brainstem A collection of structures in the vertebrate brain, including the midbrain, the pons, and the medulla oblongata; functions in homeostasis, coordination of movement, and conduction of information to higher brain centers.

branch point The representation on a phylogenetic tree of the divergence of two or more taxa from a common ancestor. A branch point is usually shown as a dichotomy in which a branch representing the ancestral lineage splits (at the branch point) into two branches, one for each of the two descendant lineages.

brassinosteroid A steroid hormone in plants that has a variety of effects, including inducing cell elongation, retarding leaf abscission, and promoting xylem differentiation.

breathing Ventilation of the lungs through alternating inhalation and exhalation.

bronchus (brong'-kus) (plural, **bronchi**) One of a pair of breathing tubes that branch from the trachea into the lungs.

brown alga A multicellular, photosynthetic protist with a characteristic brown or olive color that results from carotenoids in its plastids. Most brown algae are marine, and some have a plantlike body.

bryophyte (brī'-uh-fīt) An informal name for a moss, liverwort, or hornwort; a nonvascular plant that lives on land but lacks some of the terrestrial adaptations of vascular plants.

buffer A solution that contains a weak acid and its corresponding base. A buffer minimizes changes in pH when acids or bases are added to the solution.

bulk feeder An animal that eats relatively large pieces of food.

bulk flow The movement of a fluid due to a difference in pressure between two locations.

C₃ plant A plant that uses the Calvin cycle for the initial steps that incorporate CO_2 into organic material, forming a three-carbon compound as the first stable intermediate.

C₄ plant A plant in which the Calvin cycle is preceded by reactions that incorporate CO_2 into a four-carbon compound, the end product of which supplies CO_2 for the Calvin cycle.

callus A mass of dividing, undifferentiated cells growing in culture.

calorie (cal) The amount of heat energy required to raise the temperature of 1 g of water by 1°C; also the amount of heat energy that 1 g of water releases when it cools by 1°C. The Calorie (with a capital C), usually used to indicate the energy content of food, is a kilocalorie.

Calvin cycle The second of two major stages in photosynthesis (following the light reactions), involving fixation of atmospheric CO_2 and reduction of the fixed carbon into carbohydrate.

CAM plant A plant that uses crassulacean acid metabolism, an adaptation for photosynthesis in arid conditions. In this process, carbon dioxide entering open stomata during the night is converted to organic acids, which release CO_2 for the Calvin cycle during the day, when stomata are closed.

Cambrian explosion A relatively brief time in geologic history when many present-day phyla of animals first appeared in the fossil record. This burst of evolutionary change occurred about 535–525 million years ago and saw the emergence of the first large, hard-bodied animals.

canopy The uppermost layer of vegetation in a terrestrial biome.

capillary (kap'-il-ār'-ē) A microscopic blood vessel that penetrates the tissues and consists of a single layer of endothelial cells that allows exchange between the blood and interstitial fluid.

capillary bed A network of capillaries in a tissue or organ.

capsid The protein shell that encloses a viral genome. It may be rod-shaped, polyhedral, or more complex in shape.

capsule (1) In many prokaryotes, a dense and well-defined layer of polysaccharide or protein that surrounds the cell wall and is sticky, protecting the cell and enabling it to adhere to substrates or other cells. (2) The sporangium of a bryophyte (moss, liverwort, or hornwort).

carbohydrate (kar'-bō-hī'-drāt) A sugar (monosaccharide) or one of its dimers (disaccharides) or polymers (polysaccharides).

carbon fixation The initial incorporation of carbon from CO_2 into an organic compound by an autotrophic organism (a plant, another photosynthetic organism, or a chemoautotrophic prokaryote).

carbonyl group (kar-buh-nēl') A chemical group present in aldehydes and ketones and consisting of a carbon atom double-bonded to an oxygen atom.

carboxyl group (kar-bok'-sil) A chemical group present in organic acids and consisting of a single carbon atom double-bonded to an oxygen atom and also bonded to a hydroxyl group.

cardiac cycle (kar'-dē-ak) The alternating contractions and relaxations of the heart.

cardiac muscle A type of striated muscle that forms the contractile wall of the heart. Its cells are joined by intercalated disks that relay the electrical signals underlying each heartbeat.

cardiovascular system A closed circulatory system with a heart and branching network of arteries, capillaries, and veins. The system is characteristic of vertebrates.

carnivore An animal that mainly eats other animals.

carotenoid (kuh-rot′-uh-noyd′) An accessory pigment, either yellow or orange, in the chloroplasts of plants and in some prokaryotes. By absorbing wavelengths of light that chlorophyll cannot, carotenoids broaden the spectrum of colors that can drive photosynthesis.

carpel (kar′-pul) The ovule-producing reproductive organ of a flower, consisting of the stigma, style, and ovary.

carrier In genetics, an individual who is heterozygous at a given genetic locus for a recessively inherited disorder. The heterozygote is generally phenotypically normal for the disorder but can pass on the recessive allele to offspring.

carrying capacity The maximum population size that can be supported by the available resources, symbolized as K.

Casparian strip (ka-spār′-ē-un) A water-impermeable ring of wax in the endodermal cells of plants that blocks the passive flow of water and solutes into the stele by way of cell walls.

catabolic pathway (kat′-uh-bol′-ik) A metabolic pathway that releases energy by breaking down complex molecules to simpler molecules.

catalysis (kuh-ta′-luh-sis) A process by which a chemical agent called a catalyst selectively increases the rate of a reaction without being consumed by the reaction.

catalyst (kat′-uh-list) A chemical agent that selectively increases the rate of a reaction without being consumed by the reaction.

cation (cat′-ī′-on) A positively charged ion.

cation exchange A process in which positively charged minerals are made available to a plant when hydrogen ions in the soil displace mineral ions from the clay particles.

cecum (sē′-kum) (plural, **ceca**) The blind pouch forming one branch of the large intestine.

cell body The part of a neuron that houses the nucleus and most other organelles.

cell cycle An ordered sequence of events in the life of a cell, from its origin in the division of a parent cell until its own division into two. The eukaryotic cell cycle is composed of interphase (including G_1, S, and G_2 subphases) and M phase (including mitosis and cytokinesis).

cell cycle control system A cyclically operating set of molecules in the eukaryotic cell that both triggers and coordinates key events in the cell cycle.

cell division The reproduction of cells.

cell fractionation The disruption of a cell and separation of its parts by centrifugation at successively higher speeds.

cell plate A membrane-bounded, flattened sac located at the midline of a dividing plant cell, inside which the new cell wall forms during cytokinesis.

cell wall A protective layer external to the plasma membrane in the cells of plants, prokaryotes, fungi, and some protists. Polysaccharides such as cellulose (in plants and some protists), chitin (in fungi), and peptidoglycan (in bacteria) are important structural components of cell walls.

cell-mediated immune response The branch of adaptive immunity that involves the activation of cytotoxic T cells, which defend against infected cells.

cellular respiration The catabolic pathways of aerobic and anaerobic respiration, which break down organic molecules and use an electron transport chain for the production of ATP.

cellulose (sel′-yū-lōs) A structural polysaccharide of plant cell walls, consisting of glucose monomers joined by β glycosidic linkages.

central nervous system (CNS) The portion of the nervous system where signal integration occurs; in vertebrate animals, the brain and spinal cord.

central vacuole In a mature plant cell, a large membranous sac with diverse roles in growth, storage, and sequestration of toxic substances.

centriole (sen′-trē-ōl) A structure in the centrosome of an animal cell composed of a cylinder of microtubule triplets arranged in a 9 + 0 pattern. A centrosome has a pair of centrioles.

centromere (sen′-trō-mēr) In a duplicated chromosome, the region on each sister chromatid where it is most closely attached to its sister chromatid by proteins that bind to specific DNA sequences; this close attachment causes a constriction in the condensed chromosome. (An uncondensed, unduplicated chromosome has a single centromere, identified by its DNA sequence.)

centrosome (sen′-trō-sōm) A structure present in the cytoplasm of animal cells that functions as a microtubule-organizing center and is important during cell division. A centrosome has two centrioles.

cercozoan An amoeboid or flagellated protist that feeds with threadlike pseudopodia.

cerebellum (sār′-ruh-bel′-um) Part of the vertebrate hindbrain located dorsally; functions in unconscious coordination of movement and balance.

cerebral cortex (suh-rē′-brul) The surface of the cerebrum; the largest and most complex part of the mammalian brain, containing nerve cell bodies of the cerebrum; the part of the vertebrate brain most changed through evolution.

cerebrum (suh-rē′-brum) The dorsal portion of the vertebrate forebrain, composed of right and left hemispheres; the integrating center for memory, learning, emotions, and other highly complex functions of the central nervous system.

cervix (ser′-viks) The neck of the uterus, which opens into the vagina.

chaparral A scrubland biome of dense, spiny evergreen shrubs found at midlatitudes along coasts where cold ocean currents circulate offshore; characterized by mild, rainy winters and long, hot, dry summers.

character An observable heritable feature that may vary among individuals.

character displacement The tendency for characteristics to be more divergent in sympatric populations of two species than in allopatric populations of the same two species.

checkpoint A control point in the cell cycle where stop and go-ahead signals can regulate the cycle.

chemical bond An attraction between two atoms, resulting from a sharing of outer-shell electrons or the presence of opposite charges on the atoms. The bonded atoms gain complete outer electron shells.

chemical energy Energy available in molecules for release in a chemical reaction; a form of potential energy.

chemical equilibrium In a chemical reaction, the state in which the rate of the forward reaction equals the rate of the reverse reaction, so that the relative concentrations of the reactants and products do not change with time.

chemical reaction The making and breaking of chemical bonds, leading to changes in the composition of matter.

chemiosmosis (kem′-ē-oz-mō′-sis) An energy-coupling mechanism that uses energy stored in the form of a hydrogen ion gradient across a membrane to drive cellular work, such as the synthesis of ATP. Under aerobic conditions, most ATP synthesis in cells occurs by chemiosmosis.

chemoreceptor A sensory receptor that responds to a chemical stimulus, such as a solute or an odorant.

chiasma (plural, **chiasmata**) (kī-az′-muh, kī-az′-muh-tuh) The X-shaped, microscopically visible region where crossing over has occurred earlier in prophase I between homologous nonsister chromatids. Chiasmata become visible after synapsis ends, with the two homologs remaining associated due to sister chromatid cohesion.

chitin (kī′-tin) A structural polysaccharide, consisting of amino sugar monomers, found in many fungal cell walls and in the exoskeletons of all arthropods.

chlorophyll (klōr′-ō-fil) A green pigment located in membranes within the chloroplasts of plants and algae and in the membranes of certain prokaryotes. Chlorophyll *a* participates directly in the light reactions, which convert solar energy to chemical energy.

chlorophyll *a* A photosynthetic pigment that participates directly in the light reactions, which convert solar energy to chemical energy.

chlorophyll *b* An accessory photosynthetic pigment that transfers energy to chlorophyll *a*.

chloroplast (klōr′-ō-plast) An organelle found in plants and photosynthetic protists that absorbs sunlight and uses it to drive the synthesis of organic compounds from carbon dioxide and water.

choanocyte (kō-an′-uh-sīt) A flagellated feeding cell found in sponges. Also called a collar cell, it has a collar-like ring that traps food particles around the base of its flagellum.

cholesterol (kō-les′-tuh-rol) A steroid that forms an essential component of animal cell membranes and acts as a precursor molecule for the synthesis of other biologically important steroids, such as many hormones.

chondrichthyan (kon-drik′-thē-an) Member of the class Chondrichthyes, vertebrates with skeletons made mostly of cartilage, such as sharks and rays.

chordate Member of the phylum Chordata, animals that at some point during their development have a notochord; a dorsal, hollow nerve cord; pharyngeal slits or clefts; and a muscular, post-anal tail.

chromatin (krō′-muh-tin) The complex of DNA and proteins that makes up eukaryotic chromosomes. When the cell is not dividing, chromatin exists in its dispersed form, as a mass of very long, thin fibers that are not visible with a light microscope.

chromosome (krō′-muh-sōm) A cellular structure consisting of one DNA molecule and associated protein molecules. (In some contexts, such as genome sequencing, the term may refer to the DNA alone.) A eukaryotic cell typically has multiple, linear chromosomes, which are located in the nucleus. A prokaryotic cell often has a single, circular chromosome, which is found in the nucleoid, a region that is not enclosed by a membrane. *See also* chromatin.

chromosome theory of inheritance A basic principle in biology stating that genes are located at specific positions (loci) on chromosomes and that the behavior of chromosomes during meiosis accounts for inheritance patterns.

chylomicron (kī′-lō-mī′-kron) A lipid transport globule composed of fats mixed with cholesterol and coated with proteins.

chyme (kīm) The mixture of partially digested food and digestive juices formed in the stomach.

ciliate (sil′-ē-it) A type of protist that moves by means of cilia.

cilium (sil′-ē-um) (plural, **cilia**) A short appendage containing microtubules in eukaryotic cells. A motile cilium is specialized for locomotion or moving fluid past the cell; it is formed from a core of nine outer doublet microtubules and two inner single microtubules (the "9 + 2" arrangement) ensheathed in an extension of the plasma membrane. A primary cilium is usually nonmotile and plays a sensory and signaling role; it lacks the two inner microtubules (the "9 + 0" arrangement).

circadian rhythm (ser-kā′-dē-un) A physiological cycle of about 24 hours that persists even in the absence of external cues.

***cis-trans* isomer** One of two or more compounds that have the same molecular formula and covalent bonds between atoms but differ in the spatial arrangements of their atoms owing to the inflexibility of double bonds; formerly called a geometric isomer.

citric acid cycle A chemical cycle involving eight steps that completes the metabolic breakdown of glucose molecules begun in glycolysis by oxidizing acetyl CoA (derived from pyruvate) to carbon dioxide; occurs within the mitochondrion in eukaryotic cells and in the cytosol of prokaryotes; together with pyruvate oxidation, the second major stage in cellular respiration.

clade (klād) A group of species that includes an ancestral species and all of its descendants.

cladistics (kluh-dis′-tiks) An approach to systematics in which organisms are placed into groups called clades based primarily on common descent.

class In Linnaean classification, the taxonomic category above the level of order.

cleavage (1) The process of cytokinesis in animal cells, characterized by pinching of the plasma membrane. (2) The succession of rapid cell divisions without significant growth during early embryonic development that converts the zygote to a ball of cells.

cleavage furrow The first sign of cleavage in an animal cell; a shallow groove around the cell in the cell surface near the old metaphase plate.

climate The long-term prevailing weather conditions at a given place.

climate change A directional change in temperature, precipitation, or other aspect of the global climate that lasts for three decades or more.

climograph A plot of the temperature and precipitation in a particular region.

clitoris (klit′-uh-ris) An organ at the upper intersection of the labia minora that engorges with blood and becomes erect during sexual arousal.

cloaca (klō-ā′-kuh) A common opening for the digestive, urinary, and reproductive tracts found in many nonmammalian vertebrates but in few mammals.

clonal selection The process by which an antigen selectively binds to and activates only those lymphocytes bearing receptors specific for the antigen. The selected lymphocytes proliferate and differentiate into a clone of effector cells and a clone of memory cells specific for the stimulating antigen.

clone (1) A lineage of genetically identical individuals or cells. (2) In popular usage, an individual that is genetically identical to another individual. (3) As a verb, to make one or more genetic replicas of an individual or cell. *See also* gene cloning.

cloning vector In genetic engineering, a DNA molecule that can carry foreign DNA into a host cell and replicate there. Cloning vectors include plasmids.

closed circulatory system A circulatory system in which blood is confined to vessels and is kept separate from the interstitial fluid.

cochlea (kok′-lē-uh) The complex, coiled organ of hearing that contains the organ of Corti.

codominance The situation in which the phenotypes of both alleles are exhibited in the heterozygote because both alleles affect the phenotype in separate, distinguishable ways.

codon (kō′-don) A three-nucleotide sequence of DNA or mRNA that specifies a particular amino acid or termination signal; the basic unit of the genetic code.

coefficient of relatedness The fraction of genes that, on average, are shared by two individuals.

coenzyme (kō-en′-zīm) An organic molecule serving as a cofactor. Most vitamins function as coenzymes in metabolic reactions.

coevolution The joint evolution of two interacting species, each in response to selection imposed by the other.

cofactor Any nonprotein molecule or ion that is required for the proper functioning of an enzyme. Cofactors can be permanently bound to the active site or may bind loosely and reversibly, along with the substrate, during catalysis.

cognition The process of knowing that may include awareness, reasoning, recollection, and judgment.

cognitive map A neural representation of the abstract spatial relationships between objects in an animal's surroundings.

cohesion The linking together of like molecules, often by hydrogen bonds.

cohesion-tension hypothesis The leading explanation for the ascent of xylem sap. It states that transpiration exerts pull on xylem sap, putting the sap under negative pressure or tension, and that the cohesion of water molecules transmits this pull along the entire length of the xylem from shoots to roots.

cohort A group of individuals of the same age in a population.

coleoptile (kō′-lē-op′-tul) The covering of the young shoot of the embryo of a grass seed.

coleorhiza (kō′-lē-uh-rī′-zuh) The covering of the young root of the embryo of a grass seed.

collagen A glycoprotein in the extracellular matrix of animal cells that forms strong fibers, found extensively in connective tissue and bone; the most abundant protein in the animal kingdom.

collecting duct The location in the kidney where processed filtrate, called urine, is collected from the renal tubules.

collenchyma cell (kō-len′-kim-uh) A flexible plant cell type that occurs in strands or cylinders that support young parts of the plant without restraining growth.

colon (kō′-len) The largest section of the vertebrate large intestine; functions in water absorption and formation of feces.

commensalism (kuh-men′-suh-lizm) A +/0 ecological interaction in which one organism benefits but the other is neither helped nor harmed.

communication In animal behavior, a process involving transmission of, reception of, and response to signals. The term is also used in connection with other organisms, as well as individual cells of multicellular organisms.

community All the organisms that inhabit a particular area; an assemblage of populations of different species living close enough together for potential interaction.

community ecology The study of how interactions between species affect community structure and organization.

companion cell A type of plant cell that is connected to a sieve-tube element by many plasmodesmata and whose nucleus and ribosomes may serve one or more adjacent sieve-tube elements.

competitive exclusion The concept that when populations of two similar species compete for the same limited resources, one population will use the resources more efficiently and have a reproductive advantage that will eventually lead to the elimination of the other population.

competitive inhibitor A substance that reduces the activity of an enzyme by entering the active site in place of the substrate, whose structure it mimics.

complement system A group of about 30 blood proteins that may amplify the inflammatory response, enhance phagocytosis, or directly lyse extracellular pathogens.

complementary DNA (cDNA) A double-stranded DNA molecule made *in vitro* using mRNA as a template and the enzymes reverse transcriptase and DNA polymerase. A cDNA molecule corresponds to the exons of a gene.

complete dominance The situation in which the phenotypes of the heterozygote and dominant homozygote are indistinguishable.

complete flower A flower that has all four basic floral organs: sepals, petals, stamens, and carpels.

compound A substance consisting of two or more different elements combined in a fixed ratio.

compound eye A type of multifaceted eye in insects and crustaceans consisting of up to several thousand light-detecting, focusing ommatidia.

concentration gradient A region along which the density of a chemical substance increases or decreases.

conception The fertilization of an egg by a sperm in humans.

cone A cone-shaped cell in the retina of the vertebrate eye, sensitive to color.

conformer An animal for which an internal condition conforms to (changes in accordance with) changes in an environmental variable.

conifer Member of the largest gymnosperm phylum. Most conifers are cone-bearing trees, such as pines and firs.

conjugation (kon'-jŭ-gā'-shun) (1) In prokaryotes, the direct transfer of DNA between two cells that are temporarily joined. When the two cells are members of different species, conjugation results in horizontal gene transfer. (2) In ciliates, a sexual process in which two cells exchange haploid micronuclei but do not reproduce.

connective tissue Animal tissue that functions mainly to bind and support other tissues, having a sparse population of cells scattered through an extracellular matrix.

conservation biology The integrated study of ecology, evolutionary biology, physiology, molecular biology, and genetics to sustain biological diversity at all levels.

contraception The deliberate prevention of pregnancy.

contractile vacuole A membranous sac that helps move excess water out of certain freshwater protists.

control element A segment of noncoding DNA that helps regulate transcription of a gene by serving as a binding site for a transcription factor. Multiple control elements are present in a eukaryotic gene's enhancer.

control group In a controlled experiment, a set of subjects that lacks (or does not receive) the specific factor being tested. Ideally, the control group should be identical to the experimental group in other respects.

controlled experiment An experiment designed to compare an experimental group with a control group; ideally, the two groups differ only in the factor being tested.

convergent evolution The evolution of similar features in independent evolutionary lineages.

cooperativity A kind of allosteric regulation whereby a shape change in one subunit of a protein caused by substrate binding is transmitted to all the other subunits, facilitating binding of additional substrate molecules to those subunits.

coral reef Typically a warm-water, tropical ecosystem dominated by the hard skeletal structures secreted primarily by corals. Some coral reefs also exist in cold, deep waters.

corepressor A small molecule that binds to a bacterial repressor protein and changes the protein's shape, allowing it to bind to the operator and switch an operon off.

cork cambium (kam'-bē-um) A cylinder of meristematic tissue in woody plants that replaces the epidermis with thicker, tougher cork cells.

corpus callosum (kor'-pus kuh-lō'-sum) The thick band of nerve fibers that connects the right and left cerebral hemispheres in mammals, enabling the hemispheres to process information together.

corpus luteum (kor'-pus lū'-tē-um) A secreting tissue in the ovary that forms from the collapsed follicle after ovulation and produces progesterone.

cortex (1) The outer region of cytoplasm in a eukaryotic cell, lying just under the plasma membrane, that has a more gel-like consistency than the inner regions due to the presence of multiple microfilaments. (2) In plants, ground tissue that is between the vascular tissue and dermal tissue in a root or eudicot stem.

cortical nephron In mammals and birds, a nephron with a loop of Henle located almost entirely in the renal cortex.

cotransport The coupling of the "downhill" diffusion of one substance to the "uphill" transport of another against its own concentration gradient.

countercurrent exchange The exchange of a substance or heat between two fluids flowing in opposite directions. For example, blood in a fish gill flows in the opposite direction of water passing over the gill, maximizing diffusion of oxygen into and carbon dioxide out of the blood.

countercurrent multiplier system A countercurrent system in which energy is expended in active transport to facilitate exchange of materials and generate concentration gradients.

covalent bond (kō-vā'-lent) A type of strong chemical bond in which two atoms share one or more pairs of valence electrons.

crassulacean acid metabolism (CAM) (crass-yū-lā'-shen) An adaptation for photosynthesis in arid conditions, first discovered in the family Crassulaceae. In this process, a plant takes up CO_2 at night when stomata are open and incorporates it into a variety of organic acids; during the day, when stomata are closed, CO_2 is released from the organic acids for use in the Calvin cycle.

crista (plural, **cristae**) (kris'-tuh, kris'-tē) An infolding of the inner membrane of a mitochondrion. The inner membrane houses electron transport chains and molecules of the enzyme catalyzing the synthesis of ATP (ATP synthase).

critical load The amount of added nutrient, usually nitrogen or phosphorus, that can be absorbed by plants without damaging ecosystem integrity.

cross-fostering study A behavioral study in which the young of one species are placed in the care of adults from another species.

crossing over The reciprocal exchange of genetic material between nonsister chromatids during prophase I of meiosis.

cryptic coloration Camouflage that makes a potential prey difficult to spot against its background.

culture A system of information transfer through social learning or teaching that influences the behavior of individuals in a population.

cuticle (kyū'-tuh-kul) (1) A waxy covering on the surface of stems and leaves that prevents desiccation in terrestrial plants. (2) The exoskeleton of an arthropod, consisting of layers of protein and chitin that are variously modified for different functions. (3) A tough coat that covers the body of a nematode.

cyclic AMP (cAMP) Cyclic adenosine monophosphate, a ring-shaped molecule made from ATP that is a common intracellular signaling molecule (second messenger) in eukaryotic cells. It is also a regulator of some bacterial operons.

cyclostome (sī'-cluh-stōm) Member of one of the two main clades of vertebrates; cyclostomes lack jaws and include lampreys and hagfishes. *See also* gnathostome.

cystic fibrosis (sis'-tik fī-brō'-sis) A human genetic disorder caused by a recessive allele for a chloride channel protein; characterized by an excessive secretion of mucus and consequent vulnerability to infection; fatal if untreated.

cytochrome (sī'-tō-krōm) An iron-containing protein that is a component of electron transport chains in the mitochondria and chloroplasts of eukaryotic cells and the plasma membranes of prokaryotic cells.

cytogenetic map A map of a chromosome that locates genes with respect to chromosomal features distinguishable in a microscope.

cytokine (sī'-tō-kīn') Any of a group of small proteins secreted by a number of cell types, including macrophages and helper T cells, that regulate the function of other cells.

cytokinesis (sī'-tō-kuh-nē'-sis) The division of the cytoplasm to form two separate daughter cells immediately after mitosis, meiosis I, or meiosis II.

cytokinin (sī'-tō-kī'-nin) Any of a class of related plant hormones that retard aging and act in concert with auxin to stimulate cell division, influence the pathway of differentiation, and control apical dominance.

cytoplasm (sī'-tō-plaz'-um) The contents of the cell enclosed by the plasma membrane;

in eukaryotes, the portion exclusive of the nucleus.

cytoplasmic determinant A maternal substance, such as a protein or RNA, that when placed into an egg influences the course of early development by regulating the expression of genes that affect the developmental fate of cells.

cytoskeleton A network of microtubules, microfilaments, and intermediate filaments that extends throughout the cytoplasm and serves a variety of mechanical, transport, and signaling functions.

cytosol (sī′-tō-sol) The semifluid portion of the cytoplasm.

cytotoxic T cell A type of lymphocyte that, when activated, kills infected cells as well as certain cancer cells and transplanted cells.

dalton A measure of mass for atoms and subatomic particles; the same as the atomic mass unit, or amu.

data Recorded observations.

day-neutral plant A plant in which flower formation is not controlled by photoperiod or day length.

decomposer An organism that absorbs nutrients from nonliving organic material such as corpses, fallen plant material, and the wastes of living organisms and converts them to inorganic forms; a detritivore.

deductive reasoning A type of logic in which specific results are predicted from a general premise.

deep-sea hydrothermal vent A dark, hot, oxygen-deficient environment associated with volcanic activity on or near the seafloor. The producers in a vent community are chemoautotrophic prokaryotes.

de-etiolation The changes a plant shoot undergoes in response to sunlight; also known informally as greening.

dehydration reaction A chemical reaction in which two molecules become covalently bonded to each other with the removal of a water molecule.

deletion (1) A deficiency in a chromosome resulting from the loss of a fragment through breakage. (2) A mutational loss of one or more nucleotide pairs from a gene.

demography The study of changes over time in the vital statistics of populations, especially birth rates and death rates.

denaturation (dē-nā′-chur-ā′-shun) In proteins, a process in which a protein loses its native shape due to the disruption of weak chemical bonds and interactions, thereby becoming biologically inactive; in DNA, the separation of the two strands of the double helix. Denaturation occurs under extreme (noncellular) conditions of pH, salt concentration, or temperature.

dendrite (den′-drīt) One of usually numerous, short, highly branched extensions of a neuron that receive signals from other neurons.

density The number of individuals per unit area or volume.

density dependent Referring to any characteristic that varies with population density.

density independent Referring to any characteristic that is not affected by population density.

density-dependent inhibition The phenomenon observed in normal animal cells that causes them to stop dividing when they come into contact with one another.

deoxyribonucleic acid (DNA) (dē-ok′-sē-rī′-bō-nū-klā′-ik) A nucleic acid molecule, usually a double-stranded helix, in which each polynucleotide strand consists of nucleotide monomers with a deoxyribose sugar and the nitrogenous bases adenine (A), cytosine (C), guanine (G), and thymine (T); capable of being replicated and determining the inherited structure of a cell's proteins.

deoxyribose (dē-ok′-si-rī′-bōs) The sugar component of DNA nucleotides, having one fewer hydroxyl group than ribose, the sugar component of RNA nucleotides.

dependent variable A factor whose value is measured in an experiment to see whether it is influenced by changes in another factor (the independent variable).

depolarization A change in a cell's membrane potential such that the inside of the membrane is made less negative relative to the outside. For example, a neuron membrane is depolarized if a stimulus decreases its voltage from the resting potential of −70 mV in the direction of zero voltage.

dermal tissue system The outer protective covering of plants.

desert A terrestrial biome characterized by very low precipitation.

desmosome A type of intercellular junction in animal cells that functions as a rivet, fastening cells together.

determinate growth A type of growth characteristic of most animals and some plant organs, in which growth stops after a certain size is reached.

determination The progressive restriction of developmental potential whereby the possible fate of each cell becomes more limited as an embryo develops. At the end of determination, a cell is committed to its fate.

detritivore (deh-trī′-tuh-vōr) A consumer that derives its energy and nutrients from nonliving organic material such as corpses, fallen plant material, and the wastes of living organisms; a decomposer.

detritus (di-trī′-tus) Dead organic matter.

diabetes mellitus (dī′-uh-bē′-tis mel′-uh-tus) An endocrine disorder marked by an inability to maintain glucose homeostasis. The type 1 form results from autoimmune destruction of insulin-secreting cells; treatment usually requires daily insulin injections. The type 2 form most commonly results from reduced responsiveness of target cells to insulin; obesity and lack of exercise are risk factors.

diaphragm (dī′-uh-fram′) (1) A sheet of muscle that forms the bottom wall of the thoracic cavity in mammals. Contraction of the diaphragm pulls air into the lungs. (2) A dome-shaped rubber cup fitted into the upper portion of the vagina before sexual intercourse. It serves as a physical barrier to the passage of sperm into the uterus.

diastole (dī-as′-tō-lē) The stage of the cardiac cycle in which a heart chamber is relaxed and fills with blood.

diatom A photosynthetic protist in the stramenopile clade; diatoms have a unique glass-like wall made of silicon dioxide embedded in an organic matrix.

differential gene expression The expression of different sets of genes by cells with the same genome.

differentiation The process by which a cell or group of cells becomes specialized in structure and function.

diffusion The random thermal motion of particles of liquids, gases, or solids. In the presence of a concentration or electrochemical gradient, diffusion results in the net movement of a substance from a region where it is more concentrated to a region where it is less concentrated.

digestion The second stage of food processing in animals: the breaking down of food into molecules small enough for the body to absorb.

dihybrid (dī′-hī′-brid) An organism that is heterozygous with respect to two genes of interest. All the offspring from a cross between parents doubly homozygous for different alleles are dihybrids. For example, parents of genotypes *AABB* and *aabb* produce a dihybrid of genotype *AaBb*.

dihybrid cross A cross between two organisms that are each heterozygous for both of the characters being followed (or the self-pollination of a plant that is heterozygous for both characters).

dinoflagellate (dī′-nō-flaj′-uh-let) Member of a group of mostly unicellular photosynthetic algae with two flagella situated in perpendicular grooves in cellulose plates covering the cell.

dioecious (dī-ē′-shus) In plant biology, having the male and female reproductive parts on different individuals of the same species.

diploid cell (dip′-loyd) A cell containing two sets of chromosomes (2*n*), one set inherited from each parent.

diplomonad A protist that has modified mitochondria and multiple flagella.

directional selection Natural selection in which individuals at one end of the phenotypic range survive or reproduce more successfully than do other individuals.

disaccharide (dī-sak′-uh-rīd) A double sugar, consisting of two monosaccharides joined by a glycosidic linkage formed by a dehydration reaction.

dispersal The movement of individuals or gametes away from their parent location. This movement sometimes expands the geographic range of a population or species.

dispersion The pattern of spacing among individuals within the boundaries of a population.

disruptive selection Natural selection in which individuals on both extremes of a phenotypic range survive or reproduce more successfully than do individuals with intermediate phenotypes.

distal tubule In the vertebrate kidney, the portion of a nephron that helps refine filtrate and empties it into a collecting duct.

disturbance A natural or human-caused event that changes a biological community and usually removes organisms from it. Disturbances, such as fires and storms, play a pivotal role in structuring many communities.

disulfide bridge A strong covalent bond formed when the sulfur of one cysteine monomer bonds to the sulfur of another cysteine monomer.

DNA (deoxyribonucleic acid) (dē-ok′-sē-rī′-bō-nū-klā′-ik) A nucleic acid molecule, usually a double-stranded helix, in which each polynucleotide strand consists of nucleotide monomers with a deoxyribose sugar and the nitrogenous bases adenine (A), cytosine (C), guanine (G), and thymine (T); capable of being replicated and determining the inherited structure of a cell's proteins.

DNA ligase (lī′-gās) A linking enzyme essential for DNA replication; catalyzes the covalent bonding of the 3′ end of one DNA fragment (such as an Okazaki fragment) to the 5′ end of another DNA fragment (such as a growing DNA chain).

DNA methylation The presence of methyl groups on the DNA bases (usually cytosine) of plants, animals, and fungi. (The term also refers to the process of adding methyl groups to DNA bases.)

DNA microarray assay A method to detect and measure the expression of thousands of genes at one time. Tiny amounts of a large number of single-stranded DNA fragments representing different genes are fixed to a glass slide and tested for hybridization with samples of labeled cDNA.

DNA polymerase (puh-lim′-er-ās) An enzyme that catalyzes the elongation of new DNA (for example, at a replication fork) by the addition of nucleotides to the 3′ end of an existing chain. There are several different DNA polymerases; DNA polymerase III and DNA polymerase I play major roles in DNA replication in *E. coli.*

DNA replication The process by which a DNA molecule is copied; also called DNA synthesis.

DNA sequencing Determining the order of nucleotide bases in a gene or DNA fragment.

domain (1) A taxonomic category above the kingdom level. The three domains are Archaea, Bacteria, and Eukarya. (2) A discrete structural and functional region of a protein.

dominant allele An allele that is fully expressed in the phenotype of a heterozygote.

dominant species A species with substantially higher abundance or biomass than other species in a community. Dominant species exert a powerful control over the occurrence and distribution of other species.

dormancy A condition typified by extremely low metabolic rate and a suspension of growth and development.

dorsal Pertaining to the top of an animal with radial or bilateral symmetry.

double bond A double covalent bond; the sharing of two pairs of valence electrons by two atoms.

double circulation A circulatory system consisting of separate pulmonary and systemic circuits, in which blood passes through the heart after completing each circuit.

double fertilization A mechanism of fertilization in angiosperms in which two sperm cells unite with two cells in the female gametophyte (embryo sac) to form the zygote and endosperm.

double helix The form of native DNA, referring to its two adjacent antiparallel polynucleotide strands wound around an imaginary axis into a spiral shape.

Down syndrome A human genetic disease usually caused by the presence of an extra chromosome 21; characterized by developmental delays and heart and other defects that are generally treatable or non-life-threatening.

Duchenne muscular dystrophy (duh-shen′) A human genetic disease caused by a sex-linked recessive allele; characterized by progressive weakening and a loss of muscle tissue.

duodenum (dū′-uh-dēn′-um) The first section of the small intestine, where chyme from the stomach mixes with digestive juices from the pancreas, liver, and gallbladder as well as from gland cells of the intestinal wall.

duplication An aberration in chromosome structure due to fusion with a fragment from a homologous chromosome, such that a portion of a chromosome is duplicated.

dynein (dī′-nē-un) In cilia and flagella, a large motor protein extending from one microtubule doublet to the adjacent doublet. ATP hydrolysis drives changes in dynein shape that lead to bending of cilia and flagella.

E site One of a ribosome's three binding sites for tRNA during translation. The E site is the place where discharged tRNAs leave the ribosome. (E stands for exit.)

ecological footprint The aggregate land and water area required by a person, city, or nation to produce all of the resources it consumes and to absorb all of the waste it generates.

ecological niche (nich) The sum of a species' use of the biotic and abiotic resources in its environment.

ecological species concept Definition of a species in terms of ecological niche, the sum of how members of the species interact with the nonliving and living parts of their environment.

ecological succession Transition in the species composition of a community following a disturbance; establishment of a community in an area virtually barren of life.

ecology The study of how organisms interact with each other and their environment.

ecosystem All the organisms in a given area as well as the abiotic factors with which they interact; one or more communities and the physical environment around them.

ecosystem ecology The study of energy flow and the cycling of chemicals among the various biotic and abiotic components in an ecosystem.

ecosystem engineer An organism that influences community structure by causing physical changes in the environment.

ecosystem service A function performed by an ecosystem that directly or indirectly benefits humans.

ecotone The transition from one type of habitat or ecosystem to another, such as the transition from a forest to a grassland.

ectoderm (ek′-tō-durm) The outermost of the three primary germ layers in animal embryos; gives rise to the outer covering and, in some phyla, the nervous system, inner ear, and lens of the eye.

ectomycorrhizae (ek′-tō-mī′-kō-rī′-zē) Associations of a fungus with a plant root system in which the fungus surrounds the roots but does not cause invagination of the host (plant) cell's plasma membrane.

ectomycorrhizal fungus A symbiotic fungus that forms sheaths of hyphae over the surface of plant roots and also grows into extracellular spaces of the root cortex.

ectoparasite A parasite that feeds on the external surface of a host.

ectothermic Referring to organisms for which external sources provide most of the heat for temperature regulation.

Ediacaran biota (ē′-dē-uh-keh′-run bī-ō′-tuh) An early group of macroscopic, soft-bodied, multicellular eukaryotes known from fossils that range in age from 635 million to 535 million years old.

effective population size An estimate of the size of a population based on the numbers of females and males that successfully breed; generally smaller than the total population.

effector A pathogen-encoded protein that cripples a plant's innate immune system.

effector cell (1) A muscle cell or gland cell that performs the body's response to stimuli as directed by signals from the brain or other processing center of the nervous system. (2) A lymphocyte that has undergone clonal selection and is capable of mediating an adaptive immune response.

egg The female gamete.

ejaculation The propulsion of sperm from the epididymis through the muscular vas deferens, ejaculatory duct, and urethra.

ejaculatory duct In mammals, the short section of the ejaculatory route formed by the convergence of the vas deferens and a duct from the seminal vesicle. The ejaculatory duct transports sperm from the vas deferens to the urethra.

electrocardiogram (ECG or **EKG)** A record of the electrical impulses that travel through heart muscle during the cardiac cycle.

electrochemical gradient The diffusion gradient of an ion, which is affected by both the concentration difference of an ion across a membrane (a chemical force) and the ion's tendency to move relative to the membrane potential (an electrical force).

electrogenic pump An active transport protein that generates voltage across a membrane while pumping ions.

electromagnetic receptor A receptor of electromagnetic energy, such as visible light, electricity, or magnetism.

electromagnetic spectrum The entire spectrum of electromagnetic radiation, ranging in wavelength from less than a nanometer to more than a kilometer.

electron A subatomic particle with a single negative electrical charge and a mass about 1/2,000 that of a neutron or proton. One or more electrons move around the nucleus of an atom.

electron microscope (EM) A microscope that uses magnets to focus an electron beam on or through a specimen, resulting in a practical resolution 100-fold greater than that of a light microscope using standard techniques. A transmission electron microscope (TEM) is used to study the internal structure of thin sections of cells. A scanning electron microscope (SEM) is used to study the fine details of cell surfaces.

electron shell An energy level of electrons at a characteristic average distance from the nucleus of an atom.

electron transport chain A sequence of electron carrier molecules (membrane proteins) that shuttle electrons down a series of redox reactions that release energy used to make ATP.

electronegativity The attraction of a given atom for the electrons of a covalent bond.

element Any substance that cannot be broken down to any other substance by chemical reactions.

elimination The fourth and final stage of food processing in animals: the passing of undigested material out of the body.

embryo sac (em′-brē-ō) The female gametophyte of angiosperms, formed from the growth and division of the megaspore into a multicellular structure that typically has eight haploid nuclei.

embryonic lethal A mutation with a phenotype leading to death of an embryo or larva.

embryophyte Alternate name for plants that refers to their shared derived trait of multicellular, dependent embryos.

emergent properties New properties that arise with each step upward in the hierarchy of life, owing to the arrangement and interactions of parts as complexity increases.

emigration The movement of individuals out of a population.

enantiomer One of two compounds that are mirror images of each other and that differ in shape due to the presence of an asymmetric carbon.

endangered species A species that is in danger of extinction throughout all or a significant portion of its range.

endemic (en-dem′-ik) Referring to a species that is confined to a specific geographic area.

endergonic reaction (en′-der-gon′-ik) A nonspontaneous chemical reaction, in which free energy is absorbed from the surroundings.

endocrine gland (en′-dō-krin) A gland that secretes hormones directly into the interstitial fluid, from which they diffuse into the bloodstream.

endocrine system The internal system of communication involving hormones, the ductless glands that secrete hormones, and the molecular receptors on or in target cells that respond to hormones; functions in concert with the nervous system to effect internal regulation and maintain homeostasis.

endocytosis (en′-dō-sī-tō′-sis) Cellular uptake of biological molecules and particulate matter via formation of vesicles from the plasma membrane.

endoderm (en′-dō-durm) The innermost of the three primary germ layers in animal embryos; lines the archenteron and gives rise to the liver, pancreas, lungs, and the lining of the digestive tract in species that have these structures.

endodermis In plant roots, the innermost layer of the cortex that surrounds the vascular cylinder.

endomembrane system The collection of membranes inside and surrounding a eukaryotic cell, related either through direct physical contact or by the transfer of membranous vesicles; includes the plasma membrane, the nuclear envelope, the smooth and rough endoplasmic reticulum, the Golgi apparatus, lysosomes, vesicles, and vacuoles.

endometrium (en′-dō-mē′-trē-um) The inner lining of the uterus, which is richly supplied with blood vessels.

endoparasite A parasite that lives within a host.

endophyte A fungus that lives inside a leaf or other plant part without causing harm to the plant.

endoplasmic reticulum (ER) (en′-dō-plaz′-mik ruh-tik′-yū-lum) An extensive membranous network in eukaryotic cells, continuous with the outer nuclear membrane and composed of ribosome-studded (rough) and ribosome-free (smooth) regions.

endorphin (en-dōr′-fin) Any of several hormones produced in the brain and anterior pituitary that inhibit pain perception.

endoskeleton A hard skeleton buried within the soft tissues of an animal.

endosperm In angiosperms, a nutrient-rich tissue formed by the union of a sperm with two polar nuclei during double fertilization. The endosperm provides nourishment to the developing embryo in angiosperm seeds.

endospore A thick-coated, resistant cell produced by some bacterial cells when they are exposed to harsh conditions.

endosymbiont theory The theory that mitochondria and plastids, including chloroplasts, originated as prokaryotic cells engulfed by host cells. The engulfed cell and its host cell then evolved into a single organism. *See also* endosymbiosis.

endosymbiosis A mutually beneficial relationship between two species in which one organism lives inside the cell or cells of another organism.

endothelium (en′-dō-thē′-lē-um) The simple squamous layer of cells lining the lumen of blood vessels.

endothermic Referring to organisms that are warmed by heat generated by their own metabolism. This heat usually maintains a relatively stable body temperature higher than that of the external environment.

endotoxin A toxic component of the outer membrane of certain gram-negative bacteria that is released only when the bacteria die.

energy The capacity to cause change, especially to do work (to move matter against an opposing force).

energy coupling In cellular metabolism, the use of energy released from an exergonic reaction to drive an endergonic reaction.

enhancer A segment of eukaryotic DNA containing multiple control elements, usually located far from the gene whose transcription it regulates.

enteric division One of three divisions of the autonomic nervous system; consists of networks of neurons in the digestive tract, pancreas, and gallbladder; normally regulated by the sympathetic and parasympathetic divisions of the autonomic nervous system.

entropy A measure of disorder, or randomness.

enzyme (en′-zīm) A macromolecule serving as a catalyst, a chemical agent that increases the rate of a reaction without being consumed by the reaction. Most enzymes are proteins.

enzyme-substrate complex A temporary complex formed when an enzyme binds to its substrate molecule(s).

epicotyl (ep′-uh-kot′-ul) In an angiosperm embryo, the embryonic axis above the point of attachment of the cotyledon(s) and below the first pair of miniature leaves.

epidemic A general outbreak of a disease.

epidermis (1) The dermal tissue system of nonwoody plants, usually consisting of a single layer of tightly packed cells. (2) The outermost layer of cells in an animal.

epididymis (ep′-uh-did′-uh-mus) A coiled tubule located adjacent to the mammalian testis where sperm are stored.

epigenetic inheritance Inheritance of traits transmitted by mechanisms not directly involving the nucleotide sequence of a genome.

epinephrine (ep′-i-nef′-rin) A catecholamine that, when secreted as a hormone by the adrenal medulla, mediates "fight-or-flight" responses to short-term stresses; also released by some neurons as a neurotransmitter; also known as adrenaline.

epiphyte (ep′-uh-fīt) A plant that nourishes itself but grows on the surface of another plant for support, usually on the branches or trunks of trees.

epistasis (ep′-i-stā′-sis) A type of gene interaction in which the phenotypic expression of one gene alters that of another independently inherited gene.

epithelial tissue (ep′-uh-thē′-lē-ul) Sheets of tightly packed cells that line organs and body cavities as well as external surfaces; also called epithelium.

epithelium An epithelial tissue.

epitope A small, accessible region of an antigen to which an antigen receptor or antibody binds; also called an antigenic determinant.

equilibrium potential (E_{ion}) The magnitude of a cell's membrane voltage at equilibrium, calculated using the Nernst equation.

erythrocyte (eh-rith′-ruh-sīt) A blood cell that contains hemoglobin, which transports oxygen; also called a red blood cell.

esophagus (eh-sof′-uh-gus) A muscular tube that conducts food, by peristalsis, from the pharynx to the stomach.

essential amino acid An amino acid that an animal cannot synthesize itself and must be obtained from food in prefabricated form.

essential element A chemical element required for an organism to survive, grow, and reproduce.

essential fatty acid An unsaturated fatty acid that an animal needs but cannot make.

essential nutrient A substance that an organism cannot synthesize from any other material and therefore must absorb in preassembled form.

estradiol (es′-truh-dī′-ol) A steroid hormone that stimulates the development and maintenance of the female reproductive system and secondary sex characteristics; the major estrogen in mammals.

estrogen (es′-trō-jen) Any steroid hormone, such as estradiol, that stimulates the development and maintenance of the female reproductive system and secondary sex characteristics.

estrous cycle (es′-trus) A reproductive cycle characteristic of female mammals except humans and certain other primates, in which the nonpregnant endometrium is reabsorbed rather than shed, and sexual response occurs only during mid-cycle at estrus.

estuary The area where a freshwater stream or river merges with the ocean.

ethylene (eth′-uh-lēn) A gaseous plant hormone involved in responses to mechanical stress, programmed cell death, leaf abscission, and fruit ripening.

etiolation Plant morphological adaptations for growing in darkness.

euchromatin (yū-krō′-muh-tin) The less condensed form of eukaryotic chromatin that is available for transcription.

euglenozoan Member of a diverse clade of flagellated protists that includes predatory heterotrophs, photosynthetic autotrophs, and pathogenic parasites.

Eukarya (yū-kar′-ē-uh) The domain that includes all eukaryotic organisms.

eukaryotic cell (yū′-ker-ē-ot′-ik) A type of cell with a membrane-enclosed nucleus and membrane-enclosed organelles. Organisms with eukaryotic cells (protists, plants, fungi, and animals) are called eukaryotes.

eumetazoan (yū′-met-uh-zō′-un) Member of a clade of animals with true tissues. All animals except sponges and a few other groups are eumetazoans.

Eustachian tube (yū-stā′-shun) The tube that connects the middle ear to the pharynx.

eutherian (yū-thēr′-ē-un) Placental mammal; mammal whose young complete their embryonic development within the uterus, joined to the mother by the placenta.

eutrophic lake (yū-trōf′-ik) A lake that has a high rate of biological productivity supported by a high rate of nutrient cycling.

eutrophication A process by which nutrients, particularly phosphorus and nitrogen, become highly concentrated in a body of water, leading to increased growth of organisms such as algae or cyanobacteria.

evaporative cooling The process in which the surface of an object becomes cooler during evaporation, a result of the molecules with the greatest kinetic energy changing from the liquid to the gaseous state.

evapotranspiration The total evaporation of water from an ecosystem, including water transpired by plants and evaporated from a landscape, usually measured in millimeters and estimated for a year.

evo-devo Evolutionary developmental biology; a field of biology that compares developmental processes of different multicellular organisms to understand how these processes have evolved and how changes can modify existing organismal features or lead to new ones.

evolution Descent with modification; the idea that living species are descendants of ancestral species that were different from the present-day ones; also defined more narrowly as the change in the genetic composition of a population from generation to generation.

Excavata One of four supergroups of eukaryotes proposed in a current hypothesis of the evolutionary history of eukaryotes. Excavates have unique cytoskeletal features, and some species have an "excavated" feeding groove on one side of the cell body. *See also* SAR, Archaeplastida, and Unikonta.

excitatory postsynaptic potential (EPSP) An electrical change (depolarization) in the membrane of a postsynaptic cell caused by the binding of an excitatory neurotransmitter from a presynaptic cell to a postsynaptic receptor; makes it more likely for a postsynaptic cell to generate an action potential.

excretion The disposal of nitrogen-containing metabolites and other waste products.

exergonic reaction (ek′-ser-gon′-ik) A spontaneous chemical reaction, in which there is a net release of free energy.

exocrine gland (ek′-sō-krin) A gland that secretes substances through a duct onto a body surface or into a body cavity.

exocytosis (ek′-sō-sī-tō′-sis) The cellular secretion of biological molecules by the fusion of vesicles containing them with the plasma membrane.

exon A sequence within a primary transcript that remains in the RNA after RNA processing; also refers to the region of DNA from which this sequence was transcribed.

exoskeleton A hard encasement on the surface of an animal, such as the shell of a mollusc or the cuticle of an arthropod, that provides protection and points of attachment for muscles.

exotoxin (ek′-sō-tok′-sin) A toxic protein that is secreted by a prokaryote or other pathogen and that produces specific symptoms, even if the pathogen is no longer present.

expansin Plant enzyme that breaks the cross-links (hydrogen bonds) between cellulose microfibrils and other cell wall constituents, loosening the wall's fabric.

experiment A scientific test. Often carried out under controlled conditions that involve manipulating one factor in a system in order to see the effects of changing that factor.

experimental group A set of subjects that has (or receives) the specific factor being tested in a controlled experiment. Ideally, the experimental group should be identical to the control group for all other factors.

exploitation A +/− ecological interaction in which one species benefits by feeding on the other species, which is harmed. Exploitative interactions include predation, herbivory, and parasitism.

exponential population growth Growth of a population in an ideal, unlimited environment, represented by a J-shaped curve when population size is plotted over time.

extinction vortex A downward population spiral in which inbreeding and genetic drift combine to cause a small population to shrink and, unless the spiral is reversed, become extinct.

extracellular matrix (ECM) The meshwork surrounding animal cells, consisting of glycoproteins, polysaccharides, and proteoglycans synthesized and secreted by the cells.

extreme halophile An organism that lives in a highly saline environment, such as the Great Salt Lake or the Dead Sea.

extreme thermophile An organism that thrives in hot environments (often 60–80°C or hotter).

extremophile An organism that lives in environmental conditions so extreme that few other species can survive there. Extremophiles include extreme halophiles ("salt lovers") and extreme thermophiles ("heat lovers").

F factor In bacteria, the DNA segment that confers the ability to form pili for conjugation and associated functions required for the transfer of DNA from donor to recipient. The F factor may exist as a plasmid or be integrated into the bacterial chromosome.

F plasmid The plasmid form of the F factor.

F₁ generation The first filial, hybrid (heterozygous) offspring arising from a parental (P generation) cross.

F₂ generation The offspring resulting from interbreeding (or self-pollination) of the hybrid F₁ generation.

facilitated diffusion The passage of molecules or ions down their electrochemical gradient across a biological membrane with the assistance of specific transmembrane transport proteins, requiring no energy expenditure.

facultative anaerobe (fak′-ul-tā′-tiv an′-uh-rōb) An organism that makes ATP by aerobic respiration if oxygen is present but that switches to anaerobic respiration or fermentation if oxygen is not present.

family In Linnaean classification, the taxonomic category above genus.

fast-twitch fiber A muscle fiber used for rapid, powerful contractions.

fat A lipid consisting of three fatty acids linked to one glycerol molecule; also called a triacylglycerol or triglyceride.

fatty acid A carboxylic acid with a long carbon chain. Fatty acids vary in length and in the number and location of double bonds; three fatty acids linked to a glycerol molecule form a fat molecule, also known as a triacylglycerol or triglyceride.

feces (fē'-sēz) The wastes of the digestive tract.

feedback inhibition A method of metabolic control in which the end product of a metabolic pathway acts as an inhibitor of an enzyme within that pathway.

fermentation A catabolic process that makes a limited amount of ATP from glucose (or other organic molecules) without an electron transport chain and that produces a characteristic end product, such as ethyl alcohol or lactic acid.

fertilization (1) The union of haploid gametes to produce a diploid zygote. (2) The addition of mineral nutrients to the soil.

fetus (fē'-tus) A developing mammal that has all the major structures of an adult. In humans, the fetal stage lasts from the 9th week of gestation until birth.

fiber A lignified cell type that reinforces the xylem of angiosperms and functions in mechanical support; a slender, tapered sclerenchyma cell that usually occurs in bundles.

fibronectin An extracellular glycoprotein secreted by animal cells that helps them attach to the extracellular matrix.

filter feeder An animal that feeds by using a filtration mechanism to strain small organisms or food particles from its surroundings.

filtrate Cell-free fluid extracted from the body fluid by the excretory system.

filtration In excretory systems, the extraction of water and small solutes, including metabolic wastes, from the body fluid.

fimbria (plural, **fimbriae**) A short, hairlike appendage of a prokaryotic cell that helps it adhere to the substrate or to other cells.

first law of thermodynamics The principle of conservation of energy: Energy can be transferred and transformed, but it cannot be created or destroyed.

fixed action pattern In animal behavior, a sequence of unlearned acts that is essentially unchangeable and, once initiated, usually carried to completion.

flaccid (flas'-id) Limp. Lacking turgor (stiffness or firmness), as in a plant cell in surroundings where there is a tendency for water to leave the cell. (A walled cell becomes flaccid if it has a higher water potential than its surroundings, resulting in the loss of water.)

flagellum (fluh-jel'-um) (plural, **flagella**) A long cellular appendage specialized for locomotion. Like motile cilia, eukaryotic flagella have a core with nine outer doublet microtubules and two inner single microtubules (the "9 + 2" arrangement) ensheathed in an extension of the plasma membrane. Prokaryotic flagella have a different structure.

florigen A flowering signal, probably a protein, that is made in leaves under certain conditions and that travels to the shoot apical meristems, inducing them to switch from vegetative to reproductive growth.

flower In an angiosperm, a specialized shoot with up to four sets of modified leaves, bearing structures that function in sexual reproduction.

fluid feeder An animal that lives by sucking nutrient-rich fluids from another living organism.

fluid mosaic model The currently accepted model of cell membrane structure, which envisions the membrane as a mosaic of protein molecules drifting laterally in a fluid bilayer of phospholipids.

follicle (fol'-uh-kul) A microscopic structure in the ovary that contains the developing oocyte and secretes estrogens.

follicle-stimulating hormone (FSH) A tropic hormone that is produced and secreted by the anterior pituitary and that stimulates the production of eggs by the ovaries and sperm by the testes.

follicular phase That part of the ovarian cycle during which follicles are growing and oocytes maturing.

food chain The pathway along which food energy is transferred from trophic level to trophic level, beginning with producers.

food vacuole A membranous sac formed by phagocytosis of microorganisms or particles to be used as food by the cell.

food web The interconnected feeding relationships in an ecosystem.

foot One of the three main parts of a mollusc; a muscular structure usually used for movement. *See also* mantle and visceral mass.

foraging The seeking and obtaining of food.

foram (foraminiferan) An aquatic protist that secretes a hardened shell containing calcium carbonate and extends pseudopodia through pores in the shell.

fossil A preserved remnant or impression of an organism that lived in the past.

founder effect Genetic drift that occurs when a few individuals become isolated from a larger population and form a new population whose gene pool composition is not reflective of that of the original population.

fovea (fō'-vē-uh) The place on the retina at the eye's center of focus, where cones are highly concentrated.

fragmentation A means of asexual reproduction whereby a single parent breaks into parts that regenerate into whole new individuals.

frameshift mutation A mutation occurring when nucleotides are inserted in or deleted from a gene and the number inserted or deleted is not a multiple of three, resulting in the improper grouping of the subsequent nucleotides into codons.

free energy The portion of a biological system's energy that can perform work when temperature and pressure are uniform throughout the system. The change in free energy of a system (ΔG) is $G_{\text{final state}} - G_{\text{initial state}}$. It can be calculated by the equation $\Delta G = \Delta H - T\Delta S$, where ΔH is the change in enthalpy (in biological systems, equivalent to total energy), T is the absolute temperature, and ΔS is the change in entropy.

frequency-dependent selection Selection in which the fitness of a phenotype depends on how common the phenotype is in a population.

fruit A mature ovary of a flower. The fruit protects dormant seeds and often aids in their dispersal.

functional group A specific configuration of atoms commonly attached to the carbon skeletons of organic molecules and involved in chemical reactions.

fusion In evolutionary biology, a process in which gene flow between two species that can form hybrid offspring weakens barriers to reproduction between the species. This process causes their gene pools to become increasingly alike and can cause the two species to fuse into a single species.

G protein A GTP-binding protein that relays signals from a plasma membrane signal receptor, known as a G protein-coupled receptor, to other signal transduction proteins inside the cell.

G protein-coupled receptor (GPCR) A signal receptor protein in the plasma membrane that responds to the binding of a signaling molecule by activating a G protein. Also called a G protein-linked receptor.

G₀ phase A nondividing state occupied by cells that have left the cell cycle, sometimes reversibly.

G₁ phase The first gap, or growth phase, of the cell cycle, consisting of the portion of interphase before DNA synthesis begins.

G₂ phase The second gap, or growth phase, of the cell cycle, consisting of the portion of interphase after DNA synthesis occurs.

gallbladder An organ that stores bile and releases it as needed into the small intestine.

gamete (gam'-ēt) A haploid reproductive cell, such as an egg or sperm. Gametes unite during sexual reproduction to produce a diploid zygote.

gametogenesis The process by which gametes are produced.

gametophyte (guh-mē'-tō-fīt) In organisms (plants and some algae) that have alternation of generations, the multicellular haploid form that produces haploid gametes by mitosis. The haploid gametes unite and develop into sporophytes.

ganglion (gang'-glē-uhn) (plural, **ganglia**) A cluster (functional group) of nerve cell bodies.

gap junction A type of intercellular junction in animal cells, consisting of proteins surrounding a pore that allows the passage of materials between cells.

gas exchange The uptake of molecular oxygen from the environment and the discharge of carbon dioxide to the environment.

gas exchange circuit The branch of the circulatory system that supplies the organs where gases are exchanged with the environment; in many amphibians, it supplies the lungs and skin and is called a *pulmocutaneous circuit*, whereas in birds and mammals, it supplies only the lungs and is called a *pulmonary circuit*.

gastric juice A digestive fluid secreted by the stomach.

gastrovascular cavity A central cavity with a single opening in the body of certain animals, including cnidarians and flatworms, that functions in both the digestion and distribution of nutrients.

gastrula (gas'-trū-luh) An embryonic stage in animal development encompassing the formation of three layers: ectoderm, mesoderm, and endoderm.

gastrulation (gas'-trū-lā'-shun) In animal development, a series of cell and tissue movements in which the blastula-stage embryo folds inward, producing a three-layered embryo, the gastrula.

gated channel A transmembrane protein channel that opens or closes in response to a particular stimulus.

gated ion channel A gated channel for a specific ion. The opening or closing of such channels may alter a cell's membrane potential.

gel electrophoresis (ē-lek'-trō-fōr-ē'-sis) A technique for separating nucleic acids or proteins on the basis of their size and electrical charge, both of which affect their rate of movement through an electric field in a gel made of agarose or another polymer.

gene A discrete unit of hereditary information consisting of a specific nucleotide sequence in DNA (or RNA, in some viruses).

gene cloning The production of multiple copies of a gene.

gene expression The process by which information encoded in DNA directs the synthesis of proteins or, in some cases, RNAs that are not translated into proteins and instead function as RNAs.

gene flow The transfer of alleles from one population to another, resulting from the movement of fertile individuals or their gametes.

gene pool The aggregate of all copies of every type of allele at all loci in every individual in a population. The term is also used in a more restricted sense as the aggregate of alleles for just one or a few loci in a population.

genetic drift A process in which chance events cause unpredictable fluctuations in allele frequencies from one generation to the next. Effects of genetic drift are most pronounced in small populations.

genetic engineering The direct manipulation of genes for practical purposes.

genetic map An ordered list of genetic loci (genes or other genetic markers) along a chromosome.

genetic profile An individual's unique set of genetic markers, detected most often today by PCR.

genetic recombination General term for the production of offspring with combinations of traits that differ from those found in either parent.

genetic variation Differences among individuals in the composition of their genes or other DNA segments.

genetics The scientific study of heredity and hereditary variation.

genome (jē'-nōm) The genetic material of an organism or virus; the complete complement of an organism's or virus's genes along with its noncoding nucleic acid sequences.

genomics (juh-nō'-miks) The study of whole sets of genes and their interactions within a species, as well as genome comparisons between species.

genotype (jē'-nō-tīp) The genetic makeup, or set of alleles, of an organism.

genus (jē'-nus) (plural, **genera**) A taxonomic category above the species level, designated by the first word of a species' two-part scientific name.

geologic record A standard time scale dividing Earth's history into time periods grouped into four eons—Hadean, Archaean, Proterozoic, and Phanerozoic—and further subdivided into eras, periods, and epochs.

gestation (jes-tā'-shun) Pregnancy; the state of carrying developing young within the female reproductive tract.

gibberellin (jib'-uh-rel'-in) Any of a class of related plant hormones that stimulate growth in the stem and leaves, trigger the germination of seeds and breaking of bud dormancy, and (with auxin) stimulate fruit development.

glans The rounded structure at the tip of the clitoris or penis that is involved in sexual arousal.

glia (glial cells) Cells of the nervous system that support, regulate, and augment the functions of neurons.

glomerulus (glō-mār'-yū-lus) A ball of capillaries surrounded by Bowman's capsule in the nephron and serving as the site of filtration in the vertebrate kidney.

glucagon (glū--kuh-gon) A hormone secreted by the pancreas that raises blood glucose levels. It promotes glycogen breakdown and release of glucose by the liver.

glyceraldehyde 3-phosphate (G3P) (glis'-er-al'-de-hīd) A three-carbon carbohydrate that is the direct product of the Calvin cycle; it is also an intermediate in glycolysis.

glycogen (glī'-kō-jen) An extensively branched glucose storage polysaccharide found in the liver and muscle of animals; the animal equivalent of starch.

glycolipid A lipid with one or more covalently attached carbohydrates.

glycolysis (glī-kol'-uh-sis) A series of reactions that ultimately splits glucose into pyruvate. Glycolysis occurs in almost all living cells, serving as the starting point for fermentation or cellular respiration.

glycoprotein A protein with one or more covalently attached carbohydrates.

glycosidic linkage A covalent bond formed between two monosaccharides by a dehydration reaction.

gnathostome (na'-thu-stōm) Member of one of the two main clades of vertebrates; gnathostomes have jaws and include sharks and rays, ray-finned fishes, coelacanths, lungfishes, amphibians, reptiles, and mammals. *See also* cyclostome.

Golgi apparatus (gol'-jē) An organelle in eukaryotic cells consisting of stacks of flat membranous sacs that modify, store, and route products of the endoplasmic reticulum and synthesize some products, notably noncellulose carbohydrates.

gonad (gō'-nad) A male or female gamete-producing organ.

graded potential In a neuron, a shift in the membrane potential that has an amplitude proportional to signal strength and that decays as it spreads.

gram-negative Describing the group of bacteria that have a cell wall that is structurally more complex and contains less peptidoglycan than the cell wall of gram-positive bacteria. Gram-negative bacteria are often more toxic than gram-positive bacteria.

gram-positive Describing the group of bacteria that have a cell wall that is structurally less complex and contains more peptidoglycan than the cell wall of gram-negative bacteria. Gram-positive bacteria are usually less toxic than gram-negative bacteria.

granum (gran'-um) (plural, **grana**) A stack of membrane-bounded thylakoids in the chloroplast. Grana function in the light reactions of photosynthesis.

gravitropism (grav'-uh-trō'-pizm) A response of a plant or animal to gravity.

gray matter Regions of dendrites and clustered neuron cell bodies within the CNS.

green alga A photosynthetic protist, named for green chloroplasts that are similar in structure and pigment composition to the chloroplasts of plants. Green algae are a paraphyletic group; some members are more closely related to plants than they are to other green algae.

greenhouse effect The warming of Earth due to the atmospheric accumulation of carbon dioxide and certain other gases, which absorb reflected infrared radiation and reradiate some of it back toward Earth.

gross primary production (GPP) The total primary production of an ecosystem.

ground tissue system Plant tissues that are neither vascular nor dermal, fulfilling a variety of functions, such as storage, photosynthesis, and support.

growth factor (1) A protein that must be present in the extracellular environment (culture medium or animal body) for the growth and normal development of certain types of cells. (2) A local regulator that acts on nearby cells to stimulate cell proliferation and differentiation.

guard cells The two cells that flank the stomatal pore and regulate the opening and closing of the pore.

gustation The sense of taste.

gymnosperm (jim'-nō-sperm) A vascular plant that bears naked seeds—seeds not enclosed in protective chambers.

hair cell A mechanosensory cell that alters output to the nervous system when hairlike projections on the cell surface are displaced.

half-life The amount of time it takes for 50% of a sample of a radioactive isotope to decay.

Hamilton's rule The principle that for natural selection to favor an altruistic act, the benefit to the recipient, devalued by the coefficient of relatedness, must exceed the cost to the altruist.

haploid cell (hap'-loyd) A cell containing only one set of chromosomes (*n*).

Hardy-Weinberg equilibrium The state of a population in which frequencies of alleles and genotypes remain constant from generation to generation, provided that only Mendelian segregation and recombination of alleles are at work.

heart A muscular pump that uses metabolic energy to elevate the hydrostatic pressure of the circulatory fluid (blood or hemolymph). The fluid then flows down a pressure gradient through the body and eventually returns to the heart.

heart attack The damage or death of cardiac muscle tissue resulting from prolonged blockage of one or more coronary arteries.

heart murmur A hissing sound that most often results from blood squirting backward through a leaky valve in the heart.

heat Thermal energy in transfer from one body of matter to another.

heat of vaporization The quantity of heat a liquid must absorb for 1 g of it to be converted from the liquid to the gaseous state.

heat-shock protein A protein that helps protect other proteins during heat stress. Heat-shock proteins are found in plants, animals, and microorganisms.

heavy chain One of the two types of polypeptide chains that make up an antibody molecule and B cell receptor; consists of a variable region, which contributes to the antigen-binding site, and a constant region.

helicase An enzyme that untwists the double helix of DNA at replication forks, separating the two strands and making them available as template strands.

helper T cell A type of T cell that, when activated, secretes cytokines that promote the response of B cells (humoral response) and cytotoxic T cells (cell-mediated response) to antigens.

hemoglobin (hē'-mō-glō'-bin) An iron-containing protein in red blood cells that reversibly binds oxygen.

hemolymph (hē'-mō-limf') In invertebrates with an open circulatory system, the body fluid that bathes tissues.

hemophilia (hē'-muh-fil'-ē-uh) A human genetic disease caused by a sex-linked recessive allele, resulting in the absence of one or more blood-clotting proteins; characterized by excessive bleeding following injury.

hepatic portal vein A large vessel that conveys nutrient-laden blood from the small intestine to the liver, which regulates the blood's nutrient content.

herbivore (hur'-bi-vōr') An animal that mainly eats plants or algae.

herbivory A +/− interaction in which an organism eats parts of a plant or alga.

heredity The transmission of traits from one generation to the next.

hermaphroditism (hur-maf'-rō-dī-tizm) A condition in which an individual has both female and male gonads and functions as both a male and female in sexual reproduction by producing both sperm and eggs.

heterochromatin (het'-er-ō-krō'-muh-tin) Eukaryotic chromatin that remains highly compacted during interphase and is generally not transcribed.

heterochrony (het'-uh-rok'-ruh-nē) Evolutionary change in the timing or rate of an organism's development.

heterocyst (het'-er-ō-sist) A specialized cell that engages in nitrogen fixation in some filamentous cyanobacteria; also called a heterocyte.

heterotroph (het'-er-ō-trōf) An organism that obtains organic food molecules by eating other organisms or substances derived from them.

heterozygote An organism that has two different alleles for a gene (encoding a character).

heterozygote advantage Greater reproductive success of heterozygous individuals compared with homozygotes; tends to preserve variation in a gene pool.

heterozygous (het'-er-ō-zī'-gus) Having two different alleles for a given gene.

high-density lipoprotein (HDL) A particle in the blood made up of thousands of cholesterol molecules and other lipids bound to a protein. HDL scavenges excess cholesterol.

histamine (his'-tuh-mēn) A substance released by mast cells that causes blood vessels to dilate and become more permeable in inflammatory and allergic responses.

histogram A variant of a bar graph in which a numerical independent variable is divided into equal intervals (or groups called "bins"). The height (or length) of each bar represents the value of the dependent variable for a particular interval.

histone (his'-tōn) A small protein with a high proportion of positively charged amino acids that binds to the negatively charged DNA and plays a key role in chromatin structure.

histone acetylation The attachment of acetyl groups to certain amino acids of histone proteins.

HIV (human immunodeficiency virus) The infectious agent that causes AIDS. HIV is a retrovirus.

holdfast A rootlike structure that anchors a seaweed.

homeobox (hō'-mē-ō-boks') A 180-nucleotide sequence within homeotic genes and some other developmental genes that is widely conserved in animals. Related sequences occur in plants and yeasts.

homeostasis (hō'-mē-ō-stā'-sis) The steady-state physiological condition of the body.

homeotic gene (hō-mē-o'-tik) Any of the master regulatory genes that control placement and spatial organization of body parts in animals, plants, and fungi by controlling the developmental fate of groups of cells.

hominin A group consisting of humans and the extinct species that are more closely related to us than to chimpanzees.

homologous chromosomes (hō-mol'-uh-gus) A pair of chromosomes of the same length, centromere position, and staining pattern that possess genes for the same characters at corresponding loci. One homologous chromosome is inherited from the organism's father, the other from the mother. Also called homologs, or a homologous pair.

homologous structures Structures in different species that are similar because of common ancestry.

homologs *See* homologous chromosomes.

homology (hō-mol'-ō-jē) Similarity in characteristics resulting from a shared ancestry.

homoplasy (hō'-muh-play'-zē) A similar (analogous) structure or molecular sequence that has evolved independently in two species.

homozygote An organism that has a pair of identical alleles for a gene (encoding a character).

homozygous (hō'-mō-zī'-gus) Having two identical alleles for a given gene.

horizontal gene transfer The transfer of genes from one genome to another through mechanisms such as transposable elements, plasmid exchange, viral activity, and perhaps fusions of different organisms.

hormone In multicellular organisms, one of many types of secreted chemicals that are formed in specialized cells, travel in body fluids, and act on specific target cells in other parts of the body, changing the target cells' functioning. Hormones are thus important in long-distance signaling.

host The larger participant in a symbiotic relationship, often providing a home and food source for the smaller symbiont.

host range The limited number of species whose cells can be infected by a particular virus.

Human Genome Project An international collaborative effort to map and sequence the DNA of the entire human genome.

human immunodeficiency virus (HIV) The pathogen that causes AIDS (acquired immune deficiency syndrome).

humoral immune response (hyū'-mer-ul) The branch of adaptive immunity that involves the activation of B cells and that leads to the production of antibodies, which defend against bacteria and viruses in body fluids.

humus (hyū'-mus) Decomposing organic material that is a component of topsoil.

Huntington's disease A human genetic disease caused by a dominant allele; characterized by uncontrollable body movements and degeneration of the nervous system; usually fatal 10 to 20 years after the onset of symptoms.

hybrid Offspring that results from the mating of individuals from two different species or from two true-breeding varieties of the same species.

hybrid zone A geographic region in which members of different species meet and mate, producing at least some offspring of mixed ancestry.

hybridization In genetics, the mating, or crossing, of two true-breeding varieties.

hydration shell The sphere of water molecules around a dissolved ion.

hydrocarbon An organic molecule consisting of only carbon and hydrogen.

hydrogen bond A type of weak chemical bond that is formed when the slightly positive hydrogen atom of a polar covalent bond in one molecule is attracted to the slightly negative atom of a polar covalent bond in another molecule or in another region of the same molecule.

hydrogen ion A single proton with a charge of $1+$. The dissociation of a water molecule (H_2O) leads to the generation of a hydroxide ion (OH^-) and a hydrogen ion (H^+); in water, H^+ is not found alone but associates with a water molecule to form a hydronium ion.

hydrolysis (hī-drol'-uh-sis) A chemical reaction that breaks bonds between two molecules by the addition of water; functions in disassembly of polymers to monomers.

hydronium ion A water molecule that has an extra proton bound to it; H_3O^+, commonly represented as H^+.

hydrophilic (hī'-drō-fil'-ik) Having an affinity for water.

hydrophobic (hī'-drō-fō'-bik) Having no affinity for water; tending to coalesce and form droplets in water.

hydrophobic interaction A type of weak chemical interaction caused when molecules that do not mix with water coalesce to exclude water.

hydroponic culture A method in which plants are grown in mineral solutions rather than in soil.

hydrostatic skeleton A skeletal system composed of fluid held under pressure in a closed body compartment; the main skeleton of most cnidarians, flatworms, nematodes, and annelids.

hydroxide ion A water molecule that has lost a proton; OH^-.

hydroxyl group (hī-drok'-sil) A chemical group consisting of an oxygen atom joined to a hydrogen atom. Molecules possessing this group are soluble in water and are called alcohols.

hymen A thin membrane that partly covers the vaginal opening in the human female. The hymen is ruptured by sexual intercourse or other vigorous activity.

hyperpolarization A change in a cell's membrane potential such that the inside of the membrane becomes more negative relative to the outside. Hyperpolarization reduces the chance that a neuron will transmit a nerve impulse.

hypersensitive response A plant's localized defense response to a pathogen, involving the death of cells around the site of infection.

hypertension A disorder in which blood pressure remains abnormally high.

hypertonic Referring to a solution that, when surrounding a cell, will cause the cell to lose water.

hypha (plural, **hyphae**) (hī'-fuh, hī'-fē) One of many connected filaments that collectively make up the mycelium of a fungus.

hypocotyl (hī'-puh-cot'-ul) In an angiosperm embryo, the embryonic axis below the point of attachment of the cotyledon(s) and above the radicle.

hypothalamus (hī'-pō-thal'-uh-mus) The ventral part of the vertebrate forebrain; functions in maintaining homeostasis, especially in coordinating the endocrine and nervous systems; secretes hormones of the posterior pituitary

and releasing factors that regulate the anterior pituitary.

hypothesis (hī-poth'-uh-sis) A testable explanation for a set of observations based on the available data and guided by inductive reasoning. A hypothesis is narrower in scope than a theory.

hypotonic Referring to a solution that, when surrounding a cell, will cause the cell to take up water.

imbibition The physical adsorption of water by a seed or other structure, resulting in swelling.

immigration The influx of new individuals into a population from other areas.

immune system An animal body's system of defenses against agents that cause disease.

immunization The process of generating a state of immunity by artificial means. In active immunization, also called vaccination, an inactive or weakened form of a pathogen is administered, inducing B and T cell responses and immunological memory. In passive immunization, antibodies specific for a particular microbe are administered, conferring immediate but temporary protection.

immunoglobulin (Ig) (im'-yū-nō-glob'-yū-lin) *See* antibody.

imprinting In animal behavior, the formation at a specific stage in life of a long-lasting behavioral response to a specific individual or object.

***in situ* hybridization** A technique using nucleic acid hybridization with a labeled probe to detect the location of a specific mRNA in an intact organism.

***in vitro* fertilization (IVF)** (vē'-trō) Fertilization of oocytes in laboratory containers followed by artificial implantation of the early embryo in the mother's uterus.

inclusive fitness The total effect an individual has on proliferating its genes by producing its own offspring and by providing aid that enables other close relatives to increase production of their offspring.

incomplete dominance The situation in which the phenotype of heterozygotes is intermediate between the phenotypes of individuals homozygous for either allele.

incomplete flower A flower in which one or more of the four basic floral organs (sepals, petals, stamens, or carpels) are either absent or nonfunctional.

independent variable A factor whose value is manipulated or changed during an experiment to reveal possible effects on another factor (the dependent variable).

indeterminate growth A type of growth characteristic of plants, in which the organism continues to grow as long as it lives.

induced fit Caused by entry of the substrate, the change in shape of the active site of an enzyme so that it binds more snugly to the substrate.

inducer A specific small molecule that binds to a bacterial repressor protein and changes the repressor's shape so that it cannot bind to an operator, thus switching an operon on.

induction The process in which one group of embryonic cells influences the development

of another, usually by causing changes in gene expression.

inductive reasoning A type of logic in which generalizations are based on a large number of specific observations.

inflammatory response An innate immune defense triggered by physical injury or infection of tissue involving the release of substances that promote swelling, enhance the infiltration of white blood cells, and aid in tissue repair and destruction of invading pathogens.

inflorescence A group of flowers tightly clustered together.

ingestion The first stage of food processing in animals: the act of eating.

ingroup A species or group of species whose evolutionary relationships are being examined in a given analysis.

inhibitory postsynaptic potential (IPSP) An electrical change (usually hyperpolarization) in the membrane of a postsynaptic neuron caused by the binding of an inhibitory neurotransmitter from a presynaptic cell to a postsynaptic receptor; makes it more difficult for a postsynaptic neuron to generate an action potential.

innate behavior Animal behavior that is developmentally fixed and under strong genetic control. Innate behavior is exhibited in virtually the same form by all individuals in a population despite internal and external environmental differences during development and throughout their lifetimes.

innate immunity A form of defense common to all animals that is active immediately upon exposure to pathogens and that is the same whether or not the pathogen has been encountered previously.

inner ear One of three main regions of the vertebrate ear; includes the cochlea (which in turn contains the organ of Corti) and the semicircular canals.

inquiry The search for information and explanation, often focusing on specific questions.

insertion A mutation involving the addition of one or more nucleotide pairs to a gene.

insulin (in'-suh-lin) A hormone secreted by pancreatic beta cells that lowers blood glucose levels. It promotes the uptake of glucose by most body cells and the synthesis and storage of glycogen in the liver.

integral protein A transmembrane protein with hydrophobic regions that extend into and often completely span the hydrophobic interior of the membrane and with hydrophilic regions in contact with the aqueous solution on one or both sides of the membrane (or lining the channel in the case of a channel protein).

integrin In animal cells, a transmembrane receptor protein with two subunits that interconnects the extracellular matrix and the cytoskeleton.

integument (in-teg'-yū-ment) Layer of sporophyte tissue that contributes to the structure of an ovule of a seed plant.

interferon (in'-ter-fēr'-on) A protein that has antiviral or immune regulatory functions.

For example, interferons secreted by virus-infected cells help nearby cells resist viral infection.

intermediate disturbance hypothesis The concept that moderate levels of disturbance can foster greater species diversity than low or high levels of disturbance.

intermediate filament A component of the cytoskeleton that includes filaments intermediate in size between microtubules and microfilaments.

internal fertilization The fusion of eggs and sperm within the female reproductive tract. The sperm are typically deposited in or near the tract.

interneuron An association neuron; a nerve cell within the central nervous system that forms synapses with sensory and/or motor neurons and integrates sensory input and motor output.

internode A segment of a plant stem between the points where leaves are attached.

interphase The period in the cell cycle when the cell is not dividing. During interphase, cellular metabolic activity is high, chromosomes and organelles are duplicated, and cell size may increase. Interphase often accounts for about 90% of the cell cycle.

interspecific competition Competition for resources between individuals of two or more species when resources are in short supply.

interspecific interaction A relationship between individuals of two or more species in a community.

interstitial fluid The fluid filling the spaces between cells in most animals.

intertidal zone The shallow zone of the ocean adjacent to land and between the high- and low-tide lines.

intrinsic rate of increase (*r*) In population models, the per capita rate at which an exponentially growing population increases in size at each instant in time.

introduced species A species moved by humans, either intentionally or accidentally, from its native location to a new geographic region; also called a non-native or exotic species.

intron (in'-tron) A noncoding, intervening sequence within a primary transcript that is removed from the transcript during RNA processing; also refers to the region of DNA from which this sequence was transcribed.

invasive species A species, often introduced by humans, that takes hold outside its native range.

inversion An aberration in chromosome structure resulting from reattachment of a chromosomal fragment in a reverse orientation to the chromosome from which it originated.

invertebrate An animal without a backbone. Invertebrates make up 95% of animal species.

ion (ī'-on) An atom or group of atoms that has gained or lost one or more electrons, thus acquiring a charge.

ion channel A transmembrane protein channel that allows a specific ion to diffuse across the membrane down its concentration or electrochemical gradient.

ionic bond (ī-on'-ik) A chemical bond resulting from the attraction between oppositely charged ions.

ionic compound A compound resulting from the formation of an ionic bond; also called a salt.

iris The colored part of the vertebrate eye, formed by the anterior portion of the choroid.

isomer One of two or more compounds that have the same numbers of atoms of the same elements but different structures and hence different properties.

isotonic (ī'-sō-ton'-ik) Referring to a solution that, when surrounding a cell, causes no net movement of water into or out of the cell.

isotope (ī'-sō-tōp') One of several atomic forms of an element, each with the same number of protons but a different number of neutrons, thus differing in atomic mass.

iteroparity Reproduction in which adults produce offspring over many years; also known as repeated reproduction.

joule (J) A unit of energy: 1 J = 0.239 cal; 1 cal = 4.184 J.

juxtaglomerular apparatus (JGA) (juks'-tuh-gluh-mār'-yū-ler) A specialized tissue in nephrons that releases the enzyme renin in response to a drop in blood pressure or volume.

juxtamedullary nephron In mammals and birds, a nephron with a loop of Henle that extends far into the renal medulla.

karyogamy (kār'-ē-og'-uh-mē) In fungi, the fusion of haploid nuclei contributed by the two parents; occurs as one stage of sexual reproduction, preceded by plasmogamy.

karyotype (kār'-ē-ō-tīp) A display of the chromosome pairs of a cell arranged by size and shape.

keystone species A species that is not necessarily abundant in a community yet exerts strong control on community structure by the nature of its ecological role or niche.

kidney In vertebrates, one of a pair of excretory organs where blood filtrate is formed and processed into urine.

kilocalorie (kcal) A thousand calories; the amount of heat energy required to raise the temperature of 1 kg of water by 1°C.

kin selection Natural selection that favors altruistic behavior by enhancing the reproductive success of relatives.

kinetic energy (kuh-net'-ik) The energy associated with the relative motion of objects. Moving matter can perform work by imparting motion to other matter.

kinetochore (kuh-net'-uh-kōr) A structure of proteins attached to the centromere that links each sister chromatid to the mitotic spindle.

kingdom A taxonomic category, the second broadest after domain.

***K*-selection** Selection for life history traits that are sensitive to population density; also called density-dependent selection.

labia majora A pair of thick, fatty ridges that encloses and protects the rest of the vulva.

labia minora A pair of slender skin folds that surrounds the openings of the vagina and urethra.

lacteal (lak'-tē-ul) A tiny lymph vessel extending into the core of an intestinal villus and serving as the destination for absorbed chylomicrons.

lactic acid fermentation Glycolysis followed by the reduction of pyruvate to lactate, regenerating NAD^+ with no release of carbon dioxide.

lagging strand A discontinuously synthesized DNA strand that elongates by means of Okazaki fragments, each synthesized in a 5' → 3' direction away from the replication fork.

landscape An area containing several different ecosystems linked by exchanges of energy, materials, and organisms.

landscape ecology The study of how the spatial arrangement of habitat types affects the distribution and abundance of organisms and ecosystem processes.

larynx (lār'-inks) The portion of the respiratory tract containing the vocal cords; also called the voice box.

lateral meristem (mār'-uh-stem) A meristem that thickens the roots and shoots of woody plants. The vascular cambium and cork cambium are lateral meristems.

lateral root A root that arises from the pericycle of an established root.

lateralization Segregation of functions in the cortex of the left and right cerebral hemispheres.

law of conservation of mass A physical law stating that matter can change form but cannot be created or destroyed. In a closed system, the mass of the system is constant.

law of independent assortment Mendel's second law, stating that each pair of alleles segregates, or assorts, independently of each other pair during gamete formation; applies when genes for two characters are located on different pairs of homologous chromosomes or when they are far enough apart on the same chromosome to behave as though they are on different chromosomes.

law of segregation Mendel's first law, stating that the two alleles in a pair segregate (separate from each other) into different gametes during gamete formation.

leading strand The new complementary DNA strand synthesized continuously along the template strand toward the replication fork in the mandatory 5' → 3' direction.

leaf The main photosynthetic organ of vascular plants.

leaf primordium A finger-like projection along the flank of a shoot apical meristem, from which a leaf arises.

learning The modification of behavior based on specific experiences.

lens The structure in an eye that focuses light rays onto the photoreceptors.

lenticel (len'-ti-sel) A small raised area in the bark of stems and roots that enables gas exchange between living cells and the outside air.

leukocyte (lū'-kō-sīt') A blood cell that functions in fighting infections; also called a white blood cell.

Leydig cell (lī'-dig) A cell that produces testosterone and other androgens and is located between the seminiferous tubules of the testes.

lichen A mutualistic association between a fungus and a photosynthetic alga or cyanobacterium.

life cycle The generation-to-generation sequence of stages in the reproductive history of an organism.

life history The traits that affect an organism's schedule of reproduction and survival.

life table A summary of the age-specific survival and reproductive rates of individuals in a population.

ligand (lig'-und) A molecule that binds specifically to another molecule, usually a larger one.

ligand-gated ion channel A transmembrane protein containing a pore that opens or closes as it changes shape in response to a signaling molecule (ligand), allowing or blocking the flow of specific ions; also called an ionotropic receptor.

light chain One of the two types of polypeptide chains that make up an antibody molecule and B cell receptor; consists of a variable region, which contributes to the antigen-binding site, and a constant region.

light microscope (LM) An optical instrument with lenses that refract (bend) visible light to magnify images of specimens.

light reactions The first of two major stages in photosynthesis (preceding the Calvin cycle). These reactions, which occur on the thylakoid membranes of the chloroplast or on membranes of certain prokaryotes, convert solar energy to the chemical energy of ATP and NADPH, releasing oxygen in the process.

light-harvesting complex A complex of proteins associated with pigment molecules (including chlorophyll *a*, chlorophyll *b*, and carotenoids) that captures light energy and transfers it to reaction-center pigments in a photosystem.

lignin (lig'-nin) A strong polymer embedded in the cellulose matrix of the secondary cell walls of vascular plants that provides structural support in terrestrial species.

limiting nutrient An element that must be added for production to increase in a particular area.

limnetic zone In a lake, the well-lit, open surface waters far from shore.

linear electron flow A route of electron flow during the light reactions of photosynthesis that involves both photosystems (I and II) and produces ATP, NADPH, and O_2. The net electron flow is from H_2O to $NADP^+$.

line graph A two-dimensional graph in which each data point is connected to the next point in the data set with a straight line.

linkage map A genetic map based on the frequencies of recombination between markers during crossing over of homologous chromosomes.

linked genes Genes located close enough together on a chromosome that they tend to be inherited together.

lipid (lip'-id) Any of a group of large biological molecules, including fats, phospholipids, and steroids, that mix poorly, if at all, with water.

littoral zone In a lake, the shallow, well-lit waters close to shore.

liver A large internal organ in vertebrates that performs diverse functions, such as producing bile, maintaining blood glucose level, and detoxifying poisonous chemicals in the blood.

loam The most fertile soil type, made up of roughly equal amounts of sand, silt, and clay.

lobe-fin Member of a clade of osteichthyans having rod-shaped muscular fins. The group includes coelacanths, lungfishes, and tetrapods.

local regulator A secreted molecule that influences cells near where it is secreted.

locomotion Active motion from place to place.

locus (plural, *loci*) (lō'-kus, lō'-sī) A specific place along the length of a chromosome where a given gene is located.

logistic population growth Population growth that levels off as population size approaches carrying capacity.

long-day plant A plant that flowers (usually in late spring or early summer) only when the light period is longer than a critical length.

long-term memory The ability to hold, associate, and recall information over one's lifetime.

loop of Henle The hairpin turn, with a descending and ascending limb, between the proximal and distal tubules of the vertebrate kidney; functions in water and salt reabsorption.

low-density lipoprotein (LDL) A particle in the blood made up of thousands of cholesterol molecules and other lipids bound to a protein. LDL transports cholesterol from the liver for incorporation into cell membranes.

lung An infolded respiratory surface of a terrestrial vertebrate, land snail, or spider that connects to the atmosphere by narrow tubes.

luteinizing hormone (LH) (lū'-tē-uh-nī'-zing) A tropic hormone that is produced and secreted by the anterior pituitary and that stimulates ovulation in females and androgen production in males.

lycophyte (lī'-kuh-fīt) An informal name for a member of the phylum Lycophyta, a group of seedless vascular plants that includes club mosses and their relatives.

lymph The colorless fluid, derived from interstitial fluid, in the lymphatic system of vertebrates.

lymph node An organ located along a lymph vessel. Lymph nodes filter lymph and contain cells that attack viruses and bacteria.

lymphatic system A system of vessels and nodes, separate from the circulatory system, that returns fluid, proteins, and cells to the blood.

lymphocyte A type of white blood cell that mediates immune responses. The two main classes are B cells and T cells.

lysogenic cycle (lī'-sō-jen'-ik) A type of phage replicative cycle in which the viral genome becomes incorporated into the bacterial host chromosome as a prophage, is replicated along with the chromosome, and does not kill the host.

lysosome (lī'-suh-sōm) A membrane-enclosed sac of hydrolytic enzymes found in the cytoplasm of animal cells and some protists.

lysozyme (lī'-sō-zīm) An enzyme that destroys bacterial cell walls; in mammals, found in sweat, tears, and saliva.

lytic cycle (lit'-ik) A type of phage replicative cycle resulting in the release of new phages by lysis (and death) of the host cell.

macroclimate Large-scale patterns in climate; the climate of an entire region.

macroevolution Evolutionary change above the species level. Examples of macroevolutionary change include the origin of a new group of organisms through a series of speciation events and the impact of mass extinctions on the diversity of life and its subsequent recovery.

macromolecule A giant molecule formed by the joining of smaller molecules, usually by a dehydration reaction. Polysaccharides, proteins, and nucleic acids are macromolecules.

macronutrient An essential element that an organism must obtain in relatively large amounts. *See also* micronutrient.

macrophage (mak'-rō-fāj) A phagocytic cell present in many tissues that functions in innate immunity by destroying microbes and in acquired immunity as an antigen-presenting cell.

major histocompatibility complex (MHC) molecule A host protein that functions in antigen presentation. Foreign MHC molecules on transplanted tissue can trigger T cell responses that may lead to rejection of the transplant.

malignant tumor A cancerous tumor containing cells that have significant genetic and cellular changes and are capable of invading and surviving in new sites. Malignant tumors can impair the functions of one or more organs.

mammal Member of the class Mammalia, amniotes that have hair and mammary glands (glands that produce milk).

mammary gland An exocrine gland that secretes milk to nourish the young. Mammary glands are characteristic of mammals.

mantle One of the three main parts of a mollusc; a fold of tissue that drapes over the mollusc's visceral mass and may secrete a shell. *See also* foot and visceral mass.

map unit A unit of measurement of the distance between genes. One map unit is equivalent to a 1% recombination frequency.

marine benthic zone The ocean floor.

marsupial (mar-sū'-pē-ul) A mammal, such as a koala, kangaroo, or opossum, whose young complete their embryonic development inside a maternal pouch.

mass extinction The elimination of a large number of species throughout Earth, the result of global environmental changes.

mass number The total number of protons and neutrons in an atom's nucleus.

maternal effect gene A gene that, when mutant in the mother, results in a mutant phenotype in the offspring, regardless of the offspring's genotype. Maternal effect genes, also called egg-polarity genes, were first identified in *Drosophila melanogaster*.

matter Anything that takes up space and has mass.

maximum parsimony A principle that states that when considering multiple explanations for an observation, one should first investigate the simplest explanation that is consistent with the facts.

mechanoreceptor A sensory receptor that detects physical deformation in the body's environment associated with pressure, touch, stretch, motion, or sound.

medulla oblongata (meh-dul′-uh ob′-long-go′-tuh) The lowest part of the vertebrate brain, commonly called the medulla; a swelling of the hindbrain anterior to the spinal cord that controls autonomic, homeostatic functions, including breathing, heart and blood vessel activity, swallowing, digestion, and vomiting.

megapascal (MPa) (meg′-uh-pas-kal′) A unit of pressure equivalent to about 10 atmospheres of pressure.

megaphyll A leaf with a highly branched vascular system, found in almost all vascular plants other than lycophytes.

megaspore A spore from a heterosporous plant species that develops into a female gametophyte.

meiosis (mī-ō′-sis) A modified type of cell division in sexually reproducing organisms consisting of two rounds of cell division but only one round of DNA replication. It results in cells with half the number of chromosome sets as the original cell.

meiosis I The first division of a two-stage process of cell division in sexually reproducing organisms that results in cells with half the number of chromosome sets as the original cell.

meiosis II The second division of a two-stage process of cell division in sexually reproducing organisms that results in cells with half the number of chromosome sets as the original cell.

membrane potential The difference in electrical charge (voltage) across a cell's plasma membrane due to the differential distribution of ions. Membrane potential affects the activity of excitable cells and the transmembrane movement of all charged substances.

memory cell One of a clone of long-lived lymphocytes, formed during the primary immune response, that remains in a lymphoid organ until activated by exposure to the same antigen that triggered its formation. Activated memory cells mount the secondary immune response.

menopause The cessation of ovulation and menstruation, marking the end of a human female's reproductive years.

menstrual cycle (men′-strū-ul) In humans and certain other primates, a type of reproductive cycle in which the nonpregnant endometrium is shed through the cervix into the vagina; also called the uterine cycle.

menstruation The shedding of portions of the endometrium during a uterine (menstrual) cycle.

meristem (mār′-uh-stem) Plant tissue that remains embryonic as long as the plant lives, allowing for indeterminate growth.

mesoderm (mez′-ō-derm) The middle primary germ layer in a triploblastic animal embryo; develops into the notochord, the lining of the coelom, muscles, skeleton, gonads, kidneys, and most of the circulatory system in species that have these structures.

mesophyll (mez′-ō-fil) Leaf cells specialized for photosynthesis. In C₃ and CAM plants, mesophyll cells are located between the upper and lower epidermis; in C₄ plants, they are located between the bundle-sheath cells and the epidermis.

messenger RNA (mRNA) A type of RNA, synthesized using a DNA template, that attaches to ribosomes in the cytoplasm and specifies the primary structure of a protein. (In eukaryotes, the primary RNA transcript must undergo RNA processing to become mRNA.)

metabolic pathway A series of chemical reactions that either builds a complex molecule (anabolic pathway) or breaks down a complex molecule to simpler molecules (catabolic pathway).

metabolic rate The total amount of energy an animal uses in a unit of time.

metabolism (muh-tab′-uh-lizm) The totality of an organism's chemical reactions, consisting of catabolic and anabolic pathways, which manage the material and energy resources of the organism.

metagenomics The collection and sequencing of DNA from a group of species, usually an environmental sample of microorganisms. Computer software sorts partial sequences and assembles them into genome sequences of individual species making up the sample.

metaphase The third stage of mitosis, in which the spindle is complete and the chromosomes, attached to microtubules at their kinetochores, are all aligned at the metaphase plate.

metaphase plate An imaginary structure located at a plane midway between the two poles of a cell in metaphase on which the centromeres of all the duplicated chromosomes are located.

metapopulation A group of spatially separated populations of one species that interact through immigration and emigration.

metastasis (muh-tas′-tuh-sis) The spread of cancer cells to locations distant from their original site.

methanogen (meth-an′-ō-jen) An organism that produces methane as a waste product of the way it obtains energy. All known methanogens are in domain Archaea.

methyl group A chemical group consisting of a carbon bonded to three hydrogen atoms. The methyl group may be attached to a carbon or to a different atom.

microevolution Evolutionary change below the species level; change in the allele frequencies in a population over generations.

microfilament A cable composed of actin proteins in the cytoplasm of almost every eukaryotic cell, making up part of the cytoskeleton and acting alone or with myosin to cause cell contraction; also known as an actin filament.

micronutrient An essential element that an organism needs in very small amounts. *See also* macronutrient.

microphyll A small, usually spine-shaped leaf supported by a single strand of vascular tissue, found only in lycophytes.

microRNA (miRNA) A small, single-stranded RNA molecule, generated from a hairpin structure on a precursor RNA transcribed from a particular gene. The miRNA associates with one or more proteins in a complex that can degrade or prevent translation of an mRNA with a complementary sequence.

microspore A spore from a heterosporous plant species that develops into a male gametophyte.

microtubule A hollow rod composed of tubulin proteins that makes up part of the cytoskeleton in all eukaryotic cells and is found in cilia and flagella.

microvillus (plural, **microvilli**) One of many fine, finger-like projections of the epithelial cells in the lumen of the small intestine that increase its surface area.

middle ear One of three main regions of the vertebrate ear; in mammals, a chamber containing three small bones (the malleus, incus, and stapes) that convey vibrations from the eardrum to the oval window.

middle lamella (luh-mel′-uh) In plants, a thin layer of adhesive extracellular material, primarily pectins, found between the primary walls of adjacent young cells.

migration A regular, long-distance change in location.

mineral In nutrition, a simple nutrient that is inorganic and therefore cannot be synthesized in the body.

minimum viable population (MVP) The smallest population size at which a species is able to sustain its numbers and survive.

mismatch repair The cellular process that uses specific enzymes to remove and replace incorrectly paired nucleotides.

missense mutation A nucleotide-pair substitution that results in a codon that codes for a different amino acid.

mitochondrial matrix The compartment of the mitochondrion enclosed by the inner membrane and containing enzymes and substrates for the citric acid cycle, as well as ribosomes and DNA.

mitochondrion (mī-tō-kon′-drē-un) (plural, **mitochondria**) An organelle in eukaryotic cells that serves as the site of cellular respiration; uses oxygen to break down organic molecules and synthesize ATP.

mitosis (mī-tō′-sis) A process of nuclear division in eukaryotic cells conventionally divided into five stages: prophase, prometaphase, metaphase, anaphase, and telophase. Mitosis conserves chromosome number by allocating replicated chromosomes equally to each of the daughter nuclei.

mitotic (M) phase The phase of the cell cycle that includes mitosis and cytokinesis.

mitotic spindle An assemblage of microtubules and associated proteins that is involved in the movement of chromosomes during mitosis.

mixotroph An organism that is capable of both photosynthesis and heterotrophy.

model A physical or conceptual representation of a natural phenomenon.

model organism A particular species chosen for research into broad biological principles because it is representative of a larger group and usually easy to grow in a lab.

molarity A common measure of solute concentration, referring to the number of moles of solute per liter of solution.

mole (mol) The number of grams of a substance that equals its molecular weight in daltons and contains Avogadro's number of molecules.

molecular clock A method for estimating the time required for a given amount of evolutionary change, based on the observation that some regions of genomes evolve at constant rates.

molecular mass The sum of the masses of all the atoms in a molecule; sometimes called molecular weight.

molecule Two or more atoms held together by covalent bonds.

monilophyte An informal name for a member of the phylum Monilophyta, a group of seedless vascular plants that includes ferns and their relatives.

monoclonal antibody (mon′-ō-klōn′-ul) Any of a preparation of antibodies that have been produced by a single clone of cultured cells and thus are all specific for the same epitope.

monogamous (muh-nog′-uh-mus) Referring to a type of relationship in which one male mates with just one female.

monohybrid An organism that is heterozygous with respect to a single gene of interest. All the offspring from a cross between parents homozygous for different alleles are monohybrids. For example, parents of genotypes *AA* and *aa* produce a monohybrid of genotype *Aa*.

monohybrid cross A cross between two organisms that are heterozygous for the character being followed (or the self-pollination of a heterozygous plant).

monomer (mon′-uh-mer) The subunit that serves as the building block of a polymer.

monophyletic (mon′-ō-fī-let′-ik) Pertaining to a group of taxa that consists of a common ancestor and all of its descendants. A monophyletic taxon is equivalent to a clade.

monosaccharide (mon′-ō-sak′-uh-rīd) The simplest carbohydrate, active alone or serving as a monomer for disaccharides and polysaccharides. Also known as simple sugars, monosaccharides have molecular formulas that are generally some multiple of CH_2O.

monosomic Referring to a diploid cell that has only one copy of a particular chromosome instead of the normal two.

monotreme An egg-laying mammal, such as a platypus or echidna. Like all mammals, monotremes have hair and produce milk, but they lack nipples.

morphogen A substance, such as Bicoid protein in *Drosophila*, that provides positional information in the form of a concentration gradient along an embryonic axis.

morphogenesis (môr′-fō-jen′-uh-sis) The development of the form of an organism and its structures.

morphological species concept Definition of a species in terms of measurable anatomical criteria.

motor neuron A nerve cell that transmits signals from the brain or spinal cord to muscles or glands.

motor protein A protein that interacts with cytoskeletal elements and other cell components, producing movement of the whole cell or parts of the cell.

motor system An efferent branch of the vertebrate peripheral nervous system composed of motor neurons that carry signals to skeletal muscles in response to external stimuli.

motor unit A single motor neuron and all the muscle fibers it controls.

movement corridor A series of small clumps or a narrow strip of quality habitat (usable by organisms) that connects otherwise isolated patches of quality habitat.

mucus A viscous and slippery mixture of glycoproteins, cells, salts, and water that moistens and protects the membranes lining body cavities that open to the exterior.

multifactorial Referring to a phenotypic character that is influenced by multiple genes and environmental factors.

multigene family A collection of genes with similar or identical sequences, presumably of common origin.

multiple fruit A fruit derived from an entire inflorescence.

multiplication rule A rule of probability stating that the probability of two or more independent events occurring together can be determined by multiplying their individual probabilities.

muscle tissue Tissue consisting of long muscle cells that can contract, either on its own or when stimulated by nerve impulses.

mutagen (myū′-tuh-jen) A chemical or physical agent that interacts with DNA and can cause a mutation.

mutation (myū-tā′-shun) A change in the nucleotide sequence of an organism's DNA or in the DNA or RNA of a virus.

mutualism (myū′-chū-ul-izm) A +/+ ecological interaction that benefits each of the interacting species.

mycelium (mī-sē′-lē-um) The densely branched network of hyphae in a fungus.

mycorrhiza (plural, **mycorrhizae**) (mī′-kō-rī′-zuh, mī′-kō-rī′-zē) A mutualistic association of plant roots and fungus.

myelin sheath (mī′-uh-lin) Wrapped around the axon of a neuron, an insulating coat of cell membranes from Schwann cells or oligodendrocytes. It is interrupted by nodes of Ranvier, where action potentials are generated.

myofibril (mī′-ō-fī′-bril) A longitudinal bundle in a muscle cell (fiber) that contains thin filaments of actin and regulatory proteins and thick filaments of myosin.

myoglobin (mī′-uh-glō′-bin) An oxygenstoring, pigmented protein in muscle cells.

myosin (mī′-uh-sin) A type of motor protein that associates into filaments that interact with actin filaments, causing cell contraction.

NAD⁺ Nicotinamide adenine dinucleotide, a coenzyme that cycles easily between oxidized (NAD^+) and reduced (NADH) states, thus acting as an electron carrier.

NADP⁺ Nicotinamide adenine dinucleotide phosphate, an electron acceptor that, as NADPH, temporarily stores energized electrons produced during the light reactions.

natural killer cell A type of white blood cell that can kill tumor cells and virus-infected cells as part of innate immunity.

natural selection A process in which individuals that have certain inherited traits tend to survive and reproduce at higher rates than other individuals *because of* those traits.

negative feedback A form of regulation in which accumulation of an end product of a process slows the process; in physiology, a primary mechanism of homeostasis, whereby a change in a variable triggers a response that counteracts the initial change.

negative pressure breathing A breathing system in which air is pulled into the lungs.

nephron (nef′-ron) The tubular excretory unit of the vertebrate kidney.

nerve A fiber composed primarily of the bundled axons of neurons.

nerve net A weblike system of neurons, characteristic of radially symmetric animals, such as hydras.

nervous system The fast-acting internal system of communication involving sensory receptors, networks of nerve cells, and connections to muscles and glands that respond to nerve signals; functions in concert with the endocrine system to effect internal regulation and maintain homeostasis.

nervous tissue Tissue made up of neurons and supportive cells.

net ecosystem production (NEP) The gross primary production of an ecosystem minus the energy used by all autotrophs and heterotrophs for respiration.

net primary production (NPP) The gross primary production of an ecosystem minus the energy used by the producers for respiration.

neuron (nyūr′-on) A nerve cell; the fundamental unit of the nervous system, having structure and properties that allow it to conduct signals by taking advantage of the electrical charge across its plasma membrane.

neuronal plasticity The capacity of a nervous system to change with experience.

neuropeptide A relatively short chain of amino acids that serves as a neurotransmitter.

neurotransmitter A molecule that is released from the synaptic terminal of a neuron at a chemical synapse, diffuses across the synaptic cleft, and binds to the postsynaptic cell, triggering a response.

neutral variation Genetic variation that does not provide a selective advantage or disadvantage.

neutron A subatomic particle having no electrical charge (electrically neutral), with a mass of about 1.7×10^{-24} g, found in the nucleus of an atom.

neutrophil The most abundant type of white blood cell. Neutrophils are phagocytic and tend to self-destruct as they destroy foreign invaders, limiting their life span to a few days.

nitrogen cycle The natural process by which nitrogen, either from the atmosphere or from decomposed organic material, is converted by soil bacteria to compounds assimilated by plants. This incorporated nitrogen is then taken in by other organisms and subsequently released, acted on by bacteria, and made available again to the nonliving environment.

nitrogen fixation The conversion of atmospheric nitrogen (N_2) to ammonia (NH_3). Biological nitrogen fixation is carried out by certain prokaryotes, some of which have mutualistic relationships with plants.

nociceptor (nō′-si-sep′-tur) A sensory receptor that responds to noxious or painful stimuli; also called a pain receptor.

node A point along the stem of a plant at which leaves are attached.

node of Ranvier (ron′-vē-ā′) Gap in the myelin sheath of certain axons where an action potential may be generated. In saltatory conduction, an action potential is regenerated at each node, appearing to "jump" along the axon from node to node.

nodule A swelling on the root of a legume. Nodules are composed of plant cells that contain nitrogen-fixing bacteria of the genus *Rhizobium*.

noncompetitive inhibitor A substance that reduces the activity of an enzyme by binding to a location remote from the active site, changing the enzyme's shape so that the active site no longer effectively catalyzes the conversion of substrate to product.

nondisjunction An error in meiosis or mitosis in which members of a pair of homologous chromosomes or sister chromatids fail to separate properly from each other.

nonequilibrium model A model that maintains that communities change constantly after being buffeted by disturbances.

nonpolar covalent bond A type of covalent bond in which electrons are shared equally between two atoms of similar electronegativity.

nonsense mutation A mutation that changes an amino acid codon to one of the three stop codons, resulting in a shorter and usually nonfunctional protein.

northern coniferous forest A terrestrial biome characterized by long, cold winters and dominated by cone-bearing trees.

notochord (nō′-tuh-kord′) A longitudinal, flexible rod that runs along the anterior-posterior axis of a chordate in the dorsal part of the body.

nuclear envelope In a eukaryotic cell, the double membrane that surrounds the nucleus, perforated with pores that regulate traffic with the cytoplasm. The outer membrane is continuous with the endoplasmic reticulum.

nuclear lamina A netlike array of protein filaments that lines the inner surface of the nuclear envelope and helps maintain the shape of the nucleus.

nucleariid Member of a group of unicellular, amoeboid protists that are more closely related to fungi than they are to other protists.

nuclease An enzyme that cuts DNA or RNA, either removing one or a few bases or hydrolyzing the DNA or RNA completely into its component nucleotides.

nucleic acid (nū-klā′-ik) A polymer (polynucleotide) consisting of many nucleotide monomers; serves as a blueprint for proteins and, through the actions of proteins, for all cellular activities. The two types are DNA and RNA.

nucleic acid hybridization The process of base pairing between a gene and a complementary sequence on another nucleic acid molecule.

nucleic acid probe In DNA technology, a labeled single-stranded nucleic acid molecule used to locate a specific nucleotide sequence in a nucleic acid sample. Molecules of the probe hydrogen-bond to the complementary sequence wherever it occurs; radioactive, fluorescent, or other labeling of the probe allows its location to be detected.

nucleoid (nū′-klē-oyd) A non-membrane-enclosed region in a prokaryotic cell where its chromosome is located.

nucleolus (nū-klē′-ō-lus) (plural, **nucleoli**) A specialized structure in the nucleus consisting of chromosomal regions containing ribosomal RNA (rRNA) genes along with ribosomal proteins imported from the cytoplasm; site of rRNA synthesis and ribosomal subunit assembly. *See also* ribosome.

nucleosome (nū′-klē-ō-sōm′) The basic, bead-like unit of DNA packing in eukaryotes, consisting of a segment of DNA wound around a protein core composed of two copies of each of four types of histone.

nucleotide (nū′-klē-ō-tīd′) The building block of a nucleic acid, consisting of a five-carbon sugar covalently bonded to a nitrogenous base and one to three phosphate groups.

nucleotide excision repair A repair system that removes and then correctly replaces a damaged segment of DNA using the undamaged strand as a guide.

nucleotide-pair substitution A type of point mutation in which one nucleotide in a DNA strand and its partner in the complementary strand are replaced by another pair of nucleotides.

nucleus (1) An atom's central core, containing protons and neutrons. (2) The organelle of a eukaryotic cell that contains the genetic material in the form of chromosomes, made up of chromatin. (3) A cluster of neurons.

nutrition The process by which an organism takes in and makes use of food substances.

obligate anaerobe (ob′-lig-et an′-uh-rōb) An organism that only carries out fermentation or anaerobic respiration. Such organisms cannot use oxygen and in fact may be poisoned by it.

ocean acidification The process by which the pH of the ocean is lowered (made more acidic) when excess CO_2 dissolves in seawater and forms carbonic acid (H_2CO_3).

oceanic pelagic zone Most of the ocean's waters far from shore, constantly mixed by ocean currents.

odorant A molecule that can be detected by sensory receptors of the olfactory system.

Okazaki fragment (ō′-kah-zah′-kē) A short segment of DNA synthesized away from the replication fork on a template strand during DNA replication. Many such segments are joined together to make up the lagging strand of newly synthesized DNA.

olfaction The sense of smell.

oligodendrocyte A type of glial cell that forms insulating myelin sheaths around the axons of neurons in the central nervous system.

oligotrophic lake A nutrient-poor, clear lake with few phytoplankton.

ommatidium (ōm′-uh-tid′-ē-um) (plural, **ommatidia**) One of the facets of the compound eye of arthropods and some polychaete worms.

omnivore An animal that regularly eats animals as well as plants or algae.

oncogene (on′-kō-jēn) A gene found in viral or cellular genomes that is involved in triggering molecular events that can lead to cancer.

oocyte A cell in the female reproductive system that differentiates to form an egg.

oogenesis (ō′-uh-jen′-uh-sis) The process in the ovary that results in the production of female gametes.

oogonium (ō′-uh- gō′-nē-em) (plural, **oogonia**) A cell that divides mitotically to form oocytes.

open circulatory system A circulatory system in which fluid called hemolymph bathes the tissues and organs directly and there is no distinction between the circulating fluid and the interstitial fluid.

operator In bacterial and phage DNA, a sequence of nucleotides near the start of an operon to which an active repressor can attach. The binding of the repressor prevents RNA polymerase from attaching to the promoter and transcribing the genes of the operon.

operon (op′-er-on) A unit of genetic function found in bacteria and phages, consisting of a promoter, an operator, and a coordinately regulated cluster of genes whose products function in a common pathway.

opisthokont (uh-pis′-thuh-kont′) Member of an extremely diverse clade of eukaryotes that includes fungi, animals, and several closely related groups of protists.

opposable thumb A thumb that can touch the ventral surface (fingerprint side) of the fingertip of all four fingers of the same hand with its own ventral surface.

opsin A membrane protein bound to a light-absorbing pigment molecule.

oral cavity The mouth of an animal.

order In Linnaean classification, the taxonomic category above the level of family.

organ A specialized center of body function composed of several different types of tissues.

organ of Corti The actual hearing organ of the vertebrate ear, located in the floor of the cochlear duct in the inner ear; contains the receptor cells (hair cells) of the ear.

organ system A group of organs that work together in performing vital body functions.

organelle (ōr-guh-nel′) Any of several kinds of membrane-enclosed structures with specialized functions, suspended in the cytosol of eukaryotic cells.

organic compound A chemical compound containing carbon.

organism An individual living thing, consisting of one or more cells.

organismal ecology The branch of ecology concerned with the morphological, physiological, and behavioral ways in which individual organisms meet the challenges posed by their biotic and abiotic environments.

organogenesis (ōr-gan′-ō-jen′-uh-sis) The process in which organ rudiments develop from the three germ layers after gastrulation.

origin of replication Site where the replication of a DNA molecule begins, consisting of a specific sequence of nucleotides.

osmoconformer An animal that is isoosmotic with its environment.

osmolarity (oz′-mō-lār′-uh-tē) Solute concentration expressed as molarity.

osmoregulation Regulation of solute concentrations and water balance by a cell or organism.

osmoregulator An animal that controls its internal osmolarity independent of the external environment.

osmosis (oz-mō′-sis) The diffusion of free water molecules across a selectively permeable membrane.

osteichthyan (os′-tē-ik′-thē-an) Member of a vertebrate clade with jaws and mostly bony skeletons.

outer ear One of three main regions of the ear in reptiles (including birds) and mammals; made up of the auditory canal and, in many birds and mammals, the pinna.

outgroup A species or group of species from an evolutionary lineage that is known to have diverged before the lineage that contains the group of species being studied. An outgroup is selected so that its members are closely related to the group of species being studied, but not as closely related as any study-group members are to each other.

oval window In the vertebrate ear, a membrane-covered gap in the skull bone, through which sound waves pass from the middle ear to the inner ear.

ovarian cycle (ō-vār′-ē-un) The cyclic recurrence of the follicular phase, ovulation, and the luteal phase in the mammalian ovary, regulated by hormones.

ovary (ō′-vuh-rē) (1) In flowers, the portion of a carpel in which the egg-containing ovules develop. (2) In animals, the structure that produces female gametes and reproductive hormones.

oviduct (ō′-vuh-duct) A tube passing from the ovary to the vagina in invertebrates or to the uterus in vertebrates, where it is also known as a fallopian tube.

ovulation The release of an egg from an ovary. In humans, an ovarian follicle releases an egg during each uterine (menstrual) cycle.

ovule (o′-vyūl) A structure that develops within the ovary of a seed plant and contains the female gametophyte.

oxidation The complete or partial loss of electrons from a substance involved in a redox reaction.

oxidative phosphorylation (fos′-fōr-uh-lā′-shun) The production of ATP using energy derived from the redox reactions of an electron transport chain; the third major stage of cellular respiration.

oxidizing agent The electron acceptor in a redox reaction.

oxytocin (ok′-si-tō′-sen) A hormone produced by the hypothalamus and released from the posterior pituitary. It induces contractions of the uterine muscles during labor and causes the mammary glands to eject milk during nursing.

P generation The true-breeding (homozygous) parent individuals from which F_1 hybrid offspring are derived in studies of inheritance; P stands for "parental."

P site One of a ribosome's three binding sites for tRNA during translation. The P site holds the tRNA carrying the growing polypeptide chain. (P stands for peptidyl tRNA.)

***p53* gene** A tumor-suppressor gene that codes for a specific transcription factor that promotes the synthesis of proteins that inhibit the cell cycle.

paedomorphosis (pē′-duh-mōr′-fuh-sis) The retention in an adult organism of the juvenile features of its evolutionary ancestors.

pain receptor A sensory receptor that responds to noxious or painful stimuli; also called a nociceptor.

paleontology (pā′-lē-un-tol′-ō-jē) The scientific study of fossils.

pancreas (pan′-krē-us) A gland with exocrine and endocrine tissues. The exocrine portion functions in digestion, secreting enzymes and an alkaline solution into the small intestine via a duct; the ductless endocrine portion functions in homeostasis, secreting the hormones insulin and glucagon into the blood.

pandemic A global epidemic.

Pangaea (pan-jē′-uh) The supercontinent that formed near the end of the Paleozoic era, when plate movements brought all the landmasses of Earth together.

parabasalid A protist, such as a trichomonad, with modified mitochondria.

paraphyletic (pār′-uh-fī-let′-ik) Pertaining to a group of taxa that consists of a common ancestor and some, but not all, of its descendants.

parasite (pār′-uh-sīt) An organism that feeds on the cell contents, tissues, or body fluids of another species (the host) while in or on the host organism. Parasites harm but usually do not kill their host.

parasitism (pār′-uh-sit-izm) A +/− ecological interaction in which one organism, the parasite, benefits by feeding upon another organism, the host, which is harmed; some parasites live within the host (feeding on its tissues), while others feed on the host's external surface.

parasympathetic division One of three divisions of the autonomic nervous system; generally enhances body activities that gain and conserve energy, such as digestion and reduced heart rate.

parenchyma cell (puh-ren′-ki-muh) A relatively unspecialized plant cell type that carries out most of the metabolism, synthesizes and stores organic products, and develops into a more differentiated cell type.

parental type An offspring with a phenotype that matches one of the true-breeding parental (P generation) phenotypes; also refers to the phenotype itself.

parthenogenesis (par′-thuh-nō′-jen′-uh-sis) A form of asexual reproduction in which females produce offspring from unfertilized eggs.

partial pressure The pressure exerted by a particular gas in a mixture of gases (for instance, the pressure exerted by oxygen in air).

passive transport The diffusion of a substance across a biological membrane with no expenditure of energy.

pathogen An organism or virus that causes disease.

pathogen-associated molecular pattern (PAMP) A molecular sequence that is specific to a certain pathogen.

pattern formation The development of a multicellular organism's spatial organization, the arrangement of organs and tissues in their characteristic places in three-dimensional space.

PCR *See* polymerase chain reaction.

pedigree A diagram of a family tree with conventional symbols, showing the occurrence of heritable characters in parents and offspring over multiple generations.

pelagic zone The open-water component of aquatic biomes.

penis The copulatory structure of male mammals.

pepsin An enzyme present in gastric juice that begins the hydrolysis of proteins. Pepsin is synthesized as an inactive precursor form, pepsinogen.

peptide bond The covalent bond between the carboxyl group on one amino acid and the amino group on another, formed by a dehydration reaction.

peptidoglycan (pep′-tid-ō-glī′-kan) A type of polymer in bacterial cell walls consisting of modified sugars cross-linked by short polypeptides.

perception The interpretation of sensory system input by the brain.

pericycle The outermost layer in the vascular cylinder, from which lateral roots arise.

periderm (pār′-uh-derm′) The protective coat that replaces the epidermis in woody plants during secondary growth, formed of the cork and cork cambium.

peripheral nervous system (PNS) The sensory and motor neurons that connect to the central nervous system.

peripheral protein A protein loosely bound to the surface of a membrane or to part of an integral protein and not embedded in the lipid bilayer.

peristalsis (pâr'-uh-stal'-sis) (1) Alternating waves of contraction and relaxation in the smooth muscles lining the alimentary canal that push food along the canal. (2) A type of movement on land produced by rhythmic waves of muscle contractions passing from front to back, as in many annelids.

peritubular capillary One of the tiny blood vessels that form a network surrounding the proximal and distal tubules in the kidney.

peroxisome (puh-rok'-suh-sōm') An organelle containing enzymes that transfer hydrogen atoms from various substrates to oxygen (O_2), producing and then degrading hydrogen peroxide (H_2O_2).

petal A modified leaf of a flowering plant. Petals are the often colorful parts of a flower that advertise it to insects and other pollinators.

petiole (pet'-ē-ōl) The stalk of a leaf, which joins the leaf to a node of the stem.

pH A measure of hydrogen ion concentration equal to $-\log [H^+]$ and ranging in value from 0 to 14.

phage (fāj) A virus that infects bacteria; also called a bacteriophage.

phagocytosis (fag'-ō-sī-tō'-sis) A type of endocytosis in which large particulate substances or small organisms are taken up by a cell. It is carried out by some protists and by certain immune cells of animals (in mammals, mainly macrophages, neutrophils, and dendritic cells).

pharyngeal cleft (fuh-rin'-jē-ul) In chordate embryos, one of the grooves that separate a series of pouches along the sides of the pharynx and may develop into a pharyngeal slit.

pharyngeal slit (fuh-rin'-jē-ul) In chordate embryos, one of the slits that form from the pharyngeal clefts and communicate to the outside, later developing into gill slits in many vertebrates.

pharynx (fär'-inks) (1) An area in the vertebrate throat where air and food passages cross. (2) In flatworms, the muscular tube that protrudes from the ventral side of the worm and ends in the mouth.

phenotype (fē'-nō-tīp) The observable physical and physiological traits of an organism, which are determined by its genetic makeup.

pheromone (fär'-uh-mōn) In animals and fungi, a small molecule released into the environment that functions in communication between members of the same species. In animals, it acts much like a hormone in influencing physiology and behavior.

phloem (flō'-em) Vascular plant tissue consisting of living cells arranged into elongated tubes that transport sugar and other organic nutrients throughout the plant.

phloem sap The sugar-rich solution carried through a plant's sieve tubes.

phosphate group A chemical group consisting of a phosphorus atom bonded to four oxygen atoms; important in energy transfer.

phospholipid (fos'-fō-lip'-id) A lipid made up of glycerol joined to two fatty acids and a phosphate group. The hydrocarbon chains of the fatty acids act as nonpolar, hydrophobic tails, while the rest of the molecule acts as a polar, hydrophilic head. Phospholipids form bilayers that function as biological membranes.

phosphorylated intermediate A molecule (often a reactant) with a phosphate group covalently bound to it, making it more reactive (less stable) than the unphosphorylated molecule.

photic zone (fō'-tic) The narrow top layer of an ocean or lake, where light penetrates sufficiently for photosynthesis to occur.

photomorphogenesis Effects of light on plant morphology.

photon (fō'-ton) A quantum, or discrete quantity, of light energy that behaves as if it were a particle.

photoperiodism (fō'-tō-pēr'-ē-ō-dizm) A physiological response to photoperiod, the relative lengths of night and day. An example of photoperiodism is flowering.

photophosphorylation (fō'-tō-fos'-fōr-uh-lā'-shun) The process of generating ATP from ADP and phosphate by means of chemiosmosis, using a proton-motive force generated across the thylakoid membrane of the chloroplast or the membrane of certain prokaryotes during the light reactions of photosynthesis.

phosphorylation cascade A series of chemical reactions during cell signaling mediated by enzymes (kinases), in which each kinase in turn phosphylates and activates another, ultimately leading to phosphorylation of many proteins.

photoreceptor An electromagnetic receptor that detects the radiation known as visible light.

photorespiration A metabolic pathway that consumes oxygen and ATP, releases carbon dioxide, and decreases photosynthetic output. Photorespiration generally occurs on hot, dry, bright days, when stomata close and the O_2/CO_2 ratio in the leaf increases, favoring the binding of O_2 rather than CO_2 by rubisco.

photosynthesis (fō'-tō-sin'-thi-sis) The conversion of light energy to chemical energy that is stored in sugars or other organic compounds; occurs in plants, algae, and certain prokaryotes.

photosystem A light-capturing unit located in the thylakoid membrane of the chloroplast or in the membrane of some prokaryotes, consisting of a reaction-center complex surrounded by numerous light-harvesting complexes. There are two types of photosystems, I and II; they absorb light best at different wavelengths.

photosystem I (PS I) One of two light-capturing units in a chloroplast's thylakoid membrane or in the membrane of some prokaryotes; it has two molecules of P700 chlorophyll *a* at its reaction center.

photosystem II (PS II) One of two light-capturing units in a chloroplast's thylakoid membrane or in the membrane of some prokaryotes; it has two molecules of P680 chlorophyll *a* at its reaction center.

phototropism (fō'-tō-trō'-pizm) Growth of a plant shoot toward or away from light.

phyllotaxy (fil'-uh-tak'-sē) The pattern of leaf attachment to the stem of a plant.

phylogenetic species concept Definition of a species as the smallest group of individuals that share a common ancestor, forming one branch on the tree of life.

phylogenetic tree A branching diagram that represents a hypothesis about the evolutionary history of a group of organisms.

phylogeny (fī-loj'-uh-nē) The evolutionary history of a species or group of related species.

phylum (fī'-lum) (plural, **phyla**) In Linnaean classification, the taxonomic category above class.

physiology The processes and functions of an organism.

phytochrome (fī'-tuh-krōm) A type of light receptor in plants that mostly absorbs red light and regulates many plant responses, such as seed germination and shade avoidance.

pilus (plural, **pili**) (pī'-lus, pī'-lī) In bacteria, a structure that links one cell to another at the start of conjugation; also known as a sex pilus or conjugation pilus.

pinocytosis (pī'-nō-sī-tō'-sis) A type of endocytosis in which the cell ingests extracellular fluid and its dissolved solutes.

pistil A single carpel (a simple pistil) or a group of fused carpels (a compound pistil).

pith Ground tissue that is internal to the vascular tissue in a stem; in many monocot roots, parenchyma cells that form the central core of the vascular cylinder.

pituitary gland (puh-tū'-uh-tār'-ē) An endocrine gland at the base of the hypothalamus; consists of a posterior lobe, which stores and releases two hormones produced by the hypothalamus, and an anterior lobe, which produces and secretes many hormones that regulate diverse body functions.

placenta (pluh-sen'-tuh) A structure in the pregnant uterus for nourishing a viviparous fetus with the mother's blood supply; formed from the uterine lining and embryonic membranes.

plasma (plaz'-muh) The liquid matrix of blood in which the blood cells are suspended.

plasma cell The antibody-secreting effector cell of humoral immunity. Plasma cells arise from antigen-stimulated B cells.

plasma membrane The membrane at the boundary of every cell that acts as a selective barrier, regulating the cell's chemical composition.

plasmid (plaz'-mid) A small, circular, double-stranded DNA molecule that carries accessory genes separate from those of a bacterial chromosome; in DNA cloning, can be used as a vector carrying up to about 10,000 base pairs (10 kb) of DNA.

plasmodesma (plaz'-mō-dez'-muh) (plural, **plasmodesmata**) An open channel through the cell wall that connects the cytoplasm of adjacent plant cells, allowing water, small solutes, and some larger molecules to pass between the cells.

plasmogamy (plaz-moh′-guh-mē) In fungi, the fusion of the cytoplasm of cells from two individuals; occurs as one stage of sexual reproduction, followed later by karyogamy.

plasmolysis (plaz-mol′-uh-sis) A phenomenon in walled cells in which the cytoplasm shrivels and the plasma membrane pulls away from the cell wall; occurs when the cell loses water to a hypertonic environment.

plastid One of a family of closely related organelles that includes chloroplasts, chromoplasts, and amyloplasts. Plastids are found in the cells of photosynthetic eukaryotes.

plate tectonics The theory that the continents are part of great plates of Earth's crust that float on the hot, underlying portion of the mantle. Movements in the mantle cause the continents to move slowly over time.

platelet A pinched-off cytoplasmic fragment of a specialized bone marrow cell. Platelets circulate in the blood and are important in blood clotting.

pleiotropy (plī′-o-truh-pē) The ability of a single gene to have multiple effects.

pluripotent Describing a cell that can give rise to many, but not all, parts of an organism.

point mutation A change in a single nucleotide pair of a gene.

polar covalent bond A covalent bond between atoms that differ in electronegativity. The shared electrons are pulled closer to the more electronegative atom, making it slightly negative and the other atom slightly positive.

polar molecule A molecule (such as water) with an uneven distribution of charges in different regions of the molecule.

pollen grain In seed plants, a structure consisting of the male gametophyte enclosed within a pollen wall.

pollen tube A tube that forms after germination of the pollen grain and that functions in the delivery of sperm to the ovule.

pollination (pol′-uh-nā′-shun) The transfer of pollen to the part of a seed plant containing the ovules, a process required for fertilization.

poly-A tail A sequence of 50–250 adenine nucleotides added onto the 3′ end of a pre-mRNA molecule.

polygamous Referring to a type of relationship in which an individual of one sex mates with several of the other.

polygenic inheritance (pol′-ē-jen′-ik) An additive effect of two or more genes on a single phenotypic character.

polymer (pol′-uh-mer) A long molecule consisting of many similar or identical monomers linked together by covalent bonds.

polymerase chain reaction (PCR) (puh-lim′-er-ās) A technique for amplifying DNA *in vitro* by incubating it with specific primers, a heat-resistant DNA polymerase, and nucleotides.

polynucleotide (pol′-ē-nū′-klē-ō-tīd) A polymer consisting of many nucleotide monomers in a chain. The nucleotides can be those of DNA or RNA.

polypeptide (pol′-ē-pep′-tīd) A polymer of many amino acids linked by peptide bonds.

polyphyletic (pol′-ē-fī-let′-ik) Pertaining to a group of taxa that includes distantly related organisms but does not include their most recent common ancestor.

polyploidy (pol′-ē-ploy′-dē) A chromosomal alteration in which the organism possesses more than two complete chromosome sets. It is the result of an accident of cell division.

polysaccharide (pol′-ē-sak′-uh-rīd) A polymer of many monosaccharides, formed by dehydration reactions.

polytomy (puh-lit′-uh-mē) In a phylogenetic tree, a branch point from which more than two descendant taxa emerge. A polytomy indicates that the evolutionary relationships between the descendant taxa are not yet clear.

pons A portion of the brain that participates in certain automatic, homeostatic functions, such as regulating the breathing centers in the medulla.

population A group of individuals of the same species that live in the same area and interbreed, producing fertile offspring.

population dynamics The study of how complex interactions between biotic and abiotic factors influence variations in population size.

population ecology The study of populations in relation to their environment, including environmental influences on population density and distribution, age structure, and variations in population size.

positional information Molecular cues that control pattern formation in an animal or plant embryonic structure by indicating a cell's location relative to the organism's body axes. These cues elicit a response by genes that regulate development.

positive feedback A form of regulation in which an end product of a process speeds up that process; in physiology, a control mechanism in which a change in a variable triggers a response that reinforces or amplifies the change.

positive interactions A +/+ or +/0 ecological interaction in which at least one of the interacting species benefits and neither is harmed; positive interactions include mutualism and commensalism.

positive pressure breathing A breathing system in which air is forced into the lungs.

posterior Pertaining to the rear, or tail end, of a bilaterally symmetric animal.

posterior pituitary An extension of the hypothalamus composed of nervous tissue that secretes oxytocin and antidiuretic hormone made in the hypothalamus; a temporary storage site for these hormones.

postzygotic barrier (pōst-zī-got′-ik) A reproductive barrier that prevents hybrid zygotes produced by two different species from developing into viable, fertile adults.

potential energy The energy that matter possesses as a result of its location or spatial arrangement (structure).

predation An interaction between species in which one species, the predator, eats the other, the prey.

prediction In deductive reasoning, a forecast that follows logically from a hypothesis. By testing predictions, experiments may allow certain hypotheses to be rejected.

prepuce (prē′-pyūs) A fold of skin covering the head of the clitoris or penis.

pressure potential (Ψ_P) A component of water potential that consists of the physical pressure on a solution, which can be positive, zero, or negative.

prezygotic barrier (prē-zī-got′-ik) A reproductive barrier that impedes mating between species or hinders fertilization if interspecific mating is attempted.

primary cell wall In plants, a relatively thin and flexible layer that surrounds the plasma membrane of a young cell.

primary consumer An herbivore; an organism that eats plants or other autotrophs.

primary electron acceptor In the thylakoid membrane of a chloroplast or in the membrane of some prokaryotes, a specialized molecule that shares the reaction-center complex with a pair of chlorophyll *a* molecules and that accepts an electron from them.

primary growth Growth produced by apical meristems, lengthening stems and roots.

primary immune response The initial adaptive immune response to an antigen, which appears after a lag of about 10–17 days.

primary oocyte (ō′-uh-sīt) An oocyte prior to completion of meiosis I.

primary producer An autotroph, usually a photosynthetic organism. Collectively, autotrophs make up the trophic level of an ecosystem that ultimately supports all other levels.

primary production The amount of light energy converted to chemical energy (organic compounds) by the autotrophs in an ecosystem during a given time period.

primary structure The level of protein structure referring to the specific linear sequence of amino acids.

primary succession A type of ecological succession that occurs in an area where there were originally no organisms present and where soil has not yet formed.

primary transcript An initial RNA transcript from any gene; also called pre-mRNA when transcribed from a protein-coding gene.

primase An enzyme that joins RNA nucleotides to make a primer during DNA replication, using the parental DNA strand as a template.

primer A short stretch of RNA with a free 3′ end, bound by complementary base pairing to the template strand and elongated with DNA nucleotides during DNA replication.

prion An infectious agent that is a misfolded version of a normal cellular protein. Prions appear to increase in number by converting correctly folded versions of the protein to more prions.

problem solving The cognitive activity of devising a method to proceed from one state to another in the face of real or apparent obstacles.

producer An organism that produces organic compounds from CO_2 by harnessing light energy (in photosynthesis) or by oxidizing inorganic chemicals (in chemosynthetic reactions carried out by some prokaryotes).

product A material resulting from a chemical reaction.

production efficiency The percentage of energy stored in assimilated food that is not used for respiration or eliminated as waste.

progesterone A steroid hormone that contributes to the menstrual cycle and prepares the uterus for pregnancy.

prokaryote An organism that has a prokaryotic cell; an informal term for an organism in either domain Bacteria or domain Archaea.

prokaryotic cell (prō′-kăr′-ē-ot′-ik) A type of cell lacking a membrane-enclosed nucleus and membrane-enclosed organelles. Organisms with prokaryotic cells (bacteria and archaea) are called prokaryotes.

prometaphase The second stage of mitosis, in which the nuclear envelope fragments and the spindle microtubules attach to the kinetochores of the chromosomes.

promoter A specific nucleotide sequence in the DNA of a gene that binds RNA polymerase, positioning it to start transcribing RNA at the appropriate place.

prophage (prō′-fāj) A phage genome that has been inserted into a specific site on a bacterial chromosome.

prophase The first stage of mitosis, in which the chromatin condenses into discrete chromosomes visible with a light microscope, the mitotic spindle begins to form, and the nucleolus disappears but the nucleus remains intact.

prostate gland (pros′-tāt) A gland in human males that secretes an acid-neutralizing component of semen.

protease An enzyme that digests proteins by hydrolysis.

protein (prō′-tēn) A biologically functional molecule consisting of one or more polypeptides folded and coiled into a specific three-dimensional structure.

protein kinase An enzyme that transfers phosphate groups from ATP to a protein, thus phosphorylating the protein.

protein phosphatase An enzyme that removes phosphate groups from (dephosphorylates) proteins, often functioning to reverse the effect of a protein kinase.

proteoglycan (prō′-tē-ō-glī′-kan) A large molecule consisting of a small core protein with many carbohydrate chains attached, found in the extracellular matrix of animal cells. A proteoglycan may consist of up to 95% carbohydrate.

proteome The entire set of proteins expressed by a given cell, tissue, or organism.

proteomics (prō′-tē-ō′-miks) The systematic study of the full protein sets (proteomes) encoded by genomes.

protist An informal term applied to any eukaryote that is not a plant, animal, or fungus. Most protists are unicellular, though some are colonial or multicellular.

protocell An abiotic precursor of a living cell that had a membrane-like structure and that maintained an internal chemistry different from that of its surroundings.

proton (prō′-ton) A subatomic particle with a single positive electrical charge, with a mass of about 1.7×10^{-24} g, found in the nucleus of an atom.

proton pump An active transport protein in a cell membrane that uses ATP to transport hydrogen ions out of a cell against their concentration gradient, generating a membrane potential in the process.

proton-motive force The potential energy stored in the form of a proton electrochemical gradient, generated by the pumping of hydrogen ions (H^+) across a biological membrane during chemiosmosis.

proto-oncogene (prō′-tō-on′-kō-jēn) A normal cellular gene that has the potential to become an oncogene.

protoplast The living part of a plant cell, which also includes the plasma membrane.

provirus A viral genome that is permanently inserted into a host genome.

proximal tubule In the vertebrate kidney, the portion of a nephron immediately downstream from Bowman's capsule that conveys and helps refine filtrate.

pseudogene (sū′-dō-jēn) A DNA segment that is very similar to a real gene but does not yield a functional product; a DNA segment that formerly functioned as a gene but has become inactivated in a particular species because of mutation.

pseudopodium (sū′-dō-pō′-dē-um) (plural, **pseudopodia**) A cellular extension of amoeboid cells used in moving and feeding.

pulse The rhythmic bulging of the artery walls with each heartbeat.

punctuated equilibria In the fossil record, long periods of apparent stasis, in which a species undergoes little or no morphological change, interrupted by relatively brief periods of sudden change.

Punnett square A diagram used in the study of inheritance to show the predicted genotypic results of random fertilization in genetic crosses between individuals of known genotype.

pupil The opening in the iris, which admits light into the interior of the vertebrate eye. Muscles in the iris regulate its size.

purine (pyū′-rēn) One of two types of nitrogenous bases found in nucleotides, characterized by a six-membered ring fused to a five-membered ring. Adenine (A) and guanine (G) are purines.

pyrimidine (puh-rim′-uh-dēn) One of two types of nitrogenous bases found in nucleotides, characterized by a six-membered ring. Cytosine (C), thymine (T), and uracil (U) are pyrimidines.

quantitative character A heritable feature that varies continuously over a range rather than in an either-or fashion.

quaternary structure (kwot′-er-nār′-ē) The particular shape of a complex, aggregate protein, defined by the characteristic three-dimensional arrangement of its constituent subunits, each a polypeptide.

R plasmid A bacterial plasmid carrying genes that confer resistance to certain antibiotics.

radial symmetry Symmetry in which the body is shaped like a pie or barrel (lacking a left side and a right side) and can be divided into mirror-imaged halves by any plane through its central axis.

radicle An embryonic root of a plant.

radioactive isotope An isotope (an atomic form of a chemical element) that is unstable; the nucleus decays spontaneously, giving off detectable particles and energy.

radiometric dating A method for determining the absolute age of rocks and fossils, based on the half-life of radioactive isotopes.

ras gene A gene that codes for Ras, a G protein that relays a growth signal from a growth factor receptor on the plasma membrane to a cascade of protein kinases, ultimately resulting in stimulation of the cell cycle.

ray-finned fish Member of the class Actinopterygii, aquatic osteichthyans with fins supported by long, flexible rays, including tuna, bass, and herring.

reabsorption In excretory systems, the recovery of solutes and water from filtrate.

reactant A starting material in a chemical reaction.

reaction-center complex A complex of proteins associated with a special pair of chlorophyll *a* molecules and a primary electron acceptor. Located centrally in a photosystem, this complex triggers the light reactions of photosynthesis. Excited by light energy, the pair of chlorophylls donates an electron to the primary electron acceptor, which passes an electron to an electron transport chain.

reading frame On an mRNA, the triplet grouping of ribonucleotides used by the translation machinery during polypeptide synthesis.

receptacle The base of a flower; the part of the stem that is the site of attachment of the floral organs.

reception The binding of a signaling molecule to a receptor protein, activating the receptor by causing it to change shape. *See also* sensory reception.

receptor potential An initial response of a receptor cell to a stimulus, consisting of a change in voltage across the receptor membrane proportional to the stimulus strength.

receptor-mediated endocytosis (en′-dō-sī-tō′-sis) The movement of specific molecules into a cell by the inward budding of vesicles containing proteins with receptor sites specific to the molecules being taken in; enables a cell to acquire bulk quantities of specific substances.

recessive allele An allele whose phenotypic effect is not observed in a heterozygote.

recombinant chromosome A chromosome created when crossing over combines DNA from two parents into a single chromosome.

recombinant DNA molecule A DNA molecule made *in vitro* with segments from different sources.

recombinant type (recombinant) An offspring whose phenotype differs from that of the true-breeding P generation parents; also refers to the phenotype itself.

rectum The terminal portion of the large intestine, where the feces are stored prior to elimination.

red alga A photosynthetic protist, named for its color, which results from a red pigment that masks the green of chlorophyll. Most red algae are multicellular and marine.

redox reaction (rē′-doks) A chemical reaction involving the complete or partial transfer of one or more electrons from one reactant to another; short for **red**uction-**ox**idation reaction.

reducing agent The electron donor in a redox reaction.

reduction The complete or partial addition of electrons to a substance involved in a redox reaction.

reflex An automatic reaction to a stimulus, mediated by the spinal cord or lower brain.

refractory period (rē-frakt′-ōr-ē) The short time immediately after an action potential in which the neuron cannot respond to another stimulus, owing to the inactivation of voltage-gated sodium channels.

regression line A line drawn through a scatter plot that shows the general trend of the data. It represents an equation that is calculated mathematically to best fit the data and can be used to predict the value of the dependent variable for any value of the independent variable.

regulator An animal for which mechanisms of homeostasis moderate internal changes in a particular variable in the face of external fluctuation of that variable.

regulatory gene A gene that codes for a protein, such as a repressor, that controls the transcription of another gene or group of genes.

reinforcement In evolutionary biology, a process in which natural selection strengthens prezygotic barriers to reproduction, thus reducing the chances of hybrid formation. Such a process is likely to occur only if hybrid offspring are less fit than members of the parent species.

relative abundance The proportional abundance of different species in a community.

relative fitness The contribution an individual makes to the gene pool of the next generation, relative to the contributions of other individuals in the population.

renal cortex The outer portion of the vertebrate kidney.

renal medulla The inner portion of the vertebrate kidney, beneath the renal cortex.

renal pelvis The funnel-shaped chamber that receives processed filtrate from the vertebrate kidney's collecting ducts and is drained by the ureter.

repetitive DNA Nucleotide sequences, usually noncoding, that are present in many copies in a eukaryotic genome. The repeated units may be short and arranged tandemly (in series) or long and dispersed in the genome.

replication fork A Y-shaped region on a replicating DNA molecule where the parental strands are being unwound and new strands are being synthesized.

repressor A protein that inhibits gene transcription. In prokaryotes, repressors bind to the DNA in or near the promoter. In eukaryotes, repressors may bind to control elements within enhancers, to activators, or to other proteins in a way that blocks activators from binding to DNA.

reproductive isolation The existence of biological factors (barriers) that impede members of two species from producing viable, fertile offspring.

reptile Member of the clade of amniotes that includes tuataras, lizards, snakes, turtles, crocodilians, and birds.

residual volume The amount of air that remains in the lungs after forceful exhalation.

resource partitioning The division of environmental resources by coexisting species such that the niche of each species differs by one or more significant factors from the niches of all coexisting species.

respiratory pigment A protein that transports oxygen in blood or hemolymph.

response (1) In cellular communication, the change in a specific cellular activity brought about by a transduced signal from outside the cell. (2) In feedback regulation, a physiological activity triggered by a change in a variable.

resting potential The membrane potential characteristic of a nonconducting excitable cell, with the inside of the cell more negative than the outside.

restriction enzyme An endonuclease (type of enzyme) that recognizes and cuts DNA molecules foreign to a bacterium (such as phage genomes). The enzyme cuts at specific nucleotide sequences (restriction sites).

restriction fragment A DNA segment that results from the cutting of DNA by a restriction enzyme.

restriction site A specific sequence on a DNA strand that is recognized and cut by a restriction enzyme.

retina (ret′-i-nuh) The innermost layer of the vertebrate eye, containing photoreceptor cells (rods and cones) and neurons; transmits images formed by the lens to the brain via the optic nerve.

retinal The light-absorbing pigment in rods and cones of the vertebrate eye.

retrotransposon (re′-trō-trans-pō′-zon) A transposable element that moves within a genome by means of an RNA intermediate, a transcript of the retrotransposon DNA.

retrovirus (re′-trō-vī′-rus) An RNA virus that replicates by transcribing its RNA into DNA and then inserting the DNA into a cellular chromosome; an important class of cancer-causing viruses.

reverse transcriptase (tran-skrip′-tās) An enzyme encoded by certain viruses (retroviruses) that uses RNA as a template for DNA synthesis.

reverse transcriptase–polymerase chain reaction (RT-PCR) A technique for determining expression of a particular gene. It uses reverse transcriptase and DNA polymerase to synthesize cDNA from all the mRNA in a sample and then subjects the cDNA to PCR amplification using primers specific for the gene of interest.

rhizarians (rī-za′-rē-uhns) One of the three major subgroups for which the SAR eukaryotic supergroup is named. Many species in this clade are amoebas characterized by threadlike pseudopodia.

rhizobacterium A soil bacterium whose population size is much enhanced in the rhizosphere, the soil region close to a plant's roots.

rhizoid (rī′-zoyd) A long, tubular single cell or filament of cells that anchors bryophytes to the ground. Unlike roots, rhizoids are not composed of tissues, lack specialized conducting cells, and do not play a primary role in water and mineral absorption.

rhizosphere The soil region close to plant roots and characterized by a high level of microbiological activity.

rhodopsin (rō-dop′-sin) A visual pigment consisting of retinal and opsin. Upon absorbing light, the retinal changes shape and dissociates from the opsin.

ribonucleic acid (RNA) (rī′-bō-nū-klā′-ik) A type of nucleic acid consisting of a polynucleotide made up of nucleotide monomers with a ribose sugar and the nitrogenous bases adenine (A), cytosine (C), guanine (G), and uracil (U); usually single-stranded; functions in protein synthesis, gene regulation, and as the genome of some viruses.

ribose The sugar component of RNA nucleotides.

ribosomal RNA (rRNA) (rī′-buh-sō′-mul) RNA molecules that, together with proteins, make up ribosomes; the most abundant type of RNA.

ribosome (rī′-buh-sōm′) A complex of rRNA and protein molecules that functions as a site of protein synthesis in the cytoplasm; consists of a large subunit and a small subunit. In eukaryotic cells, each subunit is assembled in the nucleolus. *See also* nucleolus.

ribozyme (rī′-buh-zīm) An RNA molecule that functions as an enzyme, such as an intron that catalyzes its own removal during RNA splicing.

RNA interference (RNAi) A technique used to silence the expression of selected genes. RNAi uses synthetic double-stranded RNA molecules that match the sequence of a particular gene to trigger the breakdown of the gene's messenger RNA.

RNA polymerase An enzyme that links ribonucleotides into a growing RNA chain during transcription, based on complementary binding to nucleotides on a DNA template strand.

RNA processing Modification of RNA primary transcripts, including splicing out of introns, joining together of exons, and alteration of the 5′ and 3′ ends.

RNA splicing After synthesis of a eukaryotic primary RNA transcript, the removal of portions of the transcript (introns) that will not be included in the mRNA and the joining together of the remaining portions (exons).

rod A rodlike cell in the retina of the vertebrate eye, sensitive to low light intensity.

root An organ in vascular plants that anchors the plant and enables it to absorb water and minerals from the soil.

root cap A cone of cells at the tip of a plant root that protects the apical meristem.

root hair A tiny extension of a root epidermal cell, growing just behind the root tip and increasing surface area for absorption of water and minerals.

root system All of a plant's roots, which anchor it in the soil, absorb and transport minerals and water, and store food.

rooted Describing a phylogenetic tree that contains a branch point (often, the one farthest to the left) representing the most recent common ancestor of all taxa in the tree.

rough ER That portion of the endoplasmic reticulum with ribosomes attached.

round window In the mammalian ear, the point of contact where vibrations of the stapes create a traveling series of pressure waves in the fluid of the cochlea.

***r*-selection** Selection for life history traits that maximize reproductive success in uncrowded environments; also called density-independent selection.

rubisco (rū-bis'-kō) Ribulose bisphosphate (RuBP) carboxylase, the enzyme that catalyzes the first step of the Calvin cycle (the addition of CO_2 to RuBP).

ruminant (rū'-muh-nent) A cud-chewing animal, such as a cow or a sheep, with multiple stomach compartments specialized for an herbivorous diet.

S phase The synthesis phase of the cell cycle; the portion of interphase during which DNA is replicated.

saccule (sack'-yū-uhl) In the vertebrate ear, a chamber in the vestibule behind the oval window that participates in the sense of balance.

salicylic acid (sal'-i-sil'-ik) A signaling molecule in plants that may be partially responsible for activating systemic acquired resistance to pathogens.

salivary gland A gland associated with the oral cavity that secretes substances that lubricate food and begin the process of chemical digestion.

salt A compound resulting from the formation of an ionic bond; also called an ionic compound.

saltatory conduction (sol'-tuh-tōr'-ē) Rapid transmission of a nerve impulse along an axon, resulting from the action potential jumping from one node of Ranvier to another, skipping the myelin-sheathed regions of membrane.

SAR clade One of four supergroups of eukaryotes proposed in a current hypothesis of the evolutionary history of eukaryotes. This supergroup contains a large, extremely diverse collection of protists from three major subgroups: stramenopiles, alveolates, and rhizarians. *See also* Excavata, Archaeplastida, and Unikonta.

sarcomere (sar'-kō-mēr) The fundamental, repeating unit of striated muscle, delimited by the Z lines.

sarcoplasmic reticulum (SR) (sar'-kō-plaz'-mik ruh-tik'-yū-lum) A specialized endoplasmic reticulum that regulates the calcium concentration in the cytosol of muscle cells.

saturated fatty acid A fatty acid in which all carbons in the hydrocarbon tail are connected by single bonds, thus maximizing the number of hydrogen atoms attached to the carbon skeleton.

savanna A tropical grassland biome with scattered trees and large herbivores and maintained by occasional fires and drought.

scanning electron microscope (SEM) A microscope that uses an electron beam to scan the surface of a sample, coated with metal atoms, to study details of its topography.

scatter plot A graph in which each piece of data is represented by a point, but individual points are not connected by lines.

Schwann cell A type of glial cell that forms insulating myelin sheaths around the axons of neurons in the peripheral nervous system.

science An approach to understanding the natural world.

scion (sī'-un) The twig grafted onto the stock when making a graft.

sclereid (sklār'-ē-id) A short, irregular sclerenchyma cell in nutshells and seed coats. Sclereids are scattered throughout the parenchyma of some plants.

sclerenchyma cell (skluh-ren'-kim-uh) A rigid, supportive plant cell type usually lacking a protoplast and possessing thick secondary walls strengthened by lignin at maturity.

scrotum A pouch of skin outside the abdomen that houses the testes; functions in maintaining the testes at the lower temperature required for spermatogenesis.

second law of thermodynamics The principle stating that every energy transfer or transformation increases the entropy of the universe. Usable forms of energy are at least partly converted to heat.

second messenger A small, nonprotein, water-soluble molecule or ion, such as a calcium ion (Ca^{2+}) or cyclic AMP, that relays a signal to a cell's interior in response to a signaling molecule bound by a signal receptor protein.

secondary cell wall In plant cells, a strong and durable matrix that is often deposited in several laminated layers around the plasma membrane and that provides protection and support.

secondary consumer A carnivore that eats herbivores.

secondary endosymbiosis A process in eukaryotic evolution in which a heterotrophic eukaryotic cell engulfed a photosynthetic eukaryotic cell, which survived in a symbiotic relationship inside the heterotrophic cell.

secondary growth Growth produced by lateral meristems, thickening the roots and shoots of woody plants.

secondary immune response The adaptive immune response elicited on second or subsequent exposures to a particular antigen. The secondary immune response is more rapid, of greater magnitude, and of longer duration than the primary immune response.

secondary oocyte (ō'-uh-sīt) An oocyte that has completed the first of the two meiotic divisions.

secondary production The amount of chemical energy in consumers' food that is converted to their own new biomass during a given time period.

secondary structure Regions of repetitive coiling or folding of the polypeptide backbone of a protein due to hydrogen bonding between constituents of the backbone (not the side chains).

secondary succession A type of succession that occurs where an existing community has been cleared by some disturbance that leaves the soil or substrate intact.

secretion (1) The discharge of molecules synthesized by a cell. (2) The discharge of wastes from the body fluid into the filtrate.

seed An adaptation of some terrestrial plants consisting of an embryo packaged along with a store of food within a protective coat.

seed coat A tough outer covering of a seed, formed from the outer coat of an ovule. In a flowering plant, the seed coat encloses and protects the embryo and endosperm.

seedless vascular plant An informal name for a plant that has vascular tissue but lacks seeds. Seedless vascular plants form a paraphyletic group that includes the phyla Lycophyta (club mosses and their relatives) and Monilophyta (ferns and their relatives).

selective permeability A property of biological membranes that allows them to regulate the passage of substances across them.

self-incompatibility The ability of a seed plant to reject its own pollen and sometimes the pollen of closely related individuals.

semelparity Reproduction in which an organism produces all of its offspring in a single event; also known as big-bang reproduction.

semen (sē'-mun) The fluid that is ejaculated by the male during orgasm; contains sperm and secretions from several glands of the male reproductive tract.

semicircular canals A three-part chamber of the inner ear that functions in maintaining equilibrium.

semiconservative model Type of DNA replication in which the replicated double helix consists of one old strand, derived from the parental molecule, and one newly made strand.

semilunar valve A valve located at each exit of the heart, where the aorta leaves the left ventricle and the pulmonary artery leaves the right ventricle.

seminal vesicle (sem'-i-nul ves'-i-kul) A gland in males that secretes a fluid component of semen that lubricates and nourishes sperm.

seminiferous tubule (sem'-i-nif'-er-us) A highly coiled tube in the testis in which sperm are produced.

senescence (se-nes'-ens) The growth phase in a plant or plant part (as a leaf) from full maturity to death.

sensitive period A limited phase in an animal's development when learning of particular behaviors can take place; also called a critical period.

sensor In homeostasis, a receptor that detects a stimulus.

sensory adaptation The tendency of sensory neurons to become less sensitive when they are stimulated repeatedly.

sensory neuron A nerve cell that receives information from the internal or external environment and transmits signals to the central nervous system.

sensory reception The detection of a stimulus by sensory cells.

sensory receptor An organ, cell, or structure within a cell that responds to specific stimuli from an organism's external or internal environment.

sensory transduction The conversion of stimulus energy to a change in the membrane potential of a sensory receptor cell.

sepal (sē'-pul) A modified leaf in angiosperms that helps enclose and protect a flower bud before it opens.

serial endosymbiosis A hypothesis for the origin of eukaryotes consisting of a sequence of endosymbiotic events in which mitochondria, chloroplasts, and perhaps other cellular structures were derived from small prokaryotes that had been engulfed by larger cells.

Sertoli cell A support cell of the seminiferous tubule that surrounds and nourishes developing sperm.

set point In homeostasis in animals, a value maintained for a particular variable, such as body temperature or solute concentration.

sex chromosome A chromosome responsible for determining the sex of an individual.

sex-linked gene A gene located on either sex chromosome. Most sex-linked genes are on the X chromosome and show distinctive patterns of inheritance; there are very few genes on the Y chromosome.

sexual dimorphism (dī-mōr'-fizm) Differences between the secondary sex characteristics of males and females of the same species.

sexual reproduction A type of reproduction in which two parents give rise to offspring that have unique combinations of genes inherited from both parents via the gametes.

sexual selection A process in which individuals with certain inherited characteristics are more likely than other individuals of the same sex to obtain mates.

Shannon diversity index An index of community diversity symbolized by H and represented by the equation $H = -(p_A \ln p_A + p_B \ln p_B + p_C \ln p_C + \ldots)$, where A, B, C . . . are species, p is the relative abundance of each species, and ln is the natural logarithm.

shared ancestral character A character that is shared by members of a particular clade but that originated in an ancestor that is not a member of that clade.

shared derived character An evolutionary novelty that is unique to a particular clade.

shoot system The aerial portion of a plant body, consisting of stems, leaves, and (in angiosperms) flowers.

short tandem repeat (STR) Simple sequence DNA containing multiple tandemly repeated units of two to five nucleotides. Variations in STRs act as genetic markers in STR analysis, used to prepare genetic profiles.

short-day plant A plant that flowers (usually in late summer, fall, or winter) only when the light period is shorter than a critical length.

short-term memory The ability to hold information, anticipations, or goals for a time and then release them if they become irrelevant.

sickle-cell disease A recessively inherited human blood disorder in which a single nucleotide change in the β-globin gene causes hemoglobin to aggregate, changing red blood cell shape and causing multiple symptoms in afflicted individuals.

sieve plate An end wall in a sieve-tube element, which facilitates the flow of phloem sap in angiosperm sieve tubes.

sieve-tube element A living cell that conducts sugars and other organic nutrients in the phloem of angiosperms; also called a sieve-tube member. Connected end to end, they form sieve tubes.

sign stimulus An external sensory cue that triggers a fixed action pattern by an animal.

signal In animal behavior, transmission of a stimulus from one animal to another. The term is also used in the context of communication in other kinds of organisms and in cell-to-cell communication in all multicellular organisms.

signal peptide A sequence of about 20 amino acids at or near the leading (amino) end of a polypeptide that targets it to the endoplasmic reticulum or other organelles in a eukaryotic cell.

signal transduction pathway A series of steps linking a mechanical, chemical, or electrical stimulus to a specific cellular response.

signal-recognition particle (SRP) A protein-RNA complex that recognizes a signal peptide as it emerges from a ribosome and helps direct the ribosome to the endoplasmic reticulum (ER) by binding to a receptor protein on the ER.

silent mutation A nucleotide-pair substitution that has no observable effect on the phenotype; for example, within a gene, a mutation that results in a codon that codes for the same amino acid.

simple fruit A fruit derived from a single carpel or several fused carpels.

simple sequence DNA A DNA sequence that contains many copies of tandemly repeated short sequences.

single bond A single covalent bond; the sharing of a pair of valence electrons by two atoms.

single circulation A circulatory system consisting of a single pump and circuit, in which blood passes from the sites of gas exchange to the rest of the body before returning to the heart.

single nucleotide polymorphism (SNP) A single base-pair site in a genome where nucleotide variation is found in at least 1% of the population.

single-lens eye The camera-like eye found in some jellies, polychaete worms, spiders, and many molluscs.

single-strand binding protein A protein that binds to the unpaired DNA strands during DNA replication, stabilizing them and holding them apart while they serve as templates for the synthesis of complementary strands of DNA.

sinoatrial (SA) node A region in the right atrium of the heart that sets the rate and timing at which all cardiac muscle cells contract; the pacemaker.

sister chromatids Two copies of a duplicated chromosome attached to each other by proteins at the centromere and, sometimes, along the arms. While joined, two sister chromatids make up one chromosome. Chromatids are eventually separated during mitosis or meiosis II.

sister taxa Groups of organisms that share an immediate common ancestor and hence are each other's closest relatives.

skeletal muscle A type of striated muscle that is generally responsible for the voluntary movements of the body.

sliding-filament model The idea that muscle contraction is based on the movement of thin (actin) filaments along thick (myosin) filaments, shortening the sarcomere, the basic unit of muscle organization.

slow-twitch fiber A muscle fiber that can sustain long contractions.

small interfering RNA (siRNA) One of multiple small, single-stranded RNA molecules generated by cellular machinery from a long, linear, double-stranded RNA molecule. The siRNA associates with one or more proteins in a complex that can degrade or prevent translation of an mRNA with a complementary sequence. In some cases, siRNA can also block transcription by promoting chromatin modification.

small intestine The longest section of the alimentary canal, so named because of its small diameter compared with that of the large intestine; the principal site of the enzymatic hydrolysis of food macromolecules and the absorption of nutrients.

smooth ER That portion of the endoplasmic reticulum that is free of ribosomes.

smooth muscle A type of muscle lacking the striations of skeletal and cardiac muscle because of the uniform distribution of myosin filaments in the cells; responsible for involuntary body activities.

social learning Modification of behavior through the observation of other individuals.

sodium-potassium pump A transport protein in the plasma membrane of animal cells that actively transports sodium out of the cell and potassium into the cell.

solute (sol'-yūt) A substance that is dissolved in a solution.

solute potential (Ψ_S) A component of water potential that is proportional to the molarity of a solution and that measures the effect of solutes on the direction of water movement; also called osmotic potential, it can be either zero or negative.

solution A liquid that is a homogeneous mixture of two or more substances.

solvent The dissolving agent of a solution. Water is the most versatile solvent known.

somatic cell (sō-mat'-ik) Any cell in a multicellular organism except a sperm or egg or their precursors.

spatial learning The establishment of a memory that reflects the environment's spatial structure.

speciation (spē′-sē-ā′-shun) An evolutionary process in which one species splits into two or more species.

species (spē′-sēz) A population or group of populations whose members have the potential to interbreed in nature and produce viable, fertile offspring, but do not produce viable, fertile offspring with members of other such groups.

species-area curve The biodiversity pattern that shows that the larger the geographic area of a community, the more species it has.

species diversity The number and relative abundance of species in a biological community.

species richness The number of species in a biological community.

specific heat The amount of heat that must be absorbed or lost for 1 g of a substance to change its temperature by 1°C.

spectrophotometer An instrument that measures the proportions of light of different wavelengths absorbed and transmitted by a pigment solution.

sperm The male gamete.

spermatogenesis The continuous and prolific production of mature sperm cells in the testis.

spermatogonium (plural, **spermatogonia**) A cell that divides mitotically to form spermatocytes.

sphincter (sfink′-ter) A ringlike band of muscle fibers that controls the size of an opening in the body, such as the passage between the esophagus and the stomach.

spliceosome (splī′-sō-sōm) A large complex made up of proteins and RNA molecules that splices RNA by interacting with the ends of an RNA intron, releasing the intron and joining the two adjacent exons.

spontaneous process A process that occurs without an overall input of energy; a process that is energetically favorable.

sporangium (spōr-an′-jē-um) (plural, **sporangia**) A multicellular organ in fungi and plants in which meiosis occurs and haploid cells develop.

spore (1) In the life cycle of a plant or alga undergoing alternation of generations, a haploid cell produced in the sporophyte by meiosis. A spore can divide by mitosis to develop into a multicellular haploid individual, the gametophyte, without fusing with another cell. (2) In fungi, a haploid cell, produced either sexually or asexually, that produces a mycelium after germination.

sporophyte (spō-ruh-fīt′) In organisms (plants and some algae) that have alternation of generations, the multicellular diploid form that results from the union of gametes. The sporophyte produces haploid spores by meiosis that develop into gametophytes.

sporopollenin (spōr-uh-pol′-eh-nin) A durable polymer that covers exposed zygotes of charophyte algae and forms the walls of plant spores, preventing them from drying out.

stability In evolutionary biology, a term referring to a hybrid zone in which hybrids continue to be produced; this causes the hybrid zone to be "stable" in the sense of persisting over time.

stabilizing selection Natural selection in which intermediate phenotypes survive or reproduce more successfully than do extreme phenotypes.

stamen (stā′-men) The pollen-producing reproductive organ of a flower, consisting of an anther and a filament.

starch A storage polysaccharide in plants, consisting entirely of glucose monomers joined by α glycosidic linkages.

start point In transcription, the nucleotide position on the promoter where RNA polymerase begins synthesis of RNA.

statocyst (stat′-uh-sist′) A type of mechanoreceptor that functions in equilibrium in invertebrates by use of statoliths, which stimulate hair cells in relation to gravity.

statolith (stat′-uh-lith′) (1) In plants, a specialized plastid that contains dense starch grains and may play a role in detecting gravity. (2) In invertebrates, a dense particle that settles in response to gravity and is found in sensory organs that function in equilibrium.

stele (stēl) The vascular tissue of a stem or root.

stem A vascular plant organ consisting of an alternating system of nodes and internodes that support the leaves and reproductive structures.

stem cell Any relatively unspecialized cell that can produce, during a single division, one identical daughter cell and one more specialized daughter cell that can undergo further differentiation.

steroid A type of lipid characterized by a carbon skeleton consisting of four fused rings with various chemical groups attached.

sticky end A single-stranded end of a double-stranded restriction fragment.

stigma (plural, **stigmata**) The sticky part of a flower's carpel, which receives pollen grains.

stimulus In feedback regulation, a fluctuation in a variable that triggers a response.

stipe A stemlike structure of a seaweed.

stock The plant that provides the root system when making a graft.

stoma (stō′-muh) (plural, **stomata**) A microscopic pore surrounded by guard cells in the epidermis of leaves and stems that allows gas exchange between the environment and the interior of the plant.

stomach An organ of the digestive system that stores food and performs preliminary steps of digestion.

stramenopiles One of the three major subgroups for which the SAR eukaryotic supergroup is named. This clade arose by secondary endosymbiosis and includes diatoms and brown algae.

stratum (strah′-tum) (plural, **strata**) A rock layer formed when new layers of sediment cover older ones and compress them.

stroke The death of nervous tissue in the brain, usually resulting from rupture or blockage of arteries in the head.

stroma (strō′-muh) The dense fluid within the chloroplast surrounding the thylakoid

membrane and containing ribosomes and DNA; involved in the synthesis of organic molecules from carbon dioxide and water.

stromatolite Layered rock that results from the activities of prokaryotes that bind thin films of sediment together.

structural isomer One of two or more compounds that have the same molecular formula but differ in the covalent arrangements of their atoms.

style The stalk of a flower's carpel, with the ovary at the base and the stigma at the top.

substrate The reactant on which an enzyme works.

substrate feeder An animal that lives in or on its food source, eating its way through the food.

substrate-level phosphorylation The enzyme-catalyzed formation of ATP by direct transfer of a phosphate group to ADP from an intermediate substrate in catabolism.

sugar sink A plant organ that is a net consumer or storer of sugar. Growing roots, shoot tips, stems, and fruits are examples of sugar sinks supplied by phloem.

sugar source A plant organ in which sugar is being produced by either photosynthesis or the breakdown of starch. Mature leaves are the primary sugar sources of plants.

sulfhydryl group A chemical group consisting of a sulfur atom bonded to a hydrogen atom.

summation A phenomenon of neural integration in which the membrane potential of the postsynaptic cell is determined by the combined effect of EPSPs or IPSPs produced in rapid succession at one synapse or simultaneously at different synapses.

suprachiasmatic nucleus (SCN) A group of neurons in the hypothalamus of mammals that functions as a biological clock.

surface tension A measure of how difficult it is to stretch or break the surface of a liquid.

surfactant A substance secreted by alveoli that decreases surface tension in the fluid that coats the alveoli.

survivorship curve A plot of the number of members of a cohort that are still alive at each age; one way to represent age-specific mortality.

suspension feeder An animal that feeds by removing suspended food particles from the surrounding medium by a capture, trapping, or filtration mechanism.

sustainable development Development that meets the needs of people today without limiting the ability of future generations to meet their needs.

symbiont (sim′-bē-ont) The smaller participant in a symbiotic relationship, living in or on the host.

symbiosis An ecological relationship between organisms of two different species that live together in direct and intimate contact.

sympathetic division One of three divisions of the autonomic nervous system; generally increases energy expenditure and prepares the body for action.

sympatric speciation (sim-pat′-rik) The formation of new species in populations that live in the same geographic area.

symplast In plants, the continuum of cytoplasm connected by plasmodesmata between cells.

synapse (sin'-aps) The junction where a neuron communicates with another cell across a narrow gap via a neurotransmitter or an electrical coupling.

synapsid Member of an amniote clade distinguished by a single hole on each side of the skull. Synapsids include the mammals.

synapsis (si-nap'-sis) The pairing and physical connection of duplicated homologous chromosomes during prophase I of meiosis.

synaptonemal complex A zipper-like structure composed of proteins, which connects two homologous chromosomes tightly along their lengths during part of prophase I of meiosis.

systematics A scientific discipline focused on classifying organisms and determining their evolutionary relationships.

systemic acquired resistance A defensive response in infected plants that helps protect healthy tissue from pathogenic invasion.

systemic circuit The branch of the circulatory system that supplies oxygenated blood to and carries deoxygenated blood away from organs and tissues throughout the body.

systems biology An approach to studying biology that aims to model the dynamic behavior of whole biological systems based on a study of the interactions among the system's parts.

systole (sis'-tō-lē) The stage of the cardiac cycle in which a heart chamber contracts and pumps blood.

T cells The class of lymphocytes that mature in the thymus; they include both effector cells for the cell-mediated immune response and helper cells required for both branches of adaptive immunity.

taproot A main vertical root that develops from an embryonic root and gives rise to lateral (branch) roots.

tastant Any chemical that stimulates the sensory receptors in a taste bud.

taste bud A collection of modified epithelial cells on the tongue or in the mouth that are receptors for taste in mammals.

TATA box A DNA sequence in eukaryotic promoters crucial in forming the transcription initiation complex.

taxis (tak'-sis) An oriented movement toward or away from a stimulus.

taxon (plural, **taxa**) A named taxonomic unit at any given level of classification.

taxonomy (tak-son'-uh-mē) A scientific discipline concerned with naming and classifying the diverse forms of life.

Tay-Sachs disease A human genetic disease caused by a recessive allele for a dysfunctional enzyme, leading to accumulation of certain lipids in the brain. Seizures, blindness, and degeneration of motor and mental performance usually become manifest a few months after birth, followed by death within a few years.

technology The application of scientific knowledge for a specific purpose, often involving industry or commerce but also including uses in basic research.

telomere (tel'-uh-mēr) The tandemly repetitive DNA at the end of a eukaryotic chromosome's DNA molecule. Telomeres protect the organism's genes from being eroded during successive rounds of replication. *See also* repetitive DNA.

telophase The fifth and final stage of mitosis, in which daughter nuclei are forming and cytokinesis has typically begun.

temperate broadleaf forest A biome located throughout midlatitude regions where there is sufficient moisture to support the growth of large, broadleaf deciduous trees.

temperate grassland A terrestrial biome that exists at midlatitude regions and is dominated by grasses and forbs.

temperate phage A phage that is capable of replicating by either a lytic or lysogenic cycle.

temperature A measure in degrees of the average kinetic energy (thermal energy) of the atoms and molecules in a body of matter.

template strand The DNA strand that provides the pattern, or template, for ordering, by complementary base pairing, the sequence of nucleotides in an RNA transcript.

terminator In bacteria, a sequence of nucleotides in DNA that marks the end of a gene and signals RNA polymerase to release the newly made RNA molecule and detach from the DNA.

territoriality A behavior in which an animal defends a bounded physical space against encroachment by other individuals, usually of its own species.

tertiary consumer (ter'-shē-ār'-ē) A carnivore that eats other carnivores.

tertiary structure The overall shape of a protein molecule due to interactions of amino acid side chains, including hydrophobic interactions, ionic bonds, hydrogen bonds, and disulfide bridges.

test In foram protists, a porous shell that consists of a single piece of organic material hardened with calcium carbonate.

testcross Breeding an organism of unknown genotype with a homozygous recessive individual to determine the unknown genotype. The ratio of phenotypes in the offspring reveals the unknown genotype.

testis (plural, **testes**) The male reproductive organ, or gonad, in which sperm and reproductive hormones are produced.

testosterone A steroid hormone required for development of the male reproductive system, spermatogenesis, and male secondary sex characteristics; the major androgen in mammals.

tetanus (tet'-uh-nus) The maximal, sustained contraction of a skeletal muscle, caused by a very high frequency of action potentials elicited by continual stimulation.

tetrapod Member of a vertebrate clade characterized by limbs with digits. Tetrapods include mammals, amphibians, and birds and other reptiles.

thalamus (thal'-uh-mus) An integrating center of the vertebrate forebrain. Neurons with cell bodies in the thalamus relay neural input to specific areas in the cerebral cortex and regulate what information goes to the cerebral cortex.

theory An explanation that is broader in scope than a hypothesis, generates new hypotheses, and is supported by a large body of evidence.

thermal energy Kinetic energy due to the random motion of atoms and molecules; energy in its most random form. *See also* heat.

thermocline A narrow stratum of abrupt temperature change in the ocean and in many temperate-zone lakes.

thermodynamics (ther'-mō-dī-nam'-iks) The study of energy transformations that occur in a collection of matter. *See also* first law of thermodynamics; second law of thermodynamics.

thermoreceptor A receptor stimulated by either heat or cold.

thermoregulation The maintenance of internal body temperature within a tolerable range.

thick filament A filament composed of staggered arrays of myosin molecules; a component of myofibrils in muscle fibers.

thigmomorphogenesis A response in plants to chronic mechanical stimulation, resulting from increased ethylene production. An example is thickening stems in response to strong winds.

thigmotropism (thig-mo'-truh-pizm) A directional growth of a plant in response to touch.

thin filament A filament consisting of two strands of actin and two strands of regulatory protein coiled around one another; a component of myofibrils in muscle fibers.

threatened species A species that is considered likely to become endangered in the foreseeable future.

threshold The potential that an excitable cell membrane must reach for an action potential to be initiated.

thrombus A fibrin-containing clot that forms in a blood vessel and blocks the flow of blood.

thylakoid (thī'-luh-koyd) A flattened, membranous sac inside a chloroplast. Thylakoids often exist in stacks called grana that are interconnected; their membranes contain molecular "machinery" used to convert light energy to chemical energy.

thymus (thī'-mus) A small organ in the thoracic cavity of vertebrates where maturation of T cells is completed.

tidal volume The volume of air a mammal inhales and exhales with each breath.

tight junction A type of intercellular junction between animal cells that prevents the leakage of material through the space between cells.

tissue An integrated group of cells with a common structure, function, or both.

Toll-like receptor (TLR) A membrane receptor on a phagocytic white blood cell that recognizes fragments of molecules common to a set of pathogens.

tonicity The ability of a solution surrounding a cell to cause that cell to gain or lose water.

top-down model A model of community organization in which predation influences community organization by controlling herbivore numbers, which in turn control plant or phytoplankton numbers, which in turn control nutrient levels; also called the trophic cascade model.

topoisomerase A protein that breaks, swivels, and rejoins DNA strands. During DNA replication, topoisomerase helps to relieve strain in the double helix ahead of the replication fork.

totipotent (tō′-tuh-pōt′-ent) Describing a cell that can give rise to all parts of the embryo and adult, as well as extraembryonic membranes in species that have them.

trace element An element indispensable for life but required in extremely minute amounts.

trachea (trā′-kē-uh) The portion of the respiratory tract that passes from the larynx to the bronchi; also called the windpipe.

tracheal system In insects, a system of branched, air-filled tubes that extends throughout the body and carries oxygen directly to cells.

tracheid (trā′-kē-id) A long, tapered water-conducting cell found in the xylem of nearly all vascular plants. Functioning tracheids are no longer living.

trait One of two or more detectable variants in a genetic character.

transcription The synthesis of RNA using a DNA template.

transcription factor A regulatory protein that binds to DNA and affects transcription of specific genes.

transcription initiation complex The completed assembly of transcription factors and RNA polymerase bound to a promoter.

transcription unit A region of DNA that is transcribed into an RNA molecule.

transduction (1) A process in which phages (viruses) carry bacterial DNA from one bacterial cell to another. When these two cells are members of different species, transduction results in horizontal gene transfer. (2) In cellular communication, the conversion of a signal from outside the cell to a form that can bring about a specific cellular response; also called signal transduction.

***trans* fats** An unsaturated fat, formed artificially during hydrogenation of oils, containing one or more *trans* double bonds.

transfer RNA (tRNA) An RNA molecule that functions as a translator between nucleic acid and protein languages by picking up a specific amino acid and carrying it to the ribosome, where the tRNA recognizes the appropriate codon in the mRNA.

transformation (1) The process by which a cell in culture acquires the ability to divide indefinitely, similar to the division of cancer cells. (2) A change in genotype and phenotype due to the assimilation of external DNA by a cell. When the external DNA is from a member of a different species, transformation results in horizontal gene transfer.

transgenic Pertaining to an organism whose genome contains DNA introduced from another organism of the same or a different species.

translation The synthesis of a polypeptide using the genetic information encoded in an mRNA molecule. There is a change of "language" from nucleotides to amino acids.

translocation (1) An aberration in chromosome structure resulting from attachment of a chromosomal fragment to a nonhomologous chromosome. (2) During protein synthesis, the third stage in the elongation cycle, when the RNA carrying the growing polypeptide moves from the A site to the P site on the ribosome. (3) The transport of organic nutrients in the phloem of vascular plants.

transmission electron microscope (TEM) A microscope that passes an electron beam through very thin sections stained with metal atoms and is primarily used to study the internal ultrastructure of cells.

transpiration The evaporative loss of water from a plant.

transport epithelium One or more layers of specialized epithelial cells that carry out and regulate solute movement.

transport protein A transmembrane protein that helps a certain substance or class of closely related substances to cross the membrane.

transport vesicle A small membranous sac in a eukaryotic cell's cytoplasm carrying molecules produced by the cell.

transposable element A segment of DNA that can move within the genome of a cell by means of a DNA or RNA intermediate; also called a transposable genetic element.

transposon A transposable element that moves within a genome by means of a DNA intermediate.

transverse (T) tubule An infolding of the plasma membrane of skeletal muscle cells.

triacylglycerol (trī-as′-ul-glis′-uh-rol) A lipid consisting of three fatty acids linked to one glycerol molecule; also called a fat or triglyceride.

triple response A plant growth maneuver in response to mechanical stress, involving slowing of stem elongation, thickening of the stem, and a curvature that causes the stem to start growing horizontally.

triplet code A genetic information system in which a series of three-nucleotide-long words specifies a sequence of amino acids for a polypeptide chain.

trisomic Referring to a diploid cell that has three copies of a particular chromosome instead of the normal two.

trophic efficiency The percentage of production transferred from one trophic level to the next.

trophic structure The different feeding relationships in an ecosystem, which determine the route of energy flow and the pattern of chemical cycling.

trophoblast The outer epithelium of a mammalian blastocyst. It forms the fetal part of the placenta, supporting embryonic development but not forming part of the embryo proper.

tropic hormone A hormone that has an endocrine gland or endocrine cells as a target.

tropical dry forest A terrestrial biome characterized by relatively high temperatures and precipitation overall but with a pronounced dry season.

tropical rain forest A terrestrial biome characterized by relatively high precipitation and temperatures year-round.

tropics Latitudes between 23.5° north and south.

tropism A growth response that results in the curvature of whole plant organs toward or away from stimuli due to differential rates of cell elongation.

tropomyosin The regulatory protein that blocks the myosin-binding sites on actin molecules.

troponin complex The regulatory proteins that control the position of tropomyosin on the thin filament.

true-breeding Referring to organisms that produce offspring of the same variety over many generations of self-pollination.

tumor-suppressor gene A gene whose protein product inhibits cell division, thereby preventing the uncontrolled cell growth that contributes to cancer.

tundra A terrestrial biome at the extreme limits of plant growth. At the northernmost limits, it is called arctic tundra, and at high altitudes, where plant forms are limited to low shrubby or matlike vegetation, it is called alpine tundra.

turgid (ter′-jid) Swollen or distended, as in plant cells. (A walled cell becomes turgid if it has a lower water potential than its surroundings, resulting in entry of water.)

turgor pressure The force directed against a plant cell wall after the influx of water and swelling of the cell due to osmosis.

twin study A behavioral study in which researchers compare the behavior of identical twins raised apart with that of identical twins raised in the same household.

tympanic membrane Another name for the eardrum, the membrane between the outer and middle ear.

Unikonta (yū′-ni-kon′-tuh) One of four supergroups of eukaryotes proposed in a current hypothesis of the evolutionary history of eukaryotes. This clade, which is supported by studies of myosin proteins and DNA, consists of amoebozoans and opisthokonts. *See also* Excavata, SAR, and Archaeplastida.

unsaturated fatty acid A fatty acid that has one or more double bonds between carbons in the hydrocarbon tail. Such bonding reduces the number of hydrogen atoms attached to the carbon skeleton.

urea A soluble nitrogenous waste produced in the liver by a metabolic cycle that combines ammonia with carbon dioxide.

ureter (yū-rē′-ter) A duct leading from the kidney to the urinary bladder.

urethra (yū-rē′-thruh) A tube that releases urine from the mammalian body near the vagina in females and through the penis in males; also serves in males as the exit tube for the reproductive system.

uric acid A product of protein and purine metabolism and the major nitrogenous waste product of insects, land snails, and many reptiles. Uric acid is relatively nontoxic and largely insoluble.

urinary bladder The pouch where urine is stored prior to elimination.

uterine cycle The changes that occur in the uterus during the reproductive cycle of the human female; also called the menstrual cycle.

uterus A female organ where eggs are fertilized and/or development of the young occurs.

utricle (yū′-trick-uhl) In the vertebrate ear, a chamber in the vestibule behind the oval window that opens into the three semicircular canals.

vaccine A harmless variant or derivative of a pathogen that stimulates a host's immune system to mount defenses against the pathogen.

vacuole (vak′-yū-ōl′) A membrane-bounded vesicle whose specialized function varies in different kinds of cells.

vagina Part of the female reproductive system between the uterus and the outside opening; the birth canal in mammals. During copulation, the vagina accommodates the male's penis and receives sperm.

valence The bonding capacity of a given atom; the number of covalent bonds an atom can form, which usually equals the number of unpaired electrons in its outermost (valence) shell.

valence electron An electron in the outermost electron shell.

valence shell The outermost energy shell of an atom, containing the valence electrons involved in the chemical reactions of that atom.

van der Waals interactions Weak attractions between molecules or parts of molecules that result from transient local partial charges.

variable A factor that varies during an experiment.

variation Differences between members of the same species.

vas deferens In mammals, the tube in the male reproductive system in which sperm travel from the epididymis to the urethra.

vasa recta The capillary system in the kidney that serves the loop of Henle.

vascular cambium A cylinder of meristematic tissue in woody plants that adds layers of secondary vascular tissue called secondary xylem (wood) and secondary phloem.

vascular plant A plant with vascular tissue. Vascular plants include all living plant species except liverworts, mosses, and hornworts.

vascular tissue Plant tissue consisting of cells joined into tubes that transport water and nutrients throughout the plant body.

vascular tissue system A transport system formed by xylem and phloem throughout a vascular plant. Xylem transports water and minerals; phloem transports sugars, the products of photosynthesis.

vasoconstriction A decrease in the diameter of blood vessels caused by contraction of smooth muscles in the vessel walls.

vasodilation An increase in the diameter of blood vessels caused by relaxation of smooth muscles in the vessel walls.

vasopressin *See* antidiuretic hormone (ADH).

vector An organism that transmits pathogens from one host to another.

vegetative propagation Cloning of plants by humans.

vegetative reproduction Cloning of plants in nature.

vein (1) In animals, a vessel that carries blood toward the heart. (2) In plants, a vascular bundle in a leaf.

ventilation The flow of air or water over a respiratory surface.

ventral Pertaining to the underside, or bottom, of an animal with radial or bilateral symmetry.

ventricle (ven′-tri-kul) (1) A heart chamber that pumps blood out of the heart. (2) A space in the vertebrate brain, filled with cerebrospinal fluid.

vernalization The use of cold treatment to induce a plant to flower.

vertebrate A chordate animal with a backbone. Vertebrates include sharks and rays, ray-finned fishes, coelacanths, lungfishes, amphibians, reptiles, and mammals.

vesicle (ves′-i-kul) A membranous sac in the cytoplasm of a eukaryotic cell.

vessel A nonliving, water-conducting tube found in most angiosperms and a few nonflowering vascular plants that is formed by the end-to-end connection of vessel elements.

vessel element A short, wide, water-conducting cell found in the xylem of most angiosperms and a few nonflowering vascular plants. Dead at maturity, vessel elements are aligned end to end to form vessels.

vestigial structure A feature of an organism that is a historical remnant of a structure that served a function in the organism's ancestors.

villus (plural, **villi**) (1) A finger-like projection of the inner surface of the small intestine. (2) A finger-like projection of the chorion of the mammalian placenta. Large numbers of villi increase the surface areas of these organs.

viral envelope A membrane, derived from membranes of the host cell, that cloaks the capsid, which in turn encloses a viral genome.

virulent phage A phage that replicates only by a lytic cycle.

virus An infectious particle incapable of replicating outside of a cell, consisting of an RNA or DNA genome surrounded by a protein coat (capsid) and, for some viruses, a membranous envelope.

visceral mass One of the three main parts of a mollusc; the part containing most of the internal organs. *See also* foot and mantle.

visible light That portion of the electromagnetic spectrum that can be detected as various colors by the human eye, ranging in wavelength from about 380 nm to about 750 nm.

vital capacity The maximum volume of air that a mammal can inhale and exhale with each breath.

vitamin An organic molecule required in the diet in very small amounts. Many vitamins serve as coenzymes or parts of coenzymes.

voltage-gated ion channel A specialized ion channel that opens or closes in response to changes in membrane potential.

vulva Collective term for the female external genitalia.

water potential (Ψ) The physical property predicting the direction in which water will flow, governed by solute concentration and applied pressure.

wavelength The distance between crests of waves, such as those of the electromagnetic spectrum.

wetland A habitat that is inundated by water at least some of the time and that supports plants adapted to water-saturated soil.

white matter Tracts of axons within the CNS.

whole-genome shotgun approach Procedure for genome sequencing in which the genome is randomly cut into many overlapping short segments that are sequenced; computer software then assembles the complete sequence.

wild type The phenotype most commonly observed in natural populations; also refers to the individual with that phenotype.

wilting The drooping of leaves and stems that occurs when plant cells become flaccid.

wobble Flexibility in the base-pairing rules in which the nucleotide at the 5′ end of a tRNA anticodon can form hydrogen bonds with more than one kind of base in the third position (3′ end) of a codon.

xerophyte A plant adapted to an arid climate.

X-linked gene A gene located on the X chromosome; such genes show a distinctive pattern of inheritance.

X-ray crystallography A technique used to study the three-dimensional structure of molecules. It depends on the diffraction of an X-ray beam by the individual atoms of a crystallized molecule.

xylem (zī′-lum) Vascular plant tissue consisting mainly of tubular dead cells that conduct most of the water and minerals upward from the roots to the rest of the plant.

xylem sap The dilute solution of water and dissolved minerals carried through vessels and tracheids.

yeast Single-celled fungus. Yeasts reproduce asexually by binary fission or by the pinching of small buds off a parent cell. Many fungal species can grow both as yeasts and as a network of filaments; relatively few species grow only as yeasts.

zero population growth (ZPG) A period of stability in population size, when additions to the population through births and immigration are balanced by subtractions through deaths and emigration.

zoned reserve An extensive region that includes areas relatively undisturbed by humans surrounded by areas that have been changed by human activity and are used for economic gain.

zoonotic pathogen A disease-causing agent that is transmitted to humans from other animals.

zygote (zī′-gōt) The diploid cell produced by the union of haploid gametes during fertilization; a fertilized egg.

Index

1-Butene, 45*f*
2,4-D (2,4-dichlorophenoxyacetic acid), 644
2-Butene, 45*f*
2-Methylbutane, 46*f*
2-Methylpropane, 45*f*
3-D shape, protein, 43*f*, 63*f*
3′ end, 65, 286, 287*f*
3-Phosphoglycerate, 174*f*, 177*f*
5′ cap, **286**, 287*f*
5′ end, polynucleotide, 65
5-Methylcytosine, 47*f*
10-nm fibers, 268*f*
30-nm fibers, 268, 269*f*
300-nm fibers, 269*f*

A

ABA. *See* Abscisic acid
ABC hypothesis, **620**, 621*f*
abdominal-A (*abd-A*) gene, 554*f*
Abiotic factors, **843**
  in community equilibrium, 878
  in pollination, 624*f*
  population effects of, 854, 855*f*–856*ft*, 857
  in species distributions, 843, 853–854
Abiotic stresses, plant responses to, **655**–656, 657*f*
Abiotic synthesis, organic compound, 475*f*, 476
Abnormal chromosome numbers, 248*f*–250*f*
ABO blood groups, 104, 224, 225*f*, 746
Abomasum, 700*f*
Abortions, spontaneous, 248, 768
Abscisic acid (ABA), **613**–614, 642*t*, **645**, 646*f*, 655
Abscission, leaf, 645, 647, 648*f*
Absolute dating, 454
Absorption, 666*f*, **691**
  fungal feeding by, 524*f*, 525
  in large intestine, 697–698
  in small intestine, 696*f*–697*f*
  soil as source of essential elements for, by roots, 599*f*–602*f*
  of water and minerals by root cells, 609
Absorption spectrum, **166**, 167*f*
Abstinence, contraception by, 768, 769*f*
Acacia, 603*f*
Acacia trees, 872*f*
Acanthocephalan worms, 872
Acceleration, mechanoreceptors and, 806, 807*f*
Accessory fruits, **628***f*
Accessory glands, male reproductive, 756*f*
Acclimatization, thermoregulation and, 676
ACE. *See* Angiotensin converting enzyme
Acer rubrum, 582
Acetic acid, 47*f*
Acetone, 47*f*
Acetylation, histone, 309*f*, 331
Acetylcholine, 785, 786*t*, 817*f*–818*f*
Acetylcholinesterase, 785, 818
Acetyl CoA (Acetyl coenzyme A), **148***f*–149*f*
Achillea lanulosa, 866
Achondroplasia, 231*f*
Acid growth hypothesis, 642, 643*f*
Acidic amino acids, 58
Acidic side chains, 57*f*
Acidification, ocean, 39*f*, 40

Acid precipitation, 618, 911*f*
Acid reflux, 695
Acids, **37**–40
Acinonyx jubatus, 863*f*
Acorn woodpeckers, 838
Acorn worm, 552*f*
Acquired immunity. *See* Adaptive immunity
Acquired immunodeficiency syndrome (AIDS). *See* AIDS (acquired immunodeficiency syndrome)
Acquired traits, inheritance of, 381*f*
Acropora cervicornis, 883
Acropora palmata, 883
Acrosomal reaction, animal fertilization, 765*f*
Acrosomes, **758***f*
ACTH. *See* Adrenocorticotropic hormone
Actin, 93*f*, 94, 190. *See also* Thick filaments (actin)
Actinistia, 556*f*
Actinomycetes, 489*f*
Actinopterygii, 556*f*
Action potentials, **779**
  axon structure and, 782*f*
  conduction of, in neurons, 781*f*
  evolution of, 789
  generation of, in neurons, 779, 780*f*, 781
  graded potentials and, 778, 779*f*
  of heart muscles, 820
  hyperpolarization and depolarization of, 778, 779*f*
  in plants, **655**
  in sensory transmission, 802*f*
  of skeletal muscles, 818*f*–819*f*
  of smooth muscles, 820–821
Action spectrum, **166**, 167*f*, 648, 649*f*
Activation, allosteric, 137*f*, 138
Activation energy, **131***f*, 132*f*
Activators, 137*f*, **307**, 311*f*–312*f*
Active immunity, 745–746
Active sites, enzyme, **132**, 133*f*, 134
Active transport, **109**, 110*f*–111*f*, 112, 179*f*, 596–597. *See also* Passive transport; Sodium-potassium pump
Actual range, of species, 853
Acyclovir, 351
Acyrthosiphon pisum, 410
Adaptation, sensory, 802
Adaptations, **383**. *See also* Evolution; Natural selection
  adaptive evolution and, 424, 425*f*–430*f*
  for animal gas exchange, 728*f*–729*f*, 730
  artificial selection, natural selection, and, 385*f*–386*f*
  of axon structure, 782*f*
  circulatory, for thermoregulation, 675
  evolution and, 9
  floral, that prevent self-fertilization, 631*f*
  fungal, for feeding by absorption, 524*f*, 525
  in herbivory, 871
  mouse coat coloration, 2, 16*f*–17*f*
  of pathogens, 747–748
  in predation, 870, 871*f*, 885
  prokaryotic, 474, 475*f*, 478*f*–483*f*
  research by Charles Darwin on, 383*f*, 384
  respiratory, of diving mammals, 730
  sexual reproduction patterns as, 753–754
  terrestrial, of fungi and plants, 175*f*, 176, 521*f*–524*f*, 527*f*, 533, 534*f*–535*f*, 536
  for terrestrial nutrient limitations, 892
  vascular plant evaporative water loss, 614*f*, 615
  vascular plant nutritional, 602, 603*f*–608*f*
  vascular plant resource acquisition, 593–596
  of vertebrate digestive systems, 698*f*–700*f*
  of vertebrate kidneys to diverse environments, 684*f*
Adaptive evolution, **424**, 425*f*–430*f*. *See also* Adaptations
  biodiversity from, 466

  directional, disruptive, and stabilizing selection in, 425*f*, 426
  natural selection in, 421, 426*f*, 430–431
  preservation of genetic variation in, 426–427
  relative fitness and, 425
  sexual selection in, 427*f*, 430*f*
Adaptive immunity, **734**, 737–749
  active and passive immunization in, 745–746
  allergies and, 746*f*, 747
  antibodies produced by, as tools in medicine, 746
  antigen recognition by B cells and T cells in, 737, 738*f*–739*f*
  autoimmune diseases and, 747*f*
  B cell and T cell development in, 739, 740*f*–742*f*
  B cells and antibodies as responses to extracellular pathogens in, 743*f*–744*f*
  cancer and, 748–749
  cytotoxic T cells as responses to infected cells in, 744*f*
  evolution of immune system avoidance and immunodeficiency, 747–748
  helper T cells as responses to antigens in, 742, 743*f*
  human disorders from disruptions in, 746*f*–747*f*, 748–749
  humoral and cell-mediated immune responses in, 742*f*–745*f*
  immune rejection in, 746
  immunological memory in, 741, 742*f*
  innate immunity vs., 734*f*
  origin of self-tolerance in, 740
  overview of, 745*f*
Adaptive radiations, 463*f*–464*f*, 465. *See also* Radiations
Addiction, brain reward system and, 797, 798*f*
Addition rule, **222**
Adenine (A), 65*f*, 66, 256*f*, 258, 259*f*, 428*f*, 644
Adenoid, 716*f*
Adenomatous polyposis coli (APC) gene, 337*f*
Adenosine diphosphate. *See* ADP
Adenosine triphosphate. *See* ATP
Adenoviruses, 343*f*
Adenylyl cyclase, 118, 119*f*
ADH. *See* Antidiuretic hormone
Adhesion, 33*f*, 612
Adipose tissue, 702
ADP (adenosine diphosphate)
  ATP synthesis from, 130*f*, 146*f*–147*f*, 148, 151*f*–152*f*, 153
  as enzyme activator, 137
  hydrolysis of ATP to, 128*f*–130*f*
  in muscle contraction, 816*f*, 817
  as organic phosphate compound, 48
Adrenal cortex, 669*f*
Adrenal glands, 117, 669*f*, 672
Adrenaline. *See* Epinephrine
Adrenal medulla, 669*f*
Adrenocorticotropic hormone (ACTH), 669*f*
Adult stem cells, 332, 333*f*
Adventitious roots, 577, 632
Aerial roots, 577*f*
Aerobic prokaryotes, 481*f*
Aerobic respiration, **142**, 820. *See also* Cellular respiration
  fermentation compared with, 154, 156, 157*f*
Afferent neurons, 792*f*, 793
African-Americans, sickle-cell disease in, 230
African blood lily, 183*f*
African buffalo, 873*f*
African elephants, 384*f*, 385, 858–859*f*, 910, 911*f*
African gray parrots, 800
Africans
  genomes of, 374
  malaria and sickle-cell alleles in, 428*f*–429*f*
  sickle-cell disease in, 230

Agar, 279
Agave, 125f, 624f
Age-related macular degeneration, 333
Aggregate fruits, **628f**
Aggression, animal, 826f, 828f
Aging
  cytokinins in plant, 644
  telomeric DNA and, 267
Aglaophyton major, 524f, 527f
Agonistic behavior, 833
Agriculture. *See also* Crop plants
  artificial selection and breeding in, 619, 633f, 634
  biodiversity benefits for, 908
  C_3 plants in, 175
  C_4 plants in, 175f
  community disturbances by, 880
  effects of atmospheric carbon dioxide on
    productivity of, 176
  fertilizers in, 892, 897f
  importance of mycorrhizae to, 607
  nutrient enrichment caused by, 919f, 920
  plant biotechnology and genetic engineering in,
    634, 635f, 636
  polyploidy in, 442
  prokaryotes in disease-suppressive soil and, 493
  soil management in, 601
  viral diseases and, 354f
Agrobacterium, 488f, 501
Agrostis stolonifera, 636
AIDS (acquired immunodeficiency syndrome), **349**,
  350f, 416, 747–748. *See also* HIV
Ailuropoda melanoleuca, 362t
Ain, Michael C., 231f
Air circulation
  climate and, 842f–844f
  global patterns of, 842f
Airfoils, wings as, 824
Air roots, 577f
Air sacs, 726
Åland Islands, 864f
Alanine, 57f
Alarm signals, 827–828
Alberta, Canada, lake biome in, 850f
Albinism, 229f, 278f
Albumin, 312f
Alcohol, 47f, 863f
Alcohol fermentation, **156f**
Aldehyde compounds, 47f
Alder, 880f
Aldosterone, 117, 685
Aleuria aurantia, 528f
Algae
  biomanipulation of, 877f
  blooms of, 890, 920
  cells of, 79f. *See also* Eukaryotic cells
  chloroplasts of, 89f
  in eukaryotic phylogeny, 507f
  evolution of plants from green, 521f, 523f–524f
  in fossil record, 498f–499f
  land animals vs., 558f
  lichens as symbioses of fungi and, 539f
  in marine ecosystems, 568f, 569
  origins of photosynthetic, 502f, 503
  as photoautotrophs, 162f
  sexual life cycles in, 204f
  wavelengths of light driving photosynthesis in, 167f
Alimentary canal, **692f**, 693, 698, 699f
Alkaptonuria, 235, 279
Allantois, 563f
Alleles, **217**
  alteration in frequencies of, in populations,
    413–414, 421f–424f
  behavior of recessive, 229f, 230
  combinations of, 213
  correlating behavior of chromosome pairs with,
    238, 239f
  dominant, 223f, 224
  dominant vs. recessive, 217f–218f, 228f
  evolution and genetic variation from, 212
  frequencies of, in populations, 417f–419f, 420
  genetic variation and, 210, 426–427
  homozygous vs. heterozygous organisms and, 218
  in meiosis, 205

microevolution as alteration in frequencies of, in
    populations, 413–414
  multiple, and ABO blood groups, 224, 225f
  mutations as sources of new, 248, 415–416
Allergens, 635, 746f, 747
Allergies, 746f, 747
Alliaria petiolata, 607
Alligators, 564f
Alligator snapping turtles, 871
Allohexaploid, 442, 451
Allolactose, 306
Allopatric speciation, **439**
  character displacement and, 869f
  continental drift and, 460f
  evidence of, 440f, 441
  identifying dependent and independent variables,
    making scatter plots, and interpreting data
    on, 441t
  mate choice and, 451
  process of, 439f
  sympatric speciation vs., 439f
Allopolyploids, **442f**
All-or-none responses, 779
Allosteric regulation, **137f–138f**
Alpha (α) carbon, 56
Alpha cells, 702, 703f
Alpha proteobacteria, 488f, 501–502
α-amylase, 645f
α chain, antigen, 739f
α-globin genes, 366f
α glucose ring structure, polysaccharide, 52f
α helix, 60f–61f, 103f
α-lactalbumin, 369
Alpheus genus, 440f, 441
Alpine chickweed, 925f
Alpine woodsorrel, 631f
ALS. *See* Amyotrophic lateral sclerosis
Alsomitra macrocarpa, 629f
Alternate phyllotaxy, 595
Alternation of generations, **204f**, **522f**, 523
Alternative RNA splicing, **288**, **314f**, 362
Altruism, **835f**
Alu elements, 365, 373
Aluminum, bioremediation of, 899
Alveolates, 507f, **510f**, 511, 517f, 518
Alveoli, 510f, **725f**, 727
Alzheimer's disease, 63, 355
Amacrine cells, 808f, 810
Amanita muscaria, 528f
Amazon River basin, 916f
Amborella trichopoda, 537f–538f
American beech, 923f
American pika, 924f
Amine compounds, 47f
Amino acids, **56**
  abiotic synthesis of, 475f, 476
  activation of, in translation, 290f–291f, 293f, 297f
  in anabolism, 158
  analyzing sequence data of, 67, 69
  for animal nutrition, 689f, 690
  in catabolism, 158f
  for DNA-binding regions, 71
  evolution and sequence of, 71
  evolution of human globin gene sequences of, 370
  genetic code for, 282f–284f
  neurotransmitters as, 786t
  polypeptides as polymers of, 56–58
  in protein structure, 60f
  in sickle-cell disease, 62f
  side chains (R groups) of, 57f
Amino acid sequence identity tables, 370t
Aminoacyl-tRNA synthetases, **290f–291f**, 293f
Amino end, polypeptide, 58f
Amino group, 47f, 48, 56
Aminopeptidases, 695f
Amitochondriate hypothesis, 513
Amitochondriate protists, 505
Ammonia, 30f, 37–38, 129f, 675, **678**, 679f
Ammonifying bacteria, 605f
Ammonium, 897f
Ammonium chloride, 29
Amnion, 560, 561f
Amniotes, **562**, 563f–569f

Amniotic eggs, **560**, 561f
Amoebas, 94, 183f, 507f, **511**, 513, 519
Amoebocytes, 546f, **547**
Amoeboid movement, 94
Amoebozoans, **513**, 514f
Amphibians, **561**
  circulatory systems of, 708, 709f
  gills of, 706
  parental care in, 833f
  skin as respiratory organ for, 722
  as terrestrial vertebrates, 561, 562f
Amphipathic molecules, 100
Amplification
  cancer gene, 334f, 335
  sensory, **802**
Amplification, DNA, 272, 273f
Amplification, PCR. *See* Polymerase chain reaction
Amygdala, 796f
Amylase, **693**, 695f
Amylopectin, 52
Amyloplasts, 90
Amylose, 51f, 52
Amyotrophic lateral sclerosis (ALS), 818
Anabaena, 482f
Anableps anableps, 303f
Anabolic pathways, **123**, 158
Anabrus simplex, 362t
Anacystis nidulans, 501
Anaerobic respiration, 142, 154–155, 156f–157f,
  481–**482**
  fermentation compared with, 156, 157f
Analgesics, 786
Analogies, **399f**, 400
Analogous structures, **390**
Anaphase, **185**, 186f–187f, 189f–190f, 209f
Anaphase I, 206f, 209f
Anaphase II, 207f
Anaphylactic shock, 747
Anatomical homologies, 389f, 390
Anatomy, **663**
Ancestry, common, 389f, 390, 397f, 398, 401f–402f
Anchorage dependence, 194f, **195**
Anchoring cell junctions, 96f
Androgens, 669f, 760f–761f
Anemia, 718
Anesthetics, 789
Aneuploidies, **248f–250f**
Angina pectoris, 720
Angiosperms, **533**, 619–638. *See also* Crop plants;
  Plants
  bulk flow translocation in, 616
  development of. *See* Plant development
  engineering of, 619, 633–634, 635f, 636
  evolution of, 536, 537f–538f
  evolution of organs of, 576, 577f–578f
  flowers, seeds, and fruits of, 536f, 619f–629f.
    See also Flowers; Fruits; Seeds
  gametophyte-sporophyte relationship in, 532f
  insect radiations and radiation of, 559f–560f
  life cycles of, 623f
  meristematic control of flowering of, 584
  monocot vs. eudicot, 575, 576f
  overview of structure of, 577f
  phylogeny of, 530f, 537f–538f
  as seed plants, 533
  sexual and asexual reproduction in, 630f–633f
Angiotensin converting enzyme (ACE), 685
Angiotensin II, 685
Angraecum sesquipedale, 569f
Angular motion, mechanoreceptors and, 806, 807f
Animal behaviors, 814–838
  altruism and inclusive fitness in, 835f–836f
  animal brains and, 800
  behavioral ecology and, 825
  behavioral rhythms of, 826
  experience, learning, and, 828–831. *See also*
    Learning
  fixed action patterns, 826f
  foraging, 831f, 832
  genetics and evolution of, 831f–836f
  innate, 828f
  mating and mate choice, 832f–833f
  migration, 826

Animal behaviors (*Cont.*)
 muscle function in, 815–821. *See also* Muscle
  contraction; Muscles
 nervous systems, motor systems, and, 814–815.
  See also Motor systems; Nervous systems
 sensory inputs stimulating, 825, 826*f*–827*f*, 828
 signals and communication, 826, 827*f*
 skeletal systems and locomotion in, 821*f*–824*f*, 825
 species dispersal, 852–853
Animal cells. *See also* Eukaryotic cells
 active transport in, 111
 apoptosis of, 324, 326*f*
 bioenergetics in, 140
 blood, 717*f*–719*f*
 cell cycle of, 182*f*. *See also* Cell cycle
 cell junctions in, 96*f*, 97
 cellular respiration by mitochondria of, 87–88, 89*f*
 circulatory systems, gas exchange surfaces, and, 707*f*
 cotransport in, 111–112
 cytokinesis in, 188, 189*f*, 190
 endocytosis in, 112, 113*f*
 extracellular matrix of, 95*f*, 96
 local and long-distance cell signaling of, 114*f*
 meiosis in, 206*f*–207*f*
 microtubules of, 92
 mitosis in, 185*f*–190*f*
 nuclear transplantation of differentiated, in
  cloning, 330*f*–331*f*
 organelles of, 78*f*
 plasma membranes of, 78*f*, 101*f*. *See also* Plasma
  membranes
 reproductive cloning of mammalian, 331*f*
 of sponges, 546*f*, 547
 stem cells, 332*f*–333*f*, 334
 water balance and tonicity of, 107*f*
Animalia, kingdom, 10*f*, 11, 408
Animal nutrition, **688**
 dietary requirements for, 689*f*, 690
 evolutionary adaptations for, 698*f*–700*f*
 feedback circuits in, 700, 701*f*–703*f*
 food processing, 691*f*–692*f*, 693
 organs for, 693*f*–697*f*, 698
Animal reproduction, 751–771. *See also* Human
  reproduction
 asexual, 752*f*
 asexual vs. sexual, 201*f*
 embryonic development in, 764–770
 fertilization mechanisms in, 754*f*
 hormonal regulation of mammalian/human,
  760–764
 rates of, 857
 reproductive cycles in, 753*f*
 reproductive organs in, 755–760
 sexual, as evolutionary enigma, 752*f*
 sexual life cycles in, 204*f*. *See also* Sexual life cycles
 variations in patterns of sexual, 753–754
Animals, 545–574. *See also* Birds; Eukaryotes; Fishes;
  Humans; Insects; Invertebrates; Mammals;
  Vertebrates
 anatomy-physiology correlation in, 663
 aquatic vs. terrestrial, 558*f*. *See also* Aquatic
  animals; Land animals
 bacteria mutualism with, 603*f*
 behaviors of. *See* Animal behaviors
 body plans of, 549, 550*f*
 brains of. *See* Brains
 Cambrian explosion and bilaterian radiation of,
  547, 548*f*–549*f*
 catabolism and diets of, 141*f*, 142, 157–158
 cells of. *See* Animal cells
 chitin as structural polysaccharide of, 53
 circulation and gas exchange in. *See*
  Cardiovascular systems; Circulatory systems;
  Gas exchange
 cloning of, 330*f*–331*f*
 colonization of land by, 558*f*–568*f*
 comparing genomes of, 372*f*–373*f*, 374. *See also*
  Genomes
 development processes of, 374*f*–375*f*. *See also*
  Embryonic development
 diseases and disorders of, 343*f*, 344, 351*f*, 352, 863*f*
 domain Eukarya and, 10*f*
 ecological and evolutionary effects of, 568–572

embryonic development of. *See* Embryonic
  development
 in energy flow and chemical cycling, 8*f*
 evolution of, 504*f*–505*f*
 flower pollination by, 624*f*
 in fossil record, 452, 453*f*–454*f*, 455*t*, 456, 457*f*, 548*f*
 fruit and seed dispersal by, 629*f*
 fungi mutualism with, 603*f*
 herbivore adaptations in, 387*f*, 388
 hierarchical organization of tissues, organs, and
  organ systems in, 664*t*, 665*f*
 homeostasis in. *See* Homeostasis
 immune systems of. *See* Immune systems
 interactions of, 8
 nutrition in. *See* Animal nutrition; Digestive
  systems
 origination of, in sponges and cnidarians, 545, 546*f*
 phylogeny of, 550, 551*f*
 plant defenses against herbivory by, 658
 plant interactions with, 541, 542*f*
 plant mutualism with, 603*f*
 in predation. *See* Predation
 radiations of aquatic, 549, 550*f*–557*f*. *See also*
  Aquatic animals
 reproduction of. *See* Animal reproduction
 saturated and unsaturated fats of, 54*f*
 storage polysaccharides of, 51*f*, 52
 Unikonta supergroup and, 512, 513*f*–514*f*
 viruses affecting, 347, 348*f*–352*f*, 353–354
Anions, **29**, 110–111
Ankle bones, 390*f*
Annelids, 548*f*, 551*f*–552*f*, 707*f*, 708, 821, 822*f*
Annuals, plant, 584
Anolis lizards, 868*f*
Anomalocaris, 548*f*
Anopheles mosquitoes, 517*f*, 518
Anorexia nervosa, 690
Anser anser, 829*f*
Antagonistic functions, autonomic nervous
  system, 793
Antagonistic interactions, 855
Antagonistic muscle pairs, 821*f*
Antarctica, trophic structure in, 875, 876*f*
Antarctic Circle, 842*f*
Antennae, mechanoreceptors and, 804
Anterior ends, **550***f*
Anterior pituitary gland, 669*f*, **671**, 672*f*, 760–764, 768
Anthers, 536*f*, **620***f*
Anthoceros, 531*f*
Anthozoa, 547*f*
Anthrax, 489*f*
Anti-aging, plant cytokinins in, 644
Antibiotic drugs
 bacterial infections and, 291
 bacterial resistance to, 388*f*, 389, 485–486, 492, 570
 for cystic fibrosis, 230
 as enzyme inhibitors, 136
 gram-positive bacteria and, 489*f*
 peptidoglycan and, 479
 prokaryotic ribosomes and, 481
 viruses and, 351
Antibodies, **738**
 antigen recognition by, 738*f*
 in B cell and T cell diversity, 739, 740*f*
 binding of, to proteins, 59*f*
 in humoral immune response, 743*f*–744*f*
 in medical diagnosis and treatment, 746
 role of, in immunity, 745–746
Anticodons, 289*f*–**290***f*
Antidiuretic hormone (ADH), 669*f*, 670–671, 684, 685*f*
Antifreeze proteins, 657
Antigen fragments, 739*f*
Antigenic determinant, **737**
Antigenic variation, 747–748
Antigen presentation, **739**
Antigen-presenting cells, **742**, 743*f*
Antigen receptors, 737, 738*f*–739*f*
Antigens, **737**
 helper T cells as responses to, 742, 743*f*
 recognition of, by B cells and T cells, 737, 738*f*–739*f*
 variations in, and immune system evasion, 747–748
Antihistamines, 746
Antimicrobial peptides, 736

Antiparallel DNA backbones, **66***f*, 256*f*, **258***f*–259
Antivenin, 746
Antiviral drugs, 351
Ants, 22*f*, 394, 559*f*, 603*f*, 629*f*, 872*f*
Anus, 692*f*–693*f*, 698, 766*f*, 767
Anvil (incus), 805*f*
Apes, 566, 567*f*
Aphelocoma californica, 800
Aphids, 410
Aphotic zone, **849***f*
Apical buds, 577*f*, **578**
Apical dominance, **586**, 643–644
Apical meristems, 522*f*, **523**, **582**, 583*f*, 661
Apical surface, epithelial, 665*f*
Apicomplexans, 517*f*, 518
Apicoplast, 517*f*, 518
Apis mellifera, 827*f*
Apomixis, **630**, 636
Apoplast, 596*f*
Apoplastic transport route, 596*f*, 609*f*, 618
Apoptosis, **324**, 326*f*
 cancer and, 195
 p53 gene and, 336*f*
 as plant response to flooding, 655–656, 657*f*
 plant senescence and, 647
 role of, in proper functioning, 341
Aposematic coloration, **870**, 871*f*
Appendages, arthropod jointed, 553
Appendix, **697***f*, 716*f*
Appetite, 703, 704*t*
Apple fruit, 628*f*
Apple maggot fly, 436*f*, 442–443
Aquaporins, **105**, 598–**599**, **682**
 in facilitated diffusion, 108
 in kidney function, 683*f*
 in passive transport, 106
 in plasma membrane selective permeability, 100*f*
Aquatic animals, 549, 550*f*–557*f*. *See also* Animals
 body plans of, 549, 550*f*
 diversification of, 550, 551*f*
 gills for gas exchange in, 723*f*
 radiation of invertebrate, 551*f*–554*f*
 radiation of vertebrate, 554, 555*f*–557*f*
 terrestrial animals vs., 558*f*
Aquatic biomes, 849*f*–851*f*, 852
 climate influences of, 843, 844*f*, 849
 coral reefs, 851*f*
 decomposition and nutrient cycling rates in, 895
 food chains and webs in, 875*f*–876*f*
 intertidal zones, 850*f*
 inverted biomass pyramids of, 894*f*
 lakes, 850*f*
 locomotion in, 824
 photosynthetic protists in, 515*f*, 516
 primary production in, 890, 891*ft*
 streams and rivers, 850*f*
 wetlands and estuaries, 849*f*
 zonation in, 849*f*
Aquatic lobe-fin, 558*f*
Aqueous humor, 808*f*
Aqueous solutions, 36–37, 106
Arabidopsis thaliana (mustard plant), 583–584
 ABC hypothesis and, 621*f*
 altering gene expression by touch in, 654*f*
 carotenoid-biosynthesis enzymes of, 410
 genetic engineering of herbivore defenses in, 658
 genome size of, 362*t*
 photoreceptors of, 649, 650*f*
 stem elongation of, 645
 triple response in, 647*f*
Arachnids, 552*f*
Arbuscular mycorrhizae, **527***f*–528*f*, **606**, 607*f*
Archaea, **11**. *See also* Archaea, domain; Prokaryotes
 cells of. *See* Prokaryotic cells
 eukaryotic features derived from, 500*t*
 genome size and number of genes in species of,
  362*t*, 363
 membrane lipid composition in, 102
Archaea, domain, 10*f*, 11. *See also* Archaea
 compared to Bacteria and Eukarya, 487*t*
 evolutionary relationships of, 372*f*
 horizontal gene transfer and, 409*f*, 410
 phylogeny of, 487, 490

Archaean eon, 455*t*
Archaefructus sinensis, 536, 537*f*
Archaeoglobus fulgidus, 362*t*
Archaeplastida, 506*f*–507*f*, **511**, 512*f*
Archenteron, 766*f*, 767
Arctic, tundra in, 848*f*, 902*f*–903*f*
Arctic Circle, 842*f*
Arctic fox, 886*f*, 902*f*
Arctic sea ice, climate change effects on, 923
Ardipithecus ramidus, 567*f*
Area effects, 882*f*
Arginine, 57*f*, 279*f*–280*f*
Argyroneta aquatica, 732
Arid conditions, plants and, 175*f*, 176, 592
Ariolimax californicus, 834–835
Aristotle, 380
Arizona, desert biome in, 847*f*
Arms, chromatid, 184
Arms race, evolutionary, 569
Artemia, 467*f*
Arteries, **708**, 709*f*, 713*f*–714*f*, 715, 720
Arterioles, 708, 713*f*, 714*f*, 715
Arthropods, **553**
   appearance of, 548*f*, 551*f*
   chitin as structural polysaccharide of, 53
   compound eyes of, 808*f*
   diversity of, 552*f*
   exoskeletons of, 822
   general characteristics of, 559*f*
   insects as, 559*f*–560*f*
   nervous systems of, 791*f*
   origins of, 553*f*–554*f*
   skeletal muscles of, 821
Artificial selection, **385***f*, 386, 619, 633*f*, 634
Ascocarps, 528*f*
Ascomycetes, 528*f*
Asexual reproduction, **201**, 630, **752**
   allocation of energy in, 632
   angiosperm, 630*f*–633*f*
   chromosome behavior in, 252
   disease and, 213
   fungal, 529*f*, 530
   mechanisms of, 752
   reproductive cycles in, 753
   sexual reproduction vs., 201*f*, 213, 630–631, 752*f*.
      See also Sexual reproduction
   of single-cell eukaryotes, 190
Asian climbing gourd, 629*f*
Asian elephants, 384*f*, 385
Asian ladybird beetles, 385*f*
A site (aminoacyl-tRNA binding site), **291***f*, 293*f*
Asparagine, 57*f*
Aspartic acid, 57*f*
Aspen trees, 593, 630*f*
Aspidoscelis uniparens, 753*f*
Aspirin, 803
Assembly stage, phage lytic cycle, 345*f*
Associative learning, **830**, 831*f*
Asteroid collision, mass extinction from, 461*f*–462*f*
Asters, **185**, 186*f*
Asthma, 716
Astragalus bones, 390*f*
Astrocytes, 791*f*, 792
Atherosclerosis, 55, 112, 719, 720*f*
Athletes, blood doping by, 718
Atmosphere
   Cambrian explosion and changes to Earth's, 548
   carbon dioxide (CO_2) concentrations in, 515,
      613–614, 635, 921, 922*f*, 924*f*, 926, 931
   Earth's early, 475–477*f*, 478
   greenhouse effect of, 922, 923*f*
Atomic mass, **24**
Atomic nucleus, **24**
Atomic number, **24**
Atoms, 23–31
   atomic number and atomic mass of, 24
   electron distribution of, and chemical properties
      of, 26*f*, 27
   energy levels of electrons of, 25*f*, 26
   formation and function of molecules by chemical
      bonding of, 27–31
   isotopes of, 24, 25*f*

subatomic particles of, 24*f*
   tracking, through photosynthesis, 163, 164*f*
ATP (adenosine triphosphate), **48**, **128**
   aminoacyl-tRNA synthetases and, 290*f*
   anaerobic respiration synthesis of, 154–155,
      156*f*, 157
   in bioenergetics, 140
   catabolic pathways synthesis of, 142, 143*f*–144*f*, 145
   cellular respiration production of, 141*f*
   chemiosmosis synthesis of, 151*f*–152*f*
   citric acid cycle production of, 148*f*–149*f*
   conversion of, to cyclic AMP, 118, 119*f*
   dietary requirements for synthesis of, 689,
      700, 701*f*
   as energy for active transport, 109, 110*f*
   fermentation synthesis of, 154–155, 156*f*, 157
   glycolysis production of, 146*f*–147*f*
   mitochondria and, 87–88, 97
   in muscle contraction, 816*f*, 817
   nucleotides and, 263
   as organic phosphate compound, 48
   oxidative phosphorylation synthesis of, 145*f*, 146
   phosphofructokinase and, 160
   in plant cells, 179*f*
   regeneration of, 130*f*
   regulation of regeneration of, 137
   structure and hydrolysis of, 128*f*–130*f*
   substrate-level phosphorylation synthesis of, 146*f*
   synthesis of, by cellular respiration. *See* Cellular
      respiration
   synthesis of, in light reactions of photosynthesis,
      164, 170*f*–173*f*, 176, 177*f*
   types of work and energy coupling by, 128
   yield of, in cellular respiration, 153*f*, 154
   yield of, in fermentation, 156*f*
ATP cycle, 130*f*
ATP synthase, **151***f*–152*f*, 173*f*
   evolution of, 160
   pH and, 181
Atria, heart, **708**, 709*f*, 710*f*–711*f*
Atrioventricular (AV) node, **712***f*
Atrioventricular (AV) valve, **711***f*
Attachment function, membrane protein, 103*f*
Attachment stage, phage lytic cycle, 345*f*
Auditory canal, 805*f*
Auditory communication, 827
Auditory cortex, 799*f*
Auditory nerve, 805*f*, 806
Australia, 390*f*, 852, 870
Australian moles, 399*f*, 400
Autism, 801
Autoimmune diseases, 747*f*
Autonomic nervous system, vertebrate, **793**
Autophagy, 86*f*
Autopolyploids, **442***f*
Autosomes, **203**
Autotrophs, **161**, 481*t*, 490, 666*f*, 888–889. *See also*
      Primary producers
Auxin, **642***f*
   in cell differentiation, 644
   in cell elongation, 642, 643*f*
   discovery of, 640, 641*f*
   in leaf abscission, 647, 648*f*
   overview of, 642*t*
   in plant development, 643–644
   in plant gravitropism, 654*f*
   polar transport of, 643*f*
   practical uses of, 644
Avery, Mary Ellen, 725–726
Avery, Oswald, 254
Avian brains, 800
Avian flu, 354, 883–884
AV node. *See* Atrioventricular (AV) node
Avogadro's number, 37
AV valve. *See* Atrioventricular (AV) valve
Axel, Richard, 803
Axillary buds, 577*f*, **578**
Axis establishment, 328*f*–329*f*
Axolotl salamanders, 466*f*, 706*f*
Axons, **773**
   in central nervous systems, 792
   evolution of structure of, 782*f*

in nervous system signaling, 668*f*
   nervous tissue and, 665*f*
   structure and function of, 773*f*
Azidothymidine (AZT), 351
Azolla, 603*f*
AZT. *See* Azidothymidine
Azure vase sponge, 546*f*

B
Bacilli, 478*f*
Bacillus anthracis, 489*f*
Bacillus thuringiensis, 634
Backbones
   nucleic acid, 65*f*, 66, 256*f*, 258*f*–259*f*
   polypeptide, 58*f*, 60*f*–61*f*
Bacteria, **11**. *See also* Bacteria, domain; Prokaryotes
   alcohol fermentation by, 156*f*
   anaerobic respiration in, 155
   animal mutualism with, 603*f*
   antibiotic drugs and infections by, 291
   antibiotic resistance in, 388*f*, 389, 485–486,
      492, 570
   bioremediation using, 901*f*
   cells of. *See* Prokaryotic cells
   chromosomes and binary fission in, 190, 191*f*
   diversity of, 874*f*
   in DNA cloning, 270
   DNA packing in chromosomes of, 267
   DNA replication in, 260, 261*f*–265*f*
   in energy flow and chemical cycling, 8*f*
   eukaryotic features derived from, 500*t*
   evidence that DNA can transform, 254*f*
   fungi mutualism with, 603*f*
   gene expression in, 281*f*. *See also* Bacterial gene
      regulation
   genome size and number of genes in species of,
      362*t*, 363
   Gram staining of, 478, 479*f*
   horizontal gene transfer and, 409*f*, 410, 484, 492
   infection by, 356
   inhabiting human bodies, 474, 475*f*
   innate immunity and, 734, 735*f*–736*f*, 737
   macrophages and, 97*f*, 733*f*
   membrane lipid composition in, 102
   mutualistic, 491–492
   mutualistic, in digestion, 698, 699*f*
   origin of mitochondria and plastids in,
      500*ft*–502*f*, 503
   origins of photosynthesis in, 162
   pathogenic, 492*f*
   in Permian mass extinction, 461
   phage defense of, 347*f*
   as photoautotrophs, 162*f*
   photosynthetic. *See* Cyanobacteria
   phylogeny of, 487, 488*f*–489*f*
   plant nutrition and soil, 604*f*–606*f*
   reproduction rate of, 496
   root communities of, 604*f*
   size of, 496
   synthesis of multiple polypeptides during
      translation in, 296*f*
   transcription in, 284–285
   viral infections of. *See* Phages
Bacteria, domain, 10*f*, 11. *See also* Bacteria
   compared to Archaea and Eukarya, 487*t*
   evolutionary relationships of, 372*f*
   genome size and number of genes for, 362*t*
   horizontal gene transfer and, 409*f*, 410
   phylogeny of, 487, 488*f*–489*f*
Bacterial gene regulation. *See also* Gene regulation
   negative, 305, 306*f*, 307
   operon model of, 304, 305*f*
   positive, 307*f*
   regulation of metabolic pathways in, 304*f*
Bacteriophages (phages). *See* Phages
Bacteriorhodopsin, 103*f*
Bacteroides thetaiotaomicron, 492
Bacteroids, **606**
Baculum, 757
Baker, C. S., 398*f*
Balance
   locomotion and, 824*f*
   mechanoreceptors for hearing and, 804*f*–807*f*

Balancing selection, **426**, 427*f*
Balanus balanoides, 869*f*
Ball-and-socket joints, 823*f*
Ball-and-stick models, 30*f*, 44*f*
Banana, 213
Banana slugs, 834, 835
Bangiomorpha, 498*f*–499*f*
Barbiturates, 83
Bar graphs in Scientific Skills Exercises and Scientific
        Skills Review, 18*f*, 155*t*, 313*f*, 325*f*, 392*f*, 493*t*,
        570*f*, 582*t*, 656*f*, 870*t*, F-2*f*
Bark, 590*f*, **591**
Barley, 645*f*
Barnacles, 869*f*
Barr, Murray, 241
Barr body, **241**–242
Barrier defenses, immune system, 733, 734*f*, 735
Barrier methods, contraceptive, 769*f*
Basal animals, 547, 551
Basal body, **92**, 93*f*
Basal lamina, epithelial, 665*f*
Basal-like breast cancer, 339*f*
Basal metabolic rate (BMR), 702
Basal nuclei, 795*f*
Basal taxon, 397*f*, **398**
Base pairing, nucleic acid, 66*f*, 258*f*–259*f*, 260*f*–261*f*
Bases, **37**–39
    nitrogenous, 65*f*–66*f*
Basic amino acids, 58
Basic side chains, 57*f*
Basidiomycetes, 528*f*, 529
Basilar membrane, 805*f*, 806
Basophils, 717*f*–718*f*
Batesian mimicry, 870, 871*f*, 885
Bats, 399–400, 466*f*, 624*f*, 824, 908*f*
B cells, **737**
    antigen recognition by, 737, 738*f*
    development of, 739, 740*f*–742*f*, 750
    in humoral immune response, 743*f*–744*f*
    T cells and, 718*f*
Bdellovibrios, 488*f*
Beach mouse, 2*f*, 16*f*–17*f*
Beadle, George, 279–280
Beagle, Charles Darwin's voyage on HMS, 382*f*, 383
Beaks
    finch, 13*f*, 17, 383*f*, 413*f*
    soapberry bug, 387*f*, 388
Beans, 626*f*, 627*f*, 651*f*
Bears, 124*f*, 438*f*
Beavers, 877*f*
Bed bugs, 559*f*
Beech tree, 923*f*
Bees, 559*f*, 624*f*, 827*f*
Beetles, 385*f*, 573, 624*f*
Behavior, **814**. *See also* Animal behaviors
Behavioral ecology, **825**
Behavioral isolation, 436*f*
Belding's ground squirrels, 835, 855, 856*ft*, 857
Belostoma, 755*f*
Beluga whales, 803*f*
Benign tumors, **195***f*, 196–197
Bennettitales, 537*f*
Bentgrass, 636
Benthic zone, **849***f*–851*f*
Benthos, **849**
Benzene, 45*f*
Beta-carotene, 634, 635*f*, 690
Beta cells, 702, 703*f*
Beta oxidation, **158**
Beta proteobacteria, 488*f*
β chain, antigen, 739*f*
β-galactosidase, 306
β-globin, 69, 302, 366*f*
β glucose ring structure, polysaccharide, 52*f*
β pleated sheet, protein, 60*f*–61*f*
BGI (formerly Beijing Genome Institute), 359
Bicarbonate, 695, 701*f*, 705
Bicarbonate ions, 39*f*, 40, 670
Biceps, 821*f*
Bicoid protein, 329*f*
bicoid gene, 328*f*–329*f*, 375
Biennials, plant, 584
Bilateral symmetry, 326–327, 541, 549, 550*f*

Bilaterians, **548**, 551. *See also* Invertebrates;
        Vertebrates
    in animal phylogeny, 551
    Cambrian explosion and origins of, 548, 549*f*
    in predation, 569*f*–571*f*
    tissue layers in, 550*f*
Bilayers, phospholipid. *See* Phospholipid bilayers
Bile, **696**, 701*f*
Binary fission, 190, 191*f*, 482, 483*f*, 484
Binding sites, ribosome, 291*f*, 293*f*, 294
Binomial names (taxonomy), 380, **396**
Biochemistry, 75. *See also* Chemistry
Biodiversity. *See also* Species diversity
    from adaptive evolution by natural selection, 466
    branching phylogeny and, 571
    effects of adaptive radiations on, 463*f*–464*f*, 465
    effects of mass extinctions on, 461*f*, 462, 463*f*
    evolution of, 379–380, 384
    human welfare and, 908–909
    landscape and regional conservation for, 915,
        916*f*–918*f*, 919, 931
    levels of, 907*f*–908*f*
    sustainable development in conservation
        of, 928, 929*f*
    threats to, 907*f*–911*f*, 931
Biodiversity hot spot, **917***f*
Bioenergetics, **123**, 140, **700**, 701*f*, 702–703. *See also*
        Energy; Energy flow
Biofilms, **482**
Biofuels, **635**
Biogenic amines, 786*t*
Biogeochemical cycles, **895**, 896*f*–897*f*, 898, 905
Biogeographic factors, community diversity effects of,
        881*f*–882*f*
Biogeography, 391–392
    island, 882*f*
Bioinformatics, **8**, 67, **357**
    centralized resources for, 359, 360*f*
    genomics, proteomics and, 8, 67–68*f*
    genomics and, 357. *See also* Genomics
    protein structure and function and, 63
    proteomics, systems biology, medicine, and, 361
    understanding functions of protein-coding genes
        in, 359–360
    understanding genes and gene expression in,
        360–361
Biological augmentation, **901**
Biological clocks, 650, 651*f*, **796**. *See also* Circadian
        rhythms
Biological Dynamics of Forest Fragments
        Project, 916*f*
Biological magnification, **920***f*–921*f*
Biological molecules
    carbohydrates, 49–53. *See also* Carbohydrates
    genomics and proteomics in study of, 68*f*
    lipids, 53*f*–55*f*. *See also* Lipids
    nucleic acids, 64*f*–66*f*. *See also* Nucleic acids
    as organic compounds and macromolecules, 43,
        48–49. *See also* Organic compounds
    proteins, 55, 56*f*–63*f*. *See also* Proteins
    shape and function of, 30*f*–31*f*
Biological species concept, **435***f*–438*f*
Biology, **2**
    behavioral ecology in, 825. *See also* Animal
        behaviors
    biogeography in, 391–392. *See also* Species
        distributions
    cells in. *See* Cells
    connection of chemistry and. *See* Chemistry
    conservation biology in, 882
    cytology and biochemistry in, 75
    demography in, 856*ft*, 857
    evolution as core theme of, 2, 9, 10*f*–13*f*. *See also*
        Evolution
    genetics in, 6*f*–7*f*, 200. *See also* Bioinformatics;
        Genetics; Genomics
    genomics and proteomics in, 68*f*
    island biogeography in, 882*f*
    metagenomics in, 486
    molecular genealogy and molecular, 67
    radioactive isotopes in, 25*f*
    science and inquiry in, 13–19. *See also* Research
        methods; Science; Scientific skills

systematics and taxonomy in, 396*f*–398*f*, 404*f*.
        See also Systematics; Taxonomy
    themes of, 3–9. *See also* Life
Bioluminescence, 122*f*, 491*f*
Biomanipulation, **877***f*
Biomass, **635**, **875**
    in secondary production, 892, 893*f*
    standing crop measure of, 889
    total accumulation of, 890
Biomass pyramid, 894*f*
Biomes, **844**. *See also* Aquatic biomes; Biosphere;
        Ecosystems; Terrestrial biomes
    aquatic. *See* Aquatic biomes
    climate influences on distribution of, 844,
        845*f*–848*f*
    disturbances of, 845
    terrestrial. *See* Terrestrial biomes
Biophilia, 908, 929*f*
Bioremediation, 23, **494***f*, 891, **899**, 900*f*–901*f*
Biosphere, **4***f*, 490, 491*f*, **841***f*. *See also* Biomes;
        Ecosystems
    future of, 929*f*
Biosynthesis, 123, 158, 689*f*, 700, 701*f*, 702
Biotechnology. *See also* Genetic engineering
    organismal cloning, 330*f*–334*f*
    plant, 634, 635*f*, 636
    prokaryotes in, 492, 493*f*–494*f*
Biotic factors, **843**
    in community equilibrium, 878
    in pollination, 624*f*
    population effects of, 854, 855*f*–856*ft*, 857
    in species distributions, 843, 853*f*
Biotic interactions. *See* Interactions, ecological
Biotic stresses, plant responses to, **655**, 657, 658*f*–660*f*
Bipedal animals, 824
Bipolar cells, 808*f*, 810
Birds, 563, 564*f*–565*f*
    applying parsimony in molecular systematics
        of, 404*f*
    avian flu and, 354, 883–884
    bats vs., 399–400
    breathing by, 726
    as descended from dinosaurs, 405*f*–406*f*
    digestive system of, 692*f*
    double circulation in, 709–710
    evolution of brains and cognition in, 800
    field research on, by Charles Darwin, 382*f*, 383*f*
    flower pollination by, 449*f*, 624*f*
    gene flow in great *Parus major*, 424*f*
    genetic drift in greater prairie chickens, 422, 423*f*
    kidney adaptations of, 684
    learning by, 829, 830*f*
    locomotion of, 824
    natural selection in, 12, 13*f*, 17, 413*f*
    problem solving of, 831
    production efficiency of, 893
    structure and function correlation in, 3
    unity and diversity among, 11*f*
Birth control. *See* Contraception, human
Birth control pills, 769*f*
Birth rates, 902*f*
    demographics and, 856*ft*, 857
    of human population, 927*f*
    population change and, 862, 864*f*
    population dynamics and, 855*f*
    population growth and, 857–858
    regulation of, 862*f*
Biscuit star, 125*f*
Bitter tastants, 803, 804*f*
Bivalves, 553*f*, 822
Black rush plants, 872
Black snakes, 870
Blades, **509***f*
    leaf, 577*f*, **578**
Blarina brevicauda, 883*f*
Blastocoel, **766***f*
Blastocysts, 332*f*, 767*f*
Blastopore, 766*f*, 767
BLAST program, 359
Blastula, 764, **766***f*
Blebbing, 326*f*
Blending hypothesis in heredity, 214

Blindness, 422, 489*f*, 690
color, 811
Blind spot, 808*f*
Blood, 707*f*, **708**. *See also* Blood pressure; Blood vessels
ABO blood groups for human, 104, 224, 225*f*, 746
apoptosis of human white blood cells of, 326*f*
cell division of bone marrow cells and, 182, 183*f*
in closed circulatory systems, 707*f*–709*f*, 710
clotting of, 241, 718, 719*f*
components of, 717*f*
composition and function of, 717*f*–720*f*
connective tissue of, 665*f*
countercurrent exchange and fish, 723*f*
flow velocity of, 713, 714*f*
gas exchange adaptations of, 728*f*–729*f*, 730
hemophilia and clotting of, 241
immune rejection of transfusions of, 746
osmolarity of, 684
pH of human, 38*f*, 39
processing of filtrate from, by kidneys, 682, 683*f*
sickle-cell disease and, 428*f*–429*f*
volume and pressure of, in kidney regulation, 685
Blood-brain barrier, 792
Blood doping, 718
Blood flukes, 872
Bloodhound, 813
Blood poisoning, 488*f*
Blood pressure
in cardiovascular systems, 714, 715*f*
in circulatory systems, 708–709
hypertension and, 720
kidney homeostasis and, 685
temporal changes in, 732
Blood proteins, 60*f*–61*f*
Blood types, human, 104, 224, 225*f*, 746
Blood vessels
adaptations of, for thermoregulation, 675, 676*f*
blood flow velocity in, 713, 714*f*
blood pressure in, 714, 715*f*
capillary function, 715
in circulatory systems, 707*f*, 708
diseases of, 719, 720*f*
structure and function of, 713*f*
Blooms, 510, 515
algal, 890, 920
phytoplankton, 919*f*, 920
Blowflies, 619
Blueberry maggot fly, 436*f*
Blue crab, 885
Blue-footed boobies, 436*f*
Bluehead wrasse, 753–754
Blue jays, 830, 831*f*
Blue-light photoreceptors, **649**, 651
Blue whales, 398*f*
BMR. *See* Basal metabolic rate
Bobcat, 666*f*
Bodies, animal, 664*t*, 665*f*, 822
Body cavities, animal, **550**
Body fat, 703
Body hairs, insect, 804
Body plans, **549**
animal, 549
apoptosis and, 324, 326*f*
arthropod, 553
fungal, 526*f*
homeotic genes and, 374*f*–375*f*
macroevolution of, from changes in developmental genes, 465*f*–468*f*
pattern formation and, 326, 327*f*–329*f*
symmetry, tissues, and body cavities in animal, 549, 550*f*
unity and diversity of bird, 11*f*
Bohr shift, **729***f*
Boletus edulis, 525*f*
Bolting, 644, 645*f*
Bolus, **693**–694
Bombina, 444*f*, 445–446
Bonasa umbellus, 916
Bonding, parental, 829
Bone cells, 332*f*
Bone marrow, 182, 183*f*, 332*f*, 737

Bones. *See also* Skeletal systems
endoskeletons of, 822, 823*f*
for flight, 565*f*
human middle ear, 805*f*, 806
of human skeleton, 822, 823*f*
Bonneia, 499*f*
Bonnemaisonia hamifera, 512*f*
Bonobo, 373
Boquila trifoliata, 639*f*
Borisy, Gary, 189*f*
Borrelia burgdorferi, 489*f*, 492*f*
Botox, 786
Bottleneck effect, 422*f*–423*f*
Bottlenose dolphins, 796*f*
Bottom-up model, **877**
of trophic control, 877
Botulism, 116, 346, 489*f*, 492, 786
Boundaries
community, 867
ecosystem, 886, 887*f*, 916
population, 854
Bound ribosomes, 82*f*, 295*f*
Boveri, Theodor, 236
Bowman's capsule, **681***f*, 682
Boysen-Jensen, Peter, 640, 641*f*
Brachiopods, 548*f*, 551*f*
Braconid wasp, 872
Bradybaena, 436*f*
Brainbow technology, 790*f*
Brain cancer, 196, 361
Brains, **772**
arousal and sleep functions of, 793, 796*f*
biological clock regulation by, 796
breathing control centers in human, 727*f*, 728
in central nervous systems, 791, 792*f*
cerebral cortex functions in, 798, 799*f*–801*f*
drug addiction and reward system of, 797, 798*f*
evolution of cognition in, 799, 800*f*
frontal lobe function in, 799*f*
functional brain imaging of, 793*f*
information processing by, 799
language and speech functions of, 798, 799*f*
lateralization of cortical function in, 798
limbic system of, and emotions, 796*f*
mammalian, 773*f*
memory and learning in, 801
neuronal plasticity of, 800*f*, 801
neurons in, 772, 773*f*–774*f*. *See also* Neurons
opiate receptors in mammalian, 786–787
organization of human, 794*f*–795*f*
sensory systems and, 801–811. *See also* Sensory systems
size of, 573
songbird vs. human, 800*f*
stem cells of, 332
strokes in, 720
structure of human, 794*f*–795*f*, 800*f*
vertebrate, 793–801
visual information processing in, 810, 811*f*
Brainstem, 794*f*–795*f*
Brain waves, 796*f*
Branching
carbon skeleton, 45*f*
plant stem, 524, 586, 595
surface area and, 526*f*
Branching evolution, 471
Branch length, phylogenetic tree, 402*f*–404*f*, 405
Branch points, phylogenetic tree, **397***f*, 398
Brassinosteroids, 642*t*, 645
Brazil nut trees, 861*f*
BRCA1 and *BRCA2* genes, 337, 338*f*–339*f*, 340
Bread mold, 279*f*–280*f*
Breakdown pathways, 123
Breast cancer, 195*f*, 337, 338*f*–339*f*, 340
Breasts, human, 757
Breathing, **726***f*–727*f*, 728
gait and, 573
Breathing control centers, 727*f*, 728
Breeding, 385*f*, 386, 619, 633*f*, 855
Brewer's yeast, 863*f*. *See also Saccharomyces cerevisiae*
Briggs, Robert, 330
Brightfield microscopy, 74*f*
Brine shrimp, 375*f*, 467*f*

Broadleaf tree, 161*f*
Broca, Pierre, 798
Broca's area, 798, 799*f*
Bronchi, **724**, 725*f*
Bronchioles, 725*f*
Brooding, 405*f*–406*f*
Brown algae, **509***f*, 510
Brown bears, 124*f*
Brown fat, 154
Brown-headed cowbird, 916, 931
Brown tree snake, 910
Brundtland, G. H., 908
Brush border, 696
Bryophytes, **530***f*–531*f*
Bryozoans, 552*f*
Bt toxin, 634
Bubo scandiacus, 863*f*
Buchloe dactyloides, 595
Buck, Linda, 803
Budding, 78*f*, 201*f*, 210, 752
Buffalo grass, 595
Buffers, **39**
Bufo marinus, 870
Bugs, 559*f*
Bulbourethral glands, 756*f*
Bulk feeders, 691*f*
Bulk flow, vascular plant, **599**, 610, 611*f*, 612, 616
Bulk transport, 112, 113*f*
Bumblebees, 449*f*
Bundle-sheath cells, 175*f*, 587*f*
Burgess Shale fossil bed, 453*f*
Burkholderia glathei, 491*f*
Burkitt's lymphoma, 340
Butane, 45*f*
Butterflies, 252, 472, 559*f*, 624*f*, 635–636, 830, 831*f*, 864*f*

C
C. *See* Calorie
C₃ plants, **175**
C₄ plants, **175***f*
Cactus, 614*f*, 624*f*, 847*f*
Cactus-eater finches, 383*f*
Caddisflies, 472
Cadherins, 504, 505*f*
Caecilians, 561, 562*f*
Caenorhabditis elegans, 326, 360, 362*t*
cal. *See* Calorie
Calcification, 40
Calcitonin, 669*f*
Calcium, 23*t*
dietary requirements for, 690
Calcium carbonate, 39*f*, 40
Calcium ions, 83–84, 118, 783, 817*f*–818*f*, 820–821
California, chaparral biome in, 847*f*
California Current, 844*f*
California mouse, 828*t*
Callus, **632**
Callyspongia plicifera, 546*f*
Calmodulin, 820–821
Calorie (cal), **34**, 701. *See also* Kilocalorie
Calvin, Melvin, 164–165
Calvin cycle, **164**. *See also* Photosynthesis
evolution of alternative mechanisms of, 175*f*, 176
overview of, 165*f*, 174*f*, 177*f*
phases of, 173, 174*f*
as stage of photosynthesis, 164, 165*f*
Cambrian explosion, 466, 499*f*, **547**–557
Camouflage, 16*f*–17*f*, 386*f*, 870, 871*f*
CAM (crassulacean acid metabolism) plants, 175*f*, **176**, 614*f*, 615
cAMP (cyclic adenosine monophosphate), **118**, 119*f*, **307***f*, 785
cAMP receptor protein (CRP), 307*f*
Campylobacter, 488*f*
Canada goose, 676*f*
Canadian Forest Service, 895*f*
Cancer
biodiversity benefits for treatment of, 909
brain cancer, 196, 361
breast cancer, 195*f*, 337, 338*f*–339*f*, 340
carcinogen screening and, 300
cell-signaling pathways, 335*f*–336*f*

Cancer (*Cont.*)
    chromosomal translocations and, 250, 251*f*
    contributing to, 337, 340
    development of, from abnormal cell cycle control, 334*f*–339*f*, 340
    DNA mismatch repair and colon, 265
    evolutionary processes of, 341
    genomics, cell signaling and, 338*f*–339*f*
    genomics and proteomics in study and treatment of, 68*f*
    HIV and, 747
    immunity and, 748–749
    interpreting histograms on inhibition of cell cycle of, 196*f*
    loss of cell cycle controls in, 194*f*–195*f*, 196–197
    multistep model of development of, 336, 337*f*
    protein kinases in, 118
    radioactive isotopes in PET scans for, 25*f*
    skin, 266
    systems biology approach to, 361
    telomeres and treatment of, 267
    types of genes associated with, 334*f*, 335
Cancer Genome Atlas, 361
Cane toads, 870
Canis, 451
Canopy, **846**
Canyon tree frog, 871*f*
Capillaries, 677*f*, **708**, 709*f*, 713*f*–714*f*, 715, 728*f*
Capillary beds, 708, 713*f*–714*f*, 715
Capsaicin, 803
Capsids, **343***f*, 344
Capsomeres, 343
Capsule, 76*f*, **479***f*
Carbohydrates, **49**
    catabolism of, 142, 157, 158*f*
    digestion of, 695*f*
    membrane, 101*f*, 104
    monosaccharide and disaccharide sugars, 49, 50*f*–51*f*
    as organic compounds and macromolecules, 43
    as polymers of monomers, 48–49
    polysaccharides, 51*f*–52*f*, 53
    as product of photosynthesis, 177
    types of, 49
Carbon
    as essential element, 23*t*
    isotopes of, 24–25, 454
    in organic compounds, 43*f*–45*f*. *See also* Organic compounds
Carbon-12, 454
Carbon-14, 454
Carbonate ions, 40
Carbon cycle, 540, 896*f*, 903*f*
Carbon dioxide (CO₂)
    aerobic respiration and, 142, 666*f*
    in alternative carbon fixation mechanisms, 175*f*, 176
    atmospheric concentration of, 177, 515, 613, 635, 921, 922*f*, 924*f*, 926, 931
    in capillaries, 715
    carbon bonds in, 45
    in carbon cycle, 896*f*
    in circulation and gas exchange, 707. *See also* Circulatory systems; Gas exchange
    in citric acid cycle, 148*f*–149*f*
    in climate change, 515–516
    effects of atmospheric, on crop productivity, 176
    effects of removal of, by plants, 540
    gas exchange adaptations for transport of, 729–730
    greenhouse effect of, 922, 923*f*
    inhibition of fruit ripening with, 648
    in interspecific interactions, 8, 9*f*
    in mammalian cardiovascular systems, 710*f*
    in methane combustion, 142, 143*f*
    net ecosystem production and, 890
    in ocean acidification, 39*f*, 40
    in photosynthesis, 31, 32*f*, 161, 163, 164*f*–165*f*
    in plant cells, 179*f*
    in regulation of human breathing, 727*f*, 728
    rubisco as acceptor for, in Calvin cycle, 174*f*, 175
    as stimulus for stomatal opening and closing, 613
    and stomatal density, 613

Carbon fixation, **165**, 174*f*–175*f*, 176
Carbonic acid, 38–40
Carboniferous period, 533, 535, 540*f*
Carbon monoxide, 787
Carbon skeletons
    of fatty acids, 53*f*
    molecular diversity of, 45*f*–46*f*
    of steroid lipids, 55*f*
    of sugars, 50
Carbonyl group, 47*f*, 48, 50*f*
Carboxyl end, polypeptide, 58*f*
Carboxyl group, 47*f*, 48, 53, 56
Carboxylic acid, 47*f*
Carboxypeptidases, 695*f*
Carcinogens, 300. *See also* Cancer
Carcinus maenas, 570
Cardiac cycle, **711***f*, 714, 732
Cardiac muscle, 665*f*, **820**
Cardiovascular diseases, 719–721, 769
Cardiovascular systems, **708**. *See also* Circulatory systems
    blood composition and function in, 717*f*–720*f*
    blood vessels, blood flow, and blood pressure in, 712, 713*f*–716*f*
    coordination of gas exchange and, 728*f*. *See also* Gas exchange
    gas exchange adaptations in, 728*f*–729*f*, 730
    hearts in mammalian, 710, 711*f*–712*f*
    human diseases of, 719–721, 769
    lymphatic systems and, 715, 716*f*
    single and double circulation in vertebrate, 708, 709*f*, 710
Caribou, 417*f*, 753, 902*f*–903*f*, 925*f*
Carnivora, 10
Carnivores, 397*f*, **688**
    alimentary canals of, 698, 699*f*
    dentition and diet of, 698*f*
    in ecosystem trophic structure, 888
Carnivorous plant, 607, 608*f*
Carotenoids, 167*f*, **168**, 410
Carpellate flowers, 631*f*
Carpels, 215*f*, **536***f*, **620***f*
Carrier crabs, 867*f*
Carrier proteins
    in cotransport, 111*f*
    in facilitated diffusion, 108*f*
    as transport proteins, 105
Carriers, **229***f*
Carroll, Scott, 387*f*
Carrot plants, 330
Carrying capacity, 858, **859***f*, 860
    global, 927, 928*f*
Carson, Rachel, 920, 921*f*
Cartilage, 822
Cartilage fish, 557
Cas9 protein, 347, 493*f*. *See also* CRISPR-Cas systems
Casparian strip, 609*f*, **610**
Cassava, 634, 635*f*
Castor bean seeds, 626
Catabolic pathways, **123**. *See also* Cellular respiration
    ATP production and, 142
    cellular respiration as, 123
    redox reactions of, 142, 143*f*–144*f*, 145
    versatility of, 157, 158*f*
    water production in, 565*f*
Cataglyphis, 663*f*
Catalysis, **132**
Catalysts, **55**, **131**. *See also* Enzymatic catalysis
Catalytic cycle, 133*f*, 134
Caterpillars, 379, 415*f*, 559*f*, 658*f*, 661
    production efficiency of, 892, 893*f*
Cation exchange, **602***f*
Cations, **29**, 110–111
Cats, 235, 241, 242*f*, 302, 331*f*, 802
Catskill Mountains, 909
Cattle egrets, 873*f*
Caulerpa, 512*f*
Cavalier-Smith, Thomas, 513*f*
Cavendish banana, 213
Cave painting, 929*f*
CC (Carbon Copy, cloned cat), 331*f*
CCD protein domain, 505*f*

CCK. *See* Cholecystokinin
CDD. *See* Conserved Domain Database
cDNA. *See* Complementary DNA
Cecum, **697***f*
Cedar Creek Ecosystem Science Reserve, 875*f*
Celera Genomics, 358
Cell body, neuron, 773*f*, 784*f*
Cell-cell recognition, 103*f*, 104
Cell cycle, **182**–198
    bacterial binary fission in, 190, 191*f*
    cancer development from abnormal regulation of, 334*f*–339*f*, 340
    cytokinesis in, 188, 189*f*, 190
    depolymerization of kinetochore microtubules during, 189*f*
    determining phase of, arrested by inhibitor, 196
    evolution of mitosis in, 191*f*
    genetic material and cell division process in, 182, 183*f*–184*f*
    phases of, 185*f*–191*f*
    phases of, in animal cells, 186*f*–187*f*
    phases of, in plant cells, 189*f*–190*f*
    regulation of, by cell cycle control system, 192*f*–195*f*, 196–197
Cell cycle control system, **192**
    cancer development from abnormal, 334*f*–339*f*, 340
    checkpoints of, 192*f*–194*f*, 195
    evidence for cytoplasmic signals in, 192*f*
    loss of, in cancer cells, 195*f*, 196–197
    regulation of cell division by, 192
Cell cycle–inhibiting pathway, 336*f*
Cell cycle–stimulating pathway, 335*f*
Cell differentiation. *See* Differentiation, cellular
Cell division, **182**. *See also* Cell cycle
    bacterial fission, 190, 191*f*
    cancer development and, 334*f*–339*f*, 340
    cytokinins and, 644
    DNA replication in, 6*f*
    effects of platelet-derived growth factor on, 194*f*
    embryonic development and, 322*f*
    environment and mutations in, 277
    evolution of mitosis in, 191*f*
    fluorescence micrographs of, 182*f*
    genetic material and, 182, 183*f*–184*f*
    in meiosis, 205*f*–209*f*, 210
    in mitosis, 208, 209*f*, 210
    time required for human, 185
Cell fractionation, **75**
Cell junctions, 96*f*, 97, 103*f*
Cell-mediated immune response, 734*f*, 742*f*–745*f*, 750
Cell plate, 189*f*, **190**
Cells, 5*f*, 72–99. *See also* Animal cells; Plant cells
    apoptosis (programmed death) of, 324, 326*f*
    auxin in differentiation of, 644
    auxin in elongation of, 642, 643*f*
    cell cycle of. *See* Cell cycle
    cellular integration of, 97*f*
    cellular respiration and fermentation by. *See* Cellular respiration; Fermentation
    climate change effects on, 924*f*
    cytokinins in division and differentiation of, 644
    differentiation of. *See* Differentiation, cellular
    eukaryotic vs. prokaryotic, 75, 76*f*–77*f*. *See also* Eukaryotic cells; Prokaryotic cells
    evolution of, 72, 99
    as fundamental units of life, 3–4, 72
    in hierarchy of biological organization, 5*f*
    locations of enzymes in, 138*f*
    metabolism of. *See* Metabolism
    microscopy and biochemistry in study of, 73*f*–75*f*
    pH of, 39
    photosynthesis by. *See* Photosynthesis
    plasma membranes of. *See* Plasma membranes
    prokaryotic, as Earth's first, 474*f*
    protein synthesis in, 64*f*
    protocells as first, 475, 476*f*
    in sickle-cell disease, 428*f*–429*f*
    size range of, 73*f*
    surface-to-volume ratios of, 77*f*
    using scale bars to calculate volume and surface area of, 80
    viral infections of, 342*f*. *See also* Viruses
    water balance of, 106*f*–108*f*

INDEX

Cell sap, 86
Cell signaling, 114f–119f
  cancer development from interference with, 335f–336f
  in cell cycle control system, 192–197
  cilia and, 92
  in endocrine signaling, 668f–673f
  extracellular matrix in, 95–96
  genomics, cancer and, 338f–339f
  induction in, 323f
  local and long-distance, 114f
  membrane proteins in, 103f
  plant responses to. See Plant responses
  receptor proteins and reception stage of, 115f–117f
  response stage of, 119f
  three stages of, 115f
  transduction stage of, 117, 118f–119f
Cell-type specific transcription, 312f
Cellular innate immune defenses, 735f, 736
Cellular membranes. See also Plasma membranes
  of chloroplasts, 89f, 90
  internal eukaryotic, 77
  of mitochondria, 88, 89f
  movement across, 179f
  in plant response to cold stress, 657
  specialized prokaryotic, 480, 481f
  synthesis of, by rough ER, 84
  vesicles and, 82–83
Cellular respiration, 141–154, 142. See also Metabolism
  anaerobic respiration compared with, 154
  ATP production by, 141f
  ATP yield during, 153f, 154
  as catabolic pathway, 123
  catabolic pathways of, 142
  citric acid cycle, 145f, 148f–149f
  diffusion in, 106
  energy flow and chemical recycling in, 141f
  fermentation compared with, 154
  glucose in, 50
  glycolysis, 145f–147f
  mitochondria in, 77, 87, 88, 89f
  overall reaction for, 126
  oxidative phosphorylation, 145f, 146, 149, 150f–153f, 154
  photosynthesis vs., 163, 164
  in plant cells, 179f
  pyruvate oxidation, 148f
  redox reactions of, 142, 143f–144f, 145
  in secondary production, 892, 893f
  stages of, 145f–146f
  thyroid hormone and, 155, 155t
Cellular slime molds, 513, 514f
Cellulose, 52
  in cell walls, 94
  digestion of, 699
  in digestive system, 697
  as hydrophilic substance, 36–37
  as product of photosynthesis, 177
  proteins synthesizing, 521f
  as storage polysaccharide, 51f
  as structural polysaccharide, 52f
Cellulose synthase, 94
Cell walls, 94
  cellulose-synthesizing proteins and, 521f
  functions of, 94f, 95
  in plants, 79f, 178f
  prokaryotic, 76f, 478, 479f, 480
  protistan, 79f
  water balance and, 107f, 108
Cenozoic era, 455t, 460f
Central America, deforestation in, 909
Central canal, central nervous system, 792
Central dogma, DNA, 281
Centralized resources, genomic, 359, 360f
Central nervous system (CNS), 774, 791
  neuronal plasticity of, 800f, 801
  neurotransmitters and, 785–786
  peripheral nervous systems and, 791, 792f
  sensory systems and, 801f, 802. See also Sensory systems
  vertebrate, 791f–792f
Central vacuoles, 79f, 86f, 87

Centrifuges, 75
Centrioles, 92f, 185
Centromeres, 184f, 186f
Centromeric DNA, 365
Centrosomes, 78f, 92f, 185f–189f, 206f
Centrostephanus rodgersii, 925f
Cephalization, 791
Cephalocereus senilis, 614f
Cercozoans, 511f
Cerebellum, 794f–795f, 799f
Cerebral cortex, 795f, 798–801, 811f
Cerebral hemispheres, 795f, 813
Cerebral palsy, 795f
Cerebrospinal fluid, 727f, 792
Cerebrum, 794f–795f
Certainty of paternity, 832, 833f
Cervix, 757f
Cetaceans, 390f, 391
Chameleon, 545f
Chamois, 690f
Chance, natural selection and, 431
Channel proteins, 105, 108f. See also Aquaporins
Chaparral, 847f
Character displacement, 869f, 885
Characters, 215
  construction of phylogenetic trees from shared, 401f–406f
  genetic variation of phenotypic, 414f–415f
  multifactorial, 226
  taxonomy and, 397
  traits and, 215
Character tables, 402f
Chargaff, Erwin, 256–257
Chargaff's rules, 256, 258–259
Charophytes, 512, 521f
Chase, Martha, 255–256
Checkpoints, cell cycle control system, 192f–194f, 195
Cheetahs, 863f
Chemical bonds, 27–32
  covalent bonds, 27f–28f
  hydrogen bonds, 30f
  ionic bonds, 29f
  making and breaking of, by chemical reactions, 31–32
  molecular shape and function from, 30f–31f
  van der Waals interactions, 30
  weak, 30
Chemical cycling
  biogeochemical cycles in, 895, 896f–897f, 898, 905. See also Biogeochemical cycles
  as biological theme, 8f
  decomposition effects on rate of, 895f
  deforestation effects on, 898f, 899
  in ecosystems, 141f, 903f
  effects of plants and fungi on, 539f–540f
  energy flow and, in ecosystems, 886–887, 888f. See also Energy flow
  in Hubbard Brook Experimental Forest, 898f, 899
  physical laws governing, 887
  prokaryotic, 490, 491f
  trophic levels and, 888f
Chemical digestion, 691. See also Digestion; Digestive systems
  in human digestive system, 695f
  in small intestine, 695f, 696
  in stomach, 694f
Chemical energy, 123
  conversion of, by mitochondria, 88, 89f. See also Cellular respiration
  conversion of light energy to, by chloroplasts, 89–90, 162, 163f–165f. See also Photosynthesis
  diet and, 689f, 690
  in energy flow and chemical cycling, 8f. See also Energy flow
Chemical equilibrium, 32, 125, 126f–127f, 128
Chemical groups, 46, 47f–48f
Chemical mutagens, 300
Chemical reactions, 31
  activation energy barrier of, 131f, 132
  in aqueous solutions, 37
  chemical energy in, 123
  free energy and, 126f
  functional groups in, 48

making and breaking of chemical bonds by, 31–32
  metabolism and, 122
  in photosynthesis, 163, 164f
Chemical recycling. See Chemical cycling
Chemical signaling
  extracellular matrix in, 95–96
  neurons and, 772. See also Chemical synapses; Neurons
Chemical signals, plant, 658f
Chemical structure, DNA, 258f
Chemical synapses, 783–787
  generation of postsynaptic potentials at, 784
  modulated signaling at, 784–785
  neurotransmitters and, 783f, 784, 785, 786t, 787
  overview of, 783f
  summation of postsynaptic potentials at, 784f, 785f
Chemical work, 128, 129f, 130
Chemiosmosis, 151
  ATP yield during, 153f
  in cellular respiration, 145, 145f
  in chloroplasts vs. in mitochondria, 171f–173f
  in light reactions of photosynthesis, 164
  in oxidative phosphorylation, 151f–152f, 153
Chemistry, 22–42
  atomic structure and properties of elements in, 23–27
  connection of biology and. See Biology
  formation and function of molecules through chemical bonding of atoms in. See Molecules
  hydrogen bonding and properties of water in, 32–40. See also Water
  making and breaking of chemical bonds through chemical reactions in, 31–32
  matter as pure elements and compounds, 22–23
  organic compounds in. See Organic compounds
Chemoautotrophs, 481t, 851f, 889
Chemoheterotrophs, 481t
Chemoreceptors, 803, 804f
Chemosynthetic organisms, 886–887, 888f
Chemotaxis, 480
Chemotherapy, 196
Chemotrophs, 481t
Chen caerulescens, 569f
Chesapeake Bay, 885
Chestnut blight, 541, 660
Chiasmata, 206f, 208f
Chicxulub crater, 462f
Chief cells, 694f
Childbirth, human, 768
Chimpanzees (Pan troglodytes)
  comparison of chromosome sequences of humans and, 367
  comparison of human genome with genome of, 372–373
  complete genome sequence for, 357f
  heterochrony and growth rates in skulls of, 465f
  HIV in, 407
  as humans closest relative, 567
  observations of, by Goodall, 13, 14f
  problem solving by, 831
  skulls of humans vs., 399–400
Chips, human gene microarray, 361f
Chi-square (χ^2) test, 246
Chitin, 53, 525, 822
Chlamydia, 489f, 770
Chlamydomonas, 79f, 503f, 504, 512
Chlorarachniophytes, 502, 511
Chloride cells, 678
Chloride ions, 775t
Chloride transport channels, cystic fibrosis and, 230
Chlorine, 23f, 29f
Chlorophyll, 89, 162–163, 166, 167f–170f, 889f
Chlorophyll a, 166, 167f–170f
Chlorophyll b, 166, 167f–168f
Chlorophytes, 512
Chloroplasts, 87
  chemiosmosis in, 153
  chemiosmosis in, vs. in mitochondria, 171f–173f
  endosymbiont theory on evolutionary origins of, 88
  energy transformation in, 179f
  genes of, 181

INDEX

Chloroplasts (*Cont.*)
light reactions in thylakoids of, 165*f*
in photosynthesis, 3, 87, 89*f*, 162, 163*f*, 177*f*, 179*f*
pigments of, 166, 167*f*–168*f*
plant cell, 79*f*
protistan cell, 79*f*
transgenic crops and DNA in, 636
Chlorosis, 600
Choanocytes, 546*f*, **547**
Choanoflagellates, 504*f*–505*f*, 514
Cholecystokinin (CCK), 701*f*
Cholera, 116, 488*f*, 492
Cholesterol, **55**
in cardiovascular diseases, 719, 720*f*, 721
effects of, on membrane fluidity, 102
of egg yolks, 71
in plasma membranes, 101*f*
receptor-mediated endocytosis of, 112
as steroid lipid, 55*f*
Chondrichthyans, 556*f*, **557**
Chondromyces crocatus, 488*f*
Chordates, 548*f*, 551*f*, **553**–554, 822
Chorion, 560, 561*f*
Choroid, 808*f*
Chromatids, 184*f*, 203*f*, 205*f*–209*f*, 210–211, 212*f*
Chromatin, **81, 183, 267**
animal cell, 78*f*
cell division and, 183*f*–184*f*
in cell nucleus, 81*f*, 82
packing of, in chromosomes, 267, 268*f*–269*f*
plant cell, 79*f*
regulation of structure of, 309*f*
remodeling of, by noncoding RNAs, 316
in reproductive cloning, 331
Chromium, bioremediation of, 901
Chromoplasts, 90
Chromosomal alterations, 248*f*–251*f*
abnormal chromosome numbers, 248*f*–250*f*
of chromosome structure, 249*f*
human disorders due to, 249, 250*f*–251*f*
Chromosomal basis of inheritance, 236–252
behavior of chromosomes as physical basis of Mendelian inheritance in, 236*f*–239*f*
chromosomal alterations as cause of genetic disorders in, 248*f*–251*f*
constructing linkage maps in, 247*f*
determining gene linkage using chi-square (χ^2) test in, 246
evolution of gene concept from, 300
genes on chromosomes as Mendel's hereditary factors, 236
linked genes and linkage in, 242*f*–247*f*, 248
sex-linked genes in, 239, 240*f*–242*f*
Chromosomes, **81, 183**
alterations of, and genetic disorders, 248*f*–251*f*
bacterial, 76*f*
bacterial binary fission and, 190, 191*f*
behavior of, as physical basis of Mendelian inheritance, 236*f*–239*f*. See also Chromosomal basis of inheritance
behavior of, in human life cycle, 203*f*, 204
in cancer cells, 195–197
cell division and distribution of, 183*f*–184*f*, 186*f*
in cell nucleus, 81*f*, 82
in cells, 75
correlating behavior of alleles with pairs of, 238, 239*f*
DNA molecules in, 64
as DNA molecules packed with proteins, 267, 268*f*–269*f*
duplication and alteration of, in genome evolution, 367*f*–369*f*
fluorescence micrographs of, 182*f*, 236*f*
genetic variation from mutations in, 416
genetic variation from sexual reproduction and homologous, 416
independent assortment of, 211*f*
inheritance of genes in, 201
locating genes along, 236, 236*f*
mapping distance between genes on, 245–246, 247*f*, 248
Mendel's model and, 217
movement of, on kinetochore microtubules, 188*f*, 189*f*, 198

number of, in human cells, 183, 184*f*
in plant mitosis, 190*f*
preparing karyotypes of, 202*f*
in prokaryotic cells, 480, 481*f*
prokaryotic genetic recombination and, 484*f*–485*f*, 486
recombinant, 211, 212*f*
reduction of number of, by meiosis, 205*f*
sets of human, 202*f*–203*f*
sex. See Sex chromosomes
in sexual reproduction, 213
in sickle-cell disease, 428*f*–429*f*
structure of, and inheritance, 252
triploid, 213
Chromosome theory of inheritance, **236***f*–239*f*. See also Chromosomal basis of inheritance
Chronic inflammation, 737
Chronic myelogenous leukemia (CML), 250, 251*f*
Chthamalus stellatus, 869*f*
Chylomicrons, **697***f*
Chyme, **694**–695, 701*f*
Chymotrypsin, 695*f*
Chytrids, 528*f*
Chytriomyces, 528*f*
Cichlid fish, 443*f*, 446
Cigarette smoke, 337, 340, 769
Cilia, **92**, 510*f*
bronchial, 725
mechanoreceptors and, 802, 804*f*
as microtubule-containing cellular extensions, 92–93
structure of, 93*f*
Ciliates, 497*f*, **510***f*, 511, 519
Circadian rhythms, **613**, 650, **651***f*, 796, 826
Circannual rhythms, 826
Circulatory systems, 707*f*–720*f*
adaptations of, for thermoregulation, 675, 676*f*
blood composition and function in, 717*f*–720*f*
blood vessels, blood flow, and blood pressure in, 712, 713*f*–716*f*
cardiovascular diseases of, 719, 720*f*, 721
cells and exchange surfaces of, 707*f*–709*f*, 710
coordination of gas exchange and, 728*f*
evolutionary variation in, 709–710
gas exchange adaptations in, 728*f*–729*f*, 730
gas exchange and, 706, 708, 709*f*, 710, 720–730.
See also Gas exchange
genetic factors in cardiovascular disease of, 721.
See also Cardiovascular diseases
hearts in mammalian double circulation, 710, 711*f*–712*f*
mammalian, 664*t*
cis face, Golgi apparatus, 84*f*, 85, 87*f*
cis-retinal, 809*f*, 810
Cisternae, Golgi apparatus, 84*f*, 85
Cisternal maturation model, 84*f*, 85
cis-trans isomers, 46*f*
Citric acid cycle, **145***f*, 148*f*–149*f*
in anabolic pathways, 158
ATP yield during, 153*f*, 154
in catabolic pathways, 157, 158*f*
in cellular respiration, 145*f*, 148*f*–149*f*
Citrulline, 280*f*
Clades, **401***f*
Cladistic analysis, Darwin and, 412
Cladistics, **401***f*–402*f*
Clams, 821, 822, 885
Clark's nutcracker, 830
Classes (taxonomy), **396***f*. See also Taxonomy
Classification. See Taxonomy
Classification of life, E-1*f*, E-2*f*
Clausen, Jens, 866
Claw-waving behavior, 814*f*, 826
Clear cutting, 542*f*
Cleavage, 188, 189*f*, 190, 764–**765**, 766*f*, 767
Cleavage furrows, 187*f*, 188, 189*f*, 190
Clements, F. E., 878
Climate, **843**. See also Climate change
community equilibrium and, 878
continental drift and changes in, 460
effects of large bodies of water on, 34*f*, 843, 844*f*, 849
global patterns of, 842*f*–843

latitudinal gradients of species diversity and, 881*f*
mass extinctions and changes in, 462*f*
physical components of, 842*f*–843*f*
primary production in terrestrial biomes and, 891, 892*f*
regional effects of, 843*f*–844*f*
terrestrial biome distribution and, 844, 845*f*–848*f*
using dendrochronology to study changes in, 590
Climate change, 9*f*, **921**–926
biofuels and, 634–635
biological effects of, 922, 923*f*–925*f*, 926
continental drift and, 460
deforestation and, 926
effects of, on amphibians, 562
effects of, on caribou, 753, 925*f*
effects of, on coral reefs, 851*f*, 926
effects of, on kelp, 925*f*
effects of, on lizards, 9*f*
effects of, on marine producers, 516*f*
effects of, on pikas, 924*f*
effects of, on pine trees, 924*f*
effects of, on tundra, 903*f*, 923
effects of plants on, 177, 540
extinction rates and, 462*f*
fossil fuels and, 181, 634–635, 924*f*, 926
greenhouse gases and, 921, 922*f*–924*f*, 926
habitat loss and, 909
human interaction and, 8–9
Make Connections Figure, 924*f*–925*f*
ocean acidification and, 39*f*, 40, 42
in Permian mass extinction, 461
plant adaptations to, 176
solutions for, 926
using dendrochronology to study, 590
Climate science. See Climate change
Climate warming. See Climate change
Climax communities, 878
Climographs, **845***f*
Clitoris, **757***f*, 763–764
Cloaca, **755**
Clocks
biological. See Biological clocks
molecular. See Molecular clocks
Clonal selection, **741***f*
Clones, **201**. See also DNA cloning; Gene cloning; Organismal cloning
asexual reproduction and, 201
meaning of term, 330
plant cuttings as, 632
plant fragmentation and, 630*f*
plant test-tube or *in vitro*, 632, 633*f*
Cloning vectors, DNA, **271**
Closed circulatory systems, 707*f*, **708**, 709*f*, 710.
See also Cardiovascular systems
Clostridium botulinum, 489*f*, 492
Clostridium difficile, 492
Club fungi, 528*f*
Club mosses, 531*f*, 532
Clumped dispersion, 855*f*
Clutch size, 861
Cnemaspis psychedelica, 906*f*
Cnidarians, 546, 547*f*–548*f*, 550*f*–551*f*, 821, 822*f*, 824
nerve nets of, 790, 791*f*
CNS. See Central nervous system
CNVs. See Copy-number variants
CO_2. See Carbon dioxide
Coastal Japan restoration project, 900*f*
Coat coloration, mouse, 2, 16*f*–17*f*, 18
Coated pits, endocytosis and, 113*f*
Coat proteins, 113*f*
Cocci, 478*f*
Coccosteus cuspidatus, 453*f*
Cochlea, **805***f*, 806
Cochlear duct, 805*f*
Cocklebur, 652*f*, 653
Cocktails, drug, 351, 416
Coconut, 629*f*
Cod, 570, 571*f*
Coding strands, DNA, 282
Codominance, **224**
Codon recognition stage, translation elongation cycle, 293*f*

I-9   INDEX

Codons, **282**
  anticodons and, 289*f*–290*f*
  genetic code and, 282*f*–284*f*, 302
Coefficient of relatedness (r), **835**, 836*f*
Coelacanths, 556*f*, 557
Coelom, 550
Coenzyme, as essential nutrient, 689*f*
Coenzyme Q (CoQ), 150*f*, 160
Coenzymes, **135**
Coevolution, **625**
Cofactor, as essential nutrient, 689*f*
Cofactors, **135**
Cognition, 798, 799*f*–800*f*, **830**–831. *See also* Cerebral cortex
Cognitive maps, **830***f*
Cohesins, 184, 187*f*, 208*f*
Cohesion, **33***f*, 612
Cohesion-tension hypothesis, **610**, 611*f*, 612
Cohorts, **856**
Coitus, 763–764. *See also* Sexual intercourse, human
Coitus interruptus, 756, 769*f*
Cold
  plant response to, 657
  thermoreceptors and, 803
Cold viruses, 344
Coleochaete orbicularis, 521*f*
Coleoptile, **626***f*–627*f*, 640, 641*f*
Coleorhiza, **626***f*
Collagen, 61*f*, **95***f*, 369
Collapses, of populations, 864*f*
Collar cells, sponge, 547
Collecting ducts, **681***f*, 683*f*, 687
Collenchyma cells, **580***f*, 588
Colon, **697**–698, 699*f*
Colon cancer, 265
Colonial organisms, 547*f*
Colonies, multicellular, 503*f*
Colonization of land. *See* Land animals; Plants; Fungi
Coloration
  guppies, 392
  mate choice by, 443*f*
  predation and, 2, 16*f*–17*f*, 18, 870, 871*f*, 885
Color blindness, 240, 241*f*, 252, 811
Colorectal cancer, 336, 337*f*
Color vision, 811
Columbine flower, 624*f*
Comamonas testosteroni, 501
Combinatorial gene activation control, 312*f*
Comet collision, mass extinction from, 461*f*–462*f*
Commensalism, **491**, 528*f*, **872**, 873*f*
Common arrowhead (*Sagittaria latifolia*), 631*f*
Communicating cell junctions, 96*f*
Communication. *See also* Cell signaling; Language
  animal, **827**, 828*f*
  animal nervous system, 668*f*
  between drought-stressed plants, 656
  between herbivore-stressed plants, 658
  by neurons, 772. *See also* Neurons
Communities, 4*f*, **841***f*, **867**–885, 902*f*–903*f*
  biogeographic factors affecting, 881*f*–882*f*
  bottom-up and top-down controls in, 877*f*, 885
  climate change effects on, 925*f*
  community ecology and, 883*f*, 884
  comparing genomes of human, 374
  disturbances in, 878, 879*f*–881*f*
  ecological interactions between species in, 867*f*–873*f*. *See also* Interactions, ecological
  in hierarchy of biological organization, 4*f*
  interspecific interactions in, 867*f*–873*f*
  metagenomics and genome sequencing of, 358
  pathogens in, 883*f*, 884
  scientific, 18–19
  species diversity and trophic structure in, 873, 874*f*–877*f*, 878, 885
  species with large impact on, 876*f*–877*f*
  stability of, 875*f*, 878
Community ecology, **841***f*, 883*f*, 884
Companion cells, **581***f*
Competition, 902*f*–903*f*
  as density-dependent population regulation mechanism, 863*f*
  interspecific, **868***f*–869*f*
  in population dynamics, 862, 864*f*

sexual, 427*f*, 430*f*, 833*f*
  in theory of evolution by natural selection, 11*f*–12*f*
  uniform dispersion and, 855
Competitive exclusion, **868**
Competitive inhibitors, **136***f*
Complementary base pairing, nucleic acid, 66*f*. *See also* Base pairing, nucleic acid
Complementary DNA (cDNA), **317**
  DNA microarray assays and, 318, 319*f*
  reaction (RT-PCR) and, 317*f*–318*f*
Complement system, **736**, 744
Complete digestive tract, 692*f*
Complete dominance, **223**–224
Complete flowers, **620***f*. *See also* Flowers
Complete growth medium, 279*f*
Complex camera lens-type eye, 469*f*
Complex eyes, 469*f*
Compound eyes, 808*f*
Compounds, **23**. *See also* Organic compounds
  in aqueous solutions, 36*f*
  dissolving of, in aqueous solutions, 36–37
  emergent properties and elements in, 23
  isomers of, 46*f*
  pure elements vs., 28
Compromises, evolutionary, 431*f*
Computational tools, 357–361. *See also* Bioinformatics
Computer model, ribosome, 291*f*
Concentration, chemical reactant, 32
Concentration gradients, **106**
  cotransport down, 111*f*, 112
  diffusion down, 105, 106*f*
  electrochemical gradients as, 110*f*, 111
Conception, human, **767***f*, 768
Condoms, 769*f*
Conduction, 675*f*, 781*f*
Cones, 808*f*–**809***f*, 810
Cone snails, 772*f*
Confocal light microscopy, 74*f*, 75
Conformers, **673***f*
Congenital disorders, 202*f*
Coniferous forests, climate change effects on, 923, 924*f*, 926
Conifers, **535***f*
Conjugation, prokaryotic, 484*f*, 485–486
Conjunctiva, 808*f*
Connective tissue, 61*f*, **665***f*
Connell, Joseph, 869*f*
Conodonts, 555
Consanguineous mating, human, 229–230
Conservation biology, 864, 882, **906**–931
  biodiversity threats in, 907*f*–911*f*, 931
  dealing with human-caused rapid changes in, 919*f*–925*f*, 926
  genomics and proteomics in, 68*f*
  human population growth in, 926*f*–928*f*
  landscape and regional conservation in, 915, 916*f*–918*f*, 919, 931
  population conservation in, 912*f*–915*f*
  sustainable development in, 928, 929*f*
Conservation of energy, 124*f*, 887
Conservation of mass, 887
Conservative model, DNA replication, 260*f*–261*f*
Conserved Domain Database (CDD), 360*f*
Constant (C) region, antigen, 738*f*–739*f*
Constipation, 697
Consumers, 903*f*
  in ecosystem trophic structure, 875*f*, 888*f*
  in energy flow and chemical cycling, 8*f*
  producers and, 161. *See also* Producers
Consumption, regulation of, 703–704
Contact, animal fertilization, 765*f*
Continental drift, 391–392, 458*f*–460*f*
Contraception
  environmental toxins resulting from, 921*f*
  human, 756, 768, 769*f*
  human population growth and, 927*f*
Contractile proteins, 56*f*
Contractile vacuoles, **86**, 107*f*
Contraction, muscle. *See* Muscle contraction
Contrast, microscope, 73
Control center, homeostatic, 674
Control elements, **310***f*–312*f*, 313

Control groups, 16–17
Controlled experiments, **16**–17
Conus geographus, 772*f*
Convection, 675*f*
Convergent evolution, **390**, 395*f*, 399*f*, 400
Cooksonia, 524*f*
Cooling, evaporative, **35**
Cooper, Vaughn, 483*f*
Cooperation, metabolic, 482*f*
Cooperativity, **137***f*–138
Coordinately controlled genes
  bacterial, 304, 305*f*
  eukaryotic, 312–313
Coprophagy, 699, 700*f*
Copulation, human, 763–764, 767*f*–769*f*, 787
Copy-number variants (CNVs), 374
CoQ. *See* Coenzyme Q
Coral reefs, 40, 516, **851***f*, 883, 926
  loss of, 910
Corepressors, **305***f*–306*f*, 307
Cork cambium, **582***f*, 583*f*, 588, 591
Cormorant, flightless, 434
Corn (*Zea mays*, maize), 235
  action spectrum for, 649*f*
  artificial selection of, 633*f*
  complete genome sequence for, 357, 362*t*
  cytokinin in, 644
  health of transgenic Bt, 635
  mineral deficiency in, 600*f*
  precocious germination in, 646*f*
  response of, to flooding and oxygen deprivation, 657*f*
  seed germination of, 627*f*
  seed structure of, 626*f*
  transposable elements and, 364*f*
Cornea, 808*f*
Corn smut fungus, 541*f*
Coronary heart disease, 54
Corpus callosum, **795***f*, 798
Corpus luteum, **759***f*, 768
Correlation, form-function, 3, 663
Correlations, positive and negative, 632
Corridor, movement, **916**, 917*f*
Cortex, plant, **579**, 585*f*, 586, 588*f*
Cortical nephrons, 681*f*
Cortical reaction
  animal fertilization, 765*f*
  human fertilization, 767*f*
Corylus avellana, 624*f*
Corynebacterium diphtheriae, 76*f*
Costa Rica
  sustainable development in, 928–929
  tropical rain forest biome in, 846*f*
  zoned reserves in, 918*f*
Cotransport, 111*f*, 112
Cotransport proteins, 111*f*, 112
Cotton, 36–37
Cottongrass, 902*f*
Cotyledons, 575, 576*f*, 625*f*–627*f*
Coughing, 693
Counseling, genetic, 231–232, 235
Countercurrent exchange, **676***f*, 723*f*
Countercurrent multiplier system, **684**
Courtship behaviors. *See also* Mating
  behavioral isolation and, 436*f*
  external fertilization and, 754
  forms of animal communication in, 826, 827*f*
  sexual selection and, 427*f*, 430*f*
  sexual selection and female mate choice in, 833*f*
Covalent bonds, **27***f*–28*f*, 44*f*–46*f*, 61*f*
Cowbirds, 916, 931
Cows, 52–53, 331, 355, 700*f*
Coyotes, 451, 698, 699*f*
Crabs, 688*f*, 814*f*, 826, 867*f*, 885
Cranes, 829*f*
Crassulacean acid metabolism (CAM) plants, 175*f*, **176**, 614*f*, 615
Crawling, 821, 822*f*, 824
Crayfish, 804
Creatine phosphate, 816*f*, 817
Creeping juniper, 535*f*
Crenarchaeota clade, 490–491

Cretaceous mass extinction, 461*f*–462*f*, 463*f*
Creutzfeldt-Jakob disease, 355
Crick, Francis
    central dogma concept and, 281
    discovery of DNA molecular structure by, 253*f*, 257–259
    model of DNA replication of, 259*f*, 260, 261*f*
    reductionism of, 3
Crickets, 362*t*
Cri du chat, 250
CRISPR-Cas systems, 274, 275*f*, 347*f*, 493*f*
Cristae, mitochondrial, **88**, 89*f*
Critical load, **919**
Critical night length, plants and, 652*f*, 653
Crocodiles, 405*f*–406*f*, 563, 564*f*
Crohn's disease, 737
Crop, of digestive system, 692*f*
Crop plants. *See also* Agriculture; Angiosperms
    artificial selection and breeding of, 619, 633*f*, 634
    biodiversity benefits for, 908
    biotechnology and genetic engineering of, 634, 635*f*, 636
    determining effects of atmospheric carbon dioxide on productivity of, 176
    eudicots as, 538*f*
    nutrient enrichment caused by, 919*f*, 920
    polyploidy in, 442
    prokaryotes in disease-suppressive soil and, 493
    soil fertilization for, 601, 863*f*, 892, 897*f*
    viral diseases and, 354*f*
Cross-fostering studies, **828**
Crossing over, **206*f*, 244**
    evolution and, 252
    gene duplication due to unequal, 368*f*
    for genotype determination, 235
    in meiosis, 206*f*, 208*f*
    recombinant chromosomes from, in sexual life cycles, 211, 212*f*
    in recombination of linked genes, 244, 245*f*
Cross-pollination (crossing), 215*f*–216*f*, 634
CRP. *See* cAMP receptor protein
Crustaceans, 375*f*, 467, 558*f*
Crustose lichens, 539*f*
Cryphonectria parasitica, 541
Cryptic coloration, **870**, 871*f*
Cryptochromes, 649
Crypts, 614*f*
Crystallin, 312*f*, 320
Crystalline ice, 35*f*–36
Crystallin proteins, formation of, 7*f*
Ctenophora, 551*f*
C-terminus, 58*f*, 103*f*, 292
ctr mutants, ethylene and, 647*f*
Cucurbita pepo, 538*f*
Culex pipiens, 424
Culture, 830, 831*f*
Cupula, 806, 807*f*
Curl cat, 235
Currents, ocean, 843, 844*f*
Curvularia, 544
Cuscuta, 608*f*
Cuticle
    arthropod, **559**, 822
    plant, **523**, **578**
Cuttings, plant, 632, 644
Cuvier, Georges, 381
Cyanide, 635*f*
Cyanobacteria
    as bacterial group, 489*f*
    chemical cycling by, 490
    in eutrophication, 891, 920
    fossils of, 477*f*, 478
    in marine ecosystems, 568*f*, 569
    metabolic cooperation in, 482*f*
    origin of photosynthetic plastids in, 502*f*, 503
    as photoautotrophs, 162*f*
Cycas revoluta, 535*f*
Cyclical data, 922
Cyclic AMP (cyclic adenosine monophosphate, cAMP), **118**, 119*f*, **307*f***, 785
Cyclic GMP, 810*f*
Cycling, chemical. *See* Chemical cycling

Cyclins, 193
Cyclohexane, 45*f*
Cynodonts, 457*f*, 463*f*, 469
Cysteine, 47*f*, 57*f*
Cystic fibrosis, 225, **230**, 235
Cytochromes, **150**, 150*f*, 152*f*, 171*f*–173*f*
Cytogenetic maps, **248**
Cytokines, **736*f***
Cytokinesis, **184**, 187*f*–189*f*, 190, 198, 206*f*–207*f*
Cytokinins, 642*t*, **644**
Cytology, 75, 236
Cytoplasm, **76**
    cell cycle control signals in, 192*f*
    in cells, 76
    cytokinesis and division of, 184
    intracellular receptor proteins in, 117*f*
Cytoplasmic determinants, **322**, 323*f*
Cytoplasmic streaming, 94
Cytosine (C), 64, 65*f*, 66, 256, 258, 259*f*
Cytoskeletons, **90**
    animal cell, 78*f*
    components of, 91*t*, 92*f*–93*f*, 94
    in eukaryotic cells, 498
    membrane proteins and attachment to, 103*f*
    plant cell, 79*f*
    structure and function of components of, 91*t*
    structure of, 90*f*
    support and motility roles of, 90, 91*f*
Cytosol, **74**, 82*f*, 86*f*, 87, 295*f*, 296
Cytotoxic T cells, 744*f*, 745*f*

D

Dalton, **24**
Dance language, honeybee, 827*f*
Dandelions, 624*f*, 629*f*, 855*f*, 856, 861*f*
Daphnia, 860*f*
Darkness, plant flowering and, 652*f*, 653
Darwin, Charles
    Beagle voyage and field research of, on adaptations, 382, 383*f*, 384
    on genetic variation and evolution, 212
    on grandeur of evolutionary process, 393
    historical context of life and ideas of, 380*f*, 381
    on island species, 392
    on Madagascar orchid pollinator, 569*f*, 625
    on mystery of speciation, 434
    on natural selection, inheritance, and evolution, 414
    on origin of angiosperms, 536
    phylogenetic bracketing and cladistic analysis and, 412
    publication of *On the Origin of Species* by, 379, 383–384
    scientific evidence supporting theory of, 387–393
    on species diversity of tropics, 881
    study by, of phototropism in grass coleoptiles, 640, 641*f*
    theoretical aspects of theory of, 392–393
    theory of, on descent with modification by natural selection, 384*f*, 385
    theory of, on evolution by natural selection, 11*f*–12*f*
Darwin, Francis, 640, 641*f*
Data, scientific, **13**–14. *See also* Interpret the Data questions; Scientific Skills Exercises
Databases, genomic, 359, 360*f*
Data interpretation. *See* Interpret the Data questions; Scientific Skills Exercises
Dating, fossil record, 454*f*
Daughter cells, 182, 183*f*–184*f*, 198
Day-neutral plants, **652*f***
db gene, 704*t*
DDT, 136, 394, 421
DDT pesticide, 920*f*–921*f*
Dead Sea, 487
Dead zone, 919*f*, 920
Deamination, 158
Death rates, 902*f*
    demographics and, 856*ft*, 857
    population change and, 862, 864*f*
    population dynamics and, 855*f*
    population growth and, 857–858
    regulation of, 862*f*
December solstice, 843*f*
Deciduous forest, nutrient cycling in, 898*f*, 899

Decision making, 799
Declining-population approach, for population conservation, 914, 915*f*
Decomposers (detritivores), 8*f*, **490**, 875, **888*f***, 905
    effects of, on ecosystems, 569
    in energy flow between trophic levels, 892–893
    fungi as, 528*f*, 540
    as heterotrophs, 161
    nutrient cycling rates and, 895*f*
    prokaryotic, 490, 491*f*
Decomposition, 903*f*, 905
    effects of temperature on, 895*f*
    nutrient cycling rates and, 895*f*
Deductive reasoning, **14**
Deep-sea hydrothermal vents, 475, 487, 490–491, **851*f***, 888
Deer, 700, 861, 916
De-etiolation (greening), **648*f***
Defecation, 698
Defensive adaptations, predation and, 870, 871*f*, 885
Defensive proteins, 56*f*
Deficiencies, plant mineral, 600–601
Deforestation
    climate change and, 926
    as community disturbance, 880
    experimental, nutrient cycling effects of, 898*f*, 899
    in Mexico and Central America, 909
    in tropics, 906, 907*f*, 909
Degradation
    mRNA, 314
    protein, 315
Dehydration
    animal, 678
    plant, 175*f*, 176, 521, 523
Dehydration reactions, **48**
    in disaccharide formation, 50, 51*f*
    in polymer synthesis, 48, 49*f*
    in polypeptide formation, 58*f*
    in triacylglycerol synthesis, 53*f*
Dehydrogenases, 143, 144*f*, 145
Deinococcus radiodurans, 474
Deletions
    chromosome, **249**, 250
    nucleotide, **299*f***, 300, 414, 415*f*
Delta proteobacteria, 488*f*
Demographics, 856*ft*, 857
Demography, **856*ft***, 857
Denaturation, protein, 62*f*, 63
Dendrites, 665*f*, **773*f***, 784*f*, 803
Dendritic cells, 736
Dendrobates pumilio, 451
Dendrochronology, 590
Dendroctonus ponderosae, 924*f*
Density, population, **854**, 855*f*, 856, 866, 902*f*
    population dynamics and, 861*f*–864*f*
Density-dependent inhibition, **194*f***, 195
Density-dependent population regulation, **862*f*–863*f***, 866
Density-independent population regulation, 862*f*
Dental adaptations, 698*f*
Dental pulp, 332
Dentition, mammalian, 456, 457*f*
Deoxyribonucleic acid. *See* DNA
Deoxyribose, **65**, 256*f*
Dependent variables, identifying, **17**, 109, 134, 441, 870
Dephosphorylation, protein, 118*f*
Depolarization, **778**, 779*f*–780*f*, 781, 810*f*, 820
Depolymerization, 185
Depression, 786
Derivatives, plant cell, 583
Derived characters, shared, 401*f*–402*f*
Derived traits, plant, 523
Dermal tissue system, plant, **578**, 579*f*
Descent with modification, 11*f*–12*f*, 379–380, 384*f*, 385. *See also* Evolution; Natural selection
Desert ant, 663*f*
Desert mouse, 679
Deserts, 614*f*, 615, 844–845, **847*f***, 886, 887*f*
Desmodus rotundas, 684*f*
Desmognathus ochrophaeus, 441
Desmosomes, **96*f***

Determinate growth, **582**, 584
Determination, **323**, 324f, 325
Detoxification
  by peroxisomes, 90
  smooth ER and, 83
  by sunflowers, 23
Detritivores. *See* Decomposers
Detritus, **888**f, 895
Deuterostomia, 551f–552f, 553–554
Development, 321–341
  cancer development from abnormal cell cycle
    control in, 334f–339f, 340
  as cell division function, 182, 183f
  comparing genomes and processes of, 374f–375f
  DNA in, 6f
  embryonic. *See* Embryonic development
  in human life cycle, 203f
  macroevolution of, from changes in
    developmental genes, 465f–468f
  model organisms in study of, 321
  organismal cloning and stem cells in, 330f–334f
  plant. *See* Plant development
  postzygotic barriers and, 435, 437f
  vascular plant, 533
Developmental genes, 465f–468f
Devonian period, 535
DHFR (dihydrofolate reductase) enzyme, 513f
Diabetes mellitus, 333, **702**–703, 747
Diacodexis, 391f
Diagnosis, antibodies as tools in, 746
Diaphragm
  contraceptive, 769f
  respiratory system, 726f, **727**
Diarrhea, 111–112, 485, 492, 506f, 697
Diastole, **711**f
Diastolic pressure, 714, 720
Diatoms, 191f, 507f, **509**f, 519, 923
Diazepam, 786
Dichanthelium lanuginosum, 544
Dickinsonia costata, 453f, 546f
Dicrostonyx groenlandicus, 863f
Dictyostelium, 513, 514f
Didinium, 497f
Diencephalon, 794f–795f
Dietary fiber, 52
Diets. *See also* Animal nutrition
  allopatric speciation and divergence in, 440f
  of animals, 141f, 157–158
  deficiencies in, 690
  digestive system adaptations and, 698f–700f
  genetic variation in prey selection and, 834, 835
  nonheritable variation and, 415f
  nutritional needs and, 689f, 690
  phenylketonuria and, 419–420
  trophic efficiency and, 894
Differential gene expression, 303f, **308**f, 309, 322.
    See also Embryonic development; Gene
    expression; Gene regulation
Differential-interference contrast (Nomarski)
  microscopy, 74f
Differential reproductive success, 212
Differential speciation success, 471
Differentiation, cellular, **322**
  auxin and cytokinins in, 644
  cytoplasmic determinants and inductive signals
    in, 322, 323f
  in embryonic development, 322f
  in plants, 583, 584f
  sequential gene regulation during, 323, 324f–326f
Diffusion, **105**, **707**
  in circulation and gas exchange, 707
  free energy and, 126f
  as passive transport down concentration
    gradients, 105, 106f, 110f
  across respiratory surfaces, 722–723
  transport proteins in facilitated, 108
  of water across plant plasma membranes, 597,
    598f, 599
  of water and minerals into root cells, 609f, 610
Digestion, **691**. *See also* Digestive systems; Food
    processing
  endocrine signaling in, 670
  fungal, 524f, 525

human, as hydrolysis, 49
  by lysosomes, 85f–86f
  of nutrients, 695f–697f
  regulation of, 700, 701f
  vertebrate adaptations for, 698f–700f
Digestive compartments, 691, 692f, 693
Digestive systems. *See also* Animal nutrition
  compartments in, 691, 692f, 693
  evolution of vertebrate, 698f–700f
  large intestine, 697f, 698
  mammalian, 664t
  oral cavity, pharynx, and esophagus of, 693f
  small intestine, 695f–697f
  stomach, 694f, 695
Digger wasps, 829f, 830f
Dihybrid crosses, **220**f, 222
Dihybrids, **219**, 220f
Dihydrofolate reductase (DHFR) enzyme, 513f
Dimers, 92
Dimetrodon, 453f
Dimorphism, sexual, 832
Dinitrophenol (DNP), 160
Dinoflagellates, 122f, 191f, **510**f
Dinosaurs
  adaptive radiation of mammals after extinction
    of, 464
  birds as descended from, 405f–406f
  flying, 824
  in fossil record, 11f, 453f
  in geologic record, 456
  mass extinction of, 461f–462f
  phylogenetic bracketing of, 573
  as reptiles, 563, 564f
Dioecious species, **631**f
Dionaea muscipula, 608f, 655
Dipeptidases, 695f
Diphasiastrum tristachyum, 531f
Diphtheria, 346
Diploid cells, **203**
  genetic variation preserved in recessive alleles of,
    426–427
  mitosis vs. meiosis in, 208, 209f
  in sexual life cycles, 203f–204f, 205
Diploidy, 426–427
Diplomonads, 506f, **508**f
Dipnoi, 556f
Directionality, in DNA replication, 263f–264f
Directional selection, **425**f
Disaccharidases, 695f
Disaccharides, 50, 51f
Diseases and disorders, animal
  prions, 355
  viral, 343f, 344, 347–348, 351f–352f, 353–354
Diseases and disorders, human
  age-related macular degeneration, 333
  alkaptonuria, 279
  allergies, 746f, 747
  aneuploidy of sex chromosomes and, 250
  atherosclerosis, 55
  atherosclerosis and familial
    hypercholesterolemia, 112
  autism, 801
  autoimmune, 747f
  bacterial, 291, 346, 479, 484f–485f, 486,
    488f–489f, 492f
  cardiovascular diseases, 719, 720f, 721
  chromosomal alterations and genetic, 248f–251f
  color blindness, 240, 241f, 811
  community ecology and, 883f, 884
  cri du chat and chronic myelogenous leukemia,
    250, 251f
  Crohn's disease and ulcerative colitis, 737
  cystic fibrosis, 225, 230, 235
  as density-dependent population regulation
    mechanisms, 863f
  depression, 786
  diabetes, 333
  diarrhea and constipation, 111–112, 506f
  dominantly inherited, 231f
  Down syndrome, 202f, 248, 250
  drug addiction, 797, 798f
  Duchenne muscular dystrophy, 240–241
  dysentery, 485

edema, asthma, and lymphatic system, 716
  epilepsy, 781
  erectile dysfunction, 787
  essential nutrients and, 690
  fetal alcohol syndrome, 768
  food poisoning (botulism), 786
  genomics and proteomics in, 68f
  glaucoma, 808f
  gonorrhea, 479
  G protein-coupled receptors in, 116
  heart murmurs, 711–712
  hemophilia, 241, 719
  HIV/AIDS. *See* AIDS; HIV
  hormonal contraceptives and, 769
  Huntington's disease, 231, 333
  hypertension, 685, 720
  immune system disruptions and, 746f–747f,
    748–749
  immunization against, 745–746
  immunodeficiency, 747–748
  infertility, 770
  influenza. *See* Influenza viruses
  iodine deficiencies, 23
  Klinefelter syndrome and Turner syndrome, 250
  Lou Gehrig's disease (amyotrophic lateral
    sclerosis), 818
  lysosomal storage diseases, 86
  malaria, 230, 427, 428f–429f, 507f, 517f,
    518, 734
  measles, 746
  methicillin-resistant *S. aureus* and flesh-eating
    disease, 388f, 389
  from misfolding of proteins, 63
  mosaicism, 241, 242f
  multifactorial, 231
  myasthenia gravis, 818
  myotonia, 781
  neurotransmitters and, 785, 786t, 787
  Parkinson's disease, 333–334, 786
  phenylketonuria, 419–420
  pleiotropy and, 225
  pneumonia, 484f, 747
  polydactyly, 224
  prions, 355
  protists and, 516, 517f, 518
  recessively inherited, 229f–230f
  respiratory, 863f
  respiratory distress syndrome, 725–726
  retinitis pigmentosa, 422
  sexually transmitted diseases, 479, 489f, 747–748,
    769, 770
  sickle-cell disease. *See* Sickle-cell disease
  sleeping sickness, 508, 509f, 517
  stem cells in treatments for, 333–334
  Tay-Sachs disease, 224
  tuberculosis, 737, 863f
  viral, 343f, 344, 347–348, 350f, 352f, 353–354
  xeroderma pigmentosum, 266f
  X-linked disorders, 240, 241f
Diseases and disorders, plant
  community ecology and, 883
  epidemics of, 660
  fungal, 540, 541f
  plant defenses against, 658, 659f–660f
  viral, 343f, 354f
Disease-suppressive soil, 493
D isomer, 46f
Disorder, entropy and, 124f, 125
Disorders. *See* Diseases and disorders, animal;
    Diseases and disorders, human; Diseases and
    disorders, plant
Dispersal
  fruit and seed, 629f
  species, **852**–853
Dispersal modes, evolutionary rates and, 459
Dispersion, population, **854**, 855f, 856
Dispersive model, DNA replication, 260f–261f
Disruptive selection, 425f, **426**
Distal control elements, 310f–311f
Distal tubule, **681**f, 683f
Distribution of species. *See* Species distributions
Distribution patterns, making histograms and
    analyzing, 227t

Disturbances, **845**, **878**
  in biomes, 845
  characterizing of, 878, 879f
  in communities, 878, 879f–881f
  ecological succession after, 879, 880f
  ecosystem restoration after, 899f–901f
  human, 880, 881f
Disulfide bridges, 61f, 63
Diurnal animals, 828
Divergence
  of closely related species, 372f–373f
  of gene-sized regions of DNA, 368f–369f
  morphological, 399
Divergent evolution
  allopatric speciation and, 439f–441f
  speciation rates and, 447f–448f
Diversity. *See also* Biodiversity; Species diversity
  B cell and T cell, 739, 740f
  biogeographic factors affecting, 881f–882f
  in biological communities, 873, 874f–877f,
    878, 885
  community stability and, 875f, 878
  disturbances influencing, 878, 879f–881f
  eukaryotic, 498f
  evolution and unity in, 9, 11f, 20
  evolution of, 379–380
  human impacts on, 880, 881f
  of life solutions, 666f–667f
  species. *See* Species diversity
  within species, 435f
  three domains of life in classification of, 10f, 11
  trophic structure and, 875f–876f, 885
Diving bell spider, 732
Diving mammals, respiratory adaptations of, 730
Dizygotic twins, 768
Dizziness, 806
DNA (deoxyribonucleic acid), **6f**, **64**
  in animal cells, 78f
  in bacteria, 190, 191f
  as bearer of genetic information, 66–67
  cell division and distribution of, 183f–184f
  in cell nucleus, 80, 81f, 82
  changes in, during meiosis of budding yeast
    cells, 210
  in chloroplasts, 89f
  components of, 64, 65f
  constructing phylogenetic trees using,
    402f–404f, 405
  discovery of structure of, 256, 257f–259f
  editing of, genetic engineering, 274, 275f
  evaluating molecular homologies in, 400f
  evidence for, as genetic material, 254f–256f
  evidence of, for origination of animals, 546
  evolutionary significance of mutations of, 266–267
  evolution of genomes from duplication,
    rearrangement, and mutation of,
    367f–369f, 371
  gene density and noncoding, in genomes, 363
  genetic engineering and. *See* Genetic engineering
  genetic variability as nucleotide variability in,
    414f–415f
  genetic variation due to mutations in, 415–416
  genomes as complete sequences of, 7. *See also*
    Genomes
  genomics and proteomics in study of, 68f
  homeoboxes in, 374f–375f
  homologies and, 400f
  human gene microarray chips containing, 361f
  hybrids and inheritance of, 451
  inheritance of, in genes and chromosomes, 6, 201,
    213, 302
  interpreting sequence logos for, 294
  introns and exons, 287
  as measure of evolution, 67
  methylation of, 309, 331
  in mitochondria and chloroplasts, 88
  as molecular homology, 390
  monitoring gene expression and, 316,
    317f–318f, 319f
  p53 gene and repair of, 336f
  packing of proteins and, into chromosomes, 267,
    268f–269f
  phylogenies based on, 395f

  in plant cells, 79f
  prokaryotic, 480, 481f
  in prokaryotic and eukaryotic cells, 75, 76f
  prokaryotic genetic recombination of,
    484f–485f, 486
  recombinant. *See* Recombinant DNA
  repetitive and noncoding, in genomes, 363f–366f
  replication of, 253, 259f–267f. *See also* DNA
    replication
  role of, in protein synthesis, 64
  in sickle-cell disease, 428f–429f
  species identity in mitochondrial, 398f
  structure and function of, 6f–7f
  structure discovery of, 253f
  structure of molecules of, 66f
  template strands of, 282f, 283
  transcription by, 284, 285f–286f
  tree based on, 353
  viral. *See* DNA viruses
DNA amplification, 272, 273f
DNA-binding regions, 71
DNA chips, 318, 319f
DNA cloning, 270f–273f
DNA Data Bank of Japan, 359
DNA deletion experiments, analyzing, 313
DNA ligase, **264f**, 266f, 271f, 272
DNA methylation, **309**
DNA microarray assays, **318**, 319f, 338f
DNA polymerases, **263**, 264f–265f, 272, 273f,
    277, 317
DNA reference map, 910, 911f
DNA replication, **253**, 259f–267f
  antiparallel elongation of DNA strands in,
    263f–265f
  base pairing to template strands in, 260f–261f
  cell division and, 6f
  DNA replication complex of, 264, 265f
  errors in, and genome evolution, 368f–369f
  evolutionary significance of mutations during,
    266–267
  models of, 259f–261f, 265f
  proofreading and repairing of DNA during, 266f
  start of, at origins of replication, 261, 262f
  steps of, 260, 261f–265f
  synthesizing new DNA strands in, 262, 263f
  of telomeres at ends of molecules, 267f
DNA replication complex, 264, 265f, 277
DNA sequences
  amino acid sequences of polypeptides and, 69
  changes in, of developmental genes, 466, 467f
  evolution and, 320
  genes as, 300
  genomes as, 7. *See also* Genomes
  interpreting sequence logos for, 294
  noncoding, 363f–366f
  in taxonomy, 10
  types of, in human genome, 363f
DNA sequencing, **273**, 274f
  analyzing viral evolution using phylogenetic tree
    and, 353
  in cancer treatment, 197
  development of, 67
  DNA microarray assays and, 318, 319f
  genome sequencing and, 7, 358–359. *See also*
    Genome sequencing
  of ribosomal RNA of prokaryotes related to
    mitochondria, 501
  technology of, 7
DNA strands, 256f–258f, 259
DNA technology
  animal stem cells in, 332f–333f, 334
  organismal cloning in, 330f–331f
  in study of bacterial binary fission, 190–191
DNA viruses
  evolution of, 349
  as pathogens, 351f–352f, 353–354
  replicative cycles of, 345f–348f, 350f
  structure of, 342, 343f, 344
DNP. *See* Dinitrophenol
Dobzhansky, Theodosius, 67
Dodder, 608f
Dolly (cloned lamb), 331f
Dolphins, 390f–391f, 412, 796f, 908f

Domains
  protein, **369**, 504, 505f
  taxonomy, 10f, 362t, 372f, **396f**, 408, 409f, 410,
    486f, 487t. *See also* Archaea, domain;
    Bacteria, domain; Eukarya, domain
Domestication, plant, 619, 633–634
Dominance, degrees of, 223f, 224
Dominant alleles, **217f**–218f, 224, 228f, 231f, 235, 252
Dominantly inherited disorders, human, 231f
Dominant species, **876f**
Dominant traits, 216f, 228f, 231f
Dominican Republic, lizards in, 868f
Donkeys, 278f, 279, 437f
Dopamine, 786t, 797, 798f
Dormancy, 479, **626**, 645, 646f
Dorsal, hollow nerve cords, 555f
Dorsal sides, **550f**
Dorudon atrox, 452f
Double bonds, **28**
  in carbon skeletons, 45f
  covalent bonds as, 27f–28f
  isomers and, 46f
  in organic compounds, 44f–45f
  of unsaturated fatty acids, 53, 54f
Double circulation, **708**, 709f–712f. *See also*
    Cardiovascular systems
Double fertilization, angiosperm, **622**, 623f, 625f
Double helix, DNA, 6f, 66f, 253, **258f**, 259, 268f
Double membrane, nuclear envelope as, 80, 81f
Double-stranded DNA (dsDNA), 349
Douglas fir tree, 535f
Doushantuophyton, 499f
Dovrefjell-Sunndalsfjella National Park, 848f
Down syndrome, 202f, 248, **250f**
Drift, genetic, 421f–423f
Drosera, 608f
Drosophila melanogaster (fruit fly)
  changes in developmental genes of, 467f
  complete genome sequence for, 360
  correlation of allele behavior and chromosomes
    in, 238, 239f
  courtship behaviors of, 827f
  crossing over in, 244, 245f
  diploid and haploid numbers of, 203
  eye color of, 279
  foraging genes of, 831f, 832
  gene mapping in, 252
  genetic variability of, 414f–415f
  genome size of, 362t
  homeotic genes in, 374f–375
  linkage map of, 247f
  linked genes and, 242, 243f
  as model organism, 238, 321f
  natural selection and insecticide resistance in, 421
  pattern formation and body plan of, 326,
    327f–329f
  phylogenetic tree of, 403f
  reproductive anatomy of, 754f
  studying expression of single genes in, 317f–318f
  testcrosses with, 252
Drosophila pseudoobscura (fruit fly), 440f, 449
Drought
  abscisic acid in plant tolerance of, 646
  plant responses to, 655–656
Drugs
  addiction to, 797, 798f
  antibiotic. *See* Antibiotic drugs
  antiviral, 351
  cancer chemotherapy, 196
  cocktails of, in AIDS treatment, 416
  evolution of resistance to, 388f, 389, 496, 519
  opiates. *See* Opiates
  peroxisomes and, 90
  smooth ER and, 83
Dryas, 880f
Dry fruits, 628
dsDNA. *See* Double-stranded DNA
Duchenne muscular dystrophy, **240**–241
Duckweed, 79f
Ducts, male reproductive, 756f
Dune fescue grass, 862
Dung beetle, 905

Dunstan, William, 891f
Duodenum, 670, **695**
Duplications
    chromosome, **249**, 367f–369f
    gene, 416
Dusky salamanders, 441
Dwarfism, 231f
Dyes, microscopy and, 74f
Dyneins, 92, 93f
Dysentery, 485

E
Eacles, 379f
Eagles, 755
Eardrums
    human, 805f, 806
    invertebrate, 804
Ears
    bones of mammalian, 456, 457f, 469
    human, 805f
    insect, 804
Ear stones (otoliths), 806, 807f
Earth
    climate of. *See* Climate
    conditions on early, and development of life,
        475–477f, 478
    mass extinctions of life on, 460, 461f–463f
    plate tectonics of, 458f–460f
    prokaryotic cells as first cells of life on, 474f
Earthworm, digestive system of, 692f
Earthworms, 602, 707f, 708, 722, 822f. *See also*
    Caenorhabditis elegans
Eastern glass lizard, 395f, 396, 408
Ebola virus, 352f
Ecdysozoa, 551f–552f
Echinoderms, 548f, 551f–552f, 822
ECM. *See* Ectomycorrhizal mycelium; Extracellular
    matrix
Ecological footprint, **927**, 928f
Ecological interactions. *See* Interactions, ecological
Ecological niches, 438, **868f**–869f, 885
Ecological pyramids, 893, 894f
Ecological species concept, **438**
Ecological succession, **879**, 880f
Ecology, **840**–866
    aquatic biomes in, 849f–851f, 852. *See also*
        Aquatic biomes
    climate, macroclimate, and. *See* Climate
    climate and, 842f–848f
    discovering new species in, 840f
    ecological effects of animals, 568f–569f
    ecological interactions and species distributions
        in, 840, 852f–853f, 854. *See also* Interactions,
        ecological; Species distributions
    ecological interactions between species in,
        867f–873f
    importance of mycorrhizae in, 607
    mass extinctions and, 463f
    populations in, 841f, 854–864. *See also*
        Populations
    prokaryotic roles in, 490, 491f
    scope and fields of, 841f. *See also* Community
        ecology; Ecosystem ecology; Global ecology;
        Landscape ecology; Organismal ecology;
        Population ecology
    terrestrial biomes in, 843f–848f. *See also*
        Terrestrial biomes
Ecosystem diversity, 907f–908f
Ecosystem ecology, 841f
Ecosystem engineers, **876**, 877f
Ecosystems, 4f, **841f**, **886**–905
    aquatic biome diversity, 849f–851f, 852
    biogeochemical cycles in, 895, 896f–897f, 898, 905
    climate change effects on, 925f
    effects of animals on, 568f–569f
    effects of mass extinctions on, 461f, 462, 463f
    energy budgets of, 889f–890f, 905
    energy flow and chemical cycling in, 886–887,
        888f, 903f
    energy flow and chemical cycling in trophic
        structure of, 8f. *See also* Chemical cycling;
        Energy flow; Trophic structure

energy flow and chemical recycling in, 141f
energy transfer among trophic levels in, 892,
    893f–894f
evolution of, 905
genome sequencing of metagenomes in, 358–359
in hierarchy of biological organization, 4f
importance of mycorrhizae to, 607
overview of, 901, 902f–903f
prokaryotic roles in, 490, 491f
regulation of primary production in, 888,
    889f–892f, 891t
restoration of, 899f–901f
secondary production efficiency in, 892, 893f–894f
sizes of, 886, 887f
soil as, 601, 602f
terrestrial biome diversity, 843f–848f
transformations of, 886f
water and nutrient cycling in, 895f–898f, 899.
    See also Biogeochemical cycles
Ecosystem services, **909**
Ecotones, **846**
Ectoderm, **550f**, **766f**
Ectomycorrhizae, **525**, 528f, 529, **606**, 607f
Ectomycorrhizal mycelium (ECM), 529
Ectoparasites, **871**
Ectoprocts, 551f–552f
Ectothermic organisms, **563**, **674**, 675f, 676
Ectotherms, 702
Edema, 716
Edges, of habitat, 916f, 931
Ediacaran biota, 453f, 466, 499f, **546**, 548, 549f
Edidin, Michael, 102f
EEG. *See* Electroencephalogram
Eelgrass, 885
Effective population size, **913**, 914f
Effector cells, **741f**
Effectors, 658, 659f
Effector-triggered immunity, 658, 659f, 660
Efferent neurons, 792f, 793
Egg-polarity genes, 328f–329f
Eggs, **752**
    in animal fertilization, 765f
    of birds and dinosaurs, 405f–406f
    chromosomes in human, 183
    embryo survival and, 755
    enucleated, 330f, 331
    as female gametes, 752
    in human fertilization, 767f–769f
    in human oogenesis, 759f, 760
Egg yolks, 71
ein mutants, ethylene and, 646, 647f
Ejaculation, **756**, 764, 767
Ejaculatory duct, **756f**
Electrically charged side chains, 57f
Electrical membrane potential, 110f, 111
Electrical signaling, neurons and, 772. *See also*
    Neurons
Electrical synapses, 784
Electrocardiogram (ECG or EKG), **712**
Electrochemical gradients, **110f**, 111
Electroencephalogram (EEG), 796f
Electrogenic pumps, 111f
Electrolytes, blood, 717f
Electromagnetic energy or radiation, 165–166
Electromagnetic receptors, 803f
Electromagnetic spectrum, **166f**
Electron distribution diagrams, 26f, 28f
Electronegativity, **28**
Electron microscopy (EM), 73f–74f, D-1f
Electrons, **24f**
    configuration of carbon, in organic compounds,
        44f–45f
    distribution of, and chemical properties of atoms,
        26f, 27
    electron shells and energy of, 25f, 26
    in excitation of chlorophyll by light, 168, 169f
    ionic bonding and transfer of, 29f
    in light reactions of photosynthesis, 169f–173f
    in redox reactions, 142, 143f
    as subatomic particles, 24f
Electron shells, 25f, 26
Electron transport chain, **145**
    ATP yield during, 153f

in cellular respiration, 143, 144f–145f, 156–157
in fermentation, 156
in light reactions of photosynthesis, 169f–173f
in oxidative phosphorylation, 150–151, 150f
Electroreceptors, 803
Elements, **22**–27, 42
Elephantiasis, 716
Elephants, 68f, 384f, 385, 699, 858–859f, 910, 911f
Elephas maximus, 384f, 385
Elevation
    climate and, 844f
    plant species and, 866
Elimination, **691**, 698
Elk, 832f
Elkhorn coral, 883
Elodea, 32f
Elongation, antiparallel DNA, 263f–265f
Elongation factors, 292, 293f
Elongation stage
    transcription, 285f–286f
    translation, 292, 293f
Elton, Charles, 875
Elvis monkey, 906
EM. *See* Electron microscopy
Embryonic development, 321–329
    analyzing quantitative and spatial data on *Hox*
        genes in, 325
    animal, 764–770
    cytoplasmic determinants and inductive signals
        in, 322, 323f
    genes for, 377
    genetic program for, 322f
    model organisms in study of development and, 321f
    pattern formation and body plans in, 326,
        327f–329f
    sequential gene regulation in, 323, 324f–326f
Embryonic development, animal
    cleavage and gastrulation in, 765, 766f, 767
    fertilization in, 765f
    human, 767f–768f
    sex determination in, 761
    stages of, 764f
Embryonic germ layers, 767f
Embryonic lethals, **328**
Embryonic stem (ES) cells, 332, 333f
Embryophytes, **522f**
Embryos
    anatomical similarities in vertebrate, 389f
    development of plant, 625f
    ensuring survival of, 754, 755f
    monocot vs. eudicot, 576f
    mortality rates for hybrid, 249
    plant, 522f
Embryo sacs, plant, **622**, 623f
Emergent properties, 3, 4f–5f, 23, 99, 226–227
Emerging diseases, 883–884
Emerging viruses, 352f, 353–354
Emigration, **855f**, 864f
Emission, human, 764
Emotions
    limbic system and, 796f
    prefrontal cortex and, 799
Enantiomers, **46f**
Encephalitis, 352
ENCODE (Encyclopedia of DNA Elements), 360, 362
Endangered species, **907**, 908f, 931
    declining-population approach to, 914, 915f
    imprinting for, 829
    molluscs as, 571f
Endemic species, **392**
Endergonic reactions, **127**
    energy coupling of, 128f–130f
    metabolism and, 126, 127f
Endocarp, 629f
Endocrine cells, 669
Endocrine disruption, toxins causing, 920f–921f
Endocrine glands, human, **669f**
Endocrine pathways, 670f
Endocrine signaling, 668f–673f
    evolution of hormone function in, 672
    feedback regulation in, 671
    functions of endocrine and nervous systems in, 668f
    human endocrine system in, 669f–670f

Endocrine signaling (*Cont.*)
   in local cell signaling, 114*f*
   multiple effects of hormones in, 672
   neuroendocrine pathways in, 670*f*–673*f*
   regulation of, 669
   simple endocrine pathways in, 670*f*
Endocrine systems, **668**
   coordination and control functions of, 668*f*
   in digestion, 700, 701*f*
   human, 669*f*–670*f*
   mammalian, 664*t*
Endocytosis, 112, 113*f*, 179*f*, 750
Endoderm, **550***f*, **766***f*
Endodermis, **585**, **609***f*, 610
Endomembrane system, **82**, 83*f*–87*f*
   bound ribosomes and, 295*f*
   components and functions of, 82–83, 87, 97
   endoplasmic reticulum of, 83*f*, 84
   Golgi apparatus of, 84*f*, 85
   lysosomes of, 85*f*–86*f*
   organelles and functions of, 87*f*
   targeting polypeptides to, 295*f*, 296
   vacuoles of, 86*f*, 87
   vesicles of, 82–83
Endometrium, **757**
Endoparasites, **871**
Endophytes, **540**, 541*f*, **604**
Endoplasmic reticulum (ER), **83**
   animal cell, 78*f*
   plant cell, 79*f*
   ribosomes and, 82*f*
   rough ER functions, 84
   smooth ER functions, 83–84
   synthesis of membrane proteins and lipids in, 104*f*
   targeting polypeptides to, 295*f*, 296
Endorphins, 31*f*, 59, **786**
Endoskeletons, 821*f*, 822, 823*f*
Endosperm, **622**, 623*f*, 625
Endospores, **479**
Endosymbionts, 88, 500
Endosymbiont theory, 88*f*, 162, 181, **500***f*–**501***f*, 502
Endosymbiosis, 500*f t*–502*f*, 503, 519
Endothelin, 714–715
Endothelium, **713***f*
Endothermic organisms, **563**, **674**, 675*f*, 676, 709–710
Endotherms, 702
Endotoxins, **492**
Energy, **25**, **123**. *See also* Energy flow
   for active transport, 109, 110*f*
   allocation of, in angiosperm reproduction, 632
   bioenergetics, 700, 701*f*
   biofuel technology to reduce dependence on fossil
      fuels for, 634–635
   catabolic pathways and, 142, 143*f*–146*f*
   cellular use of, 141
   chemiosmosis and, 151*f*–152*f*, 153
   in citric acid cycle, 148, 149*f*
   conservation of, 887
   of diffusion, 105, 106*f*
   ecosystems and, 888*f*
   electron shells and levels of, 25*f*, 26
   forms of, 123*f*
   global carrying capacity and, 928
   in glycolysis, 147*f*
   of hydrocarbons and fats, 45, 54
   locomotion and, 824, 825
   metabolic rate, 701–702
   metabolism and cellular, 122. *See also* Metabolism
   primary production limitations caused by, 888,
      889*f*–892*f*, 891*t*
   solutions for, 666*f*
   stepwise harvest of, 143, 144*f*, 145
   storage of, 702
   thermodynamics and laws of transformation of,
      124*f*, 125, 887
   transformation of, by mitochondria, chloroplasts,
      and peroxisomes, 87, 88*f*–90*f*
   transformation of, in plant cells, 179*f*
Energy and matter
   bioenergetics, 140
   in hydrothermal vent communities, 496
   photosynthesis and, 181
   reproductive success and, 771

transfer and transformation of, as biological
      theme, 8*f*–9*f*
Energy coupling, **128**–130
Energy flow
   as biological theme, 8*f*
   chemical cycling and, in ecosystems, 886–887,
      888*f*. *See also* Chemical cycling
   ecosystem energy budgets and, 889*f*–890*f*, 905
   in ecosystems, 141*f*, 903*f*
   physical laws governing, 887
   secondary production efficiency of, between
      trophic levels, 892, 893*f*–894*f*
   between trophic levels, 892, 893*f*–894*f*
   trophic levels and, 888*f*
Energy pyramid, 894*f*
Engelmann, Theodor W., 167*f*
Engineering, genetic. *See* Genetic engineering
English Channel, 894*f*
Enhancers, **310***f*–311*f*, 320
Ensatina, 437*f*
Enteric division, 700
   peripheral nervous system, **793**
Entropy, 124*f*, 125
Entry stage, phage lytic cycle, 345*f*
Enucleated eggs, 330*f*, 331
Enveloped viruses, 348*f*
Environment
   adaptations of vertebrate kidneys to diversity in, 684*f*
   adaptive evolution as fitness to, 421, 424–425
   animal maintenance of internal, 673*f*–674*f*. *See
      also* Homeostasis
   animal regulating and conforming responses to,
      673*f*–674*f*
   aquatic physical and chemical. *See* Aquatic biomes
   behavior and stimuli from, 826
   bottleneck effect and changes in, 422*f*–423*f*
   Cambrian explosion and changes in, 548
   cancer development and, 337, 340
   chemical cycling and, 8*f*
   differential gene expression and, 303*f*. *See also*
      Gene regulation
   Earth's early, and origin of life, 475–477*f*, 478
   effects of, on protein structure, 62–63
   effects on cell division of, 192–193
   enzymatic catalysis and factors of, 135*f*–136*f*
   ethylene in plant responses to stresses from,
      646, 647*f*
   evolution and changes in, 394
   genetics vs., in animal behaviors, 828
   genome sequencing of metagenomes in, 358–359
   impact of, on phenotypes, 226
   impacts of evolution of plants and fungi on,
      539*f*–542*f*
   induction from, in cellular differentiation, 323*f*
   interaction of chance, natural selection, and, 431
   interaction of organisms with other organisms
      and, as biological theme, 8, 9*f*. *See also*
      Interactions, ecological
   ionic bond strength and, 29
   multifactorial disorders and, 231
   mutations in cell division and, 277
   plant responses to, 653, 654*f*–660*f*
   reproductive cycles and cues from, 753
   spatial learning and, 829, 830*f*
   species distributions and, 840, 852*f*–853*f*, 854
   as surroundings and organisms, 379
Environmental issues
   ecology and, 840. *See also* Ecology
   extinctions. *See* Extinctions
   honeybee population decline, 624*f*
   restoration of degraded ecosystems, 899*f*–901*f*
Enzymatic catalysis, 131*f*–138*f*
   activation energy barrier and, 131*f*, 132
   calculating rate of, 134
   cofactors, coenzymes, and, 135
   effects of environmental factors on, 135*f*–136*f*
   effects of temperature and pH on, 135*f*
   in enzyme active sites, 133*f*, 134
   enzyme inhibitors and, 136*f*
   evolution of enzymes and, 136
   lowering of activation energy barriers by, 131, 132*f*
   regulating, 136, 137*f*–138*f*
   substrate specificity of enzymes in, 132, 133*f*

Enzymatic hydrolysis, 691. *See also* Chemical
      digestion
Enzyme complexes, 138
Enzymes, **48**, **131**
   3-D structure of, 63*f*
   activation energy and, 132*f*
   allosteric regulation of, 137*f*–138*f*
   autophagy by lysosomal, 86*f*
   in cardiovascular diseases, 721
   as catalysts, 131. *See also* Enzymatic catalysis
   for cellulose digestion, 699
   in chloroplasts, 89
   evolution of, 136
   fungal, 525
   gene relationship with, in protein synthesis,
      279*f*–280*f*
   inducible and repressible, 306–307
   locations of, in cells, 138*f*
   membrane functions of, 103*f*
   in mitochondria, 77, 88
   nonenzyme proteins and, 280
   in peroxisomes, 90
   phagocytosis by lysosomal, 85*f*
   as protein catalysts, 55, 56*f*
   in protein phosphorylation and
      dephosphorylation, 118*f*
   regulation of, in bacterial gene regulation, 304,
      305*f*–306*f*, 307
   restriction, 271*f*–272*f*, 347
   of saliva, 693
   of small intestine, 695*f*, 696
   of smooth ER, 83–84
   specialized proteins as, in synthesis and
      breakdown of organic compounds, 48–49
   structure of, 59*f*
Enzyme-substrate complexes, **132**, 133*f*
Eons, geologic, 455*t*
Eosinophils, 717*f*–718*f*, 736
Ependymal cells, 791*f*
Ephrussi, Boris, 279
Epicotyl, **626***f*–627*f*
Epidemics, 352*f*, 353–354, 660
Epidermis, plant, **578**, 583, 584*f*, 658
Epididymis, **756***f*
Epigenetic inheritance, **309**
Epilepsy, 781
Epinephrine (adrenaline), 669*f*, **672**
   as biogenic amine, 786*t*
   in cell signaling, 118, 119*f*
   in fight-or-flight responses, 712
   in glycogen breakdown, 115
   in nervous systems, 793
Epiphytes, 607, 608*f*
Epistasis, **225***f*
Epithalamus, 795*f*
Epithelial milk-secreting cell, 338*f*
Epithelial tissue, 96*f*, 97, 99, **665***f*
Epithelium, **665***f*
Epitopes, **737**–738, 746
EPO. *See* Erythropoietin
Epochs, geologic, 455*t*
Epsilon proteobacteria, 488*f*
EPSP. *See* Excitatory postsynaptic potential
Epstein-Barr virus, 340
Equilibrium
   chemical. *See* Chemical equilibrium
   community, 878
   Hardy-Weinberg, 417, 418*f*–419*f*
   mechanoreceptors for hearing and, 804*f*–807*f*
   population, 862*f*
Equilibrium potential, **776**
Equinoxes, 843*f*
Equus, 392, 470*f*, 471
Eras, geologic, 455*t*
Erectile dysfunction, 756–757, 787
Erectile tissue, 756
Erection, penile, 756–757, 787
Ergot fungus, 541*f*
Errors, DNA replication, 266*f*
Erythrocytes, 717*f*–**718***f*, 729–730. *See also*
      Red blood cells
Erythropoietin (EPO), 718
ERα. *See* Estrogen receptor α

ES cells. *See* Embryonic stem cells
Escherichia coli (*E. coli*) bacteria
  binary fission in, 190, 191*f*
  complete genome sequence for, 357
  in DNA cloning, 270
  DNA replication using, 260, 261*f*–265*f*
  gene regulation in, 304, 305*f*–306*f*, 307
  genetic recombination and conjugation in, 484*f*–485*f*, 486
  genome size of, 362*t*
  in human digestive system, 698–699
  pathogenic strains of, 492
  phages and, 254, 255*f*, 256
  as proteobacteria, 488*f*
  rapid reproduction and mutation of, 483*f*, 484
  in research on origin of mitochondria, 501
  viral infection of, 344, 346*f*
E site (exit site), **291***f*, 293*f*
Esophagus, 692*f*–693*f*, **693**–695, 700*f*, 705, 724, 725*f*
Essential amino acids, **689***f*, 690
Essential elements, **23**, **599***f*–602*f*
Essential fatty acids, **689***f*
Essential nutrients, **689***f*, 690
Ester linkages, 53*f*
Estradiol, 48, 672, 753*f*, 759*f*, **760**, 762*f*, 763, 768
Estrogen medications, as environmental toxins, 921*f*
Estrogen receptor α (ERα), 338*f*–339*f*
Estrogens, 55, 341, 669*f*, 760–761, 762*f*, 763–764, 768, 769
Estrous cycles, **763**
Estuary, **849***f*
Ethane, 44*f*–45*f*
Ethanol (ethyl alcohol), 47*f*, 156*f*, 494, 863*f*, 901*f*
Ethene (ethylene), 44*f*, 114, 642*t*, **646**, 647*f*, 648, 655–656, 657*f*
Ethical issues, plant biotechnology, 635–636
Ethylene. *See* Ethene
Etiolation, **648***f*
eto mutants, ethylene and, 647
Euchromatin, **269**
Eudicots
  in angiosperm phylogenies, 537*f*–538*f*
  embryo development in, 625*f*
  monocots vs., 575, 576*f*
  overview of structure of, 577*f*
  primary growth of roots of, 584*f*
  roots of, 585*f*
  seed structure of, 626*f*
Euglenids, 508*f*
Euglenozoans, 506*f*, **508***f*
Euhadra, 448–449
Eukarya, domain, 10*f*, **11**. *See also* Eukaryotes
  compared with Bacteria and Archaea, 487*t*
  evolutionary relationships of, 372*f*
  genome size and number of genes for, 362*t*
  horizontal gene transfer and, 409*f*, 410
Eukaryotes, 497–519. *See also* Animals; Eukarya, domain; Plants
  Cambrian explosion and evolution of, 547, 548*f*–549*f*
  cell structure of, 497–498. *See also* Eukaryotic cells
  early evolution of, 498*f*–499*f*
  embryonic development of. *See* Embryonic development
  endosymbiosis in evolution of, 500*f*t–502*f*, 503
  fossil record of, 498*f*–499*f*, 500
  four supergroups in phylogeny of, 505, 506*f*–514*f*
  genomes of. *See* Eukaryotic genomes
  in geologic record, 456
  origination of animals in, 545, 546*f*–547*f*
  origination of multicellularity in, 499*f*, 503*f*–505*f*
  origins of key features of, 500*t*
  phylogenetic tree of, 506*f*–507*f*
  protists as unicellular, 497, 515*f*–517*f*, 518. *See also* Protists
  taxonomy of, 408, 409*f*, 410
  Unikonta as root of phylogenetic tree of, 513
Eukaryotic cells, **4**, **75**. *See also* Cells
  aerobic respiration of, 142
  cell cycle of. *See* Cell cycle
  cellular integration of, 97
  cellular respiration in, 145*f*–146*f*

characteristics of, 77, 497–498
chromatin packing in chromosomes of, 267, 268*f*–269*f*
cytoskeletons of, 90*f*–93*f*, 94
DNA replication in, 261, 262*f*. *See also* DNA replication
electron transport chains in, 150
endomembrane systems of, 82, 83*f*–87*f*
extracellular components of, and connections between, 94*f*–96*f*, 97
gene expression in, 281*f*
genetic instructions for, in nucleus and ribosomes of, 80, 81*f*, 82
internal membranes and functions of, 77
microscopy and biochemistry in study of, 73*f*–75*f*
mitochondria, chloroplasts, and peroxisomes of, 87, 88*f*–90*f*
mutations in, 300
organelles of animal and plant, 78*f*–79*f*. *See also* Animal cells; Plant cells
prokaryotic cells vs., 4, 5*f*, 75, 76*f*–77*f*. *See also* Prokaryotic cells
protein synthesis in, 64*f*
regulation of gene expression in. *See* Eukaryotic gene regulation
replication of telomeres at ends of DNA molecules of, 267
RNA processing after transcription in, **286**, 287*f*–288*f*
synthesis of multiple polypeptides in translation of, 296*f*–297*f*
transcription in, 284, 285*f*–286*f*
translation in, 288, 289*f*–297*f*
using scale bars to calculate volume and surface area of, 80
Eukaryotic gene regulation, 308–315. *See also* Gene regulation
  analyzing DNA deletion experiments on, 313
  differential gene expression and, 308*f*, 309
  mechanisms of post-transcriptional, 314*f*, 315
  regulation of chromatin structure in, 309*f*
  regulation of transcription initiation in, 309, 310*f*–312*f*, 313
  stages of gene expression and, 308*f*
Eukaryotic genomes, 362–371. *See also* Genomes
  evolution of, from DNA duplication, rearrangement, and mutation, 367*f*–369*f*, 371
  genes and multigene families in, 365, 366*f*
  pseudogenes and repetitive DNA in, 363*f*, 364
  simple sequence DNA and short tandem repeats in, 365
  size, number of genes, and gene density of, 362*t*, 363
  transposable elements and related sequences in, 364*f*–365*f*
Eumetazoans, 547, **551***f*
European fire salamander, 870
European green crab, 570
European honeybees, 827*f*
European Molecular Biology Laboratory, 359
Euryarchaeota clade, 490
Eustachian tube, **805***f*
Eutherians, 463*f*, **566***f*
Eutrophication, **891**, 920
Eutrophic lakes, **850***f*
Evaporation, 35, 675*f*, 687, 896*f*, 905
Evaporative cooling, **35**
Evapotranspiration, **881***f*, 892
Even-toed ungulates, 390*f*–391*f*
Evo-devo. *See* Evolutionary developmental biology
Evolution, **2**, **9**, **379**–394. *See also* Adaptations; Natural selection
  of action potentials, 789
  adaptive. *See* Adaptive evolution
  of alternative plant carbon-fixation mechanisms, 175*f*, 176
  amino acid sequences and, 71
  anatomical and molecular features, 394
  of animal hormone function, 672, 673*f*
  of animals from sponges and cnidarians, 545, 546*f*–547*f*
  of asexual and sexual reproduction, 630–631
  associative learning and, 830, 831*f*

of axon structure, 782*f*
of biological order, 125
cancer processes and, 341
of cells, 72, 99
classification of three domains of life in, 10*f*, 11
coevolution, 625
of cognition and cerebral cortex, 799, 800*f*
comparing genome sequences to study, 371, 372*f*–375*f*
constraints on, 430–431
convergent, 390*f*, 395*f*, 399*f*, 400
as core theme of biology, 2, 9, 10*f*–13*f*
crossing over and, 252
Darwin and phylogenetic bracketing and cladistic analysis, 412
as descent with modification by natural selection, 379–380, 384*f*, 385
of differences in membrane lipid composition, 102
of digestive compartments, 691, 692*f*, 693
divergent, 439*f*–441*f*, 447*f*–448*f*
DNA and proteins as measures of, 67
DNA sequences and, 320
drug development and, 519
early, of eukaryotes, 497–503
ecological niches and, 868*f*–869*f*, 885
of ecosystems, 905
effects of animals on, 569*f*–571*f*
effects of humans on, 570, 571*f*
of embryonic development genes, 377
endosymbiont theory on origins of mitochondria and chloroplasts in, 88*f*
environmental changes and, 394
of enzymes, 136
of esophagus and trachea, 705
of evaporative water loss, 687
evidence for, in biogeography and geographical distribution of species, 391–392
evidence for, in direct observations of evolutionary change, 387–389
evidence for, in fossil record, 390*f*–391*f*
evidence for, in homologies, 389–390
exaptations and, 592
extinction events in, 931
field research on, by Charles Darwin, 382, 383*f*, 384
of foraging behaviors, 831*f*, 832
of fungi, 525*f*–527*f*
gene regulation and, 329
of genetic code, 283, 284*f*, 302
genetic variation and, of animal behavior, 834*f*–836*f*
of genetic variation from genetic recombination and natural selection, 244
genetic variation within populations and, 212
of genomes from DNA duplication, rearrangement, and mutation, 367*f*–369*f*, 371
genomics and proteomics in study of, 68*f*
glycolysis and, 157
of gymnosperms, 535*f*
herbivory adaptations in, 871
hermaphroditism, 771
historical context of Darwin's ideas on, 380*f*, 381
of human globin gene amino acid sequences, 370
of humans, 451
of immune system avoidance mechanisms, 747–748
imperfections and, 433
insect size, 732
of intelligence, 813
of invertebrate defense mechanism, 750
J.-B. de Lamarck's theory of, 381
kelps and sugar transport, 618
latitudinal gradients of species diversity and, 881
of leaves, 579*f*
life history traits and, 861*f*, 862
light-sensitive germination, 661
macroevolution. *See* Macroevolution
macroevolution influences, 472
of mitosis, 191*f*, 198
molecular clocks and rates of, 406, 407*f*–408*f*
of pathogens that evade immune systems, 747–748
of patterns of sexual reproduction, 753–754
phylogenetic bracketing, 573

Evolution (*Cont.*)
phylogenies as evolutionary histories, 395*f*, 396. *See also* Phylogenies
of plant antifreeze proteins, 657
of plant defense systems, 657, 658*f*–660*f*
of plants and fungi, 521*f*–524*f*, 530*f*
plants and mass extinctions, 544
of populations. *See* Microevolution
predation adaptations in, 870, 871*f*, 885
predation and natural selection in, 392
of RNAi pathway, 316
of roots, 577*f*
of roots and leaves, 533
scientific evidence supporting theory of, 387–393
of seeds, 534*f*, 535
of sexual reproduction, 638
sexual reproduction as enigma of, 752*f*
significance of altered DNA nucleotides and mutations in, 266–267
speciation as bridge between microevolution and macroevolution, 434. *See also* Speciation
species distribution and, 866
of stems, 578*f*
subjective feelings and, 838
taxonomy and relationships in, 396*f*–398*f*
terrestrial nutrient limitations in, 892
theoretical aspects of Charles Darwin's theory on, 392–393
theory of natural selection and, 11*f*–12*f*, 20
of tolerance to toxic elements, 23
tree of life and, 12, 13*f*
tuberculosis and drug-resistance, 496
of variations in double circulation circulatory systems, 709–710
of vascular plant organs, 576, 577*f*–578*f*
of vertebrate digestive systems, 698*f*–700*f*
of viruses, 349, 353, 356
of visual perception, 807*f*–808*f*, 809
Evolutionary compromise, 431*f*
Evolutionary developmental biology (evo-devo), 329, 374*f*–375*f*, 465
Evolutionary trees, 384*f*, 385
Exaptations, 469, 480, 592
Excavata, 506*f*, 508*f*–509*f*
Excitatory postsynaptic potential (EPSP), **784**
Excited state, pigment molecule, 168*f*
Excitement phase, human sexual response, 764
Excretion, **677**, 678*f*
Excretory systems
functions of, 679, 680*f*
invertebrate, 680*f*
kidney function in, 682, 683*f*–685*f*
mammalian, 664*t*, 681*f*
vertebrate, 680, 681*f*, 682
Executive functions, brain, 799
Exergonic reactions, **126**
energy coupling of, 128*f*–130*f*
energy profile of, 131*f*, 132
metabolism and, 126, 127*f*
Exhalation, 726*f*, 727
Exit tunnel, ribosome, 291
Exocrine cells, 669
Exocytosis, 104*f*, **112**, 179*f*
Exon duplication, 369, 371*f*
Exons, 287*f*–288*f*, 362, 369, 371*f*, 414*f*–415*f*
Exon shuffling, 369, 371*f*
Exoskeletons, **822**
arthropod, 553, 559*f*
chitin as structural polysaccharide of, 53
in skeletal systems, 821*f*
Exotic species, 910*f*
Exotoxins, **492**
Expansins, 643*f*
Experimental groups, 16–17
Experiments. *See also* Inquiry Figures; Interpret the Data questions; Research Method Figures; Science; Scientific Skills Exercises
controlled, 16–17
designing, 570, 761, 797
Exploitation, **869**–870, 871*f*, 872
Exponential population growth, **858***f*–859*f*
Extant lineages, 527
Extension, muscle, 821*f*

Extensor muscles, 821*f*
External fertilization, 754, 764, 833. *See also* Fertilization, reproductive
External skeletons, 821*f*
Extinctions, 931
ecology and. *See* Ecology
in fossil record, 390*f*–391*f*, 456
habitat loss causing, 909*f*, 910
human actions as cause of, 570, 571*f*
human actions causing, 906*f*–908*f*
island equilibrium model and, 882
mass extinctions, 460–461. *See also* Mass extinctions
population dynamics and, 864
Extinction vortex, **912***f*–914*f*
Extracellular digestion, 692*f*, 693
Extracellular matrix (ECM), **95***f*, 96, 103*f*
Extreme halophiles, **487**, 490
Extreme thermophiles, **487***f*, 490
Extreme weather, 9
Extremophiles, **487**, 490
Eyecups, 469*f*
Eyes
color of fruit fly, 238*f*–239*f*, 279
compound, 808*f*
crystallin proteins of, 7*f*
differential gene expression in fish, 303*f*
evolution of, 469*f*
ocelli (eyespots) as, 807*f*, 808
single-lens, 808–809
stem cells of, 332
visual information processing in vertebrate, 810, 811*f*
Eyespots, 807

F

F$_1$ (first filial) generations, **215***f*–216*f*
F$_2$ (second filial) generations, **215**, 216*f*
Facilitated diffusion, **108**
as passive transport, 110*f*
transport proteins in, 108
of water across plant plasma membranes, 598–599
Facilitation
in ecological succession, 879, 880*f*
as interspecific interaction, 873*f*
Facultative anaerobes, **157**, 482
FAD (flavin adenine dinucleotide), 148*f*–149*f*, 154
FADH$_2$, 148*f*–150*f*, 151, 156
Fagus grandifolia, 923*f*
Falling phase, action potential, 780*f*
Familial hypercholesterolemia, 112
Families (taxonomy), **396***f*
Family histories, 228
Family resemblance, heredity and, 200*f*
Fangs, 698
Fast-twitch fibers, 819*t*, **820**
Fat cells, 332*f*
Fathead minnow, 921
Fat layer, 565
Fats, **53**
in cardiovascular diseases, 720
catabolism of, 142, 158*f*
digestion of, 695*f*–697*f*
of egg yolks, 71
energy storage in, 702
fatty acids and, 53*f*–54*f*
as hydrophobic, 45
Fat-soluble vitamins, 690
Fatty acids, 53*f*–54*f*
for animal nutrition, 689*f*, 697*f*
Feather, 565*f*
Feces, **697**
production efficiency and, 892, 893*f*
seed dispersal in, 629*f*
Feedback inhibition, **138***f*, 304*f*
Feedback mechanisms, 320
Feedback regulation. *See also* Regulation
in endocrine signaling pathways, 671
Feeding mechanisms, 524*f*, 525. *See also* Food processing
Feeding relationships, 568*f*–569*f*
Felidae, 10
Female condoms, 769*f*
Female gametophytes, angiosperm, 622, 623*f*

Females
autoimmune diseases in human, 747*f*
hormonal control of reproductive systems of human, 761, 762*f*, 763
inactivation of X-linked genes in mammalian, 241, 242*f*
mammalian sex determination of, 761
mate choice by, 427*f*, 430*f*, 833*f*
oogenesis in human, 759*f*, 760
parental care and, 832*f*–833
reproductive anatomy of human, 757*f*
reproductive rates of, 857
sex determination of, 239, 240*f*
Fermentation, **142**
aerobic respiration compared with, 154, 156, 157*f*
anaerobic respiration compared with, 156, 157*f*
oxidation in, 154–155
types of, 156*f*
Ferns, 530*f*, 531*f*, 532, 544, 603*f*
Ferrets, 354
Fertility
human, 768–770
hybrid, 437*f*
Fertilization, reproductive, **203**, **620**, **622**, 623*f*, **754**
angiosperm, 620
angiosperm double fertilization, 622, 623*f*, 625*f*
in animal embryonic development, 765*f*
cell division and, 184
ensuring offspring survival following, 754, 755*f*
external vs. internal, 754
human, 767*f*, 768
human contraception and, 768, 769*f*
human *in vitro* fertilization, 770
in human life cycle, 203*f*, 204
mechanisms preventing angiosperm self-fertilization, 631*f*
Mendel's techniques of, 215*f*, 216
parental care and internal vs. external, 833
parthenogenetic self-fertilization, 752, 753
in plant cells, 522*f*
prezygotic barriers and, 435, 436*f*–437*f*
random, 212
in sexual life cycles, 204*f*
Fertilization, soil, 601, 863*f*, 892, 897*f*
nutrient enrichment caused by, 919*f*, 920
Fe · S. *See* Iron-sulfur protein
Fescue grass, 862
Fetal alcohol syndrome, 768
Fetus, human, **768***f*
Fever, 676, 737
F factor, **485***f*
Fiber, dietary, 52
Fiber cells, **580***f*
Fibers, muscle, 815*f*–817*f*, 819*t*, 820*f*
Fibrin, 719*f*
Fibrinogen, 718, 719*f*
Fibroblasts, 194, 489*f*, 665*f*
Fibronectin, 95*f*
Fibrous proteins, 58, 60*f*–61*f*
Fibrous root systems, 576–577
Fiddler crabs, 814*f*, 826
Fields, visual, 810, 811
Fierer, Noah, 874*f*
Fight-or-flight response, 115, 672*f*, 712, 793
Filaments
flagellum, 480*f*
flower, 536*f*, 620*f*
fungi as, 530
muscle, 815*f*–817*f*
Filopodia, 97, 766*f*
Filtrate, **680***f*–683*f*
Filtration, **680***f*–681*f*
Fimbriae, 76*f*, **479***f*
Finches, 12, 13*f*, 17, 383*f*, 413*f*, 869*f*
Finland, 864*f*, 877*f*
Fin whales, 398*f*
Fire, 878, 879*f*, 926
Fire-bellied toad, 444*f*, 445–446
Firefly gene transplantation, 284*f*
Fireworm, 552*f*

First law of thermodynamics, 124f, 887
Fishapod, 560f–561f
Fishes
    allopatric speciation in, 439f
    changes in developmental gene regulation in, 467, 468f
    circulatory systems of, 708, 709f
    differential gene expression in, 303f
    effects of human overfishing, 570, 571f
    electromagnetic receptors of, 803
    estrogen effects on, 921f
    fixed action patterns in, 826f
    frequency-dependent selection and, 427f
    gills for gas exchange in, 723f
    membrane lipid composition in, 102
    mutually beneficial interaction with, 9f
    natural reserves for, 918f, 919
    osmoregulation by, 678f
    overharvesting of, 911f
    parental care in, 833f
    pheromones as alarm signals for, 827
    production efficiency of, 893
    sex reversal in, 753–754
Fission, 752
Fitness, relative, 425
FitzRoy, Robert, 382
Fixed action patterns, 826f
Fixed alleles, 417, 423
Flaccid cells, 108, 598
Flagella, 92
    animal cell, 78f
    euglenozoan, 508f
    as microtubules, 92–93
    prokaryotic, 76f, 480f
    protistan cell, 79f
    structure of, 93f
Flagellin, 658
Flame bulbs, 680
Flashlight fish, 491f
Flattening, surface area and, 526f
Flatworms, 526f, 680f, 692, 707f, 791f, 821, 822f
Flavin adenine dinucleotide. See FAD
Flavin mononucleotide (FMN), 150f
Flemming, Walther, 185
Flesh-eating disease, 388
Fleshy fruits, 628
Fletcher, W. J., 853f
Flexibility of science, 15f, 16
Flexion, muscle, 821f
Flexor muscles, 821f
Flies, 624f, 833. See also Drosophila melanogaster
Flight, 559, 560f, 565f, 824–825
Flightless cormorant, 434
FLM. See Free-living mycelium
Flooding
    as disturbance, 878, 879f
    plant responses to, 655–656, 657f
Floral meristem, 627
Florida, Kissimmee River restoration in, 900f
Florida Keys National Marine Sanctuary, 918f, 919
Florida panther, 422f
Florigen, 653f
Flower-eyed mantis, 386f
FLOWERING LOCUS T (FT) gene, 653
Flowering plants. See Angiosperms
Flowers, 536f, 619f–629f
    adaptations that prevent self-fertilization of, 631f
    double fertilization of, 622, 623f, 625f
    flowering of, 584, 651, 652f–653f
    fruit development from, 627, 628f–629f
    hypothetical florigen hormone in flowering of, 653f
    impact of pollinators on, 541–542
    monocot vs. eudicot, 576f
    photoperiodism and flowering of, 652f–653f
    pollination of, 619, 622, 623f, 624f
    preventing transgene escape with genetically engineered, 636
    reproduction and, 638
    seed development from, 625f–626f
    structure and function of, 620f–623
    structure of, 536f
Flow-gram, 274f
Fluctuation, of populations, 862, 864f

Fluid-based skeletons, 821, 822f
Fluid feeders, 691
Fluidity, membrane, 101f–102f
Fluid mosaic model, 101f–102f, 103, 105
Fluorescence, 169
Fluorescence microscopy, 74f, 182f, 190
Flu viruses. See Influenza viruses
Fly agaric, 528f
Flying. See Flight
Flying foxes, 908f
Flying squirrels, 390f
FMN. See Flavin mononucleotide
fMRI. See Functional magnetic resonance imaging
Focusing, visual, 811
Focus on Energy and Matter questions, 140, 181, 496, 771, 905
Focus on Evolution questions, 20, 42, 71, 99, 121, 140, 160, 181, 198, 213, 235, 252, 277, 302, 320, 341, 356, 377, 394, 412, 433, 451, 472, 496, 519, 544, 573, 592, 618, 638, 661, 687, 705, 732, 750, 771, 789, 813, 838, 866, 885, 905, 931
Focus on Information questions, 20, 198, 213, 235, 252, 302, 377, 412, 451, 750, 838, 866, 885
Focus on Interactions questions, 121, 320, 394, 519, 544, 618, 661, 732, 931
Focus on Organization questions, 42, 71, 99, 160, 277, 341, 356, 433, 472, 573, 592, 638, 687, 705, 789, 813
Folding
    protein, 62f, 63, 292, 295
    protein, crystallin, 7f
    surface area and, 526f
Foliose lichens, 539f
Follicles, 757f
Follicle-stimulating hormone (FSH), 669f, 759f, 760–764
Follicular phase, ovarian cycle, 762f, 763
Food
    in cellular respiration, 141–142, 157–158
    climate change and, 9f
    genetically modified organisms as, 635
    natural selection by source of, 413f
Food chains, 875f, 903f
    production efficiency in, 892, 893f
    trophic efficiency in, 893, 894f
Food poisoning, 346, 488f, 492, 786
Food processing. See also Animal nutrition; Digestive systems
    evolutionary adaptations for, 698f–700f
    feedback circuits in, 700, 701f–703f
    organs for, 693f–697f, 698
    process of, 691f–692f
Food vacuoles, 85f, 86, 113f, 510f, 692
Food webs, 515f, 516, 875f, 876f, 885
    PCBs in, 920f
Foolish seedling disease, 644
Foot, of mollusc, 553f
Foraging, 831f, 832
Foraminiferans, 511
Forams, 511
Forebrain, 794f
Foregut, 692f
Forelimbs, mammalian, 389f
Forest fire, 878, 879f
Forests
    case study on nutrient cycling in, 898f, 899
    clear-cutting of, 542
    decomposition and nutrient cycling rates in, 895
    ferns and seed plants compared with lycophytes, 544
    northern coniferous, 848f
    temperate broadleaf, 848f
    tropical, 846f
Form-function correlation, 3, 10, 663
Formic acid, 22f
Fossil fuels
    biofuel technology to reduce dependence on, 634–635
    carbon skeletons of, 45
    climate change and, 181, 924f, 926
    global carrying capacity and, 928
    increased burning of, 8–9
    ocean acidification and, 39f, 40

Fossil record
    adaptive radiations in, 463f–464f, 465
    angiosperms in, 536, 537f
    biogeography and, 391–392
    bryophytes in, 531
    Cambrian explosion and bilaterian radiation in, 547, 548f–549f
    dating of rocks and fossils in, 454f
    as documentation of history of life, 452, 453f, 454
    early eukaryotes in, 498f–499f, 500
    early land animals in, 558f–559
    evidence for evolution in, 384f, 385, 390f–391f
    evidence in, of dinosaurs as ancestors of birds, 405f–406f
    evolutionary trends in, 470f, 471
    fungi in, 525f
    geologic record and, 454, 455t, 456
    gymnosperms in, 535
    homologies vs. analogies in, 399–400
    human evolution in, 567f–568f
    insects in, 559f–560f
    mass extinctions in, 461f–463f
    origin of animals in, 545, 546f
    origin of mammals in, 457f
    origins of new groups of organisms in, 456
    phylogenetic trees in, 402f–404f, 405
    plant origin and diversification in, 523f–524f
    prokaryotes in, as evidence of early life, 477f, 478
    representative organisms in, 453f
    seedless vascular plants in, 531f–533f
    speciation patterns in, 446, 447f
    strata in, 454
    tetrapods in, 560f–561f
Fossils, 11f, 380f, 381, 474. See also Fossil record
Founder effect, 422
Fouquieria splendens, 614f
Four-chambered hearts, 710f
Fovea, 808f, 811
Fox, 886f, 902f
FOXP2 gene, 373f
F plasmids, 485f
Fractals, 575
Fragmentation
    habitat, 909f, 910, 916f–917f
    plant, 630
    reproductive, 752
Frameshift mutations, 299f, 300
Franklin, Rosalind, 257f, 258–259
Fraternal twins, human, 768
Free energy, 125, 126f–127f, 128
    ATP hydrolysis, energy coupling, and, 129f
    free-energy change, stability, equilibrium, and, 125, 126f
    metabolism and, 126, 127f, 128
Free energy, electron transport chain and, 145, 150f
Free energy of activation, 131–132
Free-living mycelium (FLM), 529
Free ribosomes, 82f, 295
Freezing, plant responses to, 657
Frequency, sound, 806
Frequency-dependent selection, 427f
Freshwater. See also Aquatic biomes
    fishes, 675–676
Freshwater biomes
    characteristics and types of, 849f–850f, 852
    primary production in, 890–891
Friction, locomotion and, 823–824
Fritillaries, 864f
Frogs
    as amphibians, 561, 562f
    continental drift and speciation of, 460f
    discovery of new species of, 840f
    evolutionary compromise of, 431f
    intersexual selection and mate choice, 430f
    life cycle of, 764f
    metamorphosis of, 672, 673f
    nuclear transplantation in, 330f, 331
    polyploidy in, 441
    in predation, 870, 871f
Fronds, 531f
Frontal lobe, 799f
Frontal lobotomy, 799f
Frost-tolerant plants, 657

Fructose
  hydrolysis of sucrose to, 131–132
  as monosaccharide, 50f
  synthesis of sucrose from, 51f
Fructose 6-phosphate, 146f, 160
Fruit fly. *See Drosophila melanogaster*; *Drosophila pseudoobscura*
Fruiting bodies, fungal, 528f
Fruitlets, **628**f
Fruit ripening, 114
Fruits, **536**, **627**
  auxin in growth of, 644
  dispersal of, 629f
  ethylene in ripening of, 648
  form and function of, 627, 628f
  gibberellins in growth of, 644, 645f
Frye, Larry, 102f
FSH. *See* Follicle-stimulating hormone
Fugu, 603f
Fumonisin, 635
Functional groups, 47f, **48**
Functional magnetic resonance imaging (fMRI), 793f
Function-form correlation, 3, 472, 663
Fundamental niches, 868, 869f
Fungi
  alcohol fermentation by, 156f
  animal mutualism with, 603f
  bacteria mutualism with, 603f
  calculate volume and surface area of, 80
  cells of, 78f. *See also* Eukaryotic cells
  chemical cycling and biotic interactions of, 539f–542f
  colonization of land by plants and, 520f, 524f–529f, 530
  in ecosystem trophic structure, 888f
  in energy flow and chemical cycling, 8f
  Eukarya domain and, 10f
  evolution of, 525f–527f
  innate immunity and, 734, 735f–736f, 737
  life cycles of, 529f
  multicellular, 525f
  mycorrhizal, 524, 527f, 595, 606, 607f, 872, 892
  nutritional adaptations of, 524f, 525
  origin of, in protists, 524f
  overproduction of, 385f
  phylogeny of, 527, 528f
  plant mutualism with, 603f
  plant toxin as, 635
  sexual and asexual reproduction of, 525f, 529f, 530
  sexual life cycles of, 204f
  structural polysaccharides and, 53
  Unikonta supergroup and, 512, 513f–514f
  vacuoles in, 86
Fungi kingdom, 10f, 11, 408
Fusarium, 635
Fusiform shape, 824
Fusion, hybrid zone, 445f, 446

G
G_0 phase, **193**f
G_1 phase, **185**f
G_1 phase checkpoint, 192f–193f
G_2 phase, **185**f–186f
G_2 phase checkpoint, 192f–193f
G3P. *See* Glyceraldehyde 3-phosphate
GABA. *See* Gamma-aminobutyric acid
Gage, Phineas, 799f
Gaia hypothesis, 905
Gait, breathing and, 573
Galápagos Islands, 12, 382f, 383, 434. *See also* Finches
  area effects on, 882f
  finches of, 869f
Gallbladder, 693f, 695f, **696**
Gälweiler, Leo, 643f
Gambusia hubbsi, 439f
Gametes, **183**, **201**
  allele combinations in, 213
  chromosomes in human, 183
  gametogenesis and, 757, 758f–759f, 760
  as haploid cells, 203
  inheritance of genes in, 201
  law of segregation of, 217–218f
  meiotic nondisjunction of, 248, 249f

Gametic isolation, 437f
Gametogenesis, **757**, 758f–759f, 760
Gametophytes, **522**f
  of bryophytes, 531f
  development of male and female, in angiosperms, 620, 622, 623f
  of plants, 522f
  reduced, in seed plants, 534
  of seedless vascular plants, 531f–533f
  sporophytes and, 204f
Gamma-aminobutyric acid (GABA), 786t, 789
Gamma proteobacteria, 488f
Ganglia, **772**, 791f
Ganglion cells, 808f, 810
Gap junctions, **96**f, 114
Garden peas, G. Mendel's, 214f–220f, 221
Garlic mustard, 607
Garrod, Archibald, 279
Garter snakes, 834, 835
GAs. *See* Gibberellins
Gas chromatography, 646
Gases, as neurotransmitters, 787
Gas exchange, 666f, 720–730
  arthropod, 559
  breathing, lung ventilation, and, 726f–727f, 728
  circulatory systems and, 706, 708, 709f, 710. *See also* Circulatory systems
  coordination of circulation and, 728f
  gills for, in aquatic animals, 723f
  ion gradients in, 777f
  lungs for, in mammalian respiratory systems, 724, 725f–726f. *See also* Respiratory systems
  mammals, 730
  partial pressure gradients in, 721–722
  respiratory media in, 722f
  respiratory pigments and adaptations for, 728f–729f, 730
  respiratory surfaces in, 722–723
  tracheal systems for, in insects, 723, 724f
Gas exchange circuits, 708, 709f
Gasterosteus aculeatus, 826f
Gastric cecae, 692f
Gastric glands, **694**f
Gastric juice, **694**f
Gastric ulcers, 694
Gastrin, 700, 701f
Gastrovascular cavities, **547**, **692**f, **707**f, 821
Gastrula, **766**f
Gastrulation, 764, **766**f
Gated channels, **108**
Gated ion channels, **778**, 779f–780f, 781, 789
Gause, G. F., 868
Gecko lizards, 30f, 906f
Geese, 569f, 829f
Gel electrophoresis, **271**f, 318f
GenBank, 359
Genealogy, molecular, 67
Gene cloning, 270f, **271**, 272, 273f. *See also* DNA cloning
Gene expression, 7, **64**f, **278**–302
  analyzing quantitative and spatial data on, 325
  basic principles of transcription and translation in, 280, 281f
  discovery of principles of, 279f–280f
  gene concept and, 300
  genetic code in, 282f–284f
  genetic engineering and transgenic, 283, 284f
  genetic information flow, protein synthesis, and, 278f
  interpreting DNA sequence logos for translation initiation in, 294
  monitoring, for single genes and for groups of genes, 316, 317f–318f, 319f
  mutations of nucleotides affecting protein structure and function in, 278, 298f–299f, 300
  overview of, 281f
  in plant development, 583, 584f
  protein synthesis in, 7f
  regulation of. *See* Gene regulation
  RNA processing after transcription in, **286**, 287f–288f
  summary of eukaryotic transcription and translation in, 297f

systems biology in study of, 360–361
  transcription as, 309
  transcription as DNA-directed RNA synthesis in, 284, 285f–286f
  translation as RNA-directed polypeptide synthesis in, 288, 289f–297f
Gene flow, **423**
  biological species concept and, 435, 438
  as cause of microevolution, 423, 424f
  geographic separation and, 443–444
  Hardy-Weinberg equilibrium and, 419–420
  speciation and, 448
Gene pools, **417**
General transcription factors, 310
Generative cells, 622, 623f
Gene regulation
  analyzing DNA deletion experiments on, 313
  analyzing quantitative and spatial gene data on, 325
  by auxin, 642t
  bacterial, 303, 304f–307f, 308
  changes in, of developmental genes, 467f–468f
  development, embryonic development, and, 321f. *See also* Development; Embryonic development
  differential gene expression and, 303f, 308f, 309
  eukaryotic, 308–315
  evolution and, 329
  faulty, in cloned animals, 331
  flowering and, 653f
  monitoring of gene expression and, 316, 317f–318f, 319f
  noncoding RNAs in, 315f, 316
  in plant development, 583, 584f
Genes, **6**, **64**, **201**. *See also* Chromosomes; DNA
  alleles as alternative versions of, 217f. *See also* Alleles
  analyzing distribution patterns in human skin pigmentation as polygenic trait, 227
  animal behavior and, 834f–836f
  appetite regulation by, 704t
  bacterial resistance, 485–486
  B cell and T cell diversity and, 739, 740f
  calibrating molecular clocks of, 406, 407f
  in cell nucleus, 80, 81f, 82
  of chloroplasts, 181
  cloning, 270f, 271, 272, 273f
  color vision and, 811
  concept of, 300
  coordinately controlled bacterial, 304, 305f
  coordinately controlled eukaryotic, 312–313
  for crystallin protein, 7f
  dating origin of HIV using, 407, 408f
  developmental. *See* Developmental genes
  DNA, nucleic acids, and, 64
  in DNA structure and function, 6f–7f
  editing of, in genetic engineering, 274, 275f. *See also* CRISPR-Cas systems
  for embryonic development, 377
  enzyme relationship with, in protein synthesis, 279f–280f
  epistasis of, 225f
  evolution of, with related and with novel functions, 368f–369f
  evolution of *FOXP2*, 373f
  extending Mendelian inheritance for multiple, 225f–226f
  extending Mendelian inheritance for single, 223f, 224, 225f
  fluorescent dye and, 236f
  foraging, 831f, 832
  gene expression and protein synthesis. *See* Gene expression
  genetic variation due to alterations of number or position of, 416
  genomics and proteomics in study of, 68f
  homeotic, 327–328, 374f–375f, 466, 467f
  homologous, 390
  horizontal gene transfer of, 409f, 410
  inheritance of, 201
  locating, along chromosomes, 236, 236f
  mapping distance between, on chromosomes, 245–246, 247f, 248
  master regulatory, 324f

maternal effect (egg-polarity), as axis establishment, 328*f*–329*f*
as measures of evolution, 67
in Mendel's particulate hypothesis of inheritance, 214
multigene families and, in genomes, 365, 366*f*
mutations, faulty proteins, and faulty, 278
mutations of. *See* Mutations
mycorrhizal, 527*f*
number and density of, in genomes, 363
organization of typical eukaryotic, 310*f*
pleiotropy of, 225
in prokaryotic and eukaryotic cells, 75, 76*f*
pseudogenes, 363*f*, 364
ras and *p53* and *p21*, in cancer development, 335*f*–336*f*
rearrangement of parts of, through exon duplication and shuffling, 369, 371*f*
regulation of. *See* Gene regulation
regulatory, **305***f*, 306
RNA splicing and split, 287*f*–288*f*
sex-linked, 240, 241*f*–242*f*
shared between organisms, 20
speciation and, 448, 449*f*
systems biology in study of, 360–361
transcription factors and, 117
transplanting of, into different species, 284*f*
transposable elements, 364*f*–365*f*
types of cancer, 334*f*, 335
understanding functions for protein-coding, 359–360
using chi-square (χ^2) test to determine linkage of, 246
Gene therapy, 277
Genetically modified (GM) organisms, 633–634, 635*f*, 636, 638
Genetic code
amino acid dictionary of, 283*f*
codons and triplet code of, 282*f*, 283, 302
deciphering, 283*f*
DNA structure and function and, 7
evolution of, 283, 284*f*
as molecular homology, 390
mutations and, 298*f*–299*f*, 300
Genetic counseling, 231–232, 235
Genetic disorders
from abnormal chromosome numbers, 248*f*–250*f*
alkaptonuria, 279
from alterations of chromosome structure, 249, 250*f*–251*f*
counseling for, 231–232
dominantly inherited, 231*f*
gene editing for, 275
multifactorial, 231
mutations and, 298*f*–299*f*, 300
preparing karyotypes for, 202*f*
recessively inherited, 229*f*–230*f*
Genetic diversity, 907*f*
benefits of, 908–909
prokaryotic, 483*f*–485*f*, 486
in small populations, 912*f*–913*f*
Genetic drift, **421***f*–423*f*
Genetic engineering, **270**
amplifying DNA for cloning using polymerase chain reaction in, 272, 273*f*
DNA cloning in, 270*f*, 271
DNA sequencing in, 273, 274*f*
editing genes and genomes, 274, 275*f*. *See also* CRISPR-Cas systems
gene transplantation in, 283, 284*f*
nucleic acid hybridization in, 270
organismal cloning in, 330*f*–334*f*
plant biotechnology and, 634, 635*f*, 636
of plant defenses against herbivores, 658
prokaryotes in, 493
resistance to, 638
using restriction enzymes to make recombinant DNA in, 271*f*–272*f*
Genetic maps, 245–246, 247*f*, 248
Genetic mutants, 704*t*, 797
Genetic profiles, **365**
Genetic prospecting, 486

Genetic recombination, **243**
evolution of genetic variation from natural selection and, 244
linked genes and, 243, 244*f*–245*f*
of linked genes through crossing over, 244, 245*f*
in prokaryotes, 484*f*–485*f*, 486
transposable elements and, 371
of unlinked genes through independent assortment of chromosomes, 244
Genetics, **200**
appetite regulation and, 704*t*
B cell and T cell diversity and, 739, 740*f*
chromosomal basis of inheritance in. *See* Chromosomal basis of inheritance
color vision and, 811
cytology and, 236
DNA structure and function in, 6*f*–7*f*. *See also* DNA
environment vs., in animal behaviors, 828
expression and transmission of genetic information as biological theme, 6*f*–7*f*, 8
flow of in plant cells, 178*f*
foraging behavior and, 831*f*, 832
gene regulation in. *See* Gene regulation
genetic basis of animal behavior, 834*f*–836*f*
genetic engineering and. *See* Genetic engineering
genomics and bioinformatics in, 7–8. *See also* Bioinformatics; Genomics
genomics and proteomics in study of, 68*f*
heredity, inheritance, variation, and, 200. *See also* Genetic variation; Inheritance
Hox genes in Cambrian explosion, 548
macroevolution of development from changes in developmental genes in, 465*f*–468*f*
of mammalian sex determination, 761
Mendelian inheritance in. *See* Mendelian inheritance
molecular basis of inheritance in. *See* Molecular basis of inheritance
molecular evidence for origination of animals, 546–547
of mycorrhizae, 527*f*
in phylogeny of animals, 550, 551*f*
prokaryotic, 480, 481*f*, 483*f*–485*f*, 486
Punnett square and, 218*f*
research on prokaryotes related to mitochondria, 501
sexual life cycles in. *See* Sexual life cycles
solving complex problems in, with rules of probability, 222
of speciation, 448, 449*f*
twin studies in, 828
Genetic variation, **414**
crossing over, recombinant chromosomes, and, 211, 212*f*
evolution and, within populations, 212
evolution of, from genetic recombination and natural selection, 244
genetic drift and loss of, 422, 423*f*
independent assortment of chromosomes and, 211*f*
microevolution and sources of, 415–416
origins of, 210–211
phylogenetic tree branch lengths and, 402*f*–404*f*, 405
preservation of, 426–427
in prey selection, 834, 835
random fertilization and, 212
in small populations, 912*f*–914*f*
types of, 414*f*–415*f*
Gene trees, 398*f*
Gene variability, 414
Genomes, 7, **183**, 357–377
bioinformatics, proteomics, and systems biology in analysis of, 359, 360*f*–361*f*
cell division and, 183, 184*f*
comparing, to study evolution and development of species, 371, 372*f*–375*f*
differential gene expression for identical, 303*f*, 308*f*, 309. *See also* Gene regulation
editing of, genetic engineering, 274, 275*f*. *See also* CRISPR-Cas systems
evolution of, from DNA duplication, rearrangement, and mutation, 367*f*–369*f*, 371

genomics, proteomics and bioinformatics in study of, 7–8, 68*f*
genomics and bioinformatics in study of, 357. *See also* Bioinformatics; Genomics; Metagenomics
horizontal gene transfer between, 409*f*, 410
Human Genome Project and genome sequencing techniques, 358–359
monitoring gene expression of groups of genes in, 318, 319*f*
noncoding DNA and multigene families in eukaryotic, 363*f*–366*f*. *See also* Eukaryotic genomes
noncoding RNAs in, 315*f*, 316
p53 gene as guardian angel of, 336*f*
predicting percentages of nucleotides in, using data in tables, 257
prokaryotic, 480, 481*f*, 486
reading amino acid sequence identity tables for, 370
size and estimated number of genes in, for organisms in three domains, 362*t*
species with complete sequences available, 357, 360, 361, 362*t*, 492
variations in size, number of genes, and gene density of, 361, 362*t*, 363
viral, 343, 345*f*–346*f*, 349
Genome sequencing, 7–8, 353, 358*f*, 359. *See also* DNA sequencing
development of, 67
Genomics, **7**–8, 66–**67**, 68*f*, **357**, 486. *See also* Bioinformatics; Genetics; Metagenomics; Systems biology; DNA sequencing
cell signaling, cancer and, 338*f*–339*f*
internet resources for, 359, 360*f*
interpreting data for, 529
new insights with, 360
Genotypes, **218**
determination of, 235
gene expression as link between phenotypes and, 278
in Hardy-Weinberg equilibrium, 418*f*–419*f*, 420
heterozygote advantage and, 426
phenotypes vs., 218, 219*f*, 226. *See also* Phenotypes
relative fitness and, 425
transformation and, 254
Genus/genera (taxonomy), **396***f*
Geographical separation, speciation with and without, 439*f*–444*f*
Geographic distribution of species. *See* Species distributions
Geologic record, 454, 455*t*, 456
Geospiza fortis, 413*f*, 414, 869*f*
Geospiza fuliginosa, 869*f*
Germ cells, 204, 267, 758*f*–759*f*
Germination, seed, 627*f*, 645*f*, **649**, 650*f*, 661
Germ layers, 550*f*, 551, 767*f*
Gestation, human, **767**–768
GH. *See* Growth hormone
Ghrelin, 703
Giant panda, 362*t*
Giant water bugs, 755*f*
Giardia intestinalis, 506*f*, 508
Gibberella, 410
Gibberellins (GAs), 642*t*, **644**, 645*f*
Gibbons, 69
Gibbs, J. Willard, 125
Gibbs free energy, 125. *See also* Free energy
Gills
for gas exchange in aquatic animals, 706, 723*f*
single circulation and, 708, 709*f*
Giraffes, 141*f*, 556*f*, 773
Gizzard, 692*f*
GLABRA-2 gene, 583, 584*f*
Glaciation, ecological succession after, 880*f*
Glacier Bay, Alaska, 880*f*
Glans
clitoris, 757*f*
penis, 756*f*, 757
Glanville fritillary, 864*f*
Glaucoma, 808*f*
Gleason, H. A., 878

Glia (glial cells), **665***f*, **773***f*, 791*f*, 792
Glioblastoma (brain cancer), 196, 361
Global carrying capacity, 927, 928*f*
Global change, 911*f*, 917. *See also* Climate change
    environmental toxins as, 920*f*–921*f*
    greenhouse gases and climate change as, 921,
        922*f*–925*f*, 926
    nutrient enrichment as, 919*f*–920*f*
Global climate change. *See* Climate change
Global climate patterns, 842*f*–843
Global ecology, 841*f*, 906–931
    biodiversity threats in, 907*f*–911*f*, 931
    human-caused rapid changes in, 919*f*–925*f*, 926
    human population growth in, 926*f*–928*f*
    landscape and regional conservation in, 915,
        916*f*–918*f*, 919, 931
    population conservation in, 912*f*–915*f*
    sustainable development in, 928, 929*f*
Global energy budget, 889
Global hectares, 928
Global net primary production, 889*f*–890*f*
Global warming. *See* Climate change
Globigerina, 507*f*
Globin genes, 366*f*–369*f*, 370
Globular proteins, 58, 60*f*–61*f*
Glomeromycetes, 528*f*
Glomerulus, **681***f*
Glomus, 528*f*
Glucagon, 669*f*, **702**, 703*f*
Glucocorticoids, 669*f*
Glucose
    ATP production from, 146
    ATP yield from, 153*f*, 154
    calculating rate of enzymatic catalysis of, 134
    in cellular respiration, 142–143. *See also* Cellular
        respiration
    diabetes mellitus and, 702–703
    effects of age on transport of, 109
    in glycolysis, 145*f*–147*f*
    homeostasis of, 702, 703*f*
    hydrolysis of sucrose to, 131–132
    linear and ring forms of, 50*f*
    as monosaccharide, 49, 50*f*
    in photosynthesis, 31–32, 163, 177*f*
    in positive gene regulation, 307
    stepwise energy harvest from, 143, 144*f*, 145
    in storage polysaccharides, 51, 52*f*
    in structural polysaccharides, 52*f*
    synthesis of sucrose from, 51*f*
    transport proteins for, 105, 108
Glucose 6-phosphatase, 134
Glucose 6-phosphate, 134
Glutamate, 786*t*, 810
Glutamic acid, 57*f*, 62*f*, 129*f*, 283*f*
Glutamine, 57*f*, 129*f*
Glyceraldehyde, 50*f*
Glyceraldehyde 3-phosphate (G3P), **173**, 174*f*, 177*f*
Glycerol, **53***f*–54*f*
Glycerol phosphate, 47*f*
Glycine, 47*f*, 57*f*, 786*t*
Glycogen, 51*f*, 52, 115, 158, 693, 702, 817
Glycogen phosphorylase, 115
Glycolipids, 101*f*, **104**
Glycolysis, **145**
    ATP yield during, 153*f*, 154
    in cellular respiration, 145*f*–147*f*
    evolutionary significance of, 157
    glycolytic muscle fibers and, 819*t*, 820
    substrate-level phosphorylation of, 155
Glycolytic muscle fibers, 819*t*
Glycoproteins, **84**, **104**
    in cell-cell recognition, 103*f*
    in extracellular matrix, 95*f*
    in Golgi apparatus, 85
    membrane carbohydrates in, 104
    in plasma membranes, 101*f*
    rough ER and, 84
    synthesis of, in endoplasmic reticulum, 104*f*
    viruses and, 343*f*, 344, 348*f*
Glycosidic linkages, 50–53
GM organisms. *See* Genetically modified organisms
Gnathostomes, **555**, 556*f*–557*f*
Goatsbeard plants, 442, 443*f*

Gobi Desert, 844
Golden Rice, 634, 690
Golgi apparatus, **84**
    in animal cell, 78*f*
    in endomembrane system, 87*f*
    functions of, 84*f*, 85
    in plant cell, 79*f*, 178*f*
    in synthesis of membrane components, 104*f*
Gonadotropin-releasing hormone (GnRH), 760–764
Gonadotropins, 760–764
Gonads, 184, 203*f*, 204, **755**, 761. *See also*
    Reproductive organs, human
Gonium, 503*f*
Gonorrhea, 479, 770
Goodall, Jane, 13, 14*f*
GPCRs. *See* G protein-coupled receptors
GPP. *See* Gross primary production
G protein-coupled receptors (GPCRs), **116***f*,
    118, 119*f*
G proteins, **116***f*, 118, 119*f*, 810
Graded muscle contraction, 818–819
Graded potentials, neuron, **778**, 779*f*, 784
Grafting, plant, 632
Grafts, tissue, 746
Gram, Hans Christian, 478
Gram-negative bacteria, **478**, 479*f*, 488*f*–489*f*
Gram-positive bacteria, **478**, 479*f*, 489*f*
Gram staining technique, 478, 479*f*
Granum (grana), **89**–90, 162, 163*f*
Grant, Peter and Rosemary, 17, 413
Grapes, 645*f*
Graphs in Scientific Skills Exercises and Scientific
    Skills Review
    bar graphs, 18*f*, 155*t*, 313*f*, 325*f*, 392*f*, 493*t*, 570*f*,
        582*t*, 656*f*, 870*t*, F-2*f*
    comparing two variables on common *x*-axis of,
        748*t*, F-1*f*
    estimating quantitative data from, and developing
        hypotheses, 459*f*
    histograms, 196*f*, 227*t*, 721*f*, F-2*f*
    line graphs, 134*t*, 210*t*, 353*f*, 748*t*, 825*f*, F-1*f*
    with log scales, 825*f*
    scatter plots, 40*f*, 109*f*, 176*t*, 441*t*, 870*t*, F-1*f*
Grass, 640, 641*f*, 862
Grasshopper, digestive system of, 692*f*
Grasshoppers, 375*f*, 707*f*, 724*f*, 821*f*
Grasslands, 592
    temperate, 847*f*
    transformation of, 886*f*
Gravitational motion, free energy and, 126*f*
Gravitropism, **654***f*
Gravity
    blood pressure and, 715
    locomotion and, 823
    mechanoreceptors for sensing, in humans,
        806, 807*f*
    mechanoreceptors for sensing, in invertebrates, 804
    plant responses to, 654*f*
Gray matter, **792**
Gray tree frogs, 430*f*, 441
Great auk, 910
Greater Mekong region, new species found in, 906*f*
Greater prairie chickens, 422, 423*f*, 912, 913*f*
Great Lakes, PCBs in, 920*f*
Great Salt Lake, 121, 487
Great tits (birds), 424*f*
Green algae, **512***f*
    cells of, 79*f*
    chloroplasts of, 89*f*
    in eukaryotic phylogeny, 507*f*
    evolution of plants from, 502*f*–504*f*, 521, 523*f*–524*f*
    land animals vs., 558*f*
Greenhouse effect, **922**, 923*f*
Greenhouse gases, climate change and, 921,
    922*f*–925*f*, 926
Greening, plant, 648*f*
Green parrot snake, 871*f*
Green slime, 525
Greylag geese, 829*f*
Griffith, Frederick, 254
Grizzly bears, 438*f*, 913, 914*f*, 918
Grolar bears, 438*f*
Gross primary production (GPP), **889**

Ground squirrels, 835, 855, 856*ft*, 857
Ground tissue system, plant, **579***f*
Groups, control and experimental, 17
Growth factors, **193**
    in cancer, 194*f*, 195
    in cell cycle control system, 193, 194*f*
    in cell signaling, 114*f*, 119
    coordinate control by, 313
Growth hormone (GH), 669*f*
Growth inhibitors, plant, 641*t*, 645, 646*f*
Growth rates
    heterochrony and, 465*f*–466*f*
    of human population, 927*f*
Growth regulators, plant, 640. *Also see* Hormones,
    plant
Growth rings, tree, 590*f*
Grundler, Michael, 840
Grus americana, 829*f*
Grus canadensis, 829*f*
GTP (guanosine triphosphate), 291, 292*f*–293*f*
    production of, 148, 149*f*
Guam, 910
Guanine (G), 65*f*, 66, 256, 258, 259*f*
Guanosine triphosphate. *See* GTP
Guard cells, **587***f*, 612, 613*f*, 614
Guinea pigs, 109
Gulf of Mexico, 919*f*, 920
Gulf Stream, 844*f*
Gulls, 829, 832*f*
Guppies, 392
Gurdon, John, 330*f*, 331, 333
Gustation, **803**
Gutenberg, Johannes, 19
Gymnosperms, **533**
    evolution of, 535*f*
    gametophyte-sporophyte relationship in, 532*f*
    ovule to seed in, 534*f*
    phylogeny of, 530*f*
    as seed plants, 533
Gynandromorph, 252

H

H1N1 virus, 352*f*, 353, 884
H5N1 virus, 354, 883–884
Habitat
    carrying capacity of, 858, **859***f*, 860
    climate change and, 9*f*
    edges of, 916*f*, 931
    islands of, 882*f*
    loss of, 909*f*, 910
    metapopulations and, 864*f*
    restoration of, 915
    sympatric speciation and differentiation of,
        442–443
Habitat corridors, 901
Habitat fragmentation, 909*f*, 910, 916*f*–917*f*
Habitat isolation, 436*f*
Hadean eon, 455*t*
Haemophilus influenzae, 362*t*
Hagfishes, 555, 556*f*
Hair, 565, 705
Hair cells, 805*f*, **806**, 807*f*
Hairs
    invertebrate, 804
    mechanoreceptors and, 802
Hakea purpurea, 592
Haldane, J. B. S., 475, 836
Half-life, **454***f*
Hallucigenia, 453*f*, 548*f*, 553
Halobacterium, 487
Halophiles, 487, 490
Halophytes, 656
Hamilton, William, 835–836
Hamilton's rule, **835**, 836*f*
Hammer (malleus), 805*f*
Hammerhead sharks, 752
Hamsters, 797
Haploid cells, **203***f*–204*f*, 205
Haplotypes, 377
Hardy-Weinberg equation, 417, 418*f*–419*f*, 420
Hardy-Weinberg equilibrium, 417, **418***f*–419*f*
Harper, John, 862
Haustoria, 608*f*

Hawaiian Islands
  adaptive radiation in, 464*f*, 465
  ages of, 464*f*, 465
  allopatric speciation in, 440
Hawaiian silversword plants, 399
Hawkmoth, 871*f*
Hazel, 624*f*
hCG. *See* Human chorionic gonadotropin
HDL. *See* High-density lipoprotein
Head, in human reproductive structures, 756*f*, 757*f*
Head structure morphogen, 328*f*–329*f*
Headwater streams, 850*f*
Hearing, mechanoreceptors for equilibrium and, 804*f*–807*f*
Heart attack, **720**
Heartbeat rhythm, 712*f*
Heartburn, 695
Heart murmurs, 711–712
Heart rate, 712
Hearts, **707**
  blood pressure and, 714, 715*f*
  cardiac muscle of, 820
  in circulatory systems, 707*f*–709*f*, 710
  control of rhythmic beating of, 712*f*
  evolutionary variation in, 709–710
  fetal, 768*f*
  mammalian, 710, 711*f*–712*f*
Heartwood, 590*f*
Heat, **34**, **123**
  from cellular respiration, 154
  in denaturation of proteins, 63
  in energy flow and chemical cycling, 8*f*
  in energy flow and chemical recycling, 141*f*
  extreme thermophiles and, 487*f*, 490
  plant response to, 656–657
  as thermal energy, 34
  thermoreceptors and, 803
Heat of vaporization, **35**
Heat-shock proteins, 656, **657**
Heavy chains, **738***f*, 740*f*
Heavy metal contamination, bioremediation of, 899, 901*f*
Heimlich maneuver, 694
HeLa cells, 195, 198
Helianthus genus, 447*f*–448*f*
Helical viruses, 343*f*
Helicases, **261***f*
Helicobacter pylori, 488*f*, 694, 699*f*
Helium, 24*f*
Helper T cells, **742**, 743*f*, 745*f*
Heme group, 150, 729*f*
Heme oxygenase, 787
Hemeroplanes ornatus, 871*f*
Hemichordates, 551*f*–552*f*
Hemipterans, 559*f*
Hemispheres, brain, 795*f*, 798
Hemizygous organisms, 240
Hemlock, 880*f*
Hemochromatosis, 705
Hemocyanin, 729
Hemocytes, 734, 735*f*
Hemoglobin, **718**
  analyzing polypeptide sequence data of, 67, 69
  cooperativity as allosteric regulation in, 138
  dissociation curves of, 732
  in erythrocytes, 718*f*
  in gas exchange, 729*f*, 730
  globin gene families and, 366*f*, 370
  sickle-cell disease and, 62*f*, 230*f*, 428*f*
  structure of, 61*f*
Hemolymph, 680, **707***f*, 708
Hemophilia, **241**, 252, 719
Hemorrhagic fever, 351*f*
Henslow, John, 382
Hepatic portal vein, **696**
Hepatitis B virus, 749
HER2, 197, 338*f*–339*f*
HER2 breast cancer, 339*f*
Herbicides
  auxin in, 644
  transgenic, 634

Herbivores, **688**
  alimentary canals of, 698, 699*f*
  as biotic factors limiting species distribution, 853
  dentition and diet of, 698*f*
  in ecosystem trophic structure, 888
  effects of, on ecosystems, 569*f*
  evolution by natural selection in, due to food source changes, 387*f*, 388
  grass and, 592
  mutualistic adaptations in, 699, 700*f*
  plant defenses against, 658*f*
  plant interactions with, 541
  production efficiency of, 892, 893*f*
Herbivory, 472, **871***f*, 902*f*–903*f*
Herceptin, 197, 339*f*
Hereditary factors, genes as, 236
Heredity, **200**. *See also* Genetics; Genetic variation; Inheritance
Hermaphroditism, **753**, 771
Heroin, 31, 59
Herpes simplex virus, 747
Herpesviruses, 348, 351, 747
Herring gulls, 920*f*
Hershey, Alfred, 255–256
Heterocephalus glaber, 835*f*
Heterochromatin, **269**, 316
Heterochrony, **465***f*–466*f*
Heterocysts (heterocytes), **482**
Heterotrophs, 161, 481*t*, 515, 524, 888
Heterozygote advantage, **426**–427, 428*f*–429*f*
Heterozygote protection, 416
Heterozygous organisms, **218**
Hexoses, 50*f*
Hibernation, 154, 826
High blood pressure, 690
High-density lipoprotein (HDL), **719**
Highly conserved genes, 372, 374*f*–375*f*
High-throughput sequencing technology, 8, 358
Hindbrain, 794*f*
Hindgut, 692*f*
Hinge joints, 823*f*
Hinges, mammalian jaw, 457*f*
Hippocampus, 796*f*, 801
Hippopotamus, 68*f*
Histamine, **736***f*, 737, 746*f*
Histidine, 57*f*
Histograms in Scientific Skills Exercises and Scientific Skills Review, 196*f*, 227*t*, 721*f*, F-2*f*
Histone acetylation, **309***f*
Histones, **268***f*, 331
HIV (human immunodeficiency virus), **349**
  AIDS and, 349, 350*f*
  antiviral drugs and, 351*f*, 352
  attacks on immune system by, 747–748
  cell infection by, 342*f*
  CRISPR-Cas9 system and treatment of, 493*f*
  dating origin of, using molecular clock, 407, 408*f*
  as emerging virus, 352
  rapid reproduction of, 416
  replicative cycle of, 350*f*
  specificity of, 344
HIV-1 M strain, 407, 408*f*
Hodgkin's lymphoma, 909
Hoekstra, Hopi, 16–17, 18
Holdfasts, 499*f*, **509***f*
Homeoboxes, 374*f*–375*f*
Homeodomains, 374*f*–375*f*
Homeostasis, **673**, 674*f*
  of fat storage and metabolism, 703
  of glucose levels, 702, 703*f*
  of human breathing, 727*f*
  kidney function in, 682, 683*f*–685*f*
  osmoregulation and excretion in, 678*f*. *See also* Excretory systems; Osmoregulation
  regulating and conforming mechanisms of, 673*f*–674*f*
  thermoregulation in, 674, 675*f*–677*f*
Homeotic genes, 327–**328**, 374*f*–375*f*, **466**, 467*f*, 583, 584*f*
Homing pigeons, 826
Hominins, **567**
Homo genus, 568
Homo habilis, 568

Homologies, **389**
  analogies vs., 399*f*, 400
  anatomical and molecular, 389*f*, 390
  convergent evolution and analogies vs., 390
  evaluating molecular, 400*f*
  as evidence for evolution, 389–390
  morphological and molecular, 399
Homologous chromosomes (homologs), **202**
  behavior of, as basis of law of segregation, 236, 237*f*
  human, 202*f*–203*f*
  independent assortment of, 211*f*
  in meiosis, 205*f*, 206*f*, 208*f*
Homologous structures, **389***f*, 390
Homo neanderthalensis. *See* Neanderthals
Homoplasies, **399**, 400*f*
Homo sapiens (human), 396, 567*f*–568*f*. *See also* Humans
Homozygous organisms, **218**
Honeybees, 624*f*, 827*f*, 830–831
Honeypot ants, 394
Hook, flagellum, 480*f*
Hooke, Robert, 73
Hopping, 824*f*
Horizontal cells, 808*f*, 810
Horizontal gene transfer, 409*f*, 410, 484, 486, 492
Horizontal transmission, viral, 354
Hormonal contraceptives, 769*f*
Hormonal signaling, 114*f*
Hormone cascade pathways, 670, 671*f*
Hormone-receptor complexes, 117*f*
Hormones, animal, **114**, **668**. *See also* Hormones, human
  antidiuretic hormone, 684, 685*f*
  coordinate control by, 313
  digestion regulation by, 700, 701*f*
  endocrine system, 668*f*
  evolution of functions of, 672, 673*f*
  in long-distance cell signaling, 114*f*
  in mammalian sex determination, 761
  membrane proteins and, 103*f*
  multiple effects of, 672*f*
  proteins as, 56*f*
  regulation of mammalian/human reproduction by, 760–764
  sex. *See* Sex hormones
  solubility of, 671–672
Hormones, human. *See also* Hormones, animal
  birth control, 768, 769*f*
  in embryonic development and childbirth, 768
  human endocrine system and, 669*f*–670*f*
  reproductive, 759*f*, 760–764
Hormones, plant, **640**, 641*f*–647*f*, 648
  abscisic acid, 642*t*, 645, 646*f*
  auxin, 640, 641*f*, 642*t*, 643*f*, 644
  brassinosteroids, 642*t*, 645
  cytokinins, 642*t*, 644
  discovery of, 640, 641*f*
  ethylene, 642*t*, 646, 647*f*, 648
  florigen, 653*f*
  gibberellins, 642*t*, 644, 645*f*
  overview of, 642*t*
  as plant growth regulators, 640
Hornworm, 872
Hornworts, 530*f*, 531*f*
Horses, 392, 414*f*, 437*f*, 470*f*, 471, 699
Horsetail, 544
Host, **871**–872
Host cells, endosymbiont, 500
Host ranges, viral, **344**
Hosts, **491**, 570, 883*f*
Hot spot, biodiversity, **917***f*
Hoxd gene, 325
Hox
  analyzing quantitative and spatial data on, 325
  as animal development genes, 375*f*
  in arthropod body plans, 554
  in macroevolution of development, 466, 467*f*
  origins of, 548
  in phylogeny of animals, 550
  wing formation, 377
HPV. *See* Human papillomavirus
HTLV-1 virus, 340

Hubbard Brook Experimental Forest
  nutrient cycling in, 898f, 899
  precipitation in, 911f
Human body
  bacterial prokaryotes and, 474, 475f, 488f–489f,
    491, 492f–493f
  bones and joints of skeleton of, 823f
  evolution of human eye, 469f
  heterochrony and growth rates in skulls of, 465f
  interaction of muscles and skeletons in
    locomotion in, 821f
  skin of, 803
  structure of ears of, 805f
  structure of eyes of, 808f–809f
Human chorionic gonadotropin (hCG), 746, 768
Human environmental impacts
  on aquatic biomes, 849f–851f
  biodiversity threats, 907f–911f, 931
  biome disturbances, 845
  in carbon cycle, 896f
  community disturbances, 880, 881f
  environmental toxin accumulation as,
    920f–921f
  greenhouse gases and climate change as, 921,
    922f–925f, 926
  in nitrogen cycle, 897f
  nutrient enrichment as, 919f–920f
  ocean acidification, 39f, 40
  restoration ecology and, 899f–901f
  species extinctions, 906f–908f
  on terrestrial biomes, 846f–848f
  on tundra, 903f
Human genetics, 228–232
  counseling in, based on Mendelian genetics,
    231–232
  dominant alleles and disorders in, 224
  dominantly inherited disorders in, 231f
  multifactorial disorders in, 231
  multiple alleles and ABO blood groups in,
    224, 225f
  pedigree analysis in, 228f, 229
  pleiotropy and disorders in, 225
  recessively inherited disorders in, 229f–230f
  skin pigmentation and polygenic inheritance in,
    226f, 227
Human genome. See also Genomes
  comparing, of different communities, 374
  comparing genomes of other species to, 360, 364,
    367f, 368, 372f–373f
  function of FOXP2 gene in, 373f
  globin gene families in, 366f–369f, 370
  Human Genome Project and complete sequence
    for, 358–359
  microarray chips containing, 361f
  size, number of genes, and gene density
    of, 362t, 363
  types of DNA sequences in, 363f
Human Genome Project, 67, 358–359
Human immunodeficiency virus (HIV). See HIV
Human papillomavirus (HPV), 749
Human population growth, 926f–928f
Human reproduction. See also Animal reproduction
  birth rates. See Birth rates
  conception, embryonic development, and birth
    in, 767f–768f
  contraception in, 756, 768, 769f
  female reproductive anatomy in, 757f
  female reproductive cycles in, 761, 762f, 763
  gametogenesis in, 757, 758f–759f, 760
  hormonal regulation of, 760–764
  infertility and in vitro fertilization in, 770
  male reproductive anatomy in, 756f, 757
  male reproductive system in, 761f
  reproductive organs in, 756f–757f
  sexual response in, 763–764
Humans. See also Animals; Mammals
  apoptosis of white blood cells of, 326f
  behavior of chromosome sets in life cycle
    of, 203f, 204
  biodiversity benefits for, 908–909
  biological species concept and diversity of, 435f
  blood types of, 104
  body. See Human body

brain and nerve cells of. See Brains; Neurons
cardiovascular systems of. See Cardiovascular
  systems
cells of, 78f. See also Animal cells
chromosome sets in cells of, 202f–203f
chromosomes in somatic cells and gametes of,
  183, 184f
communication forms of, 827
detecting pregnancy in, 746
digestion as hydrolysis in, 49
digestive system, 693f–697f, 698
disease as density-dependent population
  regulation mechanism for, 863f
disturbances by, 880, 881f
ecological impacts of, 515, 516f
embryonic development, 767f–768f. See also
  Embryonic development
endocrine system of, 669f–670f
environmental impacts of. See Human
  environmental impacts
evaporative cooling of, by sweat, 35
evolutionary effects of, 570, 571f
evolutionary tree of, 567f
evolution of, 451, 567f–568f
excretory system of, 681f
gene flow and evolution of, 424
genetics of. See Human genetics
genome of. See Human genome
genome sequencing for, 67f
genomics and proteomics in study of, 68f
homeostasis in. See Homeostasis
hormones. See Hormones, human
immune systems of. See Immune systems
impacts of, on plants, 541, 542f
karyotypes of chromosomes of, 202f
kidneys of. See Kidneys
locomotion of, 824
lymphatic systems of, 715, 716f
Neanderthals interbreeding with, 373, 568
nerve cells of, 72f
nervous systems of. See Nervous systems;
  Neurons
noncoding RNAs in genomes of, 315f, 316
number of chromosomes of, 81
nutrition. See Animal nutrition
olfactory receptor genes of, 416
phagocytosis in, 86
pH of blood of, 38f, 39
phylogenetic trees of, 403f
receptor-mediated endocytosis in, 112, 113f
reducing hunger and malnutrition in, with
  transgenic crops, 634, 635f
regulation of breathing in, 727f, 728
relatedness of rhesus monkeys, gibbons,
  and, 69
reproduction of. See Human reproduction
sex-linked genes of, and inheritance, 239,
  240f–242f
skulls of chimpanzees vs., 399–400
species name of, 396
spread of pathogens by, 884
stem cells of, 332f–333f, 334
transgenic crops and health of, 635
trophic efficiency and meat eating by, 894
twin studies of behavior of, 828
Hummingbirds, 3, 449f, 624f, 632, 691, 705
Humoral immune response, 734f, 742f–745f, 750
Humpback whales, 398f
Humus, 601–602
Hundred Heartbeat Club, 908f
Hunger, transgenic crops and reducing, 634
Huntington's disease, 231, 333
Hutton, James, 381
Hybrid breakdown, 437f
Hybridization, 215, 216f, 317, 448f, 451, 633–634
Hybrids, 435
  bears, 438f
  DNA inheritance in, 451
  gene flow and, 435
  hybrid zones and, 444f–446f
  postzygotic reproductive barriers and, 437f

sterility of, 437f, 449
sympatric speciation and, 442
Hybrid zones, 444f–446f
Hydras, 201f, 692f, 791f, 821
Hydration shells, 36
Hydrocarbons, 45f–46f, 48
Hydrocarbon tails, 102f, 168f
Hydrochloric acid, 37–38, 694f
Hydrogen
  ATP synthase and, 151–152
  in catabolic pathways, 143, 144f, 145
  covalent bonding of molecules of, 27f–28f
  as essential element, 23t
  in hydrocarbons, 45f
  peroxisomes and, 90
  in polymers, 49f
  as pure element, 28f
  in saturated and unsaturated fatty acids, 53, 54f
  valence of, and organic compounds, 44f
Hydrogenated vegetable oils, 54
Hydrogen bonds, 30f
  in DNA and tRNA structure, 66f
  of ice, 35f
  properties of water from, 32, 33f
  in protein structure, 60f–61f
  as weak chemical bonds, 30
Hydrogen ions, 37–39, 596, 618, 777f
Hydrogenosomes, 508
Hydrogen peroxide, 90
Hydrogen sulfide gas, 461
Hydrolysis, 49
  of ATP, 128f–130f
  breakdown of polymers by, 49f
  of cellulose, 53
  enzymatic, 691
  of fat, 696, 697f
  by lysosomes, 85f–86f
  of storage polysaccharides, 51, 52f
  in translation, 293f
Hydrolytic enzymes
  fungal, 525
  lysosomal, 85f–86f
Hydronium ions, 37–39
Hydrophilic substances, 36
  phospholipid heads, 54, 55f
  plasma membranes and, 77f
  side chains, 57f, 58
  water and, 36–37
Hydrophobic interactions, 61f
Hydrophobic substances, 37
  hydrocarbons and fats as, 45, 53
  phospholipid tails, 54, 55f
  plasma membranes and, 77f
  side chains, 57f, 58
  water and, 36–37
Hydroponic culture, 599f
Hydrostatic skeletons, 821, 822f
Hydrothermal vents, 475, 487, 490–491, 496, 851f, 888
Hydroxide ions, 37–39
Hydroxyl group, 47f–50f, 52f, 53–54
Hydrozoa, 547f
Hyla versicolor, 430f, 441
Hymen, 757f
Hymenophyllum tunbrigense, 533f
Hymenopterans, 559f
Hypercholesterolemia, 112
Hypermastigote, 516f
Hyperosmotic solutions, 678, 684f
Hyperpolarization, 778, 779f–780f, 781, 810f
Hypersensitive response, plant, 659f
Hypertension, 685, 720
Hypertonic solutions, 107, 121
Hyphae, fungal, 524f–525f, 527f–528f, 603f
Hypocotyl, 626f–627f
Hypoosmotic solutions, 678
Hypothalamus, 669f, 795f
  drug addiction and reward system of, 797, 798f
  kidney regulation by, 684, 685f
  regulation of mammalian/human reproduction by,
    760–764, 768
  suprachiasmatic nucleus in, 797
  thermoregulation by, 676, 677f

Hypotheses, **14**
   estimating quantitative data from graphs and developing, 459
   interpreting genomic data and generation of, 529
   phylogenetic trees as, 405*f*–406*f*
   for predators and natural selection, 20
   science and, 13–14
   theory as, in science, 393
Hypotonic solutions, **107**
Hyracotherium, 470*f*, 471

I
IBA. *See* Indolebutyric acid
Ibuprofen, 803
Ice, floating of, 35*f*–36
Iceland, ocean pelagic biome near, 851*f*
Icosahedral viruses, 343*f*
Identical DNA sequences, 366
Identical twins, human, 768
Ig. *See* Immunoglobulin
Ileum, 696
Illicium, 538*f*
Illinois, greater prairie chicken decline in, 912, 913*f*
Imaging, functional brain, 793*f*
Imbibition, **627**
Immigration, **854**, 855*f*, 864*f*
   island equilibrium model and, 882
Immune response, primary and secondary, 741, 742*f*
Immune systems, **733**–750
   adaptive immunity in. *See* Adaptive immunity
   blood plasma in, 717*f*
   cardiovascular diseases and, 719
   human disorders from disruptions in, 746*f*–747*f*, 748–749
   immunization and, 745–746
   innate immunity in, 734, 735*f*–736*f*, 737
   leukocytes in, 718*f*
   lymphatic systems and, 716
   mammalian, 664*t*
   molecular recognition and response to pathogens by, 733, 734*f*
   overview of innate and adaptive immunity in, 734*f*
   responses of, to changing pathogens, 748
Immunity, PAMP-triggered, 658
Immunization, **745**–746
Immunodeficiency, 747–748
Immunoglobulin (Ig), **738**–739, 740*f*
Immunological memory, 739, 741, 742*f*
Impala, 115
Implantation, human, 767*f*
Imprinting, **828**, 829*f*
Inclusive fitness, **835**
Incomplete dominance, **223***f*–224
Incomplete flowers, **620**. *See also* Flowers
Incomplete metamorphosis, 559*f*
Incus (anvil), 805*f*
Independent assortment, law of, 219, 220*f*, **221**, 236, 237*f*, 244
Independent assortment of chromosomes, 211*f*, 244
Independent variables, identifying, **17**, 109, 134, 441, 870
Indeterminate growth, **582**, 584
Indian corn, 364
Indian pipe, 608*f*
Indoleacetic acid (IAA). *See* Auxin
Indolebutyric acid (IBA), 644
Induced fit, **133***f*
Induced pluripotent stem (iPS) cells, 333*f*, 334
Inducers, **306***f*, 307
Inducible enzymes, 306–307
Inducible operons, 305, 306*f*, 307
Induction, **323***f*
Inductive reasoning, **14**
Inert elements, 27
Inertia, 823
Infection
   bacterial, 291, 346, 356, 479, 484*f*–485*f*, 486, 488*f*–489*f*, 492*f*
   cellular innate defenses and, 735*f*, 736
   cytotoxic T cell response to, 744*f*
   inflammatory response and, 736*f*, 737
   plant response to, 658, 659*f*–660*f*
   prions, 355*f*
   viral, 356

Infertility, human, 770
Inflammation, 719–720
Inflammatory response, 736*f*, 737
Inflorescences, **620**
Influenza viruses, 59*f*, 343*f*, 352*f*, 353–354, 356, 747, 863*f*, 883–884
Information, 8. *See also* DNA; Genetics
   B and T cell development, 750
   chromosomal behavior during sexual reproduction, 213
   chromosomal structure and behavior and inheritance, 252
   DNA inheritance, 302
   expression and transmission as biological theme, 6*f*–7*f*, 8
   flow of in plant cells, 178*f*
   hybrids and DNA, 451
   learning and heritable information, 838
   in mitosis, 198
   parental traits and genes, 235
   phylogeny reconstruction, 412
   protein-coding genes and regulatory DNA, 377
   shared genes between organisms, 20
Information processing
   in birds, 800*f*
   cerebral cortex and, 799
   ion gradients in, 777*f*
   neurons and, 774*f*
   problem solving and, 831
   vertebrate visual, 810, 811*f*
Infrared receptors, 803*f*
Ingestion, 497*f*, **691**
Ingroups, **402**
Inhalation, 726*f*, 727
Inheritance. *See also* Genetics; Genetic variation
   blending and particulate hypotheses on, 214
   of cancer predisposition, 337, 340
   C. Darwin on, 385*f*–386*f*
   chromosome theory of, 236*f*–239*f*. *See also* Chromosomal basis of inheritance
   DNA in, 6, 201, 213, 302
   epigenetic, 309
   of genes and chromosomes, 201. *See also* Sexual life cycles
   genetic variation and, 414*f*–415*f*, 416
   Mendelian. *See* Mendelian inheritance
   polygenic, 226*f*, 227
   of X-linked genes, 240, 241*f*
Inheritance of acquired characteristics principle, 381*f*
Inhibin, 761*f*
Inhibiting hormones, 669*f*
Inhibition
   allosteric, 137*f*
   cell division, 194*f*–195*f*, 196–197
   in ecological succession, 879–880
Inhibitors
   enzyme, 136*f*, 137*f*
   plant growth, 641*t*, 645, 646*f*
Inhibitory postsynaptic potential (IPSP), **784**
Initials, plant cell, 582
Initiation
   transcription, 284, 285*f*–286*f*, 309, 310*f*–312*f*, 313
   translation, 291, 292*f*, 294, 314
Initiation factors, 292*f*
Inland mouse, 2*f*, 16*f*–17*f*
Innate behavior, **828**
Innate immunity, **734**–737
   adaptive immunity vs., 734*f*
   antimicrobial peptides and proteins, 736
   barrier defenses, 733, 734*f*, 735
   cellular innate defenses, 735*f*, 736
   evasion of, by pathogens, 737
   inflammatory response, 736*f*, 737
   invertebrate, 734, 735*f*
   vertebrate, 734, 735*f*–736*f*, 737
Inner ear, **805***f*, 806, 807*f*
Inner membrane, nuclear, 81*f*
Innocence Project, The, 365
Inorganic topsoil components, 602*f*
Inquiry, **13**. *See also* Inquiry Figures; Interpret the Data questions; Research Method Figures; Science; Scientific Skills Exercises

Inquiry Figures
   allele segregation in gametes, 220*f*
   allopatric population divergence and reproductive isolation, 440*f*
   area effects on species richness, 882*f*
   arthropod body plan and *Hox* genes, 554*f*
   auxin movement, 643*f*
   Bicoid as morphogen, 329*f*
   camouflage and predation rates of mice populations, 17*f*
   coleoptile and light sensing, 641*f*
   coleoptile and growth-promoting chemical, 641*f*
   digger wasp and landmarks to find nest, 830*f*
   DNA replication, 261*f*
   endophytes and woody plants, 541*f*
   eukaryotic tree root, 513*f*
   F$_1$ hybrid cross-pollination, 216*f*
   genetic material as protein or DNA, 255*f*
   genetic trait transfer between bacterial strains, 254*f*
   hybridization and speciation, 448*f*
   interspecific competition influence on ecological niche, 869*f*
   keystone species determination, 876*f*
   kinetochore microtubules and anaphase, 189*f*
   linked genes and character inheritance, 243*f*
   mate selection, 430*f*
   membrane protein movement, 102*f*
   molecular signals and cell cycle, 192*f*
   natural selection and population's food source, 387*f*
   nucleus of differentiated animal cell, 330*f*
   nutrient limitations on phytoplankton production, 891*f*
   population decline of Illinois greater prairie chicken, 913*f*
   prokaryote evolution and environmental change, 483*f*
   respiratory distress syndrome, 726*f*
   root bacterial communities, 604*f*
   sea urchin effects on seaweed distribution, 853*f*
   seed germination and red and far-red illumination, 650*f*
   sexual selection and reproductive isolation, 443*f*
   stem cells, 333*f*
   stickleback fish and spine loss, 468*f*
   temperature effects on litter decomposition in an ecosystem, 895*f*
   wavelengths of light and photosynthesis, 167*f*
   whale meat species identification, 398*f*
   wild-type and mutant cross, 239*f*
Insect-eater finches, 383*f*
Insecticide resistance, 421, 424, 517*f*, 518
Insects
   as arthropods, 559*f*–560*f*
   body plans of, 467*f*
   camouflage in, 386*f*
   characteristics of, 558*f*
   circulatory systems of, 707*f*
   compound eyes of, 808*f*
   evolution by natural selection in, due to food source changes, 387*f*, 388
   evolution of, 379
   excretory systems of, 680
   exoskeletons of, 822
   flying, 824
   Hox genes in, 375*f*
   innate immunity in, 734, 735*f*
   insecticide resistance in, 424
   interactions of, 8
   nervous systems of, 791*f*
   nonheritable variation in, 415*f*
   parasitism in, 871–872
   plant response to herbivores and, 658*f*
   as pollinators, 449*f*, 541–542, 624*f*
   problem solving of, 830–831
   production efficiency of, 893
   reproductive organs of, 755
   size of, 732
   skeletal muscles of, 821
   tracheal systems for gas exchange in, 723, 724*f*
   transgenic crops and, 634
Insertions, nucleotide, **299***f*, 300, 414, 415*f*
In situ hybridization, **317***f*, 321*f*
Insoluble fiber, 52

Instability, free energy and, 125, 126f
Insulin, 84, 112, 280, 669f, **702**, 703f
Insulin-dependent diabetes, 703
Integral proteins, 101f, **103**
Integration
    cellular, 97f
    nervous system, 774f
Integrins, 95f
Integument, **534**f, 622
Integumentary system, 664t
Intelligence, 813
Interactions
    as biological theme, 8, 9f
    diatom populations, 519
    feedback mechanisms, 320
    forest types and, 544
    human pancreatic cell and environment, 121
    mutualism, 618
    oxygen transport, 732
    physical environment and evolution, 394
    phytochrome and shoot growth, 661
Interactions, ecological, 902f–903f. *See also* Ecology
    in communities, 867f–873f
    competition, 868f–869f, 885
    dispersion patterns and, 855f, 856
    in effects of animals on ecosystems, 568f–569f
    in effects of animals on evolution, 569f–571f
    effects of plants and fungi on, 540, 541f–542f
    exploitation, 869–870, 871f, 872
    interspecific, 867f–873f
    positive, 872f–873f
    prokaryotic, 491f
    in species distributions, 840, 852f–853f, 854
    symbols for, 868
    in vascular plant nutrition, 602, 603f–608f
Intercalary meristems, 586
Intercalated disks, 820
Intercellular joining. *See* Cell junctions
Interdisciplinary genomics research teams, 8
Interferons, **736**
Intergradation, of terrestrial biomes, 846
Intermediate disturbance hypothesis, **878**, 879f
Intermediate filaments, **94**
    animal cell, 78f
    of desmosomes, 96f
    functions of, 94
    structure and function of, 91t
Intermembrane space
    chloroplast, 89f
    mitochondrial, 88, 89f
Internal cell membranes. *See* Cellular membranes
Internal defenses, 734f
Internal fertilization, 754f, 833. *See also* Fertilization, reproductive
Internal skeletons, 821f
Internet resources, genomic, 359, 360f
Interneurons, 774f
Internodes, 577f, **578**
Interphase, **185**f–186f, 205f
Interpret the Data questions. *See also* Scientific Skills Exercises
    action potential frequency, 788f
    bacterial communities inside and outside roots, 604f
    beak length, 869f
    camouflage and predation, 17f
    climograph, 845f
    feeding relationships among sea otters, sea urchins, and kelp, 866t
    foraging behavior, 831f
    frequency-dependent selection, 427f
    genetic variation and distribution of mussels, 432f–433
    ghrelin, 40
    global water cycle, 905
    hemoglobin dissociation curves, 732f
    immune response, 742f
    mammal divergence time, 407f
    molybdenum, 891t
    next-generation sequencing, 274f
    oxygen in human body, 23t
    parthenogenetic lizards, 753f
    Permian mass extinction, 461f
    phosphofructokinase, 160f

photosynthesis and light wavelengths, 167f
plant mass vs. temperature, 544t
Rhizobium and plant mutualism, 496t
seaweed distribution, 853f
secondary production, 893f
speciation and extinction events, 458f
temperature patterns, 34f
vertebrate evolution, 403f
water gain and loss, 687t
Intersexual selection, 427f, 430f, 833
Interspecific competition, **868**f–869f, 885
Interspecific interactions, **868**, 885, 902f–903f
    in communities, 867f–873f
    genomics and proteomics in, 68f
Interspecific mating, 435
Interstitial fluid, **673**, 707f, 715, 716f
Intertidal zone, **850**f
Intestinal bacteria, 491–492
Intestine, 692f–693f, 700f. *See also* Large intestine; Small intestine
Intestines. *See* Large intestine; Small intestine
Intracellular digestion, 692
Intracellular receptor proteins, 117f
Intracellular recording, 778f
Intrasexual selection, 427f, 833
Intrauterine devices (IUDs), 769f
Intrinsic physiological factors, density-dependent population regulation and, 863f
Intrinsic rate of increase, **858**–859t
Introduced species, 910f
Introns, **287**f–288f, 363f, 414f–415f
Invagination, 766f
Invasive species, **875**
Inversions, chromosome, **249**
Invertebrates, **551**
    action potential conduction speed in, 782
    in animal phylogeny, 551
    defense mechanism of, 750
    excretory systems of, 680f
    hydrostatic skeletons of, 821, 822f
    innate immunity in, 734, 735f
    mechanoreceptors for sensing gravity and sound in, 804
    nervous systems of, 790–791
    parental care in, 755f, 833
    reproductive organs of, 755
    skeletal muscles of, 821
In vitro culturing, angiosperm, 632, 633f, 634
In vitro fertilization (IVF), **770**
Involuntary nervous system, 793
Iodine, dietary requirements for, 23t, 690
Iodine deficiencies, 23
Ion channel proteins, 781
Ion channels, **108**, **775**
    in facilitated diffusion, 108
    ligand-gated, as transmembrane receptors, 116f
    mechanoreceptors and, 802
    neuron potentials and, 775f–782f
    neuron resting potential and, 775f–776f
    in vascular plant solute transport, 596
Ionic bonds, 29f, 61f
Ionic compounds (salts), 29f, 36f
Ionotropic receptors, 784
Ion pumps
    in active transport, 110f–111f
    neuron resting potential and, 775f–776f
Ions, 29
    blood electrolytes, 717f
    concentrations of, inside and outside of mammalian neurons, 775t
    movement and gradients of, 777f
    as second messengers in cell signaling, 118, 119f
iPS cells. *See* Induced pluripotent stem (iPS) cells
IPSP. *See* Inhibitory postsynaptic potential
Iridium, 461
Iris, 808f, **809**
Irish potato famine, 660
Iron
    dietary requirements for, 689f, 690
    as essential element, 23t
    hemochromatosis and, 705
    as limiting nutrient, 891t
    plant deficiency of, 600

Iron-sulfur protein (Fe · S), 150f
Irrigation, 121
Island biogeography, 882f
Island equilibrium model, 882f
Island species, 392
Isle Royale, moose and wolf populations on, 862, 864f
Isolated systems, 124, 127f
Isoleucine, 57f, 138f
Isomers, **46**f
    retinal, 809f, 810
Isoosmotic solutions, 678
Isotonic solutions, **107**
Isotopes, 24, 25f, 898
IUDs. *See* Intrauterine devices
IVF. *See In vitro* fertilization
Ivory, 910, 911f

J

J. *See* Joule
Jackson, Rob, 874f
Jacob, François, 304, 469
Japan, coastal restoration project in, 900f
Japanese canopy plant, 362t
Japanese snails, 448–449
Jaundice, 696
Jawed vertebrates, 555, 556f–557f
Jawfish, 833
Jawless vertebrates, 555, 556f
Jaws
    mammalian, 456, 457f, 566
    snake, 426f
Jejunum, 696
Jellies (jellyfish), 284f, 547f, 867f
Jet-propulsion locomotion, 824
Jointed appendages, arthropod, 553
Joints, human, 823f
Jost, Alfred, 761
Joule (J), **34**, 701
J-shaped growth curve, 858f–859f
Jumping genes, 364
Juncus gerardii, 872
June solstice, 843f
Juniperus horizontalis, 535f
Juxtamedullary nephrons, **681**f

K

Kangaroo rats, 565f, 885
Kangaroos, 566f, 824f, 852
Kaposi's sarcoma herpesvirus, 748–749
Karyogamy, **529**f
Karyotypes, **202**
Kaufman, D. W., 18
kcal. *See* Kilocalorie
Kelps, 510, 618, 866, 925f
Kemp's ridley sea turtle, 885
Kenya, savanna biome in, 846f
Keratin, 94, 280, 705
Kernel color, 235
Ketone compounds, 47f
Keystone species, **876**f, 915
Kidneys, 565, **678**, **681**f
    adaptations of vertebrate, to diverse environments, 684f
    aldosterone and, 117
    concentration of urine in mammalian, 684
    diabetes mellitus and, 702–703
    homeostatic regulation of, 684, 685f
    mammalian/human, 681f
    osmoregulation by, 687
    processing by, of blood filtrate to urine, 682, 683f
    in vertebrate excretory systems, 680, 681f, 682
Killifish, 392
Kilocalorie (kcal), **34**, 701
Kimberella, 546f, 549
Kinases. *See* Protein kinases
Kinetic energy, **34**–35, **123**f–124f. *See also* Energy; Potential energy
Kinetochore microtubules, 186f, 188f–189f, 198, 206f–207f
Kinetochores, **185**, 186f
Kinetoplastids, 508, 509f
King, Mary-Claire, 337
King, Thomas, 330

Kingdoms, taxonomic, 10f, **396f**, 408, 521f
King penguins, 855f
Kin selection, 835–**836**
Kissimmee River restoration project, 900f
Kiwi bird, 900f
Klinefelter syndrome, 250
Knob, of ATP synthase, 151f
Knowledge, evolution of cognition and, 799, 800f
Koalas, 566f, 698, 699f
Komodo dragons, 752, 771
Korarchaeota clade, 490
Krauss's spikemoss, 533f
Krebs cycle. *See* Citric acid cycle
Krill, 875, 876f
Kruger National Park, African elephant population of, 858–859f
K-selection, **861**
Kudzu, 910f
Kuru, 355

L

Labeling, GMO food, 635
Labia majora, **757f**
Labia minora, **757f**
Labor, human childbirth, 768
Labrador Current, 844f
Laccaria bicolor, 529
Lacks, Henrietta, 195
lac operon, 305, 306f, 307
Lactate, 156f
Lactation, human, 768
Lacteal, 696f, **697f**
Lactic acid fermentation, **156**, 156f
Lactose, 50, 305, 306f, 307
Lagging strand, DNA, **264f**
Lake Erie, 920
Lakes
    as aquatic biome, 849f–850f
    biomanipulation of, 877f
    nutrient limitation in, 891
Lake Vesijärvi, biomanipulation of, 877f
Lake Victoria
    fusion of hybridized cichlid species in, 446
    sympatric speciation and sexual selection in cichlids in, 443f
Lamarck, Jean-Baptiste de, 381
λ (lambda) phage, **346f**
Lampreys, 412, 555, 556f
Lancelets, 412, 555f
Land, locomotion on, 823–824
Land animals, 558f–568f. *See also* Animals
    aquatic animals vs., 558f
    arthropods as, 559f–560f. *See also* Arthropods
    characteristics of, 558f
    evolution of, from aquatic animals, 558f–559
    vertebrates as, 560f–568f. *See also* Vertebrates
Land plants. *See* Plants
Landscape, structure and biodiversity of, 916f–917f
Landscape conservation, 915, 916f–918f, 919, 931
Landscape ecology, **841f**, 915, 916f–918f, 919, 931
Landscapes, **841f**
Language
    cerebral cortex and, 798, 799f
    FOXP2 gene and, 373f
Large intestine, 693f, **697**
    absorption in, 697f, 698
    adaptations of, 698, 699f
Largemouth bass, 673f
Large-scale mutations, 298
Larval stage, insect, 559f
Larynx, 693, **724**, 725f
Latency, viral, 747
Lateralization, **799**
Lateral meristems, **582**, 583f
Lateral roots, **576**, 577f, 586f
Latitude
    community diversity and, 881f
    sunlight intensity and, 842f–843f
Latitudinal gradients, species richness and, 881f
Law of independent assortment, 219, 220f, **221**, 236, 237f, 244
Law of segregation, 215, 216f, **217f**, 218f–219f, 236, 237f

Laws of thermodynamics, 124f, 125, 887
LDL. *See* Low-density lipoprotein
Lead, bioremediation of, 899
Leading strand, DNA, **263f**–264
Leaf (leaves), **533**, **578**. *See also* Shoots
    anatomy of, 587f, 666f
    architecture of, for light capture, 595f
    auxin in pattern formation of, 643
    brassinosteroids in abscission of, 645
    effects of transpiration on wilting and temperature of, 614
    ethylene and auxin in abscission of, 647, 648f
    evolution of, 533
    green color of, 166
    monocot vs. eudicot, 576f
    morphology of, 582
    photosynthesis in, 5f, 162, 163f–164f
    primary growth of, 586f–588f
    shape mimicry of, 639f
    in shoot systems, 577f
    structure of, 578, 579f
    tissue organization of, 587f
Leaf-cutter ants, 603f
Leaf primordia, 586
Leaf trembling, 593
Leak channels, 775
Learning, **828**–831
    associative, 830, 831f
    cerebral cortex and, 801
    cognition, problem solving, and social, 830–831
    cognitive maps and spatial, 829, 830f
    heritable information and, 838
    imprinting in, 828–829
Leefructus, 537
Left atrium, 710f–711f
Left ventricle, 710f–711f
Legionella, 488f
Legionnaires' disease, 488f
Legumes, 605, 606f, 651f
Lembeh Strait, carrier crabs in, 867f
Lemming, 863f
Length, carbon skeleton, 45f
Lens, eye, 808f, 811
    crystallin proteins of, 7f
    structure of, 813
Lens cells, differential gene expression in, 312f
Lenski, Richard, 483f
Lenticels, **591**
Leopards, 10, 396f, 397, 412
Lepidopterans, 379f, 559f
Leprosy, 489f
Leptin, 703–704
Leptonycteris curasoae yerbabuenae, 624f
Leptospira, 489f
Lesser snow goose, 569f
Lettuce seed germination, 650f
Leucine, 57f
Leukemia, 250, 251f, 340, 909
Leukocytes, 717f–**718f**, 719
Lewis, Edward B., 327
Leydig cells, **761f**
LH. *See* Luteinizing hormone
Lichen, **539f**, 603f, 902f–903f
    bioremediation using, 899, 901
Life
    adaptive radiations of, 463f–464f, 465
    biological organization hierarchy of, 4f–5f
    biology as study of, 2
    biology as study of. *See* Biology
    carbon in organic compounds of, 43
    cell division and cell cycle importance to, 182
    cells as fundamental units of, 72. *See also* Cells
    challenges and solutions in, 666f–667f
    chemistry and, 22
    classification of diversity of, 10f, 11. *See also* Systematics; Taxonomy
    conditions on early Earth for origin of, 475–477f, 478
    diversity of. *See* Biodiversity
    emergent properties of, 3, 4f–5f, 99
    energy and matter transfer and transformation in, 8f
    essential elements for, 23t

evolution of, 2, 9, 10f–13f, 380, 384. *See also* Evolution
    expression and transmission of genetic information in. *See* Genetics
    extinctions and mass extinctions of, 460, 461f–463f
    fossil record and geologic record as documentation of history of, 452, 453f–454f, 455t, 456, 457f. *See also* Fossil record; Geologic record
    genetic information expression and transmission in, 6f–7f, 8
    interaction of organisms with environment and other organisms in. *See* Interactions, ecological; Organisms
    limits of natural selection in history of, 430–431
    metabolism and energy for, 122. *See also* Metabolism
    order as characteristic of, 125
    organism interaction and, 8, 9f
    phylogenies as evolutionary history of, 395f, 396. *See also* Phylogenies
    prokaryotic cells as first cells of, 474f
    structure and function correlation in, 3
    themes of, 3–9
    three domains of, 408, 409f, 410
    transfer and transformation of energy and matter in. *See* Chemical cycling; Energy; Energy flow
    tree of, 12, 13f
    viruses and characteristics of, 342f
    water importance for, 32, 33f
    work of, 141f
Life cycles, **202**
    angiosperm, 623f
    cellular slime mold, 514f
    Drosophila melanogaster, 327f
    frog, 764f
    fungal, 529f
    human, 203f, 204
    plant, 522f, 523, 531f–533f
    Plasmodium, 517f
    sexual. *See* Sexual life cycles
Life history, **861**
    population dynamics and, 861f–864f
Life spans, plant, 584
Life tables, **856t**
Ligand-gated ion channels, **116f**, 117, 783f, **784**
Ligands, **115**
Light chains, **738f**–740f
Light-detecting organs, 807f, 808. *See also* Visual systems
Light energy
    in energy flow and chemical cycling, 8f
    in energy flow and chemical recycling, 141f
    in photosynthesis. *See* Photosynthesis
    primary production in aquatic ecosystems and limitations of, 890
    properties of, 165, 166f
    reception of, by plants. *See* Light reception, plant
    as stimulus for stomatal opening and closing, 613
    as sunlight, 141f. *See also* Sunlight
    sunlight as, 124, 128. *See also* Sunlight
Light-harvesting complexes, **169f**–170
Light microscope (LM), 73f–74f, D-1f
Light reactions, **164**–172, 173f. *See also* Photosynthesis
    determining absorption spectrum for, 167f
    determining wavelengths of light driving, 167f
    excitation of chlorophyll by light energy in, 168, 169f
    linear electron flow in, 170f–171f
    mitochondria, 171f–173f
    nature of sunlight and, 165, 166f
    overview of, 165f, 170f, 173f, 177f
    photosynthetic pigments as light receptors in, 166f–168f
    photosystems of, 169f–170
    as stage of photosynthesis, 164, 165f
Light reception, plant, 648f–653f
    biological clocks and circadian rhythms in, 650, 651f
    germination and, 661
    hypothetical flowering hormone and, 653f
    photomorphogenesis and photoreceptors in, 648f–650f

Light reception, plant (*Cont.*)
    photoperiodism and seasonal responses in, 651, 652*f*–653*f*
    phototropism and, 640, 641*f*
Lignin, **532**, **580***f*, 592
Likens, Gene, 898
Lily, African blood, 183*f*
Limbic system, 796*f*
Limbs
    evolution of tetrapod, 560*f*–561*f*
    homologous structures in, 389*f*, 390
    mammalian, 12
Limiting nutrients, **890**
    primary production and, 890, 891*ft*, 892*f*
Limnetic zone, **849***f*–850*f*
Limnodynastes peronii, 870
Limpets, 469, 853*f*
LINE-1 (*L1*) retrotransposons, 365
Linear electron flow, **170***f*–173*f*
Linear regression lines, scatter plots with, 40*f*, 176*t*, F-2*f*
Linear structure, glucose, 50*f*
Line graphs in Scientific Skills Exercises and Scientific Skills Review, 134*t*, 210*t*, 353*f*, 748*t*, 825*f*, F-1*f*
Linkage. *See* Linked genes
Linkage groups, 247
Linkage maps, **247***f*, 248
Linked genes, **242***f*–247*f*, 248
    constructing linkage maps of, 247*f*
    genetic recombination and, 243, 244*f*–245*f*
    inheritance of, 242, 243*f*
    mapping of, 245–246, 247*f*, 248
    sex-linked genes vs., 242
    using chi-square (χ^2) test to determine linkage of, 246
Linker DNA, 268*f*
Linnaean classification system, 396*f*, 397
Linnaeus, Carolus, 380, 396
Linoleic acid, 689*f*
Lionfish, 556*f*
Lions, 10
Lipase, 695*f*
Lipids, **53**
    bilayers of. *See* Phospholipid bilayers
    fats, 53*f*–54*f*
    membrane, 100*f*–102*f*, 104. *See also* Membrane lipids
    in nuclear envelopes, 80, 81*f*
    as organic compounds, 43
    phospholipids, 54, 55*f*
    in protocells, 476*f*
    steroids, 55*f*
    synthesis of, by smooth ER, 83
    Tay-Sachs disease and, 224
Lipid-soluble hormones, 672
Lipopolysaccharides, 478, 479*f*, 750
L isomer, 46*f*
Litter decomposition, 895*f*
Litter size, 861
Littoral zone, **849***f*–850*f*
Littorina obtusata, 570
Liver, **696**
    bile production by, 696
    differential gene expression in, 312*f*
    in digestive system, 693*f*, 695*f*, 700, 701*f*
    energy storage in, 702
    enzyme activity in, 140
    in glucose homeostasis, 702, 703*f*
Liverworts, 522*f*, 530*f*, 531*f*
Living topsoil components, 602
Lizards, 9*f*, 30, 395*f*, 396, 408, 563, 564*f*, 675*f*, 753*f*, 868*f*
LM. *See* Light microscope
Loams, **602**. *See also* Soil
Lobe-fins, **557**, 558*f*
Lobes, brain, 798, 799*f*
Lobopods, 553–554
Lobotomy, 799
Lobsters, 559*f*
Local cell signaling, 114*f*
Local inflammatory response, 736*f*, 737
Local regulators, 114*f*, 768
Lock-and-key specificity, viral, 344

Locomotion, **823**, 824*f*, 825
Locus, gene, **201**, 217*f*, 225
Locusts, 866
Lodgepole pines, 879*f*
Logistic population growth, **859***ft*–860*f*, 861
Log scales, 825
Long-day plants, 652*f*
Long-distance cell signaling, 114*f*
Long-distance signaling, neuron, 772. *See also* Neurons
Long-distance transport, plant, 599
Long Island, 890, 891*f*
Long-nosed bat, 624*f*
Long-term memory, **801**
Looped domains, DNA, 269*f*
Loop of Henle, **681***f*–683*f*, 687
Lophotrochozoa, 551*f*–552*f*, 553
Los Angeles, habitat fragmentation in, 909*f*
Loudness, 806
Lou Gehrig's disease, 818
Lovelock, James, 905
Low-density lipoprotein (LDL), 112, 115, **719**–721
Loxodonta, 384*f*, 385
LSD, 786
Luminal breast cancer, 339*f*
Lung cancer, 361
Lung cells, newt, 6*f*
Lungfishes, 556*f*, 557
Lungs, **724**
    breathing and ventilation of, 726*f*–727*f*, 728
    in mammalian respiratory systems, 724, 725*f*–726*f*
Lupines, 901
Lupus, 747
Luteal phase, ovarian cycle, 762*f*, 763
Luteinizing hormone (LH), **760**–764
Lycophytes, 530*f*–**531***f*, 532–533, 544
Lyell, Charles, 381–382
Lyme disease, 489*f*, 492*f*, 883*f*
Lymph, 715, **716***f*
Lymphatic system, lacteals of, 696*f*–697*f*
Lymphatic systems, **715**
    cardiovascular systems and, 715, 716*f*
    cellular innate immune defenses and, 736
    mammalian, 664*t*
Lymph nodes, **716***f*
Lymphocytes, 717*f*, 718*f*, **737**. *See also* B cells; T cells
Lymphoid stem cells, 718*f*
Lymph vessels, 716*f*
Lyon, Mary, 241–242
Lysine, 57*f*
Lysogenic cycle, 345, **346***f*
Lysosomal storage diseases, 86
Lysosomes, **85**
    animal cell, 78*f*
    in endomembrane system, 87*f*
    functions of, 85–86*f*, 97*f*
    in phagocytosis, 113*f*
    viruses and, 351
Lysozymes, 36*f*, 59*f*, 369, **734**–735
Lytic cycle, **345***f*

M

Macaca fuscata, 687
Macaques, 687
MacArthur, Robert, 882*f*
Macroclimate. *See* Climate; Climate change
Macroevolution, **434**, **452**–472. *See also* Evolution
    adaptive radiations in, 463*f*–**464***f*, 465
    of development from changes in developmental genes, 465*f*–468*f*
    effects on rates of, by differing modes of dispersal, 459
    fossil record and geologic record as documentation of, 452, 453*f*–454*f*, 455*t*, 456, 457*f*. *See also* Fossil record; Geologic record
    gene flow, genetic drift, and natural selection in, 463*f*–464*f*, 465, 472
    mass extinctions in, 460, 461*f*–463*f*
    novelties and trends in, 468, 469*f*–470*f*, 471
    plate tectonics and, 458*f*–460*f*
    speciation and, 434, 449. *See also* Speciation
    speciation and extinction rates in, 456, 458*f*–464*f*, 465

Macromolecules, **43**
    3-D structure of, 43*f*, 63*f*
    abiotic synthesis of, 476
    carbohydrates, 49–63. *See also* Carbohydrates
    diversity of polymers of, 49
    nucleic acids, 64*f*–66*f*. *See also* Nucleic acids
    as organic compounds and biological molecules, 43. *See also* Organic compounds
    as polymers of monomers, 48
    proteins, 55, 56*f*–63*f*. *See also* Proteins
    synthesis and breakdown of polymers of, 48–49
Macronutrients, plant, **599**, 600*t*
Macrophages, 86, 97*f*, 665*f*, 733*f*, **735**–736
Madagascar orchid, 569*f*, 625
Mad cow disease, 63, 355
MADS-box genes, 466
Maggot flies, 442–443
Magnesium chloride, 29
Magnesium deficiency, plant, 600
Magnetic field, Earth's, 803*f*, 826
Magnetite, 803
Magnification, microscope, 73
Magnolia grandiflora, 538*f*
Magnoliids, 538*f*
Maize. *See* Corn
Major histocompatibility complex (MHC) molecule, 739*f*, 746
Make Connections Figures
    contributions of genomics and proteomics to biology, 68*f*
    effects of climate change, 924*f*–925*f*
    genomics, cell signaling, and cancer, 338*f*–339*f*
    ion movement and gradients, 777*f*
    life challenges and solutions in plants and animals, 666*f*–667*f*
    maximizing surface area, 526*f*
    mutualism across kingdoms and domains, 603*f*
    sickle-cell allele, 428*f*–429*f*
    working cell, 178*f*–179*f*
    working ecosystem, 902*f*–903*f*
Malaria, 230, 427, 428*f*–429*f*, 507*f*, 517*f*, 518–519, 734
Malaysian orchid mantis, 386*f*
Male gametophytes, angiosperm, 622, 623*f*
Males
    female mate choice and competition between, 833*f*
    hormonal control of reproductive systems of human, 761*f*
    parental care by, 832–833*f*
    reproductive anatomy of human, 756*f*, 757
    sex determination of, 239, 240*f*, 761
    sexual competition between, 427*f*
    spermatogenesis in human, 758*f*, 760
    territorial responses of, 826
Malignant tumors, **195***f*, 196–197
Malleus (hammer), 805*f*
Malnutrition, 634, 690
Malpighian tubules, 680
Malthus, Thomas, 385–386
Maltose, 50
Mammalia, 10
Mammals, **565**. *See also* Animals
    adaptive radiations of, 463*f*, 464
    bats as flying, 824
    breathing in, 726*f*, 727
    cardiovascular systems of. *See* Cardiovascular systems
    characteristics and lineages of, 565*f*–567*f*
    digestive organs of, 693*f*–697*f*, 698
    ensuring survival of offspring of, 754, 755*f*
    excretory systems of, 681*f*
    glia in brains of, 773*f*. *See also* Neurons
    homologous structures in, 389*f*
    hormonal regulation of reproduction in, 760–764
    hormones in sex determination of, 761
    humans as, 567*f*–568*f*. *See also* Humans
    inactivation of X-linked genes in female, 241, 242*f*
    innate immunity in, 734, 735*f*–736*f*, 737
    ion concentrations inside and outside of neurons of, 775*t*
    kidney adaptations of, 684*f*
    kidney function in, 684
    lungs in respiratory systems of, 724, 725*f*–726*f*

mechanoreceptors for hearing and equilibrium in, 804f–807f
modeling neurons of, 776f
molecular clock for, 407f
natural selection of limbs of, 12
organ systems of, 664t
origination of cetaceans as land animals, 390f, 391
origin of, 456, 457f
production efficiency of, 893
reproductive cloning of, 331f
reproductive organs of, 755. See also Reproductive organs, human
respiratory adaptations of diving, 730
sex determination in, 240f
specific opiate receptors in brains of, 786–787
tissues of, 664t, 665f
Mammary gland lobule, 338f
Mammary glands, 565, **757**
Manatee, 412, 871f
Mantellinae frogs, 460f
Mantises, 386f
Mantle, 553f
Maple, 629f
Mapping, brain activity, 793f
Maps, genetic. See Genetic maps
Map units, **247**
Marchantia, 522f
March equinox, 843f
Marella, 548f
Marianas "flying fox" bat, 908f
Marine benthic zone, **851**f
Marine biomes. See also Aquatic biomes
characteristics and types of, 849f–851f, 852
effects of animals on, 568f, 569
fishes in, 672, 673f. See also Fishes
food chains and webs in, 875f–876f
photosynthetic protists as producers in, 515f, 516
primary production in, 890, 891ft
Marine crustaceans, 558f
Marine worm, 722f
Marshall, Barry, 694
Marsh gas, 490
Marsupials, 463f, **566**f, 755
Masked shrew, 883f
Mass
conservation of, 887
ecosystems and, 888f. See also Chemical cycling
Mass extinctions, **461**
consequences of, 461f, 462, 463f
extinctions vs., 460–461. See also Extinctions
first five, 461f–462f
human activities and, 570, 571f
human impacts and, 542f
plants and, 544
possibility of current sixth, 462f
Mass number, **24**
Mast cells, 736f, 737
Master regulatory genes, 324f. See also Homeotic genes; *Hox* genes
Mate choice, 430, 443f, 451, 833f
Mate recognition, 436f
Maternal age, Down syndrome and, 250
Maternal chromosomes, 211f
Maternal effect genes, 328f–329f
Mating. See also Courtship behaviors; Reproduction
animal behaviors in, 814
animal communication and, 827f
animal reproduction and, 751. See also Animal reproduction
clumped dispersion and, 855
fertilization and, 754
genetic basis of behaviors in, 834f
human, 229–230, 763–764, 787. See also Copulation, human
hybrids from interspecific, 435
hybrid zones and, 444f–446f
mating systems and parental care in, 832f–833f
mating systems and sexual dimorphism in, 832f
Mendel's techniques of cross-pollination as, 215f, 216
pheromones and, 827
prokaryotic mating bridges, 484, 485f
reproductive barriers to, 436f–437f
sexual selection and mate choice in, 833f
Mating systems, 832f–833f
Matter, **22**. See also Chemical cycling; Energy and Matter
as pure elements and compounds, 22–23
Mauna Loa monitoring station, 921, 922f
Maungatautari restoration project, 900f
Maximizing surface area, 526f
Maximum metabolic rate, 702
Maximum parsimony, 404f, 405
Maze experiments, 830–831
McClintock, Barbara, 364f
Meadowlarks, 435f
Meadow voles, 834f
Measles virus, 344, 746
Meat, human consumption of, 894
Mechanical digestion, 691, 693–694. See also Digestion; Digestive systems
Mechanical isolation, 436f
Mechanical signaling, extracellular matrix in, 95
Mechanical stimuli, plant responses to, 654f–655f
Mechanical stress, plant responses to, 646, 647f
Mechanical work, 128, 130f
Mechanoreceptors, **802**, 804f–807f
Mediator proteins, 311f, 312
Medicine. See also Diseases and disorders, human
antibodies as tools in, 746
application of systems biology to, 361f
biodiversity benefits for, 908–909
drugs in. See Drugs
as environmental toxins, 921f
genomics and proteomics contribution to, 68f
G protein-coupled receptors in, 116
radioactive isotopes as tracers in, 25f
stem cells in, 332f–333f, 334
Medium, growth, 279f, 280
Medulla oblongata, 727f, 794f–**795**f
Megapascal (MPa), **597**
Megaphylls, **533**f
Megaspores, 534f, **622**, 623f
Megasporocytes, 622, 623f
Meiosis, **204**
in animal cells, 206f–207f
changes in DNA of budding yeast cells during, 210
errors in, 248f–251f
genetic variation from errors in, 416
genome evolution and errors in, 368f–369f
human gametogenesis and, 758f–759f, 760
in human life cycle, 203f, 204
mitosis vs., 208, 209f, 210
overview of, 205f
parthenogenesis and, 771
in plant cells, 522f
production of gametes by, 184
in sexual life cycles, 204f
stages of, 205f–207f
Meiosis I, **205**, 206f, 208, 210, 211f
Meiosis II, **205**, 207f, 210
Melanerpes formicivorus, 838
Melanocyte-stimulating hormone (MSH), 669f
Melatonin, 669f
Melitaea cinxia, 864f
Membrane carbohydrates, 101f, 104
Membrane lipids, 100f–102f, 104
Membrane potentials, **110**, 111f, **775**f, 802. See also Resting potentials, neuron
Membrane proteins, 77f. See also Plasma membranes
animal cell, 95f
aquaporins, 100f, 108. See also Aquaporins
in cell junctions, 96f
exocytosis of secretory, 104f
fluid mosaic model and movement of, 101f–102f, 103
in glycoproteins, 104
phosphorylation and dephosphorylation of, 118f
receptor proteins, 103f, 113f, 115, 116f, 117
rough ER and, 84
synthesis of, in endoplasmic reticulum, 104f
targeting of polypeptides to, 295f, 296
transport proteins, 105, 108f–111f, 112. See also Transport proteins
types and functions of, 103f, 104
Membranes, cellular. See Cellular membranes
Memory, cerebral cortex and, 801
Memory cells, **741**f, 745f
Mendel, Gregor, 214f. See also Mendelian inheritance
concept of genes as hereditary factors and, 214, 236
experimental, quantitative approach of, 215f
on genetic variation, 212
law of independent assortment and, 219, 220f, 221, 244
law of segregation of, 215, 216f–219f
model of inheritance by, 414
Mendelian inheritance, 214–235
C. Darwin's theory and, 414
environmental impacts on phenotypes and, 226
evolution of gene concept from, 300
extending, for multiple genes, 225f–226f
extending, for single gene, 223f, 224, 225f
genes in particulate hypothesis of, 214
human genetics and, 228–232
integrating, with emergent properties, 226–227
law of independent assortment of, 219, 220f, 221
law of segregation of, 215, 216f–219f
laws of probability governing, 221f, 222
Mendel's experimental quantitative approach, 215f
physical basis of, in behavior of chromosomes, 236f–239f
Menopause, **763**
Menstrual cycle, **761**, 762f, 763
Menstrual flow phase, uterine cycle, 762f, 763
Menstruation, 761, **762**f, 763
Menthol, 803
Mercury pollution, 921
Meristems, **582**, 583f–584f, 627
Mescaline, 786
Meselson, Matthew, 260, 261f
Mesencephalon, 794f
Mesenchyme cells, 766f
Mesocricetus auratus, 797
Mesoderm, **550**f, 766f
Mesophyll, **162**, 163f, 175f, **587**f
Mesozoic era, 455t, 460f, 535
Messenger molecules, local cell signaling and, 114f
Messenger RNA (mRNA), **281**
in blocking translation, 314
degradation of, 314
effects of microRNAs and small interfering RNAs on, 315f, 316
genetic code and synthesis of, 282f, 283
growth factors in synthesis of, 119f
interpreting DNA sequence logos for ribosome-binding sites for, 294
in maternal effect (egg-polarity) genes, 328f–329f
monitoring gene expression and, 316, 317f–318f, 319f
in protein synthesis, 82
RNA processing of, after transcription, **286**, 287f–288f
role of, in protein synthesis, 64f
role of, in transcription and translation, 281f
in situ hybridization of, 321f
transcription and synthesis of, 281f, 284, 285f–286f
transcription factors and, 117f
in translation, 288, 289f–297f
viruses and, 349
in working cell, 178f
Metabolic defects, 279f–280f
Metabolic pathways, 122–123, 140, 303, 304f–307f, 308
Metabolic rate, **701**–702
Metabolism, **122**–140. See also Cellular respiration; Digestion; Digestive systems
ATP energy coupling of exergonic and endergonic reactions in, 128f–130f
catabolic pathways of, 142, 143f–145f, 157, 158f
chemical energy of life and, 122
enzymatic catalysis of, by lowering energy barriers, 131f–136f
enzymatic regulation of, 55
exergonic and endergonic reactions in, 126, 127f
forms of energy for, 123f
free-energy change and chemical equilibrium in, **125**, 126f–127f, 128
laws of thermodynamics and, 124f, 125
metabolic pathways of, 122–123

Metabolism (Cont.)
  prokaryotic, 481t, 482f
  protocell, 476
  regulating, by regulating enzyme activity, 136,
    137f–138f
Metabotropic receptors, 785
Metagenomics, **358**, 486, 604f
Metamorphosis
  frog, 672, 673f
  insect, 559f
Metaphase, **185**, 186f–187f, 190f, 209f
Metaphase chromosomes, 269f
Metaphase I, 206f, 209f, 210, 211f
Metaphase II, 207f
Metaphase plate, 187f, **188**f
Metapopulation, **864**f
Metastasis, 195f, **196**
Metencephalon, 794f
Meteorites, 476
Methamphetamine, 46
Methane, 28f, 30f, 44f
  combustion of, 143f
Methanogens, **487**, 490f
Methanopyrus kandleri, 490f
Methanosarcina barkeri, 362t
Methicillin, 388
Methicillin-resistant *S. aureus* (MRSA), 388f, 389
Methionine, 57f, 283f
Methods, research. *See* Research methods; Scientific
    Skills Exercises
Methylated compounds, 47f
Methylation, DNA, 309, 331
Methyl group, 47f, 48
Methylsalicylic acid, 659f
Metric system, C-1t
Mexico, deforestation in, 909
MHC (major histocompatibility complex) molecule,
    739f, 746
Mice. *See* Mouse
Microarray chips, human genome, 361f
Microbial diversity, 874f
Microbiome, 358, 699
Microevolution, **413**, **434**. *See also* Evolution
  evolution of populations as, 413–414
  gene flow as cause of, 423, 424f
  genetic drift as cause of, 421f–423f
  genetic variation and, 414f–415f, 416, 426–427
  limits of natural selection in, 430–431
  natural selection as cause of, 421
  natural selection as cause of adaptive evolution in,
    424, 425f–430f
  sexual selection in, 427f, 430f
  speciation and, 434. *See also* Speciation
  using Hardy-Weinberg equation to test,
    417f–419f, 420
Microfibrils, 52, 94–95
Microfilaments (actin filaments), **93**
  animal cell, 78f
  in animal cytokinesis, 190
  in cytoskeletons, 90f
  functions of, 93f, 94
  plant cell, 79f
  structural role of, 93f
  structure and function of, 91t
Microglia, 791f
Micronutrients, plant, **600**
Microphylls, **533**f
Micropyles, 622, 623f
MicroRNAs (miRNAs), **315**f, 316, 336
Microscopy, 73f–75f, 190, D-1f
Microsporangia, 622, 623f
Microspores, 534, **622**, 623f
Microsporocytes, 622, 623f
Microtubule-organizing center, 185
Microtubules (tubulin polymers), **92**
  animal cell, 78f
  of cilia and flagella, 93f
  in cytoskeletons, 90f
  functions of, 92, 93f
  in mitotic spindle, 185f–189f
  plant cell, 79f
  plus and minus ends of, 198
  structure and function of, 91t

Microtus ochrogaster, 834f
Microtus pennsylvanicus, 834f
Microvilli, 77, 78f, 93f, **696**f
Midbrain, 794f–795f
Middle ear, 805f, 806
Middle lamella, 94f, **95**
Midgut, 692f
Migration, **826**
  electromagnetic receptors and, 803f
  as fixed action pattern, 826
Milk duct, 338f
Miller, Stanley, 475–476
Mimicry
  endorphin, 786
  in predation, 870, 871f, 885
Mimics
  of leaf shape, 639f
  molecular, 31f, 59
Mimivirus, 349
Mimosa pudica, 655f
Mimulus, 449f, 632
Mineralocorticoids, 669f
Minerals, **690**
  for animal nutrition, 689f, 690
  plant symptoms of deficiencies in, 600–601
  root architecture and acquisition of, 595
  transpiration of, from roots to shoots via xylem,
    609f–611f, 612
  vascular plant transport of, across plasma
    membranes, 596
Minimal medium, 279f
Minimum metabolic rate, 702
Minimum viable population (MVP), **912**–913, 914f
Mining sites, bioremediation of, 899f
Minipill contraceptives, 769f
Minke whales, 398f
miRNAs. *See* MicroRNAs
Miscarriage, 248, 768
Misfolding, protein, 63
Mismatch repairs, DNA, **265**
Missense mutations, **298**, 299f
Mistletoe, 608f
Mitchell, Peter, 153
Mites, 658
Mitochondria, **87**
  in animal cells, 78f
  in cellular respiration, 77, 87, 88, 89f
  chemiosmosis in, vs. in chloroplasts, 171f–173f
  endosymbiont theory on evolutionary origins of, 88f
  enzymes in, 138f
  genetic research on prokaryotes related to, 501
  in human sperm, 758f
  origin of, in endosymbiosis, 500ft–501f, 502
  in plant cells, 79f, 179f
Mitochondrial DNA (mtDNA)
  in evidence for endosymbiosis, 501–502
  species identity in, 398f, 910–911
Mitochondrial matrix, **88**, 89f
Mitochondrion
  in brown fat, 154
  cellular respiration in, 145f, 146, 150f
  chemiosmosis in, 151f–152f
  citric acid cycle in, 148f
  pH difference across, 160f
Mitosis, **184**
  in animal cells, 185f–190f
  in chromatin packing, 268f–269f
  evolution of, 191f, 198
  in human gametogenesis, 758f–759f
  in human life cycle, 203f
  meiosis vs., 208, 209f, 210
  in plant cells, 190f, 522f
  in sexual life cycles, 204f
Mitosomes, 508
Mitotic (M) phase, **185**f
Mitotic (M) phase checkpoint, 192f–193f
Mitotic spindles, **185**f–189f
Mixotrophs, **510**, 515
M line, skeletal muscle, 815f
Mnium, 523f
Mobile genetic elements, evolution of, 349
Mobile River basin, 910
Mockingbirds, 382–383

Model organisms, **321**. *See also Arabidopsis*
    thaliana; *Caenorhabditis elegans*; *Drosophila*
    melanogaster; Mouse; *Saccharomyces*
    cerevisiae
  for DNA research, 254
  for embryonic development research, 321
  Neurospora crassa (bread mold), 279f–280f
Modified stems, 578f
Mojave Desert, 844
mol. *See* Mole
Molarity, 37
Molds, 279f–280f, 528f, 530
Mole (mol), **37**
Molecular basis of inheritance, 253–277
  chromosomes as DNA molecules packed with
    proteins in, 267, 268f–269f
  DNA as genetic material in, 254f–259f
  DNA structure and DNA replication in, 253
  evolution of gene concept from, 300
  genetic engineering and, 270f–275f
  predicting percentages of nucleotides in genomes
    and, 257
  proteins in DNA replication and repair in,
    259f–267f
Molecular biology, 67, 349
Molecular clocks, **406**
  calibration of, 406, 407f
  dating origin of HIV using, 407, 408f
  differences in clock speed of, 407
  in evidence for origination of animals, 546
  fungal lineages determined by, 525
  for mammals, 407f
  potential problems with, 407
Molecular formulas, 28f, 44f
  isomers and, 46f
Molecular genealogy, 67
Molecular homologies, 390, 399f–400f
Molecular homoplasies, 400f
Molecular mass, **37**
Molecular recognition, immune system, 733, 734f
Molecular systematics. *See also* Systematics
  applying parsimony to problems in, 404f
  evaluating molecular homologies in, 400f
  prokaryotic phylogenies of, 486f–490f
Molecules, 5f, **27**
  formation of, by chemical bonding of atoms,
    27–30
  in hierarchy of biological organization, 5f
  isomers of, 46f
  origin of self-replicating, 475–477f, 478
  polar, of water, 32, 33f
  as second messengers in cell signaling, 118, 119f
  shape and function of, 30f–31f
Mole rats, 835f
Moles, 399f, 400
Molluscs
  appearance of, 548f, 551f
  as arthropods, 553f
  body plan of, 553f
  as endangered species, 571f
  exoskeletons of, 822
  eye complexity in, 469f
  predator-prey relationships of, 570
Molothrus ater, 916
Monarch butterflies, 635–636, 830, 831f
Monera, kingdom, 408
Mongolia, grassland biome in, 847f
Monilophytes, 530f–531f, **532**
Monkey flower, 449f, 632
Monkeys, 69, 566f. *See also* Chimpanzees
Monoclonal antibodies, **746**
Monocots
  in angiosperm phylogenies, 537f–538f
  eudicots vs., 575, 576f
  roots of, 585f
  seed structure of, 626f
Monocytes, 717f–718f
Monod, Jacques, 304
Monogamous mating, **832**
Monohybrid crosses, **219**, 221
Monohybrids, **219**
Monomers, **48**, 49f
Monophyletic clades, **401**f

Monosaccharides, 49, 50*f*
Monosiga brevicollis, 504*f*–505*f*
Monosodium glutamate (MSG), 803
Monosomic zygotes, **248**–249
Monosomy X, 250
Monotremes, 463*f*, **566***f*
Monotropa uniflora, 608*f*
Monozygotic twins, 768
Montmorillonite, 476*f*
Moose, 862, 864*f*, 872
Morgan, Thomas Hunt, 238–239, 242*f*–245*f*, 254
Moriches Bay, 891*f*
"Morning-after" pills, 769*f*
Morphine, 31*f*, 59
Morphogenesis, **322**, **766**. *See also* Embryonic
    development
Morphogen gradient hypothesis, 328, 329*f*
Morphogens, **328**, 329*f*
Morphological homologies, 399
Morphological species concept, **438**
Morphology
    fungal, 525*f*–526*f*, 527
    macroevolution of, from changes in
        developmental genes, 465*f*–468*f*
    species concepts and, 434–435, 438
Mortality rates, 902*f*
    demographics and, 856*ft*, 857
    population change and, 862, 864*f*
    population dynamics and, 855*f*
    population growth and, 857–858
    regulation of, 862*f*
Mosaicism, 241, 242*f*
Mosquitoes, 394, 424, 429*f*, 517*f*, 518–519
Mosquitofish, 439*f*
Mosses, 523*f*, 530*f*–531*f*
Moths, 42*f*, 379*f*, 472, 559*f*, 569*f*, 624*f*, 625
Motility
    cell, 90*f*–93*f*, 94
    ion gradients in, 777*f*
    prokaryotic, 480*f*. *See also* Movement
Motor, flagellum, 480*f*
Motor cortex, 799*f*
Motor neurons, 774*f*, 792–793, 817*f*–818*f*
Motor output, nervous system, 774
Motor proteins, 56*f*, **91***f*–93*f*, 94, 130*f*, 188, 189*f*, 198
Motor systems, **793**, 815–825
    animal behaviors and, 814–815. *See also* Animal
        behaviors
    energy costs of locomotion in, 825
    muscle function in, 815–821. *See also* Muscles
    skeletal systems and locomotion in, 821*f*–824*f*,
        825. *See also* Skeletal systems
    in vertebrate peripheral nervous systems, 793
Motor unit, **819***f*
Mountain pine beetle, 924*f*
Mountains, climate effects of, 844*f*
Mouse (mice)
    animal behavior studies of, 828*t*
    appetite regulation in, 704*t*
    comparing human genome to genome of, 364, 373*f*
    comparison of chromosome sequences of humans
        and, 367*f*
    complete genome sequence for, 357
    density-dependent population regulation of, 863*f*
    FOXP2 gene evolution in, 373*f*
    homeotic genes in, 374*f*
    osmotic homeostasis in desert, 679
    paw development of, 325, 326*f*
    predation and coat coloration adaptations of, 2*f*,
        16*f*–17*f*, 18
    selection modes and, 425*f*
Mouth, 692*f*, 766*f*, 767
Movement. *See also* Motility
    cell. *See* Motility, cell
    ion gradients in, 777*f*
    mechanoreceptors for sensing, in humans,
        806, 807*f*
    prokaryotic, 480*f*
Movement corridor, **916**, 917*f*
MPa. *See* Megapascal
mPGES-1 gene, 313
mRNA. *See* Messenger RNA
MRSA. *See* Methicillin-resistant *S. aureus*

MSG. *See* Monosodium glutamate
MSH. *See* Melanocyte-stimulating hormone
mtDNA. *See* Mitochondrial DNA
Mucor, 528*f*
Mucous cells, **694***f*
Mucous membranes, 735
Mucus, **693**, 735
Mucus escalator, 725
Mule deer, 661
Mules, 437*f*
Muller, Hermann, 300
Multicellular asexual reproduction, 201*f*
Multicellular fungi, 525*f*
Multicellular organisms, 72, 499*f*, 503*f*–505*f*, 666*f*–667*f*
Multifactorial characters, **226**
Multifactorial disorders, human, 231
Multigene families, 365, **366***f*
Multiple fruits, **628***f*
Multiple sclerosis, 747
Multiplication rule, **221***f*, 222
Murchison meteorite, 476
Muscle cells, 72*f*, 324*f*, 670*f*
Muscle contraction, 815–821
    nervous system regulation of tension in, 818, 819*f*
    of nonskeletal muscles, 820–821
    regulation of, 817*f*–818*f*
    skeletal muscle fibers and, 819*t*, 820*f*
    skeletal muscle structure and, 815*f*
    skeletons and, 821*f*. *See also* Skeletal systems
    sliding-filament model of, 816*f*, 817
Muscles
    contraction of. *See* Muscle contraction
    energy storage in, 702
    lactic acid fermentation in, 156*f*
    mammalian, 664*t*
    nonskeletal types of, 820–821
    skeletal. *See* Skeletal muscles
    skeletal systems, locomotion, and, 821*f*–824*f*, 825
    of stomach, 694–695
Muscle tissue, **665***f*
Muscular dystrophy, 240–241
Mushrooms, fungal, 525*f*, 528*f*
Muskmelon, 359, 360*f*
Mus musculus, 357. *See also* Mouse
Mussel, 432–433, 876*f*
Mustard plant. *See Arabidopsis thaliana*
Mutagens, **300**
Mutant phenotypes, 238*f*–239*f*
Mutants
    designing experiments using genetic, 797
    nutritional, 279*f*–280*f*
Mutations, **298**
    cancer development from, 334*f*–339*f*
    color vision and, 811
    embryonic lethals and abnormal pattern
        formation by, 327*f*, 328
    emerging viruses and, 352
    environment and, 277
    as errors in DNA proofreading, 266
    evolution and genetic variation from, 212
    evolution of enzymes by, 136
    as faulty proteins from faulty genes, 278,
        298*f*–299*f*, 300
    gene editing for, 275
    genome evolution and, 367*f*–369*f*, 371
    Hardy-Weinberg equilibrium and, 419–420
    of ion channel protein genes, 781
    mutagens and spontaneous, 300
    mutant phenotypes and, 238*f*–239*f*
    nucleotide-pair insertions and deletions and
        frameshift mutations, **299***f*, 300
    nutritional mutants and, 279*f*–280*f*
    point mutations, 298*f*
    prokaryotic, 483*f*, 484
    random, as source of alleles, 248
    silent, missense, and nonsense mutations as
        nucleotide-pair substitutions, 298, 299*f*
    as sources of genetic variation, 415–416
    systems biology and cancer-causing, 361
    temperature-sensitive, 302
Mutualism, **491**, 868, **872***f*, 902*f*–903*f*
    in flower pollination, 619, 624*f*
    fungal, 527*f*, 539*f*–542*f*

in interspecific interactions, 8, 9*f*
    lichen as, 539*f*
    mycorrhizae as. *See* Mycorrhizae
    in plant nutrition, 602, 603*f*–608*f*, 618
Mutualistic bacteria, 491–492
MVP. *See* Minimum viable population
Myasthenia gravis, 818
Mycelium (mycelia), **525**
Mycobacterium tuberculosis, 492, 737
Mycoplasma capricolum, 501
Mycoplasmas, 489*f*
Mycorrhizae, 525*f*, **606**, 607*f*
    agricultural and ecological importance of, 607
    associations of, 577
    bioremediation using, 901
    disruption of, by garlic mustard, 607
    evolution of, 527*f*
    nutrient limitations and, 892
    as plant-fungi mutualism, 595, 603*f*, 872
    types of, 527, 606, 607*f*
Myelencephalon, 794*f*
Myelination, 791*f*
Myelin sheath, **782**
Myeloid stem cells, 718*f*
Myllokunmingia fengjiaoa, 554, 555*f*
Myoblasts, 324*f*
Myocardial infarctions, 720
MyoD protein, 311*f*, 324*f*
Myofibrils, **815***f*
Myoglobin, **730**, **820**
Myosin, **94**, 190. *See also* Thin filaments
Myotonia, 764, 781
Myrmecocystus, 394
Mytilus californianus, 876*f*
Mytilus edulis, 432–433
Myxini, 556*f*
Myxobacteria, 488*f*
Myxospores, 488*f*

N

NAD$^+$ (nicotinamide adenine dinucleotide), 143,
    146*f*–148*f*, 155
NADH, 143, 144*f*, 145, 146*f*–148*f*, 150*f*, 151, 153*f*,
    154–156
NADP$^+$ (nicotinamide adenine dinucleotide
    phosphate), **164**, 176, 177*f*
NADPH, **164**, 170*f*–173*f*, 176, 177*f*
NADP reductase, 173*f*
Naked mole rats, 835*f*
Naloxone, 787
Nannochloris atomus, 891*f*
Nanoarchaeota clade, 490
Nanopore, 274*f*
National Cancer Institute, 361
National Center for Biotechnology Information
    (NCBI), 359, 360*f*
National Institutes of Health (NIH), 359, 361
National Library of Medicine, 359
National Medal of Science, 726
Natural family planning, 768, 769*f*
Natural killer cells, **735**–736
Natural plastics, 493, 494*f*
Natural selection, **12**, **383**. *See also* Evolution
    biodiversity from adaptive evolution by, 466
    as cause of microevolution, 421
    C. Darwin's research focus on adaptations and,
        383*f*. *See also* Adaptations
    C. Darwin's theory of descent with modification
        by, 379–380, 384*f*–386*f*
    Darwin's theory of evolution by, 11*f*–12*f*, 20
    directional, disruptive, and stabilizing selection in,
        425*f*, 426
    ecological niches and, 868*f*–869*f*, 885
    in evolution of drug resistance, 388*f*, 389
    evolution of genetic variation from genetic
        recombination and, 244
    Hardy-Weinberg equilibrium and, 419
    herbivory adaptations in, 871
    insect evolution by, due to food source changes,
        387*f*, 388
    key role of, in adaptive evolution, 424–425, 426*f*
    life history traits and, 861*f*, 862
    limitations of, in adaptive evolution, 430–431

Natural selection (*Cont.*)
  making and testing predictions about predation, coloration of guppies, and, 392
  molecular level, 477
  mutations from altered DNA nucleotides and, 266–267
  predation adaptations in, 870, 871*f*, 885
  relative fitness and, 425
  species selection as, 471
  tree of life and, 12, 13*f*
Nature reserves, 917, 918*f*, 919, 931
Nature vs. nurture, 226, 828
Navigation, migration and, 826
NCBI. *See* National Center for Biotechnology Information
Neanderthals (*Homo neanderthalensis*), 357
  gene flow to humans from, 568*f*
  genomics and proteomics contribution to, 68*f*
  human interbreeding with, 373, 568*f*
Nectar guides, 624*f*
Negative correlations, 632
Negative feedback, **669**
  in endocrine signaling, 669
  in homeostasis, 674
  in population regulation, 862
Negative gene regulation, bacterial, 305, 306*f*, 307
Negative gravitropism, 654
Negative pressure breathing, **726***f*, 727
Neisseria gonorrhoeae, 479, 488*f*
Nematodes, 551*f*–552*f*, 821, 822*f*. *See also Caenorhabditis elegans*
Nembrotha chamberlaini, 751
Neodenticula seminae, 923
NEP. *See* Net ecosystem production
Nepenthes, 608*f*
Nephrons, **681***f*, 683*f*
Nerium oleander, 614*f*
Nerve cells
  exocytosis by, 112. *See also* Neurons
  gated channels in, 108
  human, 72*f*
Nerve cords, chordate, 555*f*
Nerve gas, 786
Nerve impulses, 670
Nerve nets, 790, 791*f*
Nerves, 774*f*, **791**
Nervous systems, **668**, 790–813
  animal behaviors and, 814. *See also* Animal behaviors
  central nervous systems and peripheral nervous systems in human, 792*f*
  control of heart rhythm by, 712*f*
  control of skeletal muscle tension by, 818, 819*f*
  coordination and control functions of, 668*f*
  diversity of, 791*f*
  glia in, 791*f*, 792
  Huntington's disease and, 231
  ligand-gated ion channels in, 116–117
  mammalian, 664*t*
  neurons, nerves, and types of, 790–791
  neurons in information processing by, **774***f*. *See also* Neurons
  sensory reception in, 801–811. *See also* Sensory reception
  synaptic signaling in, 114*f*
  vertebrate brains in, 793–801. *See also* Brains, vertebrate
  vertebrate central nervous systems, 791*f*–792*f*. *See also* Central nervous system
  vertebrate peripheral nervous systems, 791*f*–792*f*, 793. *See also* Peripheral nervous system
Nervous tissue, **665***f*
Nests, 405*f*–406*f*
Net ecosystem production (NEP), **890**, 905
Net primary production (NPP), **889***f*–890*f*, 905
Neuraminidase, 356
Neuroendocrine pathways, 670*f*–673*f*
Neuroendocrine signaling, 669
Neuromuscular junctions, 785
Neuronal plasticity, 800*f*, **801**
Neurons, 665*f*, **772**–789
  axons and action potentials of, 778, 779*f*–780*f*, 781
  electrical and chemical signaling by, 772
  in endocrine signaling, 670

glia and, in vertebrate nervous systems, 792
in human ears, 805*f*
in human eyes, 808*f*
ion concentrations inside and outside of mammalian, 775*t*
ion pumps, ion channels, and resting potentials of, 775*f*–776*f*
major neurotransmitters for, 786*t*
measuring membrane potentials of, using intracellular recording, 778*f*
nervous system information processing and, 774*f*
in sensory transmission, 802*f*
signaling of, at chemical synapses, 783–787
specific opiate receptors and, 786
structure and function of, 773*f*
vertebrate, 789
in vertebrate peripheral nervous systems, 792*f*, 793
Neuropeptides, 786–787
Neurospora crassa (bread mold), 279*f*–280*f*
Neurotransmitters, **773**
  acetylcholine, 785, 786*t*
  amino acids, 786*t*
  biogenic amines, 786*t*
  chemical synapses and, 783–787. *See also* Chemical synapses
  clearing of, from synaptic clefts, 783–784
  gases, 787
  in genetic basis of animal behavior, 834
  in local cell signaling, 114*f*
  major, 786*t*
  modulated signaling by, 784–785
  neuropeptides, 786*t*, 787
  in regulation of muscle contraction, 817*f*–818*f*
  in synaptic signaling, 114*f*
  vision and, 810
Neutralization, 743
Neutral variation, **416**
Neutrons, **24***f*
Neutrophils, 717*f*–718*f*, **735**–736
New Jersey
  bioremediation in, 899*f*
  temperate broadleaf forest biome in, 848*f*
Newt lung cells, 6*f*
Newton, Sir Isaac, 18
New Zealand, 878, 879*f*
  Maungatautari restoration project in, 900*f*
Next-generation sequencing technique, 274*f*
Niche, ecological, 438, 868*f*–869*f*, 885
Nicotinamide adenine dinucleotide. *See* NAD$^+$
Nicotine, 785–786, 871
Night length, flowering and, 652*f*–653*f*
NIH. *See* National Institutes of Health
Nirenberg, Marshall, 283
Nitrate, 897*f*
  deforestation effects on, 898*f*, 899
Nitric oxide (NO), 117, 714–715, 787
Nitrification, 605*f*
Nitrifying bacteria, 605*f*
Nitrite, 897*f*
Nitrogen
  as essential element, 23*t*
  as limiting nutrient in aquatic biomes, 890, 891*ft*
  as limiting nutrient in terrestrial biomes, 892
  pollution caused by, 919*f*, 920
  valence of, and organic compounds, 44*f*
Nitrogen cycle, 488*f*, **605***f*–606*f*, 897*f*, 903*f*
  deforestation effects on, 898*f*, 899
Nitrogen deficiency, plant, 600*f*
Nitrogen fixation, **482**, **605***f*, 892
  biological augmentation and, 901
  conservation of mass and, 887
  cyanobacteria and, 489*f*
  nitrogen cycle and, 897*f*
  prokaryotic, 482
  by *Rhizobium*, 496
Nitrogen-fixing bacteria, 605*f*–606*f*
Nitrogenous bases, nucleic acid, 64, 65*f*, 256*f*
Nitrogenous wastes, 677–678, 679*f*
Nitrosomonas, 488*f*
NO. *See* Nitric oxide
Nobel Prize winners
  Axel, R., 803
  Beadle, G., 280

  Buck, L., 803
  Crick, F., 259
  Jacob, F., 469
  Gurdon, J., 331
  Marshall, B., 694
  McClintock, B., 364
  Mitchell, P., 153
  Nüsslein-Volhard, C., 328
  Prusiner, S., 355
    for research on noncoding RNAs, 315
  Tatum, E., 280
  Tinbergen, N., 825
  Warren, R., 694
  Watson, J., 259
  Wieschaus, E., 328
  Wilkins, M., 259
  Yamanaka, S., 333
Nociceptors, **803**
Nocturnal animals, 827
Nodes
  lymph, 716*f*
  plant, 577*f*, **578**
Nodes of Ranvier, **782**
Nodules, **605**, 606*f*
Nomarski (differential-interference contrast) microscopy, 74*f*
Nonbreeding adults, territoriality and, 863*f*
Noncoding DNA, 363*f*–366*f*
Noncoding RNAs, 315*f*, 316
Noncompetitive inhibitors, **136***f*
Nondisjunction, **248***f*–250*f*
Nonequilibrium model, **878**
Nongonococcal urethritis, 489*f*
Nonheritable genetic variation, 415*f*
Nonhomologous chromosomes, 236, 237*f*
Nonidentical DNA sequences, 366
Non-insulin-dependent diabetes, 703
Nonkinetochore microtubules, 186*f*, 188*f*, 198
Non-native species, 910*f*
Nonparental types, 244, 245*f*
Nonpolar covalent bonds, **28**
Nonpolar molecules, 105
Nonpolar side chains, 57*f*, 58
Nonself recognition, immune system, 733, 734*f*
Nonsense mutations, **299***f*
Nonsister chromatids, 203*f*, 211, 212*f*
Nonspontaneous processes, 125
Nonsteroid hormones, 313
Nontemplate strands, DNA, 282
Nonvascular plants, 530*f*–532*f*
Norepinephrine (noradrenaline), 669*f*, 785, 786*t*
Nori, 512*f*
Normal range, homeostatic, 674
North America
  biomes in, 845*f*
  climate of, 842*f*–844*f*
North American moles, 399*f*, 400
North Atlantic bluefin tuna, 911*f*
Northern coniferous forests, **848***f*
Northern elephant seals, 912
Northern Hemisphere, seasonal variation in, 843*f*
Norway, coniferous forest and tundra biomes in, 848*f*
Norway spruce, 595*f*
Notochords, **555***f*
Novel functions, evolution of genes with, 369
Novelties, evolutionary, 469*f*, 470
N-P-K fertilizers, 601
NPP. *See* Net primary production
N-terminus, 58*f*, 103*f*, 268*f*, 292, 309
Nucifraga columbiana, 830
Nuclear envelope, **80**
  animal cell, 78*f*
  bound ribosomes and, 82*f*
  in endomembrane system, 87*f*
  functions of, 80, 81*f*
  in mitosis, 186*f*–187*f*
  nuclear contents and, 81*f*
  plant cell, 79*f*
  in transcription, 281*f*
Nucleariids, 514, **525**
Nuclear lamina, **81***f*
Nuclear magnetic resonance (NMR) spectroscopy, 63

Nuclear pores, 81f, 178f
Nuclear transplantation, animal cloning and, 330f–331f
Nucleases, **266**f, 695f
Nucleic acid hybridization, **270**, **317**f
Nucleic acid probes, **317**f
Nucleic acids, **64**
    components of, 48–49, 64, 65f
    digestion of, 695f
    as genetic material, 253. *See also* DNA
    as measures of evolution, 67
    as organic compounds and macromolecules, 43
    roles of, 64f
    structure of DNA and RNA molecules, 66f
    viruses as, with protein coats, 342, 343f, 344
Nucleoids, 75, **76**f, **267**, **481**
Nucleolus, 78f, 79f, 81f, **82**, 186f–187f
Nucleomorph, 502
Nucleosidases, 695f
Nucleosides, 64, 65f
Nucleosomes, **268**f
Nucleotidases, 695f
Nucleotide excision repairs, 266f
Nucleotide-pair insertions and deletions, **299**f, 300
Nucleotide-pair substitutions, 298, 299f
Nucleotides, **64**, 65f
    coding and noncoding, 287–288f
    components of, 256f
    in DNA structure and function, 6f
    evolutionary significance of altered, 266–267
    genetic triplet code of, 282f–284f
    genomics and proteomics in study of, 68f
    mutations as base-pair insertions and deletions of, **299**f, 300
    mutations as base-pair substitutions of, 298, 299f
    predicting percentages of, in genomes, 257
Nucleotide variability, 414f–415f
Nucleus, cell, **80**
    animal and fungal, 78f
    DNA in, 75, 80, 81f, 82
    in endomembrane system, 87f
    in eukaryotic cells, 498
    in eukaryotic cells vs. in prokaryotic cells, 4, 5f
    intracellular receptor proteins in, 117f
    mechanisms of cell division in, 191f
    mitosis and genetic material in, 184
    nuclear envelope and contents of, 81f
    organismal cloning by transplantation of, 330f–331f
    plant and protist, 79f, 178f
Nucleus accumbens, 797
Nudibranchs, 751
Nurture vs. nature, 226, 828
Nüsslein-Volhard, Christiane, 328, 329f
Nutrient absorption, 99
Nutrient cycling, 903f. *See also* Chemical cycling
    biogeochemical cycles in, 895, 896f–897f, 898
    climate change and, 925f
    decomposition effects on rate of, 895f
    deforestation effects on, 898f, 899
    in Hubbard Brook Experimental Forest, 898f, 899
Nutrient enrichment, 919f–920f
Nutrient enrichment experiments, 890, 891ft
Nutrient limitations
    primary production in aquatic ecosystems and, 890, 891ft
    primary production in terrestrial ecosystems and, 891, 892f
Nutrient reservoirs, 896f–897f
Nutrition, **688**
    animal. *See* Animal nutrition
    fungal, 524f, 525
    plant. *See* Plant nutrition
    prokaryotic, 481t, 482f
    protist, 515
    solutions for, 666f
Nutritional modes
    photosynthesis and, 161
    prokaryotic, 481t
Nutritional mutants, 279f–280f
Nymphaea, 538f
Nymphs, insect, 559f

O

Oak Ridge National Laboratory, 901f
Oak trees, 883
Obesity, 703
ob gene, 704t
Obligate aerobes, 481
Obligate anaerobes, **157**, 481–482
Observations, scientific, 13–14. *See also* Scientific Skills Exercises
Occam's razor, 405
Occipital lobe, 799f
Ocean acidification, **39**f, 40
    climate change and, 42
Ocean currents, climate influences of, 843, 844f
Oceanic pelagic zone, **851**f
Oceans
    anoxia in, 461
    as aquatic biome, 849, 851f
    climate influences of, 843, 844f, 849
    effects of, on climate, 34f
    human disturbances of, 880, 881f
    as marine biomes. *See* Aquatic biomes
    mass extinctions and ecology of, 463f
    primary production in, 890, 891ft
Ocelli, 807f, 808
Ochotona princeps, 924f
Ocotillo, 614f
Octopus, 553f
Odor, pheromones and, 827
Odorants, **803**
Odum, Eugene, 868
Offspring
    ensuring survival of, 754, 755f
    reproduction/survival trade-offs and, 861f
Oil spills, 494f
Okazaki fragments, **264**
Oleander, 614f
Olfaction, **803**, 813
Olfactory bulb, brain, 796f
Olfactory communication, 827–828
Olfactory receptor genes, human, 416
Oligodendrocytes, **782**, 791f
Oligotrophic lakes, **850**f
Omasum, 700f
Ommatidia, **808**f
Omnivores, **688**
    dentition and diet of, 698f
Oncogenes, **334**f–339f
One gene–one enzyme hypothesis, 280
One gene–one polypeptide hypothesis, 280
One gene–one protein hypothesis, 280f
On the Origin of Species by Means of Natural Selection (book). *See Origin of Species, The* (book)
Onychophorans, 554f
Oocytes, **757**f, 759f, 760, 767f
Oogenesis, 759f, **760**
Oogonia, **759**f
Oparin, A. I., 475
Oparin-Haldane hypothesis, 475
Open circulatory systems, **707**f, 708
Open-pit mine restoration, 899
Open systems, 124, 127f
Operators, **304**, 305f
Operon model, 304, 305f–306f, 307
Operons, **304**, 305f–306f, 307
Ophisaurus ventralis, 395f
Opiates, 31f, 59, 786
Opisthokonts, 514
Opossums, 566f
Opposable thumb, **566**
Opposite phyllotaxy, 595
Opsin, **809**f
Optic chiasm, 810, 811f
Optic disk, 808f
Optic nerves, 808f, 810, 811f
Optimal conditions, for enzyme activity, 135f
Oral cavity, 693f
Oral contraceptives, 769f
Orange peel fungus, 528f
Orangutan, 357
Orchid mantis, 386f
Order, as property of life, 125
Orders (taxonomy), 396f

Oregon, intertidal zone biome in, 850f
Organelles, **5**f, **73**
    autophagy of, by lysosomes, 86f
    determining function of, 99
    endomembrane system, 87f
    in eukaryotic cells, 498
    in hierarchy of biological organization, 5f
    microscopy in study of, 73f–75f
    in prokaryotic and eukaryotic cells, 75, 76f–79f
Organic acid, 47f
Organic compounds, **43**–69
    abiotic synthesis of, 475f–476f
    ATP as, 48
    bonds with carbon atoms in, 44f–45f
    carbohydrates, 49–53. *See also* Carbohydrates
    carbon in, and biological molecules of life, 43
    carbon skeletons of, 45f
    catabolic pathways and, 142
    chemical groups and properties of, 46, 47f–48f
    diversity of, 49
    in energy flow and chemical recycling, 141f
    isomers of, 46f
    lipids, 53f–55f. *See also* Lipids
    nucleic acids, 64f–66f. *See also* Nucleic acids
    oxidation of, 143
    in plant cells, 179f
    proteins, 55, 56f–63f. *See also* Proteins
    shape of simple, 44f
    synthesis and breakdown of, 48–49
    valences of elements of, 44f
Organic fertilizers, 601
Organic phosphate, 47f, 48
Organic topsoil components, 602
Organismal cloning, 330f–334f
Organismal ecology, **841**f
Organisms, **4**f
    in aquatic biomes. *See* Aquatic biomes
    aquatic vs. terrestrial, 558f
    cell as basic unit of structure and function for, 3–4
    climate change effects on, 924f
    correlation of structure and function in, 3
    DNA in development of, 6f
    embryonic development of. *See* Embryonic development
    in energy flow and chemical cycling, 8f
    fossil record and geologic record as documentation of history of, 452, 453f–454f, 455t, 456, 457f
    in hierarchy of biological organization, 4f
    homozygous vs. heterozygous, 218
    interactions of, with environment and other organisms as biological theme, 8, 9f. *See also* Interactions, ecological
    model. *See* Model organisms
    as open systems, 124
    organismal ecology and, 841f
    photosynthetic and chemosynthetic, in ecosystems, 886–887, 888f
    plant nutrition and relationships with, 602, 603f–608f
    prokaryotes as Earth's first, 474f, 477f, 478
    speciation and extinction rates of, 456, 458f–464f, 465
    species distributions of. *See* Species distributions
    in terrestrial biomes. *See* Terrestrial biomes
    in topsoil, 602
    transgenic, 283, 284f, 634, 635f, 636
Organization, levels of biological, 3, 4f–5f
    apoptosis role, 341
    breathing and gait, 573
    flowers and reproduction, 638
    functionality of form, 472
    lens of eye, 813
    lignin and vascular plant structure and function, 592
    osmoregulation, 687
    sickle-cell hemoglobin, 433
    vertebrate neurons, 789
    viral structure and function, 356
Organ of Corti, 805f
Organogenesis, 764, **767**f, 768f
Organophosphates, 140
Organ Pipe Cactus National Monument, 847f
Organs, **5**f

Organs, animal, **664***t*
  animal reproductive, 755
  excretory, 681*f*
  eyes and light-detecting, 807*f*–808*f*, 809
  heterochrony and development of reproductive, 466
  human reproductive, 756*f*–757*f*, 763–764
  immune system rejection of transplanted, 746
  mammalian/human digestive system. *See*
    Digestive systems
  organogenesis of, in animal embryonic
    development, 767*f*
  organogenesis of, in human embryonic
    development, 768
  smooth muscle and vertebrate, 820–821
Organs, plant, **576**, 577*f*–578*f*, **620***f*
Organ systems, animal, **664***t*
Orgasm phase, human sexual response, 764
Orientation, leaf, 595
Origin of replication. *See* Origins of replication
Origin of Species, The (book), 11*f*, 379, 383–384,
  392–393, 414
Origins of replication, **190**, 191*f*, **261**, 262*f*
Ornithine, 280*f*
Oryza nivara, 908
Oryza sativa, 362*t*, 437*f*, 644, 908. *See also* Rice
Oscillatoria, 489*f*
Oseltamivir (Tamiflu), 356
Osmoconformers, **678**
Osmolarity, **678**
Osmoreceptors, 803
Osmoregulation, **107, 677**
  challenges and mechanisms of, 678*f*
  desert mice study on, 679
  excretion and, 677
  excretory systems and, 679–681*f*, 682
  ion gradients in, 777*f*
  kidney function in, 682, 683*f*–685*f*
  membrane structures in, 687
  nitrogenous wastes and, 678, 679*f*
  osmosis, osmolarity, and, 677–678
  salinity and, 854
  water balance and, 107*f*
Osmoregulators, **678**
Osmosis, **107, 597**
  diffusion of water by, across plant plasma
    membranes, 597, 598*f*, 599
  osmoregulation and, 678*f*
  in thigmotropism, 655
  water balance and, 106*f*–108*f*
Osmotic potential, 597
Osmotic pressure, blood, 715
Ossicles, 822
Osteichthyans, 556*f*, **557**
Otoliths (ear stones), 806, 807*f*
Ouabain, 789
Outer ear, 805*f*, **805***f*
Outer membrane, nuclear, 81*f*
Outgroups, **402**
Oval window, 805*f*, 806
Ovarian cancer, 361
Ovarian cycle, **761**, 762*f*, 763
Ovaries
  human, 184, 203*f*, 204, 669*f*, **757***f*, 759*f*,
    761–763
  plant, **536***f*, **620***f*, 627
Overfishing, 570, 571*f*
Overgrazing, 880, 900*f*
Overharvesting, 570, 571*f*, 910, 911*f*
Overnourishment, 703
Overproduction, offspring, 385*f*, 386
Oviducts, **757***f*
Oviraptor dinosaurs, 406*f*
Ovulation, 753, **757**, 759*f*, 762*f*, 763, 767*f*
Ovules, **534***f*, **620***f*
Owls, 18
Oxalis alpina, 631*f*
Oxidation, **142**–143
  beta, **158**
  in fermentation, 154–155
  of glucose. *See* Glycolysis
  of organic compounds, 143
  of pyruvate, 145*f*, 148*f*
Oxidative muscle fibers, 819*t*

Oxidative phosphorylation, 145*f*, **146**, 149–150
  ATP yield during, 153*f*, 154
  chemiosmosis in, 151*f*–152*f*, 153
  electron transport chain in, 150, 150*f*
  essay question on, 160
  vs. photophosphorylation, 171*f*–173*f*
Oxidizing agent, **142**–143
Oxygen
  aerobic respiration and, 142, 666*f*
  atmospheric changes of, 456
  Cambrian explosion and increase in
    atmospheric, 548
  in capillaries, 715
  in circulation and gas exchange, 707. *See also*
    Circulatory systems; Gas exchange
  covalent bonding of molecules of, 28*f*
  electron transport chain and, 144*f*, 145
  as essential element, 23*t*
  in interspecific interactions, 8
  in mammalian cardiovascular systems, 710*f*
  in methane combustion, 142, 143*f*
  net ecosystem production and, 890
  ocean anoxia and low levels of, 461
  in photosynthesis, 31, 32*f*, 163, 164*f*–165*f*
  in plant cells, 179*f*
  plant deprivation of, 655–656, 657*f*
  as product of photosynthesis, 161, 177*f*
  as pure element, 28
  in pyruvate oxidation, 148*f*
  role of, in prokaryotic metabolism, 481–482
  species distributions and availability of, 853–854
  storage of, by diving mammals, 730
  thyroid hormones and, 155, 155*t*
  transport of, 732
  valence of, and organic compounds, 44*f*
Oxytocin, 669*f*, **670**, 671, 768

P

p21 gene, 336
p53 gene, **336***f*
P680 chlorophyll *a*, 170*f*
P700 chlorophyll *a*, 170*f*
Pacemaker, heart, 712
Pacman mechanism, 188
Paedomorphosis, **466***f*
Paedophryne amauensis, 840*f*
Paedophryne swiftorum (frog), 840*f*
Pain, 78
Paine, Robert, 876*f*
Pain receptors, **803**
Pair bonding, 829, 834
Paleontology, 11*f*, 68*f*, **381**, 454
Paleozoic era, 455*t*, 460*f*
Palisade mesophyll, 587*f*
Pallium, bird, 800*f*
Palumbi, S. R., 398*f*
PAMPs. *See* Pathogen-associated molecular patterns
PAMP-triggered immunity, 658
Pancreas, 669*f*, **671, 695**
  in digestive system, 693*f*, 695
  environment interactions of, 121
  exocytosis by, 112
  in glucose homeostasis, 702, 703*f*
  ribosomes in cells of, 82*f*
Pancreatic islets, 702, 703*f*
Pandas, 709*f*
Pandemics, 352*f*, 353–354
Pandorina, 503*f*
Pandovirus, 349
Pangaea, **391**–392, **460***f*, 472
Panicum virgatum, 635
Panthera pardus, 10, 396*f*, 397
Panthera uncia, 931
Panthers, 422*f*
Pantoea, 410
Pan troglodytes. See Chimpanzees
Papaya, 634
Papillae, 804*f*
Papillomaviruses, 340
Parabasalids, 506*f*, **508***f*, 516*f*
Parabronchi, 726
Parachutes, seed and fruit, 629*f*
Paracrine signaling, 114*f*

Parahippus, 470*f*, 471
Paralysis, 818
Paramecium, 72*f*, 107*f*, 121, 497*f*, 510*f*, 860*f*, 868
Paramyosin, 821, 838
Paraphyletic clades, **401***f*
Parasites, **491**, 871–872
  evolutionary radiations and, 570, 571*f*
  fungal, 528*f*, 541*f*
  human disorders from, 489*f*
  protists as, 508, 511, 516*f*–517*f*, 518
Parasitic plants, 607, 608*f*
Parasitism, **491**, **871**–872
Parasympathetic division, peripheral nervous
  system, **793**
Parathion, 136
Parathyroid glands, 669*f*
Parathyroid hormone (PTH), 669*f*
Parenchyma cells, **580***f*, 585*f*, 587*f*
Parental care
  ensuring offspring survival with, 754, 755*f*
  experience and behavior in, 828
  genetic basis of, 834
  mating systems and, 832*f*–833*f*
  reproduction/survival trade-offs and, 861
Parental types, **244**
Parietal cells, **694***f*
Parietal lobe, 799*f*
Paris japonica, 362*t*
Parkinson's disease, 63, 333–334, 355, 786
Parrots, 800
Parsimony, molecular systematics and, 404*f*, 405
Parthenogenesis, **752**, 753, 771
Partial pressure, **721**–722
Particles, subatomic, 24*f*
Particulate hypothesis of inheritance, 214. *See also*
  Mendelian inheritance
Parus major, 424*f*
Passive immunity, 745–746
Passive transport, **106**, 596
  active transport vs., 110*f. See also* Active transport
  diffusion down concentration gradients as, 105, 106*f*
  down electrochemical gradients, 110*f*, 111
  in plant cells, 179*f*
  transport proteins and facilitated diffusion as,
    108–109
  of water across plant plasma membranes, 597,
    598*f*, 599
  water balance and osmosis as, 106*f*–108*f*
Paternal chromosomes, 211*f*
Paternity, certainty of, 832, 833*f*
Pathogen-associated molecular patterns (PAMPs), 658
Pathogenicity, 254
Pathogens, **491, 733, 883**
  bacterial, 488*f*–489*f*, 492*f*
  B cells and antibodies as responses to extracellular,
    743*f*–744*f*
  in communities, 883*f*, 884
  cytotoxic T cell response to cells infected by, 744*f*
  evasion of innate immunity by, 737
  evolutionary adaptations of, that evade immune
    systems, 747–748
  fungal, 541*f*
  identifying hosts and vectors for, 883*f*
  immune system molecular recognition and
    response to, 733*f*–739*f*
  plant defenses against, 658, 659*f*–660*f*
  prokaryotic, 492*f*
  viruses as, 351*f*–352*f*, 353–354
  zoonotic, 883*f*, 884
Pattern, evolutionary, 379–380
Pattern formation, **326**, 327*f*–329*f*, 643
Paulinella chromatophora, 511*f*
Pauling, Linus, 256–258
Pc. *See* Plastocyanin
PCBs. *See* Polychlorinated biphenyls
PCR. *See* Polymerase chain reaction
PCSK9 enzyme, 721
PDGF. *See* Platelet-derived growth factor
Pea aphid, 410
Peacocks, 427*f*
Pea fruit, 628*f*
Pea plants, 214*f*–220*f*, 221, 235, 656
Pearl mussels, 571*f*

Peatlands, 895, 905
Pectins, 85, 95
Pediastrum, 503f
Pedigrees, **228**, 235
Pelagic zone, **849**f, 851f
Peltigera, 603f
Penguins, 855f
Penicillin, 136, 388
Penis, **756**f, 757, 763–764, 769, 787
Penny bun fungus, 525f
Pentane, 46f
Pentoses, 50f, 64, 65f
Pepsin, **694**f–695f
Pepsinogen, 694f
Peptide bonds, 55–56, **58**, 293f
Peptides, 736, 737
Peptidoglycan, **478**, 479f
Per capita rate of population growth, 858–859t
Perception
    sensory, **802**
    visual. *See* Visual systems
Perennials, plant, 584
Pericarp, 627
Pericycle, **586**f
Periderm, **578**, 591, 658
Perilymph, 807f
Periodic table of elements, 26f, B-1f
Periods, geologic, 455t
Peripheral nervous system (PNS), **774**, **791**
    central nervous system and, 791, 792f
    divisions of vertebrate, 792f, 793
    neurotransmitters and, 786
Peripheral proteins, 101f, **103**
Peripheral vision, 811
Perissodus microlepis, 427f
Peristalsis, **694**–695, **822**f, 824
Peritubular capillaries, **681**f
Periwinkle, 570
Permian mass extinction, 461f, 463f, 472
Peromyscus californicus, 828t
Peromyscus leucopus, 828t, 863f
Peromyscus polionotus, 2f, 16f–17f
Peroxisomes, **90**
    animal cell, 78f
    functions of, 90
    plant cell, 79f
    structure of, 90f
Personalized medicine, 68f
Pertussis, 116
Pesticides
    as enzyme inhibitors, 136, 140
    transgenic, 634
PET. *See* Positron-emission tomography
Petals, **536**f, **620**f
Petioles, leaf, 577f, **578**
Petromyzontida, 556f
PET scanners, 25f
Peyer's patches, 716f
Pfisteria shumwayae, 510f
Pfu polymerase, 272
P (parental) generations, **215**f–216f
pH, **38**
    adjusting soil, 601
    buffers and, 39
    in duodenum, 671
    ecological succession and, 880f
    enzymatic catalysis and, 135f
    hemoglobin dissociation and, 729f, 730
    of human cerebrospinal fluid, 727f
    ocean acidification and, 39–40
    pH scale and, 38f, 39
    of precipitation, 911f
    species distributions and soil, 854
    thylakoids and, 181
PHA (polyhydroxyalkanoate), 493, 494f
Phages (bacteriophages), **254**, **344**
    bacterial defenses against, 347f
    evidence for viral DNA in, 254f–255f, 256
    lysogenic cycle of prophages and temperate, 345, 346f
    lytic cycle of virulent, 345f
    replicative cycles of, 345f–346f
    structure of, 343f, 344
    transduction of, 484f

Phagocytosis, **85**, 112, 113f, 692, **734**f
    innate immunity and, 734, 735f–736f, 737
    by lysosomes, 85f, 86
    macrophages in, 97f
    by sponges, 546f, 547
Phalacrocorax harrisi, 434
Phanerozoic eon, 455t, 460f
Pharmaceuticals
    as environmental toxins, 921f
    from plants, 908–909
Pharyngeal arches, 389f
Pharyngeal slits (clefts), **555**f
Pharynx, 692f–**693**f, 805f
Phase-contrast microscopy, 74f
Phenotypes, **218**
    dominance and, 224
    evolution of mutant, 266–267
    gene expression as link between genotypes and, 278
    genes and, 300
    genetic variation and, 414f–415f
    genotypes vs., 218, 219f, 226. *See also* Genotypes
    impact of environment on, 226
    mutant, 238f–239f
    pleiotropy and, 225
    recessive alleles and, 235
    relative fitness and, 425
    transformation and, 254
    types of natural selection and, 425f, 426
Phenylalanine, 57f, 283f, 419–420
Phenylketonuria (PKU), 419–420
Phenylthiocarbamide (PTC), 228f, 229
Pheromones, 754, **827**–828
Philanthus triangulum, 829, 830f
Philippine eagle, 908f
Phloem, **532**, **579**, **594**
    evolution of, 594
    primary growth and, 585f
    secondary, 588, 589f–590f, 591
    sugar-conducting cells of, 581f
    sugar translocation from sources to sinks via, 615f–616f
    in vascular plant transport, 532–533
    in vascular tissue system, 579
Phloem sap, **615**f–616f
Phoenix roebelenii, 538f
Phoradendron, 608f
Phosphatases, 118, 695f
Phosphate, 897f
Phosphate deficiency, plant, 600f
Phosphate group, 47f, 48, 64, 65f, 118, 256f
Phosphodiesterase, 810f
Phosphodiester linkages, 65
Phosphofructokinase, 160
Phospholipid bilayers. *See also* Cellular membranes; Plasma membranes
    cellular membranes as, 77f, 80, 81f
    plasma membranes as, 100, 101f, 105
    structure of, 54, 55f
    synthesis of, by rough ER, 84
Phospholipids, **54**, 55f, 689f
Phosphorus, 23t, 255f, 256
    dietary requirements for, 690
    as limiting nutrient in aquatic biomes, 890, 891ft
    as limiting nutrient in terrestrial biomes, 892
Phosphorus cycle, 897f
Phosphorylated intermediates, **130**
Phosphorylation
    in light reactions of photosynthesis, 164, 165f
    oxidative. *See* Oxidative phosphorylation
    protein, 118f
    substrate-level. *See* Substrate-level phosphorylation
Phosphorylation cascade, 118f
Photic zone, **849**f, 890
Photoautotrophs, 161f–162f, 481t, 515
Photoblepharon palpebratus, 491f
Photoheterotrophs, 481t
Photomorphogenesis, **648**f–650f
Photons, **166**, 168, 169f
Photoperiodism, **652**f, 653

Photophosphorylation, **164**, 171f–173f
Photoprotection, 168
Photopsins, 811
Photoreceptors, **807**, 808f–809f, 810–811
Photorespiration, **175**, 181
Photosynthates, 576, 903f
Photosynthesis, **161**–181
    in aquatic biomes, 849
    Calvin cycle of, 164, 165f, 173, 174f
    in carbon cycle, 896f
    as chemical reaction, 31–32
    chemiosmosis in, 153
    chloroplasts as sites of, 3, 87, 89, 162, 163f. *See also* Chloroplasts
    conversion of light energy to chemical energy of food by, 162, 163f–165f
    cyanobacteria and, 489f. *See also* Cyanobacteria
    in ecosystem energy budget, 889f–890f
    effects of atmospheric carbon dioxide concentration on productivity of, 176
    electrons, electron shells, and, 26
    endosymbiont theory on evolution of chloroplasts and, 88f
    in energy flow and chemical cycling, 8f, 141f, 179f, 886–887, 888f
    evolution of alternative carbon fixation mechanisms in, 175f
    fossil evidence of prokaryotic, 477f, 478
    importance of, 161–162, 176, 177f
    levels of organization of leaves and, 5f
    light reactions of, 164–172, 173f. *See also* Light reactions
    origin of, 502f, 503, 511
    overview of, 163f, 165f, 177f
    prokaryotic, 481f
    by protists, 515–516
    satellites for determination of, 889f–890f
    sunlight availability and, 854
    tracking atoms through, 163, 164f
    two stages of, 164, 165f
    vascular plant adaptations for, 595
Photosynthetic organisms, 886–887, 888f
Photosystem I (PS I), **170**f–173f, 177f
Photosystem II (PS II), **170**f–171f, 177f
Photosystems, **169**f–173f
Phototrophs, 481t
Phototropin, 649
Phototropism, **640**, 641f
pH scale, 38f, 39. *See also* pH
Phycoerythrin, 511
Phyllotaxy, **595**, 643
Phylogenetic bracketing
    Darwin and, 412
    of dinosaurs, 573
Phylogenetic species concept, **438**
Phylogenetic trees, **397**f, 401f–406f. *See also* Phylogenies
    analyzing viral evolution using DNA sequences and, 353
    applications of, 398f
    applying parsimony to, 404f
    cladistics and, 401f–402f
    creation of, 412
    of eukaryotes, 506f–507f
    as hypotheses, 405f–406f
    identifying species identity of food sold as whale meat using, 398f
    interpreting, 398
    linking classification and phylogeny using, 397f, 398
    maximum parsimony in, 405
    prokaryotic, 486f
    proportional branch lengths of, 402f–404f, 405
Phylogenies, **395**–412
    angiosperm, 537f–538f
    of animals, 550, 551f
    applying parsimony to help evaluate the most likely, 404f
    biodiversity and branching, 571
    of eukaryotes, 505, 506f–514f
    of fungi, 528f
    horizontal gene transfer and, 409f, 410
    human, 567f–568f

Phylogenies (*Cont.*)
  inferring, from morphological and molecular data, 399*f*–400*f*
  invertebrate, 552*f*
  investigating evolutionary history of life with, 395*f*, 396. *See also* Evolution
  phylogenetic species concept and, 438
  plant, 530*f*
  prokaryotic, 486*f*–490*f*
  reconstruction of, 412
  revising, from new information, 409*f*, 410
  systematics, taxonomy, and evolutionary relationships in, 396*f*–398*f*. *See also* Systematics; Taxonomy
  three domains of life and, 408, 409*f*
  using molecular clocks to track evolutionary time for, 406, 407*f*–408*f*
  using shared characters to construct phylogenetic trees of, 401*f*–406*f*. *See also* Phylogenetic trees
  vertebrate, 556*f*
Phylum/phyla (taxonomy), **396***f*
Physical ecosystem reconstruction, 899
Physiology, **663**
Phytoalexins, 658
Phytochromes, **649**, 650*f*, 651, 661
Phytophthora, 516, 541*f*
Phytophthora ramorum, 883–884
Phytoplankton, 489*f*, 875, 876*f*, 890, 891*ft*, 894
  bloom, 919*f*, 920
Picoides borealis, 914, 915*f*
Pigeons, 826, 830
Pigmentation
  human skin, 226*f*, 227
  Siamese cats, 302
Pigmented cells, 469*f*
Pigmented epithelium, 808*f*–809*f*
Pigments
  as photosynthetic light receptors, 166*f*–168*f*
  in photosystems, 169*f*–170*f*
  respiratory, 728*f*–729*f*, 730
  visual, 809*f*, 811
Pigs, 284*f*, 352
Pikaia, 548*f*
Pikas, 924*f*
Pike-cichlid fish, 392
Pili, **479**–480, 484, 485*f*
Pimephales promelas, 921
Pineal gland, 669*f*, 795*f*
Pineapple fruit, 628*f*
Pine beetles, 924*f*
Pine trees, 924*f*
Pin flower, 631*f*
Pinhole camera-type eye, 469*f*
Pinna, 805*f*
Pinocytosis, 112, 113*f*, 692
piRNAs. *See* Piwi-associated RNAs
Pisaster ochraceus, 876*f*
Pistils, **536***f*, **620***f*
Pisum sativum, 656
Pitch, 806
Pitcher plants, 608*f*
Pith, **579**, 588*f*
Pituitary gland, 31, 669*f*, **671**, 760–764, 768, 795*f*
Pit vipers, 803*f*, 870
Pitx1 gene, 467, 468*f*
Pivot joints, 823*f*
Piwi-associated RNAs (piRNAs), 316
PKU. *See* Phenylketonuria
Placenta, **566***f*, **768**
Placental transfer cells, 522*f*
Placoderms, 453*f*
Plagiochila deltoidea, 531*f*
Planarians, 707*f*, 791*f*, 807*f*
Plankton, 852
Plantae, kingdom, 10*f*, 11, 408, 521*f*
Plant cells. *See also* Eukaryotic cells
  active transport in, 111*f*
  bioenergetics in, 140
  cell cycle of, 189*f*–190*f*. *See also* Cell cycle
  cell walls of, 94*f*, 95
  common types of, 579, 580*f*–581*f*
  cotransport in, 111*f*

gene expression, gene regulation, and differentiation of, 583, 584*f*
  meristem generation of, **582**, 583*f*–584*f*
  microtubules of, 92
  organelles of, 79*f*
  plasma membranes of. *See* Plasma membranes
  plasmodesmata in, 96
  solute and water transport across plasma membranes of, 596–597, 598*f*, 599
  vacuoles of, 86*f*, 87
  water balance and tonicity of, 107*f*, 108
  working cell of, 178*f*–179*f*
Plant development, 575–592
  auxin in, 643–644
  cells in, 579, 580*f*–581*f*
  hierarchy of organs, tissues, and cells in, 576, 577*f*–581*f*, 582
  leaf morphology in, 582
  meristems in, **582**, 583*f*–584*f*
  of monocot vs. eudicot angiosperms, 575, 576*f*
  organs in, 576, 577*f*–578*f*
  primary growth of roots and shoots in, 584*f*–588*f*
  secondary growth of stems and roots in woody plants, 588, 589*f*–590*f*, 591
Plant-growth-promoting rhizobacteria, 604
Plant growth regulators, 640. *See also* Hormones, plant
Plant nutrition. *See also* Plant transport
  essential macronutrients and micronutrients for, 599, 600*t*
  hydroponic culture and, 599*f*
  mineral deficiency symptoms and, 600–601
  relationships with organisms and adaptations for, 602, 603*f*–608*f*, 618
  resource acquisition adaptations for, 593–596
  soil management for, 601
  soil texture and composition for, 601, 602*f*
Plant reproduction. *See also* Reproduction
  allocation of energy in, 632
  alternation of generations in, 522*f*, 523
  angiosperm, 630*f*–633*f*. *See also* Flowers
  artificial selection and breeding in, 619, 633*f*, 634
  asexual vs. sexual, 201*f*
  biotechnology and genetic engineering in, 634, 635*f*, 636
  double fertilization in, 622, 623*f*, 625*f*
  meristematic control of reproductive growth in, 584
  sexual life cycles in, 204*f*. *See also* Sexual life cycles
Plant resource acquisition. *See also* Plant transport
  evolution of xylem and phloem as vascular tissues for, 594*f*
  leaf trembling and, 593
  overview of transport and, 594*f*
  root architecture and acquisition of water and minerals in, 595
  shoot architecture and light capture in, 595*f*
Plant responses, 639–661
  to attacks by herbivores and pathogens, 657, 658*f*–660*f*
  communication between plants in, 656
  to environmental stimuli other than light, 653–657
  evolution of, 657
  to gravity, 654*f*
  to light, 648*f*–653*f*. *See also* Light reception, plant
  to mechanical stimuli, 654*f*–655*f*
  plant hormones and, 640, 641*f*–647*f*, 648. *See also* Hormones, plant
Plants
  adaptations of, that reduce nutrient limitations, 892
  adaptive radiation of terrestrial, 464*f*, 465
  alternation of generations in, 522*f*, 523
  angiosperms. *See* Angiosperms
  animal mutualism with, 603*f*
  Archaeplastida supergroup and, 511, 512*f*
  area effects and, 882*f*
  bioremediation using, 899, 901
  in carbon cycle, 896*f*
  cells of. *See* Plant cells

cellulose as structural polysaccharide of, 52
characteristics of, 558*f*
chemical cycling and biotic interactions of, 539*f*–542*f*
colonization of land by fungi and, 520*f*, 524*f*–529*f*, 530. *See also* Fungi
communication between, 656
community stability and diversity of, 875*f*
crop. *See* Crop plants
defensive adaptations of, 871
determining effects of atmospheric carbon dioxide on productivity of, 176
development of. *See* Plant development
digestion of, 698, 699*f*
early evolution and terrestrial adaptations of, 521*f*–524*f*
in energy flow and chemical cycling, 8*f*
energy from, 141*f*
Eukarya domain and, 10*f*
evolution by natural selection in response to introduced species of, 387*f*, 388
evolution of alternative carbon fixation mechanisms in, 175*f*, 176
facilitation by, 873*f*
fungi mutualism with, 603*f*
genomes of. *See* Genomes
genomics and proteomics in study of, 68*f*
herbivory, 472
hormones of. *See* Hormones, plant
innate immunity in, 734
insect radiations and radiation of, 559–560
interactions of, 8
mass extinctions and, 544
in nitrogen cycle, 897*f*
nonvascular bryophytes, 530*f*–531*f*
nutrition in. *See* Plant nutrition
organismal cloning of, 330
parasites of, 516
as photoautotrophs, 161, 162*f*
photosynthesis by. *See* Photosynthesis
phylogeny of, 530*f*–532*f*, 533
polyploidy in, 249
reproduction of. *See* Plant reproduction
resource acquisition in. *See* Plant resource acquisition
responses of. *See* Plant responses
seedless vascular, 531*f*–533*f*
seed plants, 533–538. *See also* Seed plants
stomata and, 544
storage polysaccharides of, 51*f*
structural polysaccharides of, 52
sucrose uptake by, 121
sympatric speciation in, 441, 442*f*
transport in. *See* Plant transport
tumors in, 488*f*
unsaturated fats of, 54*f*
vascular. *See* Vascular plants
water transport in, 33*f*, 618
Plant transport, 593–618
  apoplastic, symplastic, and transmembrane routes in, 596*f*
  essential elements in, 600*t*
  hydroponic culture in study of, 599*f*
  nutritional relationships with organisms and, 602, 603*f*–608*f*
  overview of resource acquisition and, 594*f*
  regulation of transpiration rate by stomata in, 612–615
  resource acquisition adaptations and, 593–596
  short-distance and long-distance mechanisms of, 596–597, 598*f*, 599
  soil as source of essential elements for root absorption in, 599*f*–602*f*
  sugar-conducting cells in phloem in, 581*f*
  of sugars from sources to sinks via phloem in, 615*f*–616*f*
  temperature and water uptake by seeds in, 597
  transpiration of water and minerals from roots to shoots via xylem in, 609*f*–611*f*, 612
  water-conducting cells in xylem in, 581*f*
Plaque, 720
Plasma, **717***f*, 729–730
Plasma cells, **741***f*

Plasma membranes, **76**. *See also* Cellular membranes
    active transport across, 109, 110*f*–111*f*, 112
    animal cell, 78*f*, 95*f*
    bulk transport across, by exocytosis and
        endocytosis, 112, 113*f*
    cardiac muscle, 820
    in cell signaling, 114*f*–119*f*
    in endomembrane system, 87*f*
    evolution of differences in lipid composition of, 102
    fluidity of, 101, 102*f*
    fluid mosaic model of, 101*f*–102*f*, 103
    functions of, 75, 76*f*
    membrane carbohydrates of, in cell-cell
        recognition, 104
    membrane potentials of neuron, 775*f*–782*f*
    membrane protein types and functions in, 100,
        103*f*, 104. *See also* Membrane proteins
    microfilaments and, 93*f*
    passive transport across, 105, 106*f*–108*f*
    in plant cell, 79*f*, 178*f*
    prokaryotic, 76*f*
    selective permeability of, 100, 105
    synthesis and sidedness of, 104*f*
    targeting of polypeptides to, 295*f*, 296
    transport proteins in, 105
    vascular plant transport of solutes and water
        across, 596–597, 598*f*, 599
Plasmids, **270***f*, 349, **481**, 484*f*, 485–486
Plasmodesmata, **96**
    in local cell signaling, 114
    plant cell, 79*f*, 94*f*, 95, 96
Plasmodium, 507*f*, 517*f*, 518–519, 734
Plasmodium falciparum, 429*f*
Plasmogamy, **529***f*
Plasmolysis, **108**, **598**
Plastics, natural, 493, 494*f*
Plastids, **89**, 500*f*–502*f*, 503
Plastocyanin (Pc), 171
Plastoquinone (Pq), 171
Plateau phase, human sexual response, 764
Platelet-derived growth factor (PDGF), 194*f*
Platelets, 194, 717*f*–**718***f*
Plate tectonics, **458***f*–460*f*
Platyhelminths, 551*f*
Platypus, 566*f*, 803
Pleasure, brain activity and, 798*f*
Pleiotropy, **225**
Plesiosaur, 453*f*
Plumule, 626
Pluripotent cells, 333–**334**
Pneumatophores, 577*f*
Pneumocystis carinii, 747
Pneumonia, 254, 484, 747
PNS. *See* Peripheral nervous system
Poaching, 910, 911*f*
Poecilia reticulata, 392
Point mutations, **298***f*
    cancer genes and, 334*f*, 335
    mutagens as cause of, 300
    in sickle-cell disease, 428*f*–429*f*
    as sources of genetic variation, 415–416
Poison dart frog, 870, 871*f*
Poisons, detoxification of, 83
Polar bears, 9, 438*f*
    climate change effects on, 923
Polar bodies, 759*f*, 760
Polar covalent bonds, **28***f*
Polar molecules, **32**–33, 105
Polar side chains, 57*f*, 58
Polar transport, auxin, 642, 643*f*
Poliovirus, 351, 750
Pollen grains, 215*f*, **534***f*, 576*f*, **622**, 623*f*, 638
Pollen tubes, **622**, 623*f*
Pollination, **534***f*, **622**, 623*f*
    by animals, 624*f*, 908*f*
    asexual reproduction vs., 630
    breeding plants by cross-pollination, 634
    genetic engineering of flowers to force
        self-pollination, 636
    mechanisms of, 622, 624*f*
    Mendel's techniques of, 215*f*, 216
    mutualistic relationships in, 619
    reciprocal selection and, 569*f*, 625

reproductive isolation and pollinator choice
        for, 449*f*
    by wind, 624*f*
Pollution
    biomanipulation and, 877*f*
    bioremediation of, 494*f*, 899, 891, 901*f*
Polyadenylation signal sequence, 286
Polyandry, 832*f*
Poly-A tail, **286**, 287*f*, 317*f*
Polychlorinated biphenyls (PCBs), 920*f*–921*f*
Polyclonal antibodies, 746
Polydactyly, 224
Polygamous mating, **832**
Polygenic inheritance, **226***f*, 227
Polygyny, 832*f*
Polymerase chain reaction (PCR), 272, 273*f*, 318*f*, 486,
    487, 874*f*, 909
Polymerization, 49*f*, 185
Polymers, **48**, 49*f*
    of amino acids, 55–56
Polynucleotides, **64**, 65*f*
Polypeptides, **56**
    analyzing sequence data of, 69
    completion and targeting of, in translation, 292,
        295*f*–296*f*
    hormones as, 672
    in levels of protein structure, 60*f*–61*f*
    mutations affecting structure and function of,
        298*f*–299*f*, 300
    one gene-one polypeptide hypothesis and, 280
    peptide bonds in formation of, 58*f*
    as polymers of amino acids, 55–56
    RNA-directed synthesis of, in translation, 281,
        282*f*, 291, 292*f*–293*f*
    synthesis of multiple, in translation, 296*f*–297*f*
Polyphyletic clades, **401***f*
Polyploidy, **249**, **441**, 442*f*, 451
Polyps, 336, 337*f*, 547*f*
Polyribosomes (polysomes), 296*f*
Polysaccharides, **51**–53
    chitin, 525
    storage, 51*f*, 52
    structural, 51*f*–52*f*, 53
Polyspermy, 765, 767*f*
Polytomies, 397*f*, **398**
Polytrichum commune, 531*f*
Pongo pygmaeus, 357
Pons, 794*f*, **795***f*
Poplar trees, 635
Population conservation, 912*f*–915*f*
    conflicting demands in, 915
Population dynamics, **862**, 864*f*, 902*f*. *See also*
        Populations
    demographics in, 856*ft*, 857
    density and dispersion in, 854, 855*f*, 856
    density factors influencing, 861*f*–864*f*
    immigration, emigration, and metapopulations
        in, 864*f*
    life history traits influencing, 861*f*–864*f*
    population growth in, 857–861. *See also*
        Population growth
    population stability and fluctuation in, 862, 864*f*
Population ecology, **841***f*, 854–864. *See also*
        Populations
Population growth, 857–861. *See also* Populations
    carrying capacity in, 858, **859***f*, 860
    changes in size and, 857–858
    exponential model of, 858*f*–859*f*
    human, 926*f*–928*f*
    logistic model of, **859***ft*–860*f*, 861
    regulation of, 861*f*–864*f*
Population regulation, 861*f*–864*f*. *See also* Populations
    density and mechanisms of, 863*f*, 866
    population dynamics and, 862, 864*f*
Populations, 4*f*, **417**, **841***f*, 854–864, 902*f*
    abiotic factor effects on, 854, 855*f*–856*ft*, 857
    biotic factor effects on, 854, 855*f*–856*ft*, 857
    changes in size of, 857–858
    character displacement in, 869*f*, 885
    climate change effects on, 925*f*
    decline of honeybee, 624*f*
    declining amphibian, 562
    demographics of, 856*ft*, 857

ecological interactions and species distributions
        of, 840, 852*f*–853*f*, 854. *See also* Interactions,
        ecological; Species distributions
    evolution and genetic variation within, 212
    growth of, 857–861
    in hierarchy of biological organization, 4*f*
    human, 926*f*–928*f*
    life history traits of, 861*f*–864*f*
    microevolution as evolution of, 413–414. *See also*
        Microevolution
    natural selection and evolution of, 385*f*–386*f*
    population ecology and. *See* Ecology; Population
        ecology
    regulation of, 861*f*–864*f*, 866
    in theory of evolution by natural selection, 11*f*–12*f*
    using Hardy-Weinberg equation to test evolution
        in, 417*f*–419*f*, 420
Population size
    extinction vortex and, 912*f*–914*f*
    human, 926*f*–928*f*
Populus tremuloides, 593
Populus trichocarpa, 635
Pore complexes, 80, 81*f*
Pores, sponge, 546*f*
Porifera phylum, 546*f*, 547, 551*f*
Porphyra, 512*f*
Porphyrin ring, 168*f*
Porpoises, 390*f*–391*f*
Position, mechanoreceptors and sense of, 806, 807*f*
Positional information, **327**
Positive correlations, 632
Positive feedback, **669**
    action potentials and, 779
    in endocrine signaling, 669
Positive gene regulation, bacterial, 307*f*
Positive gravitropism, 654
Positive interactions, 872*f*–873*f*
Positive pressure breathing, **726**
Positron-emission tomography (PET), 25*f*, 793*f*
Post-anal tails, 555*f*
Postelsia, 509*f*
Posterior ends, **550***f*
Posterior pituitary gland, 669*f*, **671***f*, 768
Postsynaptic cells, 773*f*
Postsynaptic neurons, 784*f*
Postsynaptic potentials, 784, 785*f*
Post-transcriptional gene regulation, 314*f*, 315
Post-translational modifications, protein, 295
Postzygotic barriers, **435**, 436*f*–437*f*
Potassium, 23*t*, 613
Potassium ions, 775*ft*–782*f*
Potatoes, 648*f*
Potato late blight, 516, 660
Potential energy, **25**–26, 106, **123***f*–124*f*. *See also*
        Energy; Kinetic energy
Potential evapotranspiration, 881*f*
Potential range, of species, 853
Pq. *See* Plastoquinone
PR. *See* Progesterone receptor
Prairie
    loss of, 910
    restoration of, 901
Prairie chickens, 422, 423*f*
Prairie voles, 834*f*
Precipitation
    acid, 911*f*
    aquatic biomes and, 849
    climate and, 9, 842*f*–844*f*. *See also* Climate
    climographs of, 845*f*
    global patterns of, 842*f*–843
    primary production in terrestrial biomes and,
        891, 892*f*
    in water cycle, 896*f*, 905
Precocious germination, 646*f*
Precursor cell, 332*f*
Predation, 868, **870**, 902*f*–903*f*
    in Cambrian explosion, 548
    camouflage and, 379*f*
    clumped dispersion and, 855
    as density-dependent population regulation
        mechanism, 863*f*
    effects of, on ecosystems, 568*f*–569*f*
    effects of, on evolution, 545*f*, 570, 571*f*

Predation (*Cont.*)
  genetic variation in, 834, 835
  as interspecific interaction, 870, 871*f*, 885
  in molluscs, 571*f*
  mouse coat coloration and, 2, 16*f*–17*f*, 18
  natural selection, coloration in guppies, and, 392
  numbers of offspring and, 861
  population fluctuations and, 862, 864*f*
  in top-down model of trophic control, 877*f*, 885
Predators
  as biotic factors limiting species distribution, 853
  feeding adaptations of, 870–871, 885
  plant recruitment of, as herbivore defense, 658*f*
Predictions. *See also* Scientific Skills Exercises
  making and testing, 392
  of paleontology, 454
  using Hardy-Weinberg equation to interpret data
    and make, 420
Prefrontal cortex, 799, 799*f*
Pregnancy, human, 746, 767–768
Pre-mRNA, 281, 286, 287*f*–288*f*
Prepuce, of human reproductive structures, 756*f*, 757*f*
Pressure, mechanoreceptors for, 802
Pressure flow, 616
Pressure potential, **598**
Pressure waves, 806
Presynaptic cells, 773*f*
Presynaptic neurons, 784*f*
Prey. *See also* Predation
  defensive adaptations of, 870, 871*f*, 885
  genetic variation in selection of, 834, 835
Prezygotic barriers, **435**, 436*f*–437*f*
Primary cell walls, 94*f*, **95**
Primary cilia, 92
Primary consumers, 875*f*, **888***f*, 903*f*
Primary electron acceptors, **169**
Primary growth, plant, **582**
  meristem generation of cells for, **582**, 583*f*–584*f*
  overview of, 583*f*
  of roots, 584*f*–586*f*
  of woody stems, 589*f*
Primary immune response, **741**, 742*f*
Primary oocytes, 759*f*
Primary producers, 875*f*, **888***f*, 903*f*
  climate change and, 925*f*
Primary production, **889**, 903*f*, 905
  in aquatic biomes, 890, 891*ft*
  in ecosystem energy budget, 889*f*–890*f*, 905
  global patterns of, 889*f*–890*f*
  limiting factors for, 888, 889*f*–892*f*, 891*t*
  satellites for determination of, 889*f*–890*f*
  in terrestrial biomes, 891, 892*f*
Primary structure, protein, 60*f*
Primary succession, **879**, 880*f*
Primary transcripts, **281**
Primase, **262**
Primates. *See also* Chimpanzees
  cloning of, 332
  evolution of, 566, 567*f*
  HIV in, 407
  humans as, 567*f*–568*f*
  parental care in, 861
Primer, RNA, **262**
Primitive lenses, 469*f*
Primordial germ cells, human, 758*f*–759*f*
Principle of conservation of energy, 124*f*
Principles of Geology (book), 382
Printing press, 19
Prions, 355*f*
Probability, laws of, 221*f*, 222
Problem solving, **830**–831
Process, evolutionary, 379–380
Process of science. *See* Inquiry Figures; Interpret the
    Data questions; Research Method Figures;
    Science; Scientific Skills Exercises
Producers, **515**, 903*f*
  consumers and, 161. *See also* Consumers
  in ecosystem trophic structure, 875*f*, 888*f*
  effects of, on ecosystems, 569*f*
  in energy flow and chemical cycling, 8*f*, 181
  photosynthetic protists as, 515*f*
Production efficiency, 892, **893***f*
Products, chemical reaction, 31–32

Progesterone, 669*f*, 753*f*, **760**, 762*f*, 763, 768
Progesterone receptor (PR), 338*f*–339*f*
Progestin, 769*f*
Programmed cell death. *See* Apoptosis
Projections, surface area and, 526*f*
Prokaryotes, **474**–496. *See also* Archaea; Bacteria
  anaerobic respiration by, 154–155
  bioremediation using, 901*f*
  biosphere roles of, in chemical cycling and
    ecological interactions, 490, 491*f*
  cells of. *See* Prokaryotic cells
  in disease-suppressive soil, 493
  diverse evolutionary adaptations of, 474, 475*f*,
    478*f*–483*f*
  as Earth's first living organisms, 474*f*, 477*f*, 478
  fossils of, 453*f*
  genetic diversity of, 483*f*–485*f*, 486
  genetic research on, related to mitochondria, 501
  impacts of, on humans, 491, 492*f*–494*f*
  motility of, 480*f*
  nutritional and metabolic adaptations of, 481*t*, 482*f*
  origin of mitochondria and plastids in,
    500*ft*–501*f*, 502
  origins of life and, 475–477*f*, 478
  origins of photosynthesis in, 162
  phylogenies of, 486*f*–490*f*
  rapid reproduction of, by binary fission, 483*f*, 484
  shapes of, 478*f*
  size of and number of genes in genomes of, 362*t*
  summary of adaptations of, 482
  taxonomy of, 408, 409*f*, 410
  in trophic structure, 888
Prokaryotic cells, 4, **75**. *See also* Prokaryotes
  aerobic respiration of, 142
  binary fission in, 190, 191*f*
  cell-surface structures of, 478, 479*f*, 480
  cellular respiration in, 145*f*–146*f*
  DNA replication in, 260, 261*f*–265*f*
  electron transport chains in, 150
  in endosymbiont theory on origins of
    mitochondria and chloroplasts, 88*f*
  eukaryotic cells vs., 4, 5*f*, 75, 76*f*–77*f*. *See also*
    Eukaryotic cells
  gene expression in, 281*f*
  internal organization and DNA of, 480, 481*f*
  organelles of, 76*f*
  protein synthesis in, 64*f*
  regulation of gene expression in. *See* Bacterial
    gene regulation
  synthesis of multiple polypeptides in translation
    of, 296*f*
  transcription in, 284–285
Prolactin, 669*f*, 672, 768
Proliferative phase, uterine cycle, 762*f*, 763
Proline, 57*f*, 283
Prometaphase, **185**, 186*f*, 190*f*
Promoters, transcription, **284**, 285*f*
Proofreading, DNA, 266*f*
Propagation, vegetative, 644
Propanal, 47*f*
Propane, 45*f*
Properties, emergent, 3, 4*f*–5*f*
Prophages, 346*f*
Prophase, **185**, 186*f*, 190*f*, 209*f*
Prophase I, 206*f*, 208*f*–209*f*
Prophase II, 207*f*
Prostaglandins, 689*f*, 768, 803
Prostate cells, 341
Prostate glands, 756*f*
Prosthetic groups, 150
Protease, **694**
Protected areas, 917*f*–918*f*, 919
Protection, skeletal, 821
Protein Data Bank, 359
Protein kinase A, 119*f*, 672
Protein kinases, **118***f*–119*f*
Protein phosphatases, 118*f*
Proteins, **56**. *See also* Polypeptides
  3-D structure of, 43*f*, 63*f*
  amino acids of, 56, 57*f*, 58
  analyzing polypeptide sequence data of, 69
  antibiotics and prokaryotic synthesis of, 481

antibody binding to, 59*f*
antimicrobial, 736
in aqueous solutions, 36*f*
auxin transport, 643*f*
in bacterial binary fission, 190, 191*f*
in blood plasma, 717*f*
catabolism of, 142, 158*f*
in cell nucleus, 80, 81*f*, 82
cellulose-synthesizing, 521*f*
completing and targeting functional, after
    translation, 292, 295*f*–296*f*
Conserved Domains Database of structures, 360*f*
deficiency of, 690
denaturation and renaturation of, 62*f*, 63
digestion of, 695*f*
diversity of, 55, 56*f*
DNA and RNA in synthesis of, 6, 7*f*
DNA-binding, 71
in DNA replication and repair, 259*f*–267*f*
DNA vs., as genetic material, 254*f*–256*f*
of egg yolks, 71
as enzymes, 48, 55, 56*f*, 131, 136. *See also*
    Enzymatic catalysis; Enzymes
essential amino acids and, 689*f*
eukaryotic gene regulation in processing and
    degradation of, 315
exon duplication and shuffling and domains of,
    369, 371*f*
in extracellular matrix, 95*f*
in hair, 705
heat-shock and antifreeze, **657**
initiation factors, elongation factors, and release
    factors in translation, 292*f*–293*f*
levels of structure of, 59, 60*f*–63*f*
as measure of evolution, 67
membrane. *See* Membrane proteins; Receptor
    proteins; Transport proteins
motor. *See* motor proteins
mutations from faulty genes and faulty, 278
nonenzyme, 280
as organic compounds and macromolecules, 43
in origin of multicellular animals, 504, 505*f*
in pattern formation, 328*f*–329*f*
photopsin, 811
in photosystems, 169*f*–170*f*
in plant pathogen defenses, 658–659
as polymers of monomers, 48–49
prions, 355*f*
in prokaryotic flagella, 480*f*
proteomics in study of, 67, 68*f*
sequencing of, 67
Proteobacteria, 488*f*, 500*f*–502*f*
Proteoglycans, 95*f*
Proteomes, **7**, **361**
Proteomics, 7, 66–**67**, 68*f*, **361**
Proterocladus, 499*f*
Proterozoic eon, 455*t*
Protista, kingdom, 408, 505
Protists, 10*f*, 11, **497**
  cells of, 79*f*. *See also* Eukaryotic cells
  contractile vacuoles of, 86
  ecological roles and impacts of, 515*f*–517*f*, 518
  effects of, on human health, 516, 517*f*, 518
  endosymbiosis in evolution of photosynthetic,
    502*f*, 503
  Eukarya domain and, 10*f*
  four supergroups in phylogeny of eukaryotes and,
    505, 506*f*–514*f*
  in hypertonic habitats, 121
  origin of fungi in, 525
  origin of multicellular animals in, 504*f*–505*f*
  photosynthetic, 515–516
  sexual life cycles of, 204*f*
  structural and functional diversity of, 515
  symbiotic, 516*f*
  as unicellular eukaryotes, 497
Protocells, **475**, 476*f*
Protonephridia, 680*f*
Proton-motive force, **152**, 154
Proton pumps, 111*f*
  in acid growth hypothesis, 642, 643*f*
  in vascular plant solute transport, 596
Protons, **24***f*, 37, 172*f*

Proto-oncogenes, **334***f*–339*f*
Protoplast, **598**
Proviruses, **349**, 350*f*
Proximal control elements, 310*f*
Proximal tubule, **681***f*–683*f*
Proximate causation, 825
Prozac, 786
Prusiner, Stanley, 355
Pseudechis porphyriacus, 870
Pseudogenes, **363***f*, 364, 390
Pseudohypertrophic muscular dystrophy, 252
Pseudomyrmex, 872*f*
Pseudomys hermannsburgensis, 679
Pseudopodia, 97, 507*f*, 511, 513
Pseudotsuga menziesii, 535*f*
PS I. *See* Photosystem I
PS II. *See* Photosystem II
P site (peptidyl-tRNA binding site), **291***f*, 293*f*
Psittacus erithacus, 800
Psychedelic rock gecko, 906*f*
Psychoactive drugs, 786
PTC. *See* Phenylthiocarbamide
Pteropus mariannus, 908*f*
Pterosaurs, 824
PTH. *See* Parathyroid hormone
Puberty, human, 760
PubMed, 20
Puffball fungus, 385*f*
Puffer fish, 603*f*
Pulmocutaneous circuits, 708, 709*f*
Pulmonary circuits, 708, 709*f*, 711*f*
Pulp, fruit, 628
Pulse, **714**
Puma concolor coryi, 422*f*
Punctuated equilibria, **447**
Puncture vine, 629*f*
Pundamilia genus, 443*f*, 446*f*
Punnett squares, **218***f*, 225*f*, 226*f*, 244
Pupil, 808*f*, **809**
Purines, **64**, 65*f*, 258*f*–259*f*
Purple sulfur bacteria, 162*f*
Pus, 737
Pygmy date palm, 538*f*
Pyramid
    of biomass, 894*f*
    of energy, 894*f*
Pyrimidines, **64**, 65*f*, 258*f*–259*f*
Pyrococcus furiosus, 272, 487, 493
Pyruvate
    ATP yield from, 153*f*
    in fermentation, 156*f*
    oxidation of, 145*f*, 148*f*
    production of, 146*f*–147*f*
Python, 691*f*, 698
PYY, 703

Q

Q. *See* Ubiquinone
Qualitative data, 13
Quantitative characters, **226***f*
Quantitative data, 14, 679
Quantitative experimental approach, G. Mendel's, 215*f*–219*f*
Quaternary consumers, 875*f*
Quaternary structure, protein, 61*f*
Questions, scientific, 15

R

RAAS. *See* Renin-angiotensin-aldosterone system
Rabbits, 699–700, 761
Radial glia, 792
Radial symmetry, 541, **549**, 550*f*
Radiation. *See also* Ultraviolet radiation
    alterations of chromosome structure by, 249
    as cancer treatment, 196
    damage from radioactive, 25
    mutagenic, 300
    prokaryotic bioremediation of, 494
Radiation process, thermoregulation and, 675*f*
Radiations
    adaptive, 463*f*–464*f*, 465
    amniote, 563, 564*f*–566*f*
    Cambrian explosion and bilaterian, 547, 548*f*–549*f*

ecological interactions and, 569*f*, 570
    invertebrate, 551*f*–554*f*
    natural selection and, 12, 13*f*
    prokaryotic, 474
    vertebrate, 554, 555*f*–557*f*
Radicle, **626***f*–627*f*
Radioactive isotopes, **25***f*, 255*f*, 454*f*, 898
Radiometric dating, **454***f*
Raft spiders, 33*f*
Rain shadows, 844*f*
Rana pipiens, 330
Random dispersion, 855*f*, 856
Random fertilization, 212
Random mating, 417, 418*f*–419*f*
Random mutations, 248. *See also* Mutations
Randomness, entropy and, 124*f*, 125
Ranges, of species, 853
Rangifer tarandus, 417*f*, 902*f*–903*f*, 925*f*
Rapetosaurus krausei, 11*f*
Rapid eye movements (REMs), 796
Rare evolutionary event, eukaryotic, 513*f*
ras gene and Ras protein, **335***f*–336*f*
Raspberry fruit, 628*f*
Rats, 798, 830
Rattlesnakes, 698, 789, 803*f*, 870
Ravens, 831
Ray-finned fishes, 556*f*, **557**
Rays, 55
RDS. *See* Respiratory distress syndrome
Reabsorption, **680***f*, 683*f*
Reactants, chemical reaction, **31**–32
Reaction-center complexes, **169***f*–170
Reading frames, **283**, 300
Realized niches, 869*f*
Reasoning
    evolution of cognition and, 799, 800*f*
    inductive and deductive, 14
Receptacle, flower, **620**
Reception
    light. *See* Light reception, plant
    sensory, 801*f*, 802
Reception stage, cell-signaling, **115***f*–117*f*, 119*f*
Receptive fields, 810
Receptor-mediated endocytosis, 112, 113*f*
Receptor potential, **801**–802, 810*f*
Receptor proteins, 56*f*, 103*f*, 113*f*, 115, 116*f*, 117
Receptors
    cellular innate immune defense, 735*f*, 736
    dendrites as, 773
    opiate, 786
    sensory. *See* Sensory receptors
Recessive alleles, **217***f*–218*f*, 228, 229*f*–230*f*, 235, 252, 426–427
Recessively inherited human disorders, 229*f*–230*f*
Recessive traits, 216*t*, 228, 229*f*–230*f*, 240, 241*f*–242*f*
Reciprocal selection, 569*f*
Recombinant bacteria, 270–271
Recombinant chromosomes, crossing over and, **211**, 212*f*
Recombinant DNA molecule, **270***f*–271*f*
Recombinants (recombinant types), **244**, 252
Recombinase, 740
Recombination frequencies, 245–246, 247*f*, 248, 252
Recording, intracellular, 778*f*
Recruitment, motor neuron, 819*f*
Recruitment of animal predators, plant, 658*f*
Rectum, 692*f*–693*f*, **697**
Recycling, chemical. *See* Chemical cycling
Red algae, 502*f*, 503, 507*f*, **511**, 512*f*
Red blood cells, 62*f*, 109, 428*f*, 717*f*–718*f*, 729–730
Red-cockaded woodpecker, 914, 915*f*
Red deer, 861
Red mangrove, 646*f*
Red maple trees, 582
Red-necked phalaropes, 832*f*
Redox (oxidation-reduction) reactions, **142**
    in cellular respiration, 145–146
    in citric acid cycle, 148, 149*f*
    electron transport chain, 143, 144*f*, 145
    organic compound oxidation, 143
    photosynthesis as, 164
    principle of, 142, 143*f*
Red Sea, coral reef biome in, 851*f*

Red tide, 510
Reduced hybrid fertility, 437*f*
Reduced hybrid viability, 437*f*
Reducing agent, **142**–143
Reduction, **142**–143
Reductionism, 3
Reduction phase, Calvin cycle, 174*f*
Redundancy, genetic code, 283, 298
Red wolves, 451
Redwood trees, 201*f*
Reef shark, 556*f*
Reflexes, **792**
Refractory period, **781**, 820
Regeneration, 752
Regeneration phase, Calvin cycle, 174*f*, 175
Regenerative medicine, 333–334
Regional adaptive radiations, 464*f*, 465
Regional conservation, 915, 916*f*–918*f*, 919, 931
Regression lines, scatter plots with, in Scientific Skills Exercises, 40*f*, 176*t*
Regulation
    of biological clocks, 796
    of blood pressure, 714, 715*f*
    of cell cycle by cell cycle control system, 192*f*–195*f*, 196–197
    cell signaling and cellular, 119*f*
    of enzymatic catalysis, 136, 137*f*–138*f*
    of gene expression. *See* Gene regulation
    of growth, 666*f*
    homeostatic. *See* Homeostasis
    hormonal, of human embryonic development and childbirth, 768
    hormonal, of mammalian/human sexual reproduction, 760–764
    of human breathing, 727*f*, 728
    of muscle contraction, 817*f*–818*f*
    population. *See* Population regulation
    of primary production in ecosystems, 888, 889*f*–892*f*, 891*t*
Regulators, **673***f*
Regulatory genes, **305***f*, 306, 324*f*, 333*f*, 377. *See also* Homeotic genes
Regulatory proteins, 817*f*–818*f*
Reinforcement, hybrid zone, 445*f*, 446
Rejection, immune, 746
Relatedness, altruism and, 835, 836*f*
Relationships, plant nutrition and, 602, 603*f*–608*f*
Relative abundance, **873**, 874*f*
Relative fitness, **425**
Relay molecules, 115*f*, 117–118
Release factors, 292, 293*f*
Release stage, phage lytic cycle, 345*f*
Releasing hormones, 669*f*
REMs. *See* Rapid eye movements
Renal cortex, **681***f*
Renal medulla, **681***f*
Renal pelvis, **681***f*
Renaturation, protein, 62*f*, 63
Renin-angiotensin-aldosterone system (RAAS), 685
Repair, DNA, 266*f*
Repenomamus giganticus, 464
Repetitive DNA, **363***f*–366*f*
Replication, DNA. *See* DNA replication
Replication bubbles, 261, 262*f*
Replication forks, **261***f*–262
Replicative cycles, viral, 345*f*–348*f*, 350*f*
Repolarization, 781
Repressible enzymes, 306–307
Repressible operons, 305, 306*f*, 307
Repressors, **305***f*–306*f*, 307, 311*f*–312*f*
Reproduction. *See also* Animal reproduction; Human reproduction; Plant reproduction
    binary fission as rapid prokaryotic, 483*f*, 484
    as cell division function, 182, 183*f*
    climate change and, 9*f*
    evolution and success in, 212
    flowers and, 638
    fungal, 525*f*, 529*f*, 530
    heterochrony and development of organs of, 466
    overreproduction of offspring and natural selection, 385*f*, 386
    protocell, 476*f*
    rapid, as source of genetic variation in viruses, 416

Reproduction (*Cont.*)
    sexual, as source of genetic variation, 416
    sexual life cycles in. *See* Sexual life cycles
    sexual vs. asexual, 201*f*, 752*f*. *See also* Asexual
        reproduction; Sexual reproduction
    solutions to, 666*f*
    in theory of evolution by natural selection, 11*f*–12*f*
    trade-offs between survival and, 861*f*, 862
Reproductive barriers
    hybrid zones and, 444*f*–446*f*
    prezygotic and postzygotic, 436*f*–437*f*
Reproductive cells. *See* Gametes
Reproductive cloning, 331*f*
Reproductive cycles
    animal, 753*f*
    human, 760–764
Reproductive growth, plant, 584
Reproductive isolation, **435**
    allopatric speciation and, 439*f*–441*f*
    geographic separation and, 443–444
    hybrid zones and, 444*f*–446*f*
    identifying dependent and independent variables,
        making scatter plots, and interpreting data
        on, 441*t*
    pollinator choice and, 449*f*
    prezygotic and postzygotic reproductive barriers
        in, 436*f*–437*f*
    sympatric speciation and, 440–441, 442*f*–443*f*
Reproductive leaves, 579*f*
Reproductive organs
    animal, 755
    heterochrony and development of, 466
Reproductive organs, human, 756*f*–757*f*
    female, 757*f*
    gametogenesis in, 757, 758*f*–759*f*, 760
    male, 756*f*, 757
    in sexual intercourse, 763–764
Reproductive rates, 857, 863*f*
Reproductive shoots, 577*f*
Reproductive systems, mammalian, 664*t*
Reproductive technology, 770
Reptiles, 563, 564*f*
    circulatory systems of, 708, 709*f*
    diversity of, 564*f*
    flying, 824
    in geologic record, 456
Research Method Figures. *See also* Scientific Skills
        Exercises
    applying parsimony to problems in molecular
        systematics, 404*f*
    constructing linkage maps, 247*f*
    crossing pea plants, 215*f*
    determination of absorption spectrum, 167*f*
    determining microbial diversity using molecular
        tools, 874*f*
    determining primary production with satellites, 889*f*
    hydroponic culture, 599*f*
    intracellular recording, 778*f*
    polymerase chain reaction technique, 273*f*
    preparing karyotypes, 202*f*
    reverse transcriptase-polymerase chain
        reaction, 318*f*
    testcrosses, 219*f*
    X-ray crystallography, 63*f*
Reservoirs, nutrient, 896*f*–897*f*
Residual volume, **727**
Resistance genes, 485–486
Resistance (R) proteins, 659*f*
Resolution, microscope, 73
Resolution phase, human sexual response, 764
Resource acquisition. *See* Plant resource acquisition
Resource competition, density-dependent population
        regulation and, 863*f*
Resource partitioning, **868***f*–869
Respiration
    aerobic. *See* Aerobic respiration
    anaerobic. *See* Anaerobic respiration
    cellular. *See* Cellular respiration
Respiratory diseases, human, 863*f*
Respiratory distress syndrome (RDS), 725–726
Respiratory media, 722*f*
Respiratory pigments, **728**, 729*f*
Respiratory surfaces, 722–723

Respiratory systems. *See also* Gas exchange
    breathing in, 726*f*–727*f*, 728
    gas exchange adaptations in, 728*f*–729*f*, 730
    lungs in mammalian, 724, 725*f*–726*f*
    mammalian, 664*t*
    respiratory distress syndrome in, 725–726
Response, homeostatic, **674**
Responses, plant. *See* Plant responses
Response stage, cell-signaling, **115***f*
Rest and digest responses, 793
Resting potentials, neuron, 775*f*–776*f*
Resting potential state, action potential, 780*f*
Restoration ecology
    biological augmentation in, 901
    biomanipulation, 877*f*
    bioremediation in, 899, 900*f*–901*f*
    for degraded ecosystems, 899*f*–901*f*
    worldwide restoration projects, 900*f*
Restriction enzymes, **271***f*–272*f*, **347**
Restriction fragment length polymorphism
    (RFLP), 874*f*
Restriction fragments, **272**
Restriction sites, **271**
Reticulum, 700*f*
Retina, **808***f*, 810*f*, 811
Retinal, **809***f*, 810
Retinitis pigmentosa, 422
Retrotransposons, **364***f*–365*f*
Retroviral cloning vector, 333*f*
Retroviruses, 317, 333*f*, **349**, 350*f*
Reverse transcriptase, 317*f*–318*f*, **349**, 350*f*
Reverse transcriptase-polymerase chain reaction
    (RT-PCR), **317***f*–318*f*
Reverse transcripts, 317*f*–318*f*
Reversibility
    of chemical reactions, 32
    of weak chemical bonds, 30
Reward system, brain, 797, 798*f*
RFLP. *See* Restriction fragment length
    polymorphism
Rhacophorinae frogs, 460*f*
Rhagoletis, 436*f*
Rhagoletis pomonella, 442–443
Rhesus monkeys, 69
Rheumatoid arthritis, 747*f*
Rhizanthes lowii, 619
Rhizarians, 507*f*, **511***f*
Rhizobacteria, **604**
Rhizobium, 488*f*, 496, 605*f*–606*f*
Rhizoctonia solani, 493
Rhizoids, **531**, 594
Rhizomes, 578*f*
Rhizophora mangle, 646*f*
Rhizosphere, 493, **604***f*
Rhodophytes. *See* Red algae
Rhodopsin, **809***f*, 810*f*
Rhomaleosaurus victor, 453*f*
Rhythm method, contraception by, 768, 769*f*
Rhythms, behavioral, 826
Ribbon models, 59*f*
Ribonucleic acid. *See* RNA
Ribose, 50*f*, **65**, 128*f*
Ribosomal RNA (rRNA), **290**
    comparing genetic sequences of, for prokaryotes
        related to mitochondria, 501
    eukaryotic ribosomes and, 82
    gene family of, 366*f*
    horizontal gene transfer and, 409*f*, 410
    in phylogeny of animals, 550
    ribozymes and, 288
    in translation, 290, 291*f*–293*f*
Ribosomes, **82**, **281**
    animal cell, 78*f*
    in cells, 75
    in chloroplasts, 89*f*
    eukaryotic, 81*f*
    free and bound, 82*f*, 295*f*
    interpreting DNA sequence logos to identify
        binding sites for, 294
    in mitochondria and chloroplasts, 88
    plant cell, 79*f*, 178*f*
    polyribosomes, 296*f*
    prokaryotic, 76*f*, 481

in protein synthesis, 64, 82, 97
    as sites of translation, 281, 290, 291*f*–293*f*
Ribozymes, 131, **288**, **476**–**477**
Rice, 362*t*, 437*f*, 644, 908
Ricinus communis, 626
Right atrium, 710*f*–711*f*
Right ventricle, 710*f*–711*f*
RIKEN Center for Developmental Biology, 333
Ring structures, 45*f*, 50*f*, 52*f*
Rising phase, action potential, 780*f*
Risk factors, cardiovascular disease, 720
River otter, 673*f*
Rivers, 850*f*
    restoration of, 900*f*
RNA (ribonucleic acid), **64**
    ATP in, 128
    components of, 64, 65*f*
    development of self-replicating, 476–477
    in DNA replication, 262, 263*f*
    in evidence for endosymbiosis, 501
    gene density in genomes and, 363*f*
    messenger. *See* Messenger RNA
    as molecular homology, 390
    noncoding. *See* Noncoding RNAs
    in protein synthesis, 6, 7*f*
    ribosomal. *See* Ribosomal RNA
    ribozymes of, as enzymes, 131
    role of, in protein synthesis, 64
    sequencing of, 318
    structure of molecules of, 66*f*
    viral. *See* RNA viruses
RNAi. *See* RNA interference
RNA interference (RNAi), 316
RNA polymerase, **284**, 285*f*–286*f*, 345, 349
RNA polymerase II, 310
RNA processing, **286**, 287*f*–288*f*, 297*f*, 310*f*, 314*f*
RNA sequencing (RNA-seq), 318
RNA splicing, **287***f*–288*f*
    alternative, 314*f*
RNA viruses
    emerging viruses as, 352*f*, 353–354
    replicative cycles of, 344*f*, 345, 347, 348*f*–350*f*
    structure of, 342, 343*f*, 344
Rock python, 691*f*, 698
Rocks
    dating of, 454*f*
    species distributions and, 854
    weathering of, in phosphorus cycle, 897*f*
Rod, of ATP synthase, 151*f*
Rodents, 699–700, 802
Rods, 808*f*, **809***f*, 810*f*
Rod-shaped bacteria, 76*f*
Rod-shaped prokaryotes, 478*f*
Rolling circle replication, 485*f*
Romanesco, 575*f*
Root caps, **584**, 585*f*
Rooted branches, 632
Rooted phylogenetic trees, **397***f*, 398
Root hairs, **577***f*, 583, 584*f*, 609*f*, 618, 666*f*
Root pressure, 612
Roots, **533**, 576
    adventitious, 632
    apical meristems of, 523
    architecture of, and acquisition of water and
        minerals, 595
    evolution of, 533
    flooding responses of, 655–656, 657*f*
    gravitropism in, 654*f*
    monocot vs. eudicot, 576*f*
    mycorrhizal fungi and, 527, 595. *See also*
        Mycorrhizae
    primary growth of, 584*f*–586*f*
    in root systems, 577*f*
    secondary growth of, 588, 589*f*–590*f*, 591
    soil as source of essential elements for absorption
        by, 599*f*–602*f*. *See also* Soil
    transpiration of water and minerals from, to
        shoots via xylem, 609*f*–611*f*, 612
Root systems, **576**, 577*f*
Rosy periwinkle, 909
Rotifera, 551*f*–552*f*
Rotor, of ATP synthase, 151*f*

Rough ER, **83**
    animal cell, 78*f*
    in endomembrane system, 87*f*
    in eukaryotic nucleus, 81*f*
    functions of, 84
    plant cell, 79*f*, 178*f*
Round dance, honeybee, 827*f*
Round window, 805*f*, **806**
Roundworms, 552*f*, 821, 822*f*
Rous, Peyton, 340
R plasmids, **485**–486
rRNA. *See* Ribosomal RNA
r-selection, **861**–862
RT-PCR. *See* Reverse transcriptase-polymerase chain
    reaction
Rubisco (RuBP carboxylase), 174*f*, 175
Rubrivivax, 488*f*
Ruffed grouse, 916
Rule of multiplication, 418
Rumen, 700*f*
Ruminants, **700***f*
Running, 823–825
Rupicapra rupicapra, 690*f*
Rutgers University, 359
Ryther, John, 891*f*

S
Saccharomyces cerevisiae (yeast)
    calculating volume and surface area of cells of, 80
    changes in DNA content of budding cells of,
        during meiosis, 210
    density-dependent population regulation of, 863*f*
    genome size of, 362*t*
Saccule, **806**, 807*f*
Sac fungi, 528*f*
Safety issues, transgenic crop, 635–636
Sagebrush, 885
Sago palm, 535*f*
Sahara Desert, 452*f*
Sahelanthropus tchadensis, 567
Salamanders, 412, 437*f*, 441, 466*f*, 561, 562*f*, 706*f*,
    791*f*, 870
Salicylic acid, **659***f*
Salinity
    aquatic biomes and, 849
    extreme halophiles and, 487, 490
    osmosis and, 107
    plant responses to, 656
    plants and, 121
    species distributions and, 854
    species facilitation and, 873*f*
Saliva, 693
Salivary glands, **693***f*
Salmonella, 488*f*, 492
Salt, table. *See* Sodium chloride
Saltatory conduction, **782***f*
Salt concentration. *See* Salinity
Salt marshes
    energy transfer in, 893
    facilitation in, 873*f*
Salts (ionic compounds), 29*f*
    in blood plasma, 717*f*
    nitrogenous wastes. *See* Filtrate
Salty tastants, 803, 804*f*
Samoan Islands, pollination in, 908*f*
Sand dollars, 183*f*, 766*f*
Sandhill cranes, 829
Sandy inland mouse, 679
SA node. *See* Sinoatrial
Sapwood, 590*f*, 591
Sarcomeres, **815***f*–817
Sarcoplasmic reticulum (SR), **817***f*–818*f*
Sargasso Sea, 890, 891*t*
Sarin, 136, 786
Sarracenia, 608*f*
SAR supergroup, 506*f*–507*f*, **509***f*–511*f*
Satellites, determining primary production with,
    889*f*–890*f*
Satiety center, 703
Saturated enzymes, 134
Saturated fats, 53, 54*f*
Saturated fatty acids, 53, 54*f*
Saturated hydrocarbon tails, 102*f*

Savannas, **846***f*
Scala naturae (scale of nature), Aristotle's, 380
Scale, skeletal, 822, 823*f*
Scale bars, 80
Scale-eating fish, 427*f*
Scales, 563
Scanning electron microscope (SEM), **73**, 74*f*, 75
Scarlet fever, 346
Scatter plots in Scientific Skills Exercises and
        Scientific Skills Review, 40*f*, 109*f*, 176*t*, 441*t*,
        870*t*, F-1*f*
S cells, 670
Sceloporus, 9*f*
Schematic model, ribosome, 291*f*
Schmidt-Nielsen, Knut, 825
Schwann cells, **782***f*, 791*f*
Science, **13**–19. *See also* Inquiry Figures; Interpret the
        Data questions; Research Method Figures;
        Scientific Skills Exercises
    community and diversity in, as social process,
        18–19
    controlled experiments, 16–17
    data, 13–14
    deductive reasoning, 14
    flexibility of, 15*f*, 16
    hypothesis, 13–14
    inductive reasoning, 14
    inquiry, 13
    observations, 13
    questions, 15
    research methods of. *See* Research methods
    skills for. *See* Scientific Skills Exercises
    technology, 19
    theory in, 17, 393
Science, Technology, and Society questions, 121, 140,
    181, 451, 638
Scientific Inquiry questions, 20, 42, 71, 99, 121, 140,
        160, 198, 213, 235, 252, 277, 302, 320, 341,
        356, 377, 394, 412, 432–433, 451, 472, 496,
        544, 573, 592, 618, 638, 661, 705, 732, 750,
        771, 789, 813, 838, 866, 885, 905, 931. *See also*
        Inquiry Figures; Interpret the Data questions;
        Research Method Figures; Scientific Skills
        Exercises
Scientific method. *See* Inquiry Figures; Interpret the
        Data questions; Research Method Figures;
        Science; Scientific Skills Exercises
Scientific notation, 787
Scientific process. *See* Inquiry Figures; Interpret the
        Data questions; Research Method Figures;
        Science; Scientific Skills Exercises
Scientific Skills Exercises
    amino acid sequences, 69*f*, 370*t*, 410*f*
    atmospheric CO_2 concentration changes, 922*t*
    bar graphs, 18*f*, 155*t*, 313*f*, 325*f*, 392*f*, 493*t*, 570*f*,
        582*t*, 656*f*, 870*t*, F-2*f*
    Chargaff's rules data table, 257*t*
    chi-square (χ^2) test, 246*t*, F-3*t*
    converting units, 210*t*
    cyclical data, graphing, 922*t*
    DNA deletion experiments, 313*f*
    energy transfer efficiency in ecosystems, 893*t*
    experimental design, 570*f*, 761*f*, 797*f*
    gene expression data, 325*f*
    genetic mutants, 704*t*, 797*f*
    genetic sequences, 501*t*
    genomic data and generating hypotheses, 529*t*
    graphs, estimating quantitative data from, 459*f*
    graph with two variables on common *x*-axis, 748*t*,
        F-1*f*
    Hardy-Weinberg equation, 420*t*
    histograms, 196*f*, 227*t*, 721*f*, F-2*f*
    hypothesis evaluation, 155*t*
    line graphs, 134*t*, 210*t*, 353*f*, 748*t*, 825*f*, F-1*f*
    logistic equation to model population growth, 860
    log scales, 825*f*
    making and testing predictions, 392*f*
    phylogenetic trees, 353*f*
    polypeptide sequence data, 69*f*
    positive and negative correlations, 632*t*
    predation adaptation graphing, 870*t*
    protein sequence data to test evolutionary
        hypothesis, 410*f*

quantitative data, 679*t*
    ratios, 679*t*
    regression lines, 40*f*, 176*t*, F-2*f*
    scale bars, 80*f*
    scatter plots, 40*f*, 109*f*, 176*t*, 441*t*, 870*t*, F-1*f*
    scatter plot with two sets of data, 109*f*
    scientific notation, 787*t*
    sequence logos, 294*f*
    slope, 134*t*
    surface area, 80*f*
    temperature coefficients, 597*t*
    volume, 80*f*
Scientific Skills Review, F-1*f*, F-2*f*, F-3*t*
Scion, **632**
Sclera, 808*f*
Sclereids, **580***f*
Sclerenchyma cells, **580***f*, 588
SCN. *See* Suprachiasmatic nucleus
Scrapie, 355
Scr gene, 466
Scrotum, **756***f*
Scrub jays, 800, 838
Scutellum, 626*f*
Scyphozoa, 547*f*
Sea anemones, 547*f*, 751–752
Seabirds, climate change effects on, 923
Seagrass, restoration of, 900*f*
Sea lettuce, 512*f*
Seals, 730
    climate change effects on, 923
Sea otter, 688*f*, 698, 866
Sea palm, 509*f*
Sea slugs, 751
Seasonality, 843*f*
Seasons, plant photoperiodism and responses to, 651,
    652*f*–653*f*
Sea stars, 552*f*, 722*f*, 855*f*, 876*f*
Sea turtles, 9*f*, 885
Sea urchins, 256, 437*f*, 552*f*, 764, 765*f*–766*f*, 767, 853*f*,
    866, 867*f*, 925*f*
Seaweed, 507*f*, 509*f*, 510, 512*f*, 853*f*
    restoration of, 900*f*
Secondary cell walls, 94*f*, **95**
Secondary consumers, 875*f*, **888***f*, 903*f*
Secondary endosymbiosis, **502**–503
Secondary growth, plant, **582**
    cork cambium and periderm production in, 591
    meristem generation of cells for, **582**, 583*f*–584*f*
    overview of, 583*f*
    of stems and roots in woody plants, 588–591
    tissues of, 588
    vascular cambium and secondary vascular tissue
        in, 590*f*, 591
    of woody stems, 589*f*
Secondary immune response, **741**, 742*f*
Secondary oocytes, **759***f*
Secondary production, **892**, 893*f*–894*f*
Secondary structure, protein, 60*f*
Secondary succession, **879**
Secondary vascular tissue, 590*f*, 591
Second law of thermodynamics, 124*f*, 125, 887
Second messengers, 118, 119*f*, 785
Secretin, 670*f*, 671, 701*f*, 705
Secretion function, **680**
    of excretory system, 680*f*
Secretions
    of liver, 696
    of pancreas, 695*f*
    of stomach, 694*f*–695*f*
Secretory phase, uterine cycle, 762*f*, 763
Secretory proteins, 84, 104*f*
Sedimentary rock, fossils in, 454
Seed coat, 534*f*, **626***f*–627*f*
Seed-eater finches, 383*f*
Seedless vascular plants, 530*f*–531*f*, **532**, 533*f*
Seedling development, seed germination and, 627*f*
Seed plants, 533–538. *See also* Angiosperms;
        Gymnosperms; Plants
    angiosperms and gymnosperms as, 533
    gametophyte-sporophyte relationship in, 532*f*
    lycophytes compared with, 544
    origin and diversification of angiosperms, 536,
        537*f*–538*f*

Seed plants (*Cont.*)
  origin and diversification of gymnosperms, 535*f*
  phylogeny of, 530*f*
  terrestrial adaptations of, 533, 534*f*–535*f*, 536
Seed production, 861*f*
Seeds, **533**, 534*f*, **625**, 666*f*
  abscisic acid in dormancy of, 645, 646*f*
  dispersal of, 629*f*
  dormancy of, 626
  embryo development and, 625*f*
  endosperm development and, 622, 623*f*, 625
  germination of, and seedling development, 627*f*
  gibberellins in germination of, 645*f*
  phytochromes and germination of, **649**, 650*f*
  structure of mature, 626*f*
  temperature and water uptake by, 597
Segmented bodies, arthropod, 553
Segmented worms, 821, 822*f*
Segregation, law of, 215, 216*f*–219*f*, 236, 237*f*
Seizures, 781
Selaginella kraussiana, 533*f*
Selasphorus platycercus, 632
Selective breeding, 385*f*, 386
Selective inhibition, enzyme, 136
Selective permeability, **100**, 105, 775*f*–776*f*
Selective protein degradation, 315
Self-fertilization (selfing), 631*f*, 638, 771
Self-incompatibility, plant, **631**, 638
Self-pollination, 215–216
Self-pruning, 595
Self-replicating molecules, 475–477*f*, 478
Self-thinning, 616
Self-tolerance, 740
SEM. *See* Scanning electron microscope
Semen, **756***f*, 764, 767
Semicircular canals, **805***f*, 806, 807*f*
Semiconservative model, DNA replication, 260*f*–261*f*
Semilunar valves, **711***f*
Seminal vesicles, **756***f*
Seminiferous tubules, **756***f*, 758*f*, 761
Senescence, plant, **647**
Senile dementia, 63
Sensitive period, **829**
Sensitive plants, 655*f*
Sensors, homeostatic, **674**
Sensory adaptation, **802**
Sensory amplification, 802
Sensory association cortex, 799*f*
Sensory input, nervous system, 774
Sensory neurons, 774*f*, 792, 805*f*
Sensory reception, **801**
Sensory receptors, **801**
  chemoreceptors, 803, 804*f*
  electromagnetic receptors, 803*f*
  mechanoreceptors, 802
  nociceptors (pain receptors), 803
  photoreceptors, 807–811
  somatosensory, 799
  thermoreceptors, 803*f*
Sensory systems, 801–811
  cerebral cortex and, 799
  hearing, equilibrium, and mechanoreceptors in, 804*f*–807*f*
  photoreceptors and vision in, 807–811. *See also* Visual systems
  sensory amplification and adaptation in, 802
  sensory perception in, 802
  sensory reception and transduction in, 801*f*, 802
  sensory transmission in, 802
  types of sensory receptors in, 802, 803*f*–804*f*
Sensory transduction, 801*f*, **802**, 810*f*
Sepals, **536***f*, **620***f*
Separase, 188
September equinox, 843*f*
Septic shock, 737, 750
Septum, 709*f*
Sequence logos, interpreting, 294
Sequences, amino acid, 69, 370
Sequences, DNA. *See* DNA sequences
Sequencing, DNA and genome. *See* DNA sequencing; Genome sequencing
Sequencing by synthesis technique, 274*f*, 358
Serial endosymbiosis hypothesis, **500***f*–501*f*, 502

Serial transfer, 483*f*
Serine, 57*f*
Serotonin, 786*t*
Sertoli cells, **761***f*
Serum, 717
Set point, homeostatic, **674**
Sex chromosomes, **203**
  aneuploidy of human, 250
  as chromosomal basis of sex, 239, 240*f*
  human, 202*f*–203*f*
  inactivation of X-linked genes in female mammals, 241, 242*f*
  inheritance of X-linked genes, 240, 241*f*
  mammalian, 240*f*
  in mammalian sex determination, 761
  patterns of inheritance of, 239, 240*f*–242*f*
Sex determination, 239, 240*f*, 761
Sex hormones
  chemical groups of, 48
  cholesterol as steroid lipid of, 55
  production of, by smooth ER, 83
  regulation of mammalian/human reproduction by, 760–764
  as steroid hormones, 672
Sex-linked genes, **240**, 241*f*–242*f*, 252. *See also* Sex chromosomes
Sex pili, 480, 484, 485*f*
Sex reversal, 753–754
Sex steroids, as environmental toxins, 921*f*
Sexual dimorphism, **427***f*, 832
Sexual intercourse, human, 763–764, 767*f*–769*f*, 787
Sexual life cycles, 200–213
  asexual vs. sexual reproduction and, 201*f*, 213, 630–631
  changes in DNA content of budding yeast cells during meiosis, 210
  chromosome sets in human, 202*f*–203*f*, 204
  genetics, heredity, variation, and, 200
  genetic variation produced by, 210, 211*f*–212*f*
  inheritance of genes in, 201
  meiosis in, 205*f*–209*f*, 210
  of Mendelian inheritance, 236*f*–239*f*. *See also* Chromosomal basis of inheritance
  plant, 522*f*, 523
  preparing karyotypes of chromosomes and, 202*f*
  types of, 204*f*, 205
Sexually transmitted diseases (STDs), 479, 489*f*, 747–748, 769*f*, 770
Sexual reproduction, **201**, **752**
  allocation of energy in angiosperm, 632
  angiosperm, 630–631. *See also* Flowers
  asexual reproduction vs., 201*f*, 213, 630–631, 752*f*. *See also* Asexual reproduction
  chromosome behavior in, 213, 252
  effects of human overfishing on cod, 570, 571*f*
  as evolutionary enigma, 752*f*
  fungal, 529*f*, 530
  gametogenesis in, 757, 758*f*–759*f*, 760
  hormonal regulation of mammalian/human, 760–764
  human. *See* Human reproduction
  reproductive cycles in, 753*f*
  sexual selection and, 427*f*, 430*f*
  solutions for, 666*f*
  as source of genetic variation, 416
  variations in patterns of, 753–754
Sexual response, human, 763–764
Sexual selection, **427***f*
  adaptive evolution and, 427*f*, 430*f*
  female mate choice in, 833*f*
  sympatric speciation and, 443*f*
S-genes, 631
Shade avoidance, plant, 650
Shaffer, Mark, 913, 914*f*
Shannon diversity index, **874***f*
Shape
  of carrier proteins, 108*f*
  chemical groups and, of organic compounds, 48
  cytoskeletons and cell, 90
  of enzymes and proteins, 43*f*, 63*f*
  intermediate filaments and cell, 94
  molecular, 30*f*–31*f*
  of proteins, 58, 59*f*–63*f*
  swimming and body, 824

Shapes
  allosteric regulation and enzyme, 137*f*
  enzyme, 132, 133*f*
  prokaryotic, 478*f*
  protist, 497*f*
Shared ancestral characters, **402**
Shared derived characters, **402***f*
Sharks, 556*f*, 557, 752, 813
Sheep, 331*f*, 355, 700
Shell, amniotic egg, 562, 563*f*
Shewanella oneidensis, 901
Shigella, 485
Shoots. *See also* Leaf; Stems
  apical meristems of, 523
  auxin polar transport in, 643*f*
  gravitropism in, 654*f*
  light capture and architecture of, 595*f*
  phytochrome and, 661
  primary growth of, 586*f*–588*f*
  transpiration of water and minerals from roots to, via xylem, 609*f*–611*f*, 612
Shoot systems, **576**, 577*f*–578*f*
Short-day plants, **652***f*
Short-distance signaling, neuron, 772. *See also* Neurons
Short-distance transport, plant, 596–597, 598*f*, 599
Short-finned pilot whale, 68*f*
Short-tailed shrew, 883*f*
Short tandem repeats (STRs), **365**
Short-term memory, **801**
Shrews, 883*f*
Shrimp, 375*f*, 440*f*, 441, 467*f*
Siamese cats, 302
Sickle-cell disease, **62***f*, **230***f*, **718**
  hemoglobin protein structure and, 62*f*
  malaria and evolutionary implications of, 230
  malaria and heterozygote advantage in, 426–427, 428*f*–429*f*
  pleiotropy and, 225
  point mutations and, 298*f*, 415
Sickle-cell trait, 429*f*
Side chains, amino acid, 56, 57*f*, 58, 61*f*
Sierra Nevada, 866
Sieve plates, **581***f*, 615*f*
Sieve-tube elements, **581***f*, 615*f*
Signaling, neurons and, 772. *See also* Neurons
Signal peptides, **295***f*, 296
Signal-recognition particles (SRPs), **295***f*, 296
Signals, animal, **827**, 828*f*
Signal transduction pathways, **115**
  in cell signaling, 115*f*, 118, 119*f*
  induction in, 323*f*
  neurotransmitters and, 785
  in plant light reception. *See* Light reception, plant; Plant responses
  in sensory systems, 802
  in visual sensory transduction, 810, 811*f*
  water-soluble hormones and, 672
Sign language, 813
Sign stimulus, **826**
Silencing, transcription, 312
Silent extinction, 571*f*
Silent mutations, **298**, 299*f*
Silent Spring (book), 920, 921*f*
Silicosis, 725
Silk fibers, 60*f*
Silkworm moths, 42*f*
Silversword plants, 399, 464*f*
Similarity, species and, 435*f*
Simple fruits, **628***f*
Simple sequence DNA, **365**
Single bonds, **28**, 44*f*–46*f*
Single-celled organisms, 72. *See also* Prokaryotic cells; Protists
Single circulation, **708**, 709*f*
Single-lens eyes, **808**–809
Single nucleotide polymorphisms (SNPs), **373**–374*f*
Single-strand binding proteins, **261***f*, 277
Sinoatrial (SA) node, **712***f*
siRNAs. *See* Small interfering RNAs
Sister cells, 182, 183*f*–184*f*
Sister chromatid cohesion, 184, 205, 208

Sister chromatids, **184***f*, 203*f*, 205*f*–209*f*, 210–211, 212*f*, 236*f*
Sister species, 440*f*
Sister taxa, **397***f*, 398
Size
    area effects and, 882*f*
    of cells, 73*f*
    eukaryotic cell vs. prokaryotic cell, 4, 5*f*, 76
    evolution of axon, 782*f*
    genetic drift and small population, 423
    of genomes, 362*t*
    Hardy-Weinberg equilibrium and large population, 419
    population. *See* Population dynamics; Population growth
    prokaryote, 478, 496
    of skeletons, 822, 823*f*
Skeletal muscles, **665***f*, **815***f*–820*f*
    nervous system regulation of tension of, 818, 819*f*
    regulation of contraction of, 817*f*–818*f*
    sliding-filament model of contraction for, 816*f*, 817
    structure of, 815*f*
    types of fibers of, 819*t*, 820*f*
Skeletal systems, 821*f*–824*f*, 825
    bones and joints of human, 823*f*
    endoskeletons, 822, 823*f*
    energy costs of locomotion in, 825
    exoskeletons, 822
    hydrostatic skeletons, 821, 822*f*
    locomotion in, 823, 824*f*, 825
    mammalian, 664*f*
    size and scale of skeletons in, 822, 823*f*
    skeletal muscles. *See* Skeletal muscles
    types of, 821*f*–823*f*
Skeletons, carbon, 45*f*
Skin
    as barrier defense, 735
    cancer of, 266
    as gas exchange tissue, 709
    human, 803
    mammalian, 664*f*
    pigmentation of human, 226*f*, 227
    as respiratory organ, 722
    stem cells of, 332
Skulls
    human vs. chimpanzee, 399–400, 465*f*
    mammalian, 456, 457*f*
Skunks, 436*f*
Sleep
    brain functions and, 793, 796*f*
    memory and, 801
Sleeping sickness, 508, 509*f*, 517, 748
Sleep movements, plant, 651*f*
Sliding-filament model, **816***f*, 817
Slime layer, 479
Slime molds, 513, 514*f*
Slope, line graph, 134
Slow-twitch fibers, 819*t*, **820**
Slugs, 834, 835
Small interfering RNAs (siRNAs), 316
Small intestine, 99, 693*f*
    absorption in, 696*f*–697*f*
    adaptations of, 698, 699*f*
    digestion in, 695*f*, 696
    surface area of, 526*f*
Small-population approach, for population conservation, 912*f*–914*f*
Smallpox, 351
Small-scale mutations, 298, 299*f*, 300
Smell
    pheromones and communication by, 827
    sense of, 803
Smoking, 337, 340, 720, 725, 769*f*, 785–786
Smooth ER, **83**
    animal cell, 78*f*
    in endomembrane system, 87*f*
    functions of, 83–84
    plant cell, 79*f*
Smooth muscle, 665*f*, **820**–821
SMR. *See* Standard metabolic rate
Snails, 436*f*, 448–449, 772*f*, 774*f*
Snakebite, 746, 789

Snakes, 395*f*, 396, 426*f*, 563, 564*f*, 698, 803*f*, 824, 834, 835, 870, 871*f*
Snapdragons, 223*f*
Snapping shrimp, 440*f*, 441
Snow geese, 902*f*
Snow leopard, 931
Snowy owl, 863*f*
SNPs. *See* Single nucleotide polymorphisms
Soapberry bugs, 387*f*, 388
Social interactions, 855
Social learning, **831**
Social process, science as, 18–19
Society, plant biotechnology and, 635–636
SOD. *See* Sudden oak death
Sodium, 23*f*, 29*f*
Sodium chloride (table salt). *See also* Salinity
    in aqueous solutions, 36*f*
    emergent properties of, 23*f*
    excess of, 690
    ionic bonds of, 29*f*
    kidney processing of, 682, 683*f*, 684
    plant responses to excessive, 656
    solute potential and, 618
Sodium ions, 775*ft*–782*f*
Sodium-potassium pump, 109, **110***f*, **775***f*–776*f*, 789
Software, systems biology and, 359, 360*f*
Soil
    acid precipitation and, 618
    bacteria in, 488*f*–489*f*, 490, 491*f*
    bacteria in, and plant nutrition, 604*f*–606*f*
    bioremediation of, 899, 901
    determining diversity of bacteria in, 874*f*
    disease-suppressive, 493
    in ecological succession, 880*f*
    essential elements for plants in, 599*f*–602*f*
    management of, for plant nutrition, 601
    nutrient limitations in, 892
    plant response to excessive salinity of, 656
    plants and formation of, 539
    resource competition and fertilization of, 863*f*
    root architecture and acquisition of water and minerals from, 595
    species distributions and, 854
    species facilitation and salinity of, 873*f*
    texture and composition of, 601, 602*f*
Soil worm, 326, 360, 362*t*
Solar energy. *See* Light energy; Sunlight
Solstices, 843*f*
Solute potential, **598**, 618
Solute potential equation, 618
Solutes, **36**
    chemoreceptors and, 803
    concentration of, in aqueous solutions, 37
    diffusion of, across plasma membranes, 105, 106*f*
    effects of, on water potential, 597–598
    nitrogenous wastes. *See* Filtrate
    transpiration of, from roots to shoots via xylem, 609*f*–611*f*, 612
    vascular plant transport of, across plasma membranes, 596, 599
Solutions, **36**, 106
Solvents, **36**
Somatic cells, **183**, **201**
Somatosensory cortex, 799*f*
Somatosensory receptors, 799
Songbird brains, 800*f*
Sorex cinereus, 883*f*
Soufrière Hills volcano, 472
Sound, mechanoreceptors for hearing, 804*f*–807*f*
Sour tastants, 803, 804*f*
South Africa
    elephants in, 910
    Succulent Karoo restoration project in, 900*f*
Southern Hemisphere, seasonal variation in, 843*f*
Southern magnolia, 538*f*
Soybean population, microevolution of, 420
Soybeans, 181
Space-filling models, 28*f*, 30*f*, 44*f*, 55*f*, 59*f*, 258*f*
Spanish flu, 352
Spatial learning, **829**, 830*f*
Spatial pattern, homeotic genes and, 466
Spatial summation, 784
Spawning, 754

Speciation, **434**–451
    adaptive radiations and, 463*f*–464*f*, 465
    allopatric, 439*f*–441*f*
    allopatric vs. sympatric, 439*f*, 443–444
    C. Darwin on, 384*f*–386*f*
    as conceptual bridge between microevolution and macroevolution, 434
    continental drift and, 460*f*
    differential, and species selection, 471
    genetics of, 448, 449*f*
    geographic separation and, 439*f*–444*f*
    hybrid zones, reproductive isolation, and, 444*f*–446*f*
    identifying dependent and independent variables, making scatter plots, and interpreting data on reproductive isolation in, 441*t*
    macroevolution from, 449
    morphological, ecological, and phylogenetic species concepts in, 438
    reproductive isolation and biological species concept in, 434, 435*f*–438*f*
    sympatric, 440–441, 442*f*–443*f*
    time course of, 446, 447*f*–448*f*
    unity and species concepts in, 438
Species, **435**
    of animals, 545, 546*f*
    bilaterian invertebrate, 552*f*
    biological species concept of, 434, 435*f*–438*f*
    C. Darwin's interest in geographic distribution of, 382–383
    C. Darwin's theory of origin of, 384*f*–386*f*
    classification of, 396*f*–398*f*
    climate change effects on, 925*f*
    in communities, 4*f*, 867*f*–873*f*, 902*f*–903*f*. *See also* Communities
    comparing developmental processes of, 374*f*–375*f*
    comparing genomes of, 372*f*–373*f*, 374
    with complete genome sequences available, 357, 360, 362
    discovery of, 840*f*
    diversity of. *See* Species diversity
    dominant and keystone, 876*f*
    endemic, 392
    extinctions of. *See* Extinctions
    of fungi, 527
    genomes of. *See* Genomes
    geographic distribution of. *See* Species distributions
    identifying, of whale meat, 398*f*
    interactions between. *See* Interactions, ecological; Interspecific interactions
    introduced, 910*f*
    loss of plant, 542*f*
    morphological, ecological, and phylogenetic species concepts of, 438
    morphology and, 434–435
    origin of. *See* Speciation
    phylogenies as evolutionary histories of. *See* Phylogenies
    taxonomic classification of, 380–381
Species-area curve, **882**
Species distributions
    abiotic factors in, 843, 853–854
    in aquatic biomes, 849*f*–851*f*, 852. *See also* Aquatic biomes
    biogeography and, 391–392
    biotic factors in, 843, 853*f*
    climate and. *See* Climate
    climate influence on, 843–844
    dispersal factors in, 852–853
    ecology, populations, and, 840, 852*f*–853*f*, 854. *See also* Ecology; Populations
    factors limiting, 852*f*–853*f*, 854
    in terrestrial biomes, 843–845, 846*f*–848*f*. *See also* Terrestrial biomes
Species diversity, **873**, 874*f*, 907*f*–908*f*. *See also* Biodiversity
    benefits of, 908–909
    biogeographic factors affecting, 881*f*–882*f*
    community stability and, 875*f*, 878
    disturbances influencing, 878, 879*f*–881*f*
    human impacts on, 880, 881*f*
    trophic structure and, 875*f*–876*f*, 885

Species interactions, **868**, 885, 902*f*–903*f*
 in communities, 867*f*–873*f*
 genomics and proteomics in, 68*f*
Species richness, **873**, 874*f*
 area effects on, 882*f*
 latitudinal gradients of, 881*f*
Species selection, 471
Specific heat, **34**
Specificity
 of B and T cells, 738
 enzyme-substrate, 132, 133*f*
 viral, 344
Specific transcription factors, 310*f*–311*f*, 312
Specimen preparation, 75
Spectrophotometer, **166**, 167*f*
Speech, cerebral cortex and, 798, 799*f*
Sperm, **752**
 in animal fertilization, 765*f*
 chromosomes in human, 183
 flagella of, 92
 in human fertilization, 767*f*–769*f*
 human reproductive organs and, 756
 human sexual intercourse and, 764
 human spermatogenesis and, 758*f*, 760
 as male gametes, 752
 mammalian sex determination and, 240*f*
Spermathecae, 755
Spermatids, 758*f*
Spermatocytes, 758*f*
Spermatogenesis, human, 758*f*, **760**, 771
Spermatogonia, **758***f*, 771
Spermicidal foam or jelly, 769*f*
Spermophilus beldingi, 855, 856*ft*, 857
Sphagnum moss, 880*f*
S phase, **185***f*
Spherical prokaryotes, 478*f*
Sphincter, **694**–695
Spiders, 33*f*, 60*f*, 552*f*, 732
Spilogale, 436*f*
Spinal cords, 791*f*–792*f*
Spines, 579*f*
Spiny acritarch, 549*f*
Spiny anteaters, 566*f*
Spiral phyllotaxy, 595
Spiral prokaryotes, 478*f*
Spirilla, 478*f*
Spirochetes, 478*f*, 489*f*
Spirodela oligorrhiza, 79*f*
Spirogyra crassa, 89*f*
Spleen, 716*f*
Spliceosomes, **288***f*
Sponges, 546*f*–548*f*, 550*f*–551*f*
Spongy mesophyll, 587*f*
Spontaneous abortions, 248, 768
Spontaneous mutations, 300
Spontaneous processes, **125***f*–127*f*, 128
Sporangia, 522*f*, **523***f*, 524*f*
Spores, 522*f*
 fossilized, 523*f*
 fungal, 525*f*, 529*f*
 in plant reproduction, 204*f*
 of seedless vascular plants, 531*f*
 seeds vs., 534
 walled, in plants, 523*f*
Sporophytes, **522***f*
 of bryophytes, 531*f*
 fossilized, 523*f*
 life cycles with, 532*f*
 in plant reproduction, 204*f*
 of plants, 522*f*
 of seedless vascular plants, 531*f*–533*f*
 seed plant, 534
Sporopollenin, **521**, 523, 534
Spotted skunks, 436*f*
Spriggina floundersi, 499*f*
Spruce, 880*f*
Squamates, 563, 564*f*
Squirrels, 390*f*, 629*f*
SR. *See* Sarcoplasmic reticulum
SRPs. *See* Signal-recognition particles
S-shaped logistic growth curve, 859*f*–860*f*
Stability
 community, 875*f*, 878

free energy and, 125, 126*f*
 hybrid zone, 445*f*, 446
 of populations, 862, 864*f*
Stabilizing selection, 425*f*, **426**
Stable isotopes, 25
Staghorn coral, 883
Staghorn fern, 608*f*
Stahl, Franklin, 260, 261*f*
Stained specimen brightfield microscopy, 74*f*
Stalk-eyed flies, 833*f*
Stamens, 215*f*, **536***f*, **620***f*
Staminate flowers, 631*f*
Standard metabolic rate (SMR), 702
Standing crop, 889, 894*f*
Stapes (stirrup), 805*f*
Staphylococcus, 388*f*, 389, 410, 475*f*, 489*f*
Star anise, 538*f*
Starches, **51***f*
 catabolism of, 142, 157–158
 as product of photosynthesis, 177
 structure of, 52*f*
Starfish. *See* Sea stars
Start codons, 283*f*
Start point, transcription, **284**, 285*f*
Statins, 720
Statocysts, **804***f*
Statoliths, 654*f*, 804*f*
Stator, of ATP synthase, 151*f*
Stechmann, Alexandra, 513*f*
Stele, **579**, 585*f*
Stem cells, **330**, 332*f*–333*f*, 334, 582, **718***f*, 771, 792
Stems, **578**. *See also* Shoots
 architecture of, for light capture, 595
 ethylene in triple response of, to mechanical
  stress, 646, 647*f*
 gibberellins in elongation of, 644, 645*f*
 monocot vs. eudicot, 576*f*
 primary and secondary growth of, 583*f*
 primary and secondary growth of woody, 589*f*
 primary growth of, 586*f*–588*f*
 secondary growth of woody, 588, 589*f*–590*f*, 591
 in shoot systems, 577*f*
 structure of, 578*f*
 tissue organization of, 587, 588*f*
Stents, 720
Sterility, 437*f*, 449, 636
Sterilization, 769*f*
Steroids, **55**
 coordinate control by, 313
 in evidence for origin of animals, 546
 intracellular receptors and, 117*f*
 as lipids, 55*f*
 production of, by smooth ER, 83
 regulation of mammalian/human reproduction
  by, 760–764
 sex hormones as, 672
Steward, F. C., 330
Stickleback fish, 390, 467, 468*f*, 826*f*
Sticky ends, DNA, **271***f*, **272**
Stigma, 536*f*, **620***f*
Stimulus
 homeostatic, **674***f*
 imprinting, 829
 plant responses to environmental, 653, 654*f*–660*f*
 sensory reception and transduction of, 801*f*, 802
 sign, 826
Stimulus-response chains, 827
Stink bugs, 559*f*
Stipes, **509***f*
Stirrup (stapes), 805*f*
Stock, plant, **632**
Stolons, 578*f*
Stomach, 692*f*–693*f*, **694**
 adaptations of, 698, 699*f*
 digestion in, 694*f*, 695
 flowchart question about, 705
 hormonal control of, 700, 701*f*
Stomach acid, 671
Stomach ulcers, 488*f*
Stomata, **162**, 163*f*, **523**, **587***f*
 abscisic acid and, 646
 of CAM plants, 175*f*, 176
 in plants, 523, 544

regulation of transpiration by, 612–615
 transpiration and, 175
Stop codons, 283*f*, 292, 293*f*
Storage leaves, 579*f*
Storage polysaccharides, 51*f*, 52
Storage proteins, 56*f*
Storage roots, 577*f*
Storms, 878
Stramenopiles, 507*f*, **509***f*, 510, 516
Strands, DNA, 6*f*
Strangling aerial roots, 577*f*
Strata, 380*f*, **381**, 454
Strawberry poison dart frogs, 451
Streams, 850*f*
 disturbances in, 878, 879*f*
 reconstruction of, 899
Streptococcus, 254*f*, 479*f*, 484, 489*f*, 737
Streptomyces, 489*f*
Stresses, plant responses to environmental, 655–656,
  657*f*–660*f*
Stretch receptors, 802
Striated muscles, 665*f*, 815. *See also* Skeletal muscles
Strigolactones, 643
Strobili, 531*f*
Stroke, **720**
Stroke volume, blood, 711
Stroma, 89*f*, **90**, 162, 163*f*, 172*f*–173*f*
Stromatolites, 453*f*, **456**, 477*f*, 478
STRs. *See* Short tandem repeats
Structural formulas, 28*f*, 44*f*, 55*f*
Structural isomers, **46***f*
Structural polysaccharides, 51*f*–52*f*, 53
Structural proteins, 56*f*
Structure-function correlation, 5, 10
Strychnine, 871
Strychnos toxifera, 871
Sturtevant, Alfred H., 245–248
Style, flower, 536*f*, **620***f*
Subatomic particles, 24*f*
Suberin, 591
Subjective feelings, 838
Substance P, 786
Substrate feeders, 691
Substrate-level phosphorylation, **146**, 146*f*
 ATP yield during, 153*f*, 154
 of glycolysis, 155
Substrates, **132**, 133*f*
Succulent Karoo restoration project, 900*f*
Succulent plants, 175*f*, 176
 restoration of, 900*f*
Sucrase, 131–132
Sucrose
 cotransport of, 111*f*
 as disaccharide, 50, 51*f*
 hydrolysis of, to glucose and fructose, 131–132
 plant uptake of, 121
 as product of photosynthesis, 177*f*
 translocation of, in vascular plants, 615*f*–616*f*
Sudden oak death (SOD), 516, 660, 883
Sugar beets, 493
Sugar gliders, 390*f*
Sugar-phosphate backbone, DNA, 65*f*, 66, 256*f*, 258, 259*f*
Sugars
 in aqueous solutions, 36–37
 conduction of, in plant cells, 581*f*
 kelp transport of, 618
 monosaccharide and disaccharide, as
  carbohydrates, 49, 50*f*–51*f*
 in nucleic acids, 64, 65*f*
 in photosynthesis, 163, 164*f*–165*f*
 as products of Calvin cycle, 165*f*, 173,
  174*f*–175*f*, 176
 translocation of, from sources to sinks via phloem,
  615*f*–616*f*
Sugar sinks, **615***f*–616*f*
Sugar sources, **615***f*–616*f*
Suicide genes, 336
Sulfate-reducing bacteria, 155
Sulfhydryl group, 47*f*, 48
Sulfolobus, 487
Sulfur, 23*t*, 255*f*
Sulfur bacteria, 488*f*
Sulfur dioxide emissions, 911*f*

Sumner, Francis B., 16
Sundew, 608f
Sunflowers, 23, 447f–448f, 666f
Sunlight. *See also* Light energy; Ultraviolet radiation
  aquatic biomes and, 849
  cancer and, 340
  climate and, 842f–844f. *See also* Climate
  DNA damage from, 266
  ecosystem energy from, 886–887, 888f, 889
  in energy flow and chemical cycling, 8f
  as energy for life, 141
  latitudinal variation in intensity of, 842f–843f
  as light energy, 124, 128. *See also* Light energy
  in photosynthesis, 31–32
  photosynthesis and, 161f
  primary production in aquatic ecosystems and limitations of, 890
  properties of, 165, 166f
  species distributions and availability of, 854
Supercontinent, 458, 460f
Supergroups, eukaryotic, 505, 506f–507f, 508
Supplements, dietary, 690
Support
  cell, 90
  skeletal, 821
Suprachiasmatic nucleus (SCN), 797
Surface area
  cell, 76, 77f, 80
  maximizing of, 526f
Surface area-to-volume ratios, 76, 77f
Surface tension, 33f
Surfactants, **725**–726
Surroundings, system, 124
Survival
  adaptations, natural selection and, 385f–386f
  trade-offs between reproduction and, 861f, 862
Survivorship curves, **856**f, 857
Suspension feeders, **547**, 568f, 691
Suspensor cells, 625f
Suspensory ligament, 808f
Sustainability, 928
Sustainable development, **928**, 929f
Sustainable resource management, 900f
Sutherland, Earl W., 115, 118
Sutton, Walter S., 236
Swallowing, 693
Sweat, human, 35, 674
Sweet tastants, 803, 804f
Swimming, 824–825
Swine flu, 352f, 353, 884
Switchgrass, 635
Symbionts, **491**, 528f
Symbiosis, **491**
  of anthozoans, 547f
  in flower pollination, 619
  fungal, 540–541
  lichen as, 539f
  plant-fungal, 524f
  protistan, 516f
sym genes, 527
Symmetry, animal body, 549, 550f
Sympathetic division, peripheral nervous system, **793**
Sympatric populations, character displacement in, 869f
Sympatric speciation, **440**
  allopatric speciation vs., 439f, 443–444
  habitat differentiation in, 442–443
  mate choice and, 451
  polyploidy in, 441, 442f
  sexual selection in, 443f
Symplast, 596f
Symplastic transport route, 596f, 609f, 618
Synapses, **773**. *See also* Chemical synapses
  electrical and chemical, 783–787
  neuronal plasticity, memory, learning and, 800f, 801
  regulation of muscle contraction and, 817f–818f
  structure and function of, 773f
Synapsids, 457f, **566**
Synapsis, **208**f–209f
Synaptic signaling, 114f
Synaptic terminals, 773f
Synaptonemal complex, **208**f
Syndromes, 250

Synergids, 622, 623f
Synthesis stage, lytic cycle, 345f
Synthetic estrogen or progestin, 769f
Syphilis, 489f
Systematics, **396**. *See also* Phylogenies; Taxonomy
  applying parsimony to problems in molecular, 404f
  constructing phylogenetic trees from shared characters in, 401f–406f
  evaluating molecular homologies in molecular, 400f
  interpreting phylogenies using, 396
  prokaryotic phylogenies of molecular, 486f–490f
Systemic acquired resistance, 659f
Systemic circuits, **708**, 709f, 711f
Systemic inflammatory response, 737
Systemic lupus erythematosus, 747
Systems
  chemical equilibrium and work in, 127f, 128
  thermodynamics and, 124
Systems biology, 3, **361**
  emergent properties and reductionism in, 3
  in study of genomes, genes, and gene expression, 360–361
Systole, **711**f
Systolic pressure, 714, 720
Szent-Györgyi, Albert, 689

T

T2 phage, 254f–255f, 256
T4 phage, 343f, 345f
Tables, data in, 257, 893
Table salt. *See* Sodium chloride
Tadpole, 673f
Tags, molecular identification, 85
Taiga, 848f
Tails
  histone, 268f
  post-anal, 555f
Takahashi, Masayo, 333
Takahe bird, 900f
Tallgrass prairie restoration, 901
TAL protein, 277
Tamiflu, 356
Tamoxifen, 197
Tansley, A. G., 878
Tappania, 453f, 498f
Taproots, **576**, 577f
Taq polymerase, 272, 909
Taraxacum officinale, 624f
Target cells, endocrine signaling, 668f, 672
Tar spot fungus, 541f
Tastants, 803, 804f
Taste
  pheromones and communication by, 827
  sense of, 803, 804f
Taste buds, **804**f
TATA boxes, 285f, **286**
Tatum, Edward, 279–280
Taxis, **480**
Taxol, 196
Taxonomy, **396**f–398f. *See also* Systematics
  binomial nomenclature in, 396
  early schemes of, 380–381
  hierarchical classification in, 396f, 397
  phylogenies and, 397f, 398. *See also* Phylogenies
  possible plant kingdoms, 521f
  three-domain system of, 10f, 11, 408, 409f
Taxon/taxa (taxonomy), 397f, 398, 401f
Tay-Sachs disease, 86, **224**, 229
TB. *See* Tuberculosis
T cells, **737**
  antigen recognition by, 737–738, 739f
  B cells and, 718f
  cytotoxic T cells, 744f
  development of, 739, 740f–742f, 750
  helper T cells, 742, 743f
  in humoral and cell-mediated immune response, 742f–745f
Teal, John, 893
Technology, **19**
  genomics, 358–361
  prokaryotes in research and, 492, 493f–494f
  science and, 19

Tectonic plates, 458, 459f
Tectorial membrane, 805f
Teeth
  adaptations of, 698f
  mammalian, 456, 457f, 566
Telencephalon, 794f
Telomerase, **267**
Telomeres, 267f
Telomeric DNA, 365
Telophase, **185**, 186f–187f, 190f, 209f
Telophase I, 206f, 209f
Telophase II, 207f
TEM. *See* Transmission electron microscope
Temperate broadleaf forests, **848**f
Temperate grasslands, **847**f
Temperate phages, **346**f
Temperature, **34**
  aquatic biomes and, 849
  atmospheric CO_2 concentrations and, 921, 922f, 924f
  calculating and interpreting coefficients for, 597
  climate and, 842f–844f. *See also* Climate
  climographs of, 845f
  in denaturation of proteins, 63
  effects of, on litter decomposition in ecosystems, 895f
  effects of transpiration on leaf, 614
  enzymatic catalysis and, 135f
  as kinetic energy, 34
  mass extinctions and, 462f
  membrane lipid composition and, 102
  moderation of, by water, 34f, 35
  plant mass and, 544
  plant responses to high and low, 656–657
  primary production in terrestrial biomes and, 891–892
  species distributions and, 853
  thermoreceptors and, 803
  thermoregulation and. *See* Thermoregulation
  water uptake by seeds and, 597
Temperature coefficient, 597
Templates, viral, 349
Template strands, DNA, 260f–261f, 263f–265f, 282f, 283
Tempo, speciation, 446, 447f–448f
Temporal fenestra, 457f
Temporal isolation, 436f
Temporal lobe, 799f
Temporal summation, 784
Tendrils, 579f
Tension, muscle, 818, 819f
Termination codons, 283f
Termination stage
  transcription, 285f, 286
  translation, 292, 293f
Terminators, transcription, **284**
Termites, 53, 516f, 699
Terrestrial adaptations. *See also* Animals; Plants; Fungi
  of fungi and plants, 521f–524f, 527f
  of seed plants, 533, 534f–535f, 536
Terrestrial animals. *See* Land animals
Terrestrial biomes, 843f–848f
  adaptations to, 175f, 176
  chaparral, 847f
  climate influences on distribution of, 844, 845f–848f
  climographs for, 845f
  decomposition and nutrient cycling rates in, 895
  deserts, 847f
  disturbances of, 845
  effects of animals on, 569f
  food chains in, 875f
  general features of, 845, 846f–848f
  locomotion in, 823
  northern coniferous forests, 848f
  primary production in, 891, 892f
  savannas, 846f
  temperate broadleaf forests, 848f
  temperate grasslands, 847f
  tropical forests, 846f
  tundra, 848f
Terrestrial plants. *See* Plants

Terrestrial vertebrates, 558f, 560–568. *See also* Vertebrates
  amniotes, 562, 563f–569f
  amphibians, 561, 562f
  tetrapods, 560f–561f
Territoriality, **855f**, 863f
Tertiary consumers, 875f, **888f**
Tertiary structure, protein, 61f
Testcrosses, **219f**, 242f–245f, 252
Testes, 184, 203f, 204, 669f, **756f**, 761f
Testicles, **756f**
Testosterone, 48, 55, 341, 672, **760**, 761f
Tests (shells), **511**
Test-tube cloning, plant, 632, 633f
Tetanus, **819f**, 820
Tetraploids, 249, 442f
Tetrapods, 456, 457f, 556f, **557**, 560f–561f
Tetrodotoxin, 603f
Texture, soil, 601
Thalamus, **795f**–796f
Thalassoma bifasciatum, 753–754
Thamnophis, 834, 835
Themes, biological, 3–9
  emergent properties at levels of biological organization, 3, 4f–5f
  evolution, 9
  expression and transmission of genetic information, 6f–7f, 8
  interaction of organisms with environment and other organisms, 8, 9f
  transfer and transformation of energy and matter, 8f
Theobroma cacao, 541f
Theories, scientific, **17**, 393
Therapeutic cloning, 333–334
Therapsids, 457f
Thermal energy, **34**, 105, 106f, **123**. *See also* Heat
Thermocline, **849**
Thermodynamics, 124f, 125, 887
Thermoreceptors, **803f**
Thermoregulation, **674**
  acclimatization in, 676
  balancing heat loss and gain in, 675f
  circulatory adaptations for, 675, 676f
  desert ant, 663
  in endothermic and ectothermic animals, 674f, 675
  physiological thermostats and fever in, 676, 677f
  regulators and conformers in, 673f
Thermus aquaticus, 272, 909
Thick filaments (actin), 805f, **815f**, 816f, 817
Thigmomorphogenesis, **654f**, 655
Thigmotropism, 654f, **655**
Thin filaments (myosin), **815f**, 816f, 817
Thiol compounds, 47f
Thiomargarita namibiensis, 478, 488f
Third-generation sequencing technique, 274f
Thirst, 803
Thompson seedless grapes, 645f
Thoracic cavities, 726f, 727
Threatened species, **907**, 908f
  declining-population approach to, 914, 915f
Three-chambered hearts, 709
Three-spined stickleback fish, 467, 468f, 826f
Threonine, 57, 138f
Threshold, **779**
Thrombin, 719f
Thrombus, **719**
Thrum flower, 631f
Thumb, opposable, 566
Thylakoid membranes, 162, 163f, 172f–173f, 181, 526f
Thylakoids, **89f**, **162**, 163f, 165f, 181
Thylakoid space, 162, 163f, 181
Thymidylate synthase (TS) enzyme, 513f
Thymine (T), 64, 65f, 66, 256, 258, 259f, 280, 282f, 428f
Thymine dimers, 266f
Thymus, 716f, **737**
Thyroid gland, 669f
  hormones of, as chemical messengers, 117
  iodine deficiencies and, 23
Thyroid hormone (T$_3$ and T$_4$), 669f, 672
Thyroid hormone, cellular respiration and, 155, 155t
Thyroid-stimulating hormone (TSH), 669f, 670, 671f
Thyrotropin, 671f

Thyrotropin-releasing hormone (TRH), 673f
Ticks, 871–872, 883f
Tidal rhythms, 826
Tidal volume, **727**
Tigers, 10, 235
Tiger swallowtail, 252
Tight junctions, **96f**
Tiktaalik, 453f, 560f–561f
Time
  hybrid zones over, 445f–446f
  phylogenetic tree branch lengths and, 402f–404f, 405
  required for human cell division, 185
  speciation over, 446, 447f–448f
Timing, developmental, 465f–466f
Tinbergen, Niko, 825–826, 829–830
Tissue culture methods, plant, 644
Tissue plasminogen activator (TPA), 369, 371f
Tissues, **5f**
Tissues, animal, **547**, **664f**
  bilaterian, 550f
  in hierarchical organization of animal bodies, 664t, 665f
  immune system rejection of transplanted, 746
  lack of, by sponges, 547
  proteins specific to, 323, 324f, 325
  renewal of, as cell division function, 182, 183f
Tissues, plant, **576**
Tissue-specific proteins, 323, 324f, 325
Tissue systems, plant, 578f–579f, 584f–588f
TLR. *See* Toll-like receptor
TMV. *See* Tobacco mosaic virus
Toadfish, 820f
Toads, 444f, 445–446, 562
Tobacco hornworm, 872
Tobacco mosaic virus (TMV), 343f, 354
Tobacco plant, 284f, 871
Tobacco smoke, 720, 725, 785–786
Toll-like receptor (TLR), 735f, 736, 750
Tomatoes, 644
Tongue, 693f, 804f
Tonicity, **107**
Tonsils, 716f
Tools
  antibodies as, 746
  computational, 357–361. *See also* Bioinformatics
Top-down model, **877**
  of trophic control, 877f, 885
Topoisomerase, **261f**
Topsoil composition, 602. *See also* Soil
Torpedo shape, 824
Tortoiseshell cats, 241, 242f
Total biomass accumulation, 890
Totipotent cells, **330–331**
Totipotent organisms, **631**
Touch
  animal mechanoreceptors and sense of, 802
  plant response to, 654f, 655
Toxic elements
  in denaturation of proteins, 63
  evolution of tolerance to, 23
Toxic wastes
  bioremediation of, 899, 901f
  as density-dependent population regulation mechanism, 863f
Toxins
  Bt toxin and plant, 634
  environmental accumulation of, 920f–921f
  enzymatic catalysis and, 136
  neurotransmission and, 786
  in predation, 870, 871f
TPA. *See* Tissue plasminogen activator
Trace elements, **23**
Tracers, radioactive, 25f, 164
Trachea, 705
Trachea (windpipe), **724**, 725f
Tracheal systems, 559, 723, **724f**
Tracheids, **532**, **581f**
Trade-offs, life histories and, 861f, 862
Tragopogon, 442, 443f
Traits, **215**
  characters and, 215
  dominant vs. recessive, 216t, 228f–229f

  inheritance of, 385f–386f
  inheritance of acquired, 381f
  inheritance of X-linked genes and recessive, 240, 241f–242f
  plant, derived, 523
  in theory of evolution by natural selection, 11f–12f
Transcription, **280**
  analyzing DNA deletion experiments on eukaryotic, 313
  basic principles of translation and, 280–281
  coupling of translation and, 296f
  of crystallin protein, 7f
  DNA template strands in, 282f, 283
  effects of noncoding RNAs on eukaryotic, 315f, 316
  eukaryotic gene regulation after, 314f, 315
  eukaryotic regulation of initiation of, 309, 310f–312f, 313
  as gene expression, 309
  genetic code and, 283f
  molecular components of, 284, 285f
  overview of, in gene expression, 281f
  regulation of bacterial, 303, 304f–307f, 308
  RNA processing after, 286, 287f–288f
  summary of eukaryotic translation and, 297f
  three stages of synthesis of RNA transcripts in, 284, 285f–286f
Transcription factors, 117, **285f**, 286, 310f–311f, 312, 325
Transcription initiation complex, **285f**, 286, 310, 311f
Transcription units, **284**, 285f
Transduction
  prokaryotic, 484f
  sensory, 801f, 802, 810f
Transduction stage, cell-signaling, **115f**, 117, 118f–119f
trans face, Golgi apparatus, 84f, 85, 87f
Trans fats, **54**, 720
Transfer RNA (tRNA), 66f, **288**, 289f–293f, 297f
Transformation
  cancer, **195**
  energy, 124f–125f. *See also* Energy
  prokaryotic, 484f
Transformation, DNA, **254**
Transfusions, blood, 746
Transgene escape, 636
Transgenes, **634**, 636
Transgenic organisms, 283, 284f, 634, 635f, 636
trans isomers, **46f**
Transitional ER, 83f, 84
Transition state, 131
Translation, **281**, 288, 289f–297f
  basic concept of, 289f
  basic principles of transcription and, 280–281
  completing and targeting functional proteins in, 292, 295f–296f
  coupling of transcription and, 296f
  of crystallin protein, 7f
  eukaryotic gene regulation at initiation of, 314
  genetic code and, 282f
  interpreting DNA sequence logos to identify ribosome-binding sites in, 294
  molecular components of, 288, 289f–291f
  overview of, in gene expression, 281f
  summary of eukaryotic transcription and, 297f
  synthesis of multiple polypeptides in, 296f–297f
  three stages of polypeptide synthesis in, 291, 292f–293f
Translation initiation complex, 292f
Translation initiation factors, 314
Translocation
  cancer gene, 334f, 335
  chromosome, **249**, 250, 251f
  vascular plant, **615f**–616f
Translocation stage, translation elongation cycle, 293f
Transmembrane proteins, 103
Transmembrane receptor proteins, 115, 116f, 117
Transmembrane transport route, 596f, 609f
Transmission, sensory, 802f
Transmission electron microscope (TEM), 74f, **75**
Transmission rate, disease, 863f

Transpiration, **610**, 896*f*
    regulation of, by stomata, 612–615
    transport of water and minerals from roots to
        shoots via xylem by, 609*f*–611*f*, 612
Transpirational pull, 610, 611*f*
Transplants
    immune system rejection of tissue, 746
    of species, 853
Transport, 666*f*
    plant. *See* Plant transport
Transport epithelia, **679**, 682, 683*f*
Transport proteins, **105**. *See also* Aquaporins; Carrier
    proteins; Channel proteins
    in active transport, 109, 110*f*–111*f*
    in cotransport, 111*f*, 112
    in facilitated diffusion, 108*f*
    functions of, 56*f*, 103*f*
    transport work and, 130*f*
    types and functions of, in plasma membranes, 105
    in vascular plant transport, 596, 599
Transport vesicles, **84**
    in endomembrane system, 87*f*
    in exocytosis, 112
    Golgi apparatus and, 84*f*, 85
Transport work, 128, 130*f*
Transposable elements, **364**
    contribution of, to genome evolution, 371
    transposons and retroposons in genomes,
        364*f*–365*f*
Transposition process, 364, 371
Transposons, 316, 349, **364***f*–365*f*
trans-retinal, 809*f*, 810
Transthyretin, 60*f*–61*f*, 63*f*
Transverse (T) tubules, **817***f*–818*f*
Trawling, community disturbances by, 880, 881*f*
Tree frogs, mate selection of, 430*f*
Treehopper, 377
Tree of life. *See also* Phylogenetic trees; Phylogenies
    C. Darwin's, 384*f*, 385
    Darwin's, 12, 13*f*
    phylogenies and three-domain taxonomy of, 408,
        409*f*, 410
Tree rings, 590*f*
Trees, 201*f*
    disruption of mycorrhizae of, by garlic mustard, 607
    leaf morphology of, 582
    trunk anatomy of, 590*f*
Trends, evolutionary, 470*f*, 471
Treponema pallidum, 489*f*
TRH. *See* Thyrotropin-releasing hormone
Triacylglycerols, 53*f*–54*f*
Tribulus terrestris, 629*f*
Triceps, 821*f*
Triceratium morlandii, 509*f*
Trichechus manatus, 412, 871*f*
Trichomes, 578
Trichomonas vaginalis, 508*f*
Triglycerides, 53*f*–54*f*, 697*f*
Trilobites, 554*f*
Trimesters, human pregnancy, 768
Trioses, 50*f*
Triple response, plant, **646**, 647*f*
Triplet code, **282***f*–284*f*
Triploid (chromosomes), 213
Triploidy, 249
Trisomic zygotes, 248*f*–250*f*
Trisomy X (XXX), 250
Tristan da Cunha, 422
Triticum aestivum, 442, 451, 501, 652, 863*f*
tRNA. *See* Transfer RNA
Trophic cascade model, 877
Trophic efficiency, **893**, 894*f*
Trophic structure, **875***f*–876*f*, 885
    of biological communities, 873, 874*f*–877*f*, 878, 885
    bottom-up and top-down controls of, 877*f*, 885
    in ecosystem energy flow and chemical cycling, 888*f*
    energy transfer and, 892, 893*f*–894*f*, 903*f*
    species with large impact on, 876*f*–877*f*
    trophic efficiency and ecological pyramids in,
        893, 894*f*
Trophoblast, **768**
Tropical dry forests, **846***f*
Tropical rain forests, 181, 542*f*, **846***f*, 895

Tropical tree lizards, 868*f*
Tropic hormones (tropins), 671*f*, **760**–764
Tropic of Cancer, 842*f*
Tropic of Capricorn, 842*f*
Tropics, 842*f*
    deforestation in, 906, 907*f*, 909
    species richness in, 881*f*
    undiscovered species in, 906
Tropisms, **640**
Tropomyosin, **817***f*–818*f*
Troponin complex, **817***f*–818*f*
Troponin T gene, 314*f*
trp operon, 304, 305*f*, 306–307
True-breeding organisms, **215**, 235
Trypanosoma, 508, 509*f*, 517, 748
Trypsin, 695*f*
Tryptophan, 57*f*, 304, 305*f*, 306–307, 786
TS (Thymidylate synthase) enzyme, 513*f*
TSH. *See* Thyroid-stimulating hormone
T tubules. *See* Transverse (T) tubules
Tuataras, 563, 564*f*
Tubal ligation, 769*f*
Tube cells, 622, 623*f*
Tuberculosis, 863*f*
Tuberculosis (TB), 489*f*, 492, 496, 737
Tubers, 578*f*
Tubulinid amoeba, 519
Tubulin protein, 92
Tumbleweeds, 629*f*
Tumors, cancer, 195*f*, 196–197
Tumor-suppressor genes, **335**
Tumor viruses, 340
Tuna, 412, 911*f*
Tundra, **848***f*, 902*f*–903*f*, 923
    grassland transformation into, 886*f*
Túngara frog, 431*f*
Tunicates, 555*f*
Turgid cells, **108**, **598***f*
Turgor movements, plant, 655*f*
Turgor pressure, 108, **598**, 613*f*
Turner syndrome, 250
Turtle, 412, 885
Turtles, 563, 564*f*, 871
Tutu, Desmond, 374
Twins, human, 768
Twin studies, **828**
Tympanic canal, 805*f*
Tympanic membrane (eardrum), **805***f*, 806
    invertebrate, 804
Tympanuchus cupido, 422, 423*f*, 912, 913*f*
Type 1 diabetes, 703, 747
Type 2 diabetes, 703, 747
Typhoid fever, 492
Tyrosine, 57*f*, 786
Tyrosine kinase, 197

U

Ubiquinone (Q), 150*f*, 152*f*
Ulcerative colitis, 737
Ultimate causation, 825
Ultrabithorax (*Ubx*) gene, 466, 467*f*, 554*f*
Ultraviolet (UV) radiation. *See also* Radiation;
    Sunlight
    cancer and, 340
    DNA damage from, 266*f*
    mutagenic, 300
    nectar guides, 624*f*
Ulva, 512*f*
Umami tastant, 803, 804*f*
Undernourishment, 690
Undershoot phase, action potential, 780*f*
Ungulates, 390*f*–391*f*
Unicellular eukaryotes. *See* Protists
Unicellular photoautotrophs, 162*f*
Uniform dispersion, 855*f*
Unikonta, 506*f*–507*f*, **512**, 513*f*–514*f*
Unisexual flowers, 620
United Kingdom, wetland biome in, 849*f*
Unity
    evolution of diversity and, 9, 11*f*, 20,
        379–380, 384

of life solutions, 666*f*–667*f*
    universality of genetic code and, 284
University of California, San Diego, 359
Unlinked genes
    mapping, 245–246, 247*f*, 248
    recombination of, through independent
        assortment of chromosomes, 244
Unpaired electrons, 27
Unsaturated fats, 53, 54*f*
Unsaturated fatty acids, 53, 54*f*
Unsaturated hydrocarbon tails, 102*f*
Unselfish behavior, 835–836
Unstained specimen brightfield microscopy, 74*f*
Untranslated regions (UTRs), 287*f*, 314
Upwellings, 891
Uracil (U), 64, 65*f*, 66, 280, 282*f*, 283
Uranium, bioremediation of, 901*f*
Uranium-238, 454
Urea, **679**, 683*f*
Ureter, 681*f*
Urethra, **681***f*, **756***f*
Urey, Harold, 475–476
Uric acid, **679**
Urinary bladder, **681***f*
Urine
    concentration of, in mammalian kidney, 684
    excretory system production of, 680*f*
    kidney production of, 682, 683*f*
    territoriality and, 863*f*
Ursus, 438
Ursus arctos horribilis, 913, 914*f*
USA300 bacteria, 388*f*
Use and disuse principle, 381
Ustilago, 410
Uterine cycle, **761**, 762*f*, 763
Uterus, 78*f*, 755, **757***f*, 762*f*, 763, 768
Utricle, **806**, 807*f*
UTRs. *See* Untranslated regions

V

Vaccines, **351**, 745–746, 750
Vacuoles, 79*f*, **86***f*, 87, 107*f*
Vagina, **757***f*, 764, 769
Vaginal pouch, 769*f*
Valence, **28**, **44***f*–45*f*
Valence electrons, **27**
Valence shells, **27**
Valeria, 549*f*
Valine, 57*f*, 62*f*
Valium, 785
Valley of Whales, 452*f*
Valves, heart, 711*f*
Vampire bats, 684*f*
van der Waals interactions, **30**, 61*f*
van Leeuwenhoek, Antoni, 73
van Niel, C. B., 164
Vaporization, 35
Variable (V) region, antigen, 738*f*–739*f*
Variables, **17**
    experimental, 16–17
    identifying dependent and independent, 441
Variation, **200**. *See also* Genetic variation
Vasa recta, **681***f*
Vascular bundles, 579, **588***f*
Vascular cambium, **582**, 583*f*, 588, 590*f*, 591
Vascular cylinder, 579
Vascular plants, **530**. *See also* Angiosperms; Plants
    evolution of organs of, 576, 577*f*–578*f*
    gametophyte-sporophyte relationship in, 532*f*
    lignin in, 592
    overview of resource acquisition and transport
        in, 594*f*
    phylogeny of, 530*f*
    resource acquisition adaptations of, 593–596
    seedless, 531*f*–533*f*
    soil as source of essential elements for, 599*f*–602*f*
    transport in. *See* Plant transport
    vascular tissue in, 530, 532–533
Vascular rays, 590*f*
Vascular tissue, plant, **529**, 532–533, 594*f*, 595.
    See also Phloem; Xylem
Vascular tissue system, plant, **579***f*, 581*f*
Vas deferens, **756***f*

Vasectomy, 769f
Vasocongestion, 764
Vasoconstriction, 675, **714**, 715f
Vasodilation, 675, **714**, 715f, 757
Vasopressin, 669f, 670, 684, 685f, 834
Vectors, **883**f
Vegetable oil, hydrophobic, 37
Vegetal plate, 766f
Vegetation
   in terrestrial biomes, 845, 846f–848f
   terrestrial biomes and. *See* Terrestrial biomes
Vegetative growth, plant, 584, 627
Vegetative propagation, **632**, 644
Vegetative reproduction, 630f–633f
Vegetative shoots, 577f
Veins
   blood, **708**, 709f, 713f–715f
   leaf, 162, 163f, 576f, **578**, 587f
Venomous snails, 772f
Venter, Craig, 358
Ventilation, 723f
Ventral sides, **550**f
Ventral tegmental area (VTA), 797
Ventricles
   central nervous system, 791f, 792
   heart, **708**, 709f, 710f–711f
Venules, 708, 713f
Venus flytrap, 608f, 655
Vernalization, 652–**653**
Vertebrates, **551**. *See also* Animals
   action potential conduction speed in, 782
   adaptive immunity in, 734, 737. *See also* Adaptive
     immunity
   amniotes as terrestrial, 562, 563f–569f. *See also*
     Amniotes
   amphibians as terrestrial, 561, 562f. *See also*
     Amphibians
   anatomical similarities in embryos of, 389f
   in animal phylogeny, 551
   cardiovascular systems of. *See* Cardiovascular
     systems
   digestive system adaptations of, 698f–700f
   evolutionary adaptations of digestive systems of.
     See Digestive systems
   evolution of brains of, 799, 800f. *See also* Brains
   excretory systems of, 680, 681f, 682
   innate immunity in, 734, 735f–736f, 737
   mechanoreceptors for hearing and equilibrium in,
     804f–807f
   nervous systems of, 791f–792f
   origins of tetrapods as, 560f–561f
   reproductive organs of, 755
   skeletal muscles of. *See* Skeletal muscles
   swimming, 824
   terrestrial, 558f, 560f–568f
   visual systems of, 808–811
Vertical layering, in terrestrial biomes, 846
Vertical transmission, viral, 354
Vesicles, **82**
   abiotically produced, as protocells, 476f
   in bulk transport, 112, 113f
   in endomembrane system, 82–83, 87f
   in lysosomal autophagy, 86f
   in plant cells, 178f
   in plant cytokinesis, 189f, 190
   transport. *See* Transport vesicles
Vessel elements, **581**f
Vessels
   circulatory, 707f, 708. *See also* Blood vessels
   lymphatic, 716f
   xylem, 581f
Vestibular canal, 805f, 806
Vestibular glands, 757f
Vestigial structures, **389**–390
Viagra, 757, 787
Vibrio, 603f
Vibrio cholerae, 488f, 492
Vietnam
   deforestation in, 906, 907f
   new species found in, 906f
Villi, 526f, 666f, **696**f
Viral envelopes, **343**f, 344, 348f
Viral integration, 340

Virchow, Rudolf, 182
Viridiplantae, 512, 521f
Virulent pathogens, 658
Virulent phages, **345**f
Viruses, **254**, 342–356
   analyzing DNA sequence-based phylogenetic tree
     to understand evolution of influenza, 353
   in cancer development, 340, 748–749
   characteristics of life and, 342f
   community structure effects of, 883–884
   evidence for viral DNA in bacteriophages,
     254f–255f, 256
   evolution of, 349, 356
   importance of, for molecular biology, 349
   infection by, 356
   interferons and, 736
   latency of, 747
   as pathogens, 351f–352f, 353–354
   rapid reproduction of, as source of genetic
     variation, 416
   replicative cycles of, 345f–350f
   RNAi pathways and, 316
   structure of, 342, 343f, 344
Visceral mass, 553f
Visible light, **166**f
Vision. *See* Visual systems
Visual association cortex, 799f
Visual communication, 827
Visual cortex, 799f
Visual fields, 810, 811
Visual pigments, 809f, 811
Visual systems, 807–811
   color vision in, 811
   compound eyes in, 808f
   evolution of, 807f–808f, 809
   light-detecting organs in, 807f, 808
   sensory transduction in, 810f
   single-lens eyes in, 808–809
   structure of human eyes in, 808f–809f
   vertebrate, 808–811
   visual fields in, 811
   visual information processing in brain in, 810, 811f
   visual information processing in retina in, 810
Vital capacity, **727**
Vitamin A, 634, 635f, 690
Vitamin B, 689
Vitamin C, 689–690
Vitamin D, 690
Vitamin E, 690
Vitamin K, 690
Vitamins, **689**
   for animal nutrition, 689f, 690
Vitreous humor, 808f
Vocal cords and vocal folds, 724
Vocalization, *FOXP2* gene and, 373f
Volcanic springs, 487f
Volcanoes, 461, 472, 475f
Voles, 834f
Voltage, membrane potential, 110f–111f
Voltage-gated ion channels, **778**f–782f
Volume
   cell, 76, 77f, 80
   sound, 806
Voluntary nervous system, 793
Volvox, 503f, 504, 507f, 512
von Frisch, Karl, 827
von Humboldt, Alexander, 882
VTA. *See* Ventral tegmental area
Vulpes lagopus, 886f
Vulpia fasciculata, 862
Vulva, **757**f

W

Wadi Hitan, 452f
Waggle dance, honeybee, 827f
Waists, chromatid, 184
Wakefulness, brain functions and, 796f
Walking, 824
Wallace, Alfred Russel, 383f, 881
Walnut trees, 861
Walrus, 675f
Warren, Robin, 694
Washington, stream biome in, 850f

Wasps, 559f, 658f, 830f, 871–872
Water, 32–40
   acids, bases, buffers, and pH of solutions of,
     37–39
   aerobic respiration and, 142
   aqueous solutions and, as solvent of life, 36–37
   biomanipulation and quality of, 877f
   bioremediation of polluted, 891, 901f
   in blood plasma, 717f
   catabolic pathways and production of, 565f
   cell balance of. *See* Water balance
   cell membrane diffusion of, 179f
   cohesion and adhesion of, 33f
   as compound, 28
   conduction of, in plant cells, 581f
   covalent bonding of, 28f
   digestive recovery of, 697
   ecosystem purification of, 909
   effect of large bodies of, on climate, 34f, 843,
     844f, 849
   elements of, 23f
   evapotranspiration of, 881f
   evolution of alternative plant mechanisms to
     reduce loss of, 175f, 176
   floating of ice on liquid, 35f–36
   fruit and seed dispersal by, 629f
   hydrogen bonds and properties of, 30f, 32, 33f
   kidney conservation of, 684
   in methane combustion, 142, 143f
   moderation of temperature by, 34f, 35
   molecular shape of, 30f
   nitrogen pollution of, 919f, 920
   ocean acidification and, 39f, 40
   pH of, 38f
   in photosynthesis, 31, 32f
   plant responses to flooding, 655–656, 657f
   plants and, 521, 523
   regulation of plant transpiration and loss of, 612–615
   root architecture and acquisition of, 595
   seed germination and imbibition of, 627f
   species distributions and availability of, 853–854
   splitting of, in photosynthesis, 163, 164f–165f
   temperature and uptake of, by seeds, 597
   in thigmotropism, 655
   transpiration of, from roots to shoots via xylem,
     609f–611f, 612
   transport of, in plants, 33f, 618
   vascular plant transport of, across plasma
     membranes, 597, 598f, 599
Water balance
   evolution of, 687
   kidney processing and, 680–682, 683f
   osmoregulation and, 678f
   osmosis and, 106f–108f
Water bugs, 755f
Water cycle, 896f, 905
Water fleas, 860f
Water lilies, 538f
Water potential, **597**
   in plant transpiration, 610, 611f
   solute potential and, 618
   in vascular plant water transport, 597, 598f, 599
Water-soluble hormones, 671–672
Water-soluble vitamins, 689–690
Watkinson, Andrew, 862
Watson, James
   discovery of DNA molecular structure by, 253f,
     257–259
   model of DNA replication of, 259f–261f
   reductionism of, 3
Wavelengths, light, **166**f–168f
WD40 domain, 359, 360f
Weak acids, 38
Weak chemical bonds, 30
Weather, population fluctuations and, 864f. *See also*
   Climate
Weathering, in phosphorus cycle, 897f
Websites, genomic, 359, 360f
Weddell seals, 730
Weeds, transgene escape and, 636
Welch, Allison, 430f
Went, Frits, 640, 641f
Wernicke, Karl, 798

Wernicke's area, 798, 799f
Westemeier, Ronald, 913f
Western garter snakes, 834, 835
Western gulls, 832f
Western scrub jays, 800
West Indian manatee, 412
West Nile virus, 344, 352, 424
Wetlands, **849f**
    restoration of, 900f
Whales, 68f, 390f–391f, 398f, 452f, 466, 803f,
        910–911
Wheat, 442, 451, 501, 652, 863f
Whiptail lizards, 753f
Whiskers, 802
White-band disease, 883
White blood cells, 326f, 332f, 717f–718f
White-footed mouse, 828t, 863f
White matter, **792**
White-tailed deer, 916
WHO. *See* World Health Organization
Whole-genome shotgun genome-sequencing
        approach, **358f**, 529
Whooping cough, 116
Whooping cranes, 829
Whorled phyllotaxy, 595
Widow's peak pedigree analysis case, 228f, 229
Wieschaus, Eric, 328
Wildflowers, 421f, 422, 885
Wildlife management, 901
Wild mustard species, artificial selection of, 385f
Wild types, **238f–239f**
Wilkins, Maurice, 256–259
William of Occam, 405
Wilson, E. O., 882f, 908f
Wilting, 108, **598f**, 614, 646, 655
Wind
    climate and, 9, 842f–844f. *See also* Climate
    flower pollination by, 624f
    fruit and seed dispersal by, 629f
    global patterns of, 842f
Windpipe (trachea), **724**, 725f
Winged fruits and seeds, 629f
Wing formation, 377

Wings
    bat vs. bird, 399–400
    bird, 565f
    insect, 821
    locomotion by, 824
Wisconsin, prairie in, 910
Withdrawal method, contraceptive, 756, 769f
Wobble, **290**
Wolbachia, 519
Wolves, 862, 864f, 903f, 915
Wood, 95
Wood ants, 22f
Woodpeckers, 838, 914, 915f
Work
    ATP hydrolysis and, 129f–130f
    cellular respiration and, 141
    types of cellular, 128
World Health Organization (WHO), 352
Worldwide adaptive radiations, 463f–464f, 465
Worms, 326, 360, 362t, 821, 822f, 872. *See also*
        Earthworms

X

Xanthium strumarium, 652f, 653
Xanthomonas, 277
Xanthopan morganii, 569f
X chromosomes, 202f–203f, 239, 240f–242f, 761
Xenopus laevis, 330f, 331
Xeroderma pigmentosum (XP), 266f
Xerophytes, **614f**
X-linked genes, **240**, 241f–242f, 331f
XP. *See* Xeroderma pigmentosum
X-ray crystallography, 59f, **63f**, 257f, 258
X-rays, mutations and, 300
Xylem, **532**, **579**, **594**
    evolution of, 594
    primary growth and, 585f
    secondary, 588, 589f–590f, 591
    transpiration of water and minerals from roots to
        shoots via, 609f–611f, 612
    in vascular plant transport, 532–533
    in vascular tissue system, 579
    water-conducting cells of, 581f

Xylem sap, **610**, 611f, 612
X-Y sex determination system, 240f, 252

Y

Yamanaka, Shinya, 333f
Yangtze River dolphin, 908f
Yarrow plants, 866
Y chromosomes, 202f–203f, 239, 240f–242f, 761
Yeasts, **525**. *See also Saccharomyces cerevisiae* (yeast)
    alcohol fermentation by, 156f
    cell division in, 191f
    cells of, 78f. *See also* Eukaryotic cells
    density-dependent population regulation of, 863f
    fungi as, 525
Yellow-bellied toad, 444f, 445–446
Yellowstone National Park, 487f, 490, 878, 879f, 909,
        913, 914f, 915, 916f, 918
Y-linked genes, 240, 252
Yolk sac, 560, 561f

Z

Zambia, poaching in, 910, 911f
Zea mays. See Corn
Zeatin, 644
Zebra mussel, 910
Zinc deficiency, plant, 600–601
Z line, skeletal muscle, 815f
Zonation, in aquatic biomes, 849f
Zoned reserves, **918f**, 919
Zone of cell division, 584f, 585
Zone of differentiation, 584f, 585
Zone of elongation, 584f, 585
Zoonotic pathogens, **883f**, 884
Zooplankton, 875, 876f, 894
Zucchini, 538f
Zygnema, 521f
Zygomycetes, 528f
Zygotes, **203**, **752**
    abnormal chromosome numbers in, 248f–250f
    ensuring survival of, 754, 755f
    fertilization and, 765f
    human, 203f, 204, 767f